Symbols of Common Elements

Ag	silver	Cu	copper	O	oxygen
Al	aluminum	F	fluorine	P	phosphorus
As	arsenic	Fe	iron	Pb	lead
Au	gold	H	hydrogen	Pt	platinum
Ba	barium	Hg	mercury	S	sulfur
Bi	bismuth	I	iodine	Sb	antimony
Br	bromine	K	potassium	Sn	tin
C	carbon	Mg	magnesium	Sr	strontium
Ca	calcium	Mn	manganese	Ti	titanium
Cl	chlorine	N	nitrogen	U	uranium
Co	cobalt	Na	sodium	W	tungsten
Cr	chromium	Ni	nickel	Zn	zinc

Symbols of Common Polyatomic Ions

$C_2H_3O_2^-$	acetate	$Cr_2O_7^{2-}$	dichromate	NH_4^+	ammonium
ClO^-	hypochlorite	HCO_3^-	hydrogen carbonate (bicarbonate)	NO_3^-	nitrate
ClO_2^-	chlorite			NO_2^-	nitrite
ClO_3^-	chlorate	H_3O^+	hydronium	O_2^{2-}	peroxide
ClO_4^-	perchlorate	HPO_4^{2-}	hydrogen phosphate	OH^-	hydroxide
CN^-	cyanide	HSO_3^-	hydrogen sulfite	PO_4^{3-}	phosphate
CO_3^{2-}	carbonate	HSO_4^-	hydrogen sulfate	SO_3^{2-}	sulfite
CrO_4^{2-}	chromate	MnO_4^-	permanganate	SO_4^{2-}	sulfate

Other Symbols and Abbreviations

α	alpha rays	gmm	gram molecular mass	m	mass
β	beta rays	H	enthalpy	m	molality
γ	gamma rays	H_f	heat of formation	mL	milliliter (*volume*)
Δ	change in	h	hour	mm	millimeter (*length*)
δ^-, δ^+	partial ionic charge	h	Planck's constant	mol	mole (*amount*)
λ	wavelength	Hz	hertz (*frequency*)	mp	melting point
π	pi bond	J	joule (*energy*)	N	normality
σ	sigma bond	K	kelvin (*temperature*)	n^0	neutron
ν	frequency	K_a	acid dissociation constant	n	number of moles
amu	atomic mass unit	K_b	base dissociation constant	n	principal quantum number
(*aq*)	aqueous solution	K_b	molal boiling point elevation constant	P	pressure
atm	atmosphere (*pressure*)			p^+	proton
bp	boiling point	K_{eq}	equilibrium constant	Pa	pascal (*pressure*)
°C	degree Celsius (*temperature*)	K_f	molal freezing point depression constant	R	ideal gas constant
c	speed of light in a vacuum			S	entropy
cm	centimeter (*length*)	K_w	ion product constant for water	s	second
D	density			(*s*)	solid
E	energy	K_{sp}	solubility product constant	SI	International System of Units
e^-	electron	kcal	kilocalorie (*energy*)		
fp	freezing point	kg	kilogram (*mass*)	STP	standard temperature and pressure
G	Gibb's free energy	kPa	kilopascal (*pressure*)		
g	gram (*mass*)	L	liter (*volume*)	T	temperature
(*g*)	gas	(*l*)	liquid	$t_{\frac{1}{2}}$	half-life
gam	gram atomic mass	M	molarity	V	volume
gfm	gram formula mass	m	meter (*length*)	v	velocity, speed

Addison-Wesley

Chemistry

Antony C. Wilbraham

Dennis D. Staley

Michael S. Matta

Activity Reviewer and Small-Scale Laboratory Manual Author
Edward L. Waterman

Addison-Wesley Publishing Company
Menlo Park, California • Reading, Massachusetts • New York
Don Mills, Ontario • Wokingham, England • Amsterdam • Bonn
Paris • Milan • Madrid • Sydney • Singapore • Tokyo
Seoul • Taipei • Mexico City • San Juan

Activity Reviewer

Edward L. Waterman
Rocky Mountain High School
Fort Collins, Colorado

Content Reviewers

Katherine A. Anderson
Apple Valley High School
Apple Valley, Minnesota

Linda A. Badzioch
Coast High School
Cambria, California

Elizabeth M. Dabrowski
Magnificat High School
Rocky River, Ohio

Beatrice Epperson
McNary High School
Keizer, Oregon

Carole R. Goshorn
Columbus East High School
Columbus, Indiana

Elizabeth Horsch
Kelly Walsh High School
Casper, Wyoming

Mat Keller
Rancho Cotate High School
Rohnert Park, California

Zoe A. Godby Lightfoot
formerly of Carbondale
Community High School
Carbondale, Illinois

Carol V. Lloyd
University of Nebraska at Omaha
Omaha, Nebraska

Multicultural Graphics Reviewers

Mary Cage
Menlo-Atherton High School
Atherton, California

Sylvia C. Chu
South San Francisco High School
South San Francisco, California

Cheryl A. Leong
Homestead High School
Cupertino, California

James Mendoza
Gunn High School
Palo Alto, California

Miriam Motoyama
Palo Alto High School
Palo Alto, California

Multicultural Content Reviewers

Karen J. Martin
Rich Central High School
Olympia Fields, Illinois

Carol T. Mitchell
University of Nebraska at Omaha
Omaha, Nebraska

Estella W. Sheppard
Dayton Public Schools
Dayton, Ohio

Cover photographs
Paul Silverman/Fundamental Photographs; Joel Gordon (background)

ISBN 0-201-46652-X

7 8 9 10—VH—99

Contents

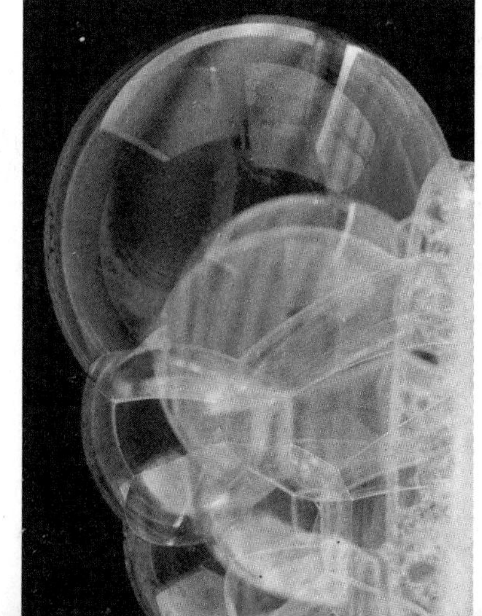

3 Problem Solving in Chemistry 58

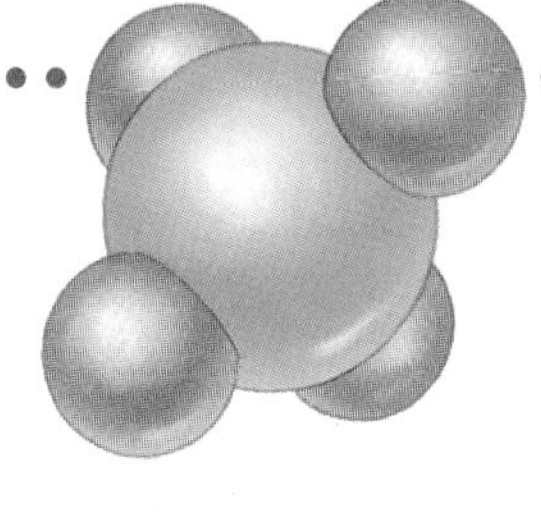

4 Atomic Structure 82

5 Chemical Names and Formulas 106

6 Chemical Quantities 140

7 Chemical Reactions 174

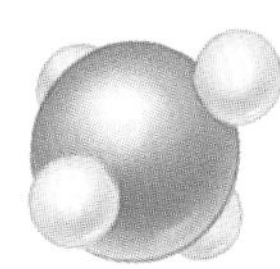

8 Stoichiometry 206

9 The States of Matter 236

10 Thermochemistry 262

11 The Behavior of Gases 290

12 Electrons in Atoms 322

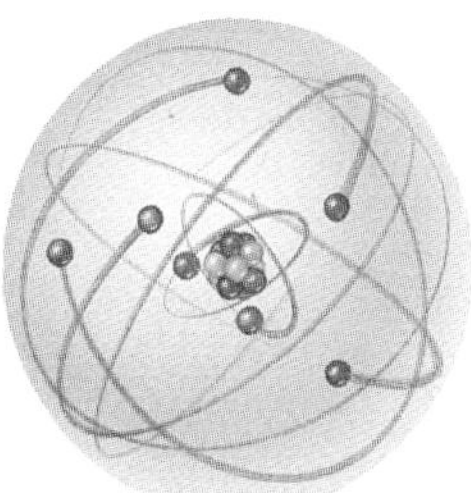

13 Chemical Periodicity 350

14 Ionic Bonds 372

15 Covalent Bonds 392

16 Water and Aqueous Systems 432

17 Properties of Solutions 458

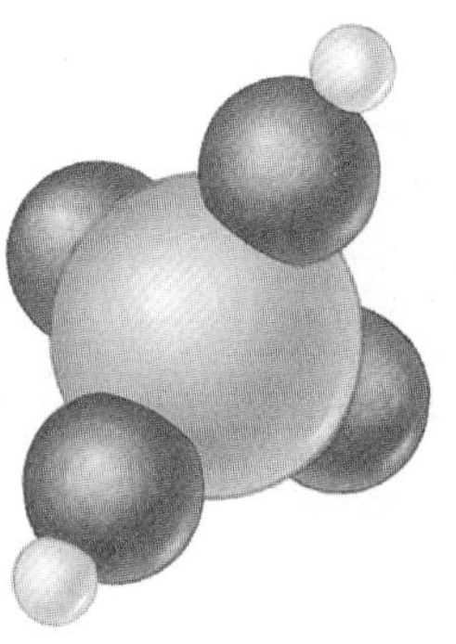

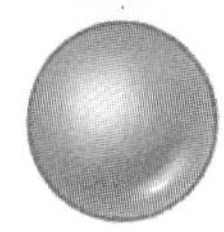

20 Neutralization 568

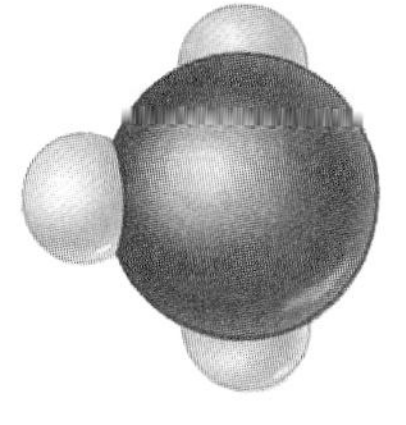

21 Oxidation–Reduction Reactions 596

22 Electrochemistry 622

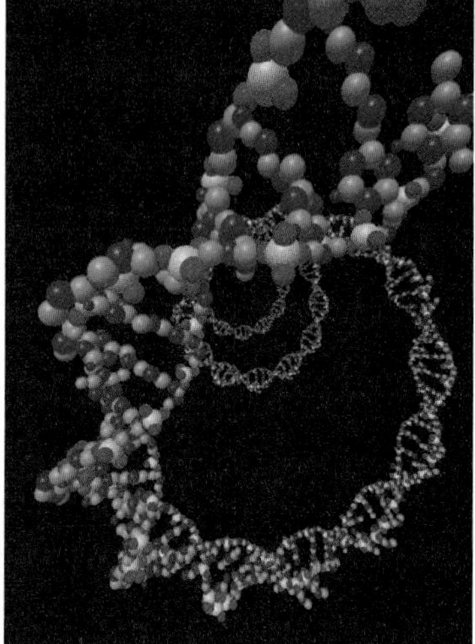

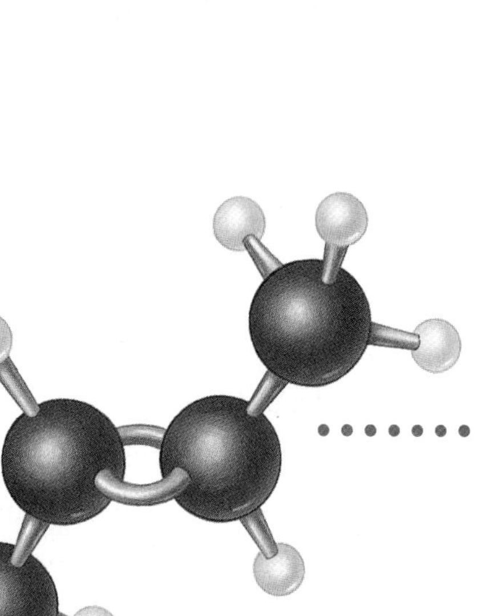

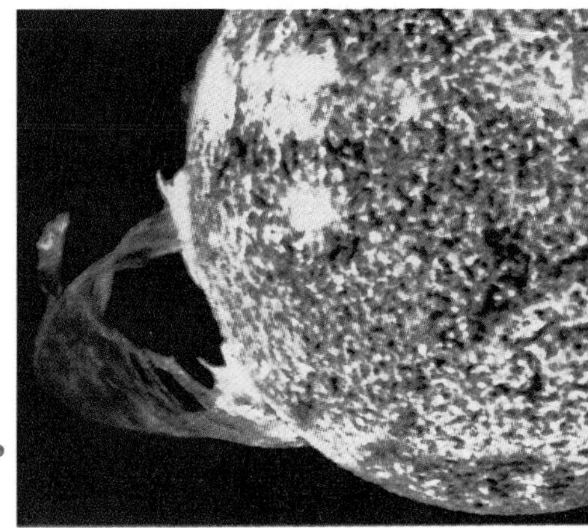

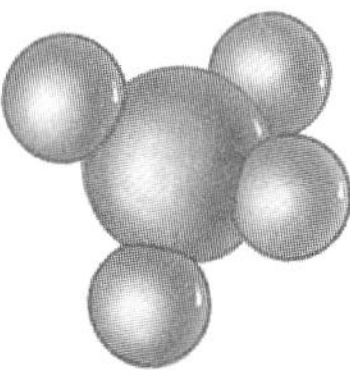

Special Features

Integrating Other Fields

Chemistry in Careers

Biographical Notes

1 Matter and Change

Goals

- Apply the scientific method to "doing science."
- Classify matter by state, as substance or mixture, as homogeneous or heterogeneous.
- Distinguish names and symbols of common elements.
- Distinguish physical changes from chemical changes of matter.

A milkshake is a tasty example of a chemical mixture. In 1988 a 40-foot milk truck was the container for a 1500-gallon milkshake.

Concept Overview

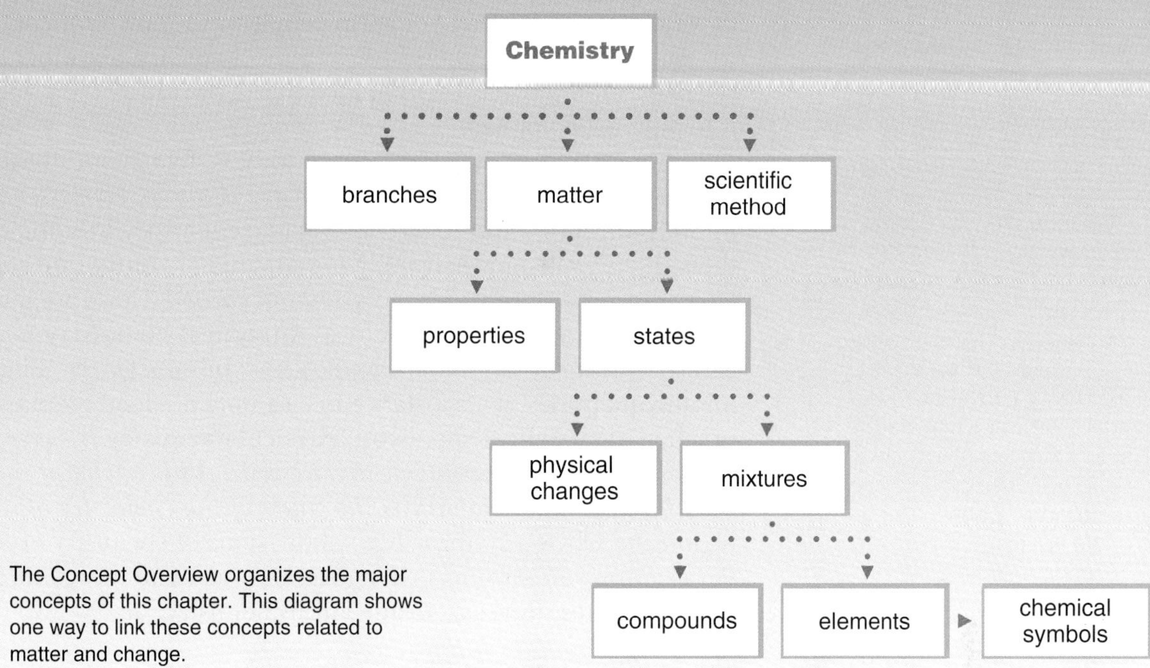

The Concept Overview organizes the major concepts of this chapter. This diagram shows one way to link these concepts related to matter and change.

1.1 Chemistry

Objective

Define chemistry and describe its five major divisions.

Does chemistry affect the things you do every day? The answer is most certainly yes! Perhaps you wear clothes made of synthetic fibers, or natural fibers that have been dyed. The pan you use to cook dinner may have a "nonstick" surface. Or perhaps you use polish remover or hair spray. Each of these actions involves chemistry. How does chemistry make all this possible?

Chemistry *is the study of the composition of substances and the changes they undergo.* In fact, as Figure 1.1 shows, the Japanese and Chinese symbols that make up the word for chemistry mean "change study." The world is complex. Chemistry reflects this complexity in the broad areas it covers. Chemistry contributes to other natural sciences, including biology, geology, and physics.

As a chemist you might do a variety of jobs. You might develop new products, such as medicines or cosmetics. Perhaps you would find methods to reduce pollution or to clean up the environment. As a chemist you could share your knowledge through teaching at any level, analyzing substances, or checking the quality of manufactured products.

Figure 1.1 The Japanese/Chinese characters for chemistry literally mean "change study."

Chemistry in Careers

Chemical Engineering
Chemical engineers are employed by many industries that manufacture or use chemicals. Chemical engineers must determine whether a reaction can be done in large enough amounts for mass production. They plan the layout of the industrial plant, design the equipment, and supervise the plant's construction and operation. They may add safety or pollution control features to comply with new regulations. Chemical engineers are responsible for ensuring that the plant operates efficiently and economically.

Most of these careers use a knowledge of chemistry to attain specific goals. These are examples of applied chemistry, or chemical technology. In applied chemistry, scientific knowledge can be used in ways that either benefit or harm people or the environment.

There is also pure chemistry. In pure chemistry, like other pure sciences, knowledge is accumulated for its own sake. Pure science is neither good nor bad.

Chemistry is usually considered to have five major divisions. *With a few exceptions,* **organic chemistry** *is the study of essentially all substances containing carbon.* Organic chemistry was originally the study of substances from living organisms. **Inorganic chemistry** *largely concerns substances without carbon.* These are mainly substances from nonliving things. **Analytical chemistry** *is concerned primarily with the composition of substances.* Finding minute quantities of a substance in a sample of blood requires the practice of analytical chemistry. **Physical chemistry** *is concerned with theories and experiments that describe the behavior of chemicals. Finally,* **biochemistry** *is the study of the chemistry of living organisms.* Obviously, these five subdivisions of chemistry overlap. For example, measuring a change in an organic or inorganic substance requires some skill in analytical chemistry.

Concept Practice

1. Distinguish between pure and applied chemistry.

2. In which divisions of chemistry might you work on the following?
a. Determining mercury levels in fish.
b. Improving the fuel characteristics of gasoline.
c. Developing new blood-clotting agents.

Objective

Explain the relationship among the terms *experiment, hypothesis, theory,* and *law* in the scientific method.

1.2 The Scientific Method

Each day you make various choices: what to eat, what to wear, when and how much to study. As a citizen of this planet you will also be asked to act on questions of much greater importance. Is nuclear power acceptable or are there better alternative energy sources? What are appropriate responses to the problems of global warming and ozone depletion? Given limited resources, what deserves the most support: the space program or finding a cure for cancer? A knowledge of the basics of science is helpful in arriving at informed opinions on these questions.

What thought processes do scientists use to find the answers to their questions? *The* **scientific method** *is an approach to the solution of scientific problems.* You have certainly used the scientific method in solving problems that you face, because it is closely related to ordinary common sense. Suppose you want to use a flashlight, but when you turn it on it does not light. You have made an *observation*—the flashlight does not light. You guess that the flashlight batteries are probably dead. You have *proposed a reason* for your observation. In the scientific method, scientists must first see, or observe, something of scientific interest. Then they propose an explanation. *A proposed reason for what is observed is called a* **hypothesis.**

You will want to test your proposal or hypothesis with an *experiment. An* **experiment** *is a means of testing a hypothesis.* Probably, you will put new batteries in the flashlight. If the flashlight lights, you are satisfied from one experiment that your hypothesis is true. Table 1.1 shows how the scientific method might be applied to a problem with a videocassette recorder. Scientists also perform experiments to test their hypotheses. For the results of an experiment to be believed, the experiment must produce the same results no matter how many times it is repeated, or by whom. The repeatability of scientific experiments distinguishes science from nonscientific fields.

Many different kinds of experiments may be needed to learn whether a hypothesis is valid. A scientific hypothesis is useful only if it accounts for what scientists observe in many situations. Suppose that the flashlight does not work after you have replaced the batteries. Your hypothesis of dead batteries is probably false. When experimental data do not fit a hypothesis, it must be scrapped or changed. The new or refined hypothesis is then subjected to further experimental testing. In flashlight repair, you may replace the flashlight bulb if replacing the batteries is not helpful. The original, false hypothesis (dead batteries) has led to a new hypothesis (burned out bulb) and a new experiment to test it. The scientific method of

Roots of Words

hypotithenai: (Greek) to suppose or propose
hypothesis a descriptive model used to explain observations.

A hypothesis can be tested by experiments.

Table 1.1 Troubleshooting Guide for a VCR (Scientific Method)

Trouble (Observation)	Possible cause (Hypothesis)	Corrective action (Experiment)
VCR is producing a poor picture on the TV.	1. VCR tracking adjustment is not set correctly. 2. Tape is defective. 3. VCR heads are dirty or magnetized. 4. Magnetic field interference.	1. Adjust tracking on VCR. 2. Try playing a different tape. 3. Clean and demagnetize the VCR's heads. 4. Move VCR away from sources of interference, such as a TV or amplifier.

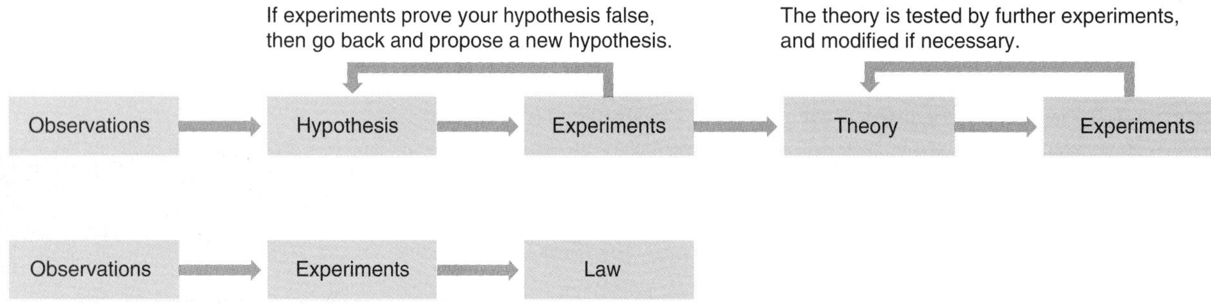

Figure 1.2 This outline of the scientific method shows how observations lead to the development of hypotheses and theories. Note that if experiments prove the hypothesis false, you must go back and propose a new hypothesis.

observing, proposing (hypothesizing), and testing (experimenting) is repeated until the hypothesis fits all of the observed experimental facts. Figure 1.2 outlines the major features of the scientific method.

Once a scientific hypothesis meets the test of repeated experimentation, it may be elevated to a higher level of ideas. *A* **theory** *is a thoroughly tested explanation of why experiments give certain results.* A theory can never be proved; it is always possible that a new experiment will disprove it. Nevertheless, theories are useful because they can help you form mental pictures of objects or processes that you cannot see. Moreover, they can give you the power to predict the behavior of natural systems under varying circumstances.

Another product of scientific research is a law. *A* **scientific law** *is a concise statement that summarizes the results of a broad spectrum of observations and experiments.* A scientific law describes a natural phenomenon, but it does not attempt to explain it. Scientific laws can often be expressed by simple mathematical relationships.

You know that a sealed container should not be thrown into a fire, because a buildup of the pressure of the gas inside might cause it to explode. The increase in pressure in a sealed container because of an increase in temperature is one of the gas laws. This law states that the pressure of a gas is directly proportional to the temperature if the volume is kept constant. This law summarizes what happens when you heat a sealed container. As a law, it does not explain why that happens. For an explanation you must look to theory.

Concept Practice

3. When you solve a problem using the scientific method, why must you have a hypothesis *before* you do experiments?

4. Later in this chapter you will learn that matter is neither created nor destroyed in any chemical change. Is this statement a theory or a law? Why?

1.A Historical Notebook

Alchemy and the Birth of Chemistry

Alchemy was practiced in China and India as early as 400 B.C. and later in the Arab world and Europe. The goal of alchemists was to change (transmute) common metals into gold. They believed that transmutation could be accomplished by a powerful transmuting agent called the *philosopher's stone.* Although alchemists did not succeed in their quest to transmute common metals into gold, they spurred the development of science through trial and error. They discovered chemicals, designed laboratory apparatus, and developed such procedures as distillation and sublimation.

A thirteenth-century English Franciscan monk named Roger Bacon believed that an understanding of the natural world could be gained through observation and experimentation. Bacon's ideas were put into practice in the sixteenth and seventeenth centuries. In his book *The Sceptical Chymist,* the Englishman Robert Boyle (1627–1691) emphasized the necessity of doing experiments to test ideas that were obtained by reason. A Frenchman, Antoine Lavoisier (1743–1794), took an important new step in doing experiments. This was to make precise measurements of the mass changes in chemical reactions. His experiments transformed chemistry from a science of observation to the science of measurement that it is today. For this reason, Lavoisier is often called the founder of modern chemistry.

Figure 1.3 Alchemists designed various types of balances, crucibles, and glassware in order to mix materials together in hundreds of different ways. Later, chemists used similar equipment in their chemical research.

Figure 1.4 Many ancient civilizations used their practical understanding of chemistry to help improve their lives. Here an Arabian druggist is distilling a cough medicine in an open-air lab.

Think About It

5. Contrast Do you think that the alchemists engaged in science? How did their approach differ from the approach of scientists in the eighteenth century?

Table 1.2 Physical Properties of Some Common Substances

Substance	Formula	State	Color	Melting point (°C)	Boiling point (°C)	Density (g/cm³)
Neon	Ne	Gas	Colorless	−249	−246	0.0009
Oxygen	O_2	Gas	Colorless	−218	−183	0.0014
Ethanol	C_2H_5OH	Liquid	Colorless	−117	78	0.789
Chlorine	Cl_2	Gas	Greenish-yellow	−101	−34	0.0032
Mercury	Hg	Liquid	Silvery-white	−39	357	13.5
Bromine	Br_2	Liquid	Red-brown	−7	59	3.12
Water	H_2O	Liquid	Colorless	0	100	1.00
Sulfur	S	Solid	Yellow	113	445	2.07
Sucrose	$C_{12}H_{22}O_{11}$	Solid	White	185	d*	1.59
Sodium chloride	$NaCl$	Solid	White	801	1413	2.17

*d, decomposes on heating.

Objective

Distinguish between matter and a substance.

1.3 Properties of Matter

Aluminum, clothing, water, air, and glass are all different kinds of matter. **Matter** *is anything that takes up space and has mass.* A golf ball contains more matter than a table-tennis ball. The golf ball has more mass. *The amount of matter that an object contains is its* **mass.**

Table sugar is 100% sugar. Table sugar (sucrose) is an example of a substance. *A* **substance** *is a particular kind of matter that has a uniform and definite composition.* Lemonade is not a substance because not all pitchers of lemonade are identical. Different pitchers of lemonade may have different amounts of sugar, lemon juice, or water and may taste different.

All crystals of sucrose taste sweet and dissolve completely in water. All samples of a substance have identical physical properties. *A* **physical property** *is a quality or condition of a substance that can be observed or measured without changing the substance's composition.* Some physical properties of matter are color, solubility, mass, odor, hardness, density, and boiling point.

Physical properties help chemists to identify substances. Scan the physical properties of the common substances in Table 1.2. A colorless liquid that boils at 100°C and melts at 0°C is probably water.

Concept Practice

6. Use Table 1.2 to find three properties of sucrose that distinguish it from sodium chloride.

1.4 The States of Matter

Objective

Name and characterize the three states of matter.

You are very familiar with the substance named water. At certain times, however, you call the same substance ice or steam. You use these three names because water, like most other substances, can exist in three different physical states: solid, liquid, and gas. The physical state of a substance is a physical property of that substance. Certain characteristics summarized in Table 1.3 distinguish each state of matter.

Coal, sugar, bone, ice, and iron are examples of solids. The shape of a solid does not depend on the shape of the container. *A* **solid** *is matter that has a definite shape and volume.* The particles in a solid are packed tightly together, as shown in Figure 1.5. As a result, solids are almost incompressible—they cannot be squashed to a smaller volume, and they expand only slightly when heated.

Water, milk, and blood are examples of liquids. The particles in a liquid are in contact with one another, but they are packed less tightly than in a solid. Liquids are almost incompressible, but they expand when heated. A liquid flows. That is, it can take the shape of the container in which it is placed. The amount of space, or volume, occupied by a sample of a liquid is the same no matter what shape it takes. The unchanging volume is said to be fixed or constant. *A* **liquid** *is a form of matter that flows, has a fixed volume, and takes the shape of its container.*

Like liquids, gases flow to take the shape of the container that holds them. The particles in a gas are spaced far apart. Unlike liquids, gases expand without limit to fill any space and are easily compressed. *Thus, a* **gas** *is matter that takes both the shape and volume of its container.*

The words *gas* and *vapor* should not be used interchangeably; there is a difference. The term *gas* is limited to substances that exist in the gaseous state at room temperature. For example, air is a mixture of gases including oxygen and nitrogen. *The word* **vapor**

Figure 1.5 Compare the structured arrangement of the particles in a solid to the less structured arrangements shown in the figures for liquids and gases. **(a)** Solids have a definite shape and a definite volume. **(b)** The particles in a liquid have more freedom to move than the particles in a solid. **(c)** The particles in a gas are free to move inside their container.

(a) Particles in a solid

(b) Particles in a liquid

(c) Particles in a gas

Table 1.3 Important Properties of the States of Matter

Property	Solid	Liquid	Gas or vapor
Mass	Definite	Definite	Definite
Shape	Rigid	Indefinite	Indefinite
Volume	Definite	Definite	Indefinite
Temperature increase	Very small expansion	Moderate expansion	Large expansion
Compressibility	Almost incompressible	Almost incompressible	Compressible

describes a substance that, although in the gaseous state, is generally a liquid or solid at room temperature. Steam, the gaseous form of water, is a vapor because water is a liquid at room temperature. Moist air contains water vapor.

Concept Practice

7. What is the physical state of each of the following at room temperature?
a. gold **b.** gasoline **c.** helium

8. Fingernail-polish remover (mostly acetone) is a liquid at room temperature. Would you describe acetone in the gaseous state as a vapor or a gas?

Objective

Identify physical changes of matter.

1.5 Physical Changes

Matter can be changed in many ways without altering its composition. Cutting, grinding, or bending a material causes such a *physical change.* A change in temperature may also bring about a physical change, as the melting of the metal gallium in Figure 1.6 shows. Melting of ice, freezing of water, conversion of water to steam, and condensation of steam to water are all examples of physical changes. These physical transformations do not change the identity of the water. The composition of the substance is unaltered by the physical change. Physical properties of water are the same for water that has been frozen and melted as they are for water that has been converted to steam and then condensed. *A* **physical change** *alters a substance without changing its composition.*

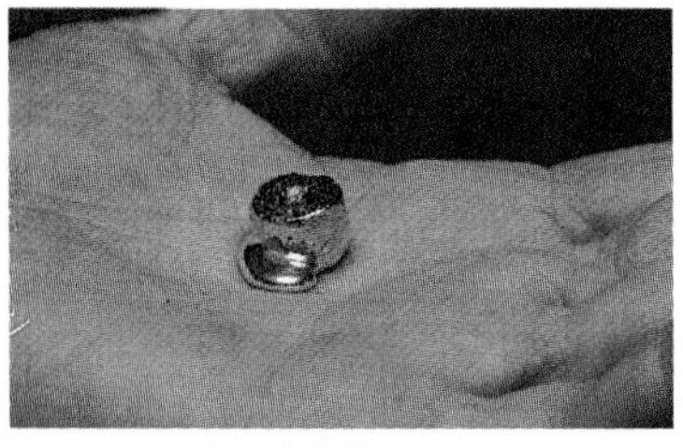

Figure 1.6 The melting point of gallium metal is 30°C. The temperature of the hand is about 37°C.

Words like boil, freeze, dissolve, melt, and condense usually signify a physical change. Other terms include break, split, crack, and crush. Sodium chloride (NaCl), or table salt, is a white solid at room temperature. Sodium chloride can also melt to form a liquid or boil to form a gas. However, the temperatures at which the changes of state occur in sodium chloride are much higher than those of the corresponding physical changes in water. Sodium chloride melts at 801°C and boils at 1413°C; water melts at 0°C and boils at 100°C.

Integrating Physics

Changing States of Matter

Thixotropic substances are solid-like substances that liquefy when subjected to shearing forces. A common example is margarine at room temperature. Margarine is a solid. However, margarine spreads like a liquid when sheared by a knife.

Concept Practice

9. Which of these are physical changes?

a. baking a potato
b. carving a wooden figurine
c. freezing mercury
d. dissolving sugar in water

10. Use Table 1.2 to identify four substances that undergo a physical change if the temperature is decreased from 50°C to –50°C.

1.6 Mixtures

Objective

Classify a sample of matter as a substance or a mixture; as homogeneous or heterogeneous.

You prepare a salad by tossing lettuce, tomatoes, cucumbers, and carrots with some vinegar and oil dressing. Besides preparing good food, you have also made a mixture. **Mixtures** *consist of a physical blend of two or more substances.* Mixtures differ from substances because they have a variable composition.

Mixtures can be heterogeneous or homogeneous. Figure 1.7 gives a few examples of each kind of mixture. *A* **heterogeneous mixture** *is not uniform in composition.* If you were to sample one portion of the mixture, its composition would be different from the composition of another portion. Soil contains bits of decayed material along with sand, silt, and/or clay. What kind of a mixture is soil? Why is the salad you prepared above heterogeneous? *By contrast, a* **homogeneous mixture** *has a completely uniform composition.* The components of the mixture are evenly distributed throughout the sample. Salt water from the ocean is the same throughout the sample. The salt water is a homogeneous mixture.

Figure 1.7 All of these items are mixtures. The toothpaste and the beverage are homogeneous; they have uniform compositions. The salad and the granite are heterogeneous; they consist of a number of phases that are not evenly distributed.

Roots of Words

homo-: (Greek) the same
genes: (Greek) kind

homogeneous mixture
a mixture that is completely uniform in composition; its components are not distinguishable.

Clear tea is a homogeneous mixture.

heteros: (Greek) different

heterogeneous mixture
a mixture that is not uniform in composition; its components are readily distinguishable.

Bean soup is a heterogeneous mixture.

Figure 1.8 The mixture of iron filings and sulfur can be separated using a magnet. The iron filings are attracted to the magnet, but the powdered sulfur is not.

One important characteristic of both heterogeneous and homogeneous mixtures is that their compositions may vary. A dinner salad can have varying amounts of tomatoes or celery added to it. The composition of air in a forest differs from that near an industrial city, particularly in the amounts and kinds of pollutants it contains.

Homogeneous mixtures are so important in chemistry that chemists give them the special name of *solutions. A* **solution** *is a homogeneous mixture.* As Table 1.4 shows, solutions may be gases, liquids, or solids. If you took a sample from any portion of a solution of sugar in water, you would find that it has the same composition as any other portion. *Any part of a system with uniform composition and properties is called a* **phase**. Thus a homogeneous mixture consists of a single phase, and a heterogeneous mixture consists of two or more phases. Vinegar-and-oil dressing is an example of a heterogeneous mixture with two phases. The separate phases are visible when the bottle of dressing is left unshaken; the oil phase floats on the water phase.

Some mixtures can be separated into their various components by simple physical methods. You might use a fork to separate a taco into meat, lettuce, cheese, and tomatoes. But how would you separate the gray-colored mixture of powdered yellow sulfur and black iron filings of Figure 1.8? The individual particles of sulfur and iron can be readily distinguished from one another under a microscope, so the mixture is heterogeneous. The iron filings can be removed from the mixture with a magnet, leaving the sulfur behind. Both the sulfur and the iron are unchanged in composition.

Tap water is a homogeneous mixture of water plus other substances that are dissolved in it. How would you separate the components in tap water? One method used to purify water is distillation. *During* **distillation** *a liquid is boiled to produce a vapor that is then condensed again to a liquid.* Figure 1.9 shows a distillation apparatus. When water is distilled, it is heated to form steam. Then the steam cools and forms droplets of pure water inside the glass tube. The water drips into a receiver, where it is collected. The solid substances originally dissolved in the water remain in the

Table 1.4 Some Common Types of Solutions

System	Examples
Gas–gas	Carbon dioxide and oxygen in nitrogen (air)
Liquid–gas	Water vapor in air (moist air)
Gas–liquid	Carbon dioxide in water (soda water)
Liquid–liquid	Acetic acid in water (vinegar)
Solid–liquid	Sodium chloride in water (brine)
Solid–solid	Copper in silver (sterling silver, an alloy)

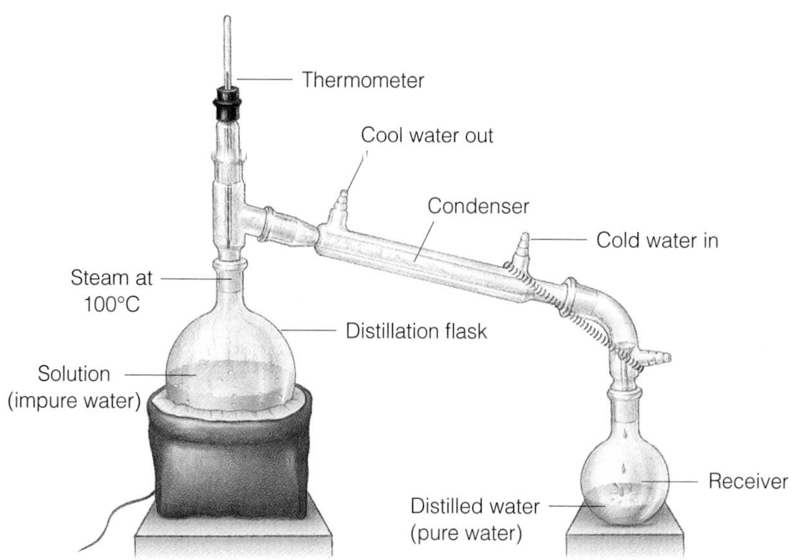

Figure 1.9 A solution of impure water is being distilled. As the water boils it turns into steam, leaving the impurities behind in the solution flask. As the steam passes through the water-cooled condenser, it is condensed into distilled water, which is collected in the receiving flask.

distillation flask because they do not change into a vapor. Distilled water is pure except for the dissolved gases it contains. Water from which the dissolved gases are removed is a pure substance. Water has unique properties: It freezes at 0°C and boils at 100°C.

Example 1 Separating Mixtures

How would you separate the following mixtures?

a. sawdust from sand

b. sand from salt

Solution

a. Add water to the mixture. The sawdust floats, while the sand sinks.

b. Add water to dissolve the salt. Pour the mixture onto a piece of cloth. The sand remains on the cloth, and the salt solution goes through. Let the water evaporate and leave solid salt.

Concept Practice

11. How many phases does every solution have?

12. Classify each of the following as homogeneous or heterogeneous mixtures.

a. blood **b.** peanut butter **c.** motor oil

Activity 1
Mixtures

Purpose

Separate a mixture by paper chromatography.

Materials

strips of filter paper
green marking pens
clear plastic drinking cups
clear plastic wrap
clear plastic tape
rubbing alcohol
water
pencil

Procedure

1. Pour rubbing alcohol into a plastic cup to a depth of 1 cm. Cover the cup with plastic wrap.

2. Draw a horizontal line with the marking pen 2 cm from one end of a strip of filter paper.

3. Tape the filter paper strip by the unmarked end to the center of a pencil so that the strip hangs down when the pencil is held horizontal.

4. Remove the plastic wrap from the cup. Rest the pencil on the rim of the cup so that the lower end of the paper strip is just in contact with the rubbing alcohol. Carefully, cover the top of the cup with plastic wrap.

5. Observe for 15 minutes.

6. If time permits, use different brands and different colors of pens and use water in place of rubbing alcohol.

Analysis and Conclusions

1. How do you know that the green ink was a mixture?

2. Approximately how far did the rubbing alcohol travel up the paper in 15 minutes?

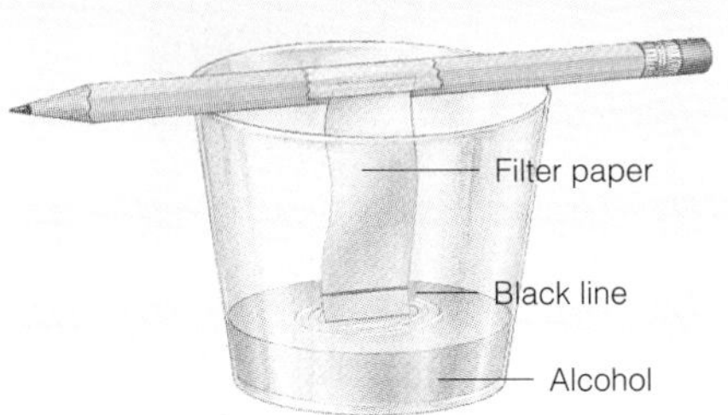

Objective

Explain the difference between an element and a compound.

1.7 Elements and Compounds

By physically separating mixtures into their component parts, you obtain pure substances. You may recall that a substance has a uniform and definite composition. Substances are divided into two groups, *elements* and *compounds.* Because you will be working with elements and compounds in the laboratory, you should be able to tell them apart. **Elements** *are the simplest forms of matter that can exist under normal laboratory conditions.* Elements cannot be separated into simpler substances by chemical reactions. Elements are the building blocks for all other substances. Two or more elements can combine chemically with one another to form compounds. **Compounds** *are substances that can be separated into simpler substances only by chemical reaction.* The different elements that make up a compound are always present in that compound in the same proportions. Every element and every compound has its own unique set of properties.

Safety

Never taste any chemical in the laboratory, even if you are sure it is safe.

You might caramelize sugar to make candied apples or a flan. Heating table sugar demonstrates the difference between elements and compounds. With gentle heating the sugar caramelizes and turns a light brown color because the sugar undergoes chemical reactions and new substances form. Upon strong heating, sugar decomposes completely to carbon and water vapor. This experiment shows that sugar is a compound, not an element. The chemical reactions caused by strongly heating sugar break the sugar down into two substances, carbon and water. Now, can the water and the carbon be broken down? The water that comes from the breakdown of the sugar can be broken down into hydrogen and oxygen by another chemical reaction. Thus water, like sugar, is a compound. Carbon, hydrogen, and oxygen cannot be broken down into simpler substances. They are elements.

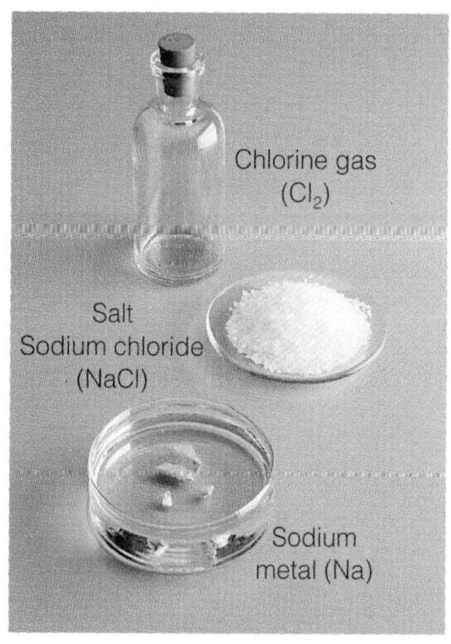

Figure 1.10 The compound sodium chloride is common table salt. It is composed of the elements sodium (a solid) and chlorine (a gas). As a safety precaution, sodium is stored under oil to prevent it from reacting with moisture in the air.

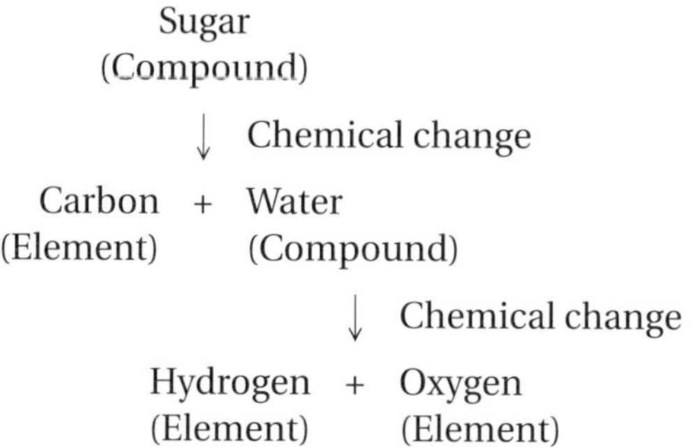

In general, the chemical and physical properties of compounds are quite different from those of their component elements. For example, table sugar is a sweet white solid, but carbon is a black tasteless solid. Water is a colorless liquid, but oxygen and hydrogen are colorless gases. Table salt (sodium chloride) is composed of the elements sodium and chlorine. Figure 1.10 shows how the physical appearances of chlorine, sodium, and sodium chloride differ.

Figure 1.11 summarizes some information about elements, compounds, and mixtures. Deciding whether a sample of matter is a substance or a homogeneous mixture can be difficult. After all, a homogeneous mixture looks like a substance. To help think about these differences, ask yourself: "Is there more than one kind of this

Figure 1.11 Any sample of matter can be classified as an element, compound, or mixture.

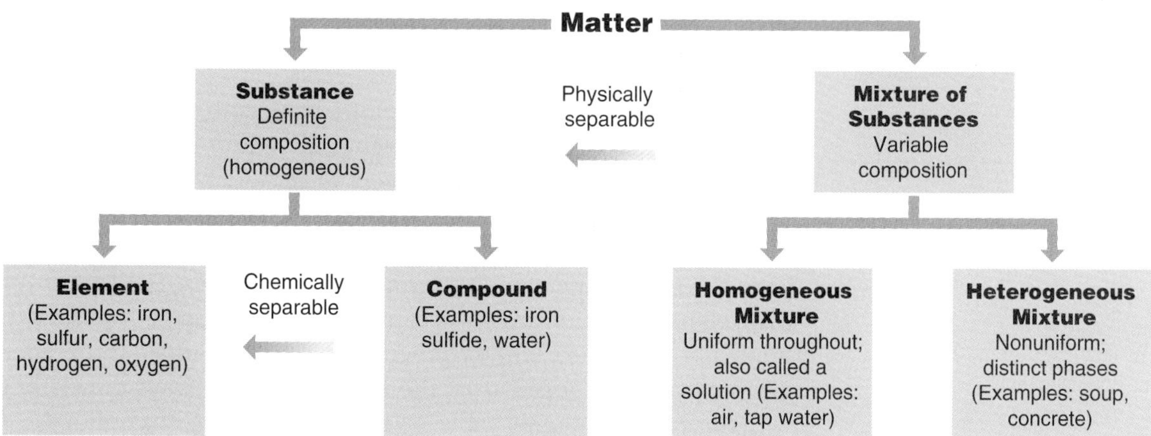

material?" For example, how would you classify gasoline? Based on its physical appearance, you might conclude that gasoline is a compound. Gasoline must be a mixture, however, because it comes in so many different grades. Gasoline has different octane ratings, and it can be leaded or unleaded. Gasoline may contain alcohol. You should also conclude that a given sample of gasoline is a homogeneous mixture because each grade is uniform throughout.

Integrating English

Origins of Element Names

Many elements are named for the people who discovered them or the places where they were discovered. Some elements were given descriptive names taken from classical Latin or Greek. Others were named for figures in mythology. Polonium is named for Poland, the native land of Marie Curie, the famous discoverer of radium. Californium was discovered at the University of California. The word *chlorine* comes from the Greek *chloros*, meaning "greenish-yellow." The name *calcium* is derived from the Latin *calx*, meaning "lime." Calcium is a major component of limestone. You can find the origins of elements' names by consulting a good dictionary or encyclopedia.

Example 2 Telling Elements and Compounds Apart

When a homogeneous blue solid is heated in the absence of air, a colorless gas and a white solid are formed. Which of these substances are elements and which are compounds? Explain.

Solution

The blue solid was homogeneous, so it was not a mixture. It separated into two substances when it was heated. Therefore, it must be a compound. The two resulting substances may be elements or compounds. You cannot tell from the information given.

Concept Practice

13. Classify these as elements, compounds, or mixtures.

a. silver **c.** orange juice **e.** iced tea
b. a pine tree **d.** oxygen **f.** air

14. A clear liquid in an open container is allowed to evaporate. After three days, a solid residue is left. Was the original liquid an element, compound, or mixture? How do you know?

Objective

Distinguish the symbols of common elements, and match the names of common elements to their symbols.

1.8 Chemical Symbols

Carbon, hydrogen, oxygen, sodium, and chlorine are only a few of the approximately 100 known elements. All matter in the universe is composed of elements. *Each element is represented by a* **chemical symbol.** The symbols for most elements consist of the first one or two letters of the name of the element. Table A.1, in the appendix, gives the names and symbols for all of the elements. The first letter of an element's name is always capitalized. If a second letter is used, it must be lowercase. Some element symbols are derived from older Latin names. In those cases, the symbol is not always consistent with the common name. Table 1.5 lists some of these exceptions.

Table 1.5 Symbols and Latin Names for Some Elements

Element	Symbol	Latin name
Sodium	Na	*Natrium*
Potassium	K	*Kalium*
Antimony	Sb	*Stibium*
Copper	Cu	*Cuprum*
Gold	Au	*Aurum*
Silver	Ag	*Argentum*
Iron	Fe	*Ferrum*
Lead	Pb	*Plumbum*
Mercury	Hg	*Hydrargyrum*
Tin	Sn	*Stannum*
Tungsten	W	From Wolfram (not Latin)

Figure 1.12 Many different symbols were developed over time to represent chemicals, processes, and phenomena.

Chemical symbols are a shorthand way to write chemical formulas of compounds. The compound water is composed of the elements hydrogen and oxygen. The formula for water is H_2O. The formula for table sugar (sucrose) is $C_{12}H_{22}O_{11}$. Sucrose is composed of the elements carbon, hydrogen, and oxygen. The numbers in subscripts in the chemical formulas represent the proportions of the various elements in the compound. A specific compound is always made up of the same elements in the same proportions throughout. Thus the formula for a specific chemical compound is always the same.

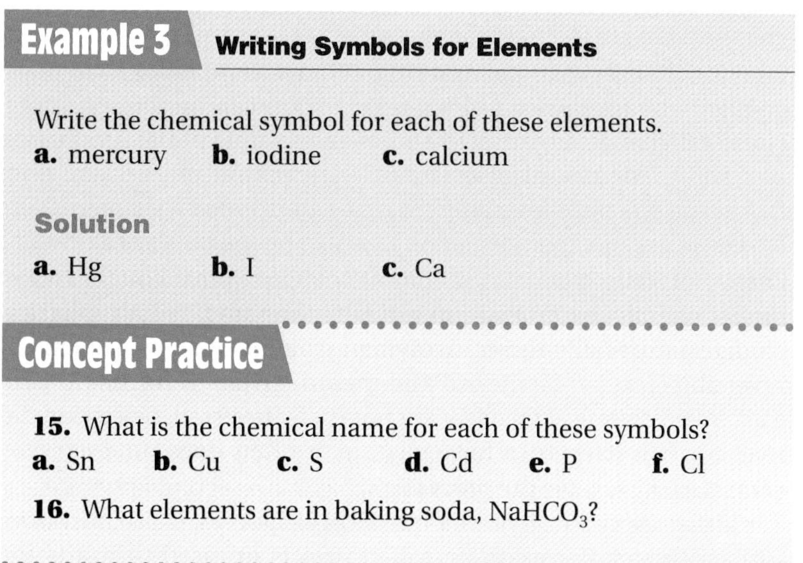

Example 3 **Writing Symbols for Elements**

Write the chemical symbol for each of these elements.

a. mercury **b.** iodine **c.** calcium

Solution

a. Hg **b.** I **c.** Ca

Concept Practice

15. What is the chemical name for each of these symbols?

a. Sn **b.** Cu **c.** S **d.** Cd **e.** P **f.** Cl

16. What elements are in baking soda, $NaHCO_3$?

Objective

Compare physical and chemical changes in matter.

1.9 Chemical Reactions

You have seen that compounds can be separated into simpler substances only by chemical reaction. For example, when table sugar is caramelized, it breaks down, and a chemical change takes place. The important point is that when the hot liquid cools, the sugar has lost its identity. The liquid does not turn back into solid sugar, because the sugar has been changed into new substances. *In a* **chemical reaction,** *one or more substances change into new substances.* The change in composition of the sugar results from a chemical reaction. *In a chemical reaction, the starting substances are called* **reactants** *and the new substances are the* **products**.

Figure 1.13 A chemical change occurs when a mixture of powdered sulfur and iron filings is heated. The reactants are converted into the product, which has different chemical and physical properties.

To help distinguish between physical and chemical changes, recall how sulfur and iron filings may be separated unchanged from a mixture. This separation is an example of a physical change. If the mixture of these two substances is heated, however, a chemical reaction takes place. The sulfur and iron change into a nonmagnetic substance, iron sulfide. Chemists use an arrow as a shorthand form of the phrase "are changed into." Using the shorthand expression, this change can be written as follows.

$$\underset{\text{Reactants}}{\text{Iron + sulfur}} \xrightarrow{\text{heat}} \underset{\text{Product}}{\text{iron sulfide}}$$

Figure 1.13 shows the product of this reaction. What are some indications that a chemical reaction has occurred? Energy is always taken in or given off in chemical reactions. When you cook food it takes in or absorbs heat; when you burn coal it gives off or evolves heat. Energy is also absorbed or evolved, however, in physical changes of state. A color change, as in leaves turning in the fall, or an odor change, as in meat rotting, often accompanies a chemical change. The production of a gas or a solid can be the result of a chemical change. Figure 1.14 shows an example of the production of a solid. The chemical decay of plant matter on the lake floor forms the gas bubbles rising from the bottom of a stagnant lake. However, gas or vapor formation can also be the result of a physical change of state. When water boils, it changes from a liquid to a gas, but its chemical composition remains the same. Finally, physical changes, especially those involving a change of state, are usually reversible. Ice can be melted and then the water refrozen. In contrast, most chemical changes are not easily reversed. Once iron has reacted with oxygen to form rust, as it often does on a car, you cannot easily reverse the process.

Figure 1.14 Here, red silver chromate forms when a solution of sodium chromate is added to a solution of silver nitrate.

Just as every substance has physical properties, it also has *chemical properties.* For example, when iron is exposed to water and oxygen, it corrodes and produces a new substance called iron oxide (rust). *The ability of a substance to undergo chemical reactions and to form new substances constitutes its* **chemical properties.** Rusting is a chemical property of iron. Chemical properties are observed only when a substance undergoes a change in composition and therefore a chemical change. Words like rot, rust, decompose, ferment, corrode, grow, decay, and sprout usually signify a chemical change.

Concept Practice

17. List four probable indications of chemical change.

18. Classify the following changes as physical or chemical.

a. Bread is baked.

b. Salt dissolves in water.

c. Milk spoils.

d. A snowflake melts.

1.10 Conservation of Mass

Objective

State the law of conservation of mass.

Combustion, or burning, is an example of one of the most familiar chemical changes. When you burn a piece of coal, atmospheric oxygen combines with the carbon in the coal. The products are carbon dioxide gas and water vapor. There is also a large residue of ash due to the mineral impurities in the coal. Careful measurements show that the mass of the reactants (the coal and oxygen consumed) equals the mass of the products (the carbon dioxide, water vapor, and ash). During a chemical reaction, the quantity of matter is unchanged. Look at Figure 1.15. When a flash bar is used to take a picture the mass of the flash bar does not change. Similarly, when 10 grams of ice melt, 10 grams of water are obtained. Again, in this physical process, mass is conserved. Similar observations have been recorded for many chemical and physical changes. *Thus, the* **law of conservation of mass** *states that in any physical or chemical reaction, mass is neither created nor destroyed; it is conserved.* In every case, the mass of the products equals the mass of the reactants.

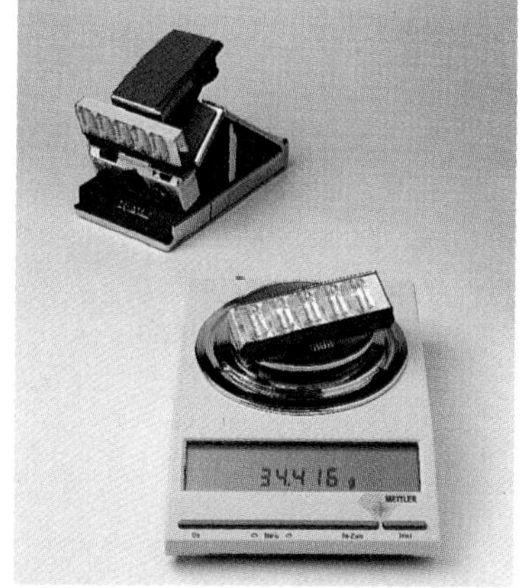

Figure 1.15 After the flash bar has been used, it looks different, indicating a chemical reaction. Magnesium has been converted into magnesium oxide, yet the mass of the flash bar does not change.

Concept Practice

19. Why is the statement of the conservation of mass a law and not a theory?

20. When powdered iron is left exposed to the air it rusts. Explain why the rust weighs more than the original powdered iron.

Practice Problem

21. Hydrogen and oxygen react chemically to form water. How much water would be formed if 4.8 grams of hydrogen reacted with 38.4 grams of oxygen?

1.B Science, Technology, and Society

Chemistry for the Sake of Art

Figure 1.17 There is a marked difference in the appearance of the interior of the Sistine Chapel before and after restoration.

Works of art reflect the culture in which they are created. For this reason, all cultures have tried to protect and restore works of art. Since the 1970s, chemists who specialize in art restoration have been applying scientific methods to their work. These chemists bring an array of instruments such as infrared spectrometers and X-ray spectrometers to their restoration efforts.

The goal of art restoration is to bring a painting or sculpture as close to its original condition as possible. The artwork must continue to represent the intentions of the artist. The restoration process must not change the piece of art. In order to retain authenticity at the microscopic level, restorers may analyze the artwork chemically. From the analysis, the exact mixtures of paints and varnishes can be reproduced and used for touch-up work. However, chemists must work with art historians to make the best decisions about what restoration techniques should be used.

The techniques of art restoration may be controversial. For example, Michelangelo's painting on the ceiling of the Sistine Chapel in Rome was recently cleaned. A mixture of sodium and ammonium hydrogen carbonates suspended in a cellulose gel was used for cleaning. Some people view the results as a great success, but critics argue that the solvent was too harsh for use on such a delicate painting. The critics claim further that the painting was irreparably altered so that its authenticity was not retained.

Think About It

22. Identify Are you aware of any pieces of art in need of restoration in your community? What would you need to know before suggesting a plan for restoration?

Materials

Labels of Civilization

Some of the materials you use for everyday activities have been developed over millions of years! In all cultures, chance discoveries have contributed to the development of materials for specific uses. Now, more than ever, there is a surge of scientific research into making specialized materials with specific tasks. This area of science, called materials science, involves many applications of chemistry.

Historically, the development of new materials has marked the ages of human development. Before you move into the New Materials Age, read about the early development of materials.

Two million years ago, the primary materials people used were stone, wood, clay, and animal skins. In fact, the distinct stone tools developed and used then gave this period of civilization its name, the Stone Age. The people of the Stone Age also used clay. Clay pottery was probably the first material to be manufactured by people. Copper compounds from copper ores were used to color the earliest Egyptian pottery with glazes.

The Stone Age ended only about 5000 years ago. Perhaps by chance, the copper ores that gave pottery its beautiful color were heated high enough to leave some copper metal behind. The smelting of copper ores, azurite and malachite, to obtain copper metal led to new materials. Soon after copper first came into use, about 2500 B.C., the toughening and hardening effect of mixing tin with copper was discovered. The product was bronze. Bronze is an alloy composed of seven parts copper and one part tin. Thus, the Bronze Age replaced the Stone Age.

Bronze was made as early as 3000 B.C. in ancient Greece but was not made in China until 1800 B.C. Bronze was used to make tools and weapons and was preferred to copper because it was easier to cast and a harder material.

By 1000 B.C., just 3000 years ago, iron was in common use. However, the temperature attainable in the furnace of the time was not sufficient to melt the crude iron. It had to be forged or hammered repeatedly, when hot, to remove impurities. As the production of iron increased, the world left the Bronze Age and entered the Iron Age.

With advancing technology, iron-smelting furnaces using forced air could attain a high enough temperature to melt iron. Africans produced cast iron in forced-draft furnaces as long as 2000 years ago. The blast furnace was used in Sweden by about A.D. 1250 and was introduced in England in the fifteenth century.

A major breakthrough was made in the Iron Age when the scarce charcoal used for fuel in the blast furnaces was replaced by coke, almost pure carbon. This made it possible to smelt iron on a much larger scale and contributed to the Industrial Revolution in Europe.

In the present time, your period of human development, people can manipulate scientific variables and develop technologies to make materials with specific properties. What are the materials that your civilization will be labeled by? Will it be called the Plastics Age? The Composites Age? Throughout this book, you will read about materials that may become the labels of your civilization.

Think About It

23. Explain In what ways are the accomplishments of humankind linked to the materials that are available to a culture at a given point in history?

Chapter 1 Review
Matter and Change

Key Terms

analytical chemistry *1.1*
biochemistry *1.1*
chemical property *1.9*
chemical reaction *1.9*
chemical symbol *1.8*
chemistry *1.1*
compound *1.7*
distillation *1.6*
element *1.7*
experiment *1.2*
gas *1.4*
heterogeneous mixture *1.6*
homogeneous mixture *1.6*
hypothesis *1.2*
inorganic chemistry *1.1*
law of conservation of mass *1.10*
liquid *1.4*
mass *1.3*
matter *1.3*
mixture *1.6*
organic chemistry *1.1*
phase *1.6*
physical change *1.5*
physical chemistry *1.1*
physical property *1.3*
product *1.9*
reactant *1.9*
scientific law *1.2*
scientific method *1.2*
solid *1.4*
solution *1.6*
substance *1.3*
theory *1.2*
vapor *1.4*

Chapter Summary

Chemistry is a natural science that deals with the composition of matter and the changes it undergoes. Matter is anything that has mass and occupies space. Matter exists in three states: solid, liquid, and gas. Chemists use the scientific method to learn how matter can be changed.

A physical combination of two or more substances is a mixture. A mixture has a variable composition and may be identified as heterogeneous or homogeneous. A mixture can be separated into its components by physical methods. Homogeneous mixtures (solutions) have uniform properties throughout. Solutions may be gases, liquids, or solids. Like all other mixtures, solutions have variable composition.

A pure substance is either an element or a compound. A pure substance is identified by its physical properties. Elements are the building blocks for all compounds. Elements are always present in the same ratio in a given compound. The properties of a compound are usually quite different from those of the elements of which it is composed. Chemical methods are required to separate compounds into their constituent elements.

A change in the properties of a substance without a change in composition is a physical change. If there is a change in the composition of a substance, however, a chemical change has occurred. In a chemical change (chemical reaction) reactants are converted to products. In any physical or chemical change mass is conserved.

Practice Questions and Problems

24. Define chemistry. *1.1*

25. List the five major divisions of chemistry. *1.1*

26. Distinguish among a theory, hypothesis, and law. *1.2*

27. What is the purpose of an experiment as part of the scientific method? *1.2*

28. Identify contributions of each of these to the development of chemistry. *1.A*

a. Arab alchemists
b. Robert Boyle
c. Antoine Lavoisier

29. Use Table 1.2 to answer the following questions. *1.3*

a. What single property do neon, ethanol, and oxygen have in common?
b. Why doesn't sucrose have a boiling point listed?
c. Make a general statement comparing the densities of gaseous substances with the densities of solid substances.

30. List four physical properties of an iron nail. *1.3*

31. In which state of matter do the following exist at room temperature and atmospheric pressure? *1.4*

a. diamond
b. oxygen
c. cooking oil
d. mercury
e. clay
f. neon

32. Match each state of matter with the terms on the left. More than one state can match each term. *1.4*

a. incompressible **1.** gas
b. indefinite shape **2.** liquid
c. definite volume **3.** solid
d. flows

33. List three substances that you have experienced in at least two physical states. *1.4*

34. What physical properties would you use to separate these mixtures? *1.5*

a. iron filings and salt **b.** salt and water

35. Name two physical properties that could be used to distinguish between these substances. *1.5*

a. water and rubbing alcohol
b. gold and aluminum
c. helium gas and oxygen gas

36. What is the difference between a heterogeneous and a homogeneous mixture? *1.6*

37. How can the various components of a mixture be separated? *1.6*

38. Identify each of the following samples of matter as homogeneous or heterogeneous. *1.6*

a. spaghetti sauce **d.** river water
b. glass **e.** cough syrup
c. table sugar **f.** nitrogen

39. How can you distinguish between an element and a compound? *1.7*

40. Classify each of the samples of matter in Problem 38 as an element, compound, or mixture. *1.7*

41. Write the chemical symbols for each of the following elements. *1.8*

a. copper **d.** silver
b. oxygen **e.** sodium
c. phosphorus **f.** helium

42. Name the elements found in each compound. *1.8*

a. ammonium chloride (NH_4Cl)
b. potassium permanganate ($KMnO_4$)
c. isopropyl alcohol (C_3H_7OH)
d. calcium iodide (CaI_2)

43. Classify each of the following as a physical or chemical change. *1.9*

a. bending a piece of wire
b. burning coal
c. cooking a steak
d. cutting grass

44. State several physical or chemical properties that could be used to distinguish between these pairs of substances and mixtures. *1.9*

a. gasoline and water
b. copper and silver
c. water and a saltwater solution

45. Describe three chemical changes that you observed today. *1.9*

46. A friend observes a burning candle and comments that the wax is *lost* as the candle burns. Having recently studied the law of conservation of mass, how would you correct your friend? *1.10*

47. When ammonium nitrate (NH_4NO_3) explodes it forms nitrogen gas (N_2), oxygen gas (O_2), and water (H_2O). When 40 grams of ammonium nitrate explode, 14 grams of nitrogen and 8 grams of oxygen are formed. How many grams of water are formed? *1.10*

Mastery Questions and Problems

48. A concept map is a concise way to show the relationships among a number of concepts and ideas. Use the chapter key terms to complete this concept map using *matter* as the key concept.

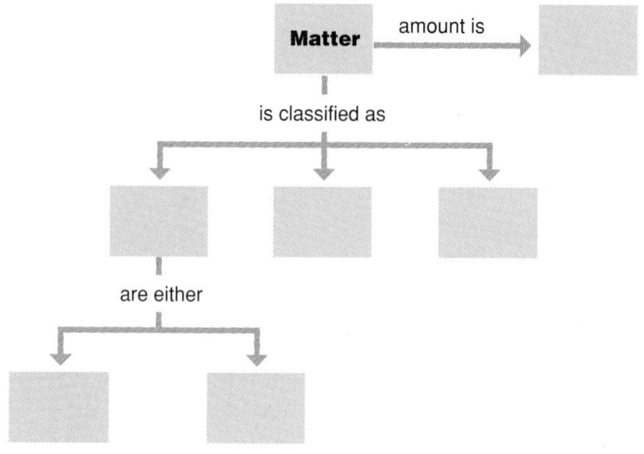

49. Devise a way to separate sand from a mixture of charcoal, sand, sugar, and water.

50. Describe two situations in which you have used at least part of the scientific method this past week.

51. Describe the difference between chemistry and chemical technology.

52. What was the major goal of the alchemists? Did they succeed in achieving this goal? What lasting contributions did the alchemists make to modern chemistry?

53. Imagine standing in the kitchen of your home and standing in the middle of a park. When you view the surroundings in each location, do you see mostly elements, compounds, or mixtures?
   a. kitchen   **b.** park

54. Use Table 1.2 to answer each question.
   a. Which property most easily distinguishes sulfur from the other solid substances?
   b. How many of these substances are elements?
   c. Which compound has the highest density?
   d. The three gases are gradually cooled. Which one will first condense to a liquid?

55. When a small amount of a red powder is heated, it darkens and then changes into a shiny silvery liquid. Is the red powder an element or a compound? Explain. Can you classify the shiny liquid with certainty? Explain.

56. Identify each of the following as a mixture or a compound. For the mixtures, classify as homogeneous or heterogeneous.
   a. soda   **e.** an egg
   b. candle wax   **f.** ice
   c. fog   **g.** blood
   d. ink   **h.** gasoline

57. Classify the following properties of the element silicon as chemical or physical properties.
   a. blue-gray color
   b. brittle
   c. insoluble in water
   d. melts at 1410°C
   e. reacts vigorously with fluorine

58. How do you know that each of these is a chemical change?
   a. Food spoils.
   b. A foaming antacid tablet fizzes in water.
   c. A ring of scum forms around your bathtub.
   d. Iron rusts.
   e. A firecracker explodes.

Critical Thinking Questions

59. Choose the term that best completes the second relationship.
   a. seed:plant   data: _____
      (1) theory   (3) experiment
      (2) law   (4) scientific method
   b. words:sentence   elements: _____
      (1) reactant   (3) compound
      (2) theory   (4) substance
   c. person:female   mixture: _____
      (1) substance   (3) seawater
      (2) compound   (4) solution

60. You do an experiment and get unexpected results. According to the scientific method, what would you do next?

61. Compare the relationships between individual particles in the three states of matter.

62. It has been said that science accepts what works and rejects what doesn't work. Comment on this idea.

63. Explain why this statement is false. "Since there is no change in composition during a physical change, the appearance of the substance will not change."

64. Two different compounds have an identical appearance. How could you distinguish between them?

Challenge Questions and Problems

65. These questions refer to the substances in Table 1.2.
   a. How many of these substances are in the liquid state at 125°C?
   b. An unidentified substance has a density of 0.0028 g/cm^3. In what state is this substance at room temperature?
   c. Is there any apparent relationship between the melting points and densities of the solid substances?
   d. The substances in the table are listed in order of increasing melting point. Propose another way these data could be arranged.

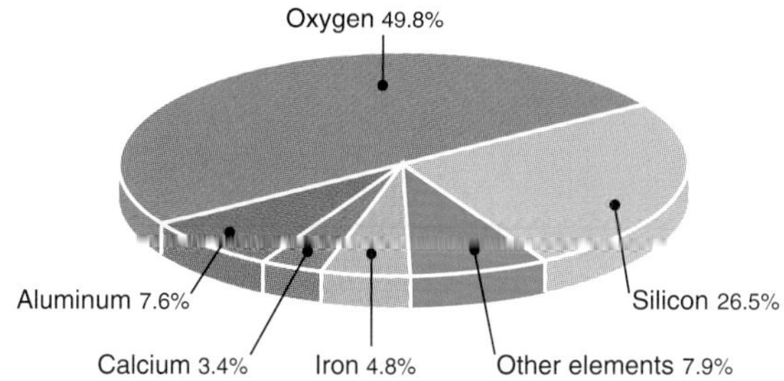

66. Five elements make up 97.9% of the mass of the human body. These elements are oxygen (64.8%), carbon (18.1%), hydrogen (10.0%), nitrogen (3.1%), and calcium (1.9%). Compare these data to those in the pie graph above, which shows the five most abundant elements by mass in the earth's crust, oceans, and atmosphere.

a. Which elements are abundant in both the earth's surface and the human body?

b. Which elements are abundant in the earth's surface but not the human body?

c. Why is the mass percent of oxygen the greatest in each case?

d. Are the compounds that make up the human body different from those found in rocks, water, and air? Explain your answer based on the evidence in the pie graph and the data above.

67. Occasionally you read about important discoveries being made "accidentally." Louis Pasteur said, "Chance favors the prepared mind." Are these two ideas contradictory? Explain.

68. Each day of your life you encounter chemical changes that are helpful and those that are harmful. Cite three examples of each. For each example list the indications that identified the change as chemical.

Connections Questions

69. Would a chemical engineer usually work in applied or pure chemistry? Explain your answer.

70. The names of elements share common origins. Name three different origins of elements' names.

71. Explain why it is important that a paint that covers in one coat be thixotropic.

Write About Chemistry

72. Write an essay describing what you observe when a candle burns.

73. Imagine that all the water in the lakes and oceans of the world is solid ice instead of liquid water. Write about the effect this could have on your life.

Readings and References

Corrick, James A. *Recent Revolutions in Chemistry.* New York: Watts, 1986.

Hann, Judith. *How Science Works.* New York: Reader's Digest Association, 1991.

Hazen, Robert M., and Trefil, James. *Science Matters, Achieving Scientific Literacy.* New York: Doubleday, 1990.

Joesten, Melvin D., *et al. The World of Chemistry.* Philadelphia: Saunders College Publishing, 1991.

Moss, Carol. *Science in Ancient Mesopotamia.* New York: Watts, 1988.

Van Sertima, Ivan. *Blacks in Science: Ancient and Modern.* New Brunswick: Transaction Books, 1990.

2 Scientific Measurement

Goals

- Calculate values from measurements using the correct number of significant figures.
- List common SI units of measurement and common prefixes used in the SI system.
- Distinguish mass, volume, density, and specific gravity from one another.
- Evaluate the accuracy of measurements using appropriate methods.

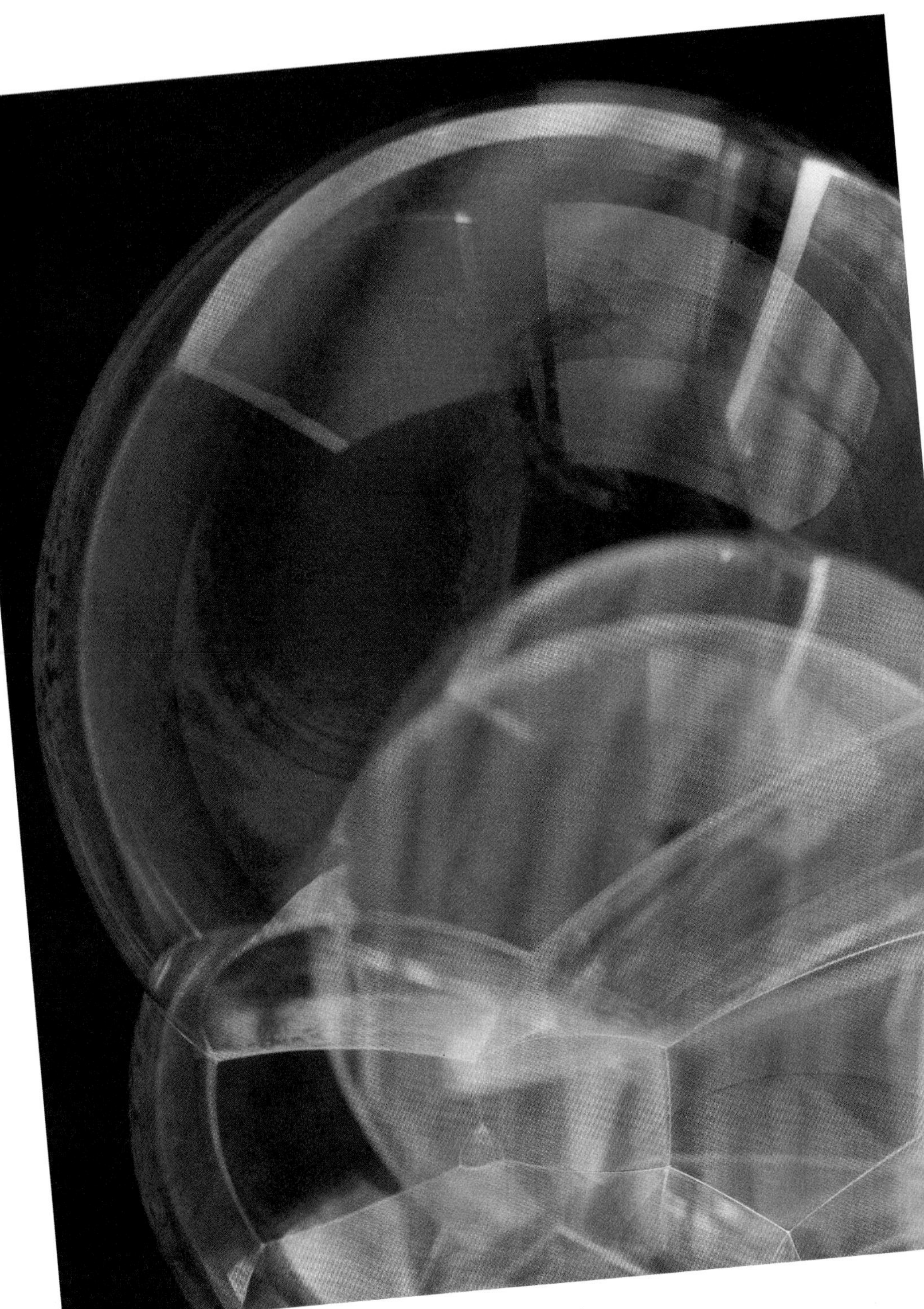

A soap bubble that measured 50 feet in length was made from a simple solution of soap and water in 1988. In SI units the soap bubble was 15 meters long. In comparison, the soap bubble shown here measured $6\frac{1}{2}$ inches or 16.5 centimeters across.

Concept Overview

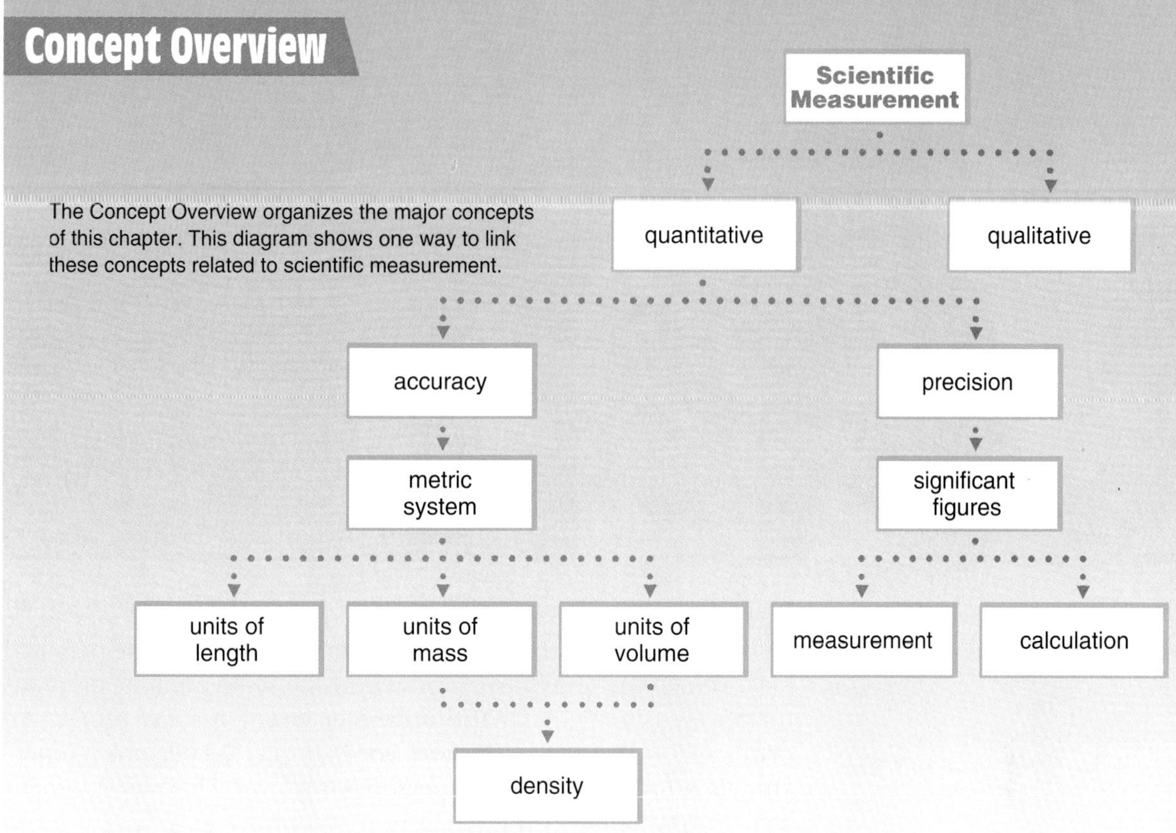

You decide how to dress in the morning based on the temperature outside. You measure the ingredients for your favorite recipe. If you were building a cabinet, you would carefully measure each piece of particleboard. Everyone makes and uses measurements.

Measurements are also fundamental to the experimental sciences. The understanding of scientific concepts is often based on measurements. For this reason, it is important to be able to make measurements and to decide whether a measurement is good or bad. In chemistry you will make measurements and express their values using the International System of Units, or the SI system.

2.1 The Importance of Measurement

Objective

Distinguish between quantitative and qualitative measurements.

How can you tell if someone has a fever? You might touch their forehead and think, "Yes! This person feels feverish." This is a qualitative evaluation. **Qualitative measurements** *give results in a descriptive nonnumeric form.* If several people touch the sick person's forehead, they might not agree with your observations. A person's own temperature influences his or her perception of how warm a sick person

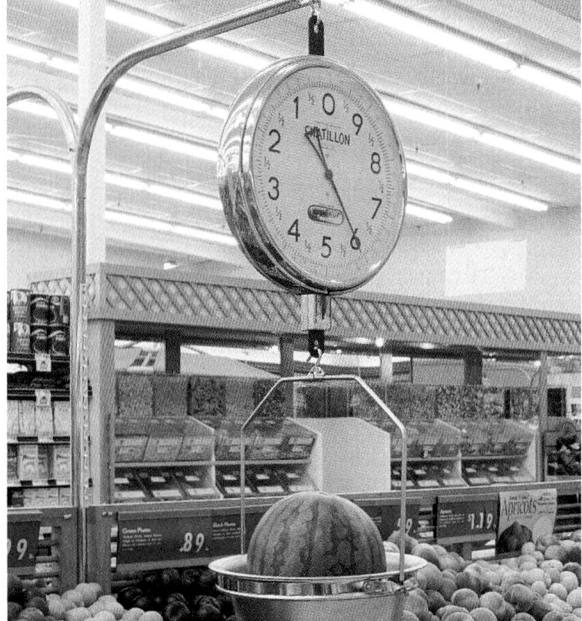

Figure 2.1 In lifting the watermelon, the child finds it heavy. This is a qualitative observation. The weight of the watermelon can also be determined with a spring scale. This is a quantitative observation.

feels. By using a thermometer, each person can eliminate personal bias. The temperature takers will report the same number, or quantitative measurement. **Quantitative measurements** *give results in a definite form, usually as numbers.* For example, the person's temperature is 39.2°C (102.5°F). This person has a fever. This measurement can be compared to the person's temperature at a later time to check for improvement. Remember, the accuracy of the thermometer has not been questioned. However, a measurement can be no more reliable than the measuring instrument.

Sometimes, as in the case of the child carrying the watermelon in Figure 2.1, a qualitative measurement conveys sufficient information. However, a quantitative measurement of the weight is necessary to determine the price of the watermelon. Before looking at some common types of measurement, you will examine the accuracy and precision of measurements.

Roots of Words

qualitativus: (Latin) related to quality or kind
qualitative descriptive, nonnumeric

Descriptions of colors are qualitative observations.

quantitativus: (Latin) having quantity as mass, size, volume, or duration in time
quantitative definite, usually numeric

Saying that a string is 100 cm long implies a quantitative measurement of the string.

Concept Practice

1. You measure 1 liter of water by filling an empty 2-liter soda bottle halfway. How could you improve the accuracy of this measurement?

2. Classify each measurement as qualitative or quantitative.
a. The basketball is brown.
b. The diameter of the basketball is 31 centimeters.
c. The air pressure in the basketball is 12 pounds per square inch.
d. The surface of the basketball has indented seams.

2.2 Accuracy and Precision

Objective

Distinguish between the accuracy and precision of a measurement.

Your success in the laboratory will depend on your ability to make "good" measurements. Ideally, good measurements are both correct (accurate) and reproducible (precise).

The words *accuracy* and *precision* mean the same thing to many people. In chemistry, however, their meanings are quite different. **Accuracy** *is how close a single measurement comes to the actual dimension or true value of whatever is measured.* **Precision** *is how close several measurements are to the same value.* Precise measurements are reproducible, but not necessarily accurate. Darts stuck in a dart board illustrate accuracy and precision in making measurements. Let the bull's-eye of the dart board represent the true value of what you are measuring. The closeness of a dart to the bull's-eye is a measure of your accuracy. The bull's-eye represents the true value. Let the closeness of the grouping of several darts represent the precision of your measurement. When several darts thrown at the same target are grouped together, the throws were reproducible. This represents highly precise measurements that can be produced more than once. Look at Figure 2.2 as you consider three possible outcomes of tossing three darts at the dart board.

1. All the darts stick in the bull's-eye. Each dart in the bull's-eye represents an accurate measurement of the true value. Thus, all your measurements are very accurate. The measurements are also closely grouped together. They are very reproducible, very precise.

2. All the darts are closely grouped, but they are not in the bull's-eye. Your precision is excellent because your throws are very reproducible. The throws are inaccurate, though, because they miss the bull's-eye and do not reflect the true value.

3. The darts are spread randomly around the target. Your shots are neither accurate nor precise. You missed the bull's-eye, and you have failed to throw the darts in a reproducible way.

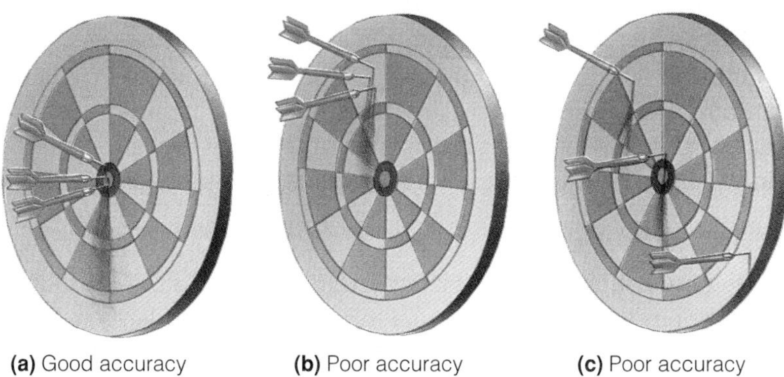

Figure 2.2 The distribution of the darts illustrates the difference between accuracy and precision. **(a)** The ideal combination is good accuracy and good precision. **(b)** Poor accuracy and good precision is probably the worst situation because it can be misleading. **(c)** Poor accuracy and poor precision point to the need for improvements.

Note that the precision of a measurement depends on more than one measurement. By contrast, an individual measurement might be accurate or inaccurate. The accuracy of real measurements depends on the quality of the measuring device. Precision depends more heavily on the skill of the person making the measurement. You usually assume that the measuring devices used in the laboratory are as accurate as their manufacturer specifies. Your job is to use these devices with sufficient skill to obtain good precision.

Concept Practice

3. Which of these synonyms or characteristics apply to the concept of *accuracy*? Which apply to the concept of *precision*?

a. multiple measurements
b. correct
c. repeatable
d. reproducible
e. single measurement
f. true value

4. Under what circumstances could a series of measurements of the same quantity be precise but inaccurate?

Objective

Rewrite measurements in scientific notation.

2.3 Scientific Notation

In chemistry you will often encounter very large and very small numbers. For example, the mass of a single atom of gold is 0.000 000 000 000 000 000 000 327 grams. Even 1 gram of the element hydrogen, a relatively small quantity, contains 301 000 000 000 000 000 000 000 hydrogen molecules. Writing and using numbers this small or this large in calculations is cumbersome. You can work more easily with these numbers by writing them in exponential or scientific notation.

In **scientific notation** *a number is written as the product of two numbers: a coefficient and a power of 10.* For example, the number 36 000 is written in scientific notation as 3.6×10^4. The coefficient in this number is 3.6. The coefficient is a number equal to or greater than one and less than ten. The power of 10, or exponent, in this example is 4. The exponent indicates how many times the coefficient 3.6 must be multiplied by 10 to equal the number 36 000.

$$3.6 \times 10^4 = 3.6 \times 10 \times 10 \times 10 \times 10 = 36\,000$$

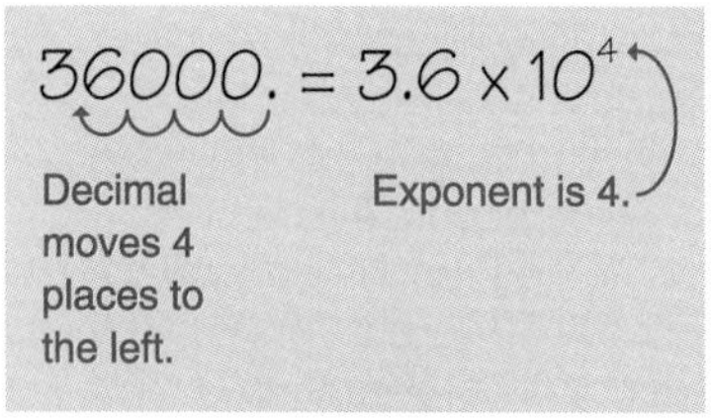

$36000. = 3.6 \times 10^4$

Decimal moves 4 places to the left. Exponent is 4.

Figure 2.3 The number of decimal places is the same as the number of the exponent.

When writing numbers greater than ten in scientific notation the exponent is positive and equal to the number of places that the decimal point has been moved to the left. Numbers less than one have a negative exponent when you write them in scientific notation. The number 0.0081 written in scientific notation is 8.1×10^{-3}. The negative exponent –3 indicates that the coefficient 8.1 must be divided three times by 10 to equal the number 0.0081. Thus

$$8.1 \times 10^{-3} = \frac{8.1}{10 \times 10 \times 10} = 0.0081$$

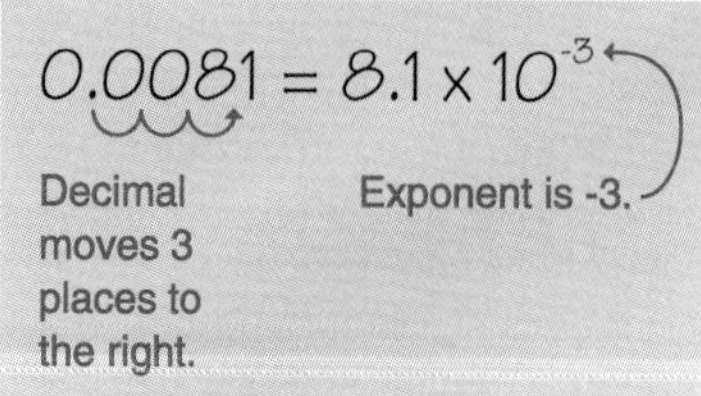

Figure 2.4 The direction in which the decimal point moves determines the sign of the exponent. What is the sign of the exponent here?

When you write a number less than one in scientific notation, the value of the exponent equals the number of places you move the decimal to the right. The sign is negative. Using scientific notation makes calculating quite straightforward.

Multiplication and Division To *multiply* numbers written in scientific notation, *multiply the coefficients and add the exponents.* To *divide* numbers written in scientific notation, *divide the coefficients and subtract the exponent in the denominator (bottom) from the exponent in the numerator (top).* When multiplying or dividing, carefully apply the arithmetic rules for using numbers with signs. For example,

$$\begin{aligned}(3 \times 10^4) \times (2 \times 10^2) &= (3 \times 2) \times 10^{4+2} \\ &= 6 \times 10^6\end{aligned}$$

Addition and Subtraction Before numbers written in scientific notation are *added or subtracted, the exponents must be made the same.* Why must you do this? The exponent determines the location of the decimal point in the number. You align the decimal points before adding two numbers together. With numbers written in scientific notation, making the exponents the same is part of the process of aligning the decimal points. For example,

$$\begin{aligned}(5.4 \times 10^3) + (0.60 \times 10^3) &= (5.4 + 0.60) \times 10^3 \\ &= 6.0 \times 10^3\end{aligned}$$

Concept Practice

5. Write the two measurements given in the first paragraph of this section in scientific notation.
a. mass of a gold atom **b.** molecules of hydrogen

6. Write these measurements in scientific notation. The abbreviation *m* stands for meter, a unit of length.
a. The length of a football field, 91.4 m
b. The diameter of a carbon atom, 0.000 000 000 154 m
c. The radius of the earth, 6 378 000 m
d. The diameter of a human hair, 0.000 008 m
e. The average distance between the centers of the sun and the earth, 149 600 000 000 m

Problem-Solving Tip

When written in scientific notation, numbers greater than 10 have positive exponents and numbers less than 1 have negative exponents.

Figure 2.5 Three different meter sticks could be used to measure the length of a board. What measurement do you get in each case? Is there a difference in the number of significant figures in the three measurements? Why or why not?

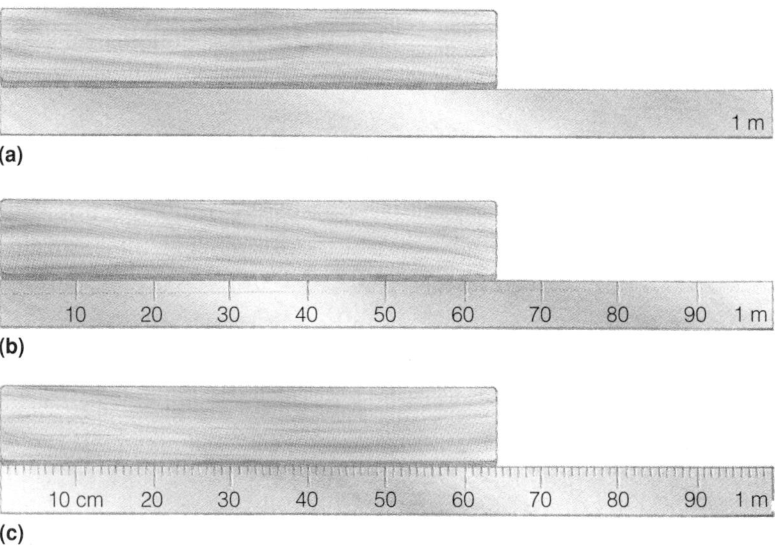

2.4 Significant Figures in Measurements

Objective

Identify the number of significant figures in a measurement.

When you read an outside thermometer marked at 1° intervals, you can easily read the temperature to the nearest degree. With this thermometer, however, you can also estimate the temperature to the nearest tenth of a degree. Suppose you estimate a temperature that lies between 24°C and 25°C to be 24.3°C. This number has three significant figures. The first two digits (2 and 4) are known with certainty. The last digit (3) has been estimated. The three-digit number is a "best guess" and involves some uncertainty. The true value of the temperature outside lies somewhere between 24.2°C and 24.4°C. Measurements must always be reported to the correct number of significant figures. *The* **significant figures** *in a measurement include all the digits that are known precisely plus one last digit that is estimated.*

By estimating the last digit in a measurement, you are able to get additional information. The digits retained in a measurement are all significant, but the last digit is uncertain. Suppose you take someone's temperature with a thermometer that is calibrated in 0.1° intervals. You can report the temperature to the nearest 0.1° and estimate it to the nearest 0.01°. You might report the temperature as 35.82°C. This measurement has four significant figures, and the last digit (2) is uncertain. Similarly, you can use the three meter sticks in Figure 2.5 to make successively more precise measurements of the board.

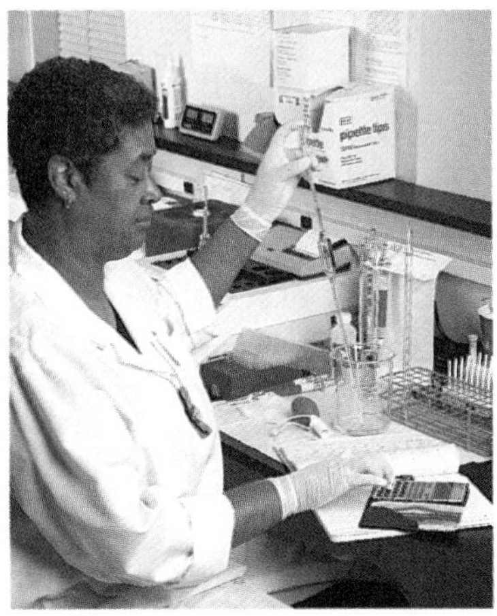

Figure 2.6 Quality control chemists use significant figures when making measurements that indicate whether the quality of a product is acceptable.

The quality control chemist shown in Figure 2.6 must be aware of significant figures in her work in the laboratory. She must report only measurements that include all digits known with certainty plus one last digit that is estimated.

The rules for determining which digits in a measurement are significant are as follows.

1. Every nonzero digit in a recorded measurement is significant. The measurements 24.7 m, 0.743 m, and 714 m all express a measure of length to three significant figures.

2. Zeros appearing between nonzero digits are significant. The measurements 7003 m, 40.79 m, and 1.503 m all have four significant figures.

3. Zeros appearing in front of all nonzero digits are *not* significant. They act as place holders. The measurements 0.0071 m, 0.42 m, and 0.000 099 m all have two significant figures. Although not significant, these particular zeros cannot be arbitrarily dropped from the measurement because they show the magnitude of the measurement. You can, however, get rid of these place-holding zeros by writing the measurements in scientific notation: 7.1×10^{-3} m, 4.2×10^{-1} m, and 9.9×10^{-5} m.

4. Zeros at the end of a number and to the right of a decimal point are always significant. The measurements 43.00 m, 1.010 m, and 9.000 m all have four significant figures.

5. Zeros at the end of a measurement and to the left of the decimal point are not significant if they just serve as place markers to show the magnitude of the number. The zeros in the measurements 300 m, 7000 m, and 27 210 m are not significant as written. The number of significant figures is one, one, and four, respectively. *However, if these zeros were measured values, then they are significant.* To avoid ambiguity, the measurements should be written in scientific notation. If these zeros were measured, you would write 3.00×10^2 m, 7.000×10^3 m, and 2.7210×10^4 m. Then the number of significant figures is three, four, and five, respectively. If the last zero in each of these measurements were not measured, then the figures would be written 3.0×10^2 m, 7.00×10^3 m, and 2.721×10^4 m. In this instance the number of significant figures is two, three, and four, respectively.

6. There are two instances in which measurements have an unlimited number of significant figures. The first involves counting. If you count 23 people in your classroom, then there are exactly 23 people and this measurement has an unlimited number of significant figures. The second instance involves exactly defined quantities usually found within a system of measurement. When you write 60 min = 1 h or 100 cm = 1 m, each of these measurements has an unlimited number of significant figures. You must recognize exact measurements to be able to round off answers correctly in calculation problems involving measurements.

Biographical Note

Antoine-Laurent Lavoisier
(1743–1794)

Lavoisier, the founder of modern chemistry, was a French scientist and dedicated public servant. He is most famous for the careful experimental measurements that led to his discovery of the true nature of combustion. In many tests, Lavoisier found that nothing could be burned in the absence of oxygen. Lavoisier was assisted in this work by his wife, Marie Ann. Lavoisier was an aristocrat. He was also a member of the despised royal taxation commission, a position he took to finance his scientific work. Although he was dedicated to improving the lives of the common people, Lavoisier was hated during the French Revolution. In 1794 he was arrested, tried, and beheaded.

Example 1 Determining Significant Figures in Measurements

How many significant figures are in each of the following measurements?

a. 123 m
b. 0.123 cm
c. 40 506 mm
d. 9.8000×10^4 m
e. 4.5600 m
f. 22 meter sticks
g. 0.070 80 m
h. 98 000 m

Solution

All nonzero digits are significant. Use rules 2 to 5 to decide about zeros.

a. 3 (rule 1)
b. 3 (rule 3)
c. 5 (rule 2)
d. 5 (rules 4 and 5)
e. 5 (rule 4)
f. unlimited (rule 6)
g. 4 (rules 2, 3, 4)
h. 2 (rule 5)

Concept Practice

7. Write each measurement in scientific notation and determine the number of significant figures in each.

a. 0.05730 m
b. 8765 dm
c. 0.000 73 mm
d. 12 basketball players
e. 0.010 km
f. 507 thumbtacks

Objective

Apply the rules for significant figures in calculations to round off numbers correctly.

2.5 Significant Figures in Calculations

The calculated area of a room that measures 7.7 m by 5.4 m is 41.58 m^2. The calculated area, 41.58 m^2, is expressed to four significant figures. However, each of the measurements used in the calculation is expressed to two significant figures. How can the calculated area be *more* precise than the measured values? It can not. The calculated area must be rounded off to make it consistent with the measurements from which it was calculated. In general *an answer cannot be more precise than the least precise measurement from which it was calculated.*

The number of significant figures in a measurement refers to the precision of the measurement. To round off a number, you must first decide how many significant figures the answer should have. Your decision will depend on the given measurements and on the arithmetic operation used to arrive at the answer. Once you know the number of significant figures your answer should have, you round to that many digits counting from the left. If the digit immediately to the right of the last significant digit is less than 5, all the digits after the last significant place are dropped. If the digit to the right is 5 or greater, the value of the digit in the last significant place is increased by 1. Rounding off to four significant figures, 56.212 m becomes 56.21 m; 56.216 m becomes 56.22 m. A calculator, as shown in Figure 2.7, will often give you an answer that must be rounded off. A calculator does not keep track of significant figures or round off answers correctly.

Figure 2.7 This calculator was used to multiply the measurements 3.24 cm and 1.78 cm. When correctly rounded off, the product is 5.77 cm^2.

Example 2 Rounding Off Measurements

Round off each of these measurements to the number of significant figures shown in parentheses. Write the answer in scientific notation.

a. 314.721 m (4)
b. 0.001 775 m (2)
c. 64.32×10^{-1} m (1)
d. 8792 m (2)

Solution

The arrow points to the digit immediately following the last significant digit.

a. 314.721 m; 2 is less than 5; 314.7 m (4) = 3.147×10^2 m
↑ (under the 2)

b. 0.001775 m; 7 is greater than 5; 0.0018 m (2) = 1.8×10^{-3} m
↑ (under the 7)

c. 64.32×10^{-1} m; 4 is less than 5; 60×10^{-1} m = 6 m
↑ (under the 4)

d. 8792 m; 9 is greater than 5; 8800 m (2) = 8.8×10^3 m
↑ (under the 9)

Concept Practice

8. Round each measurement to three significant figures and then to one. Write your answers in scientific notation.

a. 87.073 m
b. 4.3621×10^8 m
c. 0.01552 m
d. 9009 m
e. 1.7777×10^{-3} m
f. 629.55 m

Addition and Subtraction The answer to an addition or subtraction calculation should be rounded to have the same number of decimal places as the measurement with the least number of decimal places.

Integrating Engineering

Computer-Aided Design (CAD)

An engineer designing a complex new machine must specify hundreds of dimensions. Many tedious aspects of technical design have been largely replaced by computer-aided design (CAD) programs. A CAD program permits a designer to begin with a few important measurements of the object being designed. As the design progresses, the program computes the dimensions of added elements and produces drawings of the object from any perspective the designer desires. When one dimension in a design is changed, CAD programs automatically adjust all the other dimensions.

Example 3 Rounding Off Addition and Subtraction Calculations

Do the following operations and give the answer to the correct number of significant figures.

a. 12.52 m + 349.0 m + 8.24 m

b. 74.626 m – 28.34 m

Solution

a. Line up the decimal points and add the numbers.

```
 12.52 m
349.0 m
  8.24 m
369.76 m
```

Since the second measurement (349.0 m) has only one digit to the right of the decimal point, the answer must be rounded off to one digit after the decimal point. The answer is 369.8 m or 3.698×10^2 m.

b. Line up the decimal points and subtract the numbers.

```
 74.626 m
–28.34 m
 46.286 m
```

The answer must be rounded off to two digits after the decimal point. The answer is 46.29 m or 4.629×10^1 m.

Practice Problem

9. Do the following operations and give your answer to the correct number of significant figures and in scientific notation.

a. 61.2 m + 9.35 m + 8.6 m

b. 9.44 m – 2.11 m

c. 1.36 m + 10.17 m

d. 34.61 m – 17.3 m

Multiplication and Division In calculations involving multiplication and division, the answer is rounded off to the number of significant figures in the least precise term used in the calculation. The least precise term is the measurement with the least number of significant figures. You can see in Figure 2.7 that the calculator answer, 5.7672, must be rounded off to three significant figures because each measurement used in the calculation has three significant figures.

Remember, the position of the decimal point has nothing to do with the rounding-off process when multiplying and dividing measurements. The position of the decimal point is important in rounding the answer of an addition or subtraction.

Example 4 Rounding Off Multiplication and Division Calculations

Do the following operations and give the answer to the correct number of significant figures.

a. 7.55 m × 0.34 m

b. 2.10 m × 0.70 m

c. 2.4526 m ÷ 8.4

d. 0.365 m ÷ 0.0200

Solution

The calculated answer is given, then rounded off.

a. 2.567 m^2 = 2.6 m^2 (0.34 m has two significant figures)

b. 1.47 m^2 = 1.5 m^2 (0.70 m has two significant figures)

c. 0.291 976 m = 0.29 m (8.4 has two significant figures)

d. 18.25 m = 18.3 m (both numbers have three significant figures)

Practice Problem

10. Do the following problems and give your answer to the correct number of significant figures and in scientific notation.

a. 8.3 m × 2.22 m

b. $(1.8 \times 10^{-3}$ m) × $(2.9 \times 10^{-2}$ m)

c. 8432 m ÷ 12.5

d. 5.3×10^{-2} m ÷ 0.255

e. 35.2 s × 1 min/60 s

Problem-Solving Tip

Following multiplication and division, round to the *least number of significant figures.*

2.6 The International System of Units, SI

Objective

List the SI units of measurement used in chemistry.

When a measurement is made, the correct units must be assigned to the numerical value. Without the correct units, it is not possible to communicate the resulting measurement to others. Imagine the confusion that would ensue if you were instructed to "heat the solution for 20." Your immediate response would be "Twenty what? Seconds, minutes, hours, or days?"

A measurement depends on a reference standard. The standards of measurement used in science are those of the metric system. The metric system is important because of its simplicity and convenience of use. All the units are based on 10 or multiples of 10. As a result, you can easily convert one unit to another unit. The metric system was originally established in France in 1790. *The* **International System of Units** (abbreviated **SI**, after the French name Le Système International d'Unités) *is a revised version of the metric system.* SI units were adopted by international agreement in 1960. There are seven SI base units, given in Table 2.1 on the next page. From these base units, other SI units of measurement can be

Table 2.1 SI Base Units of Measurement

Quantity measured	Unit	SI symbol
Length	meter	m
Mass	kilogram	kg
Time	second	s
Electric current	ampere	A
Thermodynamic temperature	kelvin	K
Amount of substance	mole	mol
Luminous intensity	candela	cd

Table 2.2 Some Units of Measurement Used in This Text

Quantity	SI base unit or SI derived unit	Non-SI unit
Length	meter (m)	
Volume	cubic meter (m^3)	liter
Mass	kilogram (kg)	
Density	grams per cubic centimeter (g/cm^3)	
	grams per milliliter (g/mL)	
Temperature	kelvin (K)	degree Celsius (°C)
Time	second (s)	
Pressure	pascal (Pa)	atmosphere (atm)
		millimeter of mercury (mm Hg)
Energy	joule (J)	calorie (cal)

derived. These derived units are used for measurements such as volume, density, and pressure.

All measured quantities can be reported in SI units. Sometimes, however, non-SI units are preferred for convenience or for practical reasons. Table 2.2 lists some SI and non-SI units of measurement that are used in this text.

Concept Practice

11. Name the quantity measured by each SI unit and give the SI symbol or abbreviation for its units.

a. mole
b. kilogram/cubic meter
c. second
d. pascal
e. meter
f. kilogram

12. Classify each quantity in the previous question as an SI base unit or an SI derived unit.

2.A Science, Technology, and Society

The Metric System

The question of what system of measurement to use extends beyond science and technology to affect everyone in this society. A version of the metric system has been used worldwide by scientists for a long time. Citizens of most of the world's countries also use the metric system. The United States is one of only a handful of countries that have not completely adopted the metric standard of measurement. However, metric measurements are slowly creeping into everyday life in the United States. Food containers give masses in grams. Some highway signs give distances in miles and kilometers. As U.S. manufacturers attempt to expand their markets for goods to the rest of the world, they have increasingly converted to metric standards of measurement. This conversion means that goods produced in the United States are compatible with those produced in other countries. As a result, more U.S. goods can be sold abroad. For example, a European mechanic can fix an American car or a European car with the same set of metric wrenches. In the future, you can expect the strong connection between the nation's economic well-being and international trade to drive the United States further in the direction of metric conversion.

Figure 2.8 Most products you use come in nonmetric amounts. Notice that most labels list both metric and nonmetric units.

Table 2.3 Metric Units for Length

Unit	Symbol	Relationship	Examples (approximate values)	
Kilometer	km	1 km = 10^3 m	Length of about five city blocks	≈ 1 km
Meter (base unit)	m		Height of door knob from the floor	≈ 1 m
Decimeter	dm	10^1 dm = 1 m	Diameter of large orange	≈ 1 dm
Centimeter	cm	10^2 cm = 1 m	Width of shirt button	≈ 1 cm
Millimeter	mm	10^3 mm = 1 m	Thickness of dime	≈ 1 mm
Micrometer	μm	10^6 μm = 1 m	Diameter of bacterial cell	≈ 1 μm
Nanometer	nm	10^9 nm = 1 m	Thickness of RNA molecule	≈ 1 nm

Think About It

13. Compare What do you see as the advantages and disadvantages of drawing the plans for a shelf to hold a compact disc player using as the standard of length:
a. a stick you found? **b.** a yardstick? **c.** a meter stick?

14. Criticize Do you think that the conversion of the United States to the metric system should proceed more rapidly or more slowly than it is? Why?

Table 2.4 Prefixes in Common Use in the Metric System		
Prefix	**Symbol**	**Meaning**
mega	M	1 million times larger than the unit it precedes (1 000 000 or 10^6)
kilo	k	1000 times larger than the unit it precedes (1000 or 10^3)
deci	d	10 times smaller than the unit it precedes (1/10 or 10^{-1})
centi	c	100 times smaller than the unit it precedes (1 /100 or 10^{-2})
milli	m	1000 times smaller than the unit it precedes (1/1000 or 10^{-3})
micro	µ	1 million times smaller than the unit it precedes (1/1 000 000 or 10^{-6})(μ is the lowercase Greek letter "mu")
nano	n	1000 million times smaller than the unit it precedes (1/1 000 000 000 or 10^{-9})
pico	p	1 trillion times smaller than the unit it precedes (1/1 000 000 000 000 or 10^{-12})

Objective

List and define the common SI prefixes.

2.7 Units of Length

Size is an important property of matter. *The basic SI unit of length, or linear measure, is the* **meter (m)**. All measurements of length can be expressed in meters. (The length of a page in this book is about two-tenths of a meter.) For very large and very small lengths, however, it may be more convenient tc use a prefixed unit of length. Table 2.4 lists the prefixes in common use. As an example, this hyphen - is about 0.001 m long. Compare the length of this hyphen with the section of meter stick reproduced in Figure 2.9. The hyphen measures about 1 mm (millimeter), or 0.001 = 1/1000 of a meter. Both 1 mm and 0.001 m measure the same length.

For large distances, it is most appropriate to express a measurement in kilometers (km). The prefix *kilo-* means 1000 times larger; 1 km is equal to 1000 m. The marathon distance race of about 42,000 m is more conveniently expressed as 42 km (42 × 1000 m).

Roots of Words

metrum: (Latin) measure
meter the base SI unit of length

A meter is equivalent to 39.4 in.

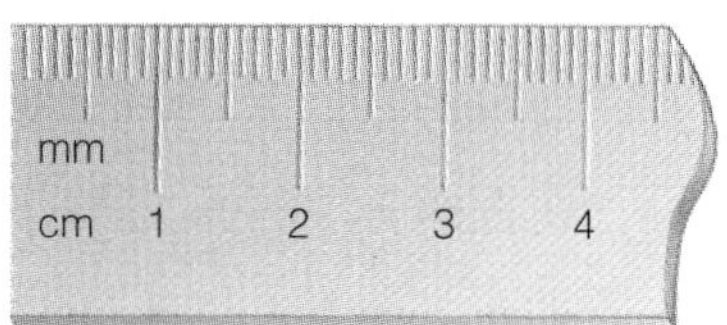

Figure 2.9 A meter stick is divided into 100 divisions. Each division is a centimeter. Each centimeter is divided into 10 millimeters. How many millimeters are there in a meter?

Concept Practice

15. Use the tables in the text to order these lengths from smallest to largest. Give each measurement in terms of meters.

a. centimeter
b. micrometer
c. kilometer
d. millimeter
e. meter
f. decimeter

16. Measure each of the following dimensions using units with the appropriate prefix.

a. the height of this letter I
b. the width of Table 2.4
c. the height of this page

2.8 Units of Volume

Objective

Explain why a milliliter and a cubic centimeter have the same volume, using a decimeter cube.

The space occupied by any sample of matter is called its **volume**. The unit for volume is derived from the SI unit for length. You calculate the volume of any cubic or rectangular solid by multiplying its length by its width by its height. The SI unit of volume is the amount of space occupied by a cube that is 1 meter along each edge. This volume is a cubic meter (m^3). An automatic dishwasher has a volume of about 1 cubic meter. A more convenient unit of volume for everyday use is the liter (L). *As shown in Figure 2.10,* a **liter** *is the volume of a cube that is 10 centimeters (cm) along each edge (10 cm × 10 cm × 10 cm = 1000 cm^3 = 1 L).* Because 10 cm is equal to one

Figure 2.10 Note that 1 mL and 1 cm^3 refer to the same volume. The face of the cube is shown in actual size.

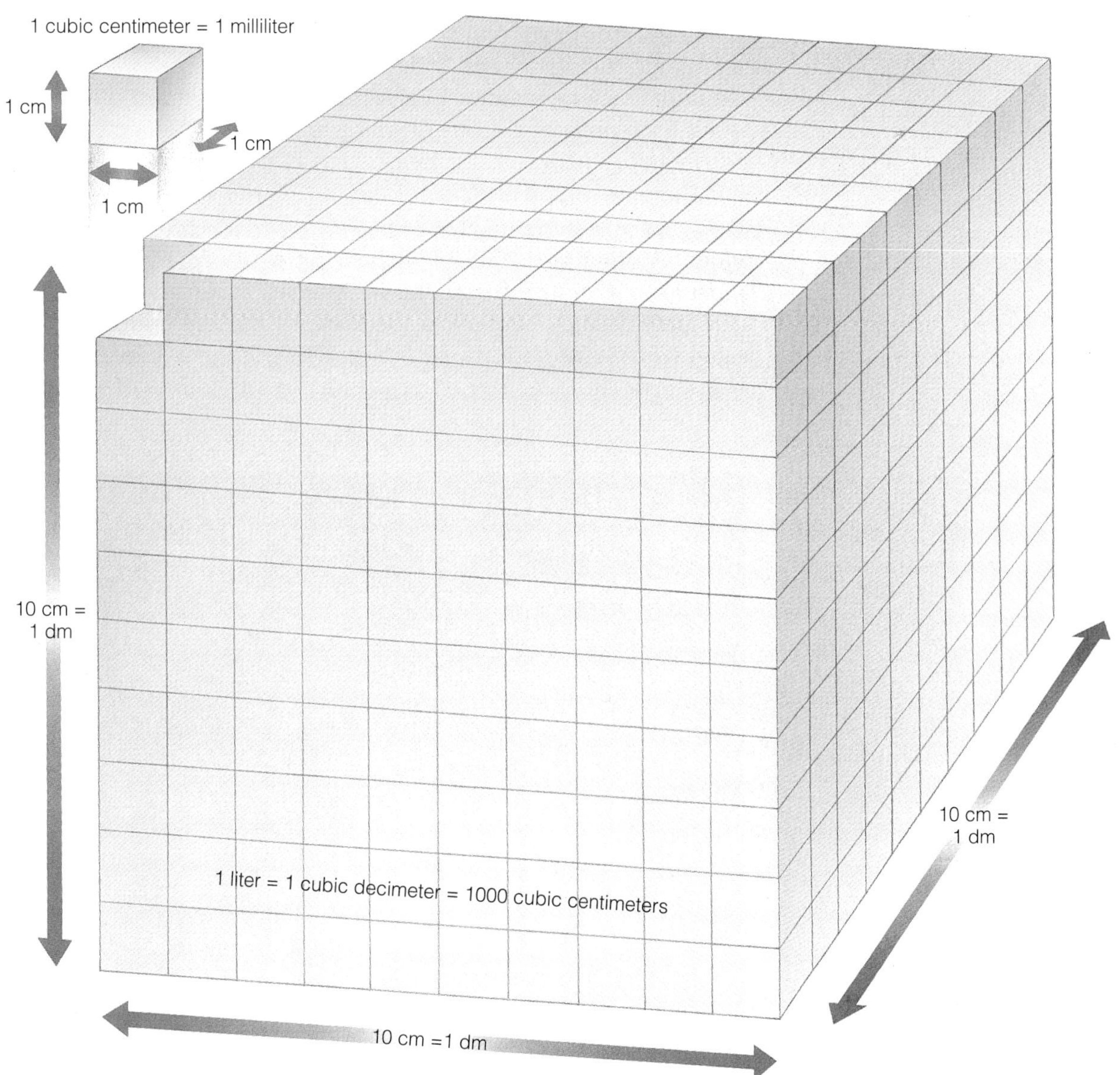

Table 2.5 Metric Units for Volume

Unit	Symbol	Relationship	Examples (approximate values)	
Liter (base unit)	L		Quart of milk	≈ 1 L
Milliliter	mL	10^3 mL = 1 L	20 drops of water	≈ 1 mL
Cubic centimeter	cm^3	1 cm^3 = 1 mL	Cube of sugar	≈ 1 cm^3
Microliter	μL	10^6 μL = 1 L	Crystal of table salt	≈ 1 μL

Figure 2.11 One cubic centimeter of water is shown in actual size. This much water has a mass of 1 g at 4°C. Twenty drops of water equals approximately 1 mL.

decimeter (dm), one liter is also equal to 1 cubic decimeter (dm^3). A smaller unit of volume is the milliliter; 1 mL is 1/1000 part of a liter. Because one liter is defined as 1000 cm^3, one milliliter and one cubic centimeter have the same volume. You can see a volume of 1 cm^3 in Figure 2.11. The units milliliter and cubic centimeter are used interchangeably. Table 2.5 summarizes the most commonly used relationships among units of volume. Note that the prefixes *milli-* and *micro-* are used with both the unit of volume, a liter, and the unit of length, a meter. This is one of the advantages of using SI units. Each prefix retains its meaning regardless of the unit of measurement to which it is attached.

There are many devices for measuring the volume of a liquid. Examples of volumetric glassware are shown in Figure 2.12. A graduated cylinder is useful for dispensing approximate volumes. A pipet or buret must be used, however, when accuracy is important. A volumetric flask contains a specified volume of liquid when it is filled to the calibration mark. Volumetric flasks are available in many sizes. A syringe is used to measure small volumes of liquids.

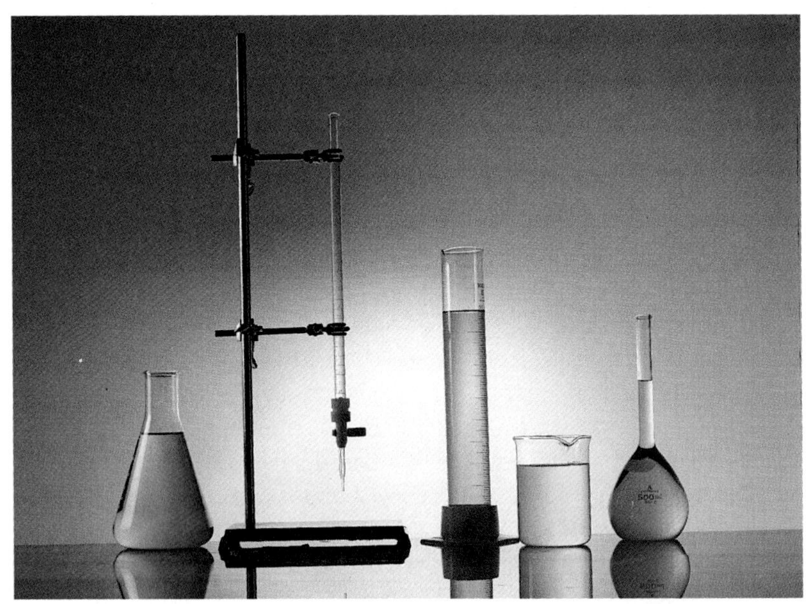

Figure 2.12 Shown left to right are five types of glassware used to measure volume: Erlenmeyer flask, buret, graduated cylinder, beaker,and volumetric flask. Beakers, Erlenmeyer flasks, and graduated cylinders are used to measure approximate volumes. Precise volumes are measured with the buret. Large volumes are measured accurately with a volumetric flask.

The volume of any solid, liquid, or gas will change with temperature. (The change in volume with a change in temperature is much more dramatic for gases than for liquids or solids.) Accurate volume-measuring devices are calibrated at a given temperature. Usually, they are calibrated at 20°C, about normal room temperature.

Concept Practice

17. From what unit is a measure of volume derived?

Practice Problems

18. What is the volume of a paperback book 21 cm tall, 12 cm wide, and 3.5 cm thick?

19. What is the volume of a glass cylinder with an inside diameter of 6.0 cm and a height of 28 cm? (Reminder: The volume of a cylinder equals π × radius squared × height, or $V = \pi r^2 h$.)

Problem-Solving Tip

Sketch and label a picture of the cylinder to help you visualize this problem.

2.9 Units of Mass

Objective

Summarize the difference between the mass and weight of an object.

If the man on the surface of the moon shown in Figure 2.13 was standing on a scale, he would weigh one-sixth of his weight on earth. A block of wood on earth has a weight that is six times its weight on the moon. The reason for this difference in weights is that the force of gravity on earth is about six times that on the moon. On a passage from the earth to the moon, the weight of the wood decreases. Whether the wood is on earth, on the moon, or in space, however, its mass does not change. Mass is the quantity of matter an object contains. Mass is not weight. **Weight** *is a force.* Weight is a measure of the pull on a given mass by the earth's gravity. Although the weight of an object can change with its location, its mass remains constant regardless of its location.

The mass of an object is measured by comparing it to a standard mass of 1 **kilogram (kg)**, *the basic SI unit of mass.* A kilogram was originally defined as the mass of 1 L of water at 4°C. (Water freezes at 0°C.) Imagine a cube of water at 4°C measuring 10 cm on each edge. This cube would have a volume of 1 L and a mass of 1000 grams (g), or a kilogram. *A* **gram** *is 1/1000 of a kilogram and is a more commonly used unit of mass because a kilogram is relatively large.* The mass of 1 cm^3 of water at 4°C, as shown in Figure 2.11, is 1 gram. The relationships among units of mass are shown in Table 2.6.

Figure 2.13 An astronaut's weight on the moon is one-sixth as much as it is on earth.

Table 2.6 Metric Units for Mass

Unit	Symbol	Relationship	Examples (approximate values)	
Kilogram (base unit)	kg	1 kg = 10^3 g	Small textbook	≈ 1 kg
Gram	g		Dollar bill	≈ 1 g
Milligram	mg	10^3 mg = 1 g	Ten grains of salt	≈ 1 mg
Microgram	μg	10^6 μg = 1 g	Particle of baking powder	≈ 1 μg

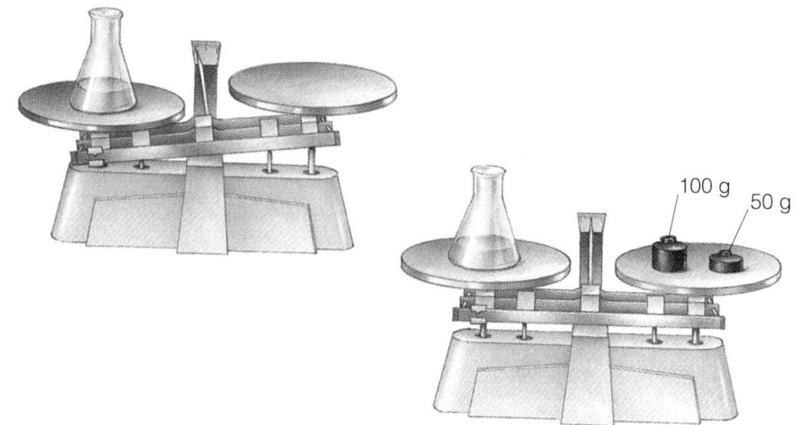

Figure 2.14 A platform balance is used to compare an unknown mass to a known mass. The mass of the unknown object is the same as the sum of the standard masses added to the right-hand pan. In this example the mass is 150 g.

You can measure the mass of an object with a platform balance. An object of unknown mass is placed on one side, and standard masses are added to the other side until the beam is in a position of balance as shown in Figure 2.14. When the beam is balanced, the unknown mass is equal to the sum of the standard masses. Look at several types of balances used in laboratories in Figure 2.15. These balances range from very sensitive instruments with a maximum capacity of only a few milligrams to devices for measuring quantities in kilograms. The analytical balance is used to measure masses of less than 100 g to the nearest 0.0001 g (0.1 mg).

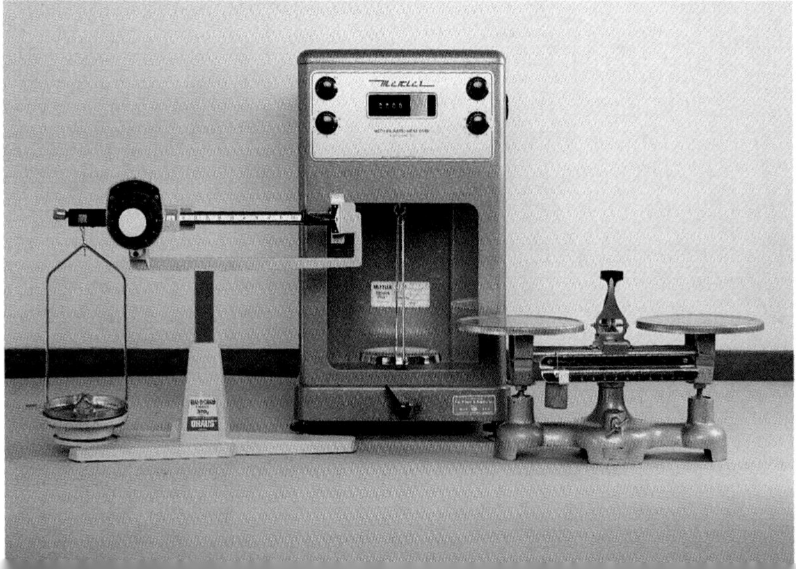

Figure 2.15 It is possible to determine mass to the nearest 0.1 g on a platform balance (right) and to the nearest 0.01 g on a triple-beam balance (left). Even greater precision is possible with an analytical balance (center).

Concept Practice

20. As you climbed a mountain and the force of gravity decreased, would your weight increase, decrease, or remain constant? How would your mass change? Explain.

21. How many grams are in each of these quantities?
a. 1 cg **b.** 1 μg **c.** 1 kg **d.** 1 mg

2.10 Measuring Density

Objective

Calculate the density of an object from experimental data.

The statement "Lead is heavier than wood" has no precise meaning. Most people take it to mean that if pieces of lead and wood of the same volume were weighed, the lead would have a greater mass than the wood. For example, 10.0 cm^3 of lead has a mass of 114 g, but a piece of wood the same size has a mass of only 5 g. This shows that it would take a much larger volume of wood to equal the mass of the lead. Thus, there is an important relationship between an object's mass and its volume. This relationship is called density.

Density *is the ratio of the mass of an object to its volume.*

$$\text{Density} = \frac{\text{mass}}{\text{volume}}$$

What is the density of lead? Using the mass and volume data given above, we see that the density of lead is

$$\frac{114 \text{ g}}{10.0 \text{ cm}^3} = 11.4 \text{ g/cm}^3$$

As seen in this example, when mass is measured in grams and volume in cubic centimeters, density has units of grams per cubic centimeter.

Table 2.7, on the next page, gives data for samples of different substances of equal mass. The volume of a 10-gram sample of each substance is shown in the table. How does the density change as the volume decreases? The volume of 10 g of lead is much smaller than the volume of 10 g of wood. As calculated above, the density of lead is much greater than the density of wood. The densities of materials are extremely important. If your bones were as dense as lead, for example, your body would collapse under its own weight.

What do you think happens when glycerine and corn oil are poured into a beaker of water? The density of corn oil is less than the density of water, so the corn oil floats on top of the water. As you can see in Figure 2.16, the glycerine sinks below the water because its density is greater than the density of water.

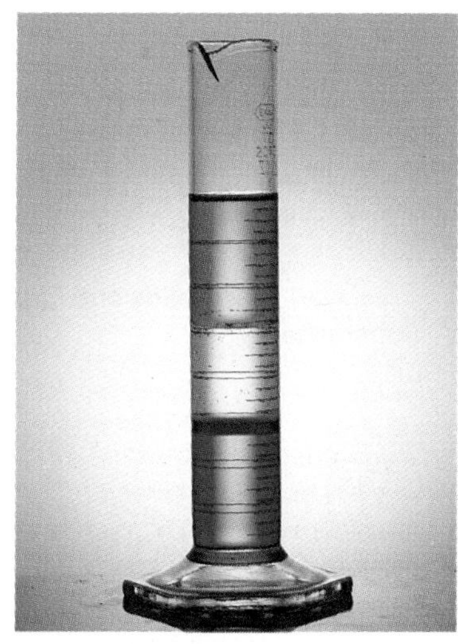

Figure 2.16 Because of differences in density, the blue-colored glycerine sinks below the surface of the water, while the corn oil floats on top of the water.

Table 2.7 Relationship Between Volume and Density for Identical Masses of Common Substances

Substance	Cube of substance (face shown actual size)	Mass (g)	Volume (cm^3)	Density (g/cm^3)
Wood		10	20	0.5
Water		10	10	1.0
Aluminum		10	3.7	2.7
Lead		10	0.88	11.4

Table 2.8 Densities of Some Common Substances

Solids and Liquids		Gases	
Substance	**Density at 20°C (g/cm^3)**	**Substance**	**Density at 20°C (g/L)**
Gold	19.3	Chlorine	2.95
Mercury	13.6	Carbon dioxide	1.83
Lead	11.4	Oxygen	1.33
Aluminum	2.70	Air	1.20
Table sugar	1.59	Nitrogen	1.17
Water (4°C)	1.000	Neon	0.84
Corn oil	0.922	Ammonia	0.718
Ice (0°C)	0.917	Methane	0.665
Ethanol	0.789	Helium	0.166
Gasoline	0.66–0.69	Hydrogen	0.084

Figure 2.17 Solid paraffin sinks in liquid paraffin (left), but solid water, ice, floats in liquid water (right). What does this tell you about the densities of these substances?

You have probably seen a helium-filled balloon disappear rapidly into the sky when it is released. Whether a gas-filled balloon will sink or float when released into the air depends on how the density of the gas compares to the density of air. The densities of the gases given in Table 2.8 allow you to determine whether a particular gas-filled balloon would sink or float in air.

What happens to the density of a substance as its temperature increases? The volume of a substance usually increases as the temperature is increased. Meanwhile, its mass remains the same. Thus, the density of a substance usually decreases as its temperature increases. Water is an important exception. Below 4°C the volume of water increases as its temperature decreases. Ice floats because it is less dense than water.

Example 5 Calculating the Density of a Substance

A copper penny has a mass of 3.1 g and a volume of 0.35 cm^3. What is the density of copper?

Solution

You can calculate the density of a substance if you know the mass and volume of a sample of the substance.

$$\text{Density} = \frac{\text{mass}}{\text{volume}} = \frac{3.1\text{ g}}{0.35\text{ cm}^3} = 8.8571 = 8.9\text{ g/cm}^3$$

(two significant figures)

Problem-Solving Tip

Check that the solution has the correct units before doing the calculation. A measurement of density should have units of mass/volume, which is true in this problem (g/cm^3).

Concept Practice

22. The density of silver is 10.5 g/cm^3 at 20°C. What happens to the density of a 68-g bar of silver that is cut in half?

Practice Problems

23. A student finds a shiny piece of metal that she thinks is aluminum. In the lab, she determines that the metal has a volume of 245 cm^3 and a mass of 612 g. Is the metal aluminum?

24. A plastic ball with a volume of 19.7 cm^3 has a mass of 15.8 g. Would this ball sink or float in a container of gasoline?

Objective

List some useful applications of the measurement of specific gravity.

2.11 Specific Gravity

Specific gravity *is a comparison of the density of a substance to the density of a reference substance, usually at the same temperature.* Water at 4°C, which has a density of 1 g/cm^3, is commonly used as the reference substance.

$$\text{Specific gravity} = \frac{\text{density of substance (g/cm}^3)}{\text{density of water (g/cm}^3)}$$

Note that the units in the equation cancel. Thus a measurement of specific gravity has no units.

The specific gravity of a liquid can be measured with a **hydrometer**. As you see in Figure 2.18, the depth to which the hydrometer sinks depends on the specific gravity of the liquid. The calibration mark on the hydrometer stem at the surface of the liquid indicates the specific gravity of the liquid.

The use of measurements of specific gravity is fairly common. A physician uses the measured specific gravity of a patient's urine to help diagnose certain diseases, such as diabetes. You can check the condition of the antifreeze of your car by measuring the specific gravity of the solution in the radiator. The hydrometer is similar to the one used by the service station attendant in Figure 2.18.

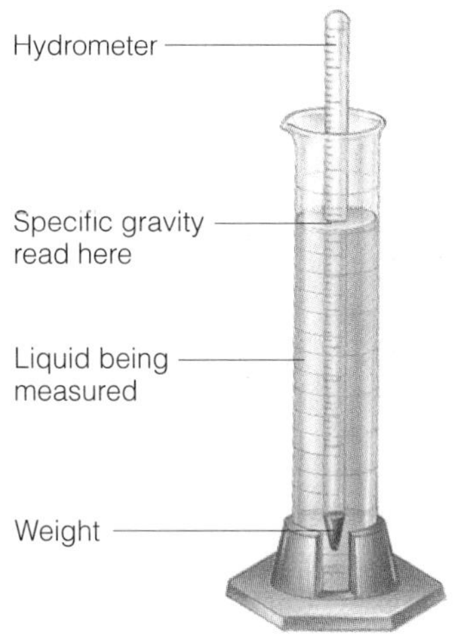

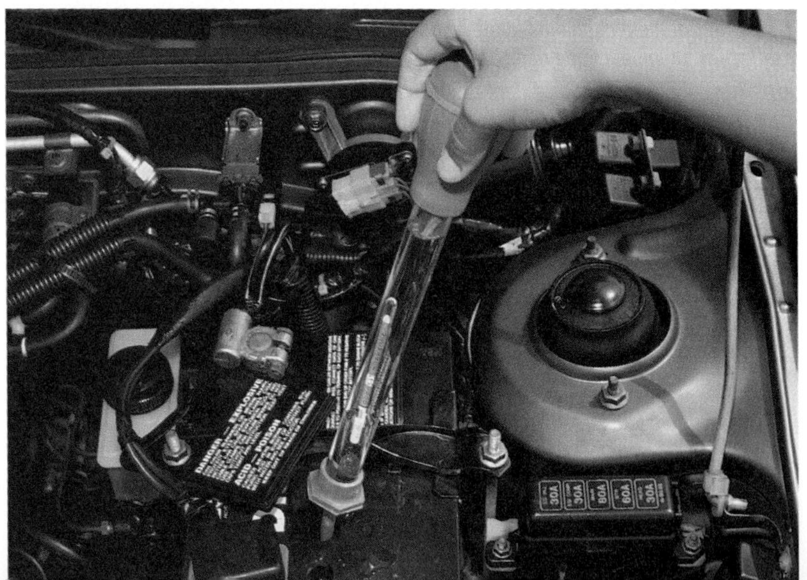

Figure 2.18 A hydrometer (above) is a sealed tube with a weight in the bottom. It is used to measure the specific gravity of a liquid. At right, a hydrometer can be used to check the amount of acid present in an automobile battery.

Concept Practice

25. Why doesn't a measurement of specific gravity have a unit?

Practice Problem

26. Use the values in Table 2.8 to calculate the specific gravity of the following substances at 20°C.
a. aluminum **b.** mercury **c.** ice

2.12 Measuring Temperature

Objective

Convert between the Celsius and Kelvin temperature scales.

When you hold a glass of hot water, it feels hot because heat is transferred from the hot glass to your hand. Your body is sensitive to temperature differences but not to specific temperatures. Temperature determines the direction of heat transfer. Heat transfer occurs when two objects at different temperatures are in contact with each other. When this happens, heat moves from the object at the higher temperature to the object at the lower temperature. **Temperature** *is the degree of hotness or coldness of an object.*

Almost all substances expand with an increase in temperature. Most substances also contract as the temperature decreases (an important exception is water). These properties are the basis for the common mercury-in-glass thermometer pictured in Figure 2.19. The mercury in the thermometer expands and contracts more than the volume of the glass bulb that holds it.

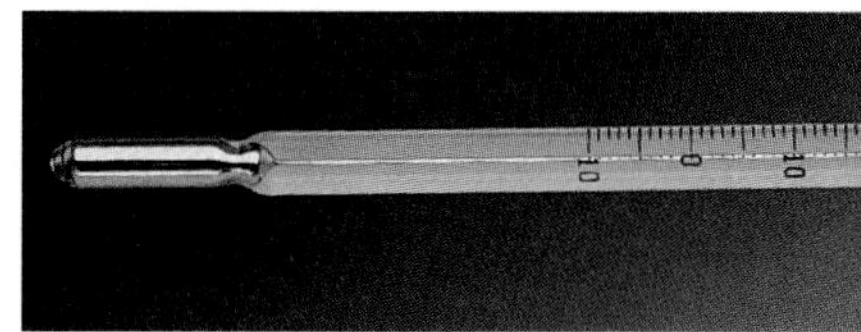

Figure 2.19 Liquid-in-glass thermometers commonly contain mercury or a red liquid. The bulb contains a large amount of liquid, which expands and contracts with temperature changes.

Several temperature scales have been devised. Two readily determined temperatures, the freezing point and the boiling point of water, are used as reference temperature values. The Celsius scale of the metric system is named after the Swedish astronomer Anders Celsius (1701–1744). *On the* **Celsius temperature scale**, *the freezing point of water is taken as 0°C and the boiling point of water as 100°C.* The distance between these two fixed points is divided into 100 equal intervals, or degrees.

Another temperature scale used in the physical sciences is the Kelvin scale, or absolute scale. This scale is named after Lord Kelvin (1824–1907), a Scottish physicist and mathematician. *On the* **Kelvin temperature scale**, *the freezing point of water is 273 K and the boiling point is 373 K.* Notice that with the Kelvin scale, the degree sign is not used. A change of 1° on the Celsius scale is the same as a change of 1 kelvin on the Kelvin scale. *The zero point on the Kelvin scale, 0 K, or* **absolute zero**, *is –273°C.* You can compare the Celsius

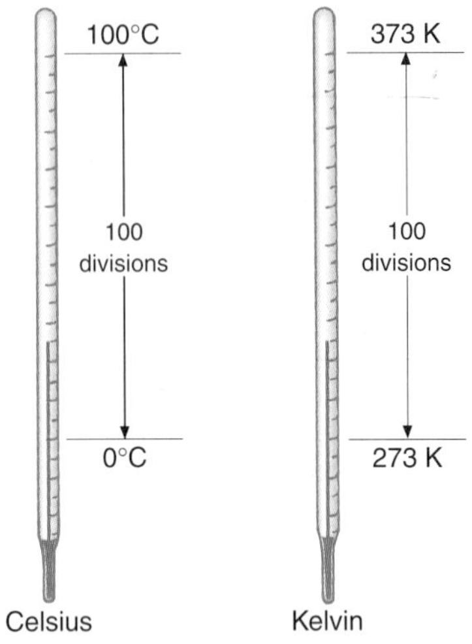

Figure 2.20 These thermometers show a comparison of the Celsius and Kelvin temperature scales. Note that a 1°C change on the Celsius scale is equal to a 1 K change on the Kelvin scale.

and Kelvin temperature scales by looking at Figure 2.20. The relationship between a temperature on the Celsius scale and one on the Kelvin scale is given by:

$$K = °C + 273 \quad \text{or} \quad °C = K - 273$$

Example 6 Converting Between Temperature Scales

Normal human body temperature is 37°C. What is your temperature in kelvins?

$$K = °C + 273 = 37 + 273 = 310$$

Practice Problems

27. Surgical instruments may be sterilized by heating at 170°C for 1.5 h. Convert 170°C to kelvins.

28. The boiling point of the element argon is 87 K. What is the boiling point of argon in °C?

Activity 2 Accuracy and Precision

Purpose

Measure an object as precisely as possible. Analyze the measurements. Apply rules for rounding off calculated answers based on the measurements.

Materials

index card, 3 inch × 5 inch

centimeter ruler

Procedure

1. Use a metric ruler to measure the length and width of an index card as precisely as you can. Your measurement should have one digit that is estimated.

2. Calculate the area (length × width) and the perimeter (2 × length + 2 × width) of the index card. Write both your unrounded answers and your correctly rounded-off answers.

3. Assume that the correct (accurate) length and width of the card are 12.70 cm and 7.62 cm, respectively. Calculate the percent error for each of your measurements.

4. If time permits, use a different ruler or different object and repeat the activity.

Analysis and Conclusions

1. How many significant figures are in your measurement of length? How many for the width?

2. How do your measurements compare with those of your classmates?

3. Do your rounded-off answers have as many significant figures as your classmates' measurements? If not, does that necessarily mean that one of you made a mistake?

2.B Consumer Chemistry

Thermometer of Choice

Choosing the right thermometer for the job, whether for taking body temperature or for use in the laboratory, depends on accuracy and safety. The common mercury thermometer has a precision of 0.2°C. There are safety concerns in using the common mercury thermometer. Because mercury thermometers are glass, they break easily. Besides the hazard due to the broken glass, this breakage exposes people to mercury vapor, which is toxic. Another kind of thermometer is a plastic strip with blocks that display a color change as the temperature changes. The colored blocks on this thermometer contain liquid crystals. These liquid crystals have the property of changing color dramatically at different temperatures. A liquid crystal thermometer is not nearly as accurate as a mercury thermometer. However, a liquid crystal thermometer is easy to use and is virtually unbreakable. Thus, depending on the degree of accuracy you want and your safety requirements, you might choose either of these thermometers for taking body temperature.

When you choose a thermometer to measure temperature in the laboratory, there are similar considerations. Most often, two kinds of thermometers are available in the laboratory. They are both long glass tubes filled with either mercury or a red liquid. The red liquid is a harmless organic compound with red dye. For each of these thermometers, both the glass and the liquid inside expand when you expose the thermometer to heat. However, the liquid expands much more than the glass. The scale on the thermometer translates the height of the liquid column into a temperature reading. The mercury actually expands more with heating than the organic material does. Thus, the mercury thermometer is slightly more accurate than the thermometer filled with organic liquid. However, what you sacrifice in accuracy you may gain in safety. The same breakage problems that apply to common mercury thermometers apply to the larger mercury thermometer for laboratory use. In fact, enough thermometers are broken by students that exposure to mercury vapor from the breakage of thermometers in school laboratories can be a significant safety hazard.

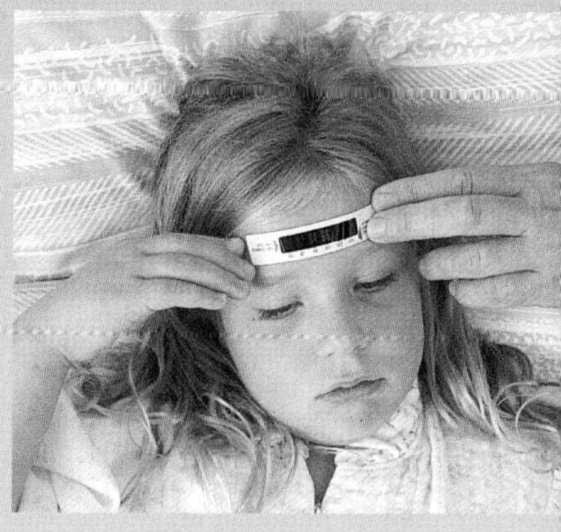

Figure 2.21 The liquid crystals in the plastic change color at different temperatures. Different strips must be used to measure room temperature and body temperature because the measurement range of liquid crystal thermometers is small.

Safety

Remember that mercury is toxic and slowly vaporizes. If you break a mercury thermometer, report it to your teacher immediately so that the mercury can be cleaned up thoroughly.

Think About It

29. Suppose You have to measure temperature in a chemistry experiment. Explain what you need to know to decide which kind of thermometer, mercury filled or organic filled, to use.

30. Analyze Would you use a less precise thermometer at home?

Objective

Calculate the percent error of an experimentally determined measurement.

2.13 Evaluating Measurements

Many experiments in the laboratory involve making measurements. Accuracy, the nearness of a measurement to its accepted or true value, depends primarily on the quality of the measuring instrument. Accuracy also depends on the skill of the person using the instrument. A error in making a measurement may have many origins. These could include improper washing or transfer of a sample, improper calibration or use of an instrument, and even color blindness.

In order to evaluate the accuracy of a measurement, you must be able to compare it to the true or accepted value. Suppose you measure the mass and volume of a silver coin at room temperature and calculate its density as 10.3 g/cm^3. According to Figure 2.22, what is the true or accepted value of the density of silver? How do you determine how close the measured value is to the accepted value?

Figure 2.22 The *Handbook of Chemistry and Physics* is a standard reference in which you can look up the accepted values of physical and chemical properties of substances.

PHYSICAL CONSTANTS OF INORGANIC COMPOUNDS (Continued)

No.	Name	Synonyms and Formulae	Mol. wt.	Crystalline form, properties and index of refraction	Density or spec. gravity	Melting point, °C	Boiling point, °C	Solubility, in grams per 100 cc		
								Cold water	Hot water	Other solvents
	Siloxane									
s123	**Siloxane, (di-), oxide.**	$[H(O)Si]_2.O$	106.19	wh volum subst		expl *ca* 300		sl s		s, d HF; d al
s124	**Silver**	Ag	107.8682±3	wh met, cub 0.54	10.5^{20}	961.93	2212	i	i	s HNO_3, h H_2SO_4, KCN; i alk
s125	acetate	$AgC_2H_3O_2$	166.91	wh pl	3.259^{15}	d		1.02^{20}	2.52^{80}	s dil HNO_3
s126	acetylide	Ag_2C_2	239.76	wh ppt		expl		i		s a; sl s al
s127	*ortho*arsenate	Ag_3AsO_4	462.52	dk red, cub	6.657^{25}	d		0.00085^{20}		s NH_4OH, ac a
s128	*ortho*arsenite	Ag_3AsO_3	446.52	yel, powd		d 150		0.00115^{20}	i	s ac a, NH_4OH, HNO_3; i al
s129	azide	AgN_3	149.89	wh rhomb pr, expl		252	297	i	0.01^{100}	s KCN, dil HNO_3; sl s NH_4OH
s130	benzoate	$AgC_7H_5O_2$	228.98	wh powd				0.262^{25}	s	0.017 al
s131	*tetra*borate	$Ag_2B_4O_7.2H_2O$	407.00	wh cr				sl s		s a
s132	bromate	$AgBrO_3$	235.77	col, tetr, 1.874, 1.920	5.206	d		0.196^{25}	1.33^{90}	s NH_4OH; sl s HNO_3
s133	bromide	Bromyrite: AgBr	187.77	pa yel, 2.253	6.473^{25}	432	d>1300	8.4×10^{-6}	0.00037^{100}	s KCN, $Na_2S_2O_3$, NaCl sol; sl s NH_4OH; i al
s134	carbonate	Ag_2CO_3	275.75	yel powd	6.077	d 218		0.0032^{20}	0.05^{100}	s NH_4OH, $Na_2S_2O_3$; i al
s135	chlorate	$AgClO_3$	191.32	wh, tetr	4.430_4^{20}	230	d 270	10^{15}	50^{80}	sl s al
s136	*per*chlorate	$AgClO_4$	207.32	wh, cr, deliq	2.806^{25}	d 486		557^{25}	s	s al; 101 tol; 5.28 bz
s137	chloride	Nat. cerargyrite. AgCl	143.32	wh, cub, 2.071	5.56	455	1550	0.000089^{10}	0.0021^{100}	s NH_4OH, $Na_2S_2O_3$, KCN
s138	chlorite	$AgClO_2$	175.32	yel cr		105 expl		0.45^{25}	2.13^{100}	
s139	chromate	Ag_2CrO_4	331.73	red, monocl	5.625			0.0014^{0}	0.008^{70}	s NH_4OH, KCN
s140	*di*chromate	$Ag_2Cr_2O_7$	**431.72**	red, tricl	4.770	d		0.0083^{15}	d	s a, NH_4OH, KCN
s141	citrate	$Ag_3C_6H_5O_7$	512.71	wh need		d		0.028^{18}	sl s	s a, NH_4OH, KCN, $Na_2S_2O_3$
s142	cyanate	AgOCN	149.89	col	4.00	d		sl s	s	s KCN, HNO_3, NH_4OH
s143	cyanide	AgCN	133.89	wh, hex	3.95	d 320		0.000023^{20}		s HNO_3, NH_4OH, KCN, $Na_2S_2O_3$
s144	ferricyanide	$Ag_3Fe(CN)_6$	535.56					0.000066^{20}		i a; s NH_4OH, h $(NH_4)_2CO_3$

The **accepted value** *is the true or correct value based on reliable references.* In some instances it may be difficult to find or to determine an accepted value. *The* **experimental value** *is the measured value determined in the experiment in the laboratory.* In this instance, the experimental value of the density of silver is 10.3 g/cm³. *The difference between the accepted value and the experimental value is the* **error**.

$$\text{Error} = \text{accepted value} - \text{experimental value}$$

For the silver coin the error is 0.2 g/cm³. The value of the error shows by what amount the experimental value is too high or too low compared to the accepted value. More often, it is useful to calculate the relative error, or the percent error. *The* **percent error** *is the error divided by the accepted value, expressed as a percentage of the accepted value.*

$$\text{Percent error} = \frac{|\,\text{error}\,|}{\text{accepted value}} \times 100\%$$

An error can be positive or negative; however, in calculating percent error the absolute value of the error is used. This means that the percent error will always be a positive value. For the silver coin the percent error is calculated as follows.

$$\text{Percent error} = \frac{|\,10.5\ \text{g/cm}^3 - 10.3\ \text{g/cm}^3\,|}{10.5\ \text{g/cm}^3} \times 100\%$$

$$= \frac{0.2\ \text{g/cm}^3}{10.5\ \text{g/cm}^3} \times 100\%$$

$$= 0.0190476 \times 100\%$$

$$= 2\%$$

Concept Practice

31. Why is the reported value of the percent error of a measurement always positive?

Practice Problem

32. A student estimated the volume of a liquid in a beaker as 200 mL. When she poured the liquid into a graduated cylinder she measured the volume as 208 mL. What is the percent error of the estimated volume from the beaker, taking the graduated cylinder measurement as the accepted value?

Integrating Art

Measurement in the Fine Arts

Although some people believe that art and science are very different, artists and scientists share many of the same methods in their work. For example, artists and scientists are both concerned with measurements. A sculptor designing a statue of a realistic human figure must be certain that the head and its features, as well as the arms, legs, and body, are in proportion. Potters must weigh or measure by volume the correct amounts of substances needed to make a particular glaze for a ceramic creation. Printmakers must mix the acids for etching solutions in correct amounts and may need to blend the inks necessary to make the prints. When an artist achieves a desirable formulation for a paint, glaze, or ink, he or she writes it down so that it can be reused by the artist or communicated to other artists.

Chapter 2 Review
Scientific Measurement

Key Terms

absolute zero *2.12*
accepted value *2.13*
accuracy *2.2*
Celsius temperature scale (degrees Celsius, °C) *2.12*
density *2.10*
error *2.13*
experimental value *2.13*
gram (g) *2.9*
hydrometer *2.11*
International System of Units (SI) *2.6*
Kelvin temperature scale (kelvins, K) *2.12*
kilogram (kg) *2.9*
liter (L) *2.8*
meter (m) *2.7*
percent error *2.13*
precision *2.2*
qualitative measurement *2.1*
quantitative measurement *2.1*
scientific notation *2.3*
significant figures *2.4*
specific gravity *2.11*
temperature *2.12*
volume *2.8*
weight *2.9*

Chapter Summary

Measurements can be qualitative or quantitative. The accuracy of a measurement is how close a measurement comes to the true value. By contrast, the precision of a measurement depends on its reproducibility.

The International System of Units (SI) is the system of measurement used by scientists. There are seven base SI units from which all other SI units of measurement are derived.

The basic SI unit of length is the meter. One cubic decimeter (liter) has a volume of 1000 cm^3. One cubic centimeter has the same volume as 1 mL.

The quantity of matter an object contains is its mass. The mass of an object is constant and independent of gravity. A balance is used to measure mass. Weight is not the same as mass. Weight is the measure of the pull of gravity on an object of given mass.

The ratio of the mass of an object to its volume is its density. The unit of density is grams per cubic centimeter. Specific gravity is the ratio of the density of a substance to the density of water. Specific gravity has no units. The specific gravity of a liquid is commonly measured with a hydrometer.

Temperature difference determines the direction of heat flow between two bodies. Heat flows from a hot body to a cold body. Temperature is measured on the Celsius and Kelvin scales.

The error in a measurement is the difference between the accepted and the experimental value. The ratio of the error to the accepted value multiplied by 100 is the percent error. Percent error is used to evaluate the accuracy of measurements.

Practice Questions and Problems

33. Identify the following as quantitative or qualitative measurements. *2.1*
a. A flame is hot.
b. A candle has a mass of 90 g.
c. Wax is soft.
d. A candle's height decreases 4.2 cm/h.

34. Distinguish between the accuracy and precision of a measurement. *2.2*

35. Comment on the accuracy and precision of these basketball free-throw shooters. *2.2*
a. 99 of 100 shots are made.
b. 99 of 100 shots hit the front of the rim and bounce off.
c. 33 of 100 shots are made; the rest miss.

36. Three students made multiple weighings of a copper cylinder, each using a different balance. The correct mass of the cylinder had been previously determined to be 47.32 g. Describe the accuracy and precision of each student's measurements. *2.2*

	Lissa	Lamont	Leigh Anne
Weighing 1	47.13	47.45	47.95
Weighing 2	47.94	47.39	47.91
Weighing 3	46.83	47.42	47.89
Weighing 4	47.47	47.41	47.93

37. How many significant figures are in each of these measurements? *2.4*

a. 143 g
b. 0.074 cm
c. 8.750×10^{-2} ng
d. 1.072 km
e. 10 800 m
f. 5.00 dm^3

38. How many significant figures are in each underlined measurement? *2.4*
a. 60 s = 1 min
b. 9 innings in a baseball game
c. 1 km = 1000 m
d. 47.70 g of copper
e. 25 computers
f. 0.0950 m of gold chain

39. Round off each of these measurements to three significant figures. *2.5*
a. 98.473 L
b. 0.000 763 21 cg
c. 57.048 m
d. 12.17°C
e. $0.007\,498\,3 \times 10^4$ mm
f. 1764.9 mL

40. Write each of the rounded-off measurements in Problem 39 in scientific notation. *2.5*

41. Round off each of the answers correctly. *2.5*
a. 8.7 g + 15.43 g + 19 g = 43.13 g
b. 4.32 cm × 1.7 cm = 7.344 cm^2
c. 853.2 L − 627.443 L = 225.757 L
d. 38.742 kg divided by 0.421 = 92.023 75 kg
e. 5.40 m × 3.21 m × 1.871 m = 32.431 914 m^3
f. 5.47 m^3 + 11 m^3 + 87.300 m^3 = 103.770 m^3

42. Express each of the rounded-off answers in Problem 41 in standard exponential form. *2.5*

43. Water with a mass of 35.4 g is added to an empty flask with a mass of 87.432 g. The mass of the flask with the water is 146.72 g after a rubber stopper is added. Express the mass of the stopper to the correct number of significant figures. *2.5*

44. Express the answer to each problem in scientific notation. *2.5*

a. $5.3 \times 10^4 + 1.3 \times 10^4 =$

b. $\dfrac{7.2 \times 10^{-4}}{1.8 \times 10^{3}} =$

c. $10^4 \times 10^{-3} \times 10^6 =$

d. $9.12 \times 10^{-1} - 4.7 \times 10^{-2} =$

e. $\dfrac{4.8 \times 10^{-5}}{(2.0 \times 10^{-2})} \times (6.0 \times 10^{3}) =$

f. $(5.4 \times 10^4) \times (3.5 \times 10^9) =$

45. List at least two advantages of using SI units for measuring. *2.6*

46. List the SI base unit of measurement for each of these quantities. *2.6*
a. time
b. length
c. temperature
d. mass

47. What is the symbol and meaning of each of these common prefixes? *2.7*
a. milli
b. nano
c. deci
d. centi

48. Match the volume with each item. *2.8*
a. an orange (1) 30 m^3
b. a basketball (2) 200 cm^3
c. a van (3) 20 L
d. an aspirin tablet (4) 200 mm^3

49. List these units in order from largest to smallest. *2.8*
a. 1 dm^3
b. 1 μL
c. 1 mL
d. 1 L
e. 1 cL
f. 1 dL

50. Astronauts in space are said to have apparent weightlessness. Explain why it is incorrect to say that they are massless. *2.9*

51. Match the approximate mass with each item. *2.9*
a. a peanut (1) 400 cg
b. a pear (2) 50 mg
c. a stamp (3) 60 kg
d. a person (4) 150 g

52. Does the density of an object depend on its size? Explain. *2.10*

53. A shiny, gold-colored bar of metal weighing 57.3 g has a volume of 4.7 cm^3. Is the metal bar pure gold? *2.10*

54. A weather balloon is inflated to a volume of 2.2×10^3 L with 37.4 g of helium. What is the density of helium in grams per liter? *2.10*

55. Three balloons filled with neon, carbon dioxide, and hydrogen are released into the atmosphere. Using the data in Table 2.8, describe the movement of each balloon. *2.10*

56. What is the unit of measure of specific gravity? Explain. *2.11*

57. Which of these substances has the highest specific gravity? Which has the lowest specific gravity? *2.11*
a. gold
b. gasoline
c. ice
d. mercury
e. lead
f. aluminum

58. The element silver melts at 960.8°C and boils at 2212°C. Express these temperatures in kelvins. *2.12*

59. Liquid nitrogen boils at 77.2 K. What is this temperature in degrees Celsius? *2.12*

60. A technician experimentally determined the boiling point of octane as 124.1°C. The actual boiling point of octane is 125.7°C. Calculate the percent error. *2.13*

Mastery Questions and Problems

61. Make a concept map using *measurement* as the central concept. Use the key terms from the chapter and the terms mass and length.

62. List two possible reasons for precise, but inaccurate, measurements.

63. Rank these numbers from smallest to largest.
   a. 5.3×10^4
   b. 57×10^3
   c. 4.9×10^{-2}
   d. 0.0057
   e. 5.1×10^{-3}
   f. 0.0072×10^2

64. Describe typical situations in which the following thermometers are used:
   a. alcohol
   b. liquid crystal
   c. mercury

65. Criticize this statement: "When two measurements are added together, the answer can have no more significant figures than the measurement with the least number of significant figures."

66. Which is larger?
   a. one centigram or one milligram
   b. one liter or one centiliter
   c. one calorie or one kilocalorie
   d. one millisecond or one centisecond
   e. one microliter or one milliliter
   f. 1 mm^3 or 1 dm^3

67. Criticize this statement: "When a number is rounded off, the last significant figure is dropped if it is less than 5."

68. A piece of wood sinks in ethanol but floats in gasoline. Give a range of possible densities for the wood.

69. Is it possible for an object to lose weight but at the same time not lose mass? Explain.

70. How has the egg been suspended in the clear liquid?

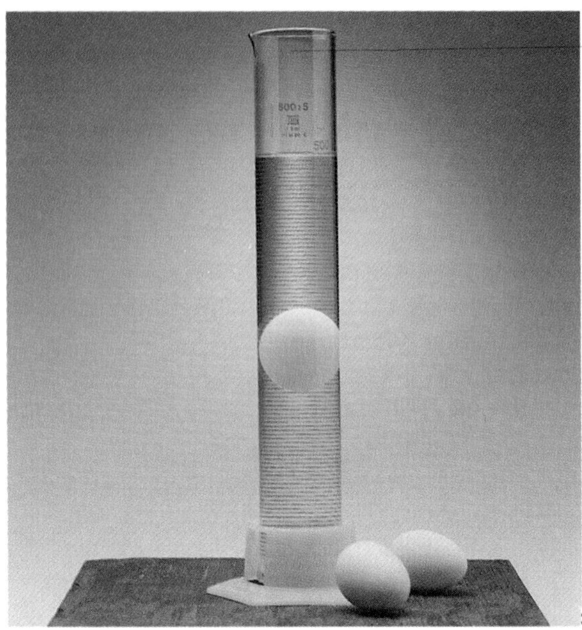

Critical Thinking Questions

71. Choose the term that best completes the second relationship.
   a. mass:kilograms   money: _____
   (1) hot   (3) coins
   (2) dollars   (4) spending
   b. temperature:thermometer   volume: _____
   (1) meter stick   (3) balance
   (2) graduated cylinder   (4) scale
   c. foot:inch   meter: _____
   (1) millimeter   (3) kilometer
   (2) liter   (4) kilogram

72. Is it possible for experimental data to have good accuracy but poor precision?

73. You are hired to count the number of ducks on three northern lakes during the summer. In the first lake, you estimate 500,000 ducks, in the second 250,000 ducks, and in the third 100,000 ducks. You write down that you have counted 850,000 ducks. As you drive away, you see 15 ducks fly in from the south and land on the third lake. Do you change the number of ducks that you report? Justify your answer.

74. Why is a range of values given for the density of gasoline in Table 2.8?

Cumulative Review

75. What is a general goal of the scientific method?

76. What is the correct symbol for each element?

a. sodium	**d.** copper
b. aluminum	**e.** sulfur
c. chlorine	**f.** strontium

77. Classify each of the following as a chemical or physical change.
    - **a.** grass growing
    - **b.** sugar dissolving in water
    - **c.** crushing a rock
    - **d.** cooking potatoes
    - **e.** bleaching clothes
    - **f.** boiling water

78. How would you separate a mixture of ground glass and salt?

79. How can you distinguish between a homogeneous mixture and a compound?

Challenge Questions and Problems

80. What if ice were more dense than water? It would certainly be easier to pour water from a pitcher of ice cubes and water. What other situations might this bring about?

81. The mass of a cube of iron is 355 g. Iron has a density of 7.87 g/cm^3. What is the mass of a cube of lead that has the same dimensions?

82. Plot these data, which show how the mass of sulfur increases with an increase in the volume. Determine the density of sulfur from the slope of the line.

Mass of sulfur (g)	Volume of sulfur (cm^3)
23.5	11.4
60.8	29.2
115	55.5
168	81.1

83. Equal amounts of mercury, water, and corn oil are added to a beaker.
    - **a.** Describe the arrangement of the layers of liquids in the beaker.
    - **b.** A small sugar cube is added to the beaker. Describe its location.
    - **c.** What will happen to the sugar cube over time?

Connections Questions

84. What substance did Lavoisier prove was necessary for combustion?

85. What is an advantage of using a computer-aided design program to design a building?

86. List two ways in which measurements are important to an artist.

Write About Chemistry

87. Write an account of your daily routine. Use SI units to describe the objects and processes in your life.

88. Write a letter to a friend explaining that you have decided to "go metric" in all of your future dealings with units and explain the reasons for your decision.

Readings and References

Frank, Sylvia. "Archimedes." *ChemMatters* (October 1987), p. 17.

Grey, Vivian. *The Chemist Who Lost His Head: The Story of Antoine Laurent Lavoisier.* New York: Coward, McCann & Geoghegan, 1982.

Morrison, Philip and Phylis, and The Office of Charles and Ray Eames. *Powers of Ten: A Book about the Relative Size of Things in the Universe and the Effect of Adding Another Zero.* New York: Scientific American (dist. by Freeman), 1982.

You'll find the graphing calculator solution to this and other problems in Appendix E, starting on page 839. Also, if you need assistance in using the graphing calculator, turn to Appendix D, page 828.

3 Problem Solving in Chemistry

Goals

- Identify several characteristics of good problem solvers.
- Apply problem-solving techniques to a variety of problem types.
- Solve problems by dimensional analysis using conversion factors.

You solve problems all the time. How can you get to something in the back of your closet without causing the things in the front to fall out? In chemistry, problem solving is getting the answer by using what you know without breaking any rules.

Concept Overview

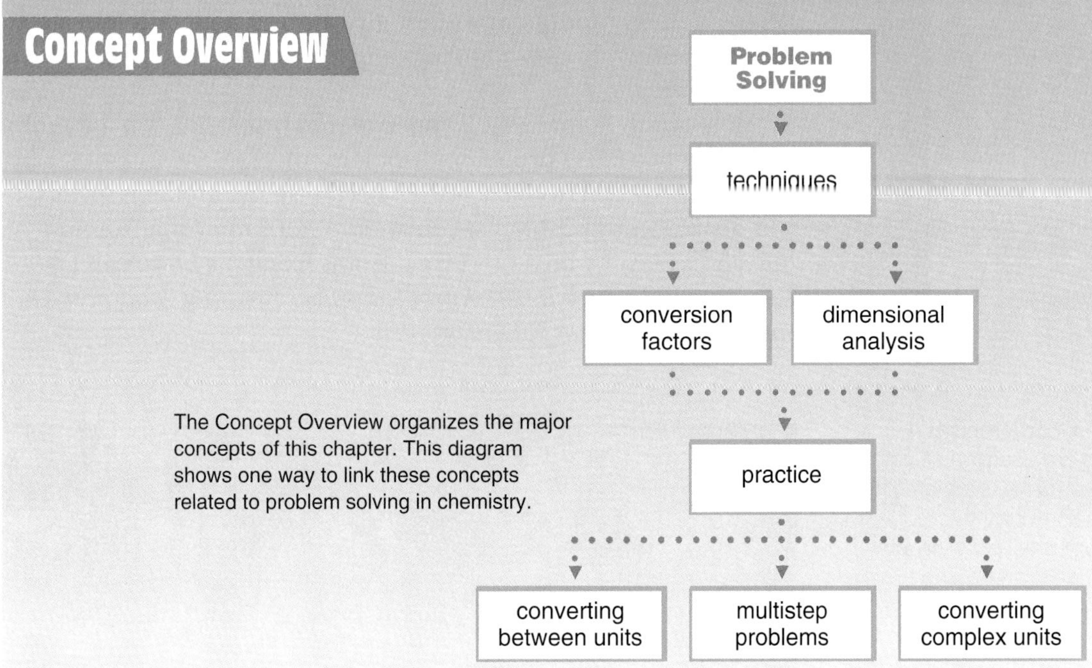

The Concept Overview organizes the major concepts of this chapter. This diagram shows one way to link these concepts related to problem solving in chemistry.

Chemistry is an experimental science aimed at solving problems. As you study chemistry and learn to think like a chemist, you will become a better problem solver. In this course, you will encounter new concepts. You will learn to look at the material world that surrounds you in a different way. As you gain an understanding of new concepts and develop your problem-solving skills, you will improve your ability to solve problems. However, problem-solving skills develop with time and practice. Give yourself the time, and plan on a lot of practice!

3.1 Word Problems

Objective

Describe how to become a better problem solver.

Do you like word problems? You know the kind: "Sally is twice as old as Sara, who is three years younger than Suzy. What will Sally's age be one year from now if Suzy is one-third as old as twelve-year-old Sonja will be nine years from now?" (Answer: Nine years old.) This problem is probably more difficult than any problem you will encounter in this class. Even with much simpler word problems, however, you might feel overwhelmed at first. Perhaps this is not your situation, but if it is, consider the following analogy.

People who like playing tennis generally fall into one of two categories. Either they are already good tennis players (at least in their own minds), or they feel they are getting better through practice.

People who try tennis and then give up are generally not good players. Neither do they want to put in the time needed to become a good player.

In much the same way, if you like word problems, you are probably already a fairly proficient problem solver. Most students who dislike word problems have not yet become good problem solvers. If you dislike word problems, you should not follow the example of the tennis player who quits. Like the girls fixing the bicycle in Figure 3.1, *you can become a better problem solver by using good problem-solving techniques as you do problems.*

Figure 3.1 Good problem-solving skills are useful in solving a variety of everyday problems. In most cases, knowing how something operates will help you figure out what is wrong and how to fix it. You need to plan how to fix it, to do the work, and check that it is fixed. What is wrong with the bicycle in the picture?

Concept Practice

1. What is your personal attitude toward word problems? Do you know why you have these feelings? Are you ready to use this course to help improve your problem-solving skills?

Practice Problem

2. Try this problem for fun, and compare your answers with your classmates' answers. The height of a graduated cylinder is 24 cm plus one-half its height. How tall is the graduated cylinder in centimeters?

Figure 3.2 Carefully planning your route helps ensure a successful trip. What are some of the possible routes for traveling from Bellaire to Jacinto City?

3.2 Techniques of Problem Solving

Objective

List five steps used in solving problems.

Suppose the family of good friends moved out of state to a distant city and then invited your family for a summertime visit. You might fly into a strange airport and then rent a car to drive to your friend's home. Before you drove there, you and your parents would need to identify your destination on a road map. On the map you see several alternative routes between the airport and your friend's city. Before you started driving you would plan a specific route to get you from your starting point to your destination. Once your planning was done, you could make a successful trip. Upon your safe arrival you could share the details of the trip with your friend and exchange news.

Solving a word problem is not too different from taking a trip to a new place. At first the problem may seem confusing, and often there may be several ways to solve the problem. No one method will work in every situation. Nevertheless, most word problems can be solved by using the following guidelines.

1. Identify the unknown. Be certain that you know what the problem is asking. Read the problem carefully. If the problem is long, you might need to read it a number of times. If the problem will have a numerical answer, what will the unit of the answer be?

2. Identify what is known or given. This usually includes a measurement and relationships between measurements. Facts might also be given that are not needed to solve the problem. Learn to recognize which information is extra, so as not to be misled.

3. Plan a solution. This is obviously the "heart" of problem solving: getting from the known to the unknown. Sketching a picture of the problem may help you see a relationship between the given and the unknown. Your sketch might also suggest a way to break down a complex problem into two or more simpler problems. At this point, you might need to look up a constant or an equation that relates a known measurement to an unknown measurement. The solutions to the simpler problems can then be combined to form the solution to the more complex problem.

Figure 3.3 Developing skills, physical or mental, takes practice and good technique.

Chemistry in Careers

Chemical Technician

Although chemists invent the chemical procedures to make a new product, chemical technicians must have the necessary skills for carrying out the chemists' ideas. A technician's job is generally hands-on and routine rather than creative. Technicians may work with standard laboratory glassware and equipment. They may also work with computerized equipment. Technicians are meticulous workers and maintain accurate records of their work. Preparation for a position as a chemical technician includes considerable on-the-job training. The technician must become familiar with the particular procedures, apparatus, and instruments used. Many community colleges, technical schools, and universities offer programs for chemical technicians.

4. Do the calculations. This is usually a straightforward step if you have done a good job planning your solution. The calculations may involve solving an equation for the unknown, substituting in known quantities, and doing the arithmetic. In some problems, you might need to convert a measurement to a different form. In such a case, you must use the relationships correctly to move from the given quantity to the unknown.

5. Finish up. The answer to a problem should always be expressed to the correct number of significant figures. Where appropriate, the answer should be written in scientific notation. Most important, **you must check your work**. Have you found what was asked for? Reread the problem. Did you copy down the given facts correctly? Check your math and check the units. Does your answer make sense? Is it reasonable? Often, you can estimate an approximate answer as a quick check.

Example 1 Calculating Volume from Density and Mass

What is the volume, in cubic centimeters, of a sample of cough syrup that has a mass of 50.0 g? The density of cough syrup is 0.950 g/cm³.

Solution

Step 1. **Identify the unknown.** The unknown is the volume, in cubic centimeters.

Step 2. **Identify what is known or given.** The knowns are the mass and density.

a. mass = 50.0 g. b. density = 0.950 g/cm³

Step 3. **Plan a solution.** The equation that relates mass, density, and volume is this.

$$\text{Density} = \frac{\text{mass}}{\text{volume}}$$

This equation can be solved for the unknown, the volume.

Step 4. **Do the calculations.** Solve for volume by multiplying each side of the equation by volume/density.

$$\cancel{\text{density}} \times \frac{\text{volume}}{\cancel{\text{density}}} = \frac{\text{mass}}{\cancel{\text{volume}}} \times \frac{\cancel{\text{volume}}}{\text{density}}$$

Substitute values for the unknown.

$$\text{Volume} = \frac{50.0\,\cancel{\text{g}}}{0.950\,\cancel{\text{g}}/\text{cm}^3} = 52.632\ \text{cm}^3$$

Step 5. **Finish up.** Volume = 52.6 cm³ (three significant figures)

Concept Practice

3. State in your own words the five suggested steps for solving word problems.

4. Match the steps taken in the trip mentioned in the first paragraph of this section with the five problem-solving steps.

Practice Problems

5. The density of silicon is 2.33 g/cm^3. What is the volume of a piece of silicon that has a mass of 62.9 g?

6. Helium has a boiling point of 4 K. This is the lowest boiling point of any liquid. Express this temperature in degrees Celsius.

7. A small piece of gold has a volume of 1.35 cm^3.
a. What is the mass if the density of gold is 19.3 g/cm^3?
b. What is the value of this piece of gold if the market value of gold is $11 per gram?

8. Normal body temperature is 37°C. What is normal body temperature on the Kelvin scale?

3.3 Conversion Factors

Objective

Construct conversion factors from equivalent measurements.

The same quantity can usually be measured or expressed in many different ways. For example, one dollar = 4 quarters = 10 dimes = 20 nickels = 100 pennies. These are all expressions, or measurements, of the same amount of money. Similarly, one meter = 10 decimeters (dm) = 100 centimeters (cm) = 1000 millimeters (mm). These are different ways to express the same length. Whenever two measurements are equal, or equivalent, a ratio of these two measurements will equal unity, or one.

For example, you can divide both sides of this equation, 1 m = 100 cm, by 100 cm or by 1 m.

$$\frac{100\text{ cm}}{100\text{ cm}} = \frac{1\text{ m}}{100\text{ cm}} = 1 \quad \text{or} \quad \frac{100\text{ cm}}{1\text{ m}} = \frac{1\text{ m}}{1\text{ m}} = 1$$

↑ conversion factors ↑

Each of these ratios of equivalent measurements is called a **conversion factor**. In a conversion factor, the measurement in the numerator (on the top) is equivalent to the measurement in the denominator (on the bottom). The conversion factors above are

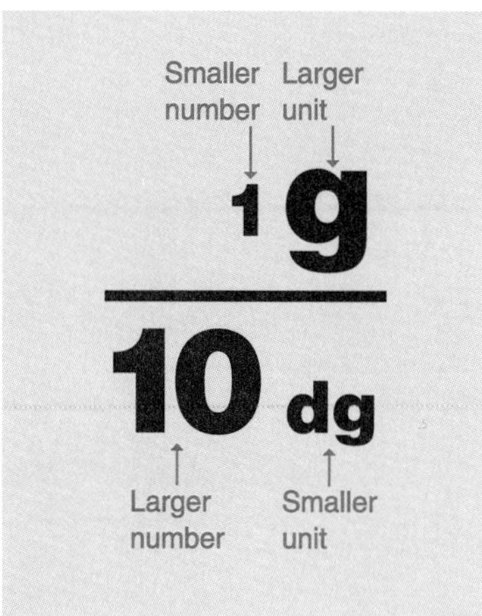

Figure 3.4 The two parts of a conversion factor, the numerator and the denominator, are equal. The smaller number is part of the quantity with the larger unit. The larger number is part of the quantity with the smaller unit.

read "one meter per one hundred centimeters" and "one hundred centimeters per one meter." Look at Figure 3.4 to see another way to look at the relationship between the two parts of a conversion factor.

As you will see in the next section, conversion factors are useful in solving problems in which a given measurement must be expressed in some other unit of measure. When a measurement is multiplied by a conversion factor, the size of the measurement remains the same. Although the *numerical value* of the measurement is changed, the change in the expressed unit compensates for this. Consider, for example, 1 g and 10 decigrams (dg). Even though the numbers in these two measurements differ, both measurements represent the same mass. Remember that conversion factors within a system of measurement are defined or exact quantities. Therefore, they have an unlimited number of significant figures.

Example 2 **Writing Conversion Factors**

Write the two possible factors for each pair of units.

a. kilograms and grams **b.** liters and milliliters

Solution

a. Since 1000 g = 1 kg, the conversion factors are

$$\frac{1000\text{ g}}{1\text{ kg}} \quad \text{and} \quad \frac{1\text{ kg}}{1000\text{ g}}$$

b. Since 1 L = 1000 ml, the conversion factors are

$$\frac{1\text{ L}}{1000\text{ ml}} \quad \text{and} \quad \frac{1000\text{ ml}}{1\text{ L}}$$

Practice Problem

9. Write six possible conversion factors involving these units of measure: 1 g = 100 cg = 10^3 mg.

Objective

Apply the technique of dimensional analysis to solving conversion problems.

3.4 Dimensional Analysis

No one method is best for solving every type of problem. However, one of the best methods available is dimensional analysis. *As the name implies, in* **dimensional analysis** *you use the units (dimensions) that are a part of measurements to help solve (analyze) the problem.* The best way to explain this problem-solving technique is to use it to solve an everyday-type problem and then apply it to chemistry.

Your school club has sold 600 tickets to a chili supper fund-raising event. In a weak moment you, unfortunately, volunteered to make the chili. You have a very large pot and a chili recipe that serves ten. The recipe calls for two teaspoons of chili powder. How much chili powder do you need for 600 servings of chili?

Let's work this problem using dimensional analysis and the problem-solving techniques from Section 3.2

Step 1. **Identify the unknown.** The unknown is the number of teaspoons of chili powder.

Step 2. **Identify what is known or given.** The knowns are as follows.
a) 600 servings of chili must be made.
b) 10 servings require two teaspoons (2 tsp) of chili powder.

Step 3. **Plan a solution.** To solve the problem, you start with the known measurement, 600 servings of chili. You can use the relationship between servings of chili and teaspoons of chili powder from the recipe to write two conversion factors.

$$\frac{10 \text{ servings}}{2 \text{ tsp chili powder}} \quad \text{and} \quad \frac{2 \text{ tsp chili powder}}{10 \text{ servings}}$$

You always use the form of the conversion factor that has the unit of the known in the denominator. This allows you to cancel the known unit and gives you an answer with the units of the unknown. Your plan then is to change the unit "servings" into the unit "teaspoons of chili powder": servings → teaspoons of chili powder.

Step 4. **Do the calculations.** The solution can now be calculated.

$$\frac{600 \text{ servings}}{1} \times \frac{2 \text{ tsp chili powder}}{10 \text{ servings}} = 600 \times \frac{2}{10} = 120 \text{ tsp}$$

Notice that the unit of the known has canceled and that you are left with the correct unit for the answer.

Step 5. **Finish up.** What have you accomplished in solving this problem? You have taken a known measurement, 600 servings, and multiplied it by a conversion factor (which equals unity). This gives you another measurement: 120 teaspoons of chili powder. According to this recipe, 120 teaspoons of chili powder are needed to make 600 servings of chili.

Now you have a problem of a different sort. Do you really take the time to measure out 120 teaspoons of chili powder or do you just estimate and dump in the whole can? The first option would be tedious; the second could be dangerous! Why not measure out the chili powder by the cup? This should be much quicker and still give a good-tasting product. The question then becomes, how many cups are 120 teaspoons of chili powder?

Step 1. **Identify the unknown.** The unknown is the number of cups of chili powder.

Integrating Business

Monetary Exchange Rates

Converting chemical units is similar to exchanging currency outside the United States. Travelers must exchange dollars for foreign currency at a given rate of exchange. For example, travelers to Britain might receive £0.6535 (British pound) for every U.S. dollar they exchange. Suppose that you have saved \$3500.00 to spend during a vacation in Britain. How many pounds will you get for your \$3500? The conversion factors that relate dollars and pounds are

$$\frac{£0.6535}{\$1.0000} \quad \text{and} \quad \frac{\$1.0000}{£0.6535}$$

Use the form of the conversion factor that allows you to cancel dollars (known amount) and gives you an answer in pounds (unknown amount).

$$\frac{\$3500.00}{1} \times \frac{£0.6535}{\$1.0000}$$
$$= £2287.25$$

Notice the similarity between using the exchange rate as a conversion factor and the use of scientific quantities for conversion factors in this chapter.

Figure 3.5 Relationships between various measurements of volume used in cooking can be found in a conversion table located inside a cookbook.

Step 2. **Identify what is known or given.** The known is 120 tsp of chili powder.

Step 3. **Plan a solution.** You start with the known, 120 tsp of chili powder. To solve this problem, you need to know how many teaspoons of chili powder are in a cup of chili powder. You find this information and other volume relationships in a cookbook, as shown in Figure 3.5.

$$3 \text{ teaspoons (tsp)} = 1 \text{ tablespoon (tbsp)}$$

$$16 \text{ tablespoons} = 1 \text{ cup}$$

You can use the first relationship to write a conversion factor that allows you to express 120 tsp as tablespoons. The conversion factor must be written with the unit teaspoons in the denominator so that the known unit will cancel. You can then use the second conversion factor to change the unit tablespoons into the unit cups. This conversion factor must be written with the unit tablespoons in the denominator.

The overall plan then is to change the unit teaspoons into the unit tablespoons; then change the unit tablespoons into the unit cups; teaspoons $\rightarrow$ tablespoons $\rightarrow$ cups.

Step 4. **Do the calculations.** The solution can now be calculated.

$$\frac{120 \cancel{\text{tsp}}}{1} \times \frac{1 \cancel{\text{tbsp}}}{3 \cancel{\text{tsp}}} \times \frac{1 \text{ cup}}{16 \cancel{\text{tbsp}}} = \frac{120 \times 1 \times 1}{1 \times 3 \times 16} = 2.5 \text{ cups}$$

Notice that the units in the numerator of the solution are the same as the units in the plan: tsp $\rightarrow$ tbsp $\rightarrow$ cups. *In every problem, it is important to check to make sure that the units cancel and that the numerator and denominator of each conversion factor are equal to each other.* You should check the conversion factors before doing the actual arithmetic to get the answer.

Roots of Words

dimensis: (Latin) to measure out
analyticus: (Latin) breaking up a whole into its component parts

dimensional analysis a technique of problem solving that uses the units that are part of a measurement to help solve the problem.

One of the best problem-solving methods available is dimensional analysis.

Step 5. **Finish up.** You have shown that 2.5 cups of chili powder is the same amount as 120 teaspoons of chili powder. You have found the answer by multiplying the known measurement by two conversion factors, each of which is equal to unity. In doing this, you have calculated a new measurement that is equivalent to the known measurement.

As noted at the beginning of this section, there is usually more than one way to solve a problem. As you read through the examples, you may have been thinking about a different way to approach some of the problems. For instance, the example in this section could also be worked using the ratio-and-proportion method. You should try the problem in Figure 3.6 right now to see that both methods will give you the same answer. Some problems are most easily worked with simple algebra. You may already be able to use these other methods of problem solving. If so, you should learn how to use dimensional analysis as well. It will broaden your problem-solving skills and allow you to choose the best way to solve each problem.

Of course, you will work to get the correct answer to a problem. At the same time though, you should try to follow the reasoning behind the steps to your solution. Use the units to help you set up the solution to the problem. More important though, *think* the solution through. Try to understand why you are using particular conversion factors in progressing from the *known* to the *unknown*. Consider every problem to be unique. Becoming proficient at a particular method of problem solving will be helpful. It will never, however, replace your ability to read and interpret the problem. With perseverance, you can learn to apply all your problem-solving skills toward the solution of problems.

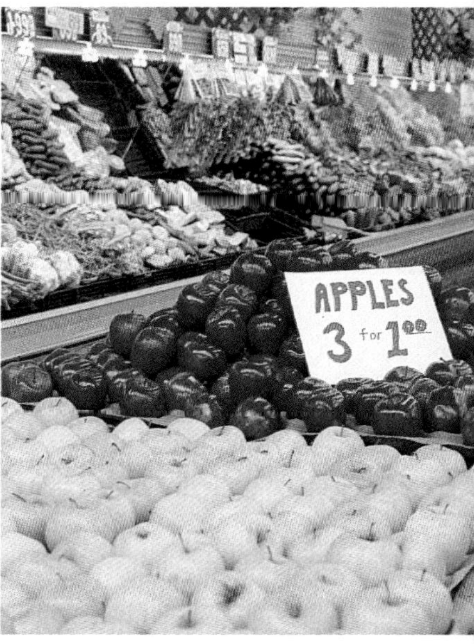

Figure 3.6 How many apples can you buy for $4.00? Work this problem using the ratio-and-proportion method and by dimensional analysis.

Example 3 Using a Conversion Factor

The directions of an experiment ask each student to measure out 1.84 g of copper, Cu, wire. The only copper wire available is a spool with a mass of 50.0 g. How many students can do the experiment before they run out of copper?

Solution

Step 1. **Identify the unknown.** The unknown is the number of students.

Step 2. **Identify what is known or given.** The knowns are as follows.

a. the mass of copper, 50.0 g
b. each student uses 1.84 g of copper

Step 3. **Plan a solution.** The conversion factor is

$$\frac{1 \text{ student}}{1.84 \text{ g Cu}}$$

Step 4. **Do the calculations.**

$$\frac{50.0 \text{ g } \cancel{\text{Cu}}}{1} \times \frac{1 \text{ student}}{1.84 \text{ g } \cancel{\text{Cu}}} = \frac{50.0}{1.84} = 27.174 \text{ students}$$

Step 5. **Finish up.** The answer is 27 students. The rules for rounding off would allow you to give the answer as 27.2 students, but this does not make any sense. Also, 27 students seems to be a reasonable answer because an approximate calculation using

$$\frac{1 \text{ student}}{2 \text{ g Cu}}$$

gives an approximate answer of 25 students.

Problem-Solving Tip

The unit in the denominator of the conversion factor must equal the unit of the given measurement. In this problem the "g Cu" cancels.

Practice Problems

10. A 1.0° increase on the Celsius scale is equivalent to a 1.8° increase on the Fahrenheit scale. If the temperature increases 48.0°C, what is the corresponding temperature increase on the Fahrenheit scale?

11. One of the first dental amalgams, used for tooth fillings, consisted of 26.0 g of silver, 10.8 g of tin, 2.4 g of copper, and 0.8 g of zinc. How much silver is in 25.0 g of this amalgam?

12. Have you ever found yourself sitting through a terrible movie counting the minutes until it was over? If a movie has 0.20 hour remaining, how many seconds of the movie remain?

Objective

Convert measurements within the SI system.

3.5 Converting Between Units

When you do chemistry it is often necessary to express a measurement in a unit different from the one given or measured initially. For example, what if a laboratory experiment requires 7.5 cg of magnesium metal and 100 students will do the experiment that day? How many grams of magnesium should your teacher have on hand? This is an example of a typical *conversion problem*. The need here is to express a given measurement in a different unit. As you have seen, conversion problems are easily solved using dimensional analysis.

Figure 3.7 Understanding the use of conversion factors can make cooking easier. It is often necessary to change a measurement given as a weight to a measurement in volume, or vice versa.

Example 4 Converting SI Mass Units

Express 750 cg in grams.

Solution

Step 1. **Identify the unknown.** The unknown is the number of grams.

Step 2. **Identify what is known or given.** The known is 750 cg.

Step 3. **Plan a solution.** The desired conversion is centigrams → grams. The expression relating the units is 100 cg = 1 g. The conversion factor is $\frac{1\text{ g}}{100\text{ cg}}$

(You want to cancel the centigram unit and be left with the unit grams.)

Step 4. **Do the calculations.** The solution is as follows.

$$\frac{750\text{ cg}}{1} \times \frac{1\text{ g}}{100\text{ cg}} = \frac{750}{100} = 7.5\text{ g}$$

Step 5. **Finish up.** Notice that the unit of the known (cg) cancels, and the answer has the correct unit, grams. Since the unit gram represents a larger mass than the unit centigram, you should expect the number of grams to be less than the given number of centigrams.

Example 5 Finding Volume Using Dimensional Analysis

What is the volume of a pure silver coin that has a mass of 14.0 g? The density of silver, Ag, is 10.5 g/cm^3.

Solution

Step 1. **Identify the unknown.** The unknown is the volume of the coin.

Step 2. **Identify what is known or given.** The knowns are as follows.

a) the mass of the coin = 14.0 g
b) the density of silver = 10.5 g/cm^3

Step 3. **Plan a solution.** You can use algebra to solve this problem, but it can also be solved as a conversion problem. You need to convert the given mass of the coin into an equivalent volume. The density measurement gives the relationship between mass and volume: 1 cm^3 Ag = 10.5 g Ag.

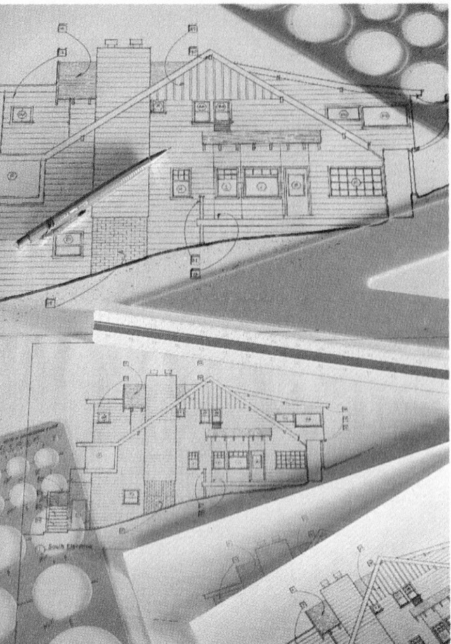

Figure 3.8 Architects use many conversion factors to draw buildings accurately to scale.

Step 4. **Do the calculations.**

$$\frac{14.0\,\cancel{\text{g Ag}}}{1} \times \frac{1\ \text{cm}^3\ \text{Ag}}{10.5\,\cancel{\text{g Ag}}} = \frac{14.0}{10.5} = 1.33333\ \text{cm}^3\ \text{Ag}$$

Step 5. **Finish up.** The answer is 1.33 cm^3. Because a mass of 10.5 grams of silver has a volume of one cubic centimeter, 14.0 g of silver should have a volume slightly larger than one cubic centimeter.

You may have noted that you could solve this problem by using algebra and the definition: density = mass/volume. You may want to rework the problem using this equation and confirm that you get the same answer.

Concept Practice

13. How do you know which unit of a conversion factor must be in the denominator (on the bottom)?

14. List at least two things you should do after you have calculated the answer to a problem on your calculator.

Practice Problems

15. Using tables from Chapter 2, make the following conversions.

a. 0.044 km to meters
b. 4.6 mg to grams
c. 8.9 m to decimeters
d. 0.107 g to centigrams
e. 15 cm^3 to liters
f. 7.38 g to kilograms
g. 6.7 s to milliseconds
h. 94.5 g to micrograms

16. Use the given densities to make the following conversions.

a. 14.8 g of boron to cubic centimeters of boron (density of boron = 2.34 g/cm^3)
b. 2.8 L of argon to grams of argon (density of argon = 1.78 g/L)
c. 4.62 g of mercury to cubic centimeters of mercury (density of mercury = 13.5 g/cm^3)

17. If you worked the density problems in the previous question by dimensional analysis, rework using the equation density = mass/volume or vice versa.

3.A Historical Notebook

Tools for Making Calculations

Figure 3.9 The abacus is an ancient, but very effective, computational device.

Throughout history, people have used various means to keep track of money and to solve numerical problems. People used their hands, pebbles, beads, and notches on sticks to help them count.

An early device used for computing was the abacus. The abacus is still used today in Japan and China. The abacus consists of beads strung on wire in a frame. Beads in the first row represent 1's, those in the next 10's, the next 100's, and so on. By sliding the beads, an experienced abacus user can add, subtract, multiply, and divide as fast as someone using a modern calculator.

Computations were greatly simplified when Scottish mathematician John Napier discovered logarithms in 1614. Calculations involving multiplication and division could now be solved by simply adding or subtracting logarithmic scales. Soon the slide rule was developed to use logarithmic scales to solve problems involving multiplication, division, reciprocals, squares, and square roots. Slide rules were used extensively by mathematicians and scientists into the 1970s, when they were replaced by the electronic calculator.

The first counting device with mechanical parts, an adding machine, was built by French scientist-philosopher Blaise Pascal in 1642. Pascal built the machine to aid him in calculations for his father's business accounts. The machine used a mechanical system of gears and number wheels to add or subtract numbers with up to eight columns of digits. However, it was not until 1820 that a machine capable of performing addition, subtraction, multiplication, and division was commercially available.

Figure 3.10 Mechanical adding machines were used extensively in businesses until the development and use of computers in the 1970s.

The advent of calculators and computers that operate electronically rendered most mechanical computational devices obsolete. Modern electronic computers and calculators can be programmed to perform extremely complex mathematical operations and yield answers faster than was previously thought possible. Computers are capable of performing millions of calculations per second.

Will electronic computers and calculators always be used? Possibly not. Scientists are always trying to improve performance and invent new technologies and devices. Currently, research is being conducted on new technologies that could render modern electronic computers as obsolete as the mechanical slide rule.

Think About It

18. Analyze A student once said, "If I had a better calculator I could work problems better." Is this a true statement? Explain.

Figure 3.11 When playing a complex piece of music for the first time, a guitarist may only play the chords without singing. In a similar way, you may break down a complex problem into simpler parts.

Objective

Apply problem-solving techniques to multistep problems.

3.6 Multistep Problems

Many complex tasks that you encounter in your everyday life, such as learning the complicated musical piece in Figure 3.11, are best handled by breaking the whole task down into more manageable parts. If you were cleaning your car before a date you might first sweep the inside, then wash the exterior, dry the exterior, and maybe even put on a fresh coat of wax. Similarly, many complex word problems are most easily solved by breaking the solution down into steps.

When converting between units, it is often necessary to use more than one conversion factor. For example, you probably don't know how many seconds are in a day. This is something that you can easily calculate using dimensional analysis and equivalent expressions of time that you do know.

Example 6 Converting Units of Time

How many seconds are in one day?

Solution

Step 1. **Identify the unknown.** The unknown is the number of seconds.

Step 2. **Identify what is known or given.** The known in this problem is one day.

Step 3. **Plan a solution.** The desired conversion is: day → seconds. This conversion can be carried out by the following sequence of conversions: day → hours → minutes → seconds. The expressions relating the units are 1 day = 24 h, 1 h = 60 min, and 1 min = 60 s.

Step 4. **Do the calculations.** The solution can be calculated in one step as shown.

$$\frac{1\,\cancel{\text{day}}}{1} \times \frac{24\,\cancel{\text{h}}}{1\,\cancel{\text{day}}} \times \frac{60\,\cancel{\text{min}}}{1\,\cancel{\text{h}}} \times \frac{60\text{ s}}{1\,\cancel{\text{min}}} = 1 \times 24 \times 60 \times 60\text{ s}$$

$$1\text{ day} = 86\,400\text{ s}$$

Each conversion factor is written so that the unit in the denominator cancels the unit in the numerator of the previous factor.

Step 5. **Finish up.** The answer in standard exponential form is 8.64×10^4 s. *Remember to check that the numerator and denominator of each conversion factor are equivalent. When the units cancel, you should be left with the unit of the unknown in the numerator.*

Example 7 Converting SI Units of Length

What is 0.073 cm in micrometers? This distance could be measured precisely with the device in Figure 3.12, called a micrometer.

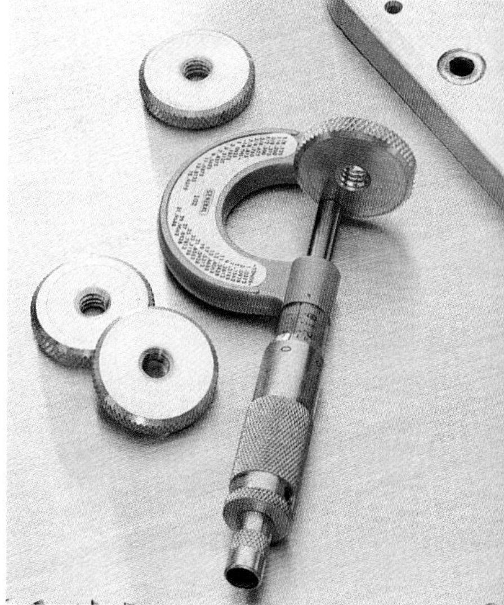

Figure 3.12 Micrometers are used to measure small lengths very accurately.

Solution

Step 1. **Identify the unknown.** The unknown is the number of micrometers.

Step 2. **Identify what is known or given.** The known is 0.073 cm.

Step 3. **Plan a solution.** The desired conversion is centimeters → micrometers. You do not have an expression that relates centimeters to micrometers. However, you do know that 100 cm = 1 m and 1 m = 10^6 μm. The problem can be solved in two steps. Change centimeters to meters, and then change meters to micrometers.

Integrating Science

Standards for Units of Measurement

The use of any system of measurements relies on the existence of a set of standards for a few fundamental quantities. The definition of metric standards has evolved as scientists have needed to make more accurate and precise measurements. Historically, in 1791, the meter was defined by the French Academy of Science as "1/10,000,000 of the quadrant of the Earth's circumference running from the North Pole through Paris to the Equator." Then, in 1889, the International Bureau of Weights and Measures established the meter as the distance between two lines on a standard bar of 90% platinum and 10% iridium. Today, the meter is defined as the distance light travels in exactly 1/299 792 458 second. This definition would not be possible if the speed of light were not known with great accuracy.

Step 4. **Do the calculations.** The solution is as follows.

$$\frac{0.073\,\text{cm}}{1} \times \frac{1\,\text{m}}{100\,\text{cm}} \times \frac{10^6\,\mu\text{m}}{1\,\text{m}} = \frac{7.3 \times 10^{-2} \times 10^6}{10^2}$$

$$= 7.3 \times 10^2\,\mu\text{m}$$

Step 5. **Finish up.** Check to make sure that the units cancel, that the conversion factors are correct, and that the answer has the correct units.

Because a micrometer is a much smaller unit than a centimeter, you should expect the answer to be larger than the given measurement.

Concept Practice

19. Look back at the solution to Example 7 and multiply together only the two conversion factors used in the problem. How does this product compare to the single conversion factor that could have been used to work this conversion problem?

Practice Problems

20. Make the following conversions.

a. 157 cs to seconds
b. 42.7 L to milliliters
c. 261 nm to millimeters
d. 0.065 km to decimeters
e. 642 cg to kilograms
f. 8.25×10^2 cg to nanograms

21. A bar of gold measures 4.5 cm by 6.5 cm by 1.6 dm. Calculate the mass of the gold bar in kilograms. The density of gold is 19.3 g/cm^3.

22. How many milliliters are contained in 1 m^3?

Objective

Apply dimensional analysis to solving complex unit conversion problems.

3.7 Converting Complex Units

Many common measurements are expressed as a ratio of two units. You measure how fast you drive your car in kilometers per hour. You measure the densities of solids and liquids in grams per cubic centimeter. If you use dimensional analysis, converting these types of measurements is just as easy as converting measurements with a single unit. As before, you need correct conversion factors. Also, you need to keep track of the cancellation of units in the numerator and in the denominator.

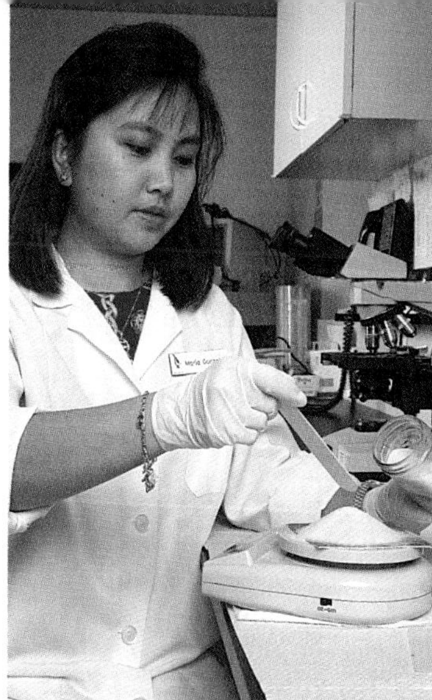

Figure 3.13 Different units are often used in different situations to express the same quantity. Density, for example, would probably be stated in kg/m^3 in an industrial setting (left) and in g/cm^3 in a laboratory setting (right).

Example 8 Converting Ratios of Units

The density of manganese is 7.21 g/cm^3. What is the density of manganese expressed in units kg/m^3?

Solution

Step 1. **Identify the unknown.** The unknown is the density in kg/m^3.

Step 2. **Identify what is known or given.** The known is a density of 7.21 g/cm^3.

Step 3. **Plan a solution.** The desired conversion is

$$\frac{\text{g}}{\text{cm}^3} \longrightarrow \frac{\text{kg}}{\text{m}^3}$$

In the numerator, the mass unit must be changed from grams to kilograms. The relationship is 10^3 g = 1 kg. In the denominator, the volume unit must be changed from cm^3 to m^3. Since 10^2 cm = 1 m, then $(10^2 \text{ cm})^3 = (1 \text{ m})^3$, or $10^6 \text{ cm}^3 = 1 \text{ m}^3$.

Step 4. **Do the calculations.**

$$\frac{7.21\,\cancel{\text{g}}}{1\,\cancel{\text{cm}^3}} \times \underset{\text{(mass conversion)}}{\frac{1\text{ kg}}{10^3\,\cancel{\text{g}}}} \times \underset{\text{(volume conversion)}}{\frac{10^6\,\cancel{\text{cm}^3}}{1\text{ m}^3}} = 7.21 \times 10^3 \text{ kg/m}^3$$

Step 5. **Finish up.** Check that the units cancel, that the conversion factors are correct, and that the answer has the correct ratio of units.

Problem-Solving Tip

When the unknown is a ratio of two units the "known" is also a ratio of two units. In this problem the conversion is from mass/volume (g/cm^3) to mass/volume (kg/m^3).

Practice Problems

23. Make the following conversions.
a. 0.44 mL/min to microliters per second
b. 7.86 g/cm^2 to milligrams per square millimeter
c. 1.54 kg/L to grams per cubic centimeter

24. Gold has a density of 19.3 g/cm^3. What is the mass, in kilograms, of a cubic meter of gold?

25. There are 7.0×10^6 red blood cells in 1.0 mm^3 of blood. How many red blood cells are in 1.0 L of blood?

Activity 3
Dimensional Analysis

Purpose

To apply the problem-solving technique of dimensional analysis to conversion problems.

Materials

3 inch × 5 inch index cards or paper cut to approximately the same size

pen

Procedure

A conversion factor is a ratio of equivalent measurements. For any relationship, you will write two ratios. On a conversion factor card you can write each ratio on one side of the card.

1. Make a conversion factor card for each metric relationship shown in Tables 2.4, 2.5, and 2.6 in Chapter 2. Show the inverse of the conversion factor on the back of each card.

2. Make a conversion factor card showing the mass-volume relationship for water (1.00 g H_2O = 1.00 mL H_2O). The factor on one side of the card should read 1.00 g H_2O/1.00 mL H_2O. The other side should read 1.00 mL H_2O/1.00 g H_2O.

3. Use the appropriate conversion factor cards to set up solutions to Example problems 4, 5, and 7 in this chapter. Notice that in each solution the unit in the denominator of the conversion factor card cancels the unit of the given quantity or unit in the numerator of the previous conversion factor.

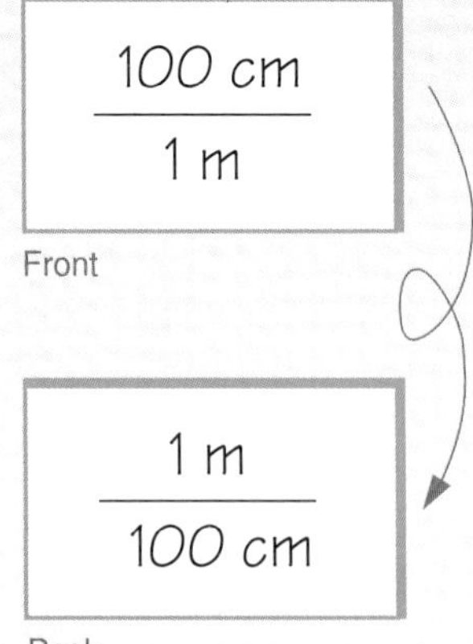

4. Use conversion factor cards to set up solutions to Problem 18 in this Chapter.

Analysis and Conclusions

1. What is the effect of multiplying a given measurement by one or more conversion factors?

2. Use your conversion factor cards to set up solutions to these problems.

a. 78.5 cm = ? meters
b. 0.056 L = ? cm^3
c. 77 kg = ? milligrams
d. 4.54 mL H_2O = ? milligrams H_2O
e. 0.087 nm = ? decimeters
f. 78.5 g H_2O = ? liters H_2O
g. 0.96 cm = ? micrometers
h. 0.0067 mm = ? nanometers

3.B Consumer Chemistry

Let's Make a Deal

As a careful shopper, you want the best value for your money. An important way to get the most for your money is by comparative shopping. Imagine that you see two different boxes of corn flakes at the supermarket. The corn flakes are comparable in quality, but one box is marked \$2.49 per 18-ounce box and the other is \$2.89 per 18-ounce box. Immediately you realize that the first box of corn flakes is a better deal. Almost instinctively you have compared two ratios or conversion factors—the price of corn flakes to the weight of corn flakes—and made a choice between the two.

Making correct decisions when comparative shopping in the real world is more difficult if the container sizes are not identical. Suppose that one brand of corn flakes is priced \$2.49 per 18-ounce box and another brand is \$1.99 per 15-ounce box. If you want the most economical buy, you must calculate the price per ounce for each box. Fortunately, many stores are now giving the price per ounce for many items on the shelf labels. This makes comparative shopping much easier.

In some instances an item is sold by different units. Suppose that strawberries are marked 99 cents/pound and \$2.79/quart. You reason that if you knew the factor for converting quarts to pounds of strawberries you could calculate the price per pound of strawberries in the quart container. However, there is no standard conversion factor between pounds and quarts of strawberries. Because you need strawberries, you may choose without a good idea of which strawberries are the better deal.

The kind of situation just described makes it difficult to be a good comparison shopper. Complete conversion to the metric system will greatly help the comparison shopper. In the meantime, compare the prices of items when you can, and be wary of sale signs—sale items are not always the best buy!

Figure 3.14 Many stores now display the unit cost of the products they sell. Which can is the best buy? What factors other than cost might affect your choice?

Think About It

26. Contrast When an item can be purchased in many amounts or sizes it is often less expensive per gram or milliliter to buy the larger amount or size. Is it always best then to buy the larger size? Explain your answer.

Diamond Coatings

A Gem of a Discovery

Diamond grinding wheel

Diamond, the crystalline form of carbon, is the hardest known material. Diamond has a number of properties that give it value in addition to its worth as a prized gem. Diamond is an excellent thermal conductor—five times better than copper, which is commonly used in kitchen cookware. Diamond is about as slippery as the nonstick surfaces on cookware. In addition, it has superb optical transparency from the infrared through the ultraviolet range of the electromagnetic spectrum. Diamond is also very resistant to radiation damage.

Thus, if it could be thinly spread, diamond could be used as a scratchproof coating on eyeglass lenses and as a supertough coating on tools. Diamond's properties also make it ideal for high-temperature, high-power, and high-speed semiconductor devices.

But how could you coat an object with a diamond film? The extreme hardness of diamond, one of its most valued characteristics, makes it difficult to work with. Once a diamond is formed, cutting or shaping it is difficult. Also, diamond does not readily stick to other surfaces. The way to coat an object with a diamond film is to grow a layer of diamond where you want it!

A group of researchers at the Naval Research Laboratory in Washington, DC grew a diamond using a process called chemical vapor deposition (CVD). In the process, a low-pressure mixture of hydrogen and methane is passed over an extremely hot tungsten filament located above the surface of a material heated to 900°C. The result is the formation of microscopic diamond crystals on the hot surface material that combine to form a thin diamond film. Scientists have actually succeeded in converting sewer gas, rich in methane and carbon dioxide, into diamond films.

In another method, scientists used an oxyacetylene torch in air instead of the tungsten filament with hydrogen and methane gases. With this method, diamond films have been grown on surfaces such as silicon wafers and copper. However, not all surfaces can withstand the intense heat that the torch produces.

There is international interest in growing diamond films because of their usefulness in optics, electronics, and cutting tools. For example, a drill bit coated with a thin diamond film would last 10 times as long as a standard, uncoated bit.

Think About It

27. Apply Suggest possible applications for diamond films that make use of their "slippery" and thermal properties.

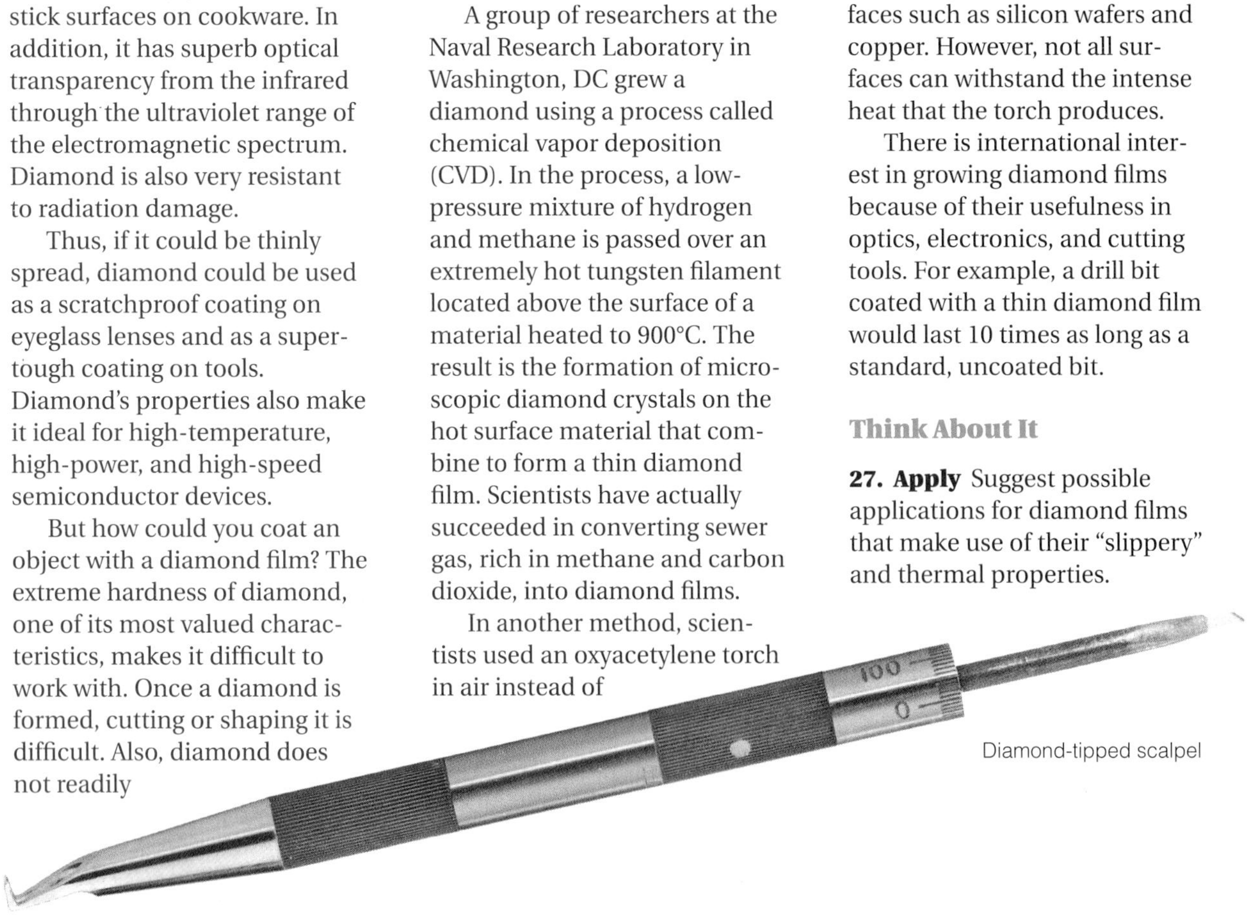

Diamond-tipped scalpel

Chapter 3 Review

Problem Solving in Chemistry

Key Terms

conversion factor *3.3*
dimensional analysis *3.4*

Chapter Summary

Problem solving is a skill learned through practice. The more you practice, the more proficient you become. To solve a word problem, you should identify both the known and unknown. You then plan a solution and do the calculations. Your answer to any problem should always be properly rounded off to the correct number of significant figures and checked.

Any two measurements that are equal to one another but expressed in different units can be written as a ratio. A ratio of equivalent measurements is called a conversion factor and is equal to unity. Conversion factors are used in the problem-solving technique of dimensional analysis. Problems in which you are asked to express a measurement in some other unit (conversion problems) are easily solved using dimensional analysis. In this technique, the units are used to help write the solution to the problem.

Practice Questions and Problems

28. Which of these statements correctly completes this sentence? Good problem solvers... *3.2*
- **a.** read a problem only once.
- **b.** check their work.
- **c.** do as much of the work as possible in their heads.
- **d.** break complex problems down into one or more simpler problems.
- **e.** look for relationships among pieces of information.

29. What must be true for a ratio of two measurements to be a conversion factor? *3.3*

30. What conversion factor would you use to convert between these pairs of units? *3.3*
- **a.** minutes and hours
- **b.** grams of water and cubic centimeters of water
- **c.** grams and milligrams
- **d.** cubic decimeters and milliliters

31. One measure of area is the hectare, which is an area of 10 000 m^2. What does the ratio 10^4 m^2/hectare equal? *3.3*

32. A 2.00-kg sample of bituminous coal is composed of 1.30 kg of carbon, 0.20 kg of ash, 0.15 kg of moisture, and 0.35 kg of volatile (gas-forming) material. How many kilograms of carbon are in 125 kg of this coal? *3.4*

33. Make the following conversions. Express your answers in standard exponential form. *3.5*
- **a.** 36 cm to meters
- **b.** 14.8 g to micrograms
- **c.** 1.44 kL to liters
- **d.** 68.9 m to decimeters
- **e.** 3.72×10^{-3} kg to grams
- **f.** 66.3 L to cubic centimeters
- **g.** 0.0371 m to kilometers

34. Which of the following linear measures is the longest? *3.5*
- **a.** 6×10^4 cm
- **b.** 6×10^6 mm
- **c.** 0.06 km
- **d.** 6×10^9 nm

35. The density of dry air at 25°C is 1.19×10^{-3} g/cm^3. What is the volume of 50.0 g of air? *3.5*

36. An atom of gold has a mass of 3.271×10^{-22} g. How many atoms of gold are in 5.00 g of gold? *3.5*

37. List some ways in which modern electronic computational devices have changed everyday life from when your parents were in school. *3.A*

38. Make the following conversions. Express your answers in standard exponential form. *3.6*
- **a.** 7.5×10^4 nm to kilometer
- **b.** 3.9×10^5 mg to decigrams
- **c.** 0.764 km to centimeters
- **d.** 2.21×10^{-4} dL to microliters

39. Complete this table so that the measurements in each horizontal line have the same value. *3.6*

mg	g	cg	kg
______	______	28.3	______
6.6×10^3	______	______	______
______	2.8×10^{-4}	______	______

40. What is the mass, in kilograms, of 14.0 L of gasoline? (Take the density of gasoline to be 0.680 g/cm^3.) *3.6*
41. A cheetah has been clocked at 112 km/h over a 100-m distance. What is this speed in meters per second? *3.7*
42. Light travels at a speed of 3.00×10^{10} cm/s. What is the speed of light in kilometers/hour? *3.7*
43. Two bottles of window cleaner are available at the store. One bottle is \$2.89 per pint and the other is \$2.25 per 12 ounces (1 pint = 16 ounces). Which bottle is the better buy? *3.B*

Mastery Questions and Problems

44. Complete this concept map, which has *problem solving* as the central concept. Use these terms to fill in the blanks: algebra, conversion factors, denominator, dimensional analysis.

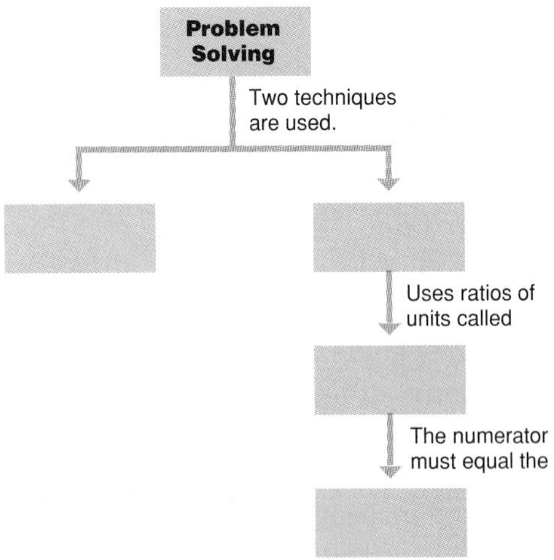

45. A tank measuring 28.6 cm by 73.0 mm by 0.72 m is filled with olive oil that has a mass of 1.64×10^4 g. What is the density of olive oil in kilograms per liter?
46. The earth is approximately 1.5×10^8 km from the sun. How many minutes does it take light to travel from the sun to the earth? The speed of light is 3.0×10^8 m/s.
47. What is the mass of a cube of aluminum that is 3.0 cm on each edge? The density of aluminum is 2.7 g/cm^3.
48. A watch loses 0.15 s every minute. How many minutes will the watch lose in 1 day?
49. The average density of the earth is 5.52 g/cm^3. Express this density in units of kg/dm^3.
50. A flask that can hold 158 g of water at 4°C can hold only 127 g of ethanol. What is the density of ethanol?
51. How many kilograms of water (at 4°C) are needed to fill an aquarium that measures 40.0 cm by 20.0 cm by 30.0 cm?

Critical Thinking Questions

52. Choose the term that best completes the second relationship.
    a. journey:route   problem:______
    (1) unknown   (3) known
    (2) plan   (4) calculate
    b. meter:100 cm   gram:______
    (1) kg   (3) 1000 mg
    (2) 100 cm   (4) 100 kg
53. You have solved many word problems up to this point. Review the techniques for solving word problems. Which step is most difficult for you? What kind of problems do you find most difficult?
54. Why are units so important in working word problems?

Cumulative Review

55. The melting point of silver is 962°C. Express this temperature in kelvins.
56. Classify each of the following as an element, compound, or mixture.
    a. an egg   **c.** dry ice, CO_2
    b. a cake   **d.** iron powder

57. Describe how the law of conservation of mass applies to a burning campfire.

58. List three physical properties of each of the following objects, which are shown in the photo.

a. the glass	**c.** the ice cube
b. the soda	**d.** the bubbles

59. Identify the larger quantity in each of these pairs of measurements.
   a. centigram and milligram
   b. deciliter and kiloliter
   c. millisecond and microsecond
   d. cubic decimeter and milliliter
   e. micrometer and nanometer

60. How many significant figures are in each of these measurements?

a. 5.12 g	**d.** 0.045 04 mm
b. 3.456×10^6 kg	**e.** 985.20 K
c. 0.000 078 dm^3	**f.** 65.02 s

61. Round each of the measurements in Problem 60 to two significant figures.

62. Name three physical and three chemical changes that you have seen today.

Challenge Questions and Problems

63. When 121 g of sulfuric acid is added to 4.00×10^2 mL of water, the resulting solution's volume is 437 mL. What is the specific gravity of the resulting solution?

64. How tall is a rectangular block of balsa wood measuring 4.4 cm wide and 3.5 cm deep that has a mass of 98.0 g? The specific gravity of balsa wood is 0.20.

65. The density of dry air at 20°C is 1.20 g/L. What is the mass of air, in kilograms, of a room that measures 25.0 m by 15.0 m by 4.0 m?

66. Different volumes of the same liquid were added to a flask on a balance. After each addition of liquid, the mass of the flask with the liquid was measured. Graph the data using mass as the dependent variable. Use the graph to answer these questions.
   a. What is the mass of the flask?
   b. What is the density of the liquid?

volume (mL)	14	27	41	55	82
mass (g)	103.0	120.4	139.1	157.9	194.1

Connections Questions

67. What are some typical tasks of a chemical technician?

68. Name a way that converting between SI units and converting between different currencies are similar.

69. Why are accurate standards needed in any system of measurement?

Write About Chemistry

70. Write a description of a shopping trip in which you try to get the best value for an item you have been wanting. Describe how you made price comparisons.

71. Scale a recipe for four people to serve 500 people. Rewrite the procedure to anticipate the practical problems of "scaling up" the recipe.

Readings and References

"Indiana's Error," *ChemMatters* (October 1989), p. 16.

Frank, Sylvia. "Archimedes," *ChemMatters* (October 1987), p. 17.

Gabel, Dorothy. *Solving Chemistry Problems.* New Jersey: Cebco Standard Publishing, 1983.

Zaugg, Harold E. "Polywater," *ChemMatters* (December 1987), pp. 10–13.

4 Atomic Structure

Goals

- Describe Dalton's atomic theory and its significance in the study of matter.
- Infer a conceptual model of the structure of an atom, including the properties of the major subatomic particles.
- Demonstrate the relationship between the atomic mass of an element and the isotopes of that element.

Shown here is the interior of a scanning tunneling microscope (STM), the most powerful microscope in the world. With a magnification of 100 million, an STM can probe matter at the atomic level, making atoms visible to the human eye!

Concept Overview

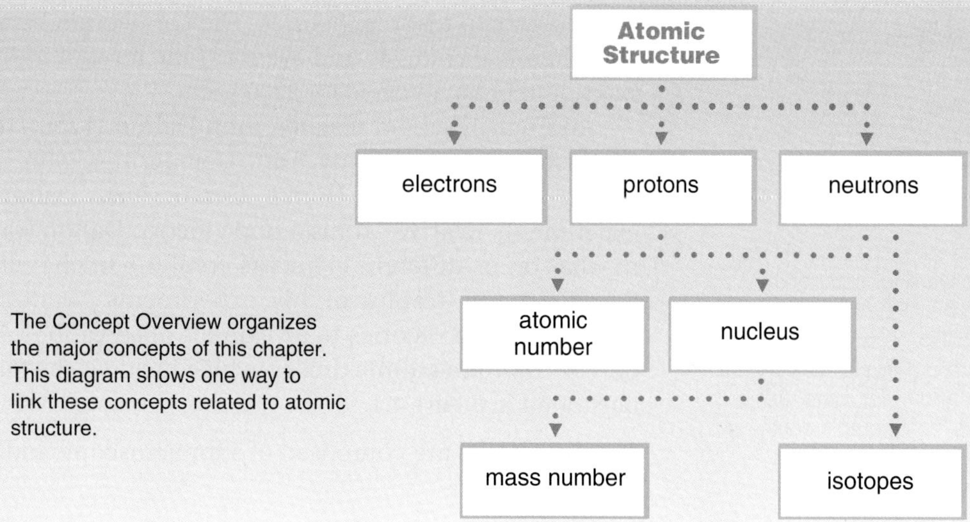

The Concept Overview organizes the major concepts of this chapter. This diagram shows one way to link these concepts related to atomic structure.

Have you ever been asked to believe in something you couldn't see? You cannot see the basic components of matter with your eyes. Yet invisible atoms are the fundamental units of which all matter is composed. Even more remarkable, the atom itself can be fractured into many pieces.

In this chapter, you will enter the world of atomic structure. You will meet some interesting people. Democritus and John Dalton were teachers separated in history by more than 2000 years. Not long after Dalton's life ended, Sir J. J. Thomson and Ernest Rutherford were born. Thomson and Rutherford were physicists who lived into this century. The story of these thinkers and experimenters is filled with ideas and discoveries that include the concept of an atom and the detection of subatomic particles.

4.1 Atoms

Objective

Summarize Dalton's atomic theory.

Democritus of Abdera, a famous teacher who lived in fourth century B.C. Greece, first suggested the idea of atoms. Democritus was part of the "Atomists" school of thought. The Atomists thought that matter was composed of tiny indivisible particles called atoms. Democritus said that atoms were invisible, indestructible, fundamental units of matter. Democritus's ideas agreed with later

Biographical Note

John Dalton
(1766–1844)

Dalton was only 12 years old when he took his first job as a school teacher. Throughout his life, he earned his living as a teacher. However, Dalton's real love and his real genius were for science. During his lifetime, he studied many different topics, including the aurora borealis, the trade winds, and color blindness. Dalton's most notable contribution to science was his reintroduction of the idea of atoms to explain chemical behavior. In spite of its flaws, Dalton's atomic theory inspired a generation of chemists to study atomic theory.

scientific theory. However, his ideas were not useful in explaining chemical behavior because they lacked experimental support. Democritus thought and talked about atoms, but scientific experiments were unknown in his world. Therefore Democritus did no experiments to test his theories. The connection between observable chemical changes and events at the level of individual atoms was not to be established for 2200 years.

An English school teacher, John Dalton (1766–1844), studied chemistry very differently from Democritus, who only philosophized about atoms. Unlike Democritus, Dalton performed experiments to arrive at his atomic theory. Dalton wanted to learn in what ratios different elements combine in chemical reactions. Based on the results of his experiments, Dalton formulated hypotheses and theories to explain his observations. Eventually he devised **Dalton's atomic theory**, which includes the following ideas, illustrated in Figure 4.1.

1. All elements are composed of submicroscopic indivisible particles called atoms.

2. Atoms of the same element are identical. The atoms of any one element are different from those of any other element.

3. Atoms of different elements can physically mix together or can chemically combine with one another in simple whole-number ratios to form compounds.

4. Chemical reactions occur when atoms are separated, joined, or rearranged. However, atoms of one element are never changed into atoms of another element as a result of a chemical reaction.

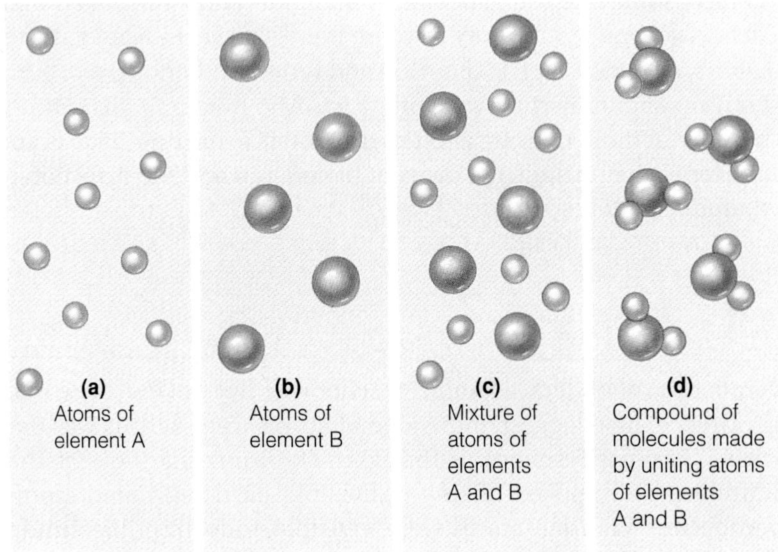

Figure 4.1 According to Dalton's atomic theory, an element is a large collection of atoms and a compound is a large collection of molecules.

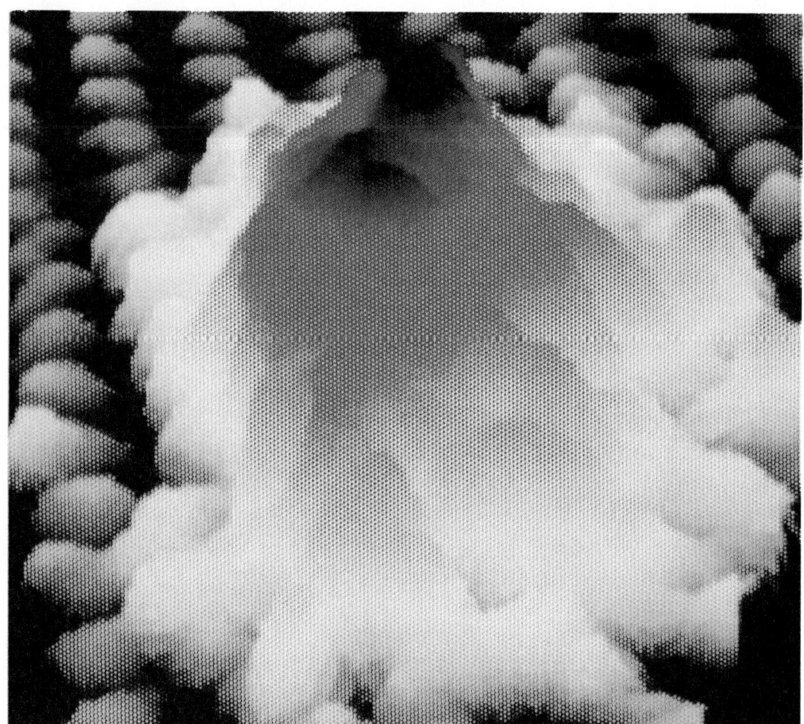

Figure 4.2 The surface of individual gold atoms appears in this photograph taken with a scanning tunneling microscope.

An ordinary coin the size of a penny but composed of pure copper (Cu) illustrates Dalton's concept of the atom. Imagine that you could grind the copper into fine dust. Each speck in your small pile of shiny red dust would still have the properties of copper. Suppose you continued to divide the specks of copper into smaller parts. Eventually, you would come upon a particle of copper that could no longer be divided and still have the properties of copper. *This final particle would be an* **atom**, *the smallest particle of an element that retains the properties of that element.*

Copper atoms are very small. Your hypothetical pure copper coin the size of a penny would contain about 2.4×10^{22} atoms. By comparison, the earth's population is about 4×10^{9} people. There are about 6×10^{12} as many atoms in your little coin as there are people on earth. Even a speck of copper dust contains an unimaginably large number of atoms.

Does seeing individual atoms seem impossible? Despite their small size, individual atoms are visible with the proper instrument. A scanning tunneling microscope visualizes individual atoms, as you can see in Figure 4.2. Individual atoms can even be arranged in patterns. The ability to move individual atoms holds promise for the future creation of atomic-size electronic devices such as circuits and computer chips. This atomic-scale technology could be applied to computers, communications, and space exploration.

Roots of Words

atomos: (Greek) indivisible
atom the smallest particle of an element that retains the properties of that element

Atoms are far too small to see with the unaided eye.

Concept Practice

1. Democritus and Dalton both proposed that matter consists of atoms. Explain how their approaches to reaching the same conclusion differed.

2. Which of these statements would John Dalton have agreed with? Use Dalton's law to explain your answer.
a. Atoms are the smallest particles of matter.
b. The mass of an iron atom is different from the mass of a copper atom.
c. Every atom of silver is identical to every other atom of silver.
d. A compound is composed of atoms of two or more different elements.

Objective

Distinguish among protons, electrons, and neutrons in terms of their relative masses and charges.

4.2 Electrons, Protons, and Neutrons

Most of Dalton's atomic theory is accepted today. One important revision is that atoms are not indivisible. Atoms can be broken down into even smaller, more fundamental particles. Dozens of these subatomic particles are unleashed when powerful atom smashers fracture atoms. In fact, no single theory of atomic structure accounts for all of the subatomic particles that are known. In chemistry you will learn about only three subatomic particles: *electrons, protons,* and *neutrons.*

Electrons are a part of the atoms of all elements. **Electrons** *are negatively charged subatomic particles.* The English physicist Sir J. J. Thomson (1856–1940) discovered electrons in 1897. Thomson performed experiments involving the flow of electric current through gases. He sealed the gases in glass tubes with metal disks called electrodes at each end. Figure 4.3 shows the apparatus. The electrodes

Under some conditions, cathode tubes emit X-rays. Care should be used in operating this equipment.

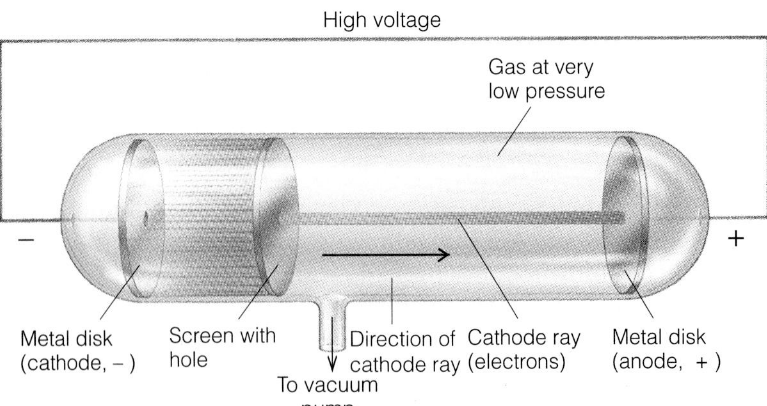

Figure 4.3 In a cathode ray tube, electrons travel as a ray from the cathode (–) to the anode (+). A television tube is a specialized type of cathode ray tube. (The color of the cathode rays in this figure implies direction, not intensity.)

were connected to a high-voltage source of electricity. One electrode, the anode, became positively charged. The other electrode, the cathode, became negatively charged. A glowing beam formed between the electrodes. *The glowing beam, which travels from the cathode to the anode, is a* **cathode ray**.

Thomson found that cathode rays were attracted to metal plates that carry a positive electrical charge. The rays were repelled by plates that carry a negative electrical charge. Figure 4.4 shows a deflection of the cathode rays. In electricity, opposite charges attract and like charges repel. Therefore Thomson proposed that a cathode ray is a stream of very small negatively charged particles, all alike, moving at high speed. He called these particles electrons. Moreover, Thomson showed that cathode rays are always composed of electrons, regardless of the kind of gas in the cathode ray tube or the kind of metal in the electrodes. Thomson concluded that electrons must be a part of the atoms of all elements. By 1900, Thomson and others had figured out that the electron carries roughly one unit of negative charge and that its mass is about 1/2000 the mass of a hydrogen atom.

Clever experiments enabled the American scientist Robert A. Millikan (1868–1953) to improve earlier estimates of the charge on an electron. Because he had accurate values of both the charge and the ratio of the charge to the mass of an electron, Millikan could calculate an accurate value for the mass of the electron. Millikan's values of charge and mass, reported in 1916, are very similar to those accepted today. An electron carries exactly one unit of negative charge and its mass is 1/1840 the mass of a hydrogen atom.

The most common form of the hydrogen atom is the lightest atom that exists. If an electron is only 1/1840 the mass of a common hydrogen atom, what is left over when one of these atoms loses an electron? You can think through this problem with four simple ideas about matter and electric charges. First, atoms have no electric charge; they are electrically neutral. The evidence for electrical

Integrating Physics

New Discoveries of Subatomic Particles

In the decades following the discovery of the neutron, physicists discovered more subatomic particles. Physicists found that when atomic nuclei were struck by high-energy particles or radiation, a target nucleus would shatter, creating unstable particles. This happened infrequently in nature, so physicists designed and built cyclotrons, synchrotrons, and linear accelerators to create collisions and study them in detail. As a result of these tools, hundreds of subatomic particles have been discovered.

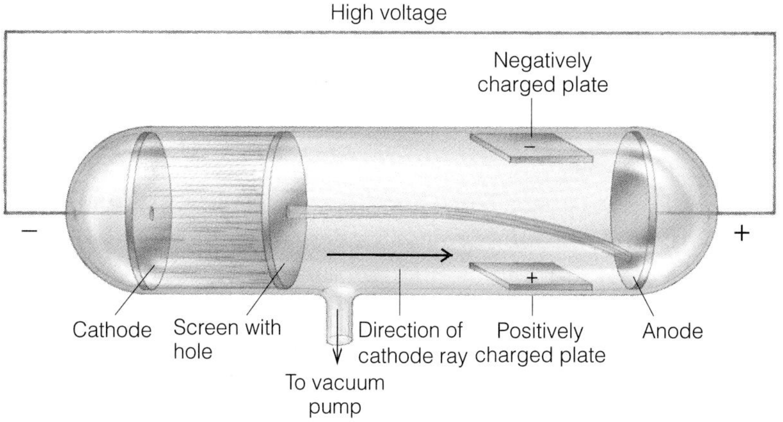

Figure 4.4 Cathode rays are attracted by a positively charged plate. This attraction shows the negatively charged character of the particles.

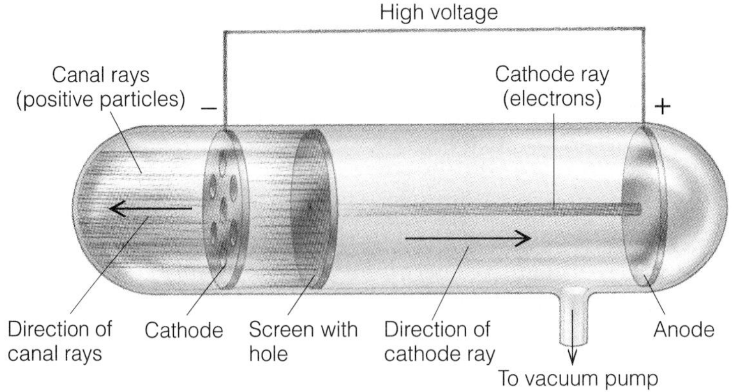

Figure 4.5 If the gas in the cathode ray tube was hydrogen, the canal rays would be made up of protons; after hydrogen gas atoms lose electrons at the cathode, only protons remain to form the canal ray.

Table 4.1 Properties of Subatomic Particles

Particle	Symbol	Relative electrical charge	Approximate relative mass (amu)*	Actual mass (g)
Electron	e^-	1–	1/1840	9.11×10^{-28}
Proton	p^+	1+	1	1.67×10^{-24}
Neutron	n^0	0	1	1.67×10^{-24}

* 1 amu = 1.66×10^{-24} g.

Roots of Words

protos: (Greek) first
proton a positively charged subatomic particle found in the nucleus of an atom

The proton was the first nuclear particle to be discovered.

elektron: (Greek) shining beam
electron a negatively charged atomic particle

The path taken by a swarm of electrons shows up as a shining beam in a cathode ray tube.

neutrality is that you do not receive an electric shock every time you touch an object. Second, electric charges are properties of particles of matter. That is, electric charges are carried by particles of matter. Third, electric charges exist in a single unit or in multiples of a single unit. There are no fractions of charges. Fourth, electric charges cancel when equal numbers of negatively charged and positively charged particles combine to form an electrically neutral particle. Thus, because an electron carries one unit of negative charge, there should be a particle with one unit of positive charge left over when a common hydrogen atom loses an electron. *This positively charged subatomic particle is called a* **proton**. In 1886 E. Goldstein, using a cathode ray tube in which the cathode had holes, observed rays traveling in the opposite direction to the cathode ray. These rays, shown in Figure 4.5, contain positively charged particles and are called canal rays.

In 1932 the English physicist Sir James Chadwick (1891–1974) confirmed the existence of yet another subatomic particle: the neutron. **Neutrons** *are subatomic particles with no charge, but their mass nearly equals that of the proton.* Thus the fundamental building blocks of atoms are the electron, the proton, and the neutron. Table 4.1 summarizes the properties of these three subatomic particles.

Concept Practice

3. Since all atoms have negatively charged electrons, shouldn't every sample of matter have a negative charge? Explain.

4. What experimental evidence did Thomson have for the following ideas?
a. Electrons have a negative charge.
b. Atoms of all elements contain electrons.

Activity 4
Electric Charge

Purpose

To describe the properties of electrical charge.

Materials

four 25-cm pieces of clear plastic tape

two round balloons

two 60-cm pieces of string

one piece of wool or acrylic material

Procedure

1. Put two 25-cm pieces of the tape on opposite sides of your smooth desk top, leaving 2 to 3 cm sticking over the edge. Grasp the ends of the tape. Pull both of the pieces of tape from the desk and slowly bring them toward one another. What do you observe?

2. You and your lab partner should each take a third 25-cm piece of tape and pull it between two of your fingers (as if you were trying to clean it). Slowly bring this piece of tape together with the fourth piece. What do you observe?

3. What would you predict might happen if you brought a piece of tape pulled up from the desk top close to a piece of tape pulled through your fingers? Try it! What happened?

4. Inflate both balloons and tie a string to each. Rub both balloons against your hair. Hold the balloons by the strings and slowly move them toward each other. What happens?

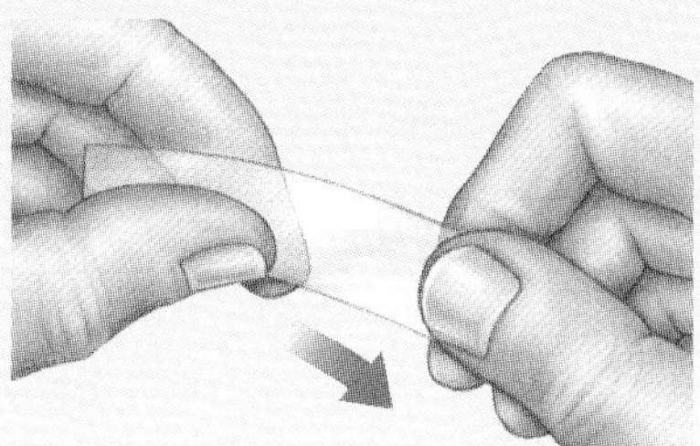

5. Rub the balloons against the piece of material, and slowly move them toward each other. Rub the balloons against your own clothes and move them together. What happens?

Analysis and Conclusions

1. How do objects with like charges react to one another? What about objects with opposite charges?

2. What subatomic particle is transferred when objects become electrically charged?

3. How does an object become positively charged?

4. Can you predict whether a piece of tape pulled from a desk top would be attracted or repelled by a balloon rubbed on wool? Explain.

5. If you knew how the tape pulled from the desk top reacted to the charged balloon, could you predict how the tape pulled through your fingers would react with the balloon? Why?

Objective

Explain the structure of an atom including the location of the proton, electron, and neutron with respect to the nucleus.

4.3 The Structure of the Nuclear Atom

Even before neutrons were discovered, scientists were wondering how electrons and protons were put together in an atom. The prevailing theory was that the protons and electrons were evenly distributed throughout the volume of an atom. In 1911, Ernest Rutherford (1871–1937) and his co-workers at the University of Manchester, England, decided to test this theory of atomic structure. For their test they chose alpha particles. Alpha particles are helium atoms that have lost two electrons and have a double positive charge from the remaining two protons. In their experiment, they directed a narrow beam of alpha particles at a very thin sheet of gold foil. According to the existing theory, they expected the alpha particles to pass straight through the gold.

To everyone's surprise, a small fraction of the alpha particles deflected, or bounced off, the gold foil at very large angles. A few alpha particles even bounced straight back toward the source. In Figure 4.6, you can see an illustration of Rutherford's apparatus.

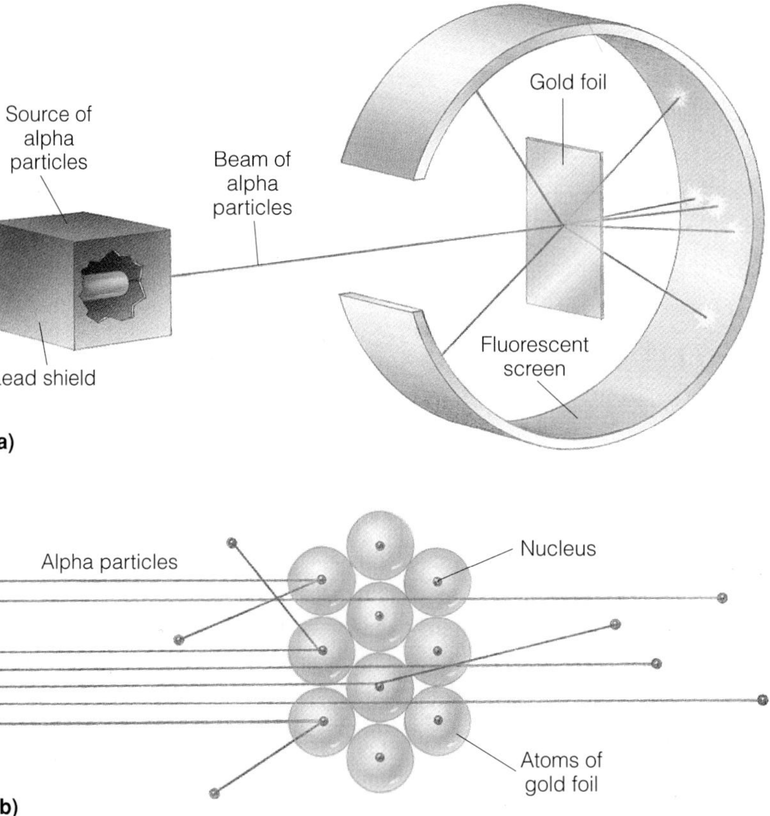

Figure 4.6 **(a)** Rutherford and Marsden aimed a beam of alpha particles at a piece of gold foil surrounded by a fluorescent screen. **(b)** Only particles that pass near or approach the nucleus directly are affected.

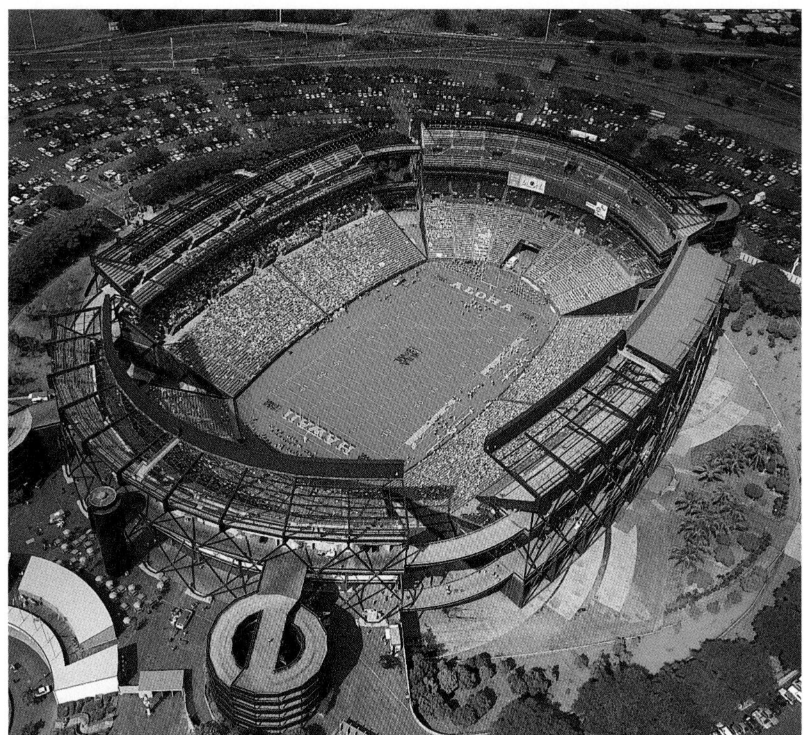

Figure 4.7 If an atom were the size of this stadium, then its nucleus would be about the size of a marble.

Proper shielding should always be used with radioactive emissions such as alpha particles.

Based on the experimental results, Rutherford suggested a new theory of the atom. He proposed that almost all the mass and all the positive charge are concentrated in a small region at the center of the atom. He called this region the nucleus. *The* **nucleus** *is the central core of an atom, composed of protons and neutrons.* Because protons and neutrons have a much greater mass than electrons, almost all of the mass of an atom is concentrated in a tiny nucleus. The nucleus is so dense that if it were the size of a pea its mass would be 2.3×10^5 kg (250 tons)! In Figure 4.7 the size of an atom is compared to that of a football stadium.

The nucleus has a positive charge, and it occupies a very small part of the volume of an atom. What about the region of the atom beyond the nucleus? Rutherford thought that the rest of the atom was more or less empty space. The negatively charged electrons in that area occupied most of the volume of the atom, but they were so small that they did not interfere with the movement of the alpha particles. So most of the alpha particles passed through undeflected. Only when an alpha particle came close to the dense, positively charged nucleus was it deflected. Alpha particles that made a "direct hit" on a gold nucleus bounced straight back. Rutherford later recollected: "It was about as credible as if you had fired a 15-inch shell at a piece of tissue paper and it came back and hit you."

Concept Practice

5. How did the results of Rutherford's gold foil experiment differ from his expectations?

6. What is the charge, positive or negative, of the nucleus of every atom?

Objective

Explain how the atomic number identifies an element.

4.4 Atomic Number

Recall that most atoms are composed of electrons, protons, and neutrons. The protons and neutrons make up the small, dense nucleus. The electrons surround the nucleus and occupy most of the volume of the atom. How are atoms of one element different from those of another element? The answer is that differences among elements result from differences in the numbers of protons in their atoms. As you can see in Table 4.2, atoms of boron (B) have five protons, atoms of carbon (C) have six protons, and fluorine (F) atoms have nine protons.

What makes an atom a hydrogen atom? Every hydrogen atom has one proton in its nucleus. Every oxygen atom has eight protons in its nucleus. *The* **atomic number** *of an element is the number of protons in the nucleus of the atom of that element.* Since all hydrogen atoms have one proton, the atomic number of hydrogen is 1.

Table 4.2 Atoms of the First Ten Elements

Name	Symbol	Atomic number	Composition of the nucleus		Mass number	Number of electrons
			Protons	Neutrons*		
Hydrogen	H	1	1	0	1	1
Helium	He	2	2	2	4	2
Lithium	Li	3	3	4	7	3
Beryllium	Be	4	4	5	9	4
Boron	B	5	5	6	11	5
Carbon	C	6	6	6	12	6
Nitrogen	N	7	7	7	14	7
Oxygen	O	8	8	8	16	8
Fluorine	F	9	9	10	19	9
Neon	Ne	10	10	10	20	10

* Number of neutrons in the most abundant isotope. Isotopes are introduced in Section 4.6.

Similarly, since oxygen atoms have eight protons, the atomic number of oxygen is 8. The atomic number identifies an element. Remember that atoms are electrically neutral. *Thus the number of protons (positively charged particles) in the nucleus of an atom must equal the number of electrons (negatively charged particles) around its nucleus.* A hydrogen atom has one electron around its nucleus, and an oxygen atom has eight electrons.

The periodic table also gives the atomic number of each element. Notice that the atomic number is a whole number written above the chemical symbol of each element. The atomic number increases as you read across each row of the periodic table from left to right.

Example 1 Finding Numbers of Protons and Electrons

The element nitrogen (N) is atomic number 7. How many protons and electrons are in a nitrogen atom?

Solution

The atomic number equals the number of protons or the number of electrons in an atom. Since the atomic number is 7, a nitrogen atom has seven protons and seven electrons.

Concept Practice

7. Why is an atom electrically neutral?

8. What is the relationship between the number of protons and the atomic number of an atom?

Practice Problem

9. Use the periodic table to complete this table.

Element	Symbol	Atomic number	Number of protons
potassium	___	___	___
___	___	5	___
___	___	___	16
___	Y	___	___

Objective

Infer the number of protons, electrons, and neutrons using the atomic number and mass number of an element.

4.5 Mass Number

You know that most of the mass of an atom is concentrated in its nucleus and depends on the number of protons and neutrons. Table 4.2 shows that a helium atom has two protons and two neutrons and a mass number of 4. A carbon atom with six protons and six neutrons in its nucleus has a mass number of 12. *Thus the total number of protons and neutrons in the nucleus is the* **mass number** *of an atom.*

You can determine the composition of an atom of any element from its atomic number and its mass number. The atom of oxygen shown in Table 4.2 has an atomic number of eight and a mass number of 16. Since the atomic number equals the number of protons and the number of electrons, an oxygen atom has eight protons and eight electrons. How can you find the number of neutrons in this atom? The mass number is 16 and is equal to the number of protons plus the number of neutrons. Oxygen, then, has eight neutrons, the difference between the mass number and the atomic number. For any atom:

$$\text{Number of neutrons} = \text{mass number} - \text{atomic number}$$

Example 2 Determining the Composition of an Atom

How many protons, electrons, and neutrons are in the following atoms?

	Atomic number	Mass number
a. Beryllium (Be)	4	9
b. Neon (Ne)	10	20
c. Sodium (Na)	11	23

Solution

a. The atomic number equals the number of electrons and the number of protons. So Be has four protons and four electrons. To find the number of neutrons, subtract the atomic number from the mass number. Thus, this Be atom has $9 - 4 = 5$ neutrons.

b. Using the same reasoning, this atom of Ne has 10 protons, 10 electrons, and $20 - 10 = 10$ neutrons.

c. The atom of Na has 11 protons, 11 electrons, and $23 - 11 = 12$ neutrons.

Practice Problem

10. Complete this table.

Atomic number	Mass number	Number of protons	Number of neutrons	Number of electrons	Symbol of element
9	___	___	10	___	___
___	___	14	15	___	___
___	47	___	___	22	___
___	55	25	___	___	___

Figure 4.8 Au is the chemical symbol for gold. How many electrons does gold have?

To represent the composition of any atom in shorthand notation, you use the chemical symbol with two additional numbers written to the left of it. The atomic number is written as a subscript (a number lowered slightly). The mass number is written as a superscript (a number raised slightly). Look at Figure 4.8. How many neutrons does gold have? Atoms of hydrogen with a mass number of 1 may be designated hydrogen-1. Atoms of helium with a mass number of 4 are designated helium-4.

Example 3 Determining the Number of Neutrons in an Atom

How many neutrons are in the following atoms?

a. ${}^{16}_{8}O$ **b.** ${}^{32}_{16}S$ **c.** ${}^{108}_{47}Ag$ **d.** ${}^{80}_{35}Br$ **e.** ${}^{207}_{82}Pb$

Solution

Recall that the superscript is the mass number and the subscript is the atomic number. The mass number minus the atomic number equals the number of neutrons.

a. $16 - 8 = 8$ **b.** 16 **c.** 61 **d.** 45 **e.** 125

Problem-Solving Tip

When the composition of an atom is represented in shorthand form, subtract the bottom number from the top number to get the number of neutrons.

Concept Practice

11. An atom is identified as platinum-195.

a. What is the number 195 called?

b. Write the symbol for this atom using superscripts and subscripts.

Practice Problem

12. Determine the number of neutrons in each atom.
a. carbon-13 **b.** nitrogen-15 **c.** radium-226

Objective

Explain how isotopes of an element differ.

4.6 Isotopes of the Elements

Most of Dalton's atomic theory is still accepted today. It is now known, however, that atoms of the same element may have different nuclear structures. The nuclei of the atoms of a given element must all contain the same number of protons, but the number of neutrons may vary. You can see in Figure 4.9 that there are three different neon atoms. How do these atoms differ? Each of the neon atoms has the same number of protons (10) and electrons (10) but a different number of neutrons. *Atoms that have the same number of protons but different numbers of neutrons are called* **isotopes**. Because isotopes of an element have different numbers of neutrons, they also have different mass numbers. Despite these differences, isotopes are chemically alike because they have identical numbers of protons and electrons. These subatomic particles are responsible for the characteristic chemical behavior of each element.

Look for hydrogen in Table 4.3. There are three known isotopes of hydrogen. Each isotope of hydrogen has one proton in the nucleus. The most common hydrogen isotope has no neutrons. It has a mass number of 1 and is called hydrogen-1 ($^{1}_{1}H$), or hydrogen. The second isotope has one neutron and a mass number of 2. It is called either hydrogen-2 ($^{2}_{1}H$) or deuterium. The third isotope has two neutrons and a mass number of 3. This isotope is hydrogen-3 ($^{3}_{1}H$) or tritium.

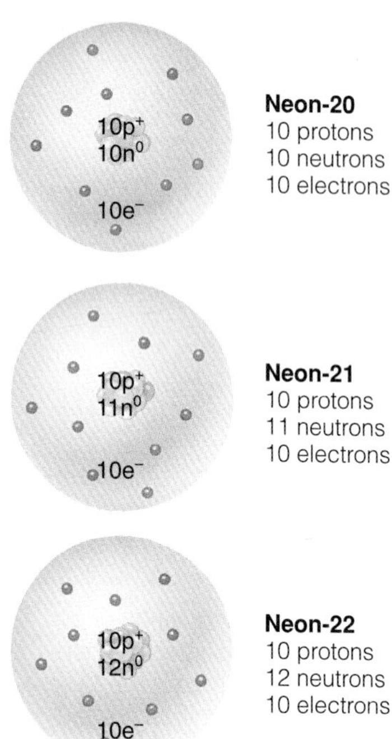

Figure 4.9 Neon-20, neon-21, and neon-22 are three isotopes of neon. How do these isotopes differ? How are they the same?

Example 4 Writing Formulas of Isotopes

Two of the isotopes of carbon are carbon-12 and carbon-13. Give the chemical symbol for each.

Solution

The mass numbers are given in the names of the isotopes. Carbon is atomic number 6. All atoms of carbon have six protons.

Carbon-12, $^{12}_{6}C$ Carbon-13, $^{13}_{6}C$

Table 4.3 Natural Percent Abundance of Stable Isotopes of Some Elements				
Name	**Symbol**	**Mass (amu)**	**Natural percent abundance**	**"Average" atomic mass**
Hydrogen	${}^{1}_{1}H$	1.0078	99.985	
	${}^{2}_{1}H$	2.0141	0.015	1.0079
	${}^{3}_{1}H$	3.0160	negligible	
Helium	${}^{3}_{2}He$	3.0160	0.0001	4.0026
	${}^{4}_{2}He$	4.0026	99.9999	
Carbon	${}^{12}_{6}C$	12.000	98.89	12.011
	${}^{13}_{6}C$	13.003	1.11	
Nitrogen	${}^{14}_{7}N$	14.003	99.63	14.007
	${}^{15}_{7}N$	15.000	0.37	
Oxygen	${}^{16}_{8}O$	15.995	99.759	
	${}^{17}_{8}O$	16.995	0.037	15.999
	${}^{18}_{8}O$	17.999	0.204	
Sulfur	${}^{32}_{16}S$	31.972	95.00	
	${}^{33}_{16}S$	32.971	0.76	32.064
	${}^{34}_{16}S$	33.967	4.22	
	${}^{36}_{16}S$	35.967	0.014	
Chlorine	${}^{35}_{17}Cl$	34.969	75.77	35.453
	${}^{37}_{17}Cl$	36.966	24.23	
Zinc	${}^{64}_{30}Zn$	63.929	48.89	
	${}^{66}_{30}Zn$	65.926	27.81	
	${}^{67}_{30}Zn$	66.927	4.11	65.37
	${}^{68}_{30}Zn$	67.925	18.57	
	${}^{70}_{30}Zn$	69.925	0.62	

Concept Practice

13. How are isotopes of the same element alike? How are they different?

Practice Problems

14. Three isotopes of oxygen are oxygen-16, oxygen-17, and oxygen-18. Write the chemical symbol, including the atomic number and mass number, for each.

15. Use Table 4.3 to determine the number of protons, electrons, and neutrons in each of the five isotopes of zinc.

4.A Environmental Awareness

Hazardous Wastes

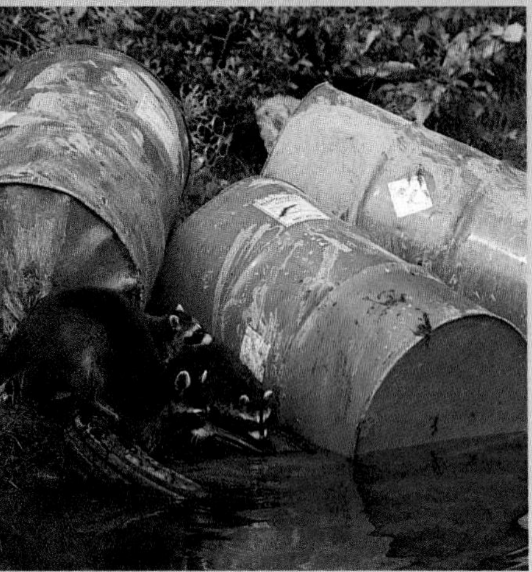

Figure 4.10 About 1200 sites throughout the United States have been designated as priority cleanup sites because they threaten human health or the environment.

In the United States there are thousands of hazardous waste sites in need of cleanup. Cleaning up waste sites is an extremely time-consuming and expensive process. In 1980, Congress passed the Comprehensive Environmental Responsibility, Compensation and Liability Act (CERCLA) to address the problem of hazardous waste cleanup. Also known as Superfund, this law authorizes the Environmental Protection Agency to clean up abandoned hazardous waste sites.

When a potential site is identified, it must first be investigated to see if it poses a threat to human health or to the environment. If so, the site is placed on a national priority cleanup list. By 1990, one decade after the passage of Superfund, approximately 1200 sites had been tabbed for the priority list. About 50 of the sites on the priority list had been cleaned up. Individual states are cleaning up an additional 1000 sites.

Cleaning up a hazardous waste site is a complex project. One project may bring together experts from the fields of chemistry, biology, hydrogeology, engineering, medicine, toxicology, law, and politics. The experts study the site and decide on the best cleanup approach to take. Traditional cleanup methods include incineration, chemical extraction, physical containment, and ground water "pump and treat."

Bioremediation is a method currently being developed to destroy toxic wastes. It involves the use of bacteria that naturally degrade hazardous materials. The cleanup site is sprayed with special fertilizers that encourage bacterial growth. The degradation process can be accelerated up to one million times the rate of normal degradation. Bioremediation has been effective in treating oil spills and city sewage. This method may also become a useful tool in cleaning up toxic wastes. With a blend of old and new technology, plus plenty of time and money, contaminated land and water can be restored to their pristine state.

Think About It

16. Apply An old adage says "An ounce of prevention is worth a pound of cure." How would you apply this saying to the problem of hazardous waste disposal?

17. Compare Of the cleanup methods listed, which do you think would be most suited to the cleanup of contaminated water? To the cleanup of contaminated land?

4.7 Atomic Mass

The mass of even the largest single atom is much too small to be measured individually on a balance. A glance back at Table 4.1 shows that the actual mass of a proton or a neutron is very small: 1.67×10^{-24} g. Even compared with this small mass, the mass of an electron is negligible: 9.11×10^{-28} g. Since the 1920s it has been possible to determine the mass of an individual atom by using a mass spectrometer. The mass of a fluorine atom was found to be 3.155×10^{-23} g and the mass of an arsenic atom is 1.244×10^{-22} g.

The masses of individual atoms are useful information, but these values are inconvenient and impractical to work with. Instead, it is more useful to compare the relative masses of atoms using an isotope of carbon, carbon-12, as a basis. This isotope of carbon was assigned a mass of exactly 12.00000 amu. *An* **atomic mass unit (amu)** *is defined as one-twelfth the mass of a carbon-12 atom.* Using these units, a helium-4 atom, with a mass of 4 amu, has about one-third the mass of a carbon-12 atom. How many carbon-12 atoms would have about the same mass as a nickel-60 atom?

You know that a carbon-12 atom has six protons and six neutrons in its nucleus and its mass is set as 12.00000 amu. Therefore the mass of a single proton or a single neutron is about 1 amu. Because the mass of any single atom depends on the number of protons and neutrons in its nucleus, you might predict that the atomic mass of an atom should be a whole number. As you can see from the periodic table, the atomic masses of sodium, phosphorus, and gold are 22.990 amu, 30.974 amu, and 196.97 amu, respectively. Each of these masses is close to a whole number. However, the atomic mass of chlorine (Cl) is 35.453 amu. How can this atomic mass be explained?

Consider the three isotopes of hydrogen discussed in the last section. According to the table, almost all naturally occurring hydrogen (more than 99.98%) is hydrogen-1. The other two isotopes are present in only trace amounts. *In nature, most elements occur as a mixture of two or more isotopes.* Each isotope of an element has a fixed mass and a natural percent abundance. Notice that the atomic mass of hydrogen in the periodic table or in Table 4.3 (1.0079 amu) is very close to the mass of hydrogen-1 (1.0078 amu). The slight difference takes into account the larger masses and lower amounts of the other two isotopes of hydrogen.

Now consider the two isotopes of chlorine: chlorine-35 and chlorine-37. The simple arithmetic average of the masses of these two isotopes is 36.9674 amu [(34.9689 amu + 36.9659 amu)/2]. The atomic mass of chlorine would average 36.9674 amu only if the two types of chlorine atoms were present in nature in equal amounts. In reality, approximately 75% of all chlorine atoms in nature have a

Objective

Explain, using the concept of isotopes, why the atomic masses of elements are not whole numbers.

Integrating Humanities

Philosophy of Science

Philosophers of science are primarily concerned with the critical analysis of scientific concepts and the way in which these concepts are expressed. These philosophers have analyzed such concepts as "number," "space," "force," and "living organism." For example, is the modern scientific method the best way to examine and explain the natural world? Or is there a better way, as yet unknown? Suppose the philosophers of science suggested an improved scientific method. Using the new method, scientists might gain startling new insights and make advances in science and technology. For this reason, philosophical questions and answers about the methods and concepts of science could be an important aid to scientific progress.

mass of approximately 35 amu (chlorine-35) and 25% have a mass of approximately 37 amu (chlorine-37). Because there is more of the chlorine-35 isotope, the atomic mass should be closer to 35 amu than to 37 amu. The atomic mass of chlorine is 35.453 amu, which is a weighted average mass of these two isotopes. *The* **atomic mass** *of an element is a weighted average mass of the atoms in a naturally occurring sample of the element.* A *weighted average mass* reflects both the mass *and* the relative abundance of the isotopes as they occur in nature. The next section discusses the actual calculation of the atomic mass of an element from isotope data.

Example 5 **Finding the Isotope of Greatest Abundance**

Copper has two isotopes: copper-63 and copper-65. Given that the atomic mass of copper from the periodic table is 63.546 amu, which of the isotopes of copper is most abundant?

Solution

The atomic mass of 63.546 amu is closer to 63 than to 65, so most of the copper atoms must be copper-63.

Concept Practice

18. What data must you have about the isotopes of an element to be able to calculate the atomic mass of the element?

19. There are three isotopes of silicon with mass numbers of 28, 29, and 30. The atomic mass of silicon is 28.086 amu. Comment on the relative abundance of these three isotopes.

Objective

Calculate the average atomic mass of an element from isotope data.

4.8 Calculating the Atomic Mass of an Element

Your grade in a class may be calculated as a weighted average. That is, some exams may have more "weight," or importance, than others. For example, your teacher might count the grade on a chapter test two times, but count a grade on a quiz or lab only once when calculating your grade average. In this way, your "average" reflects the extra weight or value of the chapter test. In the last section, you saw that the atomic mass of an element is a weighted average of the masses of its isotopes. How is atomic mass calculated?

Because the atomic mass must reflect both the masses and the relative natural abundances of the isotopes, you must know:

- The number of stable isotopes of that element
- The mass of each isotope
- The natural percent abundance of each isotope

You can look up both the mass and relative abundance values in standard chemistry reference books. Recall that Table 4.3 gives the mass and natural percent abundance and "average" atomic mass for a few elements.

In Figure 4.11 the atomic mass of chlorine is estimated much as your weighted grade average would be calculated. The number obtained in Figure 4.11 is not 35.453 amu because the mass numbers used for the estimation only approximate the actual masses of the isotopes and the ratio of the isotopes' abundances is not exactly 3 to 1. Example 6 shows a more accurate procedure for calculating atomic masses.

Ratio of chlorine atoms in natural abundance: three $^{35}_{17}Cl$ to one $^{37}_{17}Cl$

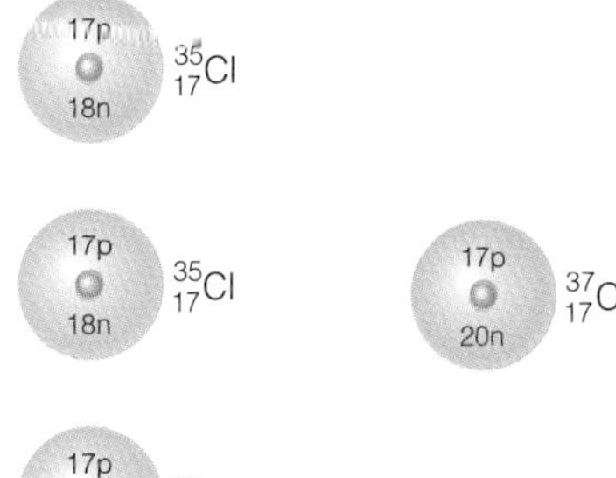

Total number of protons in three $^{35}_{17}Cl$ atoms and one $^{37}_{17}Cl$ atom (17+17+17+17)

Total number of neutrons in three $^{35}_{17}Cl$ atoms and one $^{37}_{17}Cl$ atom (18 +18 +18 +20)

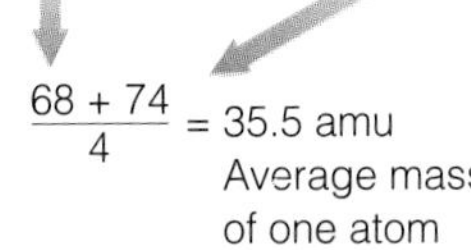

Figure 4.11 The ratio of chlorine-35 (75% abundance) to chlorine-37 (25% abundance) is about 3 to 1. Therefore the mass of three chlorine-35 atoms is averaged with the mass of one chlorine-37 atom.

Example 6 Calculating Atomic Masses

Element X has two natural isotopes. The isotope with mass 10.012 amu has a relative abundance of 19.91%. The isotope with mass 11.009 has a relative abundance of 80.09%. Calculate the atomic mass of this element and name it.

Solution

Find the mass that each isotope contributes to the weighted average by multiplying the mass by its relative abundance. Then add the products.

^{10}X	10.012 amu × 0.1991	=	1.993 amu
^{11}X	11.009 amu × 0.8009	=	8.817 amu
	Total		10.810 amu

Element X is boron, atomic number 5.

Practice Problem

20. The element copper contains the naturally occurring isotopes $^{63}_{29}Cu$ and $^{65}_{29}Cu$. The relative abundances and atomic masses are 69.2% (mass = 62.93 amu) and 30.8% (mass = 64.93 amu), respectively. Calculate the average atomic mass of copper.

4.B Science, Technology, and Society

Drug Testing

Tests used to identify traces of drugs of abuse in the body must be extremely accurate. A false-positive result could ruin a career. A false-negative result could endanger lives. The best method currently available to test for drugs of abuse is to use gas chromatography combined with mass spectrometry, or GC/MS. The gas chromatograph separates a chemical mixture into its individual components. First, the mixture is vaporized through a separation column and carried by another gas. The time required for a gaseous component to pass through the column, called retention time, is different for each compound. Retention time helps to identify the compounds in the mixture. Alone, however, the GC method is not very reliable. The component gases are swept from the GC into a mass spectrometer. The MS splits the different kinds of gaseous molecules into ions of different masses and exposes them to a magnetic field. The degree of deflection of an ion in a magnetic field is related to its mass. The identity of a component can be determined by comparing patterns of ionic deflection to the MS "deflection" of a known substance.

Used together, the GC/MS method of drug testing is very reliable—nearly 100%. But to some critics, almost 100% is not good enough. For example, poppy seeds contain small amounts of a compound that is extremely similar to opium and heroin. Based on a GC/MS test, it is remotely possible for a person who has just eaten a roll with poppy seeds to be mistaken for a heroin user! Thus chemists are busy devising new drug tests and working to improve the old ones.

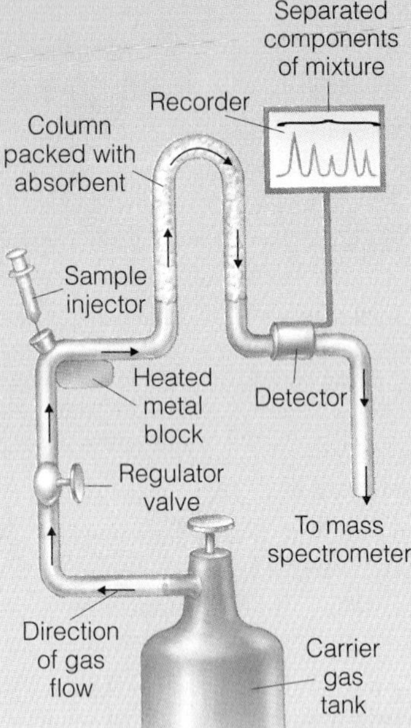

Figure 4.12 The gas chromatograph (GC) is used to separate components of mixtures.

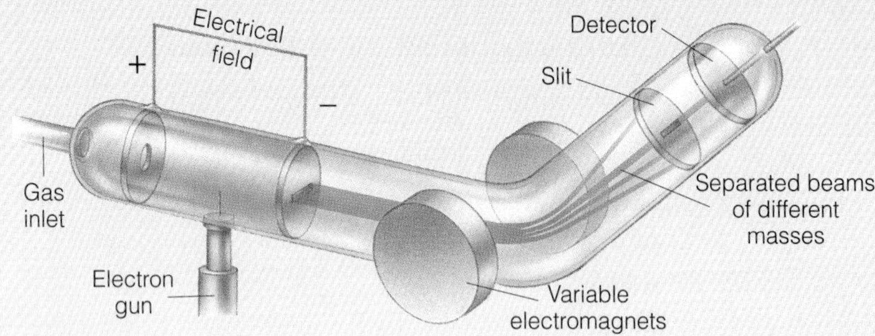

Figure 4.13 The mass spectrometer (MS) is used to find the masses of the components of the gaseous mixture. When the masses of the gaseous components are determined, the components can be accurately identified.

Think About It

21. Criticize Do you think a reliability of 95% in a drug test is adequate for an employer to make decisions about whether a person should be hired? Explain your answer.

Chapter 4 Review
Atomic Structure

Key Terms

atom *4.1*
atomic mass *4.7*
atomic mass unit *4.7*
atomic number *4.4*
cathode ray *4.2*
Dalton's atomic theory *4.1*
electron *4.2*
isotope *4.6*
mass number *4.5*
neutron *4.2*
nucleus *4.3*
proton *4.2*

Chapter Summary

Atoms are the basic building blocks of matter. Each element is composed of atoms. The atoms of a given element are different from the atoms of all other elements.

Atoms are exceedingly small. Dalton theorized that atoms were indivisible, but the discovery of the electron changed this theory. Besides negatively charged electrons, atoms contain positively charged protons and electrically neutral neutrons. The proton has a mass nearly 2000 times the mass of an electron. A proton and a neutron are nearly identical in mass.

The nucleus of the atom is composed of protons and neutrons. The nucleus contains most of the mass of the atom in a very small volume. The electrons surround the nucleus and occupy most of the volume of the atom.

The number of protons in the nucleus of the atom is the atomic number of that element. Atoms are electrically neutral. Thus an atom has the same number of protons and electrons. The sum of the protons and neutrons is the mass number. The atoms of a given element all contain the same number of protons, but the number of neutrons may vary. Atoms with the same number of protons but different numbers of neutrons are isotopes.

The atomic mass of an element is expressed in atomic mass units (amu). An atom of any element has an atomic mass that is approximately a whole number. This is because protons and neutrons each have a mass of about 1 amu. The atomic mass in the periodic table is a weighted average of all the naturally occurring isotopes of that element. For this reason, the atomic mass of most elements is generally not a whole number.

Practice Questions and Problems

22. In your own words state the main ideas of Dalton's atomic theory. *4.1*

23. Would you expect two electrons to attract or repel one another? *4.2*

24. What are the charges and relative masses of the three subatomic particles that are of most interest to chemists? *4.2*

25. What did Rutherford's gold foil experiment tell us about the structure of the atom? *4.3*

26. Describe the composition of the nucleus of the atom. *4.3*

27. What does the atomic number of each atom represent? *4.4*

28. What is meant by the statement "Atoms are electrically neutral"? *4.4*

29. What is the difference between mass number and atomic number? *4.5*

30. Complete this table. *4.5*

Element	Number protons	Mass number	Number electrons	Atomic number	Number neutrons
Si	___	___	___	___	15
___	1	2	___	___	___
___	___	50	24	___	___
___	___	88	___	38	___

31. Name two ways in which isotopes of an element differ. *4.6*

32. List the number of protons, neutrons, and electrons in each of the following atoms. *4.6*

a. $^{27}_{13}Al$ **c.** $^{3}_{1}H$ **e.** $^{78}_{34}Se$
b. $^{44}_{20}Ca$ **d.** $^{18}_{8}O$

33. What is an atomic mass unit? *4.7*
34. What is the atomic mass of an element? *4.7*
35. Uranium has three isotopes with the following percent abundances: $^{234}_{92}U$ (0.0058%), $^{235}_{92}U$ (0.71%), and $^{238}_{92}U$ (99.23%). What do you expect the atomic mass of uranium to be in whole numbers? Why? *4.7*
36. What information about an element's isotopes is needed to calculate that element's atomic mass? *4.8*

Mastery Questions and Problems

37. Make a concept map using atom as the main concept. Use the chapter key terms and the terms negative, positive, and neutral in your map.
38. Explain why the atomic masses of most elements are not whole numbers.
39. Compare the relative size and relative density of an atom to its nucleus.
40. How can there be more than 1000 different atoms when there are only about 100 different elements?
41. Imagine you are standing on top of a boron-11 nucleus. Describe the numbers and kinds of subatomic particles you would see when you look down into the nucleus and those you would see when you look out from the nucleus.
42. What parts of Dalton's atomic theory no longer agree with our current picture of the atom?
43. The four isotopes of lead are shown below, each with its percent by mass abundance and the composition of its nucleus. Using these data, calculate the atomic mass of lead.

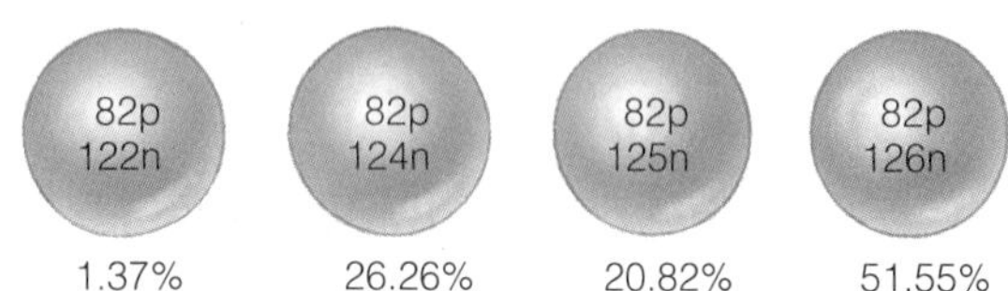

44. Dalton's atomic theory was not correct in every detail. Should this be taken as a criticism of Dalton as a scientist? Explain why or why not.
45. Why are atoms considered the "basic building blocks" of matter even though smaller particles, such as protons and electrons, exist?
46. The following table shows some data collected by Rutherford and his colleagues during their gold foil experiment.
    a. What percent of the alpha particle deflections were 5° or less?
    b. What percent were 15° or less?
    c. What percent were 60° or greater?

Angle of deflection (degrees)	Number of deflections
5	8 289 000
10	502 570
15	120 570
30	7 800
45	1 435
60	477
75	211
105	198

Critical Thinking Questions

47. Choose the term that best completes the second relationship.
    a. female:male — proton: ___
    (1) atom (3) electron
    (2) neutron (4) quark
    b. cow:horse — neutron: ___
    (1) proton (3) atom
    (2) nucleus (4) quark
    c. atom:proton — house: ___
    (1) school (3) planet
    (2) nucleus (4) brick
48. How could you modify Rutherford's experimental procedure to determine the relative sizes of different nuclei?
49. Criticize the statement: "You can't see atoms."
50. Rutherford's atomic theory proposed a dense nucleus surrounded by very small electrons. This implies that atoms are composed mainly of empty space. If all matter is mainly empty space, why is it impossible to walk through walls or pass your hand through your desk?

51. What happens when new experimental results cannot be explained by the existing theory? Base your answer on the scientific method.
52. The goal of environmental cleanup under the Superfund is to reclaim land, air, and water from chemical pollution. If efforts under Superfund continue at the present rate, how long would it take for the 1200 sites to be cleaned up? In light of this time estimate, write a paragraph supporting the current pace or an increased pace for these cleanup efforts.
53. Of every 20 drug nonabusers tested, how many might have a false-positive test result if the drug test is 95% reliable? Would it be better to take more than one drug test? Explain your answer in terms of the accuracy and precision of the drug test.

Cumulative Review

54. Oxygen and hydrogen react explosively to form water. In one reaction, 6 g of hydrogen combined with oxygen to form 54 g of water. How much oxygen was used?
55. How many significant figures are in each of these measurements?
    a. 4.607 mg
    b. 4.35×10^4 km
    c. 0.00150 mL
    d. 60.09 kg
56. Round each of the measurements in Problem 55 to two significant figures.
57. The law of conservation of mass was introduced in Chapter 1. Use Dalton's atomic theory to explain this law.
58. An aquarium measures 55.0 cm × 1.10 m × 80.0 cm. How many cm^3 of water will this aquarium hold?
59. What is the mass of 5.42 cm^3 of platinum? The density of platinum is 22.5 g/cm^3.
60. Classify each of the following as an element, compound, or mixture.
    a. sulfur
    b. salad oil
    c. newspaper
    d. orange
    e. cardboard
    f. apple juice

Challenge Questions and Problems

61. Lithium has two naturally occurring isotopes. Lithium-6 has an atomic mass of 6.015 amu; lithium-7 has an atomic mass of 7.016 amu. The atomic mass of lithium is 6.941 amu. What is the percentage of lithium-7 in nature?
62. When the masses of the particles that make up an atom are added together, the sum is always larger than the actual mass of the atom. The "missing" mass, called the mass defect, represents the matter converted into energy when the nucleus was formed from its component protons and neutrons. Calculate the mass defect of a chlorine-35 atom by using the data in Table 4.1. The actual mass of a chlorine-35 atom is 5.81×10^{-23} g.

Connections Questions

63. What was John Dalton's vocation?
64. Is it correct to say that atoms are composed of only three subatomic particles? Explain.
65. How might a philosopher of science aid scientific progress?

Write About Chemistry

66. Imagine that you are a newspaper journalist in the early 1900s. Write a 250-word account of the discovery of the neutron for your paper. Hint: Journalists try to answer five questions: Who? What? When? Where? Why?
67. Write an imaginary TV interview in which John Dalton defends his atomic theory to you, the interviewer.

Readings and References

Asimov, Isaac. *Atom: Journey Across the Subatomic Cosmos.* New York: Dutton, 1991.

Berger, Melvin. *Atoms, Molecules, and Quarks.* New York: Putnam, 1986.

5 Chemical Names and Formulas

Goals

- Explain the organization of the periodic table.
- Describe molecular and ionic compounds.
- List the names and formulas of the common polyatomic ions.
- Write formulas and names for ionic and molecular compounds.

The properties of calcium fluorite, CaF_2, shown here, are covered in *Chemical Abstracts*, the largest index in the world. This index is a listing of summaries of articles about chemistry.

Concept Overview

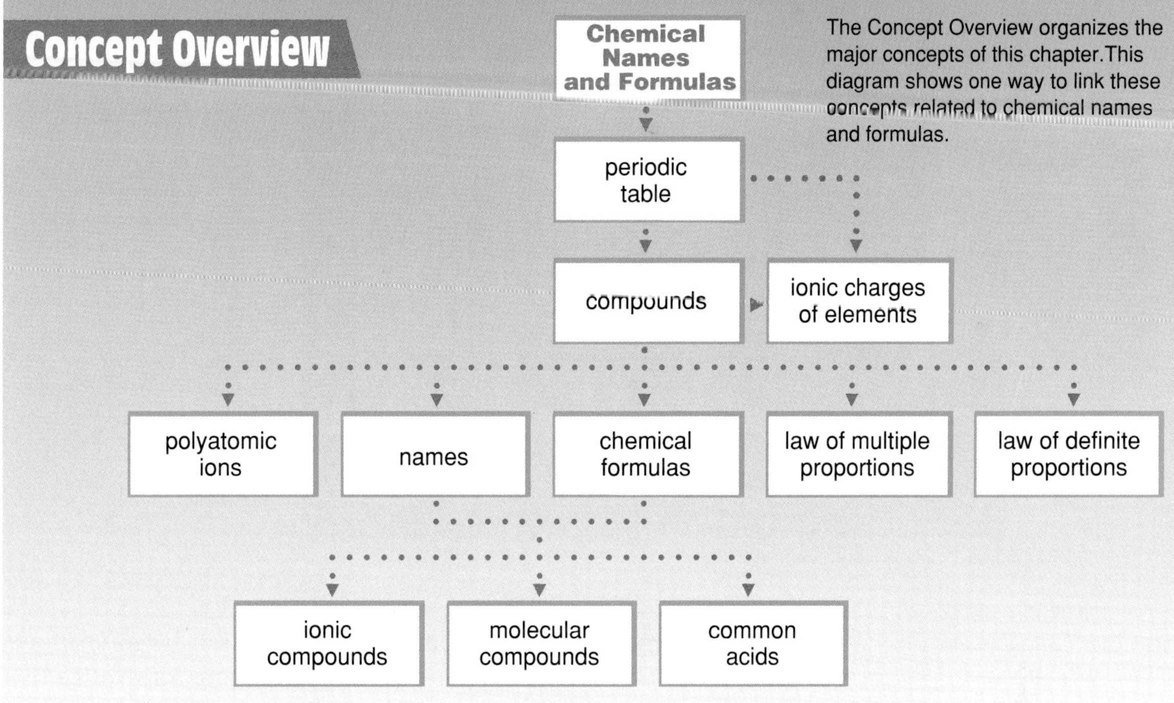

The Concept Overview organizes the major concepts of this chapter. This diagram shows one way to link these concepts related to chemical names and formulas.

Elements are the building materials for the construction of all living and nonliving things. Although there are only about 100 kinds of elements, their atoms can join in almost limitless combinations and proportions. Therefore, an enormous number of substances exist. The chemical combinations of atoms, of which there are millions, are called compounds.

With so many compounds in existence, you need a systematic way to communicate information about them. You could, for instance, identify a particular substance by listing its physical and chemical properties. This would be very time-consuming at best. Instead, each substance is identified by a unique name and chemical formula. Naming compounds is an essential skill in chemistry. Knowing the names of compounds will enable you to communicate with others about chemistry efficiently and effectively.

5.1 The Periodic Table

Objective

Locate these items on the periodic table: group, period, representative element, transition element.

The construction of a house requires many trips to a supplier of building materials. At the supplier the materials necessary to build the house are organized by categories according to their similarities. Nails, nuts, and bolts are inside the store. Plywood and lumber, cedar and pine, are in the shed. Different colored bricks are out back. You may pick and choose as you please. *Similarly, in the*

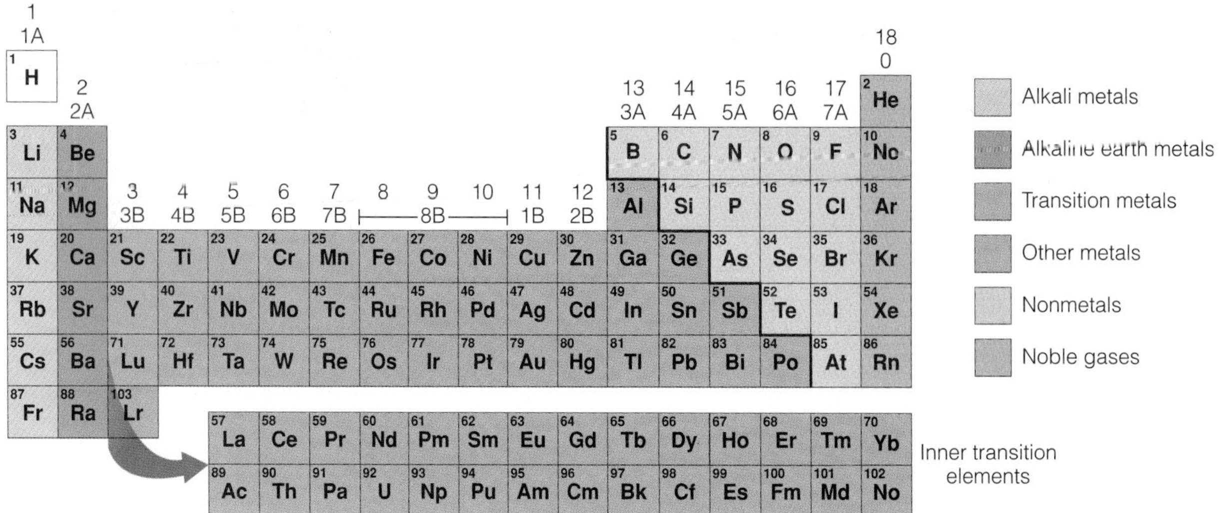

Figure 5.1 Elements are arranged in the periodic table according to their chemical properties.

periodic table, *the elements are arranged according to similarities in their properties.* Study the periodic table in Figure 5.1. Notice that the elements are listed in order of increasing atomic number as you read from left to right and from top to bottom. Hydrogen (H), the lightest element, is in the top left corner. Helium (He) is atomic number 2 at the top right. Lithium (Li) is atomic number 3 at the left side of the second row.

Each column of elements in the periodic table is known as a **group**. Each group is designated by a number-letter combination. Look at the first column on the left. It includes the elements H, Li, Na, K, Rb, and Cs. This first column is designated Group 1A. The next column to the right, starting with Be, is Group 2A, and so forth. *The Group A elements in the periodic table are known as the* **representative elements**. These elements exhibit the entire range of chemical properties. The representative elements include *metals, metalloids,* and *nonmetals.*

The elements on the left side of the periodic table are the metallic elements. **Metals** *are elements that have a high electrical conductivity and a high luster when clean.* They are ductile (can be drawn into wires) and malleable (can be beaten into thin sheets). Copper, silver, gold, and aluminum are familiar metals. Approximately 80% of all of the elements are metals. With one exception, all the metallic elements are solids at room temperature. What are the name, symbol, and physical state of this exception? *The metals include the* **transition metals**, *which are the Group B elements, and the* **inner transition metals**, *which are called the rare earths.*

Figure 5.2 Mercury, a transition metal, is the only metallic element that is a liquid at room temperature. It is used in thermometers and barometers.

The nonmetallic elements occupy the upper right corner of the periodic table. **Nonmetals** *are elements that are nonlustrous and are generally poor conductors of electricity.* Some of these elements, such as argon and chlorine, are gases. Others, such as carbon and sulfur, shown in Figure 5.3, are brittle solids. One, bromine, is a fuming dark-red liquid at room temperature. Hydrogen is a special case; it is a nonmetal in Group 1A.

Notice the heavy "stair-step" line in Figure 5.1 that divides the metals on the left from the nonmetals on the right. *Most of the elements that border this line are* **metalloids**, *elements with the properties of both metals and nonmetals.* Silicon and germanium are two important metalloids that are used in the manufacture of computer chips and solar cells.

Figure 5.3 Sulfur is a nonmetallic element that occurs as a crystalline solid or in the amorphous state. Sulfur is used primarily in the manufacture of sulfuric acid.

Concept Practice

1. Identify the following elements as metals, metalloids, or nonmetals.
a. gold **b.** silicon **c.** manganese **d.** sulfur **e.** barium

2. Which of the above elements are representative elements?

5.2 Atoms and Ions

Objective

Define the terms cation and anion and show how they are related to the terms metal and nonmetal.

As you know, each element is composed of atoms of the same kind. Recall that an atom is electrically neutral because it has equal numbers of protons and electrons. For example, an atom of sodium (Na) has 11 positively charged protons and 11 negatively charged electrons. The net charge on a sodium atom is zero [+11 + (–11) = 0]. In forming a chemical compound, an atom of sodium loses one of its electrons. Now, the number of electrons is no longer equal to the number of protons. The atom of sodium becomes an ion. Because there are more positive charges (protons) than negative charges (electrons) the sodium ion is positively charged. **Ions** *are atoms or groups of atoms that have a positive or negative charge.* An ion is formed when an atom or group of atoms loses or gains electrons.

Atoms of the metallic elements, such as sodium, tend to form positive ions by losing one or more electrons. *A* **cation** *is any atom or group of atoms with a positive charge.* Compared with an electrically neutral atom, a cation has fewer electrons. Look at Figure 5.4. Because a sodium cation has 11 protons but only 10 electrons, it must have a charge of 1+. An ionic charge is written as a number followed by a sign. If the number is 1, it is usually omitted; Na^{1+} and Na^{+} are equivalent. Similarly, magnesium (Mg) forms a magnesium cation by losing two electrons. Therefore, a magnesium cation has a charge of 2+ because it has 12 protons but only 10 electrons, Mg^{2+}.

Roots of Words

katienai: (Greek) to go down
cation any atom or group of atoms with a positive charge

When placed between oppositely charged electrodes, cations move to the negative electrode, the cathode.

Figure 5.4 A sodium atom loses an electron to become a positively charged sodium ion.

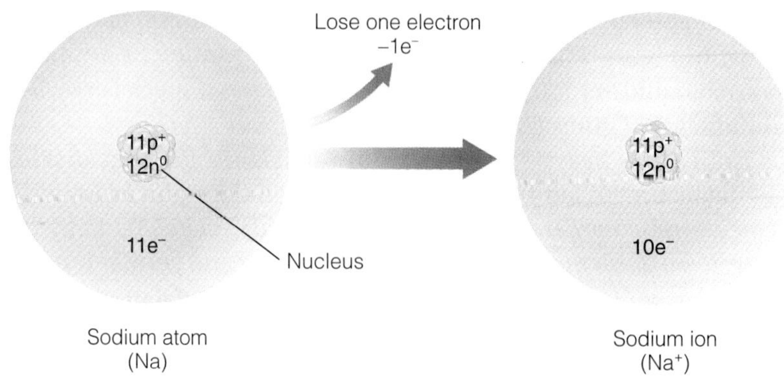

Safety

Lithium, sodium, and potassium are stored under oil to prevent them from reacting with air or water. These reactions can be violent. These metals should be used only with extreme caution.

For metallic elements, the name of a cation is exactly the same as the name of the element. Thus a lithium atom (Li) forms a lithium cation (Li^+), and an aluminum atom (Al) forms an aluminum cation (Al^{3+}). Although their names are the same, there are many important chemical differences between metals and their cations. Sodium metal, for example, reacts explosively with water. By contrast, sodium cations are a component of table salt, a compound that you know is stable in water.

Atoms of nonmetallic elements tend to form ions by gaining one or more electrons. *In this way they form* **anions**, *which are atoms or groups of atoms with a negative charge.* In comparison to an electrically neutral atom, an anion has more electrons. Look at Figure 5.5. Consider what happens when a chlorine atom (Cl) gains one electron to form an anion. The *chloride* anion has 17 protons and 18 electrons. Therefore it has an ionic charge of 1–. The chloride anion is written as Cl^-. Another common anion is the oxide anion. Because an oxygen atom gains two electrons in forming this ion, the ionic charge of the oxide anion is 2–. The oxide anion is written as O^{2-}. Notice that the name of an anion of a nonmetallic element is not the same as the element name. The name of the anion ends in *-ide.* Thus a sulfur atom (S) forms a sulfide anion (S^{2-}), and a bromine atom (Br) forms a bromide anion (Br^-).

Roots of Words

anienai: (Greek) to go up

anion any atom or group of atoms with a negative charge

Placed between oppositely charged electrodes, anions move to the positive electrode, the anode.

Figure 5.5 A chlorine atom gains an electron to become a negatively charged chloride ion.

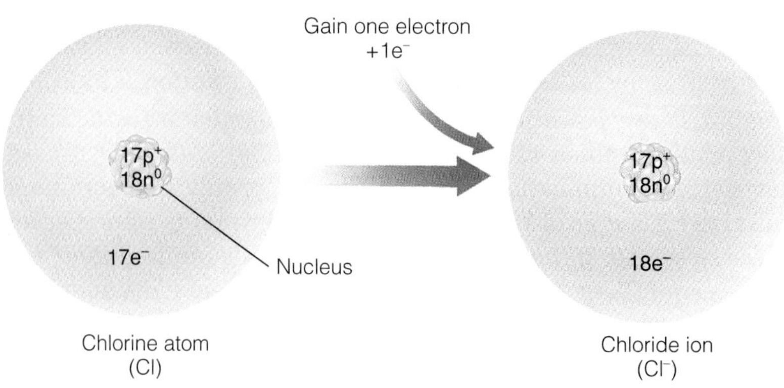

Example 1 Writing the Symbols and Names of Ions

Write the symbol and name of the ion formed.

a. A strontium atom loses two electrons.

b. An iodine atom gains one electron.

Solution

An atom that loses electrons forms a positively charged ion (cation). The names of cations of metallic elements are the same as the names of the elements.

An atom that gains electrons forms a negatively charged ion (anion). The names of anions of nonmetallic elements end in *-ide.*

a. Sr^{2+}, strontium cation **b.** I^{1-} or I^{-}, iodide anion

Problem-Solving Tip

Ion formation is like dieting: Losing (electrons) is positive (ions formed); gaining (electrons) is negative (ions formed).

Concept Practice

3. Describe two ways in which an ion forms from an atom.

Practice Problem

4. Complete this table.

	Symbol of element	Change in electrons	Formula of ion	Name of ion
a.	Al	3 electrons lost	______	______
b.	S	____________	S^{2-}	______
c.	______	____________	Ca^{2+}	______
d.	Br	1 electron gained	______	______

5.3 Compounds

Objective

Distinguish between ionic compounds and molecular compounds.

Atoms of different elements may combine to form compounds. Recall that compounds are substances composed of two or more different elements combined chemically.

In many compounds, such as water or carbon dioxide, the atoms are bound together to form a molecule. *A* **molecule** *is an electrically neutral group of atoms that act as a unit.* Molecules of a given compound are all identical, but they are different from molecules of all other compounds. For example, all molecules of water are the same; molecules of water are different from molecules of carbon dioxide.

Figure 5.6 Water is a molecular compound composed of two hydrogen atoms and one oxygen atom. Molecular compounds can be solids, liquids, or gases; water commonly exists in all three of these phases.

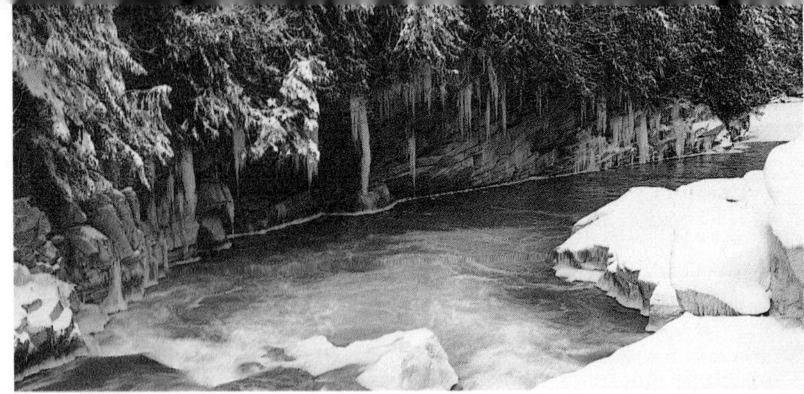

Water and carbon dioxide are examples of molecular compounds. *Compounds that are composed of molecules are* **molecular compounds**. Molecular compounds tend to have relatively low melting and boiling points. Many molecular compounds exist as gases or liquids at room temperature. The molecules in most molecular compounds are composed of two or more nonmetallic elements.

Not all compounds are composed of molecules. Ions may join to form ionic compounds such as sodium chloride, common table salt. **Ionic compounds** *are composed of positive cations and negative anions.* Although composed of ions, ionic compounds are electrically neutral. The total positive charge of the positive ions is equal to the total negative charge of the negative ions. Ionic compounds are usually formed from metallic and nonmetallic elements. Most ionic compounds are crystalline solids at room temperature.

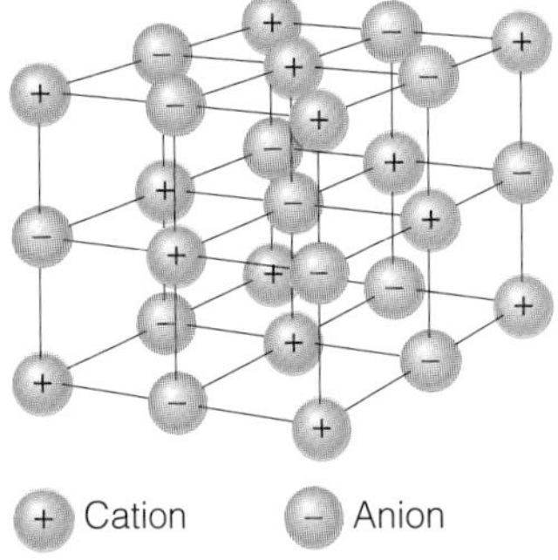

Figure 5.7 Cations and anions form an orderly three-dimensional array in ionic compounds. Each positive cation is surrounded by two or more negative anions. At the same time, each anion is surrounded by two or more cations.

Concept Practice

5. If ionic compounds are composed of charged particles (ions), why isn't every ionic compound either positively or negatively charged?

6. The melting point of a compound is 1240°C, and ice melts at 0°C. Is this compound an ionic or a molecular compound?

5.4 Chemical Formulas

Objective

Distinguish among chemical formula, molecular formula, and formula unit.

Chemists have identified more than ten million chemical compounds. Some are molecular compounds, others are ionic compounds. No two of these compounds have identical properties. Fortunately, the composition of each of these chemical substances can be represented by a chemical formula. *A* **chemical formula** *shows the kinds and numbers of atoms in the smallest representative unit of the substance.*

Water is a molecular compound. The chemical formula of a molecular compound is called a molecular formula. *A* ***molecular formula*** *shows the number and kinds of atoms present in a molecule of a compound.* A water molecule is a tightly bound unit of two hydrogen atoms and one oxygen atom. The molecular formula of water is H_2O. Notice that the number of atoms of each element is indicated by a subscript written after the symbol. The molecular formula of carbon dioxide is CO_2. This formula represents a molecule containing one carbon atom and two oxygen atoms. Ethane, a component of natural gas, is also a molecular compound. Figure 5.8 gives the molecular formula for ethane, C_2H_6. What is the composition of ethane?

Figure 5.8 The formula of a molecular compound indicates the numbers and kinds of atoms in a molecule of the compound. The arrangement of the atoms within a molecule is called the molecular structure.

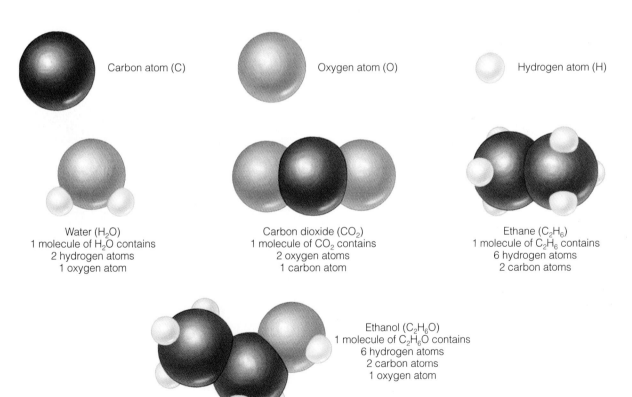

Carbon atom (C)

Oxygen atom (O)

Hydrogen atom (H)

Water (H_2O)
1 molecule of H_2O contains
2 hydrogen atoms
1 oxygen atom

Carbon dioxide (CO_2)
1 molecule of CO_2 contains
2 oxygen atoms
1 carbon atom

Ethane (C_2H_6)
1 molecule of C_2H_6 contains
6 hydrogen atoms
2 carbon atoms

Ethanol (C_2H_6O)
1 molecule of C_2H_6O contains
6 hydrogen atoms
2 carbon atoms
1 oxygen atom

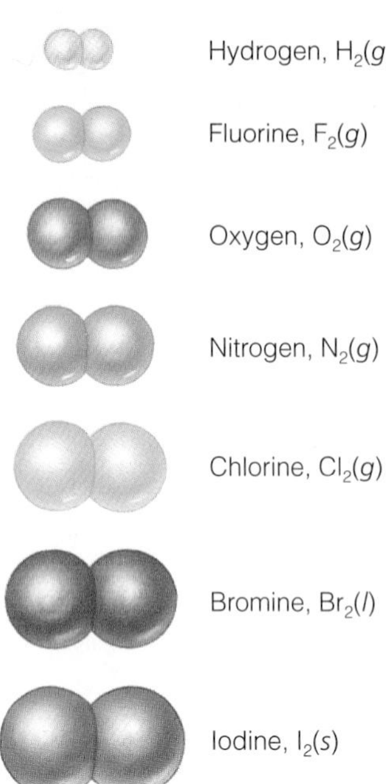

Figure 5.9 Seven elements exist as diatomic molecules.

Even some elements commonly exist as molecules. Figure 5.9 shows seven nonmetallic elements that exist as diatomic molecules. They are hydrogen, nitrogen, oxygen, fluorine, chlorine, bromine, and iodine. Diatomic molecules contain two atoms of the same element, such as N_2 or I_2. Because of their importance, it would be useful for you to memorize the names and formulas of these seven diatomic molecules.

Although a molecular formula gives the composition of a molecule, it tells you nothing about its structure. The structure of a molecule shows you how the various atoms are joined. Scientists use models and diagrams to show the arrangement of the atoms in a molecule. Look at Figure 5.8 to see the chemical formulas and structures of some molecular compounds. Based on its molecular structure, what do you know about the composition of ethanol, C_2H_6O?

Chemical formulas can also be written for ionic compounds. In this case, though, the formula does not represent a molecule. Recall that sodium chloride (table salt) is an ionic compound. Sodium chloride is composed of equal numbers of sodium cations, Na^+, and chloride anions, Cl^-. In Figure 5.10 you can see that the ions are arranged in an orderly pattern. What formula would you use to represent this compound: Na_2Cl_2, Na_3Cl_3, or NaCl? Chemists use the simplest of these formulas, a formula unit, to represent an ionic compound. *A* **formula unit** *is the lowest whole-number ratio of ions*

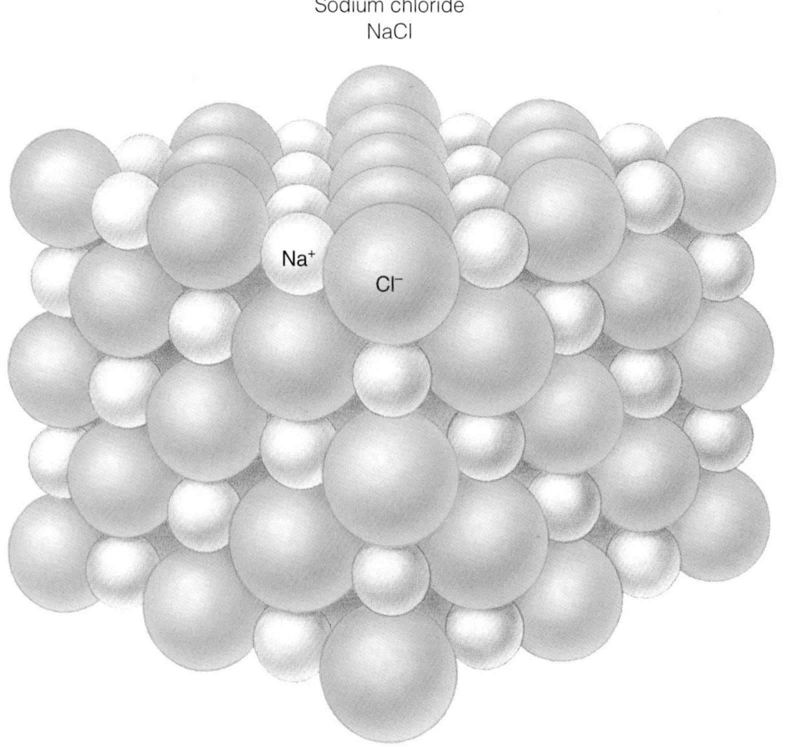

Figure 5.10 Sodium cations and chloride anions form a three-dimensional array in sodium chloride, NaCl. How many ions are part of a single formula unit of this compound?

Table 5.1 Characteristics of Ionic and Molecular Compounds

Characteristic	Ionic compound	Molecular compound
Representative unit	Formula unit (balance of oppositely charged ions)	Molecule
Type of elements	Metallic combined with nonmetallic	Nonmetallic
Physical state	Solid	Solid, liquid, or gas
Melting point	High (usually above 300°C)	Low (usually below 300°C)

in an ionic compound. For sodium chloride, the lowest whole-number ratio of the ions is 1:1 (1 Na^+ to 1 Cl^-). Thus the formula unit for sodium chloride is NaCl. Notice that although ionic charges are used to derive the correct formula, they do not appear when you write the chemical formula of the compound.

The ionic compound magnesium chloride contains magnesium cations, Mg^{2+}, and chloride anions, Cl^-. In magnesium chloride the ratio of magnesium cations to chloride anions is 1:2 (one Mg^{2+} to two Cl^-). So its formula unit is $MgCl_2$. Since there are twice as many chloride anions (with a 1^- charge) as magnesium cations (with a 2^+ charge), the compound is electrically neutral.

Remember, there is no such thing as a molecule of sodium chloride or magnesium chloride. Instead, these compounds exist as collections of positively and negatively charged ions arranged in repeating three-dimensional patterns. Table 5.1 summarizes some of the differences between ionic and molecular substances.

Concept Practice

7. Identify the number and kinds of atoms present in a molecule of each compound.

a. ascorbic acid (vitamin C), $C_6H_8O_6$
b. monosodium glutamate (MSG), $C_5H_8O_4NNa$
c. sucrose (table sugar), $C_{12}H_{22}O_{11}$
d. trinitrotoluene (TNT), $C_7H_5N_3O_6$
e. ammonium nitrate (a fertilizer), NH_4NO_3

8. Would you expect the following pairs of atoms to combine chemically to give an ionic or a molecular compound?

a. Li and S **d.** F and Cl
b. O and S **e.** I and K
c. Al and O **f.** H and N

Objective

Show that a compound obeys the law of definite proportions and that two different compounds composed of the same two elements obey the law of multiple proportions, using experimental data.

5.5 The Laws of Definite and Multiple Proportions

Consider the compound magnesium sulfide (MgS). It is produced by the combination of two kinds of ions, magnesium cations and sulfide anions. If you could take 100.00 g of magnesium sulfide and break it down into its elements, you would always obtain 43.13 g of magnesium and 56.87 g of sulfur. The ratio of these masses is 43.13/56.87 or 0.7584:1. How the magnesium sulfide was formed, or the size of the sample, does not change this mass ratio. Compounds therefore obey the **law of definite proportions**. *In samples of any chemical compound the masses of the elements are always in the same proportions.* This law is consistent with Dalton's atomic theory. If atoms combine in simple whole-number ratios as Dalton postulated, then their proportions by mass must always be the same.

In the early 1800s Dalton and others studied pairs of compounds that contain the same elements but have different physical and chemical properties. For example, Figure 5.11 shows two compounds formed by the elements hydrogen and oxygen: water and hydrogen peroxide. The formulas of these compounds were not known in Dalton's time. Both compounds obey the law of definite proportions. In every sample of hydrogen peroxide, 16.0 g of oxygen is present for each 1.0 g of hydrogen. The mass ratio of oxygen to hydrogen is always 16 to 1. In every sample of water, the mass ratio of oxygen to hydrogen is always 8 to 1. For the same mass of hydrogen, the ratio of the masses of oxygen in hydrogen peroxide and water is exactly 2:1.

$$\frac{16\text{ g O (in hydrogen peroxide)}}{8\text{ g O (in water)}} = \frac{2}{1}$$

Safety

Concentrated solutions of hydrogen peroxide enhance the combustion of other materials and can cause explosions. They also cause burns. Handle with extreme care.

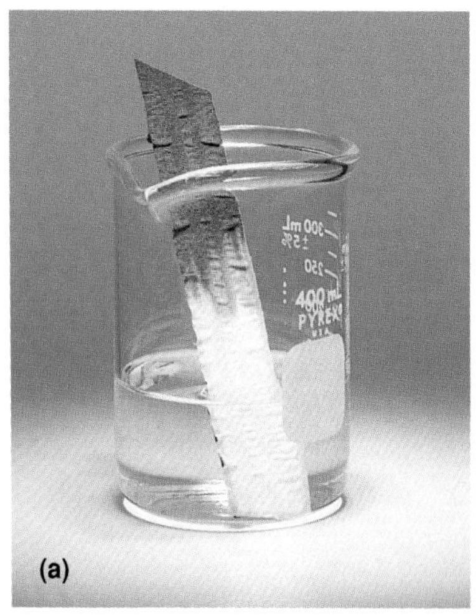

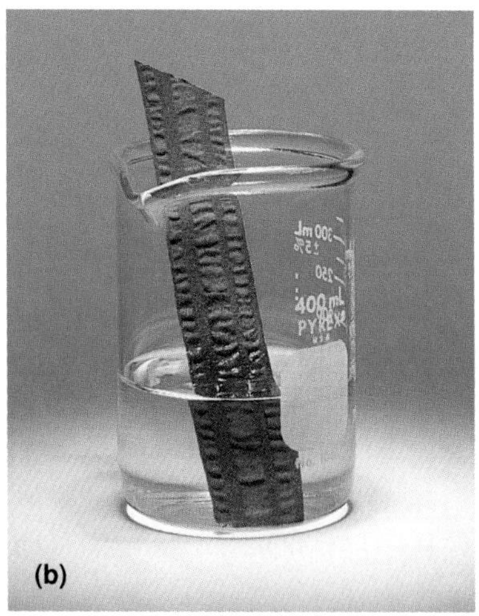

Figure 5.11 Hydrogen peroxide and water both contain only atoms of hydrogen and oxygen. Nevertheless, they have different chemical and physical properties. **(a)** Hydrogen peroxide bleaches the dye in most fabrics; **(b)** water does not.

Using the results from these kinds of experiments, Dalton stated the **law of multiple proportions.** *Whenever two elements form more than one compound, the different masses of one element that combine with the same mass of the other element are in the ratio of small whole numbers.*

Example 2 Finding Mass Ratios

Carbon reacts with oxygen to form two compounds. Compound A contains 2.41 g of carbon for each 3.22 g of oxygen. Compound B contains 6.71 g of carbon for each 17.9 g of oxygen. What is the lowest whole-number mass ratio of carbon that combines with a given mass of oxygen?

Solution

For each compound, use the law of definite proportions to find the grams of carbon that combine per 1.00 g of oxygen. Then compare the masses of carbon in each compound.

$$\text{Compound A} \quad \frac{2.41\ \text{g C}}{3.22\ \text{g O}} = \frac{0.748\ \text{g C}}{1.00\ \text{g O}}$$

$$\text{Compound B} \quad \frac{6.71\ \text{g C}}{17.9\ \text{g O}} = \frac{0.375\ \text{g C}}{1.00\ \text{g O}}$$

The mass ratio of carbon per gram of oxygen in the compounds is 2:1.

$$\frac{0.748\ \cancel{\text{g C}}\ \text{(in compound A)}}{0.375\ \cancel{\text{g C}}\ \text{(in compound B)}} = \frac{2}{1}$$

A + B = C	Ratio A:B (In C)
5 g 2 g 7 g	5:2
A + B = D	Ratio A:B (In D)
10 g 2 g 12 g	10:2

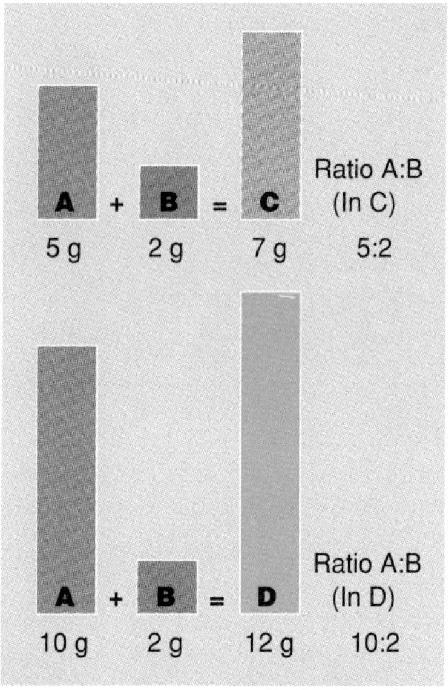

Figure 5.12 This is an example of Dalton's law of multiple proportions . The ratio of the mass of A in C to the mass of A in D (for a fixed mass of B) is 5:10 or 1:2.

Concept Practice

9. Which law would support the statement, "In every sample of carbon monoxide the mass ratio of carbon to oxygen is 3:4"? Why?

Practice Problem

10. Lead forms two compounds with oxygen. One compound contains 2.98 g of lead combined with 0.461 g of oxygen. The other compound contains 9.89 g of lead combined with 0.763 g of oxygen. What is the lowest whole-number mass ratio of lead that combines with a given mass of oxygen?

Problem-Solving Tip

To compare, divide each mass ratio to give a 1 in the denominator.

5.A Historical Notebook

Pharmacy

Figure 5.13 Modern Chinese pharmacists prepare herbal medicines using tried and tested ancient procedures.

The first person to treat a wound with a poultice of leaves was also the first pharmacist. Over 5000 years ago, Chinese physicians treated respiratory diseases with a tea brewed from a common herb, *Ephedra sinica.* The Chinese herb tea contained ephedrine, which is now used to alleviate the symptoms of allergies. The Chinese also discovered that seaweed, a rich source of iodine, is effective in the treatment of goiter, a disease that causes swelling of the thyroid gland. A traditional Chinese pharmacy, shown in Figure 5.13, may contain more than 2000 herbs and other substances. Other cultures have histories of the medicinal uses of herbs. Egyptian manuscripts from 2600 B.C. describe the use of herbs for medicinal purposes. In the seventh and eighth centuries A.D., Arabian alchemists extracted and purified essential ingredients from herbs.

A modern pharmacy is concerned with the collection, preparation, and standardization of substances used for drugs. The ancient Greeks and Romans considered pharmacy as separate and distinct from physicians, as it is today. However, in the Middle Ages (A.D. 395–1500) in Europe, physicians both treated patients and prepared medicines. This dual role of physicians ended in about 1700.

Today pharmacy is a broad science with several branches. Pharmacology is the study of the means by which medicines exert their effects on the body. Therapeutics is concerned with the use of drugs in curing diseases. Pharmacologic and therapeutic information is used by physicians in deciding which drugs to prescribe. Toxicologists focus on poisons. Pharmaceutical chemists prepare medicinal compounds from simpler materials. Many modern drugs are either partially or wholly synthesized, often from nonbiological materials. Interestingly, pharmaceutical chemists are taking renewed interest in finding new pharmaceuticals in plants, the source of many of the earliest medicines.

Figure 5.14 Today's Western pharmacists must have a broad and thorough knowledge of how various medications affect the body.

Think About It

11. Deduce Why do you think pharmaceutical chemists are interested in preserving the diversity of plant life in such regions as the world's rain forests? Would you support this effort?

12. Identify Name two common medicines that come from plant sources.

5.6 Ionic Charges of the Elements

Objective

Infer the charge on an ion using the periodic table.

In order to write chemical formulas for ionic compounds, you need to know the types of ions that atoms tend to form. That means you need to know the ionic charges of the elements. For the representative elements the ionic charges can be determined easily using the periodic table.

Recall that metallic elements tend to lose electrons. Lithium, sodium, and potassium (in Group 1A) form cations. They have a 1+ charge (Li^+, Na^+, and K^+), as do all the other Group 1A ions. Magnesium and calcium are Group 2A metals. They form cations with a 2+ charge (Mg^{2+} and Ca^{2+}), as do all the other Group 2A metals. Aluminum is the one common Group 3A metal. As you might expect, it forms a 3+ cation (Al^{3+}).

The metals in Groups 1A, 2A, and 3A lose electrons when they form cations. The ionic charge is positive and is numerically equal to the group number. The numerical charge of an ion of a Group A nonmetal is determined by subtracting the group number from 8. Because nonmetals tend to gain electrons and form anions, the sign of the charge is minus. For example, the elements in Group 7A form anions with a 1– charge, since $8 - 7 = 1$. The anions for this group are: fluoride, F^-, chloride, Cl^-, and so forth. Anions of nonmetals in Group 6A have a 2– charge ($8 - 6 = 2$); the oxide anion, O^{2-}, is an example. The three nonmetals in Group 5A can form anions with a 3– charge ($8 - 5 = 3$); one example is the nitride ion N^{3-}. Table 5.2 summarizes the ionic charges of representative elements that can be obtained from the periodic table.

The majority of the elements in the two remaining representative groups, 4A and 8A, usually do not form ions. Ordinarily, the two nonmetals in Group 4A, carbon and silicon, are found in molecular compounds. The elements in Group 8A rarely form compounds.

Unlike the cations of the Group 1A, 2A, and 3A metals, many of the transition metals have more than one common ionic charge. This is also a characteristic of tin and lead, the two metals in Group 4A. For example, the transition metal iron forms two common cations,

Table 5.2 Ionic Charges of Representative Elements

1A	2A	3A	4A	5A	6A	7A	0
Li^+	Be^{2+}			N^{3-}	O^{2-}	F^-	
Na^+	Mg^{2+}	Al^{3+}		P^{3-}	S^{2-}	Cl^-	
K^+	Ca^{2+}				Se^{2-}	Br^-	
Rb^+	Sr^{2+}					I^-	
Cs^+	Ba^{2+}						

Table 5.3 Formulas and Names of Common Metal Ions with More than One Ionic Charge

Formula	Stock name	Classical name
Cu^{1+}	Copper(I) ion	Cuprous ion
Cu^{2+}	Copper (II) ion	Cupric ion
Fe^{2+}	Iron(II) ion	Ferrous ion
Fe^{3+}	Iron(III) ion	Ferric ion
$^*Hg_2^{2+}$	Mercury(I) ion	Mercurous ion
Hg^{2+}	Mercury(II) ion	Mercuric ion
Pb^{2+}	Lead(II) ion	Plumbous ion
Pb^{4+}	Lead(IV) ion	Plumbic ion
Sn^{2+}	Tin(II) ion	Stannous ion
Sn^{4+}	Tin(IV) ion	Stannic ion
Cr^{2+}	Chromium(II) ion	Chromous ion
Cr^{3+}	Chromium(III) ion	Chromic ion
Mn^{2+}	Manganese(II) ion	Manganous ion
Mn^{3+}	Manganese(III) ion	Manganic ion
Co^{2+}	Cobalt(II) ion	Cobaltous ion
Co^{3+}	Cobalt(III) ion	Cobaltic ion

*A diatomic elemental ion.

Safety

Many transition metals are toxic. Make a habit of washing your hands thoroughly after handling any chemicals.

Fe^{2+} and Fe^{3+}. Two methods of naming such cations are used. The preferred method is called the Stock system. A Roman numeral in parentheses is used as part of the name of the element to indicate the numerical value of the charge. As you will discover if you look at Table 5.3, using the Stock system, the cation Fe^{2+} is the iron(II) ion. This is read as the "iron two" ion.

An older, less preferred method of naming these cations uses a root word with different suffixes at the end of the word. The classical name of the element is used as the root word. The suffix *-ous* is used for the name of the cation with the lower of the two ionic charges. The suffix *-ic* is used with the higher of the two ionic charges. Using

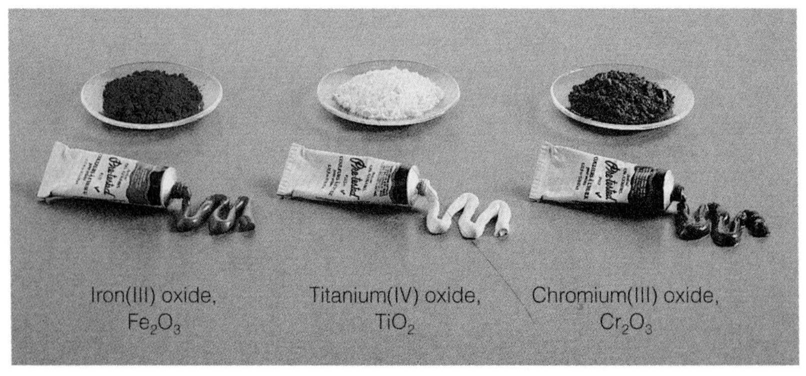

Figure 5.15 Since many transition metals form brightly colored compounds, they are used in making artists' oil paints. Shown here are some oil paint colors and the transition metal compounds used as their pigments.

this system, Fe^{2+} is the ferr*ous* cation and Fe^{3+} is the ferr*ic* cation. Notice that you can usually identify what may be an unfamiliar classical name by looking for the symbol of the element in the name. *Fe*rrous (Fe) is iron, *cu*prous (Cu) is copper, and *stan*nous (Sn) is tin. A major disadvantage of using classical names is that they do not tell you the charge of the ion. The name tells you only that the cation has either the smaller (*-ous*) or the larger (*-ic*) charge of the pair. From Figure 5.15 you can see that compounds of transition metals have a variety of colors.

A few transition metals have only one ionic charge. The names of these cations do not have a roman numeral. These "exceptions" include silver, whose cations always have a 1+ charge (Ag^+), and cadmium and zinc, whose cations always have a 2+ charge (Cd^{2+} and Zn^{2+}).

Example 3 Finding Ionic Charges

What is the charge of the ion of each of the following elements? (For metals with more than one common ionic charge, the number of electrons lost is indicated.) **a.** sulfur **b.** lead, four electrons lost **c.** zinc **d.** argon **e.** bromine **f.** copper, one electron lost.

Solution

a. 2– (in Group 6A, therefore 8 – 6 = 2) **b.** 4+ **c.** 2+
d. 0 (in Group 0) **e.** 1– (in Group 7A) **f.** 1+

Example 4 Naming and Classifying Cations and Anions

Name the ions in Example 3. List each as a cation or an anion.

Solution

The names of nonmetallic anions end in *-ide*. Metallic cations take the name of the metal. If the metal has more than one common ionic charge, a Roman numeral or classical name with a suffix is used.

a. sulfide ion, anion
b. lead(IV) or plumbic ion, cation
c. zinc ion, cation
d. no ion formed
e. bromide ion, anion
f. copper(I) or cuprous ion, cation

Chemistry in Careers

Chemical Sales Representative

A chemical company generally sells chemicals that are used in the manufacture of other products. The job of a sales representative is to find customers who have a need for his or her company's product and to provide information about it. A salesperson must know the properties, limitations, and applications of the product and communicate this information to potential customers. A college degree in chemistry and courses in business are important qualifications for someone considering a career in chemical sales.

Practice Problems

13. Write the symbol for each ion. Be sure to include the charge.
a. oxide ion **b.** lead(II) ion **c.** lithium ion
d. nitride ion **e.** cupric ion **f.** fluoride ion

14. Name the following ions. Use Table 5.3 if necessary.
a. Ba^{2+} **b.** I^- **c.** Ag^+ **d.** Hg^{2+} **e.** P^{3-} **f.** Sn^{4+}

Objective

Define a polyatomic ion and memorize the names and formulas of the common polyatomic ions.

Roots of Words

poly-: (Greek) many
atomos: (Greek) atom
polyatomic a polyatomic ion is a tightly bound group of atoms that behaves as a unit and carries a charge

The sulfate ion, SO_4^{2-}, is a polyatomic ion.

5.7 Polyatomic Ions

All of the ions mentioned in the previous section are formed from single atoms. Such ions are called monatomic ions. Unlike these ions, the sulfate anion is composed of one sulfur atom and four oxygen atoms. These five atoms together form a sulfate polyatomic anion. The sulfate ion has a 2– charge and is written SO_4^{2-}. **Polyatomic ions** *are tightly bound groups of atoms that behave as a unit and carry a charge.* You can see the structures of some polyatomic ions in Figure 5.16.

The names and formulas of some common polyatomic ions are listed in Table 5.4. There are others, of course, and your teacher may wish to expand this list. Observe that the names of most polyatomic anions end in *-ite* or *-ate.* However, there are three important exceptions to this rule: the positively charged ammon*ium* cation, NH_4^+, and two polyatomic anions that end in *-ide,* the cyanide ion (CN^-) and the hydroxide ion (OH^-).

Examine the relationships among the following polyatomic ions for which there is an *-ite*/*-ate* pair. The charge on each polyatomic ion of each pair is the same. The *-ite* name ending indicates one less oxygen atom than the *-ate* ending. However, the ending does not tell you how many oxygen atoms are in the ion.

-ite	SO_3^{2-}	NO_2^-	ClO_2^-
-ate	SO_4^{2-}	NO_3^-	ClO_3^-

Figure 5.16 These models show the arrangement of atoms in four common polyatomic ions.

NO_3^- Nitrate ion

SO_4^{2-} Sulfate ion

PO_4^{3-} Phosphate ion

NH_4^+ Ammonium ion

Table 5.4 Common Polyatomic Ions

1– charge		2– charge		3– charge	
Formula	**Name**	**Formula**	**Name**	**Formula**	**Name**
$H_2PO_4^-$	Dihydrogen phosphate	HPO_4^{2-}	Hydrogen phosphate	PO_4^{3-}	Phosphate
$C_2H_3O_2^-$	Acetate	$C_2O_4^{2-}$	Oxalate	PO_3^{3-}	Phosphite
HSO_3^-	Hydrogen sulfite	SO_3^{2-}	Sulfite		
HSO_4^-	Hydrogen sulfate	SO_4^{2-}	Sulfate		
HCO_3^-	Hydrogen carbonate	CO_3^{2-}	Carbonate		
NO_2^-	Nitrite	CrO_4^{2-}	Chromate		
NO_3^-	Nitrate	$Cr_2O_7^{2-}$	Dichromate	**1+ charge**	
CN^-	Cyanide	SiO_3^{2-}	Silicate	**Formula**	**Name**
OH^-	Hydroxide			NH_4^+	Ammonium
MnO_4^-	Permanganate				
ClO^-	Hypochlorite				
ClO_2^-	Chlorite				
ClO_3^-	Chlorate				
ClO_4^-	Perchlorate				

When the formula for a polyatomic ion begins with H (hydrogen), you can imagine it to be a hydrogen ion (H^+) combined with another polyatomic ion. For example, HCO_3^- is a combination of H^+ and CO_3^{2-}. The charge on the new ion is the algebraic sum of the ionic charges.

$$\underset{}{H^+} + \underset{\text{carbonate}}{CO_3^{2-}} \longrightarrow \underset{\text{hydrogen carbonate}}{HCO_3^-}$$

$$\underset{}{H^+} + \underset{\text{phosphate}}{PO_4^{3-}} \longrightarrow \underset{\text{hydrogen phosphate}}{HPO_4^{2-}}$$

$$\underset{}{H^+} + \underset{\text{hydrogen phosphate}}{HPO_4^{2-}} \longrightarrow \underset{\text{dihydrogen phosphate}}{H_2PO_4^-}$$

The hydrogen carbonate (HCO_3^-), hydrogen phosphate (HPO_4^{2-}), and dihydrogen phosphate ($H_2PO_4^-$) anions are essential components of living systems. The cyanide ion (CN^-) is extremely poisonous to living systems. Most laundry bleaches contain the hypochlorite anion (ClO^-).

Safety

Very poisonous ions, such as the cyanide ion, should be made into a chemically safe form before being disposed of.

Concept Practice

15. Write the name and formula of a polyatomic cation.

Activity 5 Compound Search

Purpose

To identify and write the formulas for ionic compounds found in common foods and toiletry items.

Materials

Ingredient labels from food items such as breads, cake mixes, and cereals; from toiletries such as soap, toothpaste, and antacids.

Procedure

1. Collect the ingredient labels of the suggested or similar items.

2. Make a list of compounds containing monatomic and polyatomic ions that you recognize. (There may be many compounds that you do not recognize.)

3. Write formulas for each of the compounds in step 2 and for any additional ionic compounds that you find on ingredient labels.

Analysis and Conclusions

1. Did you find the same compound in more than one product?

2. What are the most common cations and anions found in different food items?

3. Name some ions found in toiletry products that were not found in items of food.

Objective

Explain why a systematic method of naming chemical compounds is necessary.

5.8 Common and Systematic Names

In the early days of chemistry, a new compound was often named by its discoverer. It was not uncommon for the name to describe some physical or chemical property of the substance or the source of the compound. For example, a common name for potassium carbonate, K_2CO_3, is potash. The name evolved because the compound was separated by boiling wood *ashes* in iron *pots*. Laughing gas is the common name for the gaseous compound dinitrogen monoxide (N_2O). People laugh when they inhale N_2O. However, can you tell what elements are in baking soda, plaster of paris, quicksilver, and lye? Common names are often very descriptive. Unfortunately, they do not tell you anything about the chemical composition of the compound.

As the science of chemistry developed, it became apparent that some systematic method of naming chemical compounds was needed. The rest of this chapter is devoted to learning about this system for inorganic compounds. These are compounds that generally do not contain carbon.

Concept Practice

16. Why is it necessary to have a systematic method of naming chemical compounds?

5.9 Writing Formulas for Binary Ionic Compounds

Objective

Write the chemical formulas for binary ionic compounds.

The binary ionic compound potassium chloride is composed of potassium cations, K^+, and chloride anions, Cl^-. **Binary compounds**, *such as potassium chloride, are composed of two elements.* Because potassium chloride is composed of monatomic potassium cations (K^+) and monatomic chloride anions (Cl^-), it is an example of a binary ionic compound.

Keep in mind that ionic compounds are electrically neutral. So in writing the formula for potassium chloride (or any other ionic compound), the positive charge of the cation must exactly balance the negative charge of the anion. Stated another way, the net ionic charge of the formula must be zero. In potassium chloride, the charge of each K^+ cation is balanced by the charge of each Cl^- anion. The potassium and chloride ions combine in a 1:1 ratio. For each K^+ there is one Cl^-. Thus, the formula for potassium chloride is KCl. The net ionic charge of the formula is zero. Notice that in the formula for an ionic compound, the cation is always written first.

Calcium bromide is composed of calcium cations, Ca^{2+}, and bromide anions, Br^-. Each calcium ion with its 2+ charge must combine with (or be balanced by) two bromide ions, each with a 1– charge. The ions must combine in a 1:2 ratio. The formula for calcium bromide is $CaBr_2$.

In Figure 5.17, you can see an example of rust, iron(III) oxide. What is the formula for rust? Recall that a Roman numeral tells you the charge of the metal ion. Thus, this compound consists of Fe^{3+} cations combined with O^{2-} anions. Writing a balanced formula for this compound may not seem obvious. One way to balance this formula is to find the least common multiple of the charges. Since $3 \times 2 = 6$, two Fe^{3+} cations (a +6 charge) are balanced by three O^{2-} anions (a –6 charge). The balanced formula then is Fe_2O_3.

Figure 5.17 A common name for iron(III) oxide is rust. It is a binary ionic compound.

Another approach is to use the "crisscross" method. In this method, the numerical charge of each ion is crossed over and used as a subscript for the other ion. The signs of the numbers are dropped.

$$Fe^{3+} \quad O^{2-}$$

$$Fe_2O_3$$

$$2(3+) + 3(2-) = 0$$

How would you use this method to write the formula for calcium sulfide? Remember that formulas for ionic compounds are the lowest whole-number ratios of ions. The formula for calcium sulfide is CaS, not Ca_2S_2.

Ca_2S_2 reduces to CaS

Of course, if the magnitudes of the charges of the cation and anion are the same, the charges will balance. There is no reason to use the crisscross method. The ions will combine in a 1:1 ratio.

Example 5 Writing Formulas for Binary Ionic Compounds

Write formulas for these binary ionic compounds.

a. copper(II) sulfide

b. potassium nitride

Solution

Write the formula (symbol and charge) for each ion. Balance the formula using appropriate subscripts.

a. $Cu^{2+} \quad S^{2-}$

CuS

$(2+) + (2-) = 0$

b. $K^{1+} \quad N^{3-}$

K_3N

$3(1+) + (3-) = 0$

Concept Practice

17. What is the net ionic charge of every ionic compound?

Practice Problem

18. Write formulas for compounds composed of these pairs of ions.

a. Na^+, O^{2-} **b.** Sn^{4+}, S^{2-} **c.** K^+, Cl^- **d.** Mg^{2+}, N^{3-}

5.10 Naming Binary Ionic Compounds

Objective

Identify a binary ionic compound by name when given the formula of the compound.

Suppose you wanted to write the name of the binary ionic compound whose formula is CuO. Your first guess might be to write the name of the metallic cation followed by the name of the nonmetallic anion (*-ide* ending). However, the name "copper oxide" is incorrect. Recall that copper commonly forms two cations: Cu^{1+} and Cu^{2+}. How can you tell which cation forms the compound CuO? Perhaps working backward will help. The formula indicates that the copper cation and the oxide anion combine in a 1:1 ratio. You know that the oxide anion always has a 2– charge. What must be the charge of the copper cation? Obviously, the charge must be 2+ (to balance the 2– charge). When a cation has more than one common charge, a Roman numeral is used in the name. The compound must be copper(II) oxide. Iron also forms two cations: Fe^{2+} and Fe^{3+}. Examine the names and formulas of the compounds of iron displayed in Figure 5.18.

You need to know which metals have two or more common ionic charges. However, there is not much advantage to memorizing the charges given in Table 5.3. While you may know, for example, that tin forms cations with 2+ and 4+ charges, you must still determine which of these charges tin has in a particular compound. The compound SnO_2 is tin(IV) oxide. The tin(IV) cation, Sn^{4+}, balances the two oxide anions, each having a 2– charge. What is the name of the compound having the formula SnO?

In naming compounds, Roman numerals are used on an "as needed" basis. Roman numerals are not needed in naming Group 1A, 2A, and most 3A metals. The reason is that these metals form cations with only one common ionic charge. For example, sodium always forms a 1+ cation; magnesium always forms a 2+ cation. You would never write sodium(I) chloride or magnesium(II) oxide.

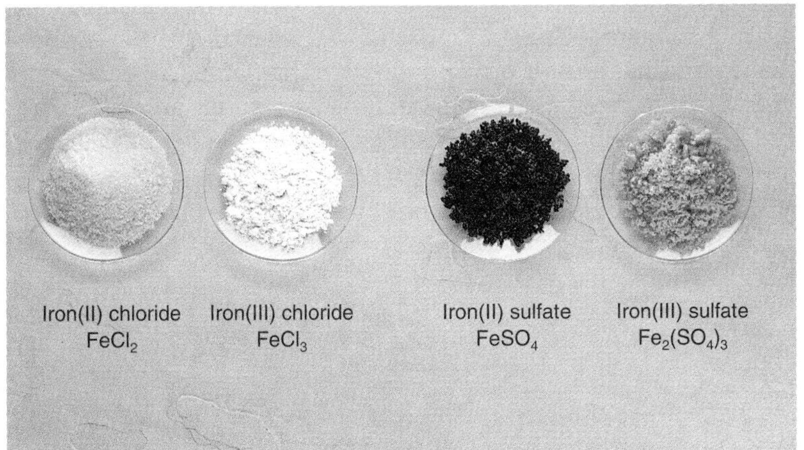

Figure 5.18 Some transition metals can exist in more than one ionic state. When combining with another ion, these metals can form more than one compound. Two examples for iron compounds are shown here, iron sulfates and iron chlorides.

Example 6 Naming Binary Ionic Compounds

Name these binary ionic compounds. **a.** CoI_2 **b.** Cs_2O

Solution

Name the cation followed by the name of the anion. Use Roman numerals when appropriate.

a. cobalt(II) iodide, or cobaltous iodide 

b. cesium oxide

Problem-Solving Tip

The Roman numeral indicates only the charge of the cation; it does not tell you how many of that ion are needed in the balanced formula.

Concept Practice

19. How do you determine the charge of a transition metal cation from the formula of an ionic compound?

Practice Problem

20. Write names for these binary ionic compounds.

a. AlF_3 **b.** FeS **c.** CaO **d.** Cu_2Se

Objective

Identify by name and write formulas of ternary ionic compounds.

5.11 Ternary Ionic Compounds

Pearls are made of calcium carbonate, an ionic compound. Calcium carbonate is a ternary ionic compound. **Ternary compounds** *contain atoms of three different elements.* Usually, ternary compounds contain a polyatomic ion. How would you write the formula of calcium nitrate? The procedure is the same as that for binary ionic compounds. In fact, the procedure is the same for ionic compounds that have more than three different elements. First, write down the formula (symbol and charge) for each ion. Then balance the charges. Remember that an *-ate* or *-ite* ending on the name of a compound indicates that the compound contains a polyatomic anion. The two common exceptions are the hydroxide and cyanide polyatomic ions.

Figure 5.19 Calcium carbonate, $CaCO_3$, is a ternary ionic compound that oysters produce to form both their shells and pearls.

Calcium nitrate is composed of calcium cations, Ca^{2+}, and polyatomic nitrate anions, NO_3^-. In calcium nitrate, two nitrate anions, each with a 1− charge, are needed to balance the 2+ charge of each calcium cation.

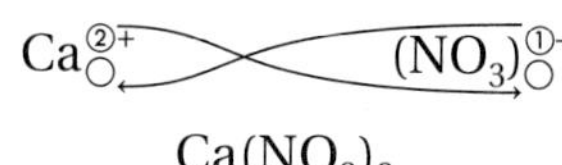

$$Ca(NO_3)_2$$

Notice that parentheses are used around the nitrate ion in the formula because two nitrate anions, $(NO_3^-)_2$ are needed.

Whenever more than a single polyatomic ion is needed to balance a formula, parentheses must be used. This is the only time they are used. For example, the formula for strontium sulfate is $SrSO_4$. Parentheses are not used in this formula because only a single polyatomic sulfate anion is needed to balance the strontium cation.

Example 7 Writing Formulas for Ternary Ionic Compounds

Write formulas for these compounds.

a. potassium sulfate **b.** magnesium hydroxide

Solution

a. $K^{1+} \quad (SO_4)^{2-}$

K_2SO_4

Two potassium cations with 1+ charges are needed to neutralize the 2– charge on one sulfate anion. The formula for potassium sulfate is K_2SO_4.

b. $Mg^{2+} \quad (OH)^{1-}$

$Mg(OH)_2$

The formula for magnesium hydroxide must have the parentheses. The formula $MgOH_2$ is incorrect.

Concept Practice

21. When, only, must parentheses be used in a formula?

Practice Problem

22. Write the formulas for these compounds.

a. calcium carbonate

b. barium hydrogen carbonate

c. lithium hypochlorite

d. tin(IV) dichromate

When naming a ternary ionic compound from its formula, you must first recognize the polyatomic ion. Like binary ionic compounds, ternary ionic compounds are named by naming the ions, cation first. For example, the compound $NaC_2H_3O_2$ is composed of sodium and acetate ions. Its name is sodium acetate. The compound $K_2Cr_2O_7$ consists of two K^+ ions combined with one $Cr_2O_7^{2-}$. Its name is potassium dichromate.

Integrating Health

Lithium Carbonate and Manic–Depression

Psychiatrists see many patients whose moods alternate between depression and hyperactivity, or mania. Such people are called manic–depressive or bipolar because they swing from one mood pole to its opposite. In the manic phase, they think they can conquer the world—until they crash into the next depression. The symptoms of manic–depressive patients are often stabilized by lithium ions, which are administered as the ternary ionic compound lithium carbonate. Dr. John Cade discovered the mood-altering effects of lithium ions in 1949. Lithium ions probably exert their effects on neurotransmission, the means by which messages are sent between brain cells.

Example 8 Naming Ternary Ionic Compounds

Name these compounds.

a. LiCN **b.** $Sr(H_2PO_4)_2$
c. $(NH_4)_2C_2O_4$ **d.** $Fe(ClO_3)_3$

Solution

a. lithium cyanide **b.** strontium dihydrogen phosphate
c. ammonium oxalate **d.** iron(III) chlorate

Problem-Solving Tip

Formulas containing more than two elements contain a polyatomic ion; you must recognize the polyatomic ions.

Practice Problems

23. Write names for these compounds.
a. $Al(OH)_3$ **b.** NaI
c. $Sn_3(PO_4)_2$ **d.** Na_2CrO_4

24. Write the name or formula as appropriate.
a. chromium(III) nitrite **b.** $Mg_3(PO_4)_2$
c. LiF **d.** sodium perchlorate
e. $Pb(C_2H_3O_2)_2$ **f.** magnesium hydrogen carbonate

Objective

Identify by name and write formulas of binary molecular compounds.

5.12 Binary Molecular Compounds

Unlike binary ionic compounds, binary molecular compounds are composed of two nonmetallic elements. This difference affects the writing of formulas for these compounds and the way they are named. Because binary molecular compounds are composed of molecules, ionic charges are *not* used to assign formulas or names to the compounds. In addition, when two nonmetallic elements combine, they often do so in more than one way. For example, the elements carbon and oxygen combine to form two different gaseous compounds, CO and CO_2. They also form two different polyatomic ions, CO_3^{2-} and $C_2O_4^{2-}$. The different compounds and the different ions have different physical and chemical properties.

How would you name a binary compound formed by the combination of carbon and oxygen atoms? It might seem satisfactory to call it "carbon oxide." This could have severe consequences, however. Sitting in a room with moderate amounts of "carbon oxide" (CO_2) in the air would not present any problems. You exhale CO_2 as a product of your body chemistry. Thus, it is normally present in the air you breathe. On the other hand, if the same amount of another "carbon oxide" (CO) were in the room, you could die of asphyxiation. The binary compound CO is a poisonous gas that interferes with the blood's ability to carry oxygen to body cells. Obviously, we need a way to distinguish between these two compounds when naming them.

You can see that Table 5.5 lists the prefixes used to name binary molecular compounds. These prefixes tell how many atoms of each element are present in each molecule (and formula) of the compound. According to the table, the prefix *mono-* would be used for the single oxygen atom in CO. The prefix *di-* would be used to indicate the two oxygen atoms in CO_2. The two compounds of carbon and oxygen, then, are named carbon monoxide (CO) and carbon dioxide (CO_2). Notice that the second element in the name is written with an *-ide* ending. *The names of all binary compounds, both ionic and molecular, end in* -ide. Also note that the vowel at the end of a prefix is dropped when the name of the element begins with a vowel. You would write monoxide, not monooxide. If there is just a single atom of the *first* element in the name, the prefix *mono-* is usually omitted. Remember, prefixes are used in naming compounds composed of two nonmetals.

Table 5.5 Prefixes Used in Naming Binary Molecular Compounds

Prefix	Number
mono-	1
di-	2
tri-	3
tetra-	4
penta-	5
hexa-	6
hepta-	7
octa-	8
nona-	9
deca-	10

Example 9 Naming Binary Molecular Compounds

Name the compounds.
a. N_2O **b.** PCl_3 **c.** $AlCl_3$ **d.** SF_6

Solution

When both elements are nonmetals, the compound is molecular, and prefixes are used to indicate numbers of atoms.
a. dinitrogen monoxide
b. phosphorus trichloride
c. aluminum chloride (This is an ionic compound, formed between a metal and a nonmetal. No prefixes are used.)
d. sulfur hexafluoride

Formulas for binary molecular compounds are among the easiest to write. Use the prefixes to tell you the subscript of each element in the formula. Then write down the correct symbols for the two elements with the appropriate subscripts. For example, the formula for tetraiodine nonoxide is I_4O_9. The prefix *tetra-* indicates four iodine atoms and the prefix *nona-* indicates nine atoms of oxygen in the compound. How would you write formulas for sulfur trioxide and phosphorus pentafluoride?

Practice Problems

25. Name these compounds.
a. CS_2 **b.** Cl_2O_7 **c.** N_2O_5 **d.** CCl_4 **e.** $CrCl_3$

26. Write formulas for these compounds.
a. carbon tetrabromide **b.** dinitrogen tetrahydride
c. boron trichloride **d.** diphosphorus trioxide

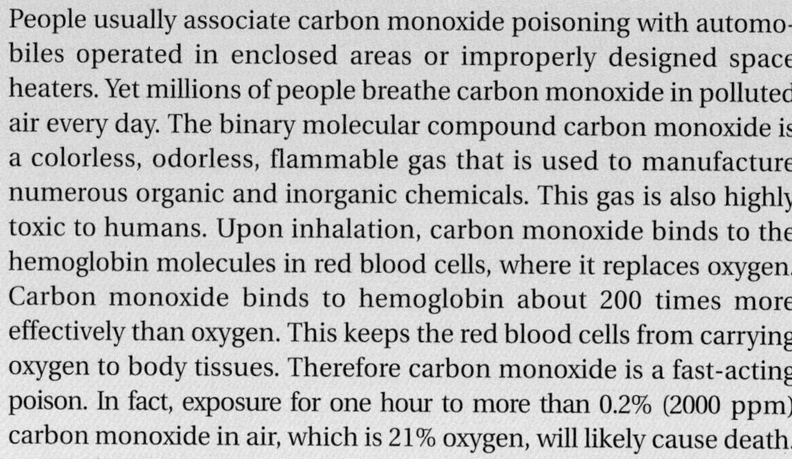

5.B Environmental Awareness

Carbon Monoxide

Figure 5.20 During peak traffic times, the carbon monoxide level in the air may cause headaches or nausea.

People usually associate carbon monoxide poisoning with automobiles operated in enclosed areas or improperly designed space heaters. Yet millions of people breathe carbon monoxide in polluted air every day. The binary molecular compound carbon monoxide is a colorless, odorless, flammable gas that is used to manufacture numerous organic and inorganic chemicals. This gas is also highly toxic to humans. Upon inhalation, carbon monoxide binds to the hemoglobin molecules in red blood cells, where it replaces oxygen. Carbon monoxide binds to hemoglobin about 200 times more effectively than oxygen. This keeps the red blood cells from carrying oxygen to body tissues. Therefore carbon monoxide is a fast-acting poison. In fact, exposure for one hour to more than 0.2% (2000 ppm) carbon monoxide in air, which is 21% oxygen, will likely cause death.

Carbon monoxide forms when compounds containing carbon burn in oxygen-poor air. At peak traffic times, the level of carbon monoxide in the air around streets and highways may reach as high as 100 ppm of air. In the United States, new automobiles must be equipped with catalytic converters that change toxic carbon monoxide to less toxic carbon dioxide.

Carbon monoxide is also present in cigarette smoke. It takes several hours to replace the carbon monoxide in a smoker's blood after only one cigarette.

Think About It

27. Apply Based on this essay, under what circumstances would you be willing to ride in a car with the windows open? Explain why.

5.13 Naming Common Acids

Objective

Identify by name and write formulas for common acids.

Acids are a group of compounds that are given special treatment in naming. You will see that acids are defined in several different ways when you look at the chemistry of acids later in the course. For now, it is sufficient to know that acids are compounds that give off hydrogen ions when dissolved in water.

Acids are used in many industrial processes, including making steel and fertilizers. There are a few acids that you will regularly use in the laboratory. You should know the formulas and names of these acids.

hydrochloric acid	HCl	acetic acid	$HC_2H_3O_2$
sulfuric acid	H_2SO_4	phosphoric acid	H_3PO_4
nitric acid	HNO_3	carbonic acid	H_2CO_3

Concept Practice

28. The formula of a common acid will always contain what element? *Hint:* Study the list above.

5.14 Summary of Naming and Formula Writing

Objective

Apply the method shown in the flowchart, Figure 5.21, to name a compound correctly.

In this chapter you have learned two skills: writing chemical formulas and naming chemical compounds. If this is your first time working with these concepts, you may feel a little overwhelmed at this point. When do you use prefixes or roman numerals in a name and when don't you use them? Should a compound's name end in *-ate*, *-ide*, or *-ite*? The flowchart in Figure 5.21 is designed to help you name compounds correctly. Follow the arrows on the flowchart to find directions for naming a particular compound. By using the flowchart while working exercises, you will increase your skill at naming compounds.

In writing a chemical formula from a chemical name, it is helpful to remember the following.

1. In an ionic compound, the net ionic charge is zero.

2. An *-ide* ending generally indicates a binary compound.

3. An *-ite* or *-ate* ending usually means there is a polyatomic anion in the formula.

Problem-Solving Tip

Look at the ending of a name to see if the compound contains a polyatomic ion (*-ite* and *-ate* endings).

Integrating Information Science

Chemical Data Banks

The job of naming chemical compounds and writing their formulas may seem like an overwhelming task. There are more than 10 million organic compounds. Each of these has a unique name. Many chemists use computers to manage this ever-growing body of data. One of the largest chemical data banks is the Chemical Information System, CIS. CIS contains data on hundreds of thousands of chemicals. Users can gain access to the system by telephone. CIS is used by government agencies, universities, and industries throughout Canada, the United States, and many other countries.

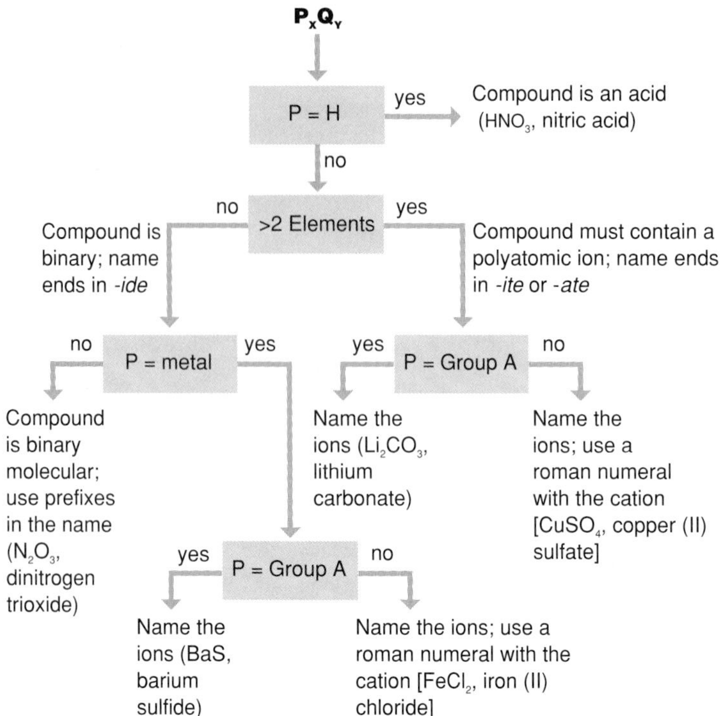

Figure 5.21 This flowchart will help you name chemical compounds. The letters P and Q in the general formula, P_xQ_y, can be atoms, monatomic ions, or polyatomic ions.

4. Prefixes in the name generally indicate that the compound is molecular. They show the number of each atom in the formula.

5. A Roman numeral shows the ionic charge of the cation.

Practice Problems

29. Name these compounds, using Figure 5.21 as an aid if necessary.

a. $CaCO_3$
b. $KMnO_4$
c. $PbCrO_4$
d. $CaHPO_4$
e. $SnCr_2O_7$
f. Mg_3P_2
g. $(NH_4)_2SO_4$
h. ICl
i. $NaNO_2$

30. Write formulas for these compounds.

a. tin(II) hydroxide
b. barium fluoride
c. tetraiodine nonoxide
d. iron(III) oxalate
e. calcium sulfide
f. aluminum hydrogen carbonate
g. sodium phosphate
h. potassium perchlorate
i. disulfur trioxide
j. magnesium nitrate

Glass

Viewing Stars Through a Grain of Sand

Imagine inventing a material with the molecular structure of a liquid but the hardness of a solid. Imagine further that it can be made into almost any size or shape. This material could take on any color you choose or be completely colorless. What if it were also a good thermal and electrical insulator and waterproof too? Impossible, right? Not at all! People have been using this material for over 4000 years. It's called glass.

Glass is made from molten materials that have been cooled without crystallizing. Solids are typically made up of molecules arranged in a crystalline structure. In glass, the molecules remain disordered, as in a liquid, even after cooling. Silica (SiO_2), the main component of sand, is one of the few substances that can be cooled without crystallizing. Most glass contains SiO_2 as its main ingredient.

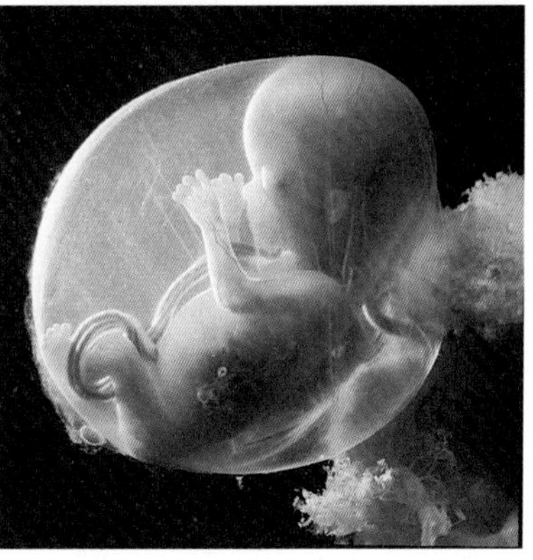

Many other ingredients can be added to the silica base to change the properties of the glass. For example, the color of glass can be changed by adding small amounts of transition metal oxides. Adding iron(III) oxide (Fe_2O_3) gives glass the green tint used in some beverage bottles and tinted windows. Blue glass contains CuO or CoO, orange glass contains Cr_2O_3, and red glass contains colloidal gold.

Adding lead(II) oxide (PbO) makes glass sparkle and also makes it easier to polish. Leaded glass is popular for making chandeliers and cut glass vases. Eyeglass lenses sometimes contain silver chloride (AgCl). In bright light, silver chloride breaks down into chlorine atoms and silver atoms. The opaque silver atoms darken the glass and reduce the amount of light that can penetrate the lens. In the dark, the atoms reassociate and the glass becomes clear again.

Optical glass is the clearest kind of glass. It is used for microscopes, telescopes, and other instruments that require maximum light transmission. Glass can be drawn into long, thin, flexible rods called optical fibers. Optical fibers can transmit light over long distances and even around corners. Like tiny periscopes, optical fibers can be used to view tissues deep within the human body. From examining a fetus in a mother's womb to charting the distant stars of the galaxy, glass has greatly expanded the limits of human vision.

Think About It

31. Explain Is glass a molecular or an ionic substance? Base your explanation on the chemical components of glass.

Chapter 5 Review
Chemical Names and Formulas

Key Terms

anion *5.2*	metal *5.1*
binary compound *5.9*	metalloid *5.1*
cation *5.2*	molecule *5.3*
chemical formula *5.4*	molecular compound *5.3*
formula unit *5.4*	molecular formula *5.4*
group *5.1*	nonmetal *5.1*
ion *5.2*	periodic table *5.1*
ionic compound *5.3*	polyatomic ion *5.7*
law of definite proportions *5.3*	representative element *5.1*
law of multiple proportions *5.5*	ternary compound *5.11*
	transition metal *5.1*

Chapter Summary

The elements in the periodic table are arranged in vertical columns called groups. Groups 1A through 8A make up the representative elements. Metals are on the left and lower side of the periodic table. Nonmetals are on the right and upper side.

Every substance is either an element or a compound. An element consists of one kind of atom. A compound consists of more than one kind of atom. A compound is molecular or ionic.

Molecular compounds are composed of two or more nonmetals. The representative particle of a molecular compound is a molecule. A molecular formula shows the number and kinds of atoms present in a molecule of a compound.

Ionic compounds are composed of oppositely charged ions (cations and anions) combined in electrically neutral groupings. The chemical formula of an ionic compound is a formula unit. A formula unit gives the lowest whole-number ratio of ions in the compound.

The charges of the ions of the representative elements can be determined by the position of these elements in the periodic table. Most transition metals have more than one common ionic charge. A polyatomic ion is a group of atoms that behaves as a unit and that has a charge.

Chemists use a systematic naming method. Binary (two-element) ionic compounds are named by writing the name of the cation followed by the name of the anion. Binary compounds end in *-ide.*

When a cation can have more than one ionic charge, a Roman numeral is used in the name. Ternary ionic compounds contain at least one polyatomic ion. The names of these compounds generally end in *-ite* or *-ate.*

Binary molecular compounds are composed of two nonmetallic elements. Prefixes are used to show how many atoms of each element are present in a molecule of the compound.

Practice Questions and Problems

32. Give the symbol of each element. *5.1*

a. a nonmetal in Group 4A

b. the inner transition metal with the lowest atomic number

c. all the nonmetals whose atomic numbers are a multiple of five

d. the two elements that are liquid at room temperature

e. a metal in Group 5A

33. What is an ion? Describe the formation of a cation and an anion. *5.2*

34. State the number of electrons either lost or gained in forming each ion. *5.2*

a. Br^- **c.** Na^+ **e.** As^{3-}

b. Ca^{2+} **d.** Cu^+ **f.** H^-

35. Name each of the ions in Problem 34. Identify them as anions and cations. *5.2*

36. Would you expect the following compounds to be ionic or molecular? *5.3*

a. CO **c.** C_2H_6

b. Na_2S **d.** N_2O_3

37. State whether each formula in Problem 36 represents a molecule or a formula unit. *5.4*

38. How is the law of multiple proportions explained by Dalton's atomic theory? *5.5*

39. Using only the periodic table, name and write the formulas of the ions of these representative elements. *5.6*
   a. potassium **b.** sulfur **c.** argon
   d. bromine **e.** beryllium **f.** sodium

40. Without consulting Table 5.4, name the following ions. *5.7*
   a. OH^- **d.** O^{2-} **g.** Al^{3+}
   b. Pb^{4+} **e.** HPO_4^{2-} **h.** ClO_2^-
   c. SO_4^{2-} **f.** $Cr_2O_7^{2-}$

41. Write the formula and charge of each of the following ions. *5.7*
   a. ammonium ion **d.** nitrate ion
   b. tin(II) ion **e.** cyanide ion
   c. chromate ion **f.** iron(III) ion

42. What condition must be met in writing a "balanced" formula for an ionic compound? *5.9*

43. Write formulas for compounds formed from these pairs of ions. *5.9*
   a. Ba^{2+}, S^{2-} **c.** Ca^{2+}, N^{3-}
   b. Li^+, O^{2-} **d.** Cu^{2+}, I^-

44. Write formulas for these compounds. *5.9*
   a. sodium iodide
   b. stannous fluoride
   c. potassium sulfide
   d. calcium iodide

45. Name these binary ionic compounds. *5.10*
   a. ZnS **b.** KCl **c.** BaO **d.** $CuBr_2$

46. When are parentheses used in writing a chemical formula? *5.11*

47. Write formulas for these compounds. *5.11*
   a. lithium hydrogen sulfate
   b. chromium(III) nitrite
   c. mercury(II) bromide
   d. ammonium dichromate

48. What are the components of a binary molecular compound? *5.12*

49. What prefix is used to indicate each of the following numbers of atoms in a formula of a molecular compound? *5.12*
   a. 3 **b.** 1 **c.** 2 **d.** 6 **e.** 5 **f.** 4

50. Name these binary molecular compounds. *5.12*
   a. OF_2 **b.** Cl_2O_8 **c.** SO_3 **d.** P_4O_{10}

51. Write formulas for the following binary molecular compounds. *5.12*
   a. nitrogen trifluoride
   b. disulfur dichloride
   c. dinitrogen tetroxide
   d. phosphorus pentachloride

52. Give the name or formula for these acids. *5.13*
   a. HCl **c.** sulfuric acid
   b. HNO_3 **d.** acetic acid

Mastery Questions and Problems

53. Make a concept map using compound as the key concept. Use at least ten of the key words from this chapter.

54. Identify each of the following sets of elements by their numbered location on the periodic table that follows. Some of the sets are made up of a combination of several numbered areas.
   a. representative elements
   b. inner transition elements
   c. nonmetals
   d. transition metals
   e. metals

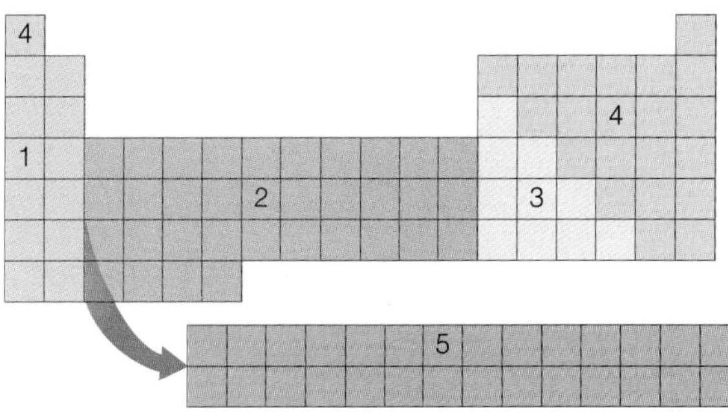

55. There is worldwide concern about the destruction of the rain forests. In what way does the history of pharmacy support these concerns?

56. Write formulas for these compounds.
   a. potassium permanganate
   b. calcium hydrogen carbonate
   c. dichlorine heptoxide
   d. trisilicon tetranitride
   e. sodium dihydrogen phosphate
   f. phosphorus pentabromide
   g. carbon tetrachloride

57. Thousands of different kinds of inorganic chemicals are produced in the United States. The amounts of the top ten inorganic chemicals produced in 1992 are shown in the following data table.

a. What percent of the total production of the top ten did lime (calcium oxide) account for?

b. Three diatomic gases are on the list. What are their names and what was their total production in 1992?

c. What percent of the total production of the top ten did the three acids account for?

d. Write formulas for the top ten inorganic chemicals.

Chemical	Amount produced (billions of kg)
Sulfuric acid	39.4
Nitrogen	25.9
Oxygen	17.7
Ammonia	15.5
Lime	15.3
Phosphoric acid	11.2
Sodium hydroxide	11.0
Chlorine	10.3
Sodium carbonate	9.3
Nitric acid	6.8

58. Name these compounds.

a. $NaClO_3$
b. Hg_2Br_2
c. K_2CrO_4
d. AlI_3
e. SnO_2
f. $Fe(C_2H_3O_2)_3$
g. $KHSO_4$
h. CaH_2

59. Name each of the following substances. Use Figure 5.21 if necessary.

a. $LiClO_4$
b. Cl_2O
c. HgF_2
d. CaO
e. $Ba_3(PO_4)_2$
f. I_2
g. $SrSO_4$
h. $CuC_2H_3O_2$

60. Write formulas for these compounds.

a. magnesium sulfide
b. nitrogen
c. barium hydroxide
d. copper(II) nitrite
e. sulfite ion
f. calcium carbonate
g. sodium bromide
h. ferric sulfate

61. Name each compound.

a. $Mg(MnO_4)_2$
b. $Be(NO_3)_2$
c. N_2H_4
d. $LiOH$
e. PI_3
f. ZnO

62. Write formulas for these compounds.

a. calcium bromide
b. silver chloride
c. aluminum carbide
d. nitrogen dioxide
e. tin(IV) cyanide
f. lithium hydride
g. strontium acetate
h. sodium silicate

Critical Thinking Questions

63. Choose the term that best completes the second relationship.

a. Black:white — cation:____
(1) anion (2) metal
(3) sodium ion (4) iron ion

b. plant:oak tree — anion:____
(1) sodium ion (2) magnesium ion
(3) cation (4) chloride ion

c. molecular compound:molecule
ionic compound:____
(1) cation (2) formula unit
(3) anion (4) metalloid

64. Compare and contrast the information conveyed by a molecular formula to that given by a formula unit of a compound.

65. Where on the periodic table will you find the two elements in a binary molecular compound?

66. Why is it important for chemists to have a common system of writing chemical names and formulas?

67. Criticize this statement: "The ionic charge of any metal can be determined from the position of the element in the periodic table."

68. One way to increase the energy efficiency of a building is to limit the amount of outside cold or hot air that enters the building. What is a potential negative aspect of this practice?

Cumulative Review

69. Make the following conversions.
- **a.** 775 mL to microliters
- **b.** –65°C to K
- **c.** 8.32 mg of Ag to centigrams of silver

70. How many protons and electrons are in each of these ions?
- **a.** magnesium ion
- **b.** bromide ion
- **c.** strontium ion
- **d.** sulfide ion

71. List five properties of the chair you are sitting in. Classify them as physical or chemical.

72. A student finds that 6.62 g of a substance occupies a volume of 12.3 cm^3. What is the density of the substance?

Challenge Questions and Problems

73. The *Handbook of Chemistry and Physics* is a reference work that contains a wealth of information about elements and compounds. Two sections of this book you might use are the "Physical Constants of Inorganic Compounds" and the "Physical Constants of Organic Compounds."

To familiarize yourself with this work, make a table with these headings: Name, Formula, Crystalline form or color, Density, Melting point (°C), Boiling point (°C), and Solubility in water. Enter these substances in the body of the table: ammonium chloride, barium, barium sulfate, bromine, calcium carbonate, chlorine, copper(II) sulfate pentahydrate, iodine, iron(II) sulfate pentahydrate, mercury, potassium carbonate, and sulfur. Use the handbook to complete the table.

74. Use the table you prepared for Problem 73 to answer the following questions.
- **a.** How would you distinguish between samples of copper(II) sulfate pentahydrate and iron(II) sulfate pentahydrate?
- **b.** A bottle contains a mixture of ammonium chloride and barium sulfate. What method could you use to separate these two compounds?
- **c.** List the *elements* in the preceding table in order of increasing density. Identify the elements as metals or nonmetals.
- **d.** Calculate the mass of 47.0 cm^3 of mercury.

Connections Questions

75. Why might a salesperson for a manufacturer of lawn care products need a good chemistry background?

76. For what condition is lithium carbonate prescribed?

77. List some occupations other than chemist for which access to chemical data banks might be needed.

Write About Chemistry

78. Are you a creative thinker? Do you like puns? You may enjoy groaning at these *elemental puns.* Each of the blanks can be completed with the name of an element. So cesium your pencil and try your luck.
- **a.** A large building for automobiles. A ____.
- **b.** A comical prisoner. A ____.
- **c.** The resort manager said, "____ view is magnificent."
- **d.** Well driller's chant. "____."
- **e.** The man was buried in the ____ the hill.
- **f.** What you do with dead cats. You ____.
- **g.** The greeting of the Greek warrior when he climbed out of the wooden horse. "____."
- **h.** Funds from your mother's sister: ____.

79. With respect to ion formation, write about how a loss can be positive and a gain can be negative.

Readings and References

Meadows, Robin. "Fossil Molecules." *ChemMatters* (April 1988), pp. 4–7.

Weast, Robert C., ed. CRC *Handbook of Chemistry and Physics: A Ready Reference Book of Chemical and Physical Data,* 67th ed. Boca Raton, FL: Chemical Rubber Co., 1993.

6 Chemical Quantities

Goals

- Explain the centrality of the mole to chemical calculations.
- Convert, using the mole, between the units of mass, representative particles, and volumes of gases at STP.
- Derive empirical and molecular formulas of compounds from experimental data.

The tallest sand castle, at 16 m, was built by 2000 people! How much sand is that? 44 000 000 kg. How many grains of sand *is* that? The question "How much?" can be answered several different ways in chemistry.

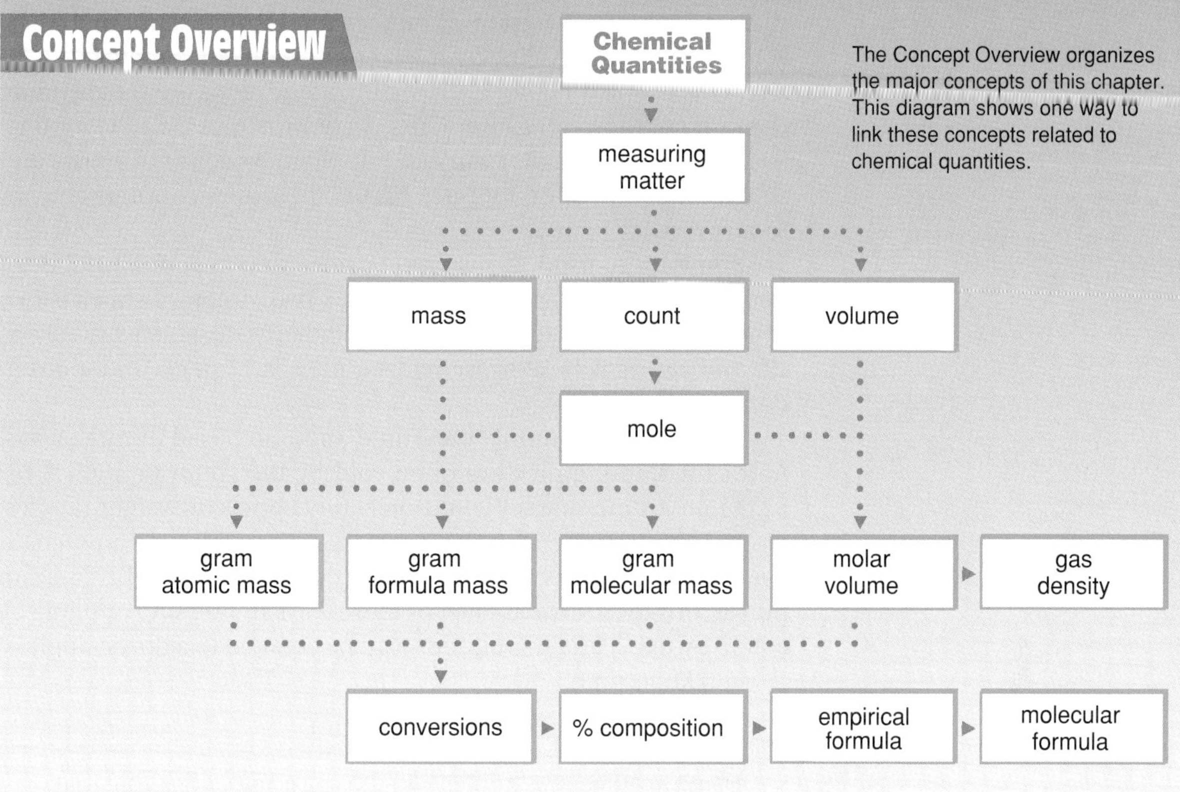

You live in a quantitative world. The grade you got on your last exam, or how many times you heard your favorite song on the radio yesterday may be important quantities to you. These are quantities that answer such questions as "how much?" or "how many?" Scientists spend time answering similar questions. How many grams of the elements hydrogen and nitrogen must be combined to make 200 g of the fertilizer ammonia, NH_3? This typical chemistry question emphasizes that chemistry is a quantitative science. In chemistry you will analyze the composition of samples of matter. You will also find that you must be able to measure the amount of matter you have.

6.1 Measuring Matter

Objective

Identify the basic SI unit for measuring the amount of a substance.

How do you measure matter? One way to measure matter is by counting how many of something you have. For example, you count the tracks on a CD or how many pins you knock down when bowling. Another way to measure the amount of matter you have is by weighing it. You may buy potatoes by the kilogram or pound and silver or gold by the gram or ounce. You also measure matter by volume. You buy gasoline by the liter or gallon, and you take cough medicine by the milliliter or teaspoon. Some items are sold by more than one of these measurements: a count, a mass, and a volume. Examples include nails (you can buy them by count or mass) and strawberries (mass or volume). Figure 6.1 shows counted units of some everyday items.

Some units used in measuring refer to a specific number of items. For example, pair always means two. A pair of shoes is two shoes and a pair of aces is two aces. Similarly, dozen always means 12. A dozen eggs is 12 eggs, a dozen pens is 12 pens, and a dozen donuts is 12 donuts.

Apples are commonly measured and purchased in three ways. At a fruit stand apples are often sold by the *count* (apples, 5 for \$2.00). In a supermarket you usually buy apples by weight (apples, \$0.89/pound) or *mass* (apples, \$1.95/kg). If you live near an orchard you can buy apples by *volume* (apples, \$9.00/bushel). You can pursue this idea further. Each of these ways to measure apples—by count, by mass, and by volume—can be equated to a dozen apples.

You know that:

1 dozen apples = 12 apples (count)

Using average-size apples you measure and determine that:

1 dozen apples = 2 kg apples (mass)

and

1 dozen apples = 0.20 bushel apples (volume)

Knowing how the count, mass, and volume of apples are related to a dozen apples allows you to convert between these different units. For example, you can calculate the mass of a bushel of apples or the mass of 90 average-size apples.

Figure 6.1 Items are often sold by different types of measurements, such as a count, a mass, or a volume. Which of these common supermarket items are being sold by mass? By volume? By count?

Example 1 Finding Mass from a Count

What is the mass of 90 average-size apples?

Step 1. The unknown is the mass of apples.

Step 2. The known is 90 apples.

Step 3. The desired conversion is:

number of apples → mass of apples

The conversion can be carried out by the following sequence of conversions:

number of apples → dozens of apples → mass of apples

The expressions relating the units are:

12 apples = 1 dozen apples
1 dozen apples = 2.0 kg apples

Step 4. The solution is:

$$90\ \cancel{\text{apples}} \times \frac{1\ \cancel{\text{dozen apples}}}{12\ \cancel{\text{apples}}} \times \frac{2.0\ \text{kg apples}}{1\ \cancel{\text{dozen apples}}} = 15\ \text{kg apples}$$

Step 5. The answer is 15 kg apples.

In the next section you will see that the mole, the SI unit that measures the "amount of substance," is a unit just like the dozen. The unit mole can be related to the number of particles (a count), the mass, and the volume of an element or a compound just as a dozen was related to these three units for apples. Work through the following problems using the apple relationships listed above.

Concept Practice

1. List two items other than those listed above that are commonly measured in at least two of these ways: by count, by mass, and by volume.

Practice Problems

2. What is the mass of 0.50 bushel of apples?

3. Assume that this variety of apples has 8 seeds in each apple. How many apple seeds are in 15 kg of apples?

6.A Environmental Awareness

Lead Poisoning

Figure 6.2 Many seemingly safe places for children to play, such as outside this home, are actually serious health threats because of lead contamination from flaking old house paint.

Lead has been a threat to the outdoor environment because of the use of tetraethyl lead as an antiknock compound in gasoline. Fortunately, the use of tetraethyl lead has been phased out in unleaded fuels. However, deteriorating lead paint continues to be a serious indoor environmental concern. Interior paint containing up to 50% lead was used in most homes built before 1950.

Millions of children are at risk of underdeveloped nervous systems and impaired intelligence because of lead dust and paint chips in their homes. More than three million children in the United States have blood levels of 10 micrograms of lead or more per deciliter. The U.S. Centers for Disease Control considers a blood level of lead above 10 micrograms per deciliter as a cause for concern. At 20 micrograms of lead per deciliter of blood, medical evaluation is recommended, and medical treatment should be administered above 45 micrograms of lead per deciliter of blood.

If you calculate the number of atoms in 10 micrograms of lead, it seems like a lot—2.92×10^{16} atoms. In reality, this is a very small amount of lead, only 4.9×10^{-8} mol. You need to get an idea of how much 10 micrograms per deciliter is. Imagine pouring 5000 two-liter soda bottles of water into a small square swimming pool that measures 3.16 m on each side and is 1 m deep. The water would fill the pool to the brim. Then, you dissolve *ten* 100-milligram aspirin tablet in the water. The water in the tub would contain 10 micrograms per deciliter of aspirin. If the water represents all the blood in your body and the aspirin represents lead, you can see that it doesn't take much lead to give cause for concern.

Covering lead paint with a nonlead paint or removing the lead paint greatly reduces the risk of lead poisoning. Many environmental and public health groups are seeking funds for environmental lead reduction. These groups maintain that the cost to society of caring for the victims of lead poisoning is higher than the substantial costs of lead removal.

Think About It

4. Evaluate List some recent efforts to reduce the amount of lead in the environment. How practical do you think these efforts are?

5. Support On what basis can you justify the expenditure of public funds to reduce the amount of lead in the environment?

6.2 The Mole

Recall that matter is composed of different kinds of particles. One way to measure the amount of a substance is to count the number of particles in that substance. Since atoms, molecules, and ions are exceedingly small, the number of individual particles in the smallest sample of any substance is very large. Counting the particles is not practical or even possible. You can "count" particles, however, if you introduce a term that represents a specified number of particles. *Just as a dozen eggs represents 12 eggs, a* **mole** *of a substance represents* 6.02×10^{23} *representative particles of that substance. The experimentally determined number* 6.02×10^{23} *is called* **Avogadro's number**, in honor of Amedeo Avogadro di Quarenga (1776–1856).

The term **representative particle** *refers to the species present in a substance: usually atoms, molecules, or formula units (ions).* The representative particle of most elements is the atom. Iron is composed of iron atoms. Seven elements, however, normally exist as diatomic molecules (H_2, N_2, O_2, F_2, Cl_2, Br_2, and I_2). The representative particle of these elements and of all molecular compounds is the molecule. The molecular compound water (H_2O) is composed of H_2O molecules. The formula unit is the representative particle of ionic compounds. Calcium chloride, an ionic compound, has the formula unit $CaCl_2$. Calcium ions and chloride ions are present in a 1:2 ratio in this formula unit. Table 6.1 summarizes the relationship between representative particles and moles of substances.

A mole refers to Avogadro's number of representative particles of any substance. A mole of a diatomic element such as nitrogen contains 6.02×10^{23} *molecules* of nitrogen. A mole of any molecular compound is composed of Avogadro's number of *molecules* regardless of the size of the molecule. A mole of dinitrogen tetroxide, N_2O_4, and a mole of sucrose, $C_{12}H_{22}O_{11}$, each contains 6.02×10^{23} molecules. In a similar fashion, a mole of any ionic compound is composed of Avogadro's number of *formula units.* A mole of NaI and a mole of $(NH_4)_3PO_4$ each contains 6.02×10^{23} formula units.

Objective

Describe how Avogadro's number is related to a mole of any substance.

Roots of Words

di-: (Greek) two
atomos: (Greek) indivisible
diatomic molecule a molecule consisting of two atoms. Nitrogen, N_2, is a diatomic molecule.

moles: (Latin) heap or pile
mole (mol) the amount of a substance that contains 6.02×10^{23} representative particles of that substance; a molar mass of any substance. One molar mass of a substance contains one mole of particles of the substance.

Table 6.1 Representative Particles and Moles

Substance	Representative particle	Chemical formula	Representative particles in 1.00 mol
Atomic nitrogen	Atom	N	6.02×10^{23}
Nitrogen gas	Molecule	N_2	6.02×10^{23}
Water	Molecule	H_2O	6.02×10^{23}
Calcium ion	Ion	Ca^{2+}	6.02×10^{23}
Calcium fluoride	Formula unit	CaF_2	6.02×10^{23}
Sucrose	Molecule	$C_{12}H_{22}O_{11}$	6.02×10^{23}

Biographical Note

Amedeo Avogadro
(1776–1856)

Count Amedeo Avogadro was an Italian lawyer who turned to the study of mathematics and physics. He soon became a professor of these subjects. Before Avogadro's time chemists used the terms "atoms" and "molecules" interchangeably. Avogadro clarified the difference between atoms and molecules. Avogadro was also responsible for Avogadro's hypothesis: equal volumes of gases at the same temperature and pressure contain the same number of molecules. Avogadro himself never calculated the number named after him. The first determination of Avogadro's number was made nine years after Avogadro's death. This important number was given his name, however, to honor him for contributions to science that were not recognized until after his death.

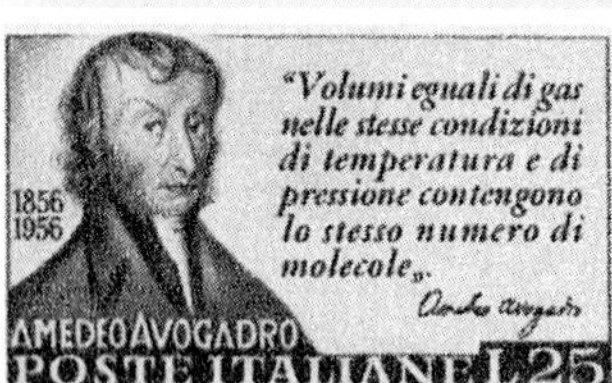

Example 2 Converting Number of Atoms to Moles

How many moles of magnesium are 3.01×10^{22} atoms of magnesium?

Solution

Step 1. The unknown is the number of moles.

Step 2. The known is the number of atoms, 3.01×10^{22} atoms.

Step 3. The desired conversion is: atoms → moles. The expression relating the units is 1 mol Mg = 6.02×10^{23} atoms Mg. The conversion factor is 1 mol Mg/6.02×10^{23} atoms Mg. (You want to cancel the unit atoms and be left with the unit moles.)

Step 4. In doing the calculation, make sure that the units cancel.

$$3.01 \times 10^{22} \,\cancel{\text{atoms Mg}} \times \frac{1 \text{ mol Mg}}{6.02 \times 10^{23} \,\cancel{\text{atoms Mg}}} = 0.500 \times 10^{-1} \text{ mol Mg}$$

Step 5. In scientific notation the answer is 5.00×10^{-2} mol Mg. The answer should have three significant figures. Since the given number of atoms was less than Avogadro's number, you would expect to have less than 1 mol of atoms.

Practice Problems

6. How many moles are 2.80×10^{24} atoms of silicon?

7. How many atoms are 0.360 mol of silver?

How many atoms are in a mole of a compound? To answer this question you must know how many atoms are in a representative particle of the compound. Consider this analogy. A package of pencils contains 12 pencils. A dozen packages of pencils contain 144 (12 × 12) pencils. Similarly, the number of atoms in a compound depends on the chemical formula. A mole of carbon dioxide, CO_2, contains Avogadro's number of CO_2 molecules. Each CO_2 molecule is composed of three atoms. Hence, a mole of carbon dioxide contains three times Avogadro's number of atoms. A mole of carbon monoxide (CO) contains two times Avogadro's number of atoms. *To find the number of atoms in a mole of a compound, you must determine the number of atoms in a representative formula of that compound.* Figure 6.3 illustrates this idea with marbles (atoms) in packages (molecules).

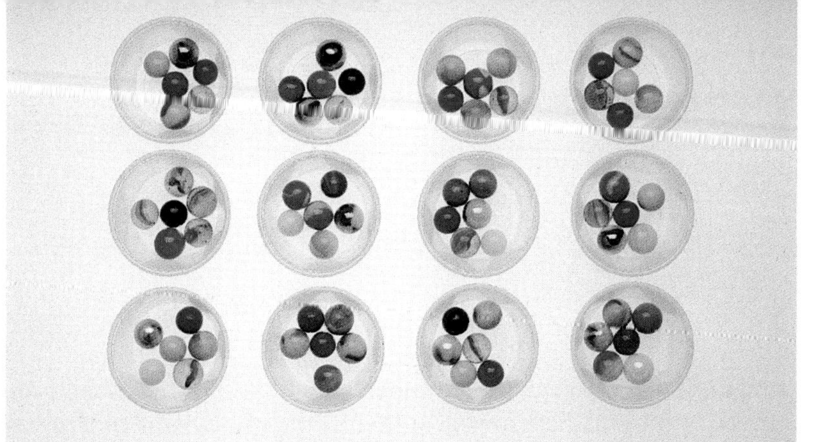

Figure 6.3 A dozen cups of marbles contain more than just one dozen marbles. Similarly, a mole of molecules contains more than a mole of atoms. How many atoms are there in one mole of molecules if each molecule consists of six atoms?

Example 3 Converting Moles to Number of Molecules

How many molecules are 4.00 mol of glucose, $C_6H_{12}O_6$?

Solution

Step 1. The unknown is the number of molecules of $C_6H_{12}O_6$.

Step 2. The known is the number of moles: 4.00 mol of $C_6H_{12}O_6$.

Step 3. The desired conversion is: moles → molecules. Thus you need a conversion factor that gives molecules/mole. Glucose is a molecular compound. You know that 6.02×10^{23} molecules of $C_6H_{12}O_6$ are 1 mol of $C_6H_{12}O_6$.

Step 4. The calculations can be done in a single step.

$$4.00\ \cancel{\text{mol}\ C_6H_{12}O_6} \times \frac{6.02 \times 10^{23}\ \text{molecules}\ C_6H_{12}O_6}{1\ \cancel{\text{mol}\ C_6H_{12}O_6}}$$

$$= 24.08 \times 10^{23}\ \text{molecules}$$

Step 5. The answer must be rounded to three significant figures and written in scientific notation: 2.41×10^{24} molecules of glucose.

Problem-Solving Tip

Estimate an approximate answer to see if your answer makes sense.

Concept Practice

8. How many oxygen atoms are in a representative particle of each substance?

a. ammonium nitrate, NH_4NO_3, a fertilizer
b. acetylsalicylic acid, $C_9H_8O_4$, aspirin
c. ozone, O_3, a disinfectant
d. nitroglycerine, $C_3H_5(NO_3)_3$, an explosive

Figure 6.4 How big is a mole?

Practice Problems

9. How many molecules are in 2.14 mol CO?

10. How many moles are contained in 4.65×10^{24} molecules NO_2?

How large is Avogadro's number? The SI unit of the mole is not related to the small burrowing animal of the same name that makes an unsightly mess of lawns and golf courses in some areas of the country. Although they are not related, we can use this mole to help develop an appreciation for the size of the number 6.02×10^{23}. Let's assume that an average animal-mole is 15 cm long, 5 cm tall, and has a mass of 150 g.

What about the mass of 6.02×10^{23} animal-moles? This many animal-moles would equal. . .

- more than 1% of the mass of the Earth
- more than 1.3 times the mass of the moon
- more than 60 times the mass of the water in all the oceans of the Earth put together

If spread over the entire surface of the Earth, Avogadro's number of animal-moles would form a layer more than 8 million animal-moles thick.

If lined up end to end, 6.02×10^{23} animal-moles would easily stretch from Earth to the nearest star, Alpha Centauri, *and back to Earth again.*

Suppose you could convince Avogadro's number of animal-moles to line up into 4 billion equal columns. Suppose further that each person on Earth counted the animal-moles in one column at the rate of 1000 animal-moles per second. Even with this many people counting this fast, it would still take more than 4500 years to count 6.02×10^{23} animal-moles.

Practice Problem

11. Construct a numerical problem to illustrate the size of Avogadro's number. Use common items such as buttons, string, etc. Here is an example problem: "A typical zipper has 8 teeth per centimeter. If you had a zipper with Avogadro's number of teeth, how long would it be in km?" Let a classmate work your problem and then compare answers together.

6.3 The Gram Formula Mass

Objective

Distinguish between the terms gram atomic mass, gram molecular mass, and gram formula mass.

You are always working with large numbers of atoms even if you are using microgram quantities. Even one billion atoms would be a very small amount of a substance. Working with grams of atoms would be much easier to do. *The* **gram atomic mass (gam)** *is the atomic mass of an element expressed in grams.* For carbon the gram atomic mass (gam) is 12.0 g. For hydrogen the gram atomic mass is 1.0 g. Figure 6.5 shows one gram atomic mass of carbon, iron, mercury, and sulfur. By checking atomic masses in the periodic table you can see that for sulfur, the gram atomic mass is 32.1 g. What are the gram atomic masses of iron and mercury?

You learned previously that the atomic mass of an element (the mass of a single atom) is expressed in atomic mass units (amu). Remember that atomic masses of atoms are relative values. The atomic masses of elements found in the periodic table are "weighted average masses" of all the isotopes of those elements. An "average" carbon atom (C) with an atomic mass of 12.0 amu is 12 times heavier than an "average" hydrogen atom (H) with a mass of 1.0 amu. One hundred carbon atoms are 12 times heavier than 100 hydrogen atoms. In fact, any number of carbon atoms is 12 times heavier than the same number of hydrogen atoms. Therefore 12.0 g of carbon atoms and 1.0 g of hydrogen atoms each contain the same number of atoms.

The gram atomic masses of any two elements must contain the same number of atoms. If you were to compare 12.0 g of carbon atoms with 16.0 g of oxygen atoms, you would find they contain the same number of atoms. How many atoms are contained in the gram atomic mass of an element? This is a quantity with which you are already familiar. The gram atomic mass of any element contains one mole of atoms (6.02×10^{23} atoms) of that element.

The mole is defined as the amount of substance that contains as many representative particles as the number of atoms in 12.0 g of carbon-12. You know that 12.0 g is the gram atomic mass of carbon-12.

Figure 6.5 One gram atomic mass (gam) is shown for carbon, sulfur, mercury, and iron. Each of these quantities contains one mole, or 6.02×10^{23} atoms, of that substance.

Carbon atoms		Hydrogen atoms		Mass ratio
number	mass (amu)	number	mass (amu)	$\frac{\text{Mass carbon}}{\text{Mass hydrogen}}$
●	12		1	$\frac{12\text{ amu}}{1\text{ amu}} = \frac{12}{1}$
●●	24 (2 × 12)		2 (2 × 1)	$\frac{24\text{ amu}}{2\text{ amu}} = \frac{12}{1}$
	120 (10 × 12)		10 (10 × 1)	$\frac{120\text{ amu}}{10\text{ amu}} = \frac{12}{1}$
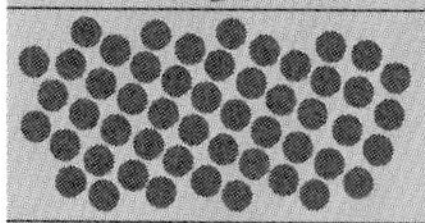	600 (50 × 12)		50 (50 × 1)	$\frac{600\text{ amu}}{50\text{ amu}} = \frac{12}{1}$
Avogadro's number	$(6.02 \times 10^{23})(12)$	**Avogadro's number**	$(6.02 \times 10^{23})(1)$	$\frac{(6.02 \times 10^{23})(12)}{(6.02 \times 10^{23})(1)} = \frac{12}{1}$

Figure 6.6 The mass ratio of equal numbers of carbon atoms to hydrogen atoms is always 12 to 1.

Thus, the gram atomic mass is the mass of one mole of atoms of any element. Since 12.0 g of carbon is the gram atomic mass of carbon, 12.0 g is 1 mol of carbon. Since 24.3 g is the gram atomic mass of magnesium, 24.3 g is 1 mol of magnesium or 6.02×10^{23} atoms of magnesium.

Practice Problem

12. What is the mass of 1 mol of each of these monatomic elements? **a.** sodium **b.** selenium **c.** lead

What is the mass of a mole of a compound? To answer this you must first know the formula of the compound. The formula of a compound tells you the number of atoms of each element in a representative particle of that compound. For example, the formula of the molecular compound sulfur trioxide is SO_3. Thus a molecule of SO_3 is composed of one atom of sulfur and three atoms of oxygen. You can calculate the molecular mass of a molecule of SO_3 by adding together the atomic masses of the atoms making up a molecule of SO_3. From the periodic table, the atomic mass of sulfur (S) is 32.1 amu. The mass of three atoms of oxygen is three times the atomic mass of oxygen (O): 3×16.0 amu = 48.0 amu. Thus, the molecular mass of SO_3 is 32.1 amu + 48.0 amu = 80.1 amu.

Now if you substitute the unit grams for atomic mass units, you obtain the gram molecular mass of SO_3. *The* **gram molecular mass**

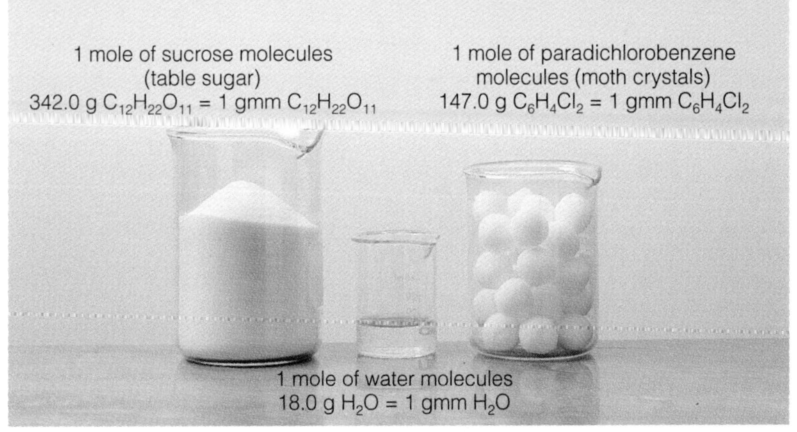

Figure 6.7 One gram molecular mass (gmm) is shown for each of three molecular compounds. Each of these quantities contains 6.02×10^{23} molecules.

(gmm) *of any molecular compound is the mass of one mole of that compound.* The gmm is equal to the molecular mass expressed in grams. Thus, 1 mol of SO_3 has a mass of 80.1 g. Gram molecular masses may be calculated directly from gram atomic masses.

Example 4 Finding the Gram Molecular Mass of a Compound

What is the gram molecular mass of hydrogen peroxide, H_2O_2?

Solution

The unknown is the number of grams in the gram molecular mass. The known is the molecular formula: H_2O_2. This tells you the number of moles of each element in a mole of compound: 2 mol of hydrogen atoms and 2 mol of oxygen atoms.

You can convert moles of atoms to grams by using conversion factors (g/mol) based on the gram atomic mass of each element: 1 mol H = 1.0 g H and 1 mol O = 16.0 g O. Now sum the masses of each element to get the gram molecular mass.

$$2\,\cancel{\text{mol}}\,\text{H} \times \frac{1.0\,\text{g H}}{1\,\cancel{\text{mol}}\,\text{H}} = 2.0\,\text{g H}$$

$$2\,\cancel{\text{mol}}\,\text{O} \times \frac{16.0\,\text{g O}}{1\,\cancel{\text{mol}}\,\text{O}} = 32.0\,\text{g O}$$

Gram molecular mass of H_2O_2 = 34.0 g

Practice Problem

13. Find the gram molecular mass of each compound.
a. C_2H_6 **b.** PCl_3 **c.** C_3H_7OH **d.** N_2O_5

Figure 6.8 One gram formula mass (gfm) is shown for each of the three ionic compounds. Each of these quantities contains 6.02×10^{23} formula units.

It is inappropriate to calculate the gram molecular mass of calcium iodide, CaI_2, because it is an ionic compound. The representative particle of an ionic compound is a formula unit, not a molecule. *The mass of 1 mol of an ionic compound is the* **gram formula mass (gfm)**. The gfm is equal to the formula mass expressed in grams. A gram formula mass is calculated the same way as a gram molecular mass. Simply sum the atomic masses of the atoms that are in the formula of the compound. The atoms are actually present as ions. For example, the gram formula mass of calcium iodide, CaI_2, is the gram atomic mass of calcium plus two times the gram atomic mass of iodine.

$$40.1 \text{ g Ca} + (2 \times 126.9 \text{ g I}) = 293.9 \text{ g CaI}_2$$

There are 293.9 g of CaI_2 in 1 gfm or 1 mol of CaI_2.

Figure 6.8 shows one gram formula mass of three ionic compounds. How many formula units are there in each sample in the picture?

Example 5 Calculating the Gram Formula Mass

What is the gram formula mass of ammonium carbonate, $(NH_4)_2CO_3$?

Solution

The unknown is the number of grams in a gram formula mass. The known is the formula unit. From the formula, you know that a mole of this ionic compound is composed of 2 mol of nitrogen atoms, 8 mol of hydrogen atoms, 1 mol of carbon atoms, and 3 mol of oxygen atoms.

Problem-Solving Tip

A subscript after parentheses in the formula of a compound multiplies the number of each atom within the parentheses.

You will convert moles of atoms to grams by using conversion factors based on the gram atomic masses. Then you will sum the masses of each element to get the gram formula mass.

$$2\ \cancel{\text{mol N}} \times \frac{14.0\ \text{g N}}{1\ \cancel{\text{mol N}}} = 28.0\ \text{g N}$$

$$8\ \cancel{\text{mol H}} \times \frac{1.0\ \text{g H}}{1\ \cancel{\text{mol H}}} = 8.0\ \text{g H}$$

$$1\ \cancel{\text{mol C}} \times \frac{12.0\ \text{g C}}{1\ \cancel{\text{mol C}}} = 12.0\ \text{g C}$$

$$3\ \cancel{\text{mol O}} \times \frac{16.0\ \text{g O}}{1\ \cancel{\text{mol O}}} = \underline{48.0\ \text{g O}}$$

Gram formula mass of $(NH_4)_2CO_3$ = 96.0 g

Practice Problem

14. Find the gram formula mass of each of these compounds.

a. strontium cyanide, $Sr(CN)_2$

b. sodium hydrogen carbonate, $NaHCO_3$

c. aluminum sulfite, $Al_2(SO_3)_3$

Activity 6 Counting by Weighing

Purpose

To make a model of counting by weighing.

Materials

100 paper clips of the same size

a centigram balance

Procedure

1. Determine the average mass of a paper clip by weighing 25 paper clips and dividing the total mass by 25. Repeat this activity using 25 different paper clips until your average masses agree.

2. Weigh about three-fourths of your total number of paper clips. Calculate how many paper clips you weighed.

3. Count the number of paper clips in your sample.

4. Repeat steps 3 and 4 with a different sample size.

Analysis and Conclusions

1. Did the number of paper clips you counted in the sample (step 3) equal the number you calculated by weighing (step 2)? If there was not agreement, propose an explanation.

2. Explain how you would use the balance to "count out" 185 paper clips.

3. What is the advantage of using a larger sample size in step 1? What is a disadvantage?

4. How are the paper clips like atoms in this experiment?

Objective

Define the relationship between the gram formula mass and molar mass of a substance.

6.4 The Molar Mass of a Substance

In the last section you learned three new terms: gram atomic mass (gam), gram molecular mass (gmm), and gram formula mass (gfm). Each term is used to represent a mole of a particular kind of substance. The gram atomic mass of an element contains a mole of atoms. The gram molecular mass of a molecular compound contains a mole of molecules. The gram formula mass of an ionic compound contains a mole of formula units. There is nothing wrong, however, with using the term gram formula mass to refer to a mole of an element, molecular compound, or ionic compound. *However, some people use the term* **molar mass** *in place of gram formula mass to refer to the mass of a mole of any element or compound.*

Which term do you use? Consider this example. What is the gram *molecular* mass of oxygen? Is it any different from the gram *formula* mass of oxygen, O_2? In the first case the name tells us that the substance is molecular oxygen, which consists of diatomic molecules (O_2). Oxygen molecules have a gram molecular mass of 32.0 g (2 × 16.0 g). In the second question the inclusion of the appropriate chemical formula is necessary. Thus, if you are given the chemical formula, think in terms of the gram formula mass. It will work for atoms, molecules, ions, or formula units.

Table 6.2 Molar Mass Names

Specific ⟶		General
gram **a**tomic **m**ass mole of atoms	**g**ram **m**olecular **m**ass mole of molecules	**g**ram **f**ormula **m**ass mole of formula units

Concept Practice

15. List the steps you would take to calculate the molar mass of any compound.

16. What is the gram molecular mass of chlorine?

Practice Problem

17. Calculate the molar mass of each substance listed in Table 6.1.

6.5 Mole–Mass Conversions

The gram formula mass of an element or compound is used to convert grams of a substance into moles.

$$\text{grams A} \times \frac{1 \text{ mol A}}{\text{gfm A}} = \text{mol A}$$

The gram formula mass can also be used to convert moles of a substance into grams.

$$\text{mol B} \times \frac{\text{gfm B}}{1 \text{ mol B}} = \text{grams B}$$

Objective

Calculate the mass of a mole of any substance and convert between moles and mass of a substance.

Example 6 Converting Moles to Grams

How many grams are in 7.20 mol of dinitrogen trioxide?

Solution

From a known number of moles of a compound you want to calculate the unknown number of grams of the compound: mol → grams. First you need to write the formula from the given name of the substance: N_2O_3. If you calculate the gram formula mass, you will know the number of grams in 1 mol of the compound.

$$2 \cancel{\text{mol N}} \times \frac{14.0 \text{ g N}}{1 \cancel{\text{mol N}}} = 28.0 \text{ g N}$$

$$3 \cancel{\text{mol O}} \times \frac{16.0 \text{ g O}}{1 \cancel{\text{mol O}}} = 48.0 \text{ g O}$$

$$1 \text{ mol } N_2O_3 = 1 \text{ gfm } N_2O_3 = 76.0 \text{ g } N_2O_3$$

Now you can use the gram formula mass to write a conversion factor. Convert moles of N_2O_3 to grams of N_2O_3.

$$7.20 \cancel{\text{mol } N_2O_3} \times \frac{76.0 \text{ g } N_2O_3}{1.00 \cancel{\text{mol } N_2O_3}} = 547.2$$

$$= 5.47 \times 10^2 \text{ g } N_2O_3$$

The answer is rounded off to three significant figures and written in scientific notation. You should expect a relatively large number for an answer because one mole of N_2O_3 has a mass of 76.0 g and you have more than seven moles of the compound.

Integrating Agriculture

Pros and Cons of Using Fertilizers

Plants need fairly large amounts of nitrogen, sulfur, phosphorus, potassium, calcium, and magnesium as well as trace amounts of iron, boron, manganese, copper, zinc, chlorine, and molybdenum. Plants get these mineral nutrients in the form of salts dissolved in soil water. When poor soils lack adequate amounts of these minerals, fertilizers can make up the difference. However, fertilizers can damage the environment. Runoff from nitrogen fertilizers can result in the overfertilization of lakes and rivers. Now farmers are required to use nitrogen fertilizers more carefully than ever before.

Practice Problem

18. Find the mass in grams of each quantity.

a. 0.720 mol Be

b. 2.40 mol N_2

c. 10.0 mol Cr

d. 3.32 mol K

e. 4.52×10^{-3} mol $C_{20}H_{42}$

f. 0.0112 mol K_2CO_3

g. 0.160 mol H_2O_2

h. 5.08 mol $Ca(NO_3)_2$

Example 7 Converting Grams to Moles

Find the number of moles in 92.2 g of iron(III) oxide, Fe_2O_3.

Solution

From a known number of grams of a compound you want to calculate the unknown number of moles of the same compound: grams → moles.

First you calculate the gram formula mass.

$$2\ \cancel{\text{mol Fe}} \times \frac{55.8\ \text{g Fe}}{1\ \cancel{\text{mol Fe}}} = 111.6\ \text{g Fe}$$

$$3\ \cancel{\text{mol O}} \times \frac{16.0\ \text{g O}}{1\ \cancel{\text{mol O}}} = 48.0\ \text{g O}$$

$$\text{gfm } Fe_2O_3 = 159.6\ \text{g}$$

Convert the number of grams to moles of Fe_2O_3 by using the gfm as a conversion factor.

$$92.2\ \cancel{\text{g } Fe_2O_3} \times \frac{1.00\ \text{mol } Fe_2O_3}{159.6\ \cancel{\text{g } Fe_2O_3}} = 0.5776 = 0.578\ \text{mol } Fe_2O_3$$

Round the answer to three significant figures. Because the given mass is less than 159.6 g, you should expect the answer to be less than one mole.

Problem-Solving Tip

The unit of the denominator of the conversion factor must equal the unit of the given measurement.

Practice Problem

19. Find the number of moles in each quantity.

a. 5.00 g hydrogen molecules

b. 0.000 264 g Li_2HPO_4

c. 72.0 g Ar

d. 3.70×10^{-1} g B

e. 11.0 g CH_4

f. 847 g $(NH_4)_2CO_3$

g. 187 g Al

h. 333 g SnF_2

6.6 The Volume of a Mole of Gas

Objective

Convert moles to volume and volume to moles, using the volume of one mole of a gas at STP (22.4 L).

If you look at Figure 6.7 you will see that one-mole amounts of different liquid and solid substances have different volumes. For example, the volume of a mole of table sugar is much larger than that of a mole of water. The volumes of moles of gases are much more predictable.

The volume of a gas varies with a change in temperature or a change in pressure. Because of this variation, the volume of a gas is usually measured at a **standard temperature and pressure (STP)**. *Standard temperature is 0°C. Standard pressure is 101.3 kPa or 1 atmosphere (atm).* At STP, 1 mol of any gas occupies a volume of 22.4 L. Look at Figure 6.9 to get an idea of the volume occupied by 22.4 L. *This quantity, 22.4 L, is known as the* **molar volume** *of a gas and is measured at STP.* A mole of any substance contains Avogadro's number of particles. Thus, 22.4 L of any gas at STP contains 6.02×10^{23} representative particles of that gas.

Would 22.4 L of one gas also have the same mass as 22.4 L of another gas at STP? Probably not. A mole of a gas (22.4 L at STP) has a mass equal to the gram formula mass. Only gases with the same gram formula masses would have equal masses for equal volumes at STP.

Example 8 Calculating the Volume of a Gas at STP

Determine the volume, in liters, of 0.600 mol of SO_2 gas at STP.

Solution

The known is the number of moles and the unknown is the number of liters of SO_2. You know that 1.00 mol SO_2 = 22.4 L of SO_2 at STP. You can express this equality as a conversion factor and use it to convert moles to liters (mol → L).

$$0.600 \cancel{\text{mol SO}_2} \times \frac{22.4 \text{ L SO}_2}{1.00 \cancel{\text{mol SO}_2}} = 13.4 \text{ L SO}_2$$

Figure 6.9 The volume of 11 two-liter soda bottles is 22 L. The volume of one mole of any gas at STP is a little more, 22.4 L.

Example 9 Converting the Volume of a Gas to Moles

Determine the number of moles in 33.6 L of He gas at STP.

Solution

Here you want to convert liters to moles of He gas: L →mol. Again, you use a conversion factor based on the molar volume of a gas at STP.

$$33.6\ \cancel{\text{L He}} \times \frac{1.00\ \text{mol He}}{22.4\ \cancel{\text{L He}}} = 1.50\ \text{mol He}$$

Concept Practice

20. Three balloons each contain the same number of molecules of three different gases at STP. Would these balloons have the same mass or the same volume? Explain.

Practice Problems

21. What is the volume at STP of these gases?
a. 3.20×10^{-3} mol CO_2 **b.** 0.960 mol CH_4 **c.** 3.70 mol N_2

22. Assuming STP, how many moles are in these volumes?
a. 67.2 L SO_2 **b.** 0.880 L He **c.** 1.00×10^3 L C_2H_6

Objective

Calculate the gram molecular mass of a gas from density measurements of gases at STP.

6.7 Gas Density and the Gram Molecular Mass

The density of a gas is usually measured in the units g/L. The experimentally determined density of a gas at STP is used to calculate the gram formula mass of that gas. The gas can be an element, such as He, or a compound, such as CO_2.

Figure 6.10 Helium is less dense than air. Thus, balloons filled with helium are always tied to strings.

Example 10 **Calculating Molar Mass of a Gas at STP**

The density of a gaseous compound of carbon and oxygen is 1.964 g/L at STP. Determine its gram formula mass. Is the compound carbon dioxide or carbon monoxide?

Solution

At STP the gram formula mass of any gas occupies a volume of 22.4 L. You can use the density as a conversion factor to convert volume, in liters, to grams: L → g.

$$22.4\,\cancel{L} \times \frac{1.964\text{ g}}{1\,\cancel{L}} = 44.0\text{ g}$$

A volume of 22.4 L of this gas has a mass of 44.0 g. This gas has a molar mass of 44.0 g/mol. To solve the problem, you must compare this mass with the gram formula masses of carbon monoxide and carbon dioxide.

gfm CO: 12 g/mol (C) + 16 g/mol (O) = 28 g/mol

gfm CO_2: 12 g/mol (C) + 2(16 g/mol) (O) = 44 g/mol

Based on your comparison, you identify the compound as carbon dioxide.

Practice Problem

23. The densities of gases A, B, and C are 1.25 g/L, 2.86 g/L, and 0.714 g/L, respectively. Calculate the gram formula mass of each of these substances. Identify each substance as ammonia (NH_3), sulfur dioxide (SO_2), chlorine (Cl_2), nitrogen (N_2), or methane (CH_4).

6.8 Converting Between Units with Moles

Objective

Convert among measurements of mass, volume, and number of particles, using the mole.

You have now examined a mole in terms of particles, mass, and, for gas, volume at STP. Figure 6.11 summarizes these relationships and shows the importance of the mole. To change from one unit to another, you use the mole as an intermediate step. The form of the conversion factor depends on whether you are going *from* moles or *to* moles. You use the mole conversion factor in the same way you used the unit dozen to convert among mass, volume, and number of apples at the beginning of this chapter.

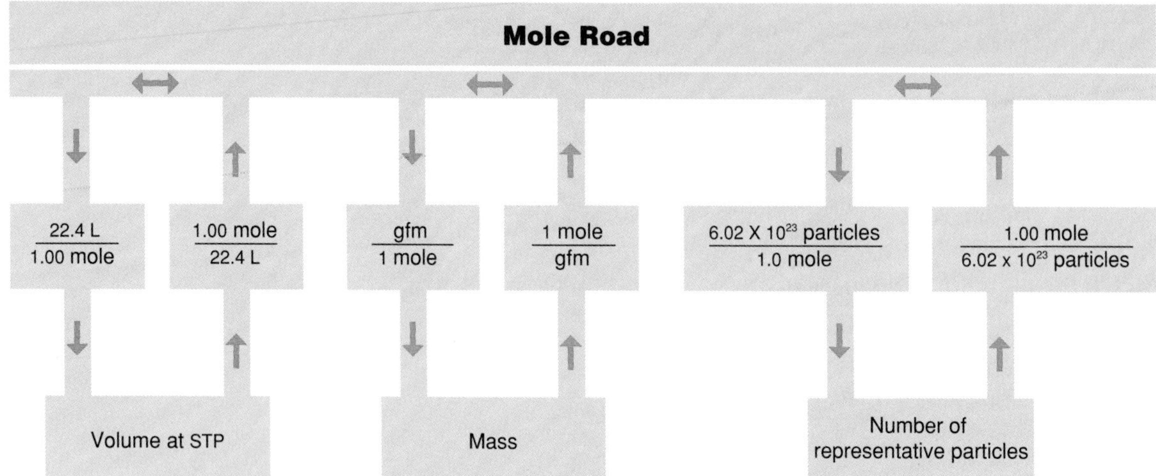

Figure 6.11 All paths lead to or from the mole road on this mole conversion roadmap.

Example 11 Calculating the Number of Atoms in a Mass

How many carbon atoms are in a 50.0-carat diamond that is pure carbon? Fifty carats is the same as 10.0 g.

Solution

Only along the mole-to-mass path does the value of the conversion factor depend on what the substance is. You want to convert from a known mass to an unknown number of atoms. Figure 6.11 shows that you will need to use moles in this process:

grams ⟶ moles ⟶ atoms (representative particles)

Starting with a given mass, you can use the gram formula mass to find the number of moles.

$$10.0\ \cancel{\text{g C}} \times \frac{1.00\ \text{mol C}}{12.0\ \cancel{\text{g C}}} = 0.833\ \text{mol C}$$

Then you can use Avogadro's number to find the number of particles, in this case atoms.

$$0.833\ \cancel{\text{mol C}} \times \frac{6.02 \times 10^{23}\ \text{atoms C}}{1.00\ \cancel{\text{mol C}}} = 5.02 \times 10^{23}\ \text{atoms C}$$

You can also set up the problem in "one solution."

$$10.0\ \cancel{\text{gram C}} \times \frac{1.00\ \cancel{\text{mol C}}}{12.0\ \cancel{\text{g C}}} \times \frac{6.02 \times 10^{23}\ \text{atoms C}}{1.00\ \cancel{\text{mol C}}} = 5.02 \times 10^{23}\ \text{atoms C}$$

Problem-Solving Tip

Check that the answer has the correct unit after canceling and before doing the numerical calculations.

Concept Practice

24. Write a conversion factor to convert between these units.
a. moles of Ar to grams of Ar
b. liters of F_2 (at STP) to mol of F_2
c. molecules of NO_2 to mol of NO_2

25. Consider the problem, "How many apples are in 30 kg of apples?" Explain the similarities between the solution of this problem and the solution of Example 11.

Practice Problems

26. What is the mass in grams of an atom of mercury (Hg)?

27. How many molecules are in a 9.00-L balloon (at STP) filled with carbon dioxide? Would your answer change if the gas was carbon monoxide? Explain your answer.

6.9 Calculating Percent Composition

Objective

Calculate the percent composition of a substance from its chemical formula or experimental data.

The amount of fertilizer that you put on the grass in your yard or on plants in your garden is important. The relative amount, or the percentage, of each nutrient in the fertilizer is also important. In the spring you may use a fertilizer that has a relatively high percentage of nitrogen, which "greens" your plants. In the fall you may use a fertilizer with a higher percentage of potassium to strengthen the root system of the plants. Thus, it is sometimes useful or important to know the relative amounts of the components of a mixture or compound.

When you make a new compound in the laboratory, you need to determine its formula. One of the first steps in doing this is to find the relative amounts of the elements in the compound. *These relative amounts are expressed as the* **percent composition**, *the percent*

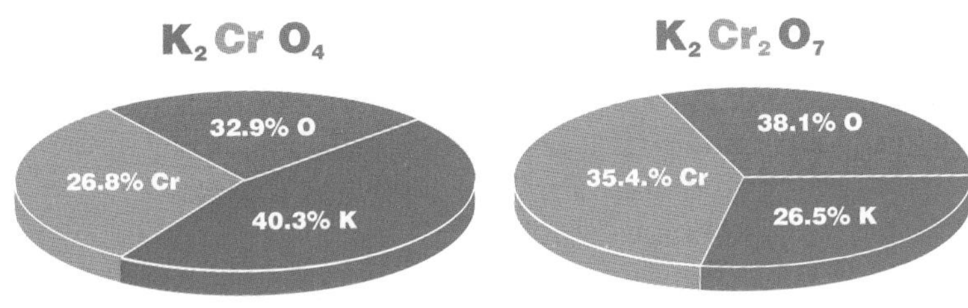

Figure 6.12 Potassium chromate, K_2CrO_4, is composed of 40.3% potassium, 26.8% chromium, and 32.9% oxygen. How does this differ from the percent composition of potassium dichromate, $K_2Cr_2O_7$?

Integrating Geology

Mining of Metal Ores

When a new source of metal ore is discovered, geologists evaluate it to see if it can be mined profitably. They determine the percentage of the mineral present in the ore and also the percentage of metal in the mineral compound. Most ores mined today contain very small percentages of metal. Thus metallurgists continually look for cheaper, more efficient ways to process these low-grade ores. All ores contain huge amounts of waste rock. Even after the metal has been separated from the concentrated ore, more wastes remain. Proper disposal of this useless material is a problem. In the past, mine operators dumped wastes wherever they chose. Today, however, such mining activities are regulated by federal and state laws.

by mass of each element in a compound. The percent composition of a compound has as many percent values as there are different elements in the compound. The percent composition of $K_2Cr_2O_7$ is K = 26.5%, Cr = 35.4%, and O = 38.1%. These percentages must add up to 100% (26.5% + 35.4% + 38.1% = 100%).

The percent by mass of an element in a compound is the number of grams of the element divided by the grams of the compound, multiplied by 100%.

$$\% \text{ mass of element E} = \frac{\text{grams of element E}}{\text{grams of compound}} \times 100\%$$

Example 12 Finding the Percent Composition of a Compound

An 8.20-g piece of magnesium combines completely with 5.40 g of oxygen to form a compound. What is the percent composition of this compound?

Solution

Since you know the mass of each element, you can add them to find the mass of the compound.

$$8.20 \text{ g} + 5.40 \text{ g} = 13.60 \text{ g}$$

Now you divide the mass of each element by the mass of the compound and multiply by 100%.

$$\% \text{ Mg} = \frac{\text{mass of Mg}}{\text{mass of compound}} \times 100\% = \frac{8.20 \text{ g}}{13.6 \text{ g}} \times 100\%$$

$$= 60.3\%$$

$$\% \text{ O} = \frac{\text{mass of O}}{\text{mass of compound}} \times 100\% = \frac{5.40 \text{ g}}{13.6 \text{ g}} \times 100\%$$

$$= 39.7\%$$

Check to be sure that the percentages of the elements add up to 100%: 60.3% + 39.7% = 100%

Practice Problem

28. Calculate the percent composition of the compounds that are formed from these reactions.

a. 9.03 g of Mg combine completely with 3.48 g of N.
b. 29.0 g of Ag combine completely with 4.30 g of S.
c. 222.6 g of Na combine completely with 77.4 g of O.

Occasionally you may want to calculate the percent composition of a known compound. To do this, you use the chemical formula to calculate the gram formula mass. This gives you the mass of one mole of the compound. Then for each element, you calculate the percent by mass in one mole of the compound. To calculate the percent by mass you divide the mass of each element in one mole of the compound by the gram formula mass and multiply this by 100%.

$$\%\ \text{mass} = \frac{\text{grams of element in 1 mol of compound}}{\text{gfm of compound}} \times 100\%$$

The subscripts in the formula of the compound are used to calculate the grams of each particular element in a mole of that compound.

Example 13 Finding the Percent Composition of a Compound

Calculate the percent composition of propane, C_3H_8.

Solution

Given the formula, you can calculate the percent composition by using the gram formula mass:

$$\text{formula} \longrightarrow \text{gfm} \longrightarrow \%\ \text{composition}$$

First calculate the gram formula mass of propane.

$$3\ \cancel{\text{mol C}} \times \frac{12.0\ \text{g C}}{1\ \cancel{\text{mol C}}} = 36.0\ \text{g C}$$

$$8\ \cancel{\text{mol H}} \times \frac{1.0\ \text{g H}}{1\ \cancel{\text{mol H}}} = 8.0\ \text{g H}$$

$$\text{Gram formula mass of } C_3H_8 = 44.0\ \text{g.}$$

Now the percent by mass for each element can be calculated. The mass of each element is divided by the mass of the compound and multiplied by 100%.

$$\%\ \text{C} = \frac{\text{grams of C}}{\text{gfm of } C_3H_8} \times 100\% = \frac{36.0\ \cancel{\text{g}}}{44.0\ \cancel{\text{g}}} \times 100\% = 81.8\%\ \text{C}$$

$$\%\ \text{H} = \frac{\text{grams of H}}{\text{gfm of } C_3H_8} \times 100\% = \frac{8.0\ \cancel{\text{g}}}{44.0\ \cancel{\text{g}}} \times 100\% = 18.2\%\ \text{H}$$

Check to be sure that the percentages of the elements add up to 100%: 81.8% + 18.2% = 100%.

Practice Problem

29. Calculate the percent composition of each of these five compounds.

a. ethane, C_2H_6

b. sodium bisulfate, $NaHSO_4$

c. calcium acetate, $Ca(C_2H_3O_2)_2$

d. hydrogen cyanide, HCN

e. water, H_2O

You can use percent composition to calculate the number of grams of an element in a specific amount of a compound. To do this, you multiply the mass of the compound by a conversion factor that is based on the percent composition.

Figure 6.13 Lawn and garden fertilizers are labeled with three numbers. These numbers represent the mass percent of the elements nitrogen, phosphorus, and potassium, respectively. One hundred kilograms of a 16-16-16 fertilizer would contain 16 kg of nitrogen (as N), 16 kg of phosphorus (as P_2O_5), and 16 kg of potassium (as K_2O).

Example 14 Finding the Mass of an Element in Given Mass of a Compound

Calculate the mass of carbon in 82.0 g of propane, C_3H_8.

Solution

Given the number of grams of propane, C_3H_8, you want to calculate the number of grams of carbon, C:

$$\text{grams } C_3H_8 \longrightarrow \text{grams C}$$

Use a conversion factor based on the percent by mass of carbon in ethane. From Example 13 you know that the percent composition of propane is 81.8% C and 18.2% H. Remember that 81.8% C means 81.8 g of C per 100 g of C_3H_8.

$$82 \text{ g } C_3H_8 \times \frac{81.8 \text{ g C}}{100 \text{ g } C_3H_8} = 67.1 \text{ g C}$$

Practice Problem

30. Using the results of Problem 29, calculate the amount of hydrogen in the following amounts of these compounds.

a. 350 g C_2H_6

b. 20.2 g $NaHSO_4$

c. 124 g $Ca(C_2H_3O_2)_2$

d. 378 g HCN

e. 100 g H_2O

6.B Historical Notebook

Saltmaking

Currently, many people are concerned with reducing the amount of salt in their diets. Nevertheless, some salt is essential to the health of humans and animals. However, salt hasn't always been plentiful.

Because of its relative scarcity, salt had great value historically. Making salt was one of the world's first mineral industries. The Chinese had a vigorous saltmaking industry by A.D. 200. Likewise, early saltmaking took place in Japan and parts of the Middle East. Herodotus, a Greek author of the fourth century B.C., described connecting routes used by traders between salt oases of the Libyan desert. Cakes of salt were used as money in Ethiopia and other parts of Africa. Roman soldiers were given an allotment of salt as part of their pay. The English word "salary" comes from the Latin name *salarium,* as this Roman salt allotment was called. If someone says you are "worth your salt," it means that your work is worthy of the salary you get, or what you are paid.

How people made salt depended on its source, but the methods were almost always quite simple. The most extensive source of salt is the oceans. About 78% of the dissolved solids in seawater is sodium chloride. Early saltmaking in coastal regions probably consisted of letting seawater fill pools. The salt was collected after the sun evaporated the water. Some inland regions have natural salt lakes, such as the Dead Sea, or brine wells. Brine is a salt solution of high concentration. People in these regions used solar evaporation or heated the brines to drive away water and obtain fairly pure salt. Other parts of the world contain beds of salt that may be many meters thick. People have mined these beds extensively for many centuries.

Figure 6.14 Seawater has long been a major source of salt. Seawater is trapped in small ponds where the sun evaporates away the water, leaving behind the salt.

Today's methods for obtaining salt are about the same as they have always been, except for the modern use of salt mines. Geologic structures called salt domes consist of halite, the mineral name for rock salt. Salt domes may be more than 1 kilometer across and at fairly shallow depths below the earth's surface.

Table salt may have a compound such as magnesium silicate added to prevent caking. Potassium iodide may also be added. This "iodized" salt prevents goiter, a swelling of the thyroid gland.

Think About It

31. Compare Why has salt been highly valued throughout history?

32. Infer What evidence have you seen in the advertising for food products that affirms the need to moderate salt consumption?

Objective

Derive the empirical formula of a compound from experimental data.

Roots of Words

empeirikos: (Greek) based on experiment alone

empirical formula a formula with the lowest whole-number ratio of elements in a compound. The empirical formula of hydrogen peroxide, H_2O_2, is HO.

6.10 Calculating Empirical Formulas

Once you make a new compound in the laboratory, you can usually determine its percent composition experimentally. Then, from the percent composition data, you can calculate the empirical formula of the compound. *The* **empirical formula** *gives the lowest whole-number ratio of the atoms of the elements in a compound.* For example, a compound may have the empirical formula CO. The empirical formula is valuable information because it tells the kinds and relative count (atoms or moles of atoms) in molecules or formula units of a compound. As you can see in Figure 6.15, empirical formulas may be interpreted at the microscopic (atoms) or macroscopic (moles of atoms) level.

If you use the mole interpretation, an empirical formula is the lowest whole-number ratio of moles of atoms that combine to form a compound. An empirical formula may or may not be the same as a molecular formula. If they are different, the molecular formula is a simple multiple of the empirical formula.

For carbon dioxide, the empirical and molecular formulas are the same, CO_2. Dinitrogen tetrahydride, whose molecular formula is N_2H_4, has an empirical formula of NH_2 because this is the simplest ratio of nitrogen to hydrogen in the compound. Figure 6.16 shows one of two compounds of carbon that have the same empirical formula but different molecular formulas.

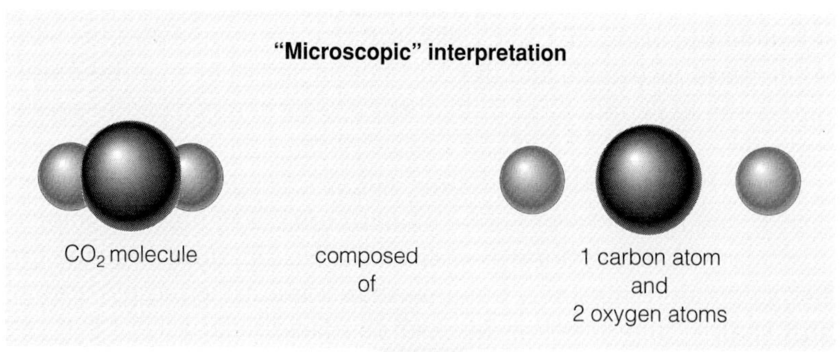
"Microscopic" interpretation
CO_2 molecule
composed of
1 carbon atom and 2 oxygen atoms
CO_2
"Macroscopic" interpretation
1 mol of CO_2 molecules
composed of
6.02×10^{23} carbon atoms (1 mol of C atoms)
and
$2 \times (6.02 \times 10^{23})$ oxygen atoms (2 mol of O atoms)

Figure 6.15 A formula can be interpreted on a microscopic level in terms of atoms or on a macroscopic level in terms of moles of atoms.

Example 15 Determining the Empirical Formula of a Compound

What is the empirical formula of a compound that is 25.9% nitrogen and 74.1% oxygen?

Solution

The unknown is the empirical formula. You want to calculate the lowest whole-number ratio of moles of nitrogen atoms to oxygen atoms. The known is the percent composition. This tells you the ratio of masses of nitrogen to oxygen in the compound. Suppose you have 100.0 g of the compound. In 100.0 g of the compound there are 25.9 g N and 74.1 g O.

You can change the ratio of *masses* to a ratio of *moles* by using conversion factors based on the gram atomic mass of each element (1 mol = gam).

$$25.9\,\cancel{\text{g N}} \times \frac{1\text{ mol N}}{14.0\,\cancel{\text{g N}}} = 1.85\text{ mol N}$$

$$74.1\,\cancel{\text{g O}} \times \frac{1\text{ mol O}}{16.0\,\cancel{\text{g O}}} = 4.63\text{ mol O}$$

You now know the mole ratio of nitrogen to oxygen: $N_{1.85}O_{4.63}$. This is not the correct empirical formula because it is not the lowest whole-number ratio. You can get the correct values by dividing both molar quantities by the smaller number of moles. This will give you a "1" for the element with the smaller number of moles. This step may not give you whole numbers for the other elements, though.

$$\frac{1.85\text{ mol N}}{1.85} = 1\text{ mol N}$$

$$\frac{4.63\text{ mol O}}{1.85} = 2.50\text{ mol O}$$

Is the final answer $N_1O_{2.5}$? No, because this is still not the lowest *whole*-number ratio. You must now multiply each part of the ratio by a number (in this case 2) to convert the fraction to a whole number.

$$1\text{ mol N} \times 2 = 2\text{ mol N}$$

$$2.5\text{ mol O} \times 2 = 5\text{ mol O}$$

The empirical formula is N_2O_5. To be sure that this is the empirical formula, check the subscripts. If they are whole numbers, it is the empirical formula.

Figure 6.16 Ethyne, C_2H_2, also called acetylene, is a gas used in welders' torches. Benzene, C_6H_6, is a flammable liquid. These two compounds have the same empirical formula.

Concept Practice

33. Which of the following molecular formulas are also empirical formulas?

a. ribose, $C_5H_{10}O_5$, sugar molecule in RNA

b. ethyl butanoate, $C_6H_{12}O_2$, a compound with the odor of pineapple

c. chlorophyll, $C_{55}H_{72}MgN_4O_5$, part of photosynthesis

d. DEET, $C_{12}H_{17}ON$, an insect repellent

e. oxalic acid, $H_2C_2O_4$, found in spinach and tea

Practice Problems

34. Calculate the empirical formula of each compound with the following percent composition.

a. 94.1% O, 5.9% H

b. 79.9% C, 20.1% H

c. 67.6% Hg, 10.8% S, 21.6% O

d. 27.59% C, 1.15% H, 16.09% N, 55.17% O

e. 17.6% Na, 39.7% Cr, 42.7% O

35. Calculate the empirical formula for each compound in Problem 28 without using the percent composition.

Objective

Derive the molecular formula of a compound from experimental data.

6.11 Calculating Molecular Formulas

Consider the two series of compounds in Table 6.3. Ethyne and benzene have the same empirical formula, CH. Glucose, ethanoic acid, and methanal all have the same empirical formula, CH_2O, but the compounds have different gram formula masses. These gram formula masses are simple whole-number multiples of the gram formula mass of the empirical formula, CH_2O. The molecular formula of a compound is either the same as its experimentally determined empirical formula, or it is some simple whole-number multiple of it.

You can determine the molecular formula of a compound if you know its empirical formula and its gram formula mass. From the empirical formula you can calculate the empirical formula mass. This is simply the gram formula mass of the empirical formula. The known gram formula mass is then divided by the empirical formula mass. This gives the number of empirical formula units in a molecule of the compound and is the multiplier to convert the empirical formula to the molecular formula.

Table 6.3 Comparison of Empirical and Molecular Formulas

Formula (name)	Classification of formula	Gram formula mass
CH	Empirical	13
C_2H_2 (ethyne)	Molecular	26 (2 × 13)
C_6H_6 (benzene)	Molecular	78 (6 × 13)
CH_2O (methanol)	Empirical and molecular	30
$C_2H_4O_2$ (ethanoic acid)	Molecular	60 (2 × 30)
$C_6H_{12}O_6$ (glucose)	Molecular	180 (6 × 30)

Example 16 Finding the Molecular Formula of a Compound

Calculate the molecular formulas of the following compounds.

	Gram formula mass	Empirical formula
a.	60 g	CH_4N
b.	78 g	NaO
c.	181.5 g	C_2HCl

Solution

First calculate the empirical formula mass (efm). Then divide the empirical formula mass (emf) into the gram formula mass (gfm). It takes this many of the empirical formula units to make up the molecular formula of the compound.

	Empirical formula	efm	gfm/efm	Molecular formula
a.	CH_4N	30	$\frac{60}{30} = 2$	$C_2H_8N_2$
b.	NaO	39	$\frac{78}{39} = 2$	Na_2O_2
c.	C_2HCl	60.5	$\frac{181.5}{60.5} = 3$	$C_6H_3Cl_3$

Practice Problems

36. The compound methyl butanoate smells like apples. Its percent composition is 58.8% C, 9.8% H, and 31.4% O. If its gram molecular mass is 102 g/mol, what is its molecular formula?

37. You find that 7.36 g of a compound has decomposed to give 6.93 g of oxygen. The rest of the compound is hydrogen. If the molecular mass of the compound is 34.0 g/mol, what is its molecular formula?

Chapter 6 Review

Chemical Quantities

Key Terms

Avogadro's number *6.2*
empirical formula *6.10*
gram atomic mass (gam) *6.3*
gram formula mass (gfm) *6.3*
gram molecular mass (gmm) *6.3*
molar mass *6.4*
molar volume *6.6*
mole (mol) *6.2*
percent composition *6.9*
representative particle *6.2*
standard temperature and pressure (STP) *6.6*

Chapter Summary

The SI unit that measures the amount of substance is the mole. A mole of any substance is composed of Avogadro's number (6.02×10^{23}) of representative particles. The representative particle of most elements is the atom. A molecule is the representative particle of diatomic elements and molecular compounds. The representative particle of ionic compounds is a formula unit.

The mass of an atom, molecule, or formula unit expressed in grams is its gram formula mass. One gram formula mass of any substance is a mole. One mole of any substance contains the same number of representative particles as one mole of any other substance. Thus, one gfm of any substance contains 6.02×10^{23} representative particles of that substance.

If you want to determine the number of moles of a gas, it may be easier to measure its volume than its mass. One mole of any gas at STP (1 atm pressure and 0°C) occupies a volume of 22.4 L.

The percent composition is the percent by mass of each element in a compound. An empirical formula is the simplest whole-number ratio of atoms of the elements in the compound. An empirical formula can be calculated from a compound's percent composition. A molecular formula will be the same as, or some simple multiple of, an empirical formula. For example, dinitrogen tetroxide has the empirical formula NO_2 and the molecular formula N_2O_4.

Practice Questions and Problems

38. List three common ways in which matter is measured, giving examples of each. *6.1*

39. Name the basic SI unit that measures the "amount of substance." *6.1*

40. Name the representative particle (atom, molecule, or formula unit) of each of the following substances. *6.2*
a. oxygen
b. sodium sulfide
c. sulfur dioxide
d. potassium

41. How many hydrogen atoms are in a representative particle of each of these substances? *6.2*
a. $Al(OH)_3$ **c.** $(NH_4)_2HPO_4$
b. $H_2C_2O_4$ **d.** $C_4H_{10}O$

42. Which contains more molecules: 1.00 mol H_2O_2, 1.00 mol C_2H_6, or 1.00 mol CO? *6.2*

43. Which contains more atoms: 1.00 mol H_2O_2, 1.00 mol C_2H_6, or 1.00 mol CO? *6.2*

44. Find the number of representative particles in each of these substances. *6.2*
a. 3.00 mol Sn **c.** 7.50 mol SO_2
b. 0.400 mol KCl **d.** 4.80×10^{-3} mol NaI

45. How many moles is each of the following? *6.2*
a. 1.50×10^{23} molecules NH_3
b. 1 billion (1×10^9) molecules O_2
c. 6.02×10^{22} molecules Br_2
d. 4.81×10^{24} atoms Li

46. Calculate the gram formula mass of each of these substances. *6.3*
a. H_3PO_4 **c.** $CaCO_3$ **e.** $C_4H_9O_2$
b. N_2O_3 **d.** $(NH_4)_2SO_4$ **f.** Br_2

47. Calculate the mass of 1.00 mol of each of these substances. *6.3*
a. SiO_2 **c.** $Fe(OH)_3$
b. N_2 **d.** Cu

48. How many moles is each of the following? *6.5*
- **a.** 15.5 g SiO_2
- **b.** 0.0688 g AgCl
- **c.** 79.3 g Cl_2
- **d.** 5.96 g KOH
- **e.** 937 g $Ca(C_2H_3O_2)_2$
- **f.** 0.800 g Ca

49. Find the mass of each of these amounts of substances. *6.5*
- **a.** 1.50 mol C_5H_{12}
- **b.** 14.4 mol F_2
- **c.** 0.780 mol $Ca(CN)_2$
- **d.** 7.00 mol H_2O_2
- **e.** 5.60 mol NaOH
- **f.** 3.21×10^{-2} mol Ni

50. Calculate the volume of each of these gases at STP. *6.6*
- **a.** 7.6 mol Ar
- **b.** 0.44 mol C_2H_6
- **c.** 1.20 mol O_2

51. What is the density of each of these gases at STP? *6.7*
- **a.** C_3H_8 **b.** Ne **c.** NO_2

52. Find each of the following quantities. *6.8*
- **a.** the volume in liters of 835 g of SO_3 (STP)
- **b.** the mass in grams of a molecule of aspirin, $C_9H_8O_4$
- **c.** the number of atoms in 5.78 mol NH_4NO_3
- **d.** the number of molecules in 60.0 g of NO_2
- **e.** the volume in liters of 3.24×10^{22} molecules Cl_2 (STP)
- **f.** the mass in grams of 18.0 L of CH_4 (STP)

53. Calculate the percent composition of each of these compounds. *6.9*
- **a.** H_2S
- **b.** $(NH_4)_2C_2O_4$
- **c.** $Mg(OH)_2$
- **d.** Na_3PO_4

54. Using your answers from Problem 53, calculate the number of grams of these elements. *6.9*
- **a.** sulfur in 3.54 g of H_2S
- **b.** nitrogen in 25.0 g of $(NH_4)_2C_2O_4$
- **c.** magnesium in 97.4 g of $Mg(OH)_2$
- **d.** phosphorus in 804 g of Na_3PO_4

55. Which of the following compounds has the highest iron content? *6.9*
- **a.** $FeCl_2$
- **b.** $Fe(C_2H_3O_2)_3$
- **c.** $Fe(OH)_2$
- **d.** FeO

56. Find the empirical formula of each compound from its percent composition. *6.10*
- **a.** 65.2% Sc and 34.8% O
- **b.** 72.4% Fe and 27.6% O
- **c.** 52.8% Sn, 12.4% Fe, 16.0% C, and 18.8% N

57. Classify each of these formulas as an empirical or a molecular formula. *6.11*
- **a.** S_2Cl_2
- **b.** $C_6H_{10}O_4$
- **c.** Na_2SO_3
- **d.** $C_5H_{10}O_5$
- **e.** $C_{17}H_{19}NO_3$
- **f.** $(NH_4)_2CO_3$

58. What is the molecular formula of each of these compounds? Each compound's empirical formula and gram formula mass is given. *6.11*
- **a.** CH_2O, 90 g/mol
- **b.** HgCl, 472.2 g/mol
- **c.** $C_3H_5O_2$, 146 g/mol

59. Determine the molecular formula of each of these compounds. *6.11*
- **a.** 94.1% O and 5.9% H; gfm = 34 g
- **b.** 40.0% C, 53.4% O, and 6.6% H; gfm = 120 g
- **c.** 54.5% C, 13.6% H, and 31.8% N; gfm = 88 g

Mastery Questions and Problems

60. Make a concept map using the term mole as the central concept. Include as many chapter key terms as you can as well as the quantities 6.02×10^{23} and 22.4.

61. Which of the following contains the largest number of atoms?
- **a.** 82.0 g Kr
- **b.** 0.842 mol C_2H_4
- **c.** 36.0 g N_2

62. What is the total mass of a mixture of 3.50×10^{22} formula units of Na_2SO_4, 0.500 mol of H_2O, and 7.23 g of AgCl?

63. An imaginary "atomic balance" is shown below. Fifteen atoms of boron on the left side of the balance are being balanced by six atoms of the unknown element E on the right side.
- **a.** What is the atomic mass of element E?
- **b.** What is the identity of element E?

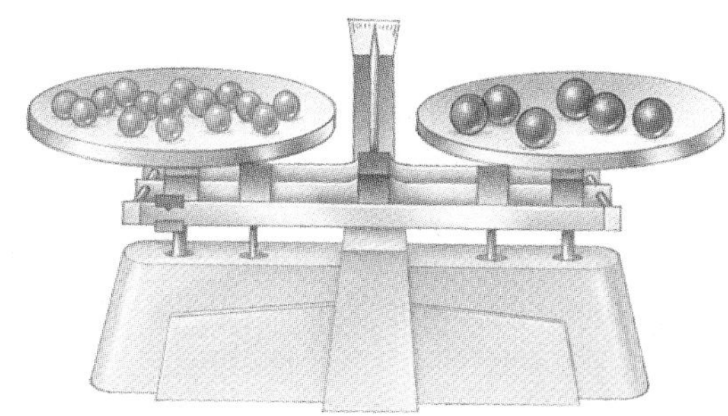

64. Explain what is wrong with each of the following statements.

a. One mole of any substance contains the same number of atoms.

b. The gram atomic mass of a compound is the atomic mass expressed in grams.

c. One gram molecular mass of CO_2 contains Avogadro's number of atoms.

65. Determine the empirical formula of each of these compounds.

a. 42.9% C and 57.1% O

b. 32.00% C, 42.66% O, 18.67% N, and 6.67% H

c. 71.72% Cl, 16.16% O, and 12.12% C

66. A typical virus particle is 5×10^{-6} cm in diameter. If Avogadro's number of these virus particles were laid in a row, how many kilometers long would the line be?

67. How many formula units of aluminum oxide, Al_2O_3, can be made from 90 aluminum ions and 90 oxide ions?

68. Calculate the empirical formula of each of these compounds.

a. The compound consists of 0.40 mol of Cu per 0.80 mol of Br.

b. The compound has 4 atoms of carbon for each 12 atoms of hydrogen.

69. What blood level of lead in micrograms per deciliter of blood requires medical treatment for lead poisoning? How many moles of lead are in that many micrograms?

Critical Thinking Questions

70. Choose the term that best completes the second relationship.

a. dozen: eggs mole: ____

(1) atoms (2) 6.02×10^{23}
(3) size (4) grams

b. gam: element gmm: ____

(1) formula unit (2) molecule
(3) ionic compound (4) molecular compound

c. mole: Avogadro's number molar volume: ____

(1) mole (2) water
(3) STP (4) 22.4 L

71. How are the empirical and molecular formulas of a compound related?

72. Why does one mole of carbon have a smaller mass than one mole of sulfur? How are the atomic structures of these elements different?

73. One mole of any gas at STP is equal to 22.4 L of that gas. It is also true that atoms of different elements have different atomic volumes, or diameters. How can you reconcile these two statements?

Cumulative Review

74. How many protons, electrons, and neutrons are in each of these isotopes?

a. zirconium-90 **c.** bromine-81
b. palladium-108 **d.** antimony-123

75. How many moles is 14.5 cm^3 of platinum? The density of platinum is 21.45 g/cm^3.

76. How does a molecule differ from an atom?

77. Do each of these conversions.

a. 4.72 g to mg

b. 2.7×10^3 cm/s to km/h

c. 4.4 mm to decimeters

78. Name these compounds.

a. $Fe(OH)_3$ **c.** Na_2CO_3
b. NH_4I **d.** CCl_4

79. Write formulas for these compounds.

a. potassium nitrate **c.** magnesium nitride
b. copper(II) oxide **d.** silver fluoride

Challenge Questions and Problems

80. Nitroglycerine contains 60% as many carbon atoms as hydrogen atoms, three times as many oxygen atoms as nitrogen atoms, and the same number of carbon and nitrogen atoms. The number of moles in a gram of nitroglycerine is 0.00441. What is the molecular formula?

81. Dry air is about 20.95% oxygen by volume. Assuming STP, how many oxygen molecules are in a 75.0-g sample of air? The density of air is 1.19 g/L.

82. The following table gives the gram formula mass (gfm) and density of seven gases at STP.

a. Plot these data, with density on the x axis.

b. What is the slope of the straight line plot?

c. What is the gfm of a gas at STP that has a density of 1.10 g/L?

d. A mole of a gas at STP weighs 56.0 g. Use the graph to determine the density of this gas.

Substance	Gram formula mass (gfm)	Density (g/l)
Oxygen	32.0	1.43
Carbon dioxide	44.0	1.96
Ethane	30.0	1.34
Hydrogen	2.00	0.0893
Sulfur dioxide	64.1	2.86
Ammonia	17.0	0.759
Fluorine	38.0	1.70

83. The element gold has properties that have made it much sought after through the ages. A cubic meter of ocean water contains 6×10^{-6} g gold. If the total mass of the water in the oceans of the world is 4×10^{20} kg, how many kilograms of gold are distributed throughout the oceans? (Assume that the density of seawater is 1 g/cm^3.) How many liters of seawater would have to be processed to recover a kilogram of gold (which has a value of about $11,000 at 1993 prices)? Do you think this recovery operation is feasible?

84. Have you ever wondered how Avogadro's number was determined? Actually, Avogadro's number has been determined independently by about 20 different methods. In one approach, Avogadro's number is calculated from the volume of a film of a fatty acid floating on water. In another method it is determined by comparing the electric charge of an electron to the electric charge of a mole of electrons. In a third method the spacing between ions in an ionic substance can be determined by using a technique called X-ray diffraction. In the X-ray diffraction of sodium chloride, it has been determined that the distance between adjacent Na^+ and Cl^- ions is 2.819×10^{-8} cm. The density of solid sodium chloride is 2.165 g/cm^3. By calculating the gram formula mass to four significant figures, you can determine Avogadro's number. What value do you obtain?

Connections Questions

85. List some of Avogadro's scientific contributions.

86. List four major and four minor nutrients that plants need for healthy growth.

87. What is a negative aspect of processing low-grade mineral ores?

Write About Chemistry

88. Write a paragraph that illustrates the magnitude of Avogadro's number.

89. Write a short poem about the SI unit, the mole.

90. Imagine that you have just tasted salt for the first time. Write a letter to a friend telling what it was like.

Readings and References

Barnwell, George M. "Salt-Gradient Solar Ponds." *ChemMatters* (December 1989), pp. 12–15.

Cook, James L. *Conversion Factors.* Oxford: Oxford University Press, 1991.

Glover, Daniel and Kenneth Kolb. "The Margarine Puzzle." *ChemMatters* (October 1990), p. 16.

7 Chemical Reactions

Goals

- Rewrite chemical equations from descriptions of chemical reactions.
- Apply the rules for balancing chemical equations.
- Categorize chemical reactions by type.

The largest barbecue on record served more than 50,000 people. Charcoal briquettes fuel barbecues through the combustion of carbon. Combustion is one of many types of chemical reactions.

Concept Overview

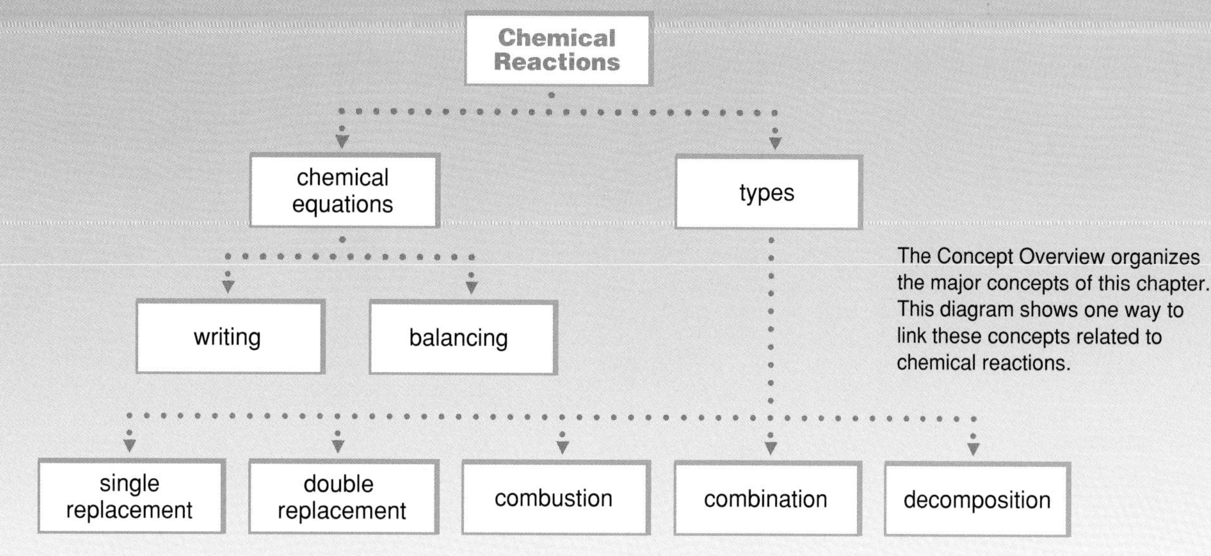

The Concept Overview organizes the major concepts of this chapter. This diagram shows one way to link these concepts related to chemical reactions.

A dynamite explosion blasts rock loose in a quarry. A rush of hot air from a propane burner keeps a hot-air balloon aloft. Oil and natural gas are converted into phonograph records, detergents, rubber tires, and many other consumer items. All of these events involve chemical reactions.

In Chapter 5 you learned the vocabulary of chemistry by writing chemical formulas and naming chemical compounds. You will now use this vocabulary to write chemical sentences called chemical equations. Chemical equations describe chemical reactions. To conform to the law of conservation of mass, equations must be balanced. While practicing your skills in balancing equations, you will learn about five general types of reactions. Knowing these reaction types will allow you to predict what will happen when substances undergo a chemical change.

7.1 Chemical Reactions

Objective

Identify the reactants and products in a chemical reaction.

Every minute of the day chemical reactions are taking place both *in* you and *around* you. After a meal, as your body digests food, a whole series of complex chemical reactions take place. The foods that you rely on for your diet, fruits, vegetables, and grains, are continually being replenished. Plants use sunlight to drive the photosynthetic processes that lead to plant growth. The chemical

Figure 7.1 The ingredients used for baking are reactants. They undergo physical and chemical changes and combine to form the product, in this case blueberry muffins.

reactions involved in photosynthesis are quite different from those involved in digestion. All of these chemical reactions are necessary to sustain life.

Not all chemical reactions involve living things directly. One useful chemical reaction takes place in a car battery. The reaction produces the energy necessary to start a car. At the same time, an undesirable chemical reaction happens between the iron in the car fender and the oxygen in the air. This reaction produces rust. Cooking food, such as baking muffins from the ingredients shown in Figure 7.1, always involves chemical reactions. All chemical reactions, whether simple or complex, desirable or undesirable, involve changing substances. One or more substances, the reactants, change into one or more new substances, the products. In writing reactions you separate the reactants from the products by writing an arrow (→). The arrow means "yields" or "reacts to produce."

$$\text{Reactants} \rightarrow \text{products}$$

An explanation for the way in which substances change in a chemical reaction was proposed by John Dalton in his atomic theory. This explanation holds true today. In a chemical reaction the ways in which atoms are joined together are changed. As reactants are converted to products, bonds that hold atoms together are broken and new bonds are formed. The atoms themselves are neither created nor destroyed. This part of Dalton's theory explains the law of conservation of mass. In any physical or chemical change mass is neither created nor destroyed. The atoms in the products are the same atoms that were in the reactants. They are just arranged differently.

Chemical reactions can be described in different ways. For the example of rusting you could say: "Iron reacts with oxygen to produce iron(III) oxide (rust)." Alternatively, you could identify the reactants and product in this reaction by writing a word equation.

$$\text{Iron} + \text{oxygen} \rightarrow \text{iron(III) oxide}$$

In a word equation, the reactants are written on the left, and the products are written on the right. Notice that the two reactants are separated by a plus sign. Had there been two or more products, they would also be separated by a plus sign.

Another example of a simple chemical reaction involves hydrogen peroxide, a common antiseptic. When you pour hydrogen peroxide on an open cut, bubbles of oxygen gas rapidly form. The production of the gas is visible evidence of a chemical change. A new substance, a gas, is produced. Actually, two substances are produced in this reaction, oxygen gas and water. The statement "hydrogen peroxide reacts to form water and oxygen gas" describes this reaction. You write the word equation as follows.

$$\text{Hydrogen peroxide} \rightarrow \text{water} + \text{oxygen}$$

Methane is the major component of natural gas, a common fuel for residential heating. When methane is burned to produce energy, a chemical reaction occurs. The word equation for this reaction must include all the reactants and products. Burning typically requires oxygen. The products of this chemical reaction are water and carbon dioxide. You write the word equation as follows.

$$\text{Methane} + \text{oxygen} \rightarrow \text{carbon dioxide} + \text{water}$$

Concept Practice

1. What are the functions of an arrow (→) and a plus sign (+) in a chemical equation?

2. Write word equations for the following chemical reactions.
a. Pure copper can be produced by heating copper(II) sulfide with oxygen. Sulfur dioxide is also produced in this reaction.
b. Water is formed by the explosive reaction between hydrogen and oxygen.
c. When baking soda (sodium hydrogen carbonate) is heated it decomposes, forming sodium carbonate, carbon dioxide, and water.

Integrating Biology

Hydrogen Peroxide

Why does hydrogen peroxide decompose to water and oxygen when the peroxide comes into contact with blood? The enzyme catalase, found in living cells, catalyzes the breakdown of hydrogen peroxide. An enzyme is a biological catalyst. Catalase is a protein that contains an iron(II) ion at its center. The iron(II) ion is the actual place on the catalase molecule that catalyzes the decomposition of hydrogen peroxide. By pouring peroxide on a cut, you bring it into contact with the iron(II) ions of catalase. This assures rapid destruction of the peroxide. Energetic oxygen atoms formed in the decomposition reaction are thought to produce the antiseptic effect of the hydrogen peroxide.

Objective

Rewrite a chemical equation from a description of a chemical reaction using appropriate symbols.

7.2 Writing Chemical Equations

Word equations adequately describe chemical reactions, but they are cumbersome. To communicate more effectively, you can use chemical formulas for writing equations. *In a* **chemical equation,** *an arrow separates the formulas of the reactants (on the left) from the formulas of the products (on the right).* For instance, here is the chemical equation for the formation of rust.

$$Fe + O_2 \rightarrow Fe_2O_3$$

Such equations, which show just the formulas of the reactants and products, are skeleton equations. *A* **skeleton equation** *is a chemical equation that does not indicate the relative amounts of the reactants and products.* Writing a skeleton equation is an important first step in obtaining a correct chemical equation.

You can indicate the physical state of a substance in the equation by putting a symbol after each formula. Use *(s)* for a solid, *(l)* for a liquid, *(g)* for a gas, and *(aq)* for an aqueous solution (a solution of a substance dissolved in water).

$$Fe(s) + O_2(g) \rightarrow Fe_2O_3(s)$$

In many chemical reactions, a catalyst is employed. *A* **catalyst** *is a substance that speeds up a reaction without being used up.* Because a catalyst is neither a reactant nor a product, its formula is written above the arrow in a chemical equation. For example, Figure 7.2 shows that the compound manganese(IV) oxide (MnO_2) catalyzes the decomposition of an aqueous solution of hydrogen peroxide (H_2O_2).

$$H_2O_2(aq) \xrightarrow{MnO_2} H_2O(l) + O_2(g)$$

Figure 7.2 Hydrogen peroxide slowly decomposes to form water and oxygen. At left, manganese(IV) oxide, MnO_2, a black powder, speeds up this reaction, causing bubbles to form. Since it is not used up in the reaction shown at right, MnO_2 is a catalyst.

Symbol	Explanation
+	Used to separate two reactants or two products
$\longrightarrow$	"Yields," separates reactants from products
$=$	An alternative to $\longrightarrow$
$\rightleftharpoons$	Used in place of a $\longrightarrow$ for reversible reactions
(s)	Designates a reactant or product in the solid state; placed after the formula
(l)	Designates a reactant or product in the liquid state; placed after the formula
(aq)	Designates an aqueous solution; the substance is dissolved in water
(g)	Designates a reactant or product in the gaseous state; placed after the formula
$\xrightarrow{\Delta}$ $\xrightarrow{\text{heat}}$	Indicates that heat is supplied to the reaction
$\xrightarrow{\text{Pt}}$	A formula written above or below the yield sign indicates its use as a catalyst (in this example, platinum)

Table 7.1 Symbols Used in Equations

To write a skeleton equation, you must write the correct formulas of the reactants and products. Put the reactants to the left of the arrow and the products to the right. Table 7.1 lists many of the symbols that are commonly used in writing chemical equations.

Example 1 Writing a Skeleton Equation

Write a skeleton equation for this chemical reaction: When calcium carbonate is heated, calcium oxide and carbon dioxide are produced.

Solution

$$CaCO_3(s) \xrightarrow{\Delta} CaO(s) + CO_2(g)$$

Concept Practice

3. Write a skeleton equation for each of these chemical reactions. Include appropriate symbols from Table 7.1.
a. Solid sulfur burns in oxygen gas to form sulfur dioxide gas.
b. Oxygen gas can be made by heating potassium chlorate in the presence of the catalyst manganese(IV) oxide. Potassium chloride is left as a solid residue.
c. When solid mercury(II) sulfide is heated with oxygen, liquid mercury metal and gaseous sulfur dioxide are produced.

Example 2 **Writing Word Equations**

Write a sentence that completely describes the chemical reaction shown in this skeleton equation.

$$NaHCO_3(s) + HCl(aq) \longrightarrow NaCl(aq) + H_2O(l) + CO_2(g)$$

Solution

Solid sodium hydrogen carbonate reacts with a solution of hydrochloric acid to produce aqueous sodium chloride, water, and carbon dioxide gas.

Concept Practice

4. Write sentences that completely describe each of the chemical reactions shown in these skeleton equations.

a. $NH_3(g) + O_2(g) \xrightarrow{Pt} NO(g) + H_2O(g)$
b. $H_2SO_4(aq) + BaCl_2(aq) \longrightarrow BaSO_4(s) + HCl(aq)$
c. $N_2O_3(g) + H_2O(l) \longrightarrow HNO_2(aq)$

Objective

Construct and balance formula equations for common items.

7.3 Balancing Everyday Equations

You can write word equations similar to chemical equations for many everyday processes. For instance, you could write a word equation for the manufacture of bicycles. What do you need to make a bicycle? To simplify your task, limit yourself to four major components: frames, wheels, handlebars and pedals. Your word equation for making a bicycle is probably:

$$\underset{\text{(reactants)}}{\text{Frame + wheel + handlebar + pedal}} \longrightarrow \underset{\text{(product)}}{\text{bicycle}}$$

Your word equation is *qualitatively* correct. It shows the reactants (the kinds of parts) you need to make a product (a bicycle). If you are responsible for ordering parts to make a bicycle, however, this word equation is inadequate. It does not show you a *quantitative* relationship because it does not indicate the number of each part needed to make a bicycle.

A standard bicycle is composed of one frame (F), two wheels (W), one handlebar (H), and two pedals (P). Using these symbols, the formula for a bicycle is FW_2HP_2. The skeleton equation for bicycle assembly is:

$$F + W + H + P \longrightarrow FW_2HP_2 \qquad \text{(unbalanced)}$$

However, this equation is unbalanced because it does not indicate the number of wheels and pedals in the reactants needed to produce the number of wheels and pedals in the product. A complete description of both the kind and the number of parts is required. The equation can be balanced by indicating the correct number of each of the parts needed to make a bicycle. These numbers, *coefficients,* are placed in front of the symbols for the respective parts.

$$F + 2W + H + 2P \longrightarrow FW_2HP_2$$

This is a balanced equation. There are equal numbers of each part on both sides of the equation.

Concept Practice

5. Balance equations for each item.

a. a basketball team

Center + forward + guard ⟶ team

$$C + F + G \longrightarrow CF_2G_2$$

b. a tricycle

Frame + wheel + seat + pedal ⟶ tricycle

$$F + W + S + P \longrightarrow FW_3SP_2$$

7.4 Balancing Chemical Equations

Objective

Apply the rules for balancing equations when given the names or formulas of all the reactants and products in a chemical reaction.

For chemical equations to represent a chemical reaction correctly, first you must write the correct formulas for the reactants and the products. This is always the first step in writing a chemical equation. The next step is to balance the chemical equation so that it is quantitatively correct. Balancing the equation is necessary to be consistent with the law of conservation of mass. Remember, in a chemical reaction, atoms are not created or destroyed; they are simply rearranged. *In every* **balanced equation,** *each side of the equation has the same number of atoms of each element.*

Biographical Note

St. Elmo Brady
(1884–1966)

In 1916 St. Elmo Brady became the first African-American man to be awarded a doctorate in chemistry. He left the University of Illinois to begin a career dedicated to inspiring young people in the study of science. Brady studied plant chemistry at Tuskegee Institute. This remained one of his research interests, along with other branches of organic chemistry. In the course of his career, he developed departments of chemistry at Tuskegee Institute, Howard University, and Fisk University. After his retirement from Fisk in 1952, he went to Tougaloo College in Mississippi to start yet another department of chemistry. Brady was known for his dedication to research and his love of teaching.

Sometimes when you write the formulas for the reactants and products in an equation, the equation may already be balanced. One example of this is the equation for the burning of carbon in the presence of oxygen to produce carbon dioxide.

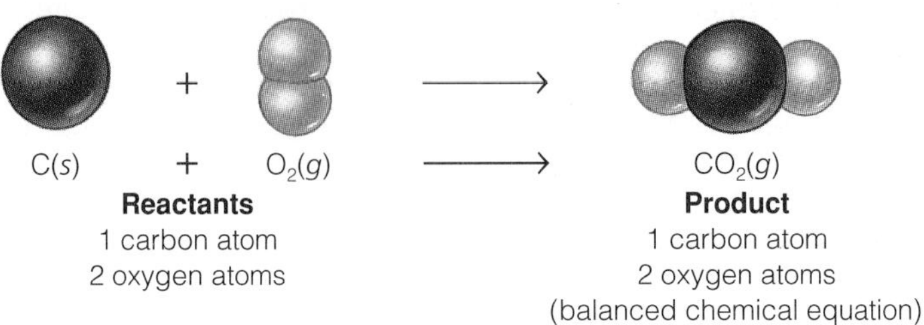

This equation is balanced. One carbon atom is on each side of the equation, and two oxygen atoms are on each side. You do not need to change the coefficients. They each remain a "one."

Another equation you have seen is the reaction of hydrogen with oxygen to form water.

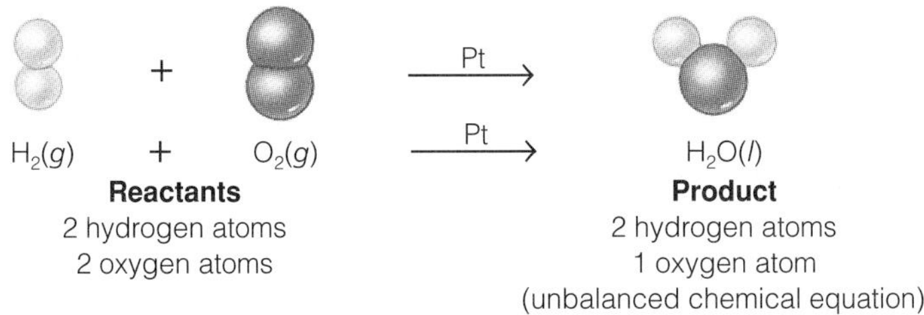

This equation is not balanced even though the formulas for all the reactants and products are correct. Count the atoms on both sides of the equation. There are two oxygen atoms on the reactant (left) side of the equation and only one oxygen atom on the product (right) side. As written, the equation does not obey the law of conservation of mass. What can you do to balance it? Many chemical equations can be balanced by trial and error. A few guidelines, however, will speed up the process.

Rules for Balancing Equations

1. Determine the correct formulas for all reactants and products.

2. Write the formulas for the reactants on the left and the formulas for the products on the right with a yields sign (arrow) in between. If two or more reactants or products are involved, separate their formulas with plus signs.

3. Count the number of atoms of each element in the reactants and products. For simplicity, a polyatomic ion appearing unchanged on both sides of the equation is counted as a single unit.

4. Balance the elements one at a time by using coefficients. *A* **coefficient** *is a small whole number that appears in front of a chemical formula in an equation.* When no coefficient is written, it is assumed to be 1. It is best to begin the balancing operation with elements that appear only once on each side of the equation. *You must not attempt to balance an equation by changing the subscripts in the chemical formula of a substance.*

5. Check each atom or polyatomic ion to be sure that the equation is balanced.

6. Finally, make sure that all the coefficients are in the lowest possible ratio.

Now let's use these rules to balance the equation for the formation of water from hydrogen and oxygen.

Example 3 Writing a Balanced Chemical Equation

When hydrogen and oxygen react, the product is water. Write a balanced equation for this reaction.

Solution

Since the chemical formulas of the reactants and products are known, you can write a skeleton equation.

$$H_2(g) + O_2(g) \rightarrow H_2O(l)$$

Hydrogen is balanced but oxygen is not. If you put a coefficient of 2 in front of H_2O, the oxygen becomes balanced.

$$H_2(g) + O_2(g) \rightarrow 2H_2O(l)$$

Now there are twice as many hydrogen atoms in the product as there are in the reactants. To correct this, put a coefficient of 2 in front of H_2. The equation is now balanced.

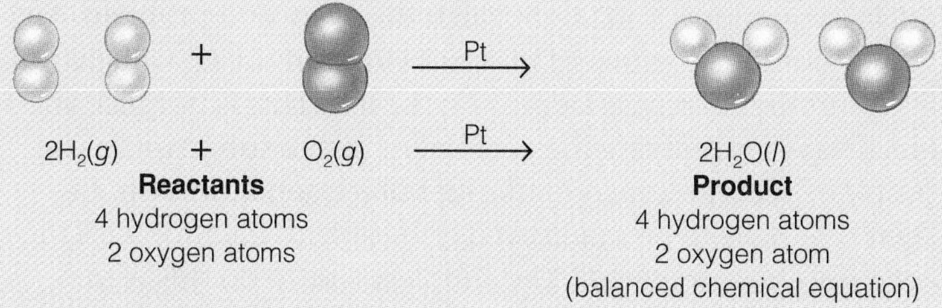

Check the coefficients. They must be in their lowest possible ratio: $2(H_2)$, $1(O_2)$, and $2(H_2O)$.

Problem-Solving Tip

Write the diatomic elements as O_2, H_2, N_2, F_2, Cl_2, Br_2, and I_2.

Figure 7.3 The copper screen reacts with silver nitrate to form copper nitrate and silver. Notice the silver plating on the copper screen and the characteristic blue-green color of the copper(II) ion in solution.

Example 4 Balancing a Chemical Equation

Figure 7.3 shows the reaction of aqueous silver nitrate and solid copper. Balance the equation for this reaction.

$$AgNO_3(aq) + Cu(s) \rightarrow Cu(NO_3)_2(aq) + Ag(s)$$

Solution

Since this reaction involves the polyatomic nitrate ion, you can save time if you consider the nitrate ion as a unit. Put a coefficient of 2 in front of $AgNO_3$ to balance the nitrate ion.

$$2AgNO_3(aq) + Cu(s) \rightarrow Cu(NO_3)_2(aq) + Ag(s)$$

By inspection you see that the silver is not balanced. Put a coefficient of 2 in front of Ag.

$$2AgNO_3(aq) + Cu(s) \rightarrow Cu(NO_3)_2(aq) + 2Ag(s)$$

The equation is balanced and obeys the law of conservation of mass.

Example 5 Balancing a Chemical Equation

Balance the following equation.

$$Al(s) + O_2(g) \rightarrow Al_2O_3(s)$$

Solution

First balance the aluminum by adding a coefficient of 2 in front of Al.

$$2Al(s) + O_2(g) \rightarrow Al_2O_3(s)$$

You now have a situation that occurs quite frequently in balancing equations. You might call it the even-odd problem. Any whole-number coefficient placed in front of the O_2 will give an even number of oxygen atoms on the left. This is because you are always multiplying the coefficient by the subscript 2. The problem becomes the odd number of oxygen atoms on the right that have to be made even to be able to balance with the even number on the left. The simplest way to do this is to begin by multiplying the formula with the odd number of oxygen atoms by 2.

$$2Al(s) + O_2(g) \rightarrow 2Al_2O_3(s)$$

Now there are six oxygens on the right. Balance the oxygens on the left with a 3 and rebalance the aluminum on the left with a 4.

$$4Al(s) + 3O_2(g) \rightarrow 2Al_2O_3(s)$$

Suppose you had written the equation for the formation of aluminum oxide as follows.

$$8Al(s) + 6O_2(g) \rightarrow 4Al_2O_3(s)$$

Since this equation obeys the law of conservation of mass, it appears to be correct. However, it is incorrect because the coefficients are not in their lowest possible ratio. Each of them can be divided by 2 to give the previous equation.

Concept Practice

6. What is the purpose of balancing an equation?

7. The equation for the formation of water from its elements,

$$H_2(g) + O_2(g) \rightarrow H_2O(l)$$

can easily be "balanced" by changing the formula of the product to H_2O_2. Explain why this is incorrect.

Practice Problems

8. Balance the following equations. In doing problems in this chapter, you may ignore the physical states of products and reactants unless they are specifically required.
a. $PbO_2 \rightarrow PbO + O_2$
b. $P + O_2 \rightarrow P_4O_{10}$
c. $Al + N_2 \rightarrow AlN$
d. $Fe(OH)_3 \rightarrow Fe_2O_3 + H_2O$
e. $(NH_4)_2CO_3 \rightarrow NH_3 + H_2O + CO_2$
f. $NaCl + H_2SO_4 \rightarrow Na_2SO_4 + HCl$
g. $H_2 + Fe_3O_4 \rightarrow Fe + H_2O$
h. $Al + CuSO_4 \rightarrow Al_2(SO_4)_3 + Cu$

9. Rewrite these word equations as balanced chemical equations.
a. carbon + oxygen → carbon monoxide
b. potassium nitrate → potassium nitrite + oxygen
c. hydrogen + sulfur → hydrogen sulfide
d. iron(III) chloride + calcium hydroxide → iron(III) hydroxide + calcium chloride
e. sodium + water → sodium hydroxide + hydrogen

7.A Science, Technology, and Society

Chemistry Rescues Crumbling Books

Figure 7.4 Many old books, such as the one shown, are becoming brittle and decaying because of the acid content of the paper they were originally printed on.

Millions of books printed since the mid-nineteenth century decay slowly as they sit on library shelves. Some of these books are extremely valuable. However, their pages are so fragile that they crumble at a touch. The cause is the acidity of the paper, which originates from alum (aluminum sulfate). For the past 150 years, alum has been used in the sizing process, to prevent inks from soaking into the paper. Before the Industrial Revolution, books were made from rag paper, which is very durable but also very expensive. From the 1850s, however, the demand for books rose dramatically. Since wood pulp was cheaper, it was used to make paper. To cut down on the absorbency of the wood-pulp paper, the sizing process using alum was introduced.

Libraries throughout the world are working with chemists to find ways to stop the acid deterioration of books. One process, which is carried out in a vacuum chamber, is called mass deacidification. After the air is pumped out of the chamber and most of the moisture is removed from the books, the compound diethyl zinc is introduced as a gas. The gas penetrates the closed pages of books and completely neutralizes any acid that is present. The gas also forms zinc oxide, which protects the paper against future acid attack. Hundreds of volumes can be treated at one time at an estimated cost of $6 to $10 per book. If books had to be treated page by page it could cost $1000 per book!

Figure 7.5 Using a vacuum chamber allows many books to be deacidified at once, keeping the cost of the treatment process down to a reasonable level.

The deacidification process extends the life of a new book three to five times. Unfortunately, the process will not reverse damage that has already taken place. For books with pages that are already brittle and beyond repair an alternative technique for saving their words, such as microfilming, is necessary. One recommendation is that new books be deacidified before they ever go onto library shelves.

Think About It

10. Analyze What are the advantages and disadvantages of having the reference materials in your library available as bound books? On microfilm?

11. Criticize Do you think that it is worth spending money to preserve old books? How would you justify your response?

7.5 Types of Reactions

Objective

Explain the usefulness of a system for classifying chemical reactions.

You can be certain what the products of a chemical reaction are only by carrying out that reaction in the laboratory. The known reactants must be allowed to react and the products must be identified.

Consider for a moment the number of possible chemical reactions. Since there are millions of known chemical compounds, it is logical to expect that millions of different chemical reactions can occur in nature or be done in the laboratory. Carrying out each reaction in the laboratory is the ideal, but it would be both time consuming and costly. You learned to name many compounds in Chapter 5 by following a system of nomenclature rather than memorizing common names for thousands of different compounds. Similarly, you can learn to recognize patterns of chemical behavior that allow you to predict the products in many chemical reactions.

There are many ways to categorize chemical reactions. One classification scheme identifies five general reaction types: combination, decomposition, single replacement, double replacement, and combustion. Not all chemical reactions, however, fit neatly into one of these classes. Occasionally, a reaction may fit equally well into two of these categories. In spite of these exceptions, recognizing a reaction as a particular type is useful. Patterns in reactions will become apparent that will allow you to predict the products of these reactions.

Concept Practice

12. How can you know with most certainty the identity of the products of a chemical reaction?

7.6 Combination Reactions

Objective

Identify a combination reaction and predict the product of a simple combination reaction.

Sulfur and oxygen react by combining to form a new compound. *As the name implies, in a* **combination reaction** *two or more substances react to form a single substance.* The reactants of most common combination reactions are either two elements or two compounds. The product of a combination (or synthesis) reaction must be a compound.

When two nonmetals react, or when a transition metal reacts with a nonmetal, more than one product is often possible. (Remember Dalton's law of multiple proportions from Chapter 5.)

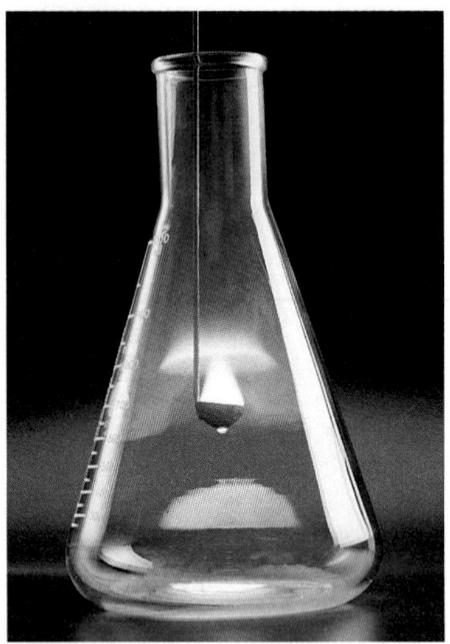

Figure 7.6 When ignited, sulfur combines with oxygen to form sulfur dioxide gas, SO_2.

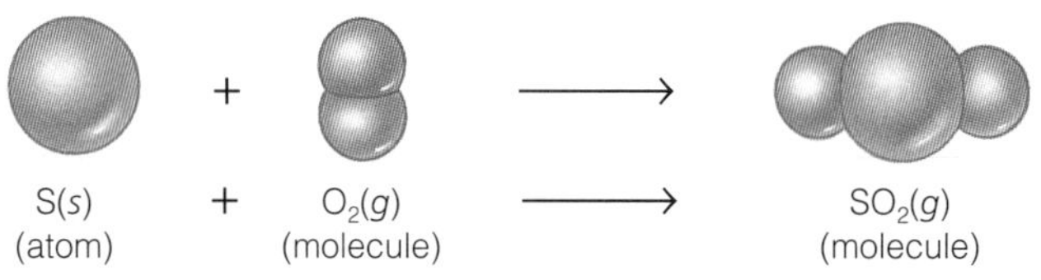

$$2S(s) + 3O_2(g) \rightarrow 2SO_3(g) \text{ sulfur trioxide}$$

$$Fe(s) + S(s) \rightarrow FeS(s) \text{ iron(II) sulfide}$$

$$2Fe(s) + 3S(s) \rightarrow Fe_2S_3(s) \text{ iron(III) sulfide}$$

When a Group A metal and a nonmetal react, the formula for the product is the compound that results from combination of the metal cation and nonmetal anion.

$$2K(s) + Cl_2(g) \rightarrow 2KCl(s)$$

Some nonmetal oxides react with water to produce an *acid*, a compound that produces hydrogen ion in aqueous solution.

$$SO_2(g) + H_2O(l) \rightarrow H_2SO_3(aq)$$

Metallic oxides react with water to give a *base*, a compound that contains hydroxide ion. Use ionic charges to derive the formula for the product.

$$CaO(s) + H_2O(l) \rightarrow Ca(OH)_2(aq)$$

Problem-Solving Tip

Often you can get the formula of the acid by "adding" the formulas of the two reacting molecules together.

Example 6 Writing Equations for Combination Reactions

Complete the following combination reactions.

a. $Al(s) + O_2(g) \rightarrow$ **b.** $Cu(s) + S(s) \rightarrow$

Solution

a. Write the correct formula for the compound aluminum oxide by using ionic charges. Then balance the equation.

$$Al(s) + O_2(g) \rightarrow Al_2O_3(s) \text{ (unbalanced)}$$

$$4Al(s) + 3O_2(g) \rightarrow 2Al_2O_3(s)$$

b. Two reactions are possible.

$$Cu(s) + S(s) \rightarrow CuS(s) \text{ [copper(II)]}$$

$$2Cu(s) + S(s) \rightarrow Cu_2S(s) \text{ [copper(I)]}$$

Concept Practice

13. How do you predict the correct formula for the combination reaction between a nonmetal and a Group A metal?

14. A compound is formed by the reaction of nitrogen with oxygen gas. Can you predict the formula of the compound formed? Explain.

Practice Problem

15. Write balanced chemical equations for the following combination reactions.

a. $Mg + O_2 \rightarrow$

b. $P + O_2 \rightarrow$ tetraphosphorus decoxide

c. $Ca + S \rightarrow$

d. $Fe + O_2 \rightarrow$ iron(II) oxide

e. $N_2O_5 + H_2O \rightarrow$

Activity 7 Balancing Chemical Equations

Purpose

To make models of the process of reactants changing into products during a chemical reaction.

Materials

12 paper clips each of three different colors (or sizes)

Procedure

1. Designate each color of paper clip to represent a single atom of an element.

2. Make three molecules each of hydrogen (H_2) and oxygen (O_2). "React" one molecule of H_2 with one molecule of O_2 by splitting the molecules and joining one oxygen atom to two hydrogen atoms. The other unreacted oxygen atom must react with another hydrogen molecule to form a second water molecule. All of the atoms of reactants must combine to form molecules of product.

3. Write a balanced equation for the formation of water from its elements. Start with the unbalanced equation: $H_2 + O_2 \rightarrow H_2O$.

4. Repeat step 2 for the reaction of methane with oxygen. Start with three molecules of methane and three molecules of oxygen.

5. Write a balanced equation for the formation of carbon dioxide and water from methane and oxygen. Use the unbalanced equation: $CH_4 + O_2 \rightarrow CO_2 + H_2O$.

Analysis and Conclusions

1. In this activity, why should there be no individual atoms left over that were originally part of a reactant molecule?

2. In the formation of water, why couldn't you take both atoms from each hydrogen and oxygen molecule and put them all together to form H_2O_2?

Objective

Identify a decomposition reaction and predict the products of a simple decomposition reaction.

7.7 Decomposition Reactions

When calcium carbonate is heated it *decomposes* into two simpler compounds. This reaction is used to make lime (calcium oxide) from limestone (primarily calcium carbonate). Many other compounds also break apart or decompose with the addition of energy.

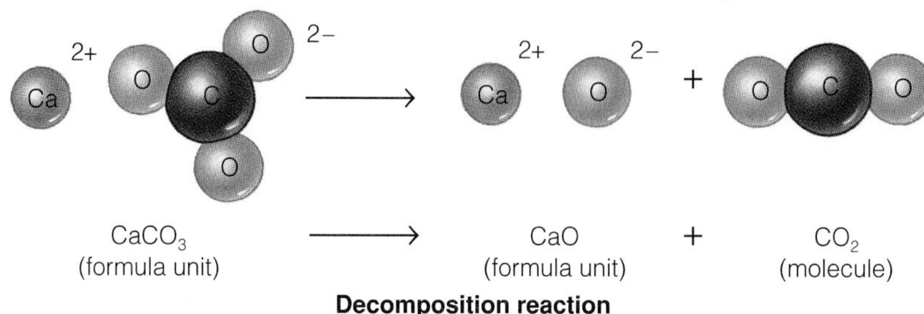

Decomposition reaction

In a **decomposition reaction** *a single compound is broken down into two or more products.* These products can be any combination of elements and compounds. It is usually very difficult to predict the products of decomposition reactions. When a simple binary compound breaks down, however, you know the products will be the constituent elements. Most decomposition reactions require energy in the form of heat, light, or electricity.

Example 7 Writing Equations for Decomposition Reactions

Write balanced equations for the following decomposition reactions.

a. $H_2O(l) \xrightarrow{\text{electricity}}$

b. Mercury(II) oxide $\xrightarrow{\Delta}$

Solution

a. Water, a binary compound, breaks down into its elements, hydrogen and oxygen. (Remember: hydrogen and oxygen are both diatomic molecules.)

$$H_2O(l) \xrightarrow{\text{electricity}} H_2(g) + O_2(g) \text{ (unbalanced)}$$

$$2H_2O(l) \xrightarrow{\text{electricity}} 2H_2(g) + O_2(g)$$

b. $HgO(s) \xrightarrow{\Delta} Hg(l) + O_2(g)$ (unbalanced)

$$2HgO(s) \xrightarrow{\Delta} 2Hg(l) + O_2(g)$$

Practice Problems

16. Write the formula for the binary compound that decomposes to each of the following sets of products.

a. $H_2 + Br_2$ **b.** $Na + Cl_2$

17. Write balanced chemical equations for these decomposition reactions.

a. $Ag_2O(s) \xrightarrow{\Delta}$

b. nickel(II) carbonate $\xrightarrow{\Delta}$ nickel(II) oxide + ____

c. ammonium nitrate $\xrightarrow{\Delta}$ dinitrogen monoxide + water

7.8 Single-Replacement Reactions

Objective

Identify a single-replacement reaction and use the activity series of metals to predict the products of single-replacement reactions.

When a small piece of potassium is dropped into a beaker of water, a violent reaction occurs. The reaction produces hydrogen gas and a large quantity of heat. The hydrogen can ignite and burn with explosive rapidity. The reaction of potassium with water is a *single-replacement* reaction. Similar but much less spectacular reactions can occur when certain elements are put in an aqueous solution of a compound. *In a* **single-replacement reaction** *atoms of an element replace the atoms of a second element in a compound.* Single-replacement reactions are also called single-displacement reactions. Whether one metal will displace another metal from a compound can be determined by the relative reactivities of the two metals. *The* **activity series of metals,** *given in Table 7.2, is a list of metals in order of decreasing reactivity.* A reactive metal will replace any metal listed below it in the activity series. Thus magnesium displaces zinc from a zinc compound in solution. Magnesium also displaces silver from a silver compound in solution. By contrast, magnesium does not displace lithium or calcium from aqueous solutions of their compounds.

$$Mg(s) + Zn(NO_3)_2(aq) \rightarrow Mg(NO_3)_2(aq) + Zn(s)$$

$$Mg(s) + 2AgNO_3(aq) \rightarrow Mg(NO_3)_2(aq) + 2Ag(s)$$

$$Mg(s) + LiNO_3(aq) \rightarrow \text{no reaction}$$

A nonmetal can also replace another nonmetal from a compound. This replacement is usually limited to the halogens (F_2, Cl_2, Br_2, and I_2). The activity of the halogens decreases as you go down Group 7A of the periodic table.

Table 7.2 Activity Series of Metals

	Name	Symbol
Decreasing activity ↓	Lithium	Li
	Potassium	K
	Calcium	Ca
	Sodium	Na
	Magnesium	Mg
	Aluminum	Al
	Zinc	Zn
	Iron	Fe
	Lead	Pb
	(Hydrogen)	(H)*
	Copper	Cu
	Mercury	Hg
	Silver	Ag

* Metals from Li to Na will replace H from acids and water; from Mg to Pb they will replace H from acids only.

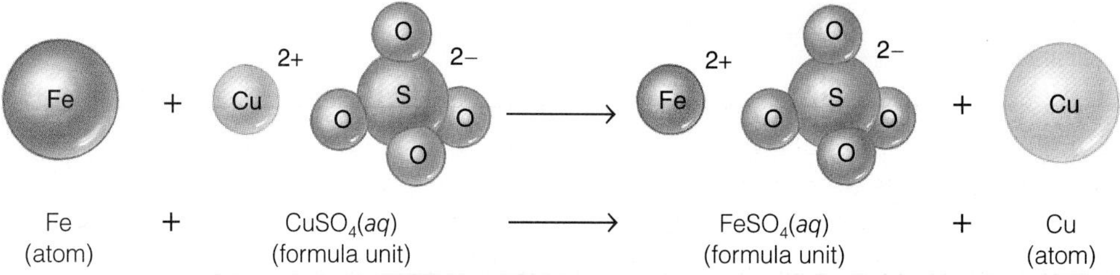

Single-replacement reaction

Example 8 Writing Equations for Single-Replacement Reactions

Write a balanced chemical equation for each of these single-replacement reactions.

a. $Zn(s) + H_2SO_4(aq) \rightarrow$ **b.** $Na(s) + H_2O(l) \rightarrow$

Solution

a. According to the activity series of metals, zinc will displace hydrogen from an acid and take its place. Hydrogen is a diatomic gas.

$$Zn(s) + H_2SO_4(aq) \rightarrow ZnSO_4(aq) + H_2(g)$$

b. Sodium will displace hydrogen from water. Write water as HOH and visualize it as being made of H^+ and OH^-.

$$Na(s) + H^+OH^-(l) \rightarrow NaOH(aq) + H_2(g) \text{ (unbalanced)}$$

$$2Na(s) + 2H^+OH^-(l) \rightarrow 2NaOH(aq) + H_2(g)$$

Problem-Solving Tip

A metal displaces a cation from a compound; a nonmetal displaces an anion.

Figure 7.7 Alkali metals such as potassium (shown here) displace hydrogen from water in a *single-replacement* reaction.

Concept Practice

18. For each pair, predict which element as an atom would displace the other element as an ion from a compound in aqueous solution.

a. iron and sodium
b. silver and tin
c. zinc and hydrogen (in HCl)

Practice Problem

19. Use the activity series of metals to write a balanced chemical equation for each of these single-replacement reactions.

a. $Ag(s) + KNO_3(aq) \rightarrow$
b. $Zn(s) + AgNO_3(aq) \rightarrow$
c. $Al(s) + H_2SO_4(aq) \rightarrow$
d. $Cl_2(l) + KI(aq) \rightarrow$
e. $Li(s) + H_2O(l) \rightarrow$
f. $Cu(s) + FeSO_4(aq) \rightarrow$

7.9 Double-Replacement Reactions

Objective

Identify a double-replacement reaction and write the products of the double-replacement reaction between two ionic compounds.

Many ionic compounds dissolve in water to form homogeneous solutions. If solutions of two ionic compounds are mixed together, either an aqueous homogeneous mixture will form or a chemical reaction will occur. Mixing solutions of sodium chloride and calcium nitrate gives a homogeneous mixture. Figure 7.8 shows that mixing aqueous solutions of barium chloride and potassium carbonate results in a chemical reaction. Barium carbonate is the white precipitate formed. Potassium chloride, the other product of the reaction, remains in solution. **Double-replacement reactions** *involve an exchange of positive ions between two compounds.* Such reactions generally take place between two ionic compounds in aqueous solution. These reactions are often characterized by one of the products coming out of solution in some way. Thus, for a double-replacement reaction to occur, one of the following is usually true.

Figure 7.8 Solutions of barium chloride and potassium carbonate react in a *double-replacement* reaction to form barium carbonate, the white precipitate.

1. One product is only slightly soluble and precipitates from solution, leaving the other product dissolved in solution. For example, the reaction of aqueous solutions of sodium sulfide and cadmium nitrate produces a yellow precipitate of cadmium sulfide.

$$Na_2S(aq) + Cd(NO_3)_2(aq) \rightarrow CdS(s) + 2NaNO_3(aq)$$

2. One product is a gas that bubbles out of the mixture. For example, hydrogen cyanide gas is produced when aqueous calcium cyanide is mixed with sulfuric acid.

$$2NaCN(aq) + H_2SO_4(aq) \rightarrow 2HCN(g) + Na_2SO_4(aq)$$

3. One product is a molecular compound such as water, which separates from the ions in solution as intact molecules. Combining solutions of calcium hydroxide and hydrochloric acid produces water as one of the products.

$$Ca(OH)_2(aq) + 2HCl(aq) \rightarrow CaCl_2(aq) + 2H_2O(l)$$

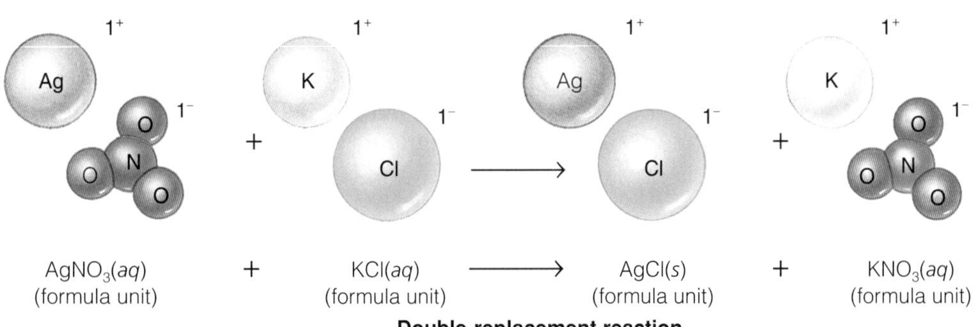

Double-replacement reaction

Example 9 Writing Equations for Double-Replacement Reactions

Write balanced chemical equations for these double-replacement reactions.

a. $BaCl_2(aq) + K_2CO_3(aq) \rightarrow$ **b.** $FeS(s) + HCl(aq) \rightarrow$

Solution

a. The driving force behind the reaction is the formation of a precipitate.

$$BaCl_2(aq) + K_2CO_3(aq) \rightarrow BaCO_3(s) + KCl(aq) \text{ (unbalanced)}$$

$$BaCl_2(aq) + K_2CO_3(aq) \rightarrow BaCO_3(s) + 2KCl(aq)$$

b. A gas is formed in this double-replacement reaction.

$$FeS(s) + HCl(aq) \rightarrow H_2S(g) + FeCl_2(aq) \text{ (unbalanced)}$$

$$FeS(s) + 2HCl(aq) \rightarrow H_2S(g) + FeCl_2(aq)$$

Problem-Solving Tip

The cation is always written first in the formula of an ionic compound.

Practice Problem

20. Write a balanced equation for each of these reactions.

a. $HCl(aq) + Ca(OH)_2(aq) \rightarrow$
b. $Ag_2SO_4(aq) + AlCl_3(aq) \rightarrow$ (silver chloride is a precipitate)
c. $KOH(aq) + H_3PO_4(aq) \rightarrow$
d. $H_2SO_4(aq) + Al(OH)_3(aq) \rightarrow$
e. $SrBr_2(aq) + (NH_4)_2CO_3(aq) \rightarrow$ (strontium carbonate is a precipitate)

Objective

Identify a combustion reaction and write the products of a combustion reaction.

7.10 Combustion Reactions

Your house or apartment may be heated with natural gas, propane, or heating oil. All of these fuels provide warmth when they are burned. *In a* **combustion reaction** *an element or a compound reacts with oxygen, often producing energy in the form of heat and light.* Combustion reactions may involve hydrocarbons, compounds of hydrogen and carbon. The complete combustion of a hydrocarbon produces carbon dioxide and water. If insufficient oxygen is available during a reaction, combustion will be incomplete. Elemental carbon and toxic carbon monoxide may be additional products. The complete combustion of a hydrocarbon releases a lot of energy as heat. Thus hydrocarbons such as methane (CH_4), propane (C_3H_8), butane (C_4H_{10}), and octane (C_8H_{18}) are important fuels.

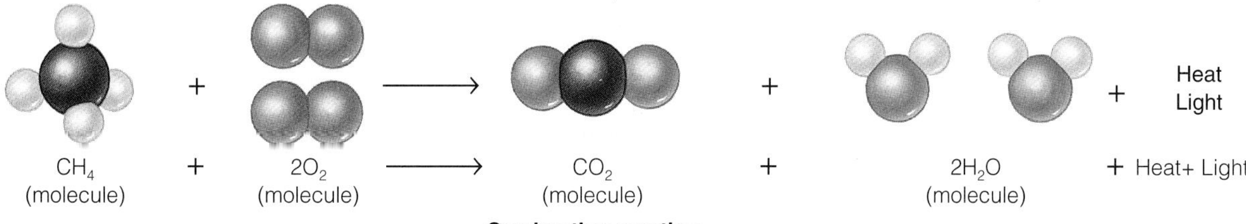

Combustion reaction

A combustion reaction between an element and oxygen is also an example of a combination reaction. For example, both magnesium and sulfur will burn by reaction with oxygen.

$$2Mg(s) + O_2(g) \rightarrow 2MgO(s)$$

$$S(s) + O_2(g) \rightarrow SO_2(g)$$

Example 10 Writing Equations for Combustion Reactions

Write a balanced equation for the complete combustion of these compounds.

a. benzene, $C_6H_6(l)$
b. methanol, $CH_3OH(l)$

Solution

a. Oxygen is the other reactant in a combustion reaction. The products are CO_2 and H_2O.

$$C_6H_6(l) + O_2(g) \rightarrow CO_2(g) + H_2O(g) \text{ (unbalanced)}$$

$$2C_6H_6(l) + 15O_2(g) \rightarrow 12CO_2(g) + 6H_2O(g)$$

b. $2CH_3OH(l) + 3O_2(g) \rightarrow 2CO_2(g) + 4H_2O(g)$

Problem-Solving Tip

The coefficients in a balanced chemical equation must be the lowest whole numbers.

Concept Practice

21. What substance is common to all combustion reactions?

22. Name the products of the combustion of a hydrocarbon.

Practice Problem

23. Write a balanced equation for the complete combustion of these compounds

a. butene(g), C_4H_8
b. glucose(s), $C_6H_{12}O_6$
c. octane(l), C_8H_{18}

7.B Science, Technology, and Society

The Chemistry of Firefighting

Figure 7.9 Uncontrolled fires can be destructive and dangerous.

In North America alone, uncontrolled fires of the kind shown in Figure 7.9 kill more than 20,000 people and cause millions of dollars in property damage each year. Controlling fires is an important application of chemistry.

Fire, or combustion, is the rapid reaction of a fuel with oxygen. The fuel is heated to start the fire. Once started, a fire can be put out in three ways: (1) by cooling the fuel, (2) by cutting off the supply of oxygen, or (3) by trapping the combustion intermediates so they cannot react with oxygen.

Firefighters are called upon most often to fight fires involving a solid fuel—such as the wooden frame of a typical house. This kind of fire is known as a Class A fire. Water is usually used to put out a Class A fire.

In a Class B fire, where the burning material is a liquid or gas, a stream of water can sometimes spread the fire. Also, because of the salt dissolved in most pressurized-water fire extinguishers, the water will conduct electricity. Thus water fire extinguishers are not used in a fire involving an energized electrical circuit, known as a Class C fire. Finally, water can actually be a source of oxygen for a Class D fire, in which a metal is burning.

Carbon dioxide extinguishers can be used on Class B and C fires. Carbon dioxide extinguishes fires by cutting off the oxygen supply. Because carbon dioxide is more dense than air, it will blanket the burning fire.

Figure 7.10 Airplanes can be used to dump fire retardant chemicals on brush and forest fires. The powder also contains a nutrient to help vegetation grow in the burned area.

Dry chemicals can be dropped from airplanes on forest fires, as shown in Figure 7.10. The simplest of these chemicals, sodium hydrogen carbonate, works by generating carbon dioxide when exposed to heat, which shuts off the oxygen supply to the fire.

$$2NaHCO_3(s) + \text{heat} \rightarrow Na_2CO_3(s) + H_2O(g) + CO_2(g)$$

Halons are a class of fire extinguishing agents that are used in automatic sprinkling systems to protect sensitive electronic equipment such as computers and in aircraft fire extinguishers. Halons put out fires quickly, leaving no residue. However, when halons are released into the atmosphere they destroy the ozone layer.

Think About It

24. Describe What three things are necessary for a fire to burn?

25. Contrast Why is it not safe to use a single kind of fire extinguisher on all fires?

7.11 Predicting Products of a Chemical Reaction

Objective

Predict the products of combination, decomposition, single-replacement, double-replacement, and combustion reactions.

To predict the products of a chemical reaction successfully you must recognize the possible type of reaction that the reactants can undergo. Keys to predicting products of a reaction are shown in Table 7.3. In a *combination reaction,* two or more elements or compounds combine chemically to form a new compound. By contrast, a single reactant is the identifying characteristic of a decomposition reaction. In a typical *decomposition reaction,* a compound is decomposed into two or more elements and/or new compounds.

Single- and double-replacement reactions are also general types of reactions. In a *single-replacement reaction* an element replaces another element from a compound in aqueous solution. A different compound and a new element are formed. The activity series of metals is used to determine whether a single-replacement reaction will occur. The element that is being displaced must be less active than the element that is doing the displacing for a single-replacement reaction to occur.

Table 7.3 Keys to Identifying Types of Chemical Reactions

General equation	Reactants	Probable reaction type	Probable products
$R + S \rightarrow RS$	Two elements	Combination	A single compound
	Two compounds, at least one a molecular compound	Combination	A single compound
$RS \rightarrow R + S$	A single binary compound	Decomposition	Two elements
	A single ternary compound	Decomposition	Two or more elements and/or compounds
$T + RS \rightarrow TS + R$	An element and a compound	Single replacement	A different element and a new compound
$R^+S^- + T^+U^- \rightarrow R^+U^- + T^+S^-$	Two ionic compounds	Double replacement	Two new compounds
$C_xH_y + (x + \frac{y}{4})O_2 \rightarrow x\,CO_2 + \frac{y}{2}H_2O$	Oxygen and a compound of C, H, (O)	Combustion	CO_2 and H_2O (with incomplete combustion, C, and/or CO may be additional products)

In a *double-replacement reaction* two ionic compounds react by exchanging cations to form two different compounds. A double-replacement reaction usually takes place in aqueous solution. Double-replacement reactions are driven by the formation of a precipitate, a gaseous product, or water.

When oxygen reacts with an element or compound *combustion* may occur. If the compound is composed of the elements carbon and hydrogen (and perhaps oxygen), the most probable products are carbon dioxide and water. If all the carbon in the product is present as carbon dioxide, the reaction is complete combustion. If carbon monoxide is formed, however, the reaction is incomplete combustion. Whether a combustion reaction is complete or incomplete depends on the amount of oxygen present. Reaction conditions such as temperature may also be important. A combustion reaction is more likely to go to completion at a high temperature.

Some reactions are not any one of these five general types. Another very important type of chemical reaction is an oxidation-reduction, or redox, reaction. This type of reaction is discussed in Chapters 21 and 22. The only way to determine the products of any reaction with certainty is to carry out the reaction in the laboratory.

Concept Practice

26. Match each type of reaction with the phrase that best describes it.

a. double replacement	(1) a single reactant
b. combustion	(2) two ionic compounds
c. decomposition	(3) oxygen and a substance
d. single replacement	(4) a single product
e. combination	(5) an element and a compound

Practice Problem

27. After balancing each of these equations, identify them as to type.

a. $Hf + N_2 \rightarrow Hf_3N_4$
b. $Mg + H_2SO_4 \rightarrow MgSO_4 + H_2$
c. $C_2H_6 + O_2 \rightarrow CO_2 + H_2O$
d. $Pb(NO_3)_2 + NaI \rightarrow PbI_2 + NaNO_3$
e. $Fe + O_2 \rightarrow Fe_3O_4$
f. $Pb(NO_3)_2 \rightarrow PbO + NO_2 + O_2$
g. $Hg(NO_3)_2 + NH_4SCN \rightarrow Hg(SCN)_2 + NH_4NO_3$
h. $(NH_4)_2SO_4 + NaOH \rightarrow NH_3 + H_2O + Na_2SO_4$

Problem-Solving Tip

There are two stepwise reactions in the equation for h.

7.12 Net Ionic Equations

The reaction between aqueous solutions of silver nitrate and sodium chloride to form silver chloride and sodium nitrate is a double-replacement reaction.

$$AgNO_3(aq) + NaCl(aq) \rightarrow AgCl(s) + NaNO_3(aq)$$

As written, this equation continues the practice of representing ionic compounds by their formula units. You can write this equation more realistically, however, if you recognize that most ionic compounds dissociate, or separate, into cations and anions when they dissolve in water. For example, when sodium chloride dissolves in water it separates into sodium ions, $Na^+(aq)$, and chloride ions, $Cl^-(aq)$. Similarly, silver nitrate dissociates into silver ions, $Ag^+(aq)$, and nitrate ions, $NO_3^-(aq)$.

You can now write a **complete ionic equation,** *an equation that shows dissolved ionic compounds as their free ions.*

$$Ag^+(aq) + NO_3^-(aq) + Na^+(aq) + Cl^-(aq) \rightarrow AgCl(s) + Na^+(aq) + NO_3^-(aq)$$

The equation can be simplified and made more useful by eliminating the ions that do not participate in the reaction. You do this by canceling the ions that appear on both sides of the equation.

$$Ag^+(aq) + \cancel{NO_3^-}(aq) + \cancel{Na^+}(aq) + Cl^-(aq) \rightarrow AgCl(s) + \cancel{Na^+}(aq) + \cancel{NO_3^-}(aq)$$

Ions that are not directly involved in a reaction are **spectator ions.** Spectator ions appear on both sides of the equation. You can rewrite this equation leaving out the spectator ions. *This gives you the* **net ionic equation,** *which indicates only the particles that actually take part in the reaction.*

$$Ag^+(aq) + Cl^-(aq) \rightarrow AgCl(s)$$

In writing balanced net ionic equations, you must also balance the electric charge. For the previous reaction the net electric charge on each side of the equation is zero and therefore balanced. In other reactions this may not be the case. For example, consider the single-replacement reaction that occurs between lead and silver nitrate.

$$Pb(s) + AgNO_3(aq) \rightarrow Ag(s) + Pb(NO_3)_2(aq)$$

The nitrate ion is the spectator ion in this reaction. The net ionic equation is

$$Pb(s) + Ag^+(aq) \rightarrow Ag(s) + Pb^{2+}(aq) \text{ (unbalanced)}$$

Although this equation is balanced with respect to atoms, the electrical charges do not balance. On the reactant side of the equation there is a single unit of positive charge. On the product side

Objective

Rewrite and balance net ionic equations.

Integrating Industrial Arts

Combustion and the Oxyacetylene Torch

The oxyacetylene torch is used in welding, cutting, and melting metals. This torch is specially constructed so that burning acetylene, C_2H_2, mixes with a large amount of air. Otherwise the acetylene, which contains a large proportion of carbon in its molecular structure, would burn incompletely and produce a sooty flame. Welders usually get acetylene from an acetylene generator, a steel tank similar to those used to store compressed, liquefied gases at high pressures. However, liquefied acetylene tends to explode. Therefore the acetylene is generated inside the tank as it is needed. Pieces of calcium carbide, CaC_2, are placed in a container sealed to the tank. These pieces are dropped onto water in the tank. The reaction of calcium carbide and water generates acetylene gas, which flows to the torch for combustion.

there are two units of positive charge. Placing a 2 in front of $Ag^+(aq)$ balances the charge. A 2 in front of $Ag(s)$ rebalances the atoms.

$$Pb(s) + 2Ag^+(aq) \rightarrow 2Ag(s) + Pb^{2+}(aq) \text{ (balanced)}$$

Of the five types of reactions, both single- and double-replacement reactions can be written as net ionic equations.

Example 11 Writing and Balancing Net Ionic Equations

Identify the spectator ions and write balanced net ionic equations for these reactions.

a. $HCl(aq) + ZnS(aq) \rightarrow H_2S(g) + ZnCl_2(aq)$
b. $Cl_2(g) + NaBr(aq) \rightarrow Br_2(l) + NaCl(aq)$

Solution

a. Write the complete ionic equation.

$$H^+(aq) + Cl^-(aq) + Zn^{2+}(aq) + S^{2-}(aq) \rightarrow H_2S(g) + Zn^{2+}(aq) + Cl^-(aq)$$

The spectator ions are Zn^{2+} and Cl^-. The balanced net ionic equation is:

$$2H^+(aq) + S^{2-}(aq) \rightarrow H_2S(g)$$

b. Write the complete ionic equation.

$$Cl_2(g) + Na^+(aq) + Br^-(aq) \rightarrow Br_2(l) + Na^+(aq) + Cl^-(aq)$$

The spectator ion is Na^+. The balanced net ionic equation is:

$$Cl_2(g) + 2Br^-(aq) \rightarrow Br_2(l) + 2Cl^-(aq)$$

Concept Practice

28. Distinguish between a complete ionic equation and a net ionic equation.

Practice Problems

29. Write a balanced net ionic equation for each reaction.
a. $Pb(ClO_4)_2(aq) + NaI(aq) \rightarrow PbI_2(s) + NaClO_4(aq)$
b. $Zn(s) + HCl(aq) \rightarrow ZnCl_2(aq) + H_2(g)$
c. $Ca(OH)_2(aq) + H_3PO_4(aq) \rightarrow Ca_3(PO_4)_2(aq) + H_2O(l)$

30. Complete each equation and write a net ionic equation.
a. $Al(s) + H_2SO_4(aq) \rightarrow$
b. $HCl(aq) + Ba(OH)_2(aq) \rightarrow$

Composites

Greater Than the Sum of Their Parts

Have you noticed that cars are "losing weight" lately? Thanks to new uses for a family of materials called composites, cars have been getting lighter in weight. Composites are less dense than metals traditionally used to manufacture cars.

Composites can be made by embedding fibers in a plastic base. The fibers may be glass, graphite, or a synthetic fabric such as nylon. The strength of the fibers, combined with the flexibility of the plastic, produces a material that is remarkably strong, yet low in density. In addition, composites are noncorrosive and they absorb vibrations. Some composites can even be made out of recycled plastic beverage containers. All these properties combine to make composites unique and valuable materials.

The advantages of manufacturing cars out of composites instead of metals are many. Cars weigh less, so they would use less fuel. Cars would also be stronger, providing better protection for the passengers. Because composites absorb vibrations, the cars would be quieter and smoother riding than steel-framed models. Also, cars made of composites would not rust or corrode. Many sports car bodies are now made almost entirely of composites. Most car manufacturers have been replacing some steel and chrome parts with composites in their newer models.

The unique properties of composites make them valuable for other applications, too. Because they are strong but low in density, composites are now being used to build satellites, military aircraft, and personal airplanes. Their shock-absorbing properties make composites ideal for sports equipment such as tennis racquets, baseball bats, and golf clubs. Thanks to composites, artificial limbs can be made that are less dense and stronger than ever before.

Surprisingly, composites are not a new idea. Fiberglass, one of the first composites to be manufactured, has been around for many years. Fiberglass was

invented during World War I as a substitute for asbestos. Materials scientists are finding new uses for composites every day. One of the newest kinds of composites is composite "lumber." Beams made from this material look like wood, can be cut and nailed like wood, but are stronger and safe from termites. Composite "lumber" can even be made from recycled plastics—saving money, trees, and the environment, too.

Think About It

31. Contrast List several advantages of using composites instead of metal in cars.

32. Analyze Many items you use are made of composites. What are the advantages to you?

Chapter 7 Review
Chemical Reactions

Key Terms

activity series of metals *7.8*
balanced equation *7.4*
catalyst *7.2*
chemical equation *7.2*
coefficient *7.4*
combination reaction *7.6*
combustion reaction *7.10*
complete ionic equation *7.12*
decomposition reaction *7.7*
double-replacement reaction *7.9*
net ionic equation *7.12*
single-replacement reaction *7.8*
skeleton equation *7.2*
spectator ion *7.12*

Chapter Summary

A chemical reaction can be concisely represented by a chemical equation. The substances that undergo a chemical change are the reactants. The new substances formed are the products. In accordance with the law of conservation of mass, a chemical equation must be balanced. In balancing an equation, coefficients are placed in front of the reactants and products so that the same number of atoms of each element appears on each side of the equation.

Special symbols are written after formulas in equations to show a substance's state. The designations for a solid, liquid, and gas are *(s)*, *(l)*, and *(g)*, respectively. A substance dissolved in water is designated *(aq)*. If a catalyst is used to increase the speed of a chemical reaction, its formula or symbol is written above the arrow.

Many chemical equations can be classified as to type. In a combination reaction, there is always a single product. The reactants are two or more elements and/or compounds. In a decomposition reaction, a single compound is broken down into two or more simpler substances.

In a single-replacement reaction, the reactants and products are an element and a compound. A double-replacement reaction involves exchange of cations (or anions) between two compounds. One of the reactants in a combustion reaction is oxygen. Both single- and double-replacement reactions can be written as net ionic equations.

Practice Questions and Problems

33. Identify the reactants and products in each chemical reaction. *7.1*
   a. Hydrogen gas and sodium hydroxide are formed when sodium is dropped into water.
   b. In photosynthesis, carbon dioxide and water react to form oxygen gas and glucose.

34. How did John Dalton explain a chemical reaction using his atomic theory? *7.1*

35. Write formulas and other symbols for these substances. *7.2*
   a. sulfur trioxide gas
   b. potassium nitrate dissolved in water
   c. heat supplied to a chemical reaction
   d. metallic copper
   e. liquid mercury
   f. zinc chloride as a catalyst

36. What is the purpose of a catalyst? *7.2*

37. Write a sentence that describes each chemical reaction. *7.2*
   a. $2KOH(aq) + H_2SO_4(aq) \rightarrow 2H_2O(l) + K_2SO_4(aq)$
   b. $2Na(s) + 2H_2O(l) \rightarrow 2NaOH(aq) + H_2(g)$
   c. $FeO(s) + C(s) \xrightarrow{\Delta} Fe(s) + CO(g)$

38. Write an equation for making an automobile from the given parts: body (B), wheel (W), engine (E), headlight (H), and taillight (T). *7.3*

39. Balance the following equations *7.4*
   a. $CS_2 + Cl_2 \rightarrow CCl_4 + S_2Cl_2$
   b. $AgNO_3 + H_2S \rightarrow Ag_2S + HNO_3$
   c. $Zn(OH)_2 + H_3PO_4 \rightarrow Zn_3(PO_4)_2 + H_2O$
   d. $CO + Fe_2O_3 \rightarrow Fe + CO_2$
   e. $C_6H_5OH + O_2 \rightarrow CO_2 + H_2O$
   f. $KClO_4 \rightarrow KCl + O_2$

40. How is the law of conservation of mass related to the balancing of a chemical equation? *7.4*

41. Why is it useful to classify reactions? *7.5*

42. What is a characteristic of every combination reaction? *7.6*

43. Complete and balance these combination reactions. *7.6*

a. $Be + O_2 \rightarrow$ **c.** $Sr + I_2 \rightarrow$

b. $SO_2 + H_2O \rightarrow$ **d.** $Mg + N_2 \rightarrow$

44. What is a distinguishing feature of every decomposition reaction? *7.7*

45. Complete and balance these decomposition reactions. In some cases one of the decomposition products is given. *7.7*

a. $OF_2 \rightarrow$ **c.** $Mg(ClO_3)_2 \rightarrow MgCl_2 + O_2$

b. $HI \rightarrow$ **d.** $H_2O_2 \rightarrow H_2O +$

46. Complete the equations for these single-replacement reactions that take place in water solution. Balance each equation. If a reaction does not occur (use the activity series), write "no reaction." *7.8*

a. $Fe + Pb(NO_3)_2 \rightarrow$ **c.** $Cu + H_2O \rightarrow$

b. $F_2 + NaBr \rightarrow$ **d.** $Al + CuSO_4 \rightarrow$

47. What are the three "driving forces" for double-replacement reactions? *7.9*

48. Write the products of these double-replacement reactions. Then balance each equation. Assume that each reaction will occur. *7.9*

a. $H_2C_2O_4 + KOH \rightarrow$

b. $CdBr_2 + Na_2S \rightarrow$

c. $NaOH + Fe(NO_3)_3 \rightarrow$

d. $Ba(NO_3)_2 + H_3PO_4 \rightarrow$

e. $NaC_2H_3O_2 + AgNO_3 \rightarrow$

49. Write a balanced equation for the complete combustion of each of these compounds. *7.10*

a. formic acid, HCOOH

b. heptane, C_7H_{16}

c. glycerol, $C_3H_8O_3$

d. acetone, C_3H_6O

50. Balance each of these equations. Identify each as to type. *7.11*

a. $Pb(NO_3)_2 + K_2CrO_4 \rightarrow PbCrO_4 + KNO_3$

b. $Cl_2 + KI \rightarrow KCl + I_2$

c. $C_3H_6 + O_2 \rightarrow CO_2 + H_2O$

d. $Al(OH)_3 \rightarrow Al_2O_3 + H_2O$

e. $Li + O_2 \rightarrow Li_2O$

51. Write a balanced net ionic equation for each reaction. *7.12*

a. $Pb(NO_3)_2(aq) + H_2SO_4(aq) \rightarrow PbSO_4(s) + HNO_3(aq)$

b. $Pb(C_2H_3O_2)_2(aq) + HCl(aq) \rightarrow PbCl_2(s) + HC_2H_3O_2(aq)$

c. $Na_3PO_4(aq) + FeCl_3(aq) \rightarrow NaCl(aq) + FePO_4(s)$

d. $(NH_4)_2S(aq) + Co(NO_3)_2(aq) \rightarrow CoS(s) + NH_4NO_3(aq)$

52. Identify the spectator ions in each of the reactions in Problem 51. *7.12*

Mastery Questions and Problems

53. Make a concept map using replacement reactions as the main concept. Include appropriate key terms from the chapter plus the following: exchange of ions, gas, ionic compounds, molecular compound, precipitate, reactants, and products.

54. Each of these equations is "balanced" but incorrect. Find the errors and correctly balance each equation.

a. $Cl_2 + NaI \rightarrow NaCl_2 + I$

b. $NH_3 \rightarrow N + H_3$

c. $Na + O_2 \rightarrow NaO_2$

d. $2Mg + H_2SO_4 \rightarrow Mg_2SO_4 + H_2$

e. $MgCl + CaOH \rightarrow MgOH + CaCl$

f. $H_2 + Cl_2 \rightarrow H_2Cl_2$

55. Write a balanced chemical equation for each of these reactions. Use the necessary symbols from Table 7.1 to describe the reaction completely.

a. Bubbling chlorine gas through a solution of potassium iodide gives elemental iodine and a solution of potassium chloride.

b. Bubbles of hydrogen gas and aqueous iron(III) chloride are produced when metallic iron is dropped into hydrochloric acid.

c. Solid tetraphosphorus decoxide reacts with water to produce phosphoric acid.

d. Solid silver oxide can be heated to give silver and oxygen gas.

56. Write balanced chemical equations for these double-replacement reactions that occur in aqueous solution.
a. Zinc sulfide is added to sulfuric acid.
b. Sodium hydroxide reacts with nitric acid.
c. A solution of calcium iodide is poured into a solution of mercury(II) nitrate.
d. Solutions of potassium fluoride and calcium nitrate are mixed.

57. Write a balanced chemical equation for each of these combination reactions.
a. sodium oxide + water →
b. hydrogen + bromine →
c. aluminum + chlorine →
d. dichlorine heptoxide + water →

58. Write a balanced chemical equation for each of these single-replacement reactions that take place in water solution. Then balance each equation. Write "no reaction" if they do not occur.
a. A piece of steel wool (iron) is placed in sulfuric acid.
b. A piece of silver jewelry is dropped in hydrochloric acid.
c. Mercury is poured into an aqueous solution of zinc nitrate.
d. Bromine reacts with aqueous barium iodide.

59. Test tubes A and B contain water. A piece of sodium metal has been dropped in one test tube, a piece of magnesium metal in the other.
a. Which tube contains the sodium metal?
b. Write an equation for the reaction in the tube containing the sodium metal.
c. What type of reaction is occurring in this tube?

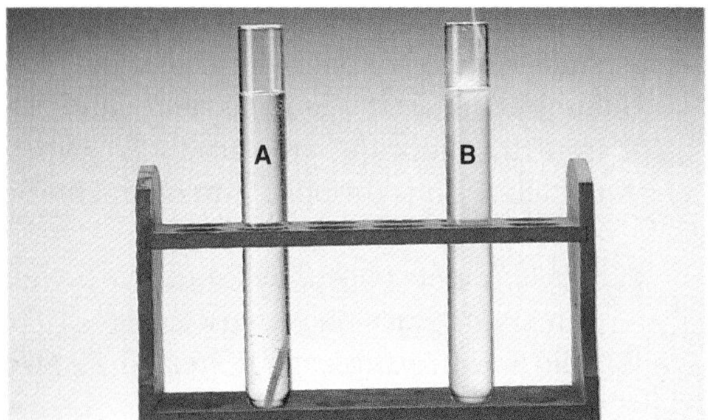

60. Write a balanced equation for the complete combustion of each compound. Assume that the products are carbon dioxide and water.
a. octane, C_8H_{18} **c.** acetylene, C_2H_2
b. glucose, $C_6H_{12}O_6$ **d.** acetic acid, $HC_2H_3O_2$

61. Write balanced chemical equations for these decomposition reactions.
a. Aluminum can be obtained from aluminum oxide with the addition of a large amount of electrical energy.
b. Heating tin(IV) hydroxide gives tin(IV) oxide and water.
c. Passing an electric current through melted crystals of magnesium chloride decomposes it into its elements.
d. Silver carbonate decomposes into silver oxide and carbon dioxide when it is heated.

62. Write a balanced net ionic equation for each of the reactions in Problem 48. The product that is *not* in solution is given.
a. H_2O **d.** $Ba_3(PO_4)_2$
b. CdS **e.** $AgC_2H_3O_2$
c. $Fe(OH)_3$

Critical Thinking Questions

63. Choose the term that best completes the second relationship.
a. charcoal:ashes reactant: ____
(1) equation (3) heat
(2) reaction (4) product
b. tool:hammer catalyst: ____
(1) reaction (3) sulfur
(2) MnO_2 (4) combustion
c. east:west combination: ____
(1) decomposition (3) coefficient
(2) reaction (4) replacement

64. Why is no smoking permitted near an oxygen source? What would happen if a match were struck in an empty room filled with oxygen?

65. A student was cooking. In the process, a pan of grease caught fire. Although a Class A fire extinguisher was available, the student put out the fire without it. Propose a method for how she put out the fire safely.

Cumulative Review

66. Calculate the number of moles in each of the following substances.
  a. 54.0 L nitrogen dioxide (at STP)
  b. 1.68 g magnesium ions
  c. 69.6 g sodium hypochlorite
  d. 4.27×10^{24} molecules carbon monoxide

67. What mass of gold (density = 19.3 g/cm^3) occupies the same volume as 2.20 mol of aluminum (density = 2.70 g/cm^3)?

68. Many coffees and colas contain the stimulant caffeine. The percent composition of caffeine is 49.5% C, 5.20% H, 16.5% O, and 28.9% N. What is the molecular formula of caffeine if its molar mass is 194.1 g/mol?

69. The white solid calcium chloride, $CaCl_2$, is used as a drying agent. The maximum amount of water absorbed by different quantities of $CaCl_2$ is given in the following table.
  a. Complete the table.
  b. Plot the moles of water absorbed (*y* axis) versus the moles of $CaCl_2$.
  c. Based on your graph, how many molecules of water does each formula unit of $CaCl_2$ absorb?

$CaCl_2$ (g)	$CaCl_2$ (mol)	H_2O (g)	H_2O (mol)
17.3	___	5.62	___
48.8	___	15.8	___
124	___	40.3	___
337	___	109	___

Challenge Questions and Problems

70. Write balanced chemical equations for each of these reactions. Classify each as to type.
  a. Sodium iodide reacts with phosphoric acid.
  b. Potassium oxide reacts with water.
  c. Heating sulfuric acid produces water, oxygen, and sulfur dioxide.
  d. Aluminum reacts with sulfuric acid.
  e. Pentane, C_5H_{12}, reacts with oxygen.

71. The mass of a proton and the mass of an electron are 1.67×10^{-24} g and 9.11×10^{-28} g, respectively. **a.** What are the masses of a mole of protons and a mole of electrons? **b.** How many electrons are equal in mass to one proton?

72. Complete and balance these equations.
  a. $H_2O_2 \rightarrow$
  b. $Al + Cl_2 \rightarrow$
  c. $Bi(NO_3)_3 + H_2S \rightarrow$
  d. $Br_2 + NaI \rightarrow$
  e. $K + H_2O \rightarrow$
  f. $C_2H_5OH + O_2 \rightarrow$
  g. $Ba(OH)_2 + HNO_3 \rightarrow$

Connections Questions

73. What is an enzyme? What is the function of the enzyme catalase?

74. List some accomplishments of St. Elmo Brady.

75. Write the balanced chemical equation for the combustion of acetylene in the oxyacetylene torch.

Write About Chemistry

76. Describe your activities in a typical day, including references to at least five chemical reactions that you observed.

77. Imagine that you are a carbon atom in a methane molecule (CH_4). Describe what happens as your methane molecule is burned.

Readings and References

Marsella, Gail. "Fireside Dreams." *ChemMatters* (December 1988), pp. 13–15.

Smith, Trevor. "Camping Stoves." *ChemMatters* (April 1992), pp. 7–11.

Zurer, Pamela. "Aviation Industry Grapples with Halon Ban." *Chemistry & Engineering News* (February 15, 1993), p. 5.

8 Stoichiometry

Goals

- Calculate quantities of reactants and products needed in chemical reactions using a balanced chemical equation.
- Identify the limiting reagent in a chemical reaction.
- Calculate the percent yield in a chemical reaction.

Do you think you could stand on one foot for 34 hours? You'd have to do better than that to beat the world record. In this feat, balance is crucial. Similarly, chemical equations must be balanced in order to be useful in calculations.

Concept Overview

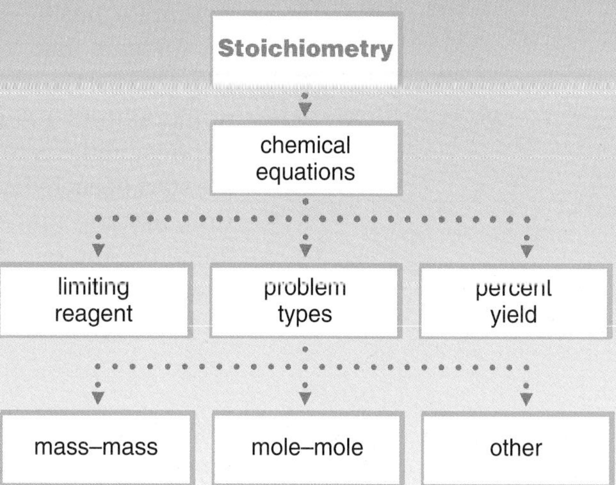

The Concept Overview organizes the major concepts of this chapter. This diagram shows one way to link these concepts related to stoichiometry.

Chemicals are used in the manufacture of almost everything you use. The cost of making anything cannot be higher than the money you pay for it, or the manufacturer could not make a profit. Therefore, the chemical processes used in manufacturing must be carried out economically. This is where balanced chemical equations help. Balanced chemical equations are the recipes that tell chemists what amounts of reactants to mix and what amounts of products to expect.

You can calculate the quantities of reactants and products in a reaction from the balanced equation. When you know the quantity of one substance in a reaction, you can calculate the quantity of any other substance created or consumed in the reaction. Quantity usually means the amount of a substance expressed in grams or moles. Quantity could just as well be in liters, tons, or molecules. **Stoichiometry** *is the calculation of quantities in chemical equations.* For chemists it is a form of bookkeeping. Calculations using balanced equations are called *stoichiometric* calculations.

Roots of Words

stoikheion: (Greek) element
metron: (Greek) to measure
stoichiometry the calculation of amounts of substances involved in chemical reactions.

8.1 Interpreting Everyday Equations

Objective

Calculate the amount of reactants required or product formed in a nonchemical process.

When you bake cookies you probably use a recipe. A cookie recipe tells you the amounts of ingredients to mix together to make a certain number of cookies. If you need a larger number of cookies than the recipe provides, the amount of ingredients can be doubled or tripled. A cookie recipe, in fact, gives you the same kind of information that a balanced chemical equation provides. The ingredients

Chemistry in Careers

Quality Control Chemist

The quality control chemist is responsible for seeing that products meet manufacturing standards. Quality control chemists work in a wide variety of industries. These include companies that process or manufacture foods, cosmetics, and plastics. Quality control chemists must know how to make and interpret measurements. Experience in analytical chemistry and the ability to develop new analytical methods are particularly important. A good quality control chemist assures that his or her company's customers receive the highest-quality products.

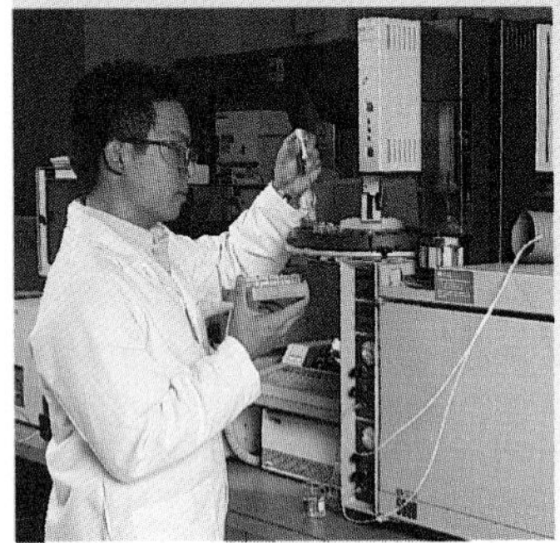

are the reactants; the cookies are the products. Similar examples exist in the business world.

Imagine that you are in charge of manufacturing for the Tiny Tike Tricycle Company. The business plan for Tiny Tike requires the production of 128 custom-made tricycles each day. One of your responsibilities is to be sure that there are enough parts available at the start of each day to make these tricycles. To simplify the discussion, assume that the major components of the tricycle are the frame (F), the seat (S), the wheels (W), the handlebars (H), and the pedals (P). The finished tricycle has a "formula" of FSW_3HP_2. The skeleton equation for making a tricycle is

$$F + S + W + H + P \rightarrow FSW_3HP_2$$

The balanced equation is

$$F + S + 3W + H + 2P \rightarrow FSW_3HP_2$$

This equation gives you the "recipe" to make a single tricycle. To make a tricycle requires one frame, one seat, three wheels, one handlebar, and two pedals. The equation also allows you to calculate the number of parts needed to make 128 tricycles.

Example 1 Using an Equation As a Recipe

How many pedals are needed to make 128 tricycles?

Solution

The unknown is the number of pedals.
The known is the number of tricycles to be made, 128 tricycles.

The balanced equation shows that two pedals are necessary to make each tricycle:

$$2P \,/\, 1\, FSW_3HP_2$$

A solution is

$$128\cancel{FSW_3HP_2} \times \frac{2P}{1\cancel{FSW_3HP_2}} = 256P$$

F + S + 3W + H + 2P → FSW_3HP_2

Figure 8.1 A balanced equation can be thought of as a recipe. In this equation the separate parts are the reactants and the tricycle is the product.

Example 2 Finding the Amount of a Reactant

In a 5-day work week, Tiny Tike is scheduled to make 640 tricycles. How many wheels should be in the plant on Monday morning to ensure that these tricycles can be made?

Solution

The unknown is the number of wheels. The known is 640 tricycles. According to the balanced equation, three wheels are required for each tricycle.

$$640\cancel{FSW_3HP_2} \times \frac{3W}{1\cancel{FSW_3HP_2}} = 1920W$$

Problem-Solving Tip

The unit of the denominator of the conversion factor must equal the unit of the given measurement.

Concept Practice

1. Write an equation that gives your own "recipe" for making a puppet or a piece of furniture.

Practice Problem

2. How many tricycle seats, wheels, and pedals are needed to make 288 tricycles?

8.2 Interpreting Chemical Equations

Objective

Interpret balanced chemical equations in terms of interacting moles, representative particles, masses, and volume (gases at STP).

Ammonia is widely used as a fertilizer. Ammonia is produced industrially by the reaction of nitrogen with hydrogen.

$$N_2(g) + 3H_2(g) \longrightarrow 2NH_3(g)$$

What kinds of information can you derive from this equation?

1. Particles One molecule of nitrogen reacts with three molecules of hydrogen to produce two molecules of ammonia. Nitrogen and hydrogen will always react to form ammonia in this 1:3:2 ratio of molecules. If you could make 10 molecules of nitrogen react with 30 molecules of hydrogen, you would expect to get 20 molecules of ammonia. Of course, it is not possible to count small numbers of molecules and allow them to react. You could, however, take Avogadro's number of nitrogen molecules and react them with three times Avogadro's number of hydrogen molecules. This would be the same 1:3 ratio of molecules of the reactants. This reaction would form two times Avogadro's number of ammonia molecules.

Integrating Philosophy

Chemistry, Is It a Science?

Jeremiah Richter, an eighteenth-century German mathematician and scientist, demonstrated some of the important mathematical relationships of chemical stoichiometry. Richter probably attended university lectures in which Immanuel Kant, the famous philosopher, discussed the nature of science. Kant proposed that because the chemistry of the time was based on observation and not mathematics, it was not a true science. Richter, however, succeeded in establishing mathematical (stoichiometric) relationships between the masses of reactants and products. Thus, chemistry met Kant's criterion for a science, as demonstrated by Richter.

2. Moles You know that Avogadro's number of representative particles is 1 mol of a substance. On the basis of the particle interpretation just given, this equation tells you the number of moles of reactants and products. One mole of nitrogen molecules reacts with three moles of hydrogen molecules. These starting materials react chemically to form two moles of ammonia molecules. This is the most important information that a chemical equation provides. *The coefficients of a balanced chemical equation give you the relative numbers of moles of reactants and products in the chemical reaction.* Using this information, you can calculate the amounts of reactants and products.

3. Mass A balanced chemical equation must obey the law of conservation of mass. The mole interpretation supports this. Remember that mass is related to the number of atoms in the chemical equation through moles. The mass of 1 mol of nitrogen (28.0 g) plus the mass of 3 mol of hydrogen (6.0 g) does equal the mass of 2 mol of ammonia (34.0 g).

4. Volume If you assume standard temperature and pressure, this equation also tells you about the volumes of gases. Recall that 1 mol of any gas at STP occupies a volume of 22.4 L. It follows that 22.4 L of nitrogen reacts with 67.2 L (3 × 22.4 L) of hydrogen to form 44.8 L (2 × 22.4 L) of ammonia.

$N_2(g)$	+	$3H_2(g)$	→	$2NH_3(g)$
	+		→	
2 atoms N	+	6 atoms H	→	2 atoms N and 6 atoms H
1 molecule N_2	+	3 molecules H_2	→	2 molecules NH_3
10 molecules N_2	+	30 molecules H_2	→	20 molecules NH_3
$1 \times \left(\begin{array}{c}6.02 \times 10^{23}\\ \text{molecules } N_2\end{array}\right)$	+	$3 \times \left(\begin{array}{c}6.02 \times 10^{23}\\ \text{molecules } H_2\end{array}\right)$	→	$2 \times \left(\begin{array}{c}6.02 \times 10^{23}\\ \text{molecules } NH_3\end{array}\right)$
1 mol N_2	+	3 mol H_2	→	2 mol NH_3
28g N_2	+	3 × 2g H_2	→	2 × 17g NH_3
		34g reactants	→	34g products
Assume STP 22.4 L 22.4 L N_2	+	22.4 L 22.4 L 22.4 L 67.2 L H_2	→	22.4 L 22.4 L 44.8 L NH_3

Figure 8.2 The balanced chemical equation for the formation of ammonia can be interpreted in several ways.

Notice in Figure 8.2 that mass and the number of atoms are conserved in this chemical reaction. Mass and atoms will be conserved in every chemical reaction. The mass of the reactants equals the mass of the products. Representative particles, moles, and volumes of gases will not necessarily be conserved, although they may. Take, for example, the formation of hydrogen iodide.

$$H_2(g) + I_2(g) \longrightarrow 2HI(g)$$

In this reaction, moles, molecules, and volume all happen to be conserved. In the majority of reactions, however, they are not. In the formation of ammonia, moles, molecules, and volume of gas are not conserved. *Recall that only mass and atoms are conserved in every chemical reaction.*

Example 3 Interpreting a Balanced Chemical Equation

Foul-smelling hydrogen sulfide gas is found in nature. Interpret this balanced chemical equation for the burning of hydrogen sulfide in terms of the interaction of relative quantities in the following three ways.

a. number of representative particles
b. number of moles
c. masses of reactants and products

$$2H_2S(g) + 3O_2(g) \longrightarrow 2SO_2(g) + 2H_2O(g)$$

Solution

a. Two molecules of H_2S react with three molecules of O_2 to form two molecules of SO_2 and two molecules of H_2O.
b. Two moles of H_2S react with 3 mol of O_2 to produce 2 mol of SO_2 and 2 mol of H_2O.
c. $2 \text{ mol } H_2S + 3 \text{ mol } O_2 \longrightarrow 2 \text{ mol } SO_2 + 2 \text{ mol } H_2O$

$$(2\,\cancel{\text{mol}} \times 34.1\text{ g}/\cancel{\text{mol}}) + (3\,\cancel{\text{mol}} \times 32.0\text{ g}/\cancel{\text{mol}}) \longrightarrow (2\,\cancel{\text{mol}} \times 64.1\text{ g}/\cancel{\text{mol}}) + (2\,\cancel{\text{mol}} \times 18.0\text{ g}/\cancel{\text{mol}})$$

$$68.2\text{ g} + 96.0\text{ g} \longrightarrow 128.2\text{ g} + 36.0\text{ g}$$

$$164.2\text{ g} = 164.2\text{ g}$$

Figure 8.3 Hydrogen sulfide (H_2S) smells like rotten eggs. It escapes from the ground through fumaroles in volcanic areas.

Concept Practice

3. Explain what information the coefficients provide in a balanced chemical equation.

4. Explain this statement: "Mass and atoms are conserved in every chemical reaction but moles are not necessarily conserved." Hint: Use balanced chemical equations to illustrate your answer.

Practice Problem

5. After balancing each of these equations, interpret them in terms of relative quantities in four ways: (1) number of representative particles, (2) number of moles, (3) masses of reactants and products, (4) volumes of gases at STP (where appropriate).
a. $H_2(g) + O_2(g) \longrightarrow H_2O(g)$
b. $C_2H_2(g) + O_2(g) \longrightarrow CO_2(g) + H_2O(l)$
c. $K(s) + H_2O(l) \longrightarrow KOH(aq) + H_2(g)$

Objective

Construct mole ratios from balanced chemical equations and apply these ratios in calculating mole–mole stoichiometric quantities.

8.3 Mole–Mole Calculations

To produce ammonia in an industrial plant like the one shown in Figure 8.4, hydrogen and nitrogen are reacted in the proper proportions. Return now to the balanced equation for the production of ammonia.

$$N_2(g) + 3H_2(g) \longrightarrow 2NH_3(g)$$

The most important interpretation of this equation is that 1 mol of nitrogen reacts with 3 mol of hydrogen to form 2 mol of ammonia. With this interpretation you can relate moles of reactants to moles of products. You use the coefficients from the balanced equation to write conversion factors. Then you calculate the number of moles of product from a given number of moles of reactant. Using other mole-quantity relationships, you can introduce mass, volume, and particles into your calculations.

Figure 8.4 This manufacturing plant produces ammonia by combining nitrogen with hydrogen. Ammonia is used in cleaning products, fertilizers, and in the manufacture of other chemicals.

Example 4 Calculating Moles of a Product

How many moles of ammonia are produced when 0.60 mol of nitrogen reacts with hydrogen?

Solution

You will work from a known number of moles of N_2 to the unknown number of moles of NH_3:

$$\text{mole } N_2 \longrightarrow \text{? mol } NH_3$$

From the balanced equation just given, you can see that 1 mol of N_2 produces 2 mol of NH_3. This relationship can be written as a conversion factor relating N_2 and NH_3. The conversion factor is called a *mole ratio.*

$$\frac{1 \text{ mol } N_2}{2 \text{ mol } NH_3} \quad or \quad \frac{2 \text{ mol } NH_3}{1 \text{ mol } N_2}$$

To solve the problem, you start with the given quantity, 0.60 mol of N_2. You then multiply it by the form of the mole ratio that allows the given unit to cancel.

$$0.60 \cancel{\text{mol } N_2} \times \frac{2 \text{ mol } NH_3}{1 \cancel{\text{mol } N_2}} = 1.2 \text{ mol } NH_3$$

Note that mole ratios from balanced equations are considered to be exact (defined numbers). They do not enter into the determination of significant figures in the answer.

Problem-Solving Tip

Stoichiometry problems are easily solved using dimensional analysis.

Example 5 Calculating Moles of a Reactant

Calculate the number of moles of (a) nitrogen and (b) hydrogen that are required to make 7.24 mol of ammonia.

$$N_2(g) + 3H_2(g) \longrightarrow 2NH_3(g)$$

Solution

The conversions are similar:

a. mol $NH_3 \longrightarrow$ mol N_2 **b.** mol $NH_3 \longrightarrow$ mol H_2.

From the balanced equation you can get mole ratios relating each of the reactants to the product.

$$\frac{1 \text{ mol } N_2}{2 \text{ mol } NH_3} \quad or \quad \frac{2 \text{ mol } NH_3}{1 \text{ mol } N_2} \quad and \quad \frac{3 \text{ mol } H_2}{2 \text{ mol } NH_3} \quad or \quad \frac{2 \text{ mol } NH_3}{3 \text{ mol } H_2}$$

In each case, start with the given amount of product. Multiply by the appropriate mole ratio so that the given unit cancels.

a. $7.24 \cancel{\text{mol NH}_3} \times \frac{1 \text{ mol N}_2}{2 \cancel{\text{mol NH}_3}} = 3.62 \text{ mol N}_2$

b. $7.24 \cancel{\text{mol NH}_3} \times \frac{3 \text{ mol H}_2}{2 \cancel{\text{mol NH}_3}} = 10.86 = 10.9 \text{ mol H}_2$

Each solution in these two examples follows the same pattern. The moles of the given quantity, (G), whether reactant or product, are multiplied by a mole ratio with the given in the denominator.

$$\frac{b \text{ moles of W}}{a \text{ moles of G}}$$

In this mole ratio, *W* is the wanted quantity. The values of *a* and *b* are the coefficients from the balanced equation. A general solution for a mole-mole problem is given by the following equation

$$\underset{\text{Given}}{\frac{x \cancel{\text{mol } G}}{1}} \times \underset{\text{Mole ratio}}{\frac{b \text{ mol } W}{a \cancel{\text{mol } G}}} = \underset{\text{Calculated}}{\frac{xb \text{ mol } W}{a}}$$

Concept Practice

6. Explain the term *mole ratio* in your own words. When would you use it?

Practice Problems

7. The formation of aluminum oxide from its constituent elements is represented by this equation.

$$4\text{Al} + 3\text{O}_2 \longrightarrow 2\text{Al}_2\text{O}_3$$

a. Write the six mole ratios that can be derived from this equation.
b. How many moles of aluminum are needed to form 3.7 mol of Al_2O_3?
c. How many moles of oxygen are required to react completely with 14.8 mol of Al?
d. Calculate the number of moles of Al_2O_3 formed when 0.78 mol of O_2 reacts with aluminum.

8.A Science, Technology, and Society

Forensic Chemistry

Does the blood on a murder victim's hand belong to the victim or to the murderer? Does the charred material from a warehouse fire show any signs that a chemical was used to spread the fire? Is the ink on a document really 20 years old, or was it forged last week?

Forensic chemistry is involved with the collection and representation of evidence that may be used in a court of law. Most forensic laboratories handle evidence involved in criminal cases. Several hundred such "crime labs" exist in the United States and Canada. Other forensic laboratories prepare evidence in cases concerning violations of federal or state regulations. These may involve the chemical compositions of pollutants, imported materials, or products sold to the public. In both types of forensic laboratories, standard methods are used for the analysis and comparison of materials. Because the materials may be used in a court case, however, they must be collected, preserved, and analyzed according to very strict and well-documented methods. Forensic chemists often testify in court as expert witnesses about evidence from a crime scene.

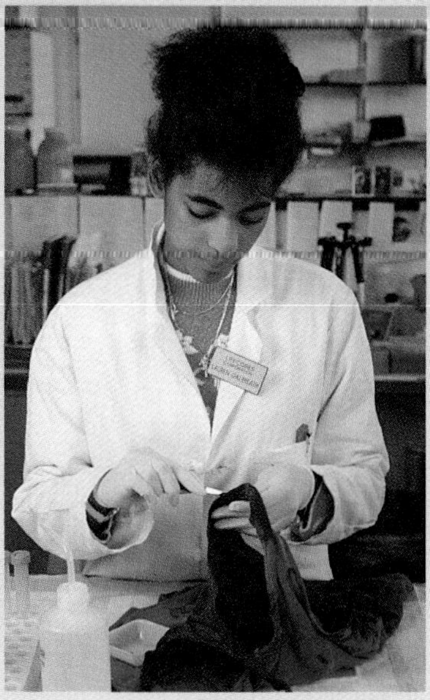

Figure 8.5 Evidence from a crime must be carefully collected, analyzed, and preserved.

In a crime laboratory body fluids and internal organs are commonly analyzed for poison, drugs, and alcohol. Similarly, analyses of other aspects of the crime scene are performed. Blood, saliva, and hair can be typed. Charred documents can be restored, and fire debris can be analyzed. Many tests must be run on very tiny samples. Sometimes the tests must measure the exact amount of some specific substance in a sample, as in the analysis of pills for drugs. This requires the techniques of quantitative analysis. Often the tests only compare a material to some other sample, as in matching the paint on a crowbar to the paint on a door. These tests employ the methods of qualitative analysis.

Think About It

8. Create Imagine that you want to become a forensic chemist. Write a list of the courses you would take and the skills you would acquire to become a successful forensic chemist.

9. Distinguish Some methods used in forensic chemistry are quantitative. Others are qualitative. Use examples to differentiate between the two types of methods.

Objective

Calculate stoichiometric quantities from balanced chemical equations using units of mass.

8.4 Mass–Mass Calculations

No laboratory balance can measure substances directly in moles. Instead, as you can see in Figure 8.6, the amount of a substance is typically determined by measuring its mass in grams. From the mass of a reactant or product, you can calculate the mass of any other reactant or product in a given chemical equation. You can do this by using the mole interpretation of a balanced equation. If the given sample is measured in grams, you can use the gram formula mass to convert the mass to moles. Then you use the mole ratio from the balanced equation to calculate the unknown. Similarly, if you need to know the mass of the unknown, you can find the number of moles of unknown first. Then you can use the gram formula mass to calculate the mass of the unknown. As in mole–mole calculations, the unknown can be either a reactant or a product.

Figure 8.6 To determine the number of moles in a sample of a compound, first measure the mass of the sample. Then use the gram formula mass to calculate the number of moles in that mass.

Problem-Solving Tip

Check that the answer has the appropriate unit after canceling and before doing the numerical calculations.

Example 6 Finding the Mass of a Product

Calculate the number of grams of NH_3 produced by the reaction of 5.40 g of hydrogen with an excess of nitrogen. The balanced equation is given.

$$N_2(g) + 3H_2(g) \longrightarrow 2NH_3(g)$$

Solution

You are given the mass, in grams, of hydrogen and asked to find the mass, in grams, of ammonia:

$$\text{g } H_2 \longrightarrow \text{g } NH_3$$

The coefficients in the equation tell you that 3 mol of H_2 can react with 1 mol of N_2 to produce 2 mol of NH_3. Thus you need two more steps to do the calculation:

$$\text{g } H_2 \longrightarrow \text{mol } H_2 \longrightarrow \text{mol } NH_3 \longrightarrow \text{g } NH_3$$

First, change the given, 5.40 g of H_2, to moles by using the gram formula mass of hydrogen: g $H_2 \longrightarrow$ mol H_2.

$$5.40 \cancel{\text{g } H_2} \times \frac{1 \text{ mol } H_2}{2.0 \cancel{\text{g } H_2}} = 2.70 \text{ mol } H_2$$

Now, use the mole ratio from the equation to calculate the number of moles of NH_3: mol $H_2 \longrightarrow$ mol NH_3.

$$2.70 \cancel{\text{mol } H_2} \times \frac{2 \text{ mol } NH_3}{3 \cancel{\text{mol } H_2}} = 1.80 \text{ mol } NH_3$$

Finally, convert 1.80 mol of NH_3 to grams: mol $NH_3 \longrightarrow$ g NH_3. The gram molecular mass of NH_3 is 17.0 g/mol.

$$1.80 \text{ mol } NH_3 \times \frac{17.0 \text{ g } NH_3}{1 \text{ mol } NH_3} = 30.6 \text{ g } NH_3$$

The three steps just described can be combined into one solution:

$$\text{g } H_2 \longrightarrow \text{mol } H_2 \longrightarrow \text{mol } NH_3 \longrightarrow \text{g } NH_3$$

$$\underset{\text{Given quantity}}{5.40 \text{ g } H_2} \times \underset{\text{Change given unit to moles}}{\frac{1 \text{ mol } H_2}{2.0 \text{ g } H_2}} \times \underset{\text{Mole ratio}}{\frac{2 \text{ mol } NH_3}{3 \text{ mol } H_2}} \times \underset{\text{Change moles of "wanted" to grams}}{\frac{17.0 \text{ g } NH_3}{1 \text{ mol } NH_3}} = 30.6 \text{ g } NH_3$$

If the law of conservation of mass is true, how is it possible to make 30.6 g of NH_3 from only 5.40 g of H_2? Check the equation for the reaction. From it you will see that another reactant, nitrogen, is also involved. The compound ammonia has been detected on other planets in our solar system such as Saturn, shown in Figure 8.7.

Figure 8.7 Clouds of condensed ammonia hide the surface of Saturn.

Example 7 Calculating the Mass of a Reactant

How many grams of nitrogen are needed to produce the 30.6 g of NH_3 in the previous example? The equation is the same:

$$N_2(g) + 3H_2(g) \longrightarrow 2NH_3(g)$$

Solution

The balanced equation tells you that 1 mol of N_2 is needed to make 2 mol of NH_3. To use this fact, change the 30.6 g of NH_3 to moles. Then use the mole ratio to find moles of N_2. Finally, change moles of N_2 to grams of N_2. The process is:

$$\text{g } NH_3 \longrightarrow \text{mol } NH_3 \longrightarrow \text{mol } N_2 \longrightarrow \text{g } N_2$$

$$\underset{\text{Given quantity}}{30.6 \text{ g } \cancel{NH_3}} \times \underset{\text{Change given unit to moles}}{\frac{1 \cancel{\text{mol } NH_3}}{17.0 \cancel{\text{g } NH_3}}} \times \underset{\text{Mole ratio}}{\frac{1 \cancel{\text{mol } N_2}}{2 \cancel{\text{mol } NH_3}}} \times \underset{\text{Change moles of "wanted" to grams}}{\frac{28.0 \text{ g } N_2}{1 \cancel{\text{mol } N_2}}} = 25.2 \text{ g } N_2$$

Your answer can be checked by using the law of conservation of mass and the answers from the last two examples.

$$\begin{aligned} \text{Mass of reactants} &= \text{mass of products} \\ \text{Mass of } N_2 + \text{mass } H_2 &= \text{mass of } NH_3 \\ 25.2 \text{ g } N_2 + 5.40 \text{ g } H_2 &= 30.6 \text{ g } NH_3 \\ 30.6 \text{ g of reactants} &= 30.6 \text{ g of product} \end{aligned}$$

You can solve mass–mass stoichiometric problems in basically the same way as mole–mole problems. Figure 8.8 shows the steps.

1. The mass of the given quantity must be changed to moles by using the ratio, 1 mol *G*/gfm *G*: mass *G* ⟶ mol *G*.

2. The moles of *G* are changed to moles of *W* (wanted unit) by using the mole ratio from the balanced equation: mol *G* ⟶ mol *W*.

3. The moles of *W* are changed to grams of *W* by using the ratio, gfm *W*/1 mol *W*: mol *W* ⟶ mass *W*.

From Figure 8.8 you can also see the steps for doing mole–mass and mass–mole stoichiometric calculations. For a mole–mass problem, you skip the first conversion (from mass to moles). For a mass–mole problem, you skip the last conversion (from moles to mass). Thus, you can use parts of the three-step process in Figure 8.8 as they are appropriate to the problem you are solving.

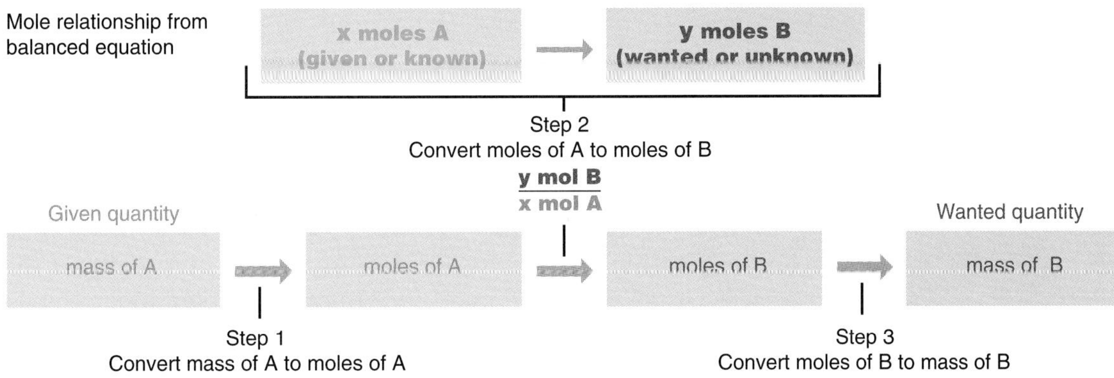

Figure 8.8 This general solution diagram for a mass–mass problem shows the order of steps necessary to convert mass to moles and then moles to mass.

Concept Practice

10. What information about a chemical reaction is derived from the coefficients in a balanced equation?

Practice Problems

11. Acetylene gas, C_2H_2, is produced by adding water to calcium carbide, CaC_2.

$$CaC_2(s) + 2H_2O(l) \longrightarrow C_2H_2(g) + Ca(OH)_2(aq)$$

a. How many moles of CaC_2 are needed to react completely with 49.0 g of H_2O?
b. How many grams of acetylene are produced by adding water to 5.00 g of CaC_2?
c. How many grams of $Ca(OH)_2$ are produced when 0.89 mol of C_2H_2 is produced?
d. How could you prove that this equation obeys the law of conservation of mass?

12. The combustion of acetylene gas is represented by this equation.

$$2C_2H_2(g) + 5O_2(g) \longrightarrow 4CO_2(g) + 2H_2O(g)$$

a. How many grams of CO_2 and grams of H_2O are produced when 52.0 g of C_2H_2 burns?
b. How many grams of oxygen are required to "burn" 52.0 g of C_2H_2?
c. Use the answers from (a) and (b) to show that this equation obeys the law of conservation of mass.

8.B Environmental Awareness

Analysis of Risks and Benefits of Technology

Figure 8.9 As scarce landfill sites fill up, people are looking for ways to decrease the amount of nonrecyclable material they dispose of.

Technologies provide alternatives for products and processes. However, you must weigh the good and bad effects of a given technology. Do the benefits of a technology outweigh the risks to people's health or to the environment?

Take, for example, the choice between reusable cloth diapers and disposable diapers. Parents like disposables for their convenience. Disposable diapers are made from plastic film, which comes from petroleum, a nonrenewable resource, and absorbent paper. Like the cotton in cloth diapers, paper comes from trees, a renewable resource. Disposable diapers are discarded after use, but diapers made from cloth are recycled. The discarded disposables contribute to filling from 0.5 to 1.8 percent of increasingly scarce landfill space. The implication is that recyclable cotton diapers are better for the environment. However, Table 8.1 shows that the situation is more complicated. The manufacture and recycling of cloth diapers waste more energy and consume more water than disposables. Currently, most experts consider that the negative effects of cloth and disposable diapers on the environment are about equal.

The story of cloth versus disposable diapers teaches some lessons about risk-benefit analysis. First, sometimes the effects of a technology are unforeseen. Second, to analyze risks versus benefits, you must gather as much relevant information as possible. Third, you may not find a clear winner among the options.

Table 8.1 Environmental Costs of Cloth and Disposable Diapers (One Week)

	Cloth	Disposable
Raw materials (pounds)	3.6	25.3
Water consumption (gallons)	144.0	23.6
Energy consumption (BTUs)	78 890	23 290
Air emissions (pounds)	0.860	0.093
Water pollution (pounds)	0.117	0.012
Solid waste (pounds)	0.24	22.16

Think About It

13. Appraise What might be the most important considerations in the risk-benefit analysis of a new chemical insecticide for agricultural use?

8.5 Other Stoichiometric Calculations

Objective

Calculate stoichiometric quantities from balanced chemical equations using units of moles, mass, representative particles, and volumes of gases at STP.

A balanced chemical equation shows you the relative number of moles of reactants and products. From this foundation, stoichiometric calculations can be expanded to include any unit of measurement that is related to the mole. The given quantity can be expressed in numbers of representative particles, units of mass, or volumes of gases at STP. The problems can include *mass–volume, volume–volume,* and *particle–mass* calculations. First you convert the given quantity to moles. Then you use the mole ratio from the balanced equation to calculate the number of moles of the wanted substance. Once you have determined this unit, you can convert the moles to any other unit of measurement.

Example 8 Calculating Moles of a Product

How many molecules of oxygen are produced when 29.2 g of water is decomposed according to this balanced equation?

$$2H_2O(l) \xrightarrow{\text{electricity}} 2H_2(g) + O_2(g)$$

Solution

Figure 8.10 shows you the steps to follow.

$$\text{mass } H_2O \longrightarrow \text{mol } H_2O \longrightarrow \text{mol } O_2 \longrightarrow \text{molecules } O_2$$

$$29.2\ \cancel{\text{g } H_2O} \times \frac{1\ \cancel{\text{mol } H_2O}}{18.0\ \cancel{\text{g } H_2O}} \times \frac{1\ \cancel{\text{mol } O_2}}{2\ \cancel{\text{mol } H_2O}} \times \frac{6.02 \times 10^{23} \text{ molecules } O_2}{1\ \cancel{\text{mol } O_2}}$$

$$= 4.88 \times 10^{23} \text{ molecules } O_2$$

Figure 8.10 With your knowledge of conversion factors and this problem-solving diagram you can solve a variety of stoichiometric problems.

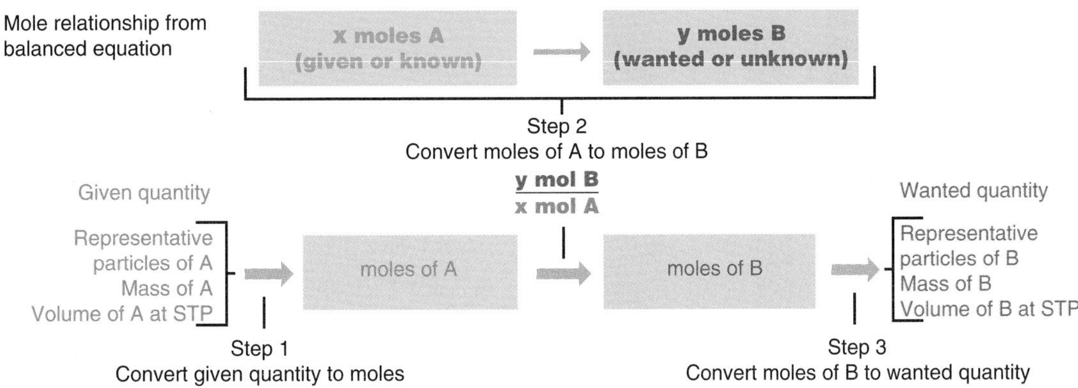

Integrating Biology

Ammonia in the Nitrogen Cycle

Nitrogen is essential to sustaining life on earth. The movement of nitrogen through the ecosystem is called the nitrogen cycle. Although 80% of the air is nitrogen gas, most living things cannot use nitrogen in this form. Ammonia plays an important role in several steps of the nitrogen cycle. Bacteria on the roots of certain plants change atmospheric nitrogen into ammonia molecules and ammonium ions (NH_4^+). Other bacteria break down the nitrogen-rich material in dead plants and animals into these same particles. The bacteria in the soil oxidize the ammonia molecules and ammonium ions into nitrate (NO_3^-), the form of nitrogen that is absorbed by plants through their roots. Also, lightning causes nitrogen to combine with oxygen in the air. The resulting oxides of nitrogen react with water to form HNO_3 and HNO_2, which are washed to earth.

Example 9 Finding the Volume of a Gas Needed for Reaction

Assuming STP, how many liters of oxygen are needed to produce 19.8 L of SO_3 according to this balanced equation?

$$2SO_2(g) + O_2(g) \longrightarrow 2SO_3(g)$$

Solution

Again using Figure 8.10 as a guide, you find the steps to follow are these:

$$\text{liters } SO_3 \longrightarrow \text{moles } SO_3 \longrightarrow \text{moles } O_2 \longrightarrow \text{liters } O_2$$

$$\underset{\text{Given quantity}}{19.8\ \cancel{\text{L } SO_3}} \times \underset{\text{Change to moles}}{\frac{1\ \cancel{\text{mol } SO_3}}{22.4\ \cancel{\text{L } SO_3}}} \times \underset{\text{Mole ratio}}{\frac{1\ \cancel{\text{mol } O_2}}{2\ \cancel{\text{mol } SO_3}}} \times \underset{\text{Change to liters}}{\frac{22.4\text{ L } O_2}{1\text{ mol } O_2}} = 9.9\text{ L } O_2$$

In the previous example, did you notice that the 22.4 L/mol factors canceled out? This will always be true in a volume–volume problem. *The coefficients in a balanced chemical equation tell you the relative number of moles. The coefficients also indicate the relative volumes of interacting gases.* The volume can be expressed in any unit: cubic decimeters, milliliters, liters, and so on.

Example 10 Volume–Volume Stoichiometric Calculations

Nitrogen monoxide and oxygen gas combine to form the brown gas nitrogen dioxide. How many milliliters of nitrogen dioxide are produced when 3.4 mL of oxygen reacts with an excess of nitrogen monoxide? Assume conditions of STP.

$$2NO(g) + O_2(g) \longrightarrow 2NO_2(g)$$

Solution

The coefficients indicate the relative number of reacting milliliters of gases. The problem is solved in one step:

$$\text{mL } O_2 \longrightarrow \text{mL } NO_2$$

$$\underset{\text{Given quantity}}{3.4\ \cancel{\text{mL } O_2}} \times \underset{\text{Volume ratios}}{\frac{2\text{ mL } NO_2}{1\ \cancel{\text{mL } O_2}}} = 6.8\text{ mL } NO_2$$

Concept Practice

14. What ratio is used to carry out these conversions?

a. moles of CH_4 to grams of CH_4

b. liters of CH_4 to moles of CH_4 (at STP)

c. molecules of CH_4 to moles of CH_4

Practice Problem

15. Tin(II) fluoride, formerly found in many toothpastes, is formed in this reaction:

$$Sn(s) + 2HF(g) \longrightarrow SnF_2(s) + H_2(g)$$

a. How many liters of HF are needed to produce 9.40 L of H_2? (Assume STP.)

b. How many molecules of H_2 are produced by the reaction of tin with 20.0 L of HF (at STP)?

c. How many grams of SnF_2 can be made by reacting 7.42×10^{24} molecules of HF with tin?

8.6 Limiting Reagent

Objective

Identify the limiting reagent in a reaction and use it to calculate stoichiometric quantities and the amount of excess reagents.

Most cooks follow a recipe when making a new dish. Sufficient quantities of all the ingredients must be available. For example, in preparing to make lasagne you find that you have more than enough meat, tomato sauce, cottage cheese, eggs, mozzarella cheese, and seasoning on hand. However, you have only half a box of noodles. The amount of lasagne you can make will be limited by the amount of noodles you have on hand. In fact, the noodles are the *limiting reagent.* Figure 8.11 illustrates another example of a limiting reagent in making sandwiches. A chemist often faces a similar situation. It is impossible for a chemist to make a certain amount of a desired compound if there is an insufficient quantity of any of the required reactants.

Figure 8.11 The amount of product is limited by the quantity of the limiting reagent. In this example, the rolls are the limiting reagent. No matter how much of all the other ingredients you have, with two rolls you can make only two sandwiches.

You can see that a balanced chemical equation is a chemist's recipe. This recipe can be interpreted on a microscopic scale (interacting particles) or on a macroscopic scale (interacting moles). Recall the familiar equation for the preparation of ammonia:

$$N_2(g) + 3H_2(g) \longrightarrow 2NH_3(g)$$

When one molecule (mole) of N_2 reacts with three molecules (moles) of H_2, two molecules (moles) of NH_3 are produced. What would happen, however, if two molecules (moles) of N_2 reacted with three molecules (moles) of H_2? Would more than two molecules (moles) of NH_3 be formed? Figure 8.12 shows both the particle and the mole interpretations of this problem.

Before the reaction takes place, nitrogen and hydrogen are present in a 2:3 molecule (mole) ratio. The reaction takes place according to the balanced equation. One molecule (mole) of N_2 reacts with three molecules (moles) of H_2 to produce two molecules (moles) of NH_3. At this point all the hydrogen has been used up, and the reaction stops. One molecule (mole) of unreacted nitrogen is left in addition to the two molecules (moles) of NH_3 that have been produced by the reaction.

In this reaction, only the hydrogen is completely used up. It is called the *limiting reagent. As the name implies, the* **limiting reagent** *limits or determines the amount of product that can be formed in a reaction.* The reaction occurs only until the limiting reagent is used up. *By contrast, the quantity of an* **excess reagent** *is more than enough to react with a limiting reagent.* In the present example, nitrogen is the excess reagent. Some nitrogen will remain unreacted.

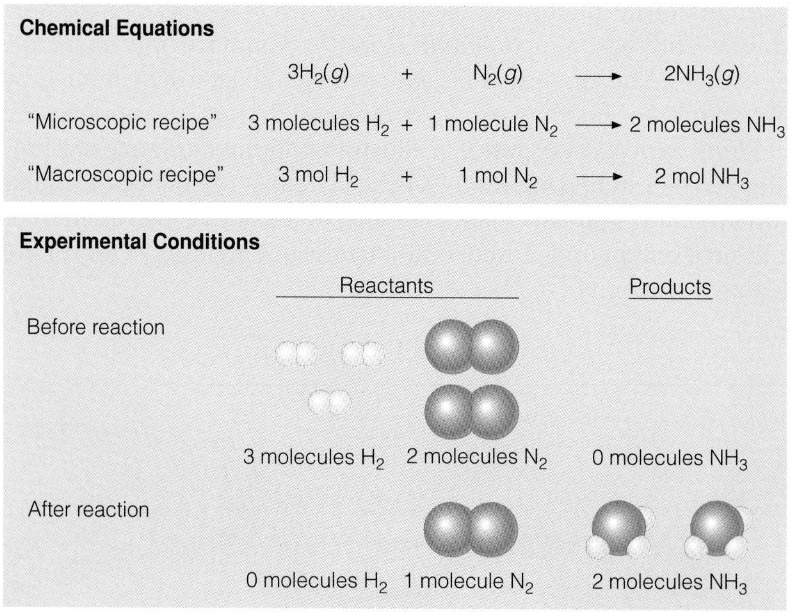

Figure 8.12 The "recipe" calls for 3 molecules of H_2 for every 1 molecule of N_2. In this particular experiment N_2 is in excess and H_2 is the limiting reagent.

Chemical Equations

	$3H_2(g)$	+	$N_2(g)$	$\longrightarrow$	$2NH_3(g)$
"Microscopic recipe"	3 molecules H_2	+	1 molecule N_2	$\longrightarrow$	2 molecules NH_3
"Macroscopic recipe"	3 mol H_2	+	1 mol N_2	$\longrightarrow$	2 mol NH_3

Experimental Conditions

	Reactants		Products
Before reaction	3 molecules H_2	2 molecules N_2	0 molecules NH_3
After reaction	0 molecules H_2	1 molecule N_2	2 molecules NH_3

Example 11 Determining the Limiting Reagent in a Reaction

Sodium chloride can be prepared by the reaction of sodium metal with chlorine gas.

$$2Na(s) + Cl_2(g) \longrightarrow 2NaCl(s)$$

What will occur when 6.70 mol of Na reacts with 3.20 mol of Cl_2?

a. What is the limiting reagent?
b. How many moles of NaCl are produced?
c. How much of the excess reagent remains unreacted?

Solution

a. Start with the known amount of one of the reactants. Use the mole ratio from the balanced equation to calculate the required amount of the other reactant. Sodium is chosen arbitrarily here: mol Na $\longrightarrow$ mol Cl_2.

$$\underset{\text{Given amount of sodium}}{6.70\ \cancel{\text{mol Na}}} \times \underset{\text{Mole ratio}}{\frac{1\ \text{mol Cl}_2}{2\ \cancel{\text{mol Na}}}} = \underset{\text{Required amount of chlorine}}{3.35\ \text{mol Cl}_2}$$

This calculation shows that 3.35 mol of Cl_2 is needed to react with 6.70 mol of Na. Because only 3.20 mol of Cl_2 is available, chlorine is the limiting reagent. The sodium, then, must be in excess.

b. The given amount of limiting reagent, 3.20 mol of Cl_2, is used to calculate the maximum amount of product that can be formed: mol $Cl_2 \longrightarrow$ mol NaCl.

$$3.20\ \cancel{\text{mol Cl}_2} \times \frac{2\ \text{mol NaCl}}{1\ \cancel{\text{mol Cl}_2}} = 6.40\ \text{mol NaCl}$$

c. The amount of the excess reagent remaining is the difference between the given amount (6.70 mol of Na) and the amount of sodium needed to react with the limiting reagent. We need to calculate the sodium that is needed: mol $Cl_2 \longrightarrow$ mol Na.

$$\underset{\text{Limiting reagent}}{3.20\ \cancel{\text{mol Cl}_2}} \times \underset{\text{Mole ratio}}{\frac{2\ \text{mol Na}}{1\ \cancel{\text{mol Cl}_2}}} = \underset{\text{Amount of excess reagent used up}}{6.40\ \text{mol Na}}$$

The amount of remaining sodium can now be calculated:

6.70 mol − 6.40 mol = 0.30 mol Na in excess

Concept Practice

16. What is the significance of the limiting reagent in a chemical process? What happens to the amount of any reagent that is present in excess?

17. The quantities of reactants and products in a reaction may be expressed in a variety of units. Give the names of some of these units.

Practice Problem

18. Two equations for the combustion of ethane, C_2H_4, are possible.

$$C_2H_4(g) + 3O_2(g) \longrightarrow 2CO_2(g) + 2H_2O(g)$$
(complete combustion)

$$C_2H_4(g) + 2O_2(g) \longrightarrow 2CO(g) + 2H_2O(g)$$
(incomplete combustion)

What will occur for each reaction if 2.70 mol of C_2H_4 is reacted with 6.30 mol of O_2?
a. Identify the limiting reagent.
b. Calculate the moles of water produced.
c. Calculate the moles of excess reagent remaining.

Figure 8.13 Black crystalline copper(II) sulfide is formed as a product when copper and sulfur reactants are heated.

The given quantities of reactants may be expressed in units other than moles. In that case, the first step in the solution of the problem is to convert the quantity of each reactant to moles. Then you can identify the limiting reagent as in the previous example. Finally, you can determine the amount of product from the given amount of limiting reagent.

Example 12 Using a Limiting Reagent to Find the Quantity of Product

As shown in Figure 8.13, the properties of copper(I) sulfide are very different from the properties of the elements copper and sulfur from which copper(I) sulfide is formed.

$$2Cu(s) + S(s) \longrightarrow Cu_2S(s)$$

What is the maximum number of grams of Cu_2S that can be formed when 80.0 g of Cu reacts with 25.0 g of S?

Solution

First, find the number of moles of each reactant: g Cu $\longrightarrow$ mol Cu, and g S $\longrightarrow$ mol S.

$$80.0\ \cancel{\text{g Cu}} \times \frac{1\ \text{mol Cu}}{63.5\ \cancel{\text{g Cu}}} = 1.26\ \text{mol Cu}$$

$$25.0\ \cancel{\text{g S}} \times \frac{1\ \text{mol S}}{32.1\ \cancel{\text{g S}}} = 0.779\ \text{mol S}$$

Next, use the balanced equation to calculate the number of moles of one reactant needed to react with the given amount of the other reactant: mol Cu $\longrightarrow$ mol S.

$$\underset{\text{Given quantity}}{1.26\ \cancel{\text{mol Cu}}} \times \underset{\text{Mole ratio}}{\frac{1\ \text{mol S}}{2\ \cancel{\text{mol Cu}}}} = \underset{\text{“Needed” amount}}{0.630\ \text{mol S}}$$

Compare the amount of sulfur needed, 0.630 mol of S, with the given amount, 0.779 mol of S. The sulfur is in excess. Therefore, in this problem copper is the limiting reagent. Finally, use the limiting reagent to calculate the maximum amount of Cu_2S formed: mol Cu $\longrightarrow$ mol Cu_2S $\longrightarrow$ g Cu_2S.

$$1.26\ \cancel{\text{mol Cu}} \times \frac{1\ \cancel{\text{mol Cu}_2\text{S}}}{2\ \cancel{\text{mol Cu}}} \times \frac{159.1\ \text{g Cu}_2\text{S}}{1\ \cancel{\text{mol Cu}_2\text{S}}} = 1.00 \times 10^2\ \text{g Cu}_2\text{S}$$

You could have begun this last step with the given quantity of copper, 80.0 g. In that case the first step in the solution of the problem would be to change to moles of copper, which we had previously done.

Practice Problems

19. Hydrogen gas can be produced in the laboratory by the reaction of magnesium metal with hydrochloric acid.

$$\text{Mg}(s) + 2\text{HCl}(aq) \longrightarrow \text{MgCl}_2(aq) + \text{H}_2(g)$$

a. How many grams of hydrogen can be produced when 6.00 g of HCl is added to 5.00 g of Mg?
b. Assuming STP, what is the volume of this hydrogen?

20. Hydrogen gas and oxygen gas combine to produce water vapor.
a. If you react 200 cm^3 of hydrogen with 150 cm^3 of oxygen, what volume of water is formed?
b. Which gas is left over, and how much?

Problem-Solving Tip

Identify the given (what you know) and the unknown (what you want to find) before you plan the solution.

Objective

Calculate the theoretical yield, actual yield, or percent yield for a chemical reaction.

8.7 Percent Yield

In theory, when a teacher gives an exam to the class, everyone should get a grade of 100%. For a variety of reasons (not all of which are the teacher's fault), this is usually not the case. Instead, the performance of the class is usually spread over a range of grades. Your exam grade, expressed as a percentage, is a quantity that shows how well you did on the exam (questions answered correctly) compared to how well you could have done (100%). This calculation is analogous to the percent yield calculation that you do when the product from a chemical reaction is less than you expected based on the balanced chemical equation.

Up to now, in doing stoichiometric problems, you have assumed that things do not "go wrong" in chemical reactions. This assumption is as faulty as assuming that all students will score 100% on an exam. *When an equation is used to calculate the amount of product that will form during a reaction, a value for the* **theoretical yield** *is obtained.* This is the maximum amount of products that could be formed from given amounts of reactants. *In contrast, the amount of product that forms when the reaction is carried out in the laboratory is called the* **actual yield.** The actual yield is often less than the theoretical yield. *The* **percent yield** *is the ratio of the actual yield to the theoretical yield expressed as a percentage.* The percent yield measures the efficiency of the reaction.

$$\text{Percent yield} = \frac{\text{actual yield}}{\text{theoretical yield}} \times 100\%$$

A percent yield should not normally be larger than 100%. Many factors cause percent yields to be less than 100%. Reactions do not always go to completion. Impure reactants and competing side reactions may cause other products to form. Some of the product may be lost during filtration or in transferring between containers. The student in Figure 8.15 must weigh both the reactants and products carefully in order to calculate an accurate percent yield.

Figure 8.14 The productivity of a farm is measured in yield. Because growing conditions may vary from year to year, the actual yield often differs from the theoretical yield.

An actual yield is an experimental value. If you do not do an experiment, you cannot calculate a percent yield unless you are given the value of an actual yield. For reactions in which percent yields have been determined, you can calculate and therefore predict an "actual" yield if the reaction conditions remain the same. A farmer's crop yield could also be expressed as a percent yield. What factors would a farmer use to project a theoretical yield?

Figure 8.15 Here the mass of sodium hydrogen carbonate, the reactant, is measured before it is heated. The mass of the product, sodium carbonate, is measured after the reaction is completed.

Example 13 Calculating the Percent Yield of a Reaction

Calcium carbonate is decomposed by heating.

$$CaCO_3(s) \longrightarrow CaO(s) + CO_2(g)$$

What is the percent yield of this reaction if 24.8 g of $CaCO_3$ is heated to give 13.1 g of CaO?

Solution

The actual yield is 13.1 g of CaO. The theoretical yield can be calculated: g $CaCO_3 \longrightarrow$ mol $CaCO_3 \longrightarrow$ mol CaO $\longrightarrow$ g CaO.

$$24.8\,\text{g}\,\cancel{CaCO_3} \times \frac{1\,\cancel{\text{mol}\,CaCO_3}}{100.1\,\cancel{\text{g}\,CaCO_3}} \times \frac{1\,\cancel{\text{mol}\,CaO}}{1\,\cancel{\text{mol}\,CaCO_3}} \times \frac{56.1\,\text{g CaO}}{1\,\cancel{\text{mol}\,CaO}}$$

$$= 13.9\,\text{g CaO}$$

$$\text{Percent yield} = \frac{\text{actual yield}}{\text{theoretical yield}} \times 100\%$$

$$= \frac{13.1\,\cancel{\text{g CaO}}}{13.9\,\cancel{\text{g CaO}}} \times 100\% = 94.2\%$$

Concept Practice

21. What is the difference between an actual yield and a theoretical yield? Show how these values are used to determine percent yield.

Practice Problems

22. What is the percent yield if 4.65 g of copper is produced when 1.87 g of aluminum reacts with an excess of copper(II) sulfate?

$$2Al(s) + 3CuSO_4(aq) \longrightarrow Al_2(SO_4)_3(aq) + 3Cu(s)$$

23. Heating an ore of antimony, Sb_2S_3, in the presence of iron gives the element antimony and iron(II) sulfide.

$$Sb_2S_3(s) + 3Fe(s) \longrightarrow 2Sb(s) + 3FeS(s)$$

When 15.0 g of Sb_2S_3 reacts with an excess of Fe, 9.84 g Sb is produced. What is the percent yield of this reaction?

Activity 8 Limiting Reagent

Purpose

To demonstrate the concept of a limiting reagent in a chemical reaction, $M_2 + 3C_2 \rightarrow 2MC_3$.

Materials

20 metal paper clips (symbol = M)

20 identically colored vinyl-coated paper clips (symbol = C)

1 plastic sandwich bag

Procedure

1. Join together pairs of paper clips of the same color to form models representing 10 diatomic molecules of each reactant. Place these molecules in the plastic bag.

2. Without looking, choose 15 molecules from the plastic bag.

3. Line up the M_2 and C_2 molecules in two adjacent vertical rows.

4. Pair up reactant molecules in the 1:3 M_2-to-C_2 ratio as shown in the equation $M_2 + 3C_2 \rightarrow 2MC_3$. Make the molecules "react" by taking them apart and forming two molecules of the products.

5. Continue making M_2 and C_2 react in a 1:3 ratio until you run out of one of the reactants.

Analysis and Conclusions

1. List the number of each type of reactant molecule that was drawn from the bag.

2. Which reactant molecule was the limiting reagent?

3. How many molecules of the product were formed?

4. How many molecules of the excess reagent remained at the completion of the reaction?

5. Relate the idea of limiting reagent to a recipe with which you are familiar.

Chapter 8 Review
Stoichiometry

Key Terms

actual yield *8.7*
excess reagent *8.6*
limiting reagent *8.6*
percent yield *8.7*
stoichiometry *8.0*
theoretical yield *8.7*

Chapter Summary

A balanced chemical equation may be interpreted in several different ways. For example, the coefficients tell you the relative number of moles of reactants and products. Chemists use moles to do chemical arithmetic, or stoichiometry. All stoichiometric calculations involving chemical reactions begin with a balanced equation. Balanced equations are necessary because mass is conserved in every chemical reaction. The number and kinds of atoms in the reactants equal the number and kinds of atoms in the products.

Stoichiometric problems are solved using conversion factors derived from a balanced chemical equation. The conversion factor relates the moles of a given substance to the moles of the desired substance. Units such as mass, volume of gases (at STP), and particles are converted to moles when working stoichiometry problems.

Whenever quantities of two or more reactants are given in a stoichiometry problem, you must identify the limiting reagent. A limiting reagent is completely used up in a chemical reaction. The amount of limiting reagent determines the amount of product that is formed in a chemical reaction. If there is a single limiting reagent in a reaction, all the other reactants are in excess.

A theoretical yield is the maximum amount of product that can be obtained from a given amount of reactants in a chemical reaction. An actual yield is the amount of product obtained when the reaction is carried out in the laboratory. The ratio of the actual yield to the theoretical yield, expressed as a percentage, is the percent yield of a reaction.

Practice Questions and Problems

24. Your school club has "adopted" a local nursing home and provides welcoming packages to new residents. Each welcoming package consists of a toothbrush (B), three washcloths (W), a hand mirror (M), two decks of cards (C), and four small bottles of skin lotion (L). *8.1*

a. Write a balanced equation for preparing a complete welcoming package, $BW_3MC_2L_4$.

b. Calculate the number of each item needed to assemble 45 care packages.

25. Interpret each of these chemical equations in terms of interacting particles. *8.2*

a. $2KClO_3(s) \rightarrow 2KCl(s) + 3O_2(g)$

b. $4NH_3(g) + 6NO(g) \rightarrow 5N_2(g) + 6H_2O(g)$

c. $4K(s) + O_2(g) \rightarrow 2K_2O(s)$

26. Interpret each of the equations in Problem 25 in terms of interacting numbers of moles of reactants and products. *8.2*

27. Calculate and compare the mass of the reactants with the mass of the products for each of the equations in Problem 25. Show that each balanced equation obeys the law of conservation of mass. *8.2*

28. Carbon disulfide is an important industrial solvent. It is prepared by the reaction of coke with sulfur dioxide. *8.3*

$$5C + 2SO_2 \rightarrow CS_2 + 4CO$$

a. How many moles of CS_2 form when 2.7 mol of C reacts?

b. How many moles of carbon are needed to react with 5.44 mol of SO_2?

c. How many moles of carbon monoxide form at the same time that 0.246 mol of CS_2 forms?

d. How many moles of SO_2 are required to make 118 mol of CS_2?

29. Oxygen is produced by the reaction of sodium peroxide and water. *8.4*

$$2Na_2O_2(s) + 2H_2O(l) \rightarrow O_2(g) + 4NaOH(aq)$$

a. Calculate the mass of Na_2O_2 in grams needed to form 4.80 g of oxygen.

b. How many grams of NaOH are produced when 4.80 g of O_2 is formed?

c. When 0.48 g of Na_2O_2 is dropped in water, how many grams of O_2 are formed?

30. Suppose you have a choice between using a polystyrene plastic cup and a paper cup for a soda. List the pros and cons for each choice. *8.B*

31. Methanol, CH_3OH, is used in the production of many chemicals. Methanol is made by reacting carbon monoxide and hydrogen at high temperature and pressure. *8.5*

$$CO(g) + 2H_2(g) \rightarrow CH_3OH(g)$$

a. How many moles of each reactant are needed to produce 3.60×10^2 g of CH_3OH?

b. Calculate the number of grams of each reactant needed to produce 4.00 mol of CH_3OH.

c. How many grams of hydrogen are necessary to react with 2.85 mol of CO?

32. The reaction of fluorine with ammonia produces dinitrogen tetrafluoride and hydrogen fluoride. *8.6*

$$5F_2(g) + 2NH_3(g) \rightarrow N_2F_4(g) + 6HF(g)$$

a. If you have 66.6 g of NH_3, how many grams of F_2 are required for complete reaction?

b. How many grams of NH_3 are required to produce 4.65 g of HF?

c. How many grams of N_2F_4 can be produced from 225 g of F_2?

33. Lithium nitride reacts with water to form ammonia and aqueous lithium hydroxide. *8.6*

$$Li_3N(s) + 3H_2O(l) \rightarrow NH_3(g) + 3LiOH(aq)$$

a. What mass of water is needed to react with 32.9 g of Li_3N?

b. When the above reaction takes place, how many molecules of NH_3 are produced?

c. Calculate the number of grams of Li_3N that must be added to an excess of water to produce 15.0 L of NH_3 (at STP).

34. How would you identify a limiting reagent in a chemical reaction? *8.6*

35. For each of these balanced equations, identify the limiting reagent for the given combination of reactants. *8.6*

a. $2Al + 3Cl_2 \rightarrow 2AlCl_3$ (2Al: 3.6 mol; $3Cl_2$: 5.3 mol)

b. $2H_2 + O_2 \rightarrow 2H_2O$ ($2H_2$: 6.4 mol; O_2: 3.4 mol)

c. $P_4O_{10} + 6H_2O \rightarrow 4H_3PO_4$ (P_4O_{10}: 0.48 mol; $6H_2O$: 1.52 mol)

d. $4P + 5O_2 \rightarrow P_4O_{10}$ (4P: 14.5 mol; $5O_2$: 18.0 mol)

36. For each of the four reactions in Problem 35, calculate the number of moles of product formed. *8.6*

37. For each of the four reactions in Problem 35, calculate the number of moles of excess reagent remaining after the reaction has used up the limiting reagent. *8.6*

38. Acetylene, C_2H_2, will burn in the presence of oxygen. *8.6*

$$2C_2H_2(g) + 5O_2(g) \rightarrow 4CO_2(g) + 2H_2O(g)$$

How many grams of water can be produced by the reaction of 2.40 mol of C_2H_2 with 7.4 mol of O_2?

39. The manufacture of compound F requires five separate chemical reactions. The initial reactant, compound A, is converted to compound B; compound B is converted to compound C, and so forth. The diagram below summarizes the stepwise manufacture of compound F, including the percent yield for each step. Provide the missing quantities or missing percent yields. Assume that the reactant and product in each step react in a one-to-one mole ratio. *8.7*

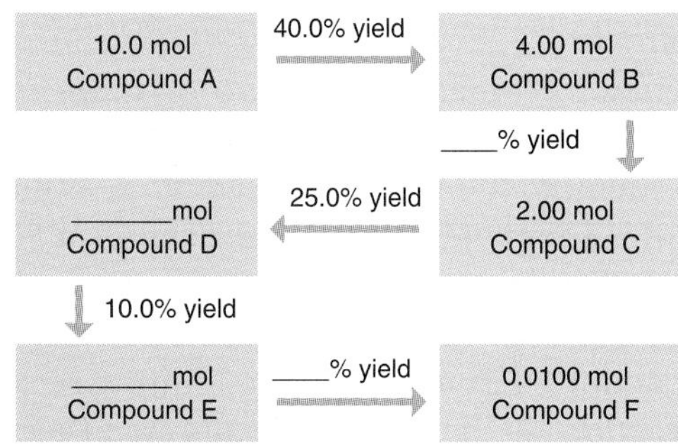

40. What is a percent yield of a chemical reaction a measure of? *8.7*

41. When 84.8 g of iron(III) oxide reacts with an excess of carbon monoxide, 54.3 g of iron is produced.

$$Fe_2O_3(s) + 3CO(g) \rightarrow 2Fe(s) + 3CO_2(g)$$

What is the percent yield of this reaction? *8.7*

42. If 50.0 g of silicon dioxide is heated with an excess of carbon, 27.9 g of silicon carbide is produced.

$$SiO_2(s) + 3C(s) \rightarrow SiC(s) + 2CO(g)$$

What is the percent yield of this reaction? *8.7*

Mastery Questions and Problems

43. Make a concept map using all the key terms in this chapter and the following terms: substances, chemical reaction, reactant, and product.

44. Calcium carbonate reacts with phosphoric acid to produce calcium phosphate, carbon dioxide, and water.

$$3CaCO_3(s) + 2H_3PO_4(aq) \rightarrow$$
$$Ca_3(PO_4)_2(aq) + 3CO_2(g) + 3H_2O(l)$$

a. How many grams of phosphoric acid react with excess calcium carbonate to produce 3.74 g of $Ca_3(PO_4)_2$?

b. Assuming STP, how many liters of carbon dioxide are produced when 5.74 g of $CaCO_3$ reacts with an excess of H_3PO_4?

45. Nitric acid and zinc react to form zinc nitrate, ammonium nitrate, and water.

$$4Zn(s) + 10HNO_3(aq) \rightarrow$$
$$4Zn(NO_3)_2(aq) + NH_4NO_3(aq) + 3H_2O(l)$$

a. How many atoms of zinc react with 1.49 g of HNO_3?

b. Calculate the number of grams of zinc that must react with an excess of HNO_3 to form 29.1 g of NH_4NO_3.

46. Elemental sulfur is one of the products of the gas-phase reaction of nitric acid and hydrogen sulfide. The other products are nitrogen monoxide and water.

$$3H_2S(s) + 2HNO_3(g) \rightarrow$$
$$2NO(g) + 4H_2O(g) + 3S(s)$$

a. How many grams of each product are formed when 18.2 g of H_2S reacts with an excess of HNO_3?

b. How many milligrams of water are produced when 43.7 mg of sulfur is formed?

47. Hydrazine, N_2H_4, is used as a rocket fuel. It reacts with oxygen to form nitrogen and water.

$$N_2H_4(l) + O_2(g) \rightarrow N_2(g) + 2H_2O(g)$$

a. How many liters of N_2 (at STP) form when 1.0 kg of N_2H_4 reacts with 1.0 kg of O_2?

b. How many grams of the excess reagent remain after the reaction?

48. When 50.0 g of silicon dioxide is heated with an excess of carbon, 32.2 g of silicon carbide is produced.

$$SiO_2(s) + 3C(s) \rightarrow SiC(s) + 2CO(g)$$

a. What is the percent yield of this reaction?

b. How many grams of CO gas are made?

49. The pollutant sulfur dioxide can be removed from the emissions of an industrial plant by reaction with calcium carbonate and oxygen.

$$2CaCO_3(s) + 2SO_2(g) + O_2(g) \rightarrow$$
$$2CaSO_4(s) + 2CO_2(g)$$

If this reaction proceeds with a 96.8% yield, how many kilograms of $CaSO_4$ are formed when 5.24 kg of SO_2 reacts with an excess of $CaCO_3$ and O_2?

50. Ammonium nitrate decomposes explosively at high temperatures to form nitrogen, oxygen, and water vapor.

$$2NH_4NO_3(s) \rightarrow 2N_2(g) + 4H_2O(g) + O_2(g)$$

a. What is the total number of liters of gas formed when 228 g of NH_4NO_3 is decomposed? (Assume STP.)

b. Calculate the number of grams of water formed when 25.0 L of N_2 is produced in this reaction. (Assume STP.)

Critical Thinking Questions

51. Given a certain quantity of reactant, you calculate that a particular reaction should produce 55 g of a product. When you perform the reaction you find that you have produced 63 g of product. What is your percent yield? What could have caused a percent yield over 100%?

52. Would the law of conservation of mass hold in a net ionic equation? Explain.

53. Choose the term that completes the second relationship.
   a. equation:coefficients   balance: _____
      (1) moles   (3) weight
      (2) standard masses   (4) atoms
   b. actual:theoretical   experimental: _____
      (1) excess   (3) real
      (2) limiting   (4) calculated
   c. mass:kilograms   volume: _____
      (1) milliliters   (3) coefficients
      (2) molecules   (4) products
54. A bicycle built for three has a frame, two wheels, six pedals, and three seats. The balanced equation for this bicycle is

$$F + 2W + 6P + 3S \rightarrow FW_2P_6S_3$$

How many of each part are needed to make 29 bicycles built for three?
   a. frames   c. pedals
   b. wheels   d. seats

58. Write a net ionic equation for each of the reactions in Problem 57.
59. Identify the spectator ions in each reaction in Problem 57.
60. How many electrons, protons, and neutrons are in an atom of each isotope?
   a. titanium-47   c. oxygen-18
   b. tin-120   d. magnesium-26
61. What is the mass, in grams, of a molecule of benzene, C_6H_6?
62. Write these formulas.
   a. aluminum carbonate
   b. silicon dioxide
   c. potassium sulfide
   d. manganese(II) chromate
   e. sodium bromide
63. What is the molecular formula of oxalic acid, gram molecular mass 90 g/mol? Its percent composition is 71.1% O, 26.7% C, and 2.2% H.

Cumulative Review

55. Write a balanced chemical equation for each of these reactions.
   a. Lead(II) nitrate when heated decomposes to form lead(II) oxide, nitrogen dioxide, and molecular oxygen.
   b. The complete combustion of isopropyl alcohol, C_3H_7OH, produces carbon dioxide and water vapor.
   c. When a mixture of aluminum and iron(II) oxide is heated, metallic iron and aluminum oxide are produced.
   d. Sodium hydrogen carbonate reacts with acetic acid to produce sodium acetate, water, and carbon dioxide.
56. How many grams of beryllium are in 147 g of the mineral beryl, $Be_3Al_2Si_6O_{18}$?
57. Balance each of these equations.
   a. $Ba(NO_3)_2(aq) + Na_2SO_4(aq) \rightarrow BaSO_4(s) + NaNO_3(aq)$
   b. $AlCl_3(aq) + AgNO_3(aq) \rightarrow AgCl(s) + Al(NO_3)_3(aq)$
   c. $H_2SO_4(aq) + Mg(OH)_2(aq) \rightarrow MgSO_4(aq) + H_2O(l)$

Challenge Questions and Problems

64. A car gets 9.2 kilometers to a liter of gasoline. Assuming that gasoline is 100% octane, C_8H_{18} (which has a specific gravity of 0.69), how many liters of air (21% oxygen by volume at STP) will be required to burn the gasoline for a 1250-km trip? Assume complete combustion.
65. Ethyl alcohol, C_2H_5OH, can be produced by the fermentation of glucose, $C_6H_{12}O_6$. If it takes 5.0 h to produce 8.0 kg of alcohol, how many days will it take to consume 1.0×10^3 kg of glucose? An enzyme (biological catalyst) is used to increase the rate of this reaction.

$$C_6H_{12}O_6 \xrightarrow{\text{enzyme}} C_2H_5OH + CO_2$$

66. The white limestone cliffs of Dover, England, contain a large percentage of calcium carbonate, $CaCO_3$. A sample of limestone weighing 84.4 g reacts with an excess of hydrochloric acid to form calcium chloride.

$$CaCO_3 + 2HCl \rightarrow CaCl_2 + H_2O + CO_2$$

The mass of calcium chloride formed is 81.8 g. What is the percentage of calcium carbonate in the limestone?

67. A 435.0-g sample of $CaCO_3$ that is 95.0% pure gives 225 L of CO_2 at STP when reacted with an excess of hydrochloric acid.

$$CaCO_3 + HCl \rightarrow CaCl_2 + CO_2 + H_2O$$

What is the density (in grams/liter) of the CO_2?

68. Aspirin, $C_9H_8O_4$, is made by the reaction of salicylic acid, $C_7H_6O_3$, and acetic anhydride, $C_4H_6O_3$.

$$C_7H_6O_3 + C_4H_6O_3 \rightarrow C_9H_8O_4 + HC_2H_3O_2$$

How many grams of each reactant should be used to produce 75.0 g of aspirin?

69. SO_3 can be produced in this two-step process.

$$FeS_2 + O_2 \rightarrow Fe_2O_3 + SO_2$$
$$SO_2 + O_2 \rightarrow SO_3$$

Assuming that all the FeS_2 reacts, how many grams of SO_3 are produced when 20.0 g of the FeS_2 reacts with 16.0 g of O_2?

Connections Questions

70. Describe the duties of a quality control chemist working for a cosmetic manufacturer.

71. Describe Jeremiah Richter's contribution to the establishment of chemistry as a true science.

72. List some natural sources of ammonia.

Write About Chemistry

73. Find out more about the methods used by forensic chemists. Write a short story that includes a mystery which is solved by a forensic chemist.

74. Write short essays that describe three nonchemistry situations in which the concept of a limiting reagent comes into play.

75. Write a letter to the editor that answers the following question: What do you think are important considerations in the risk-benefit analysis of nuclear power for the generation of electricity?

Readings and References

Saferstein, Richard. "DNA Fingerprinting." *ChemMatters* (October 1991), pp. 10–13.

Gerber, Samuel M., ed. *Chemistry and Crime: From Sherlock Holmes to Today's Courtroom.* Washington, D.C.: American Chemical Society, 1983.

9 The States of Matter

Goals

- Describe the nature of gases, liquids, and solids and the interconversion of these three states of matter.
- Explain the behavior of gases, liquids, and solids in terms of the kinetic theory.
- Explain what happens on a particle basis during changes of state using the kinetic theory.

Part of a comet's tail is made of plasma, a state of matter. An example is Comet West, shown here. The Great Comet of 1843 had a tail that was 205 million miles long.

Concept Overview

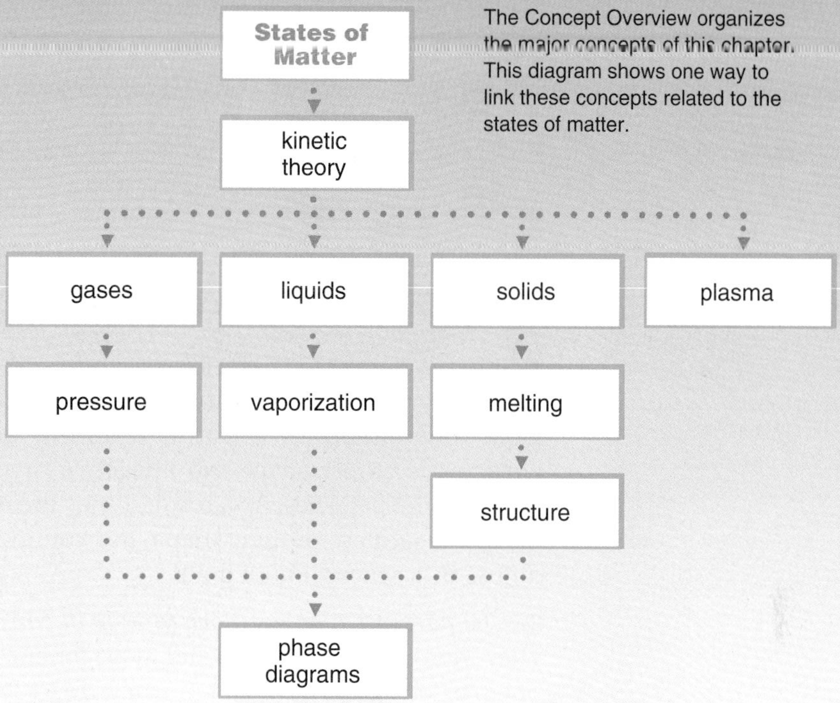

States of Matter → kinetic theory → gases, liquids, solids, plasma

gases → pressure; liquids → vaporization; solids → melting → structure

pressure, vaporization, structure → phase diagrams

The Concept Overview organizes the major concepts of this chapter. This diagram shows one way to link these concepts related to the states of matter.

An ice cube is solid water. Tap water is liquid water. Steam is gaseous water. Most substances commonly exist in one of the three states of matter: solid, liquid, and gas. But a substance in one state may change to another state with a change in temperature. When cooled, water freezes to become ice; steam condenses to form water. Why do changes in the state of matter occur with changes in temperature? You will find the answers to these questions in this chapter with the help of a model called the kinetic theory.

9.1 Kinetic Theory and the Nature of Gases

Objective

Describe the motion of particles of a gas according to the kinetic theory.

If you put on perfume, the aroma soon reaches the nose of anyone nearby. Obviously, the molecules of the perfume have moved from the wearer. This behavior and many other properties of gases can be explained by the kinetic theory.

The word *kinetic* means motion. *The energy an object has because of its motions is* **kinetic energy**. *The* **kinetic theory** *says that the tiny particles in all forms of matter are in constant motion.* Here are the basic assumptions of the kinetic theory as it applies to gases.

Figure 9.1 **(a)** Gas particles have random and chaotic movements. They are constantly colliding with one another and the walls of the container. **(b)** As a single gas particle moves through space, it frequently changes direction due to collisions with other particles.

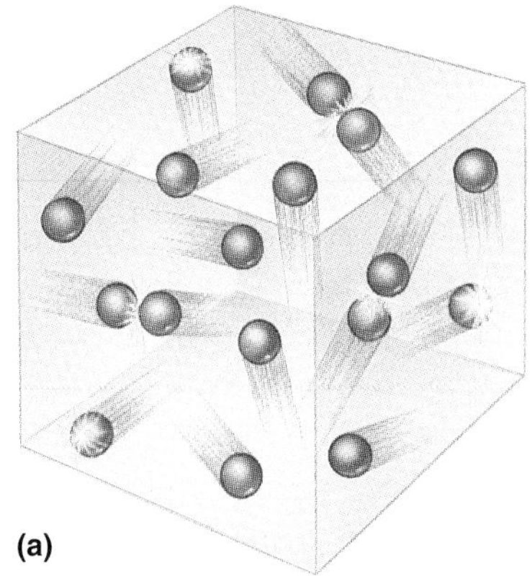

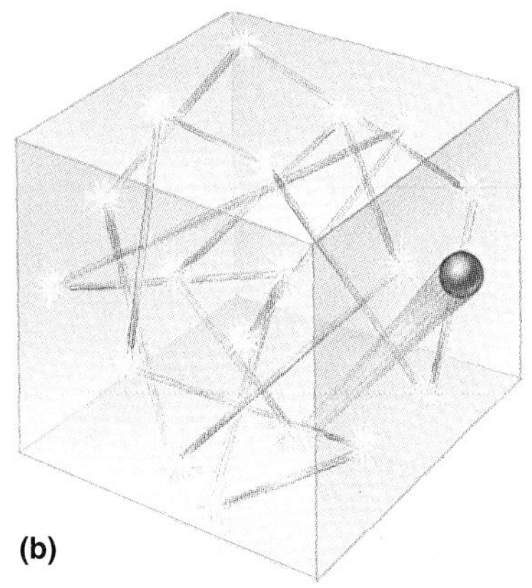

1. *A gas is composed of particles, usually molecules or atoms.* These particles are considered to be small hard spheres that have negligible volume and are far away from one another. Between the particles is empty space. No attractive or repulsive forces exist between the particles. As a result, gases in containers fill the containers regardless of their shape and volume. Uncontained gases diffuse into space without limit.

2. *The particles in a gas move rapidly in constant random motion.* They travel in straight paths and move independently of each other. The particles change direction when they rebound from collisions with one another or with other objects, as Figure 9.1 shows. Measurements indicate that the average speed of oxygen molecules in air at 20°C is about 1656 km/h. At these high speeds, the odor molecules from a hot cheese pizza in Washington, DC, should reach Mexico, DF, in about 90 minutes. They never get there, however, because their path of unimpeded travel in a straight line is very short. The odor molecules are constantly striking the molecules of air and rebounding in other directions. The aimless path they take is called a random walk. Figure 9.1 illustrates a typical random walk.

3. *All collisions are perfectly elastic.* "Perfectly elastic" means that kinetic energy is transferred from one particle to another during collisions, but the total kinetic energy remains constant.

As you will see in the next section, the kinetic theory of gases is very helpful in explaining gas pressure.

Roots of Words

kinetos: (Greek) to move
kinetic the energy an object has because of its motion is the object's kinetic energy

Gas particles are in constant motion and have kinetic energy.

Concept Practice

1. In your own words, write the three assumptions of the kinetic theory of gases.

2. Explain why a hunter always stalks prey from "downwind."

9.2 Gas Pressure

Objective

Interpret gas pressure in terms of kinetic theory.

Moving bodies exert forces when they collide with other bodies. Although a gas particle is a moving body, the force exerted by only one gas particle is extremely small. It is not hard to imagine, however, that many simultaneous collisions would produce a measurable force on an object. **Gas pressure** *is the result of simultaneous collisions of billions upon billions of gas particles with an object.* When no gas particles are present, they do not collide and cause pressure. *The resulting empty space is a* **vacuum**.

Air exerts pressure on the earth because gravity holds air molecules in the earth's atmosphere. **Atmospheric pressure** *results from the collisions of air molecules with objects.* Atmospheric pressure decreases as you climb a mountain because the air layer around the earth thins out at high elevations.

Barometers *are commonly used to measure atmospheric pressure.* This pressure varies slightly, depending on the weather. *The SI unit of pressure is the* **pascal (Pa)**. Atmospheric pressure at sea level is about 101.3 kilopascal (kPa). Two older units of pressure are millimeters of mercury and the atmosphere. The origin of these units is the early use of mercury barometers similar to the one shown in the photograph in Figure 9.2. One part of the first barometers was a straight glass tube closed at one end. The tube was filled with

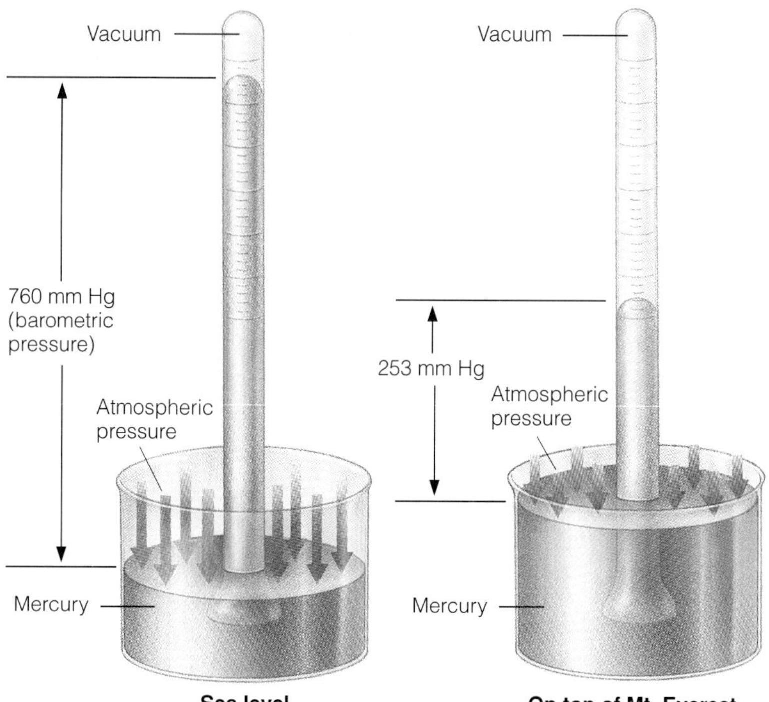

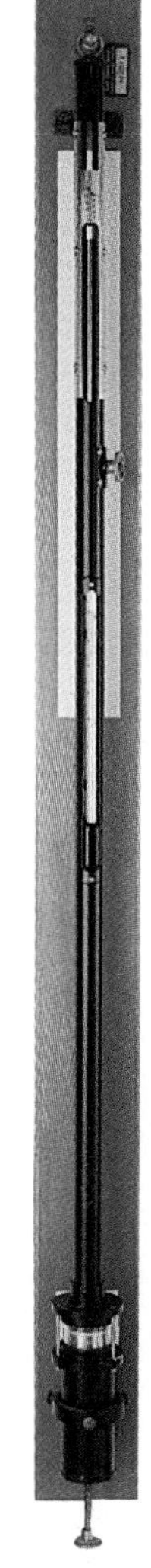

Figure 9.2 Barometers measure atmospheric pressure. This type of barometer is commonly used in laboratories. The average atmospheric pressure at sea level is 101.3 kPa, or 1 atm, or 760 mm Hg. On top of Mt. Everest (9000 m in altitude) the air pressure is only enough to support a column of mercury 253 mm high.

Biographical Note

Evangelista Torricelli
(1608–1647)

Evangelista Torricelli spent three months with Galileo before Galileo's death in 1642. During this time, Galileo suggested the problem that led Torricelli to construct the first mercury barometer. When Torricelli upended a long glass tube filled with mercury into a dish of mercury, the liquid level fell to about 760 mm. Torricelli's observation of daily changes in the level of mercury in the tube led to the concept of changing atmospheric pressure and its measurement. A unit of pressure equal to 1/760 of a standard atmosphere, or 1 mm Hg, was called the torr before the introduction of the SI unit of pressure, the pascal.

mercury and then inverted so that the open end was below the surface of mercury in a dish. The level of mercury in the tube depended on the pressure created by collisions of air molecules with the surface of the pool of mercury in the dish. At sea level, this pressure is sufficient to support a mercury column about 760 mm high. *One* **standard atmosphere (1 atm)** *is the pressure required to support 760 mm of mercury (760 mm Hg) in a mercury barometer at 25°C.* That is, 1 atm = 760 mm Hg. Similarly, only 1/760 atm of pressure is required to support a column of mercury 1 mm high. When you work with gases, *standard conditions are defined as a temperature of 0°C and a pressure of 101.3 kPa or 1 atm.* This is standard temperature and pressure or STP.

Many barometers do not contain mercury. They are called aneroid barometers. In these devices, atmospheric pressure is related to the number of collisions of air molecules with a sensitive metal diaphragm. The diaphragm controls the movement of a pointer, which in turn gives the pressure reading.

Example 1 Converting Units of Pressure

A gas is at a pressure of 1.5 atm. Convert this pressure to (a) kilopascals and (b) millimeters of mercury.

Solution

a. $1.50\ \cancel{\text{atm}} \times \dfrac{101.3\ \text{kPa}}{1\ \cancel{\text{atm}}} = 151.95\ \text{kPa} = 1.52 \times 10^2\ \text{kPa}$

b. $1.50\ \cancel{\text{atm}} \times \dfrac{760\ \text{mm Hg}}{1\ \cancel{\text{atm}}} = 1140\ \text{mm Hg} = 1.14 \times 10^3\ \text{mm Hg}$

Concept Practice

3. Explain what causes gas pressure.

4. List the various units used to measure pressure and identify the SI unit.

Practice Problems

5. Convert 190 mm Hg to (a) kilopascals and (b) atmospheres of pressure.

6. The pressure at the top of Mount Everest is 33.7 kPa. Is this greater or less than 0.25 atm?

9.A Environmental Awareness

Scrap Tires

More than 240 million scrap tires are generated every year! Add to these the approximately 2 billion tires that have accumulated nationwide in stockpiles or been dumped and you will recognize the magnitude of the scrap tire problem. Also, when stockpiles of tires catch fire they are very difficult to extinguish because air moves freely through the void spaces of the tires.

With changing technology and attitudes, used tires can be reused, recycled, and burned for energy recovery. At present, most states regulate the management of used tires. For example, whole used tires may not be disposed of in landfills. Tires can be reused on automobiles. They can be retreaded or remanufactured and have mileage guarantees and warranties similar to new tires. Barriers to their ready acceptance include the competitive prices for new tires and consumer concerns about safety and reliability.

Figure 9.3 The enormity of the problem caused by used tires can be seen in this photo of a used-tire stockpile.

Tires may contribute to the environment in many ways. Whole tires, banded together, have been buried on unstable slopes to reduce soil and beach erosion. They have also been used successfully as artificial reefs and breakwaters. Shredded or chipped tires have been used in playgrounds as a substitute for gravel and for road fill where roads cross over soft or peaty soils.

Finely ground crumb rubber offers the greatest use potential. Crumb rubber can be blended with other materials such as plastic and molded into carpet padding and floor mats. It can also be blended with asphalt and used to make paved roads. An estimated 1 million tires are consumed annually through crumb rubber asphalt applications. The federal government has passed legislation requiring that each state use recycled rubber in a portion of asphalt-paved roads financed either in whole or in part by the federal government.

Figure 9.4 Applications for used tires are being developed. Rubber from used tires is now one of the components in asphalt-paved roads financed by the federal government.

The short-term solution to stockpiles of used tires favored by the United States Environmental Protection Agency is to burn the tires to generate electrical energy. Tires can be burned alone or as a supplementary fuel at power plants, cement kilns, pulp and paper plants, and tire remanufacturing plants.

Think About It

7. Infer Sulfur is used in the vulcanization of rubber. What problems could this cause when used tires are burned?

8. Create Suggest some innovative uses that would help reduce the ever-growing piles of old tires.

Objective

Show that the temperature of a substance is a measure of the kinetic energy of the particles in the substance.

9.3 Kinetic Energy and Kelvin Temperature

What happens when a substance is heated? The particles of the substance absorb energy, some of which is stored within the particles. This stored energy does not raise the temperature of the substance. The rest of the energy goes into speeding up the particles, that is, increasing their average kinetic energy. The particles in any collection of atoms or molecules actually have a wide range of kinetic energies from very low to very high. Most of the particles have kinetic energies in the middle of this range. Therefore the term "average kinetic energy" is proper when discussing the kinetic energy of a collection of particles in a substance. Figure 9.5 shows the distribution of kinetic energies of gas particles at two different temperatures. Notice that at the higher temperature there is a wider range of kinetic energies.

Only the increase in the average kinetic energy of the particles causes the temperature of the substance to rise. As a substance cools, the particles move more slowly and their average kinetic energy declines. You could reasonably expect the particles of all substances to stop moving at some very low temperature. The particles would have no kinetic energy at this temperature because they would have no motion. Absolute zero is the temperature at which the motion of particles theoretically ceases. Absolute zero, defined as 0 K, has never been produced in the laboratory, although temperatures near 0.0001 K have been achieved.

The Kelvin temperature scale reflects the relationship between temperature and average kinetic energy. The Kelvin temperature of a substance is directly proportional to the average kinetic energy of the particles of the substance. For example, the particles in helium gas at 200 K have twice the average kinetic energy of the particles in helium gas at 100 K. However, regardless of physical state, at any

Integrating Medicine

Cryogenics

Cryogenics is the science of producing very low temperatures and studying the behavior of matter at such temperatures. At very low temperatures, biological reactions slow down or stop. Biologists use this effect to study reactions more easily. In medicine some tissues are preserved by rapid freezing and can be used in the body when later thawed. Blood, sperm, and cartilage are a few such materials. Doctors also perform cryosurgery by freezing tissue instead of cutting it. Cryosurgery minimizes bleeding during the operation, and healing is rapid with minimal scarring.

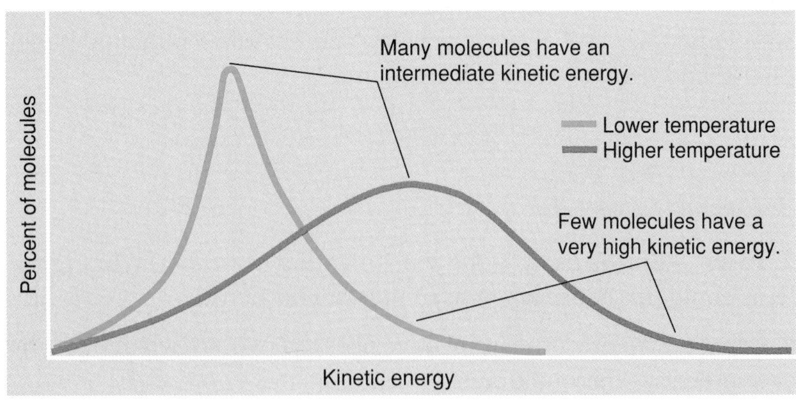

Figure 9.5 The blue curve shows the kinetic energy distribution of a typical collection of molecules. Notice that most molecules have intermediate energies. The red curve shows the energy distribution of the same molecules at a higher temperature. The average kinetic energy has increased.

given temperature the particles of all substances have the same average kinetic energy. You may recall that absolute zero or zero kelvin (0 K) is about –273°C on the Celsius scale. Negative temperatures on the Kelvin scale are not needed.

Concept Practice

9. Explain the relationship between the absolute temperature of a substance and the kinetic energy of its particles.

10. How is the average kinetic energy of water molecules affected when you pour hot tea from a kettle into cups at the same temperature as the water?

Practice Problem

11. By what factor does the average kinetic energy of the molecules of a gas in an aerosol container increase when the temperature is raised from 27°C (300 K) to 627°C (900 K)?

9.4 The Nature of Liquids

Objective

Describe the nature of a liquid in terms of the attractive forces between the particles.

You have seen that gas volume and pressure can be explained by assuming that gas particles have motion and that there is no attraction between them. The particles that constitute liquids are also in motion, as Figure 9.6 shows. Liquid particles are free to slide past one another. Hence both liquids and gases flow. However, the particles of a liquid are more strongly attracted to each other than the particles in a gas. The attractive forces between molecules are called intermolecular forces.

Because of intermolecular forces, the particles that make up liquids vibrate and spin in fixed positions and while moving from place to place. All of these motions contribute to the average kinetic energy of the particles. Even so, most of the particles do not have enough kinetic energy to overcome the intermolecular forces and escape into the gaseous state. The forces also reduce the amount of space between the particles of the liquid. Thus liquids are much denser than gases. Increasing the pressure on a liquid has hardly any effect on its volume. For this reason, liquids and also solids are known as the condensed states of matter. The interplay between the disruptive motions of particles and the attractive forces between them determines many physical properties of liquids. Two of these properties are the vapor pressure and the boiling point of a liquid.

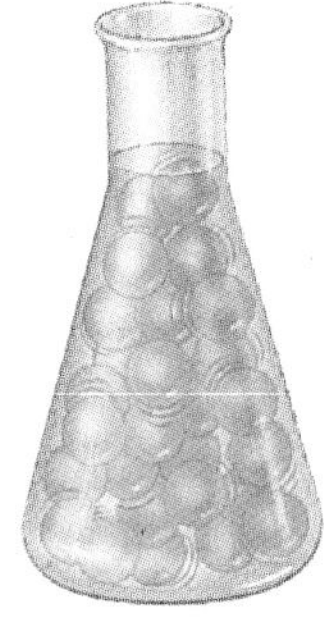

Figure 9.6 Particles in a liquid are free to move around and slide past one another. The attractive forces between the particles prevent most of them from escaping the liquid.

Figure 9.7 Both liquids and gases flow. If a gas is denser than air, it can be poured from one container into another. These pictures were taken in a fume hood because bromine vapor is both toxic and corrosive.

Concept Practice

12. Use kinetic theory to explain the differences between the particles in a gas and those in a liquid.

13. A liquid is a condensed state of matter. Explain.

Objective

Explain the vaporization of liquids, using kinetic theory.

9.5 Evaporation

You know that water in an open vessel goes into the air eventually, as shown in Figure 9.8. When you see the slow disappearance of an uncontained liquid like a puddle of water, you probably say it *evaporates. The scientific term for the conversion of a liquid to a gas or vapor below its boiling point is* **evaporation** *or* **vaporization.** In evaporation, molecules at the surface of the liquid break away and

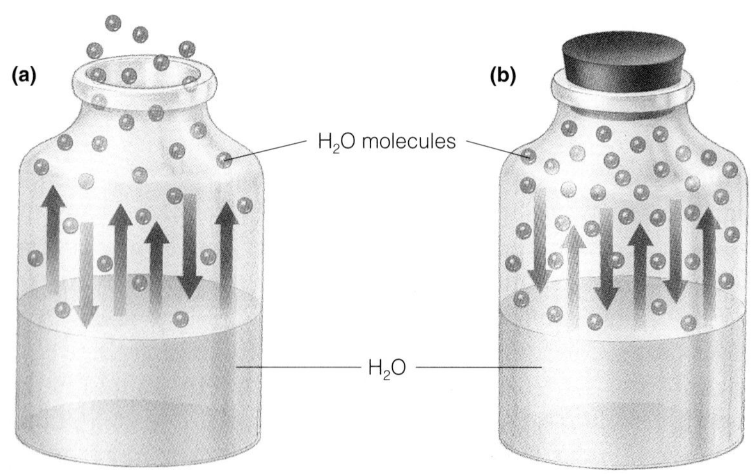

Figure 9.8 **(a)** Water molecules evaporate from the liquid and escape from an open container. No equilibrium is established. **(b)** In a closed container, water molecules do not escape but collect as a vapor above the liquid. A dynamic equilibrium between the vapor and the liquid is established.

go into the gas or vapor state. Only those molecules of the liquid with a certain minimum kinetic energy can break away from the surface. Some escaping particles collide with air molecules and rebound back into the liquid, but others escape completely into the air, into the gaseous phase.

A liquid evaporates faster when heated because the kinetic energy of its particles increases. This enables more particles to overcome the attractive forces keeping them in the liquid. However, evaporation itself is a cooling process. The reason is that the particles with the highest kinetic energy (highest temperature) escape first. The particles left in the liquid have a lower average kinetic energy (lower temperature) than the particles that have escaped. This is similar to removing the fastest runner from a race. The remaining runners have a lower average speed. When water molecules in your perspiration evaporate from your skin's surface, the remaining perspiration is cooler. Therefore the remaining perspiration cools you by absorbing more body heat.

Figure 9.9 This terrarium is at equilibrium. The rate of evaporation equals the rate of condensation. Notice the condensation on the inner surface of the glass.

The evaporation of a liquid in a closed container is somewhat different. The terrarium in Figure 9.9 is an example of a closed container in which liquid evaporates. Figure 9.8b shows that no particles can escape into the atmosphere. When a partially filled container of liquid is sealed, some of the particles in the liquid vaporize. *These particles collide with the walls of the sealed container and produce a* **vapor pressure** *above the liquid.* As the container stands, the number of particles entering the vapor increases. Eventually some of the particles will return to the liquid, or condense.

$$\text{Liquid} \underset{\text{condensation}}{\overset{\text{evaporation}}{\rightleftharpoons}} \text{vapor (gas)}$$

After a time, the number of vapor particles condensing will equal the number of liquid particles vaporizing. The container is now saturated with vapor and a *dynamic equilibrium* exists between the gas and the liquid.

$$\begin{array}{c}\text{Rate of evaporation}\\ \text{of liquid particles}\end{array} = \begin{array}{c}\text{Rate of condensation}\\ \text{of vapor particles}\end{array}$$

At equilibrium, the particles in the system are still evaporating and condensing, but there is no net change in either number of particles. One sign that equilibrium is established is that the inner walls of the container "sweat," as shown in the terrarium of Figure 9.9. Liquid that once evaporated is now condensing, but more liquid is evaporating to take its place.

An increase in the temperature of a contained liquid increases the vapor pressure because the particles in the warmed liquid have increased kinetic energy. As a result, more of them have the minimum kinetic energy necessary to escape the surface of the liquid.

Table 9.1 Vapor Pressures (kPa) of Several Substances at Various Temperatures	0°C	20°C	40°C	60°C	80°C	100°C
Water	0.61	2.33	7.37	19.92	47.34	101.33
Ethanol	1.63	5.85	18.04	47.02	108.34	225.75
Diethyl ether	24.70	58.96	122.80	230.65	399.11	647.87

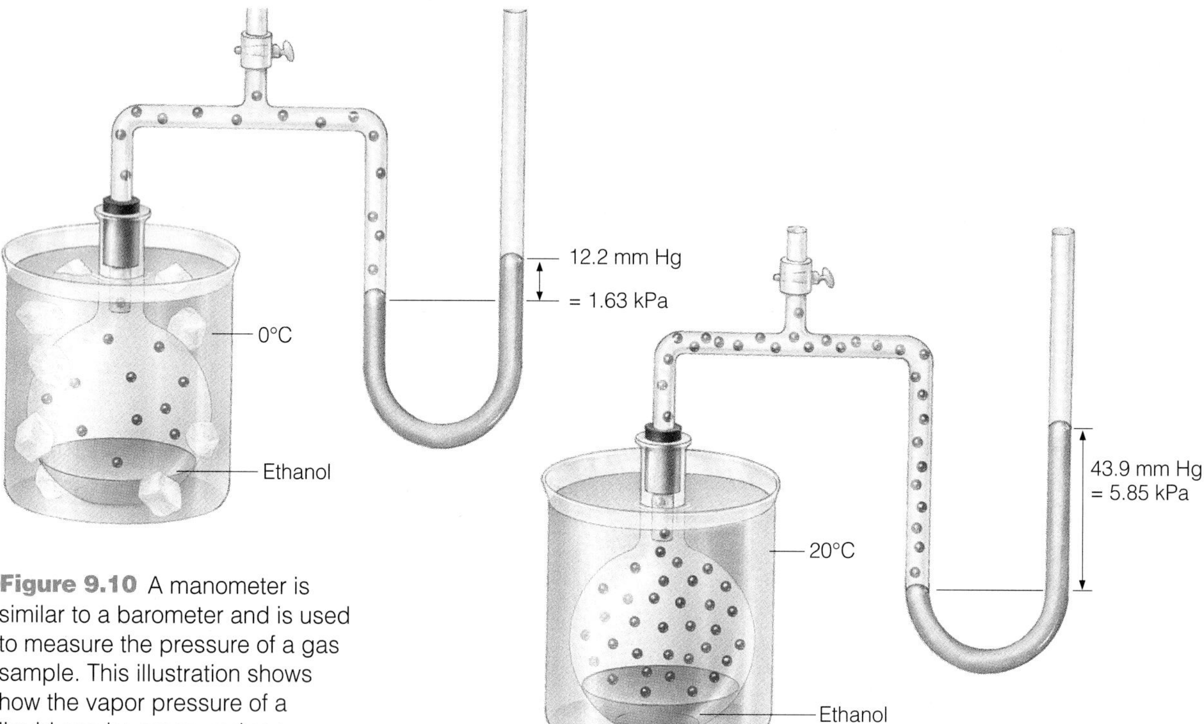

Figure 9.10 A manometer is similar to a barometer and is used to measure the pressure of a gas sample. This illustration shows how the vapor pressure of a liquid can be measured at two different temperatures. The height difference in the U-tube equals the vapor pressure at that temperature.

The particles escape the liquid and collide with greater frequency with the walls of the container. Table 9.1 gives the vapor pressures of some common liquids at various temperatures. Figure 9.10 illustrates one way to determine the vapor pressure of a liquid.

Concept Practice

14. Compare the evaporation of a contained liquid with the evaporation of an uncontained liquid.

15. In your own words, explain the terms *vapor pressure* and *dynamic equilibrium.*

9.6 The Boiling Point of a Liquid

Objective

Describe what happens on a particle level at the boiling point of a liquid.

You know that the rate of evaporation of a liquid from an open container increases with the addition of heat. Heating allows larger numbers of particles at the liquid's surface to break the attractive forces keeping them in the liquid state. The remaining particles in the liquid become agitated as they absorb the heat. Hence their average kinetic energy increases. When the liquid is finally heated to its boiling point, many of the particles throughout the liquid have enough kinetic energy to vaporize. *The* **boiling point (bp)** *is the temperature at which the vapor pressure of the liquid is just equal to the external pressure.* Bubbles of vapor form throughout the liquid. The vapor pressure in these bubbles is equal to the atmospheric pressure. Vapor escapes to the atmosphere and the liquid boils.

The **normal boiling point** *is the boiling point of a liquid at a pressure of 101 kPa.* The boiling point of a liquid changes as the external pressure changes. Figure 9.11 illustrates this point using

Table 9.2 The Normal Boiling Points of Several Common Substances

Name and formula	Boiling point (°C)
Carbon disulfide (CS_2)	46.0
Chloroform ($CHCl_3$)	61.7
Ethanol (C_2H_6O)	78.5
Water (H_2O)	100.0

Figure 9.11 A liquid boils when the vapor pressure of particles in the bulk of the liquid equals the atmospheric pressure.

101 kPa

70°C

Sea level
At 70°C and 101 kPa the atmospheric pressure at the surface of the liquid is greater than the vapor pressure of the liquid. Bubbles of vapor cannot form in the liquid.

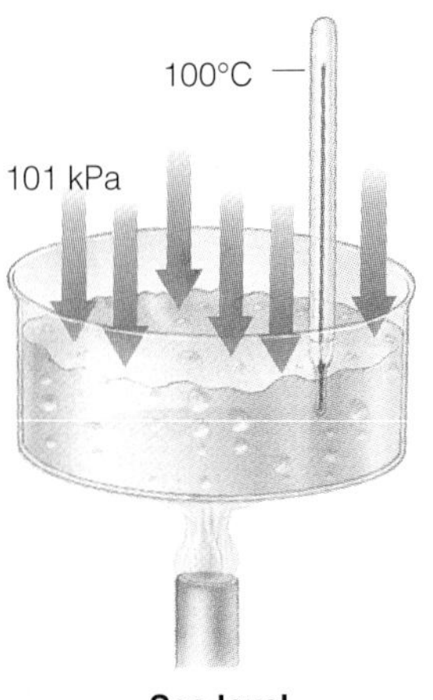

Sea level
At the boiling point the vapor pressure is equal to atmospheric pressure. Bubbles of vapor form inside the liquid, and the liquid boils.

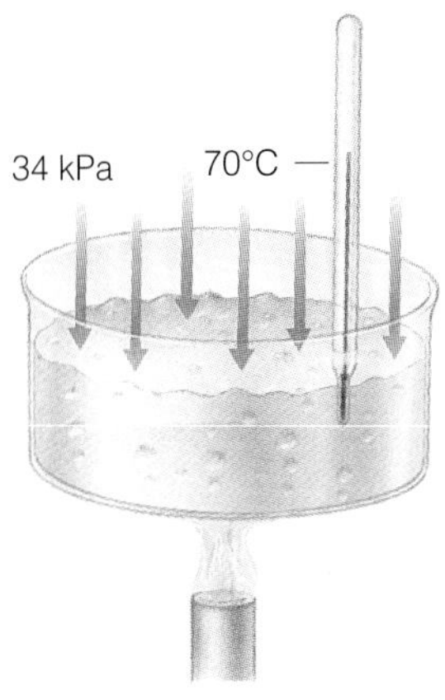

Mt. Everest
At higher altitudes the atmospheric pressure is lower than at sea level. Thus the liquid boils at a lower temperature.

Figure 9.12 A liquid boils when its vapor pressure equals the external pressure. The intersection of a curve with the 101-kPa line indicates the normal boiling point of the substance. At about what temperature would ethanol boil in Denver?

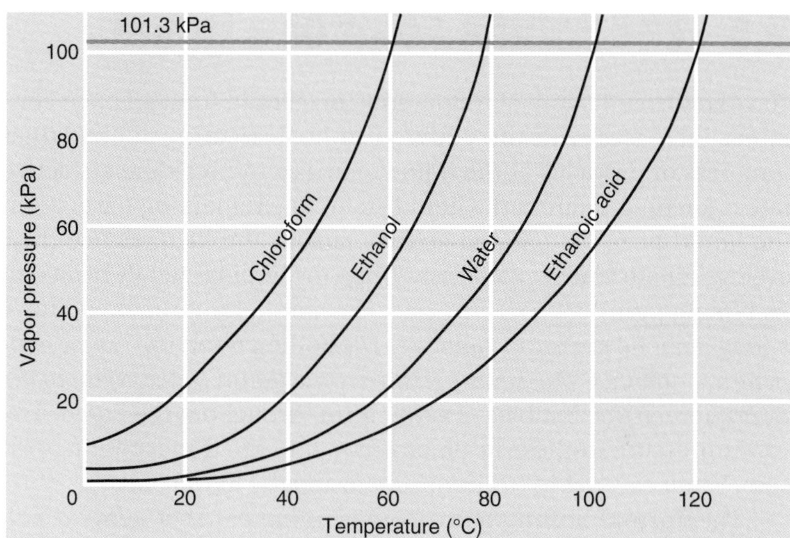

Figure 9.13 An autoclave is commonly used to sterilize medical instruments. Autoclaves are usually set at 120°C and 202.6 kPa for 15 minutes. The high pressure keeps the water at a high enough temperature to kill bacteria and their spores.

water as the example. Also look at the vapor pressure diagram of Figure 9.12. At lower atmospheric pressures, the boiling point decreases because particles leaving the liquid are less likely to collide with external air molecules or other vapor molecules. Therefore these particles need less kinetic energy to escape the liquid. The normal boiling point of water is 100°C. In Denver, however, water boils at 95°C. At 1600 m above sea level, Denver has an average atmospheric pressure of only 85.3 kPa. Similarly, at higher atmospheric pressures, a liquid's boiling point increases because the particles in the liquid need more kinetic energy to escape. You may know about pressure cookers that reduce cooking time. At the high pressure in the cooker, water boils well above 100°C. Autoclaves such as the one shown in Figure 9.13 operate in a similar way.

The particles with the highest kinetic energy escape first when a liquid is at its boiling point. If no more heat is supplied, the temperature of the liquid drops below its boiling point. If more heat is supplied, however, more particles acquire enough kinetic energy to escape. The result is a continual cooling effect on the remaining liquid. *Therefore, the temperature of a boiling liquid never rises above its boiling point.* When more heat is supplied, the liquid only boils faster. Eventually all of the liquid boils away.

Concept Practice

16. Describe what happens when the vapor pressure of a liquid just equals atmospheric pressure.

9.7 The Nature of Solids

Objective

Describe how higher organization and stronger forces between the particles distinguish solids from gases and liquids.

The motions of the particles in liquids are chaotic. However, Figure 9.14 shows that rather than sliding from place to place, solid particles tend to vibrate about fixed points. In most solids the particles are packed against one another in a highly organized pattern, as in Figure 9.15. Solids are dense and incompressible. Because of the fixed position of most of their particles, solids do not flow to fill their containers.

When you heat a solid, its particles vibrate more rapidly and begin to spin as their kinetic energy increases. The organization of particles within the solid crumbles and eventually the solid melts. *The* **melting point (mp)** *is the temperature at which the solid turns into a liquid.* At this temperature, the disruptive vibrations of the particles are strong enough to overcome the interactions that hold them in fixed positions. The melting process can be reversed by cooling the liquid. The freezing of a liquid substance is the reverse process of melting a solid substance. Thus the melting and freezing points of a substance are the same temperature. At this temperature the liquid and solid substance are in equilibrium with each other.

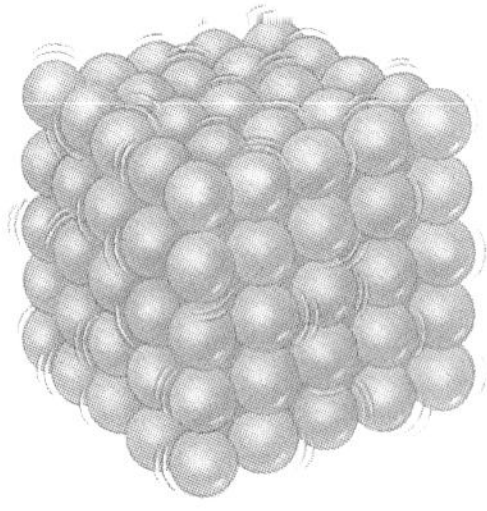

Figure 9.14 A solid melts when its temperature is raised to a point at which the vibrations of the particles become so intense that they disrupt the ordered structure.

$$\text{Solid} \underset{\text{freezing}}{\overset{\text{melting}}{\rightleftharpoons}} \text{liquid}$$

In general, ionic solids have high melting points because these solids are held together by relatively strong forces. Sodium chloride, an ionic compound, has a melting point of 801°C. By contrast, molecular solids have relatively low melting points. Molecular solids are held together by relatively weak forces. For example, hydrogen chloride, a molecular compound, melts at –112°C. Not all solids melt. Wood, for example, decomposes when heated.

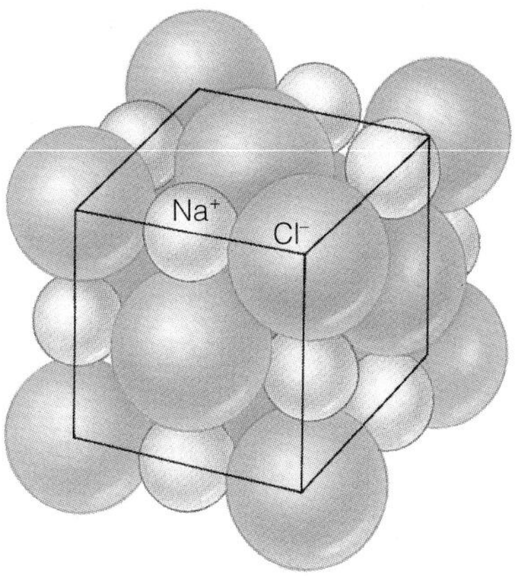

Figure 9.15 The regular shape of this sodium chloride crystal can be explained by the arrangement of sodium ions and chloride ions within the crystal.

Roots of Words

krystallos: (Greek) icelike
crystal a substance in which the particles are arranged in an orderly, three-dimensional pattern called a crystal lattice

Sodium chloride, common table salt, is a crystalline substance.

Most solid substances are crystalline. *In a* **crystal** *the atoms, ions, or molecules are arranged in an orderly, repeating, three-dimensional pattern.* This array is called the crystal lattice. All crystals have a regular shape. The shape reflects the arrangement of the particles within the solid. The angles at which the faces of a crystal intersect are always the same for a given substance and are characteristic of that substance. Crystals are classified into seven crystal systems. They have the characteristic shapes shown in Figure 9.16. The seven crystal systems differ according to the angles between the faces and how many of the edges of the faces are of equal length.

The shape of a crystal depends on the arrangement of the particles within it. *The smallest group of particles within a crystal that retains the geometric shape of the crystal is known as a* **unit cell.** A crystal lattice is a repeating array of any one of the 14 known unit cells. The three unit cells that are part of the cubic crystal system are shown in Figure 9.17. Each crystal system has one to four types of unit cells that are associated with that crystal system. The melting points of crystals are determined by how the atoms are bonded.

Figure 9.16 Crystals are classified into the seven crystal systems shown here.

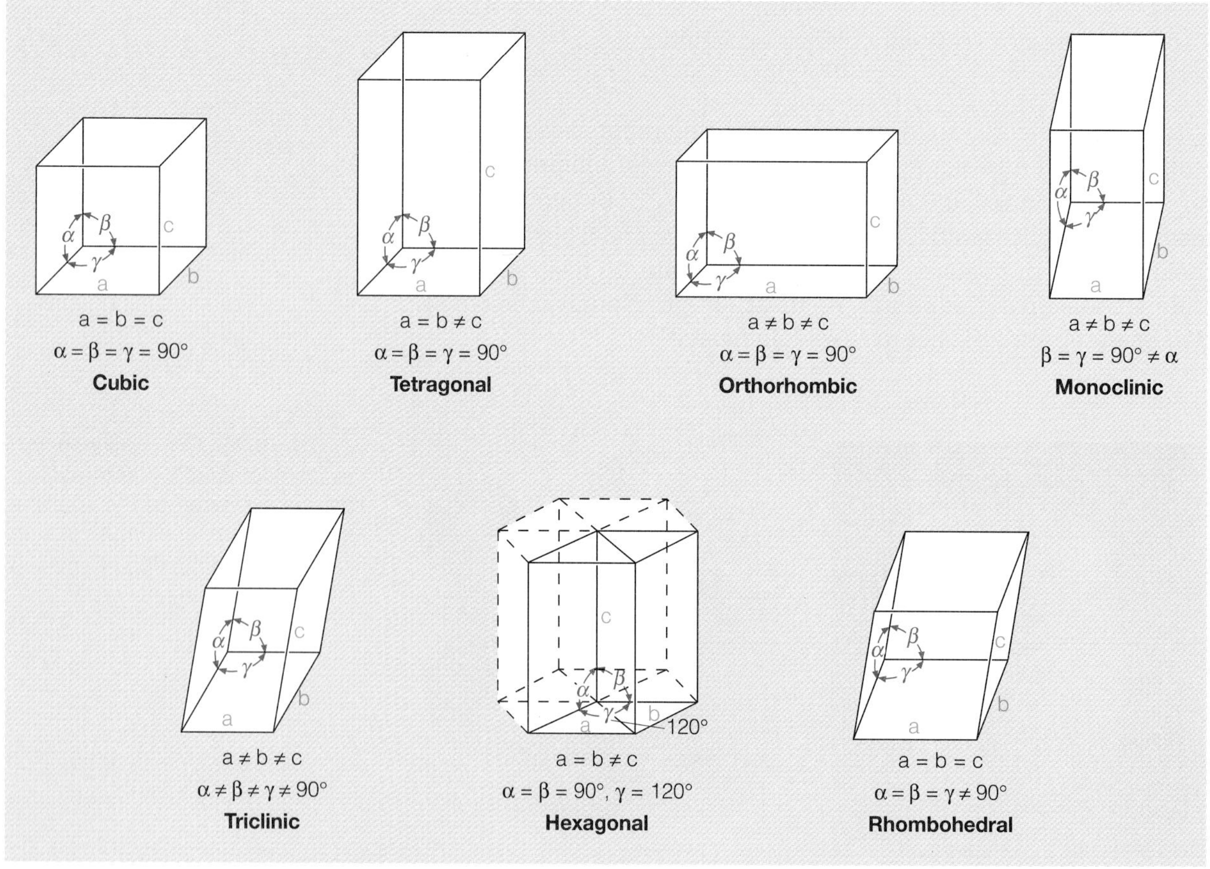

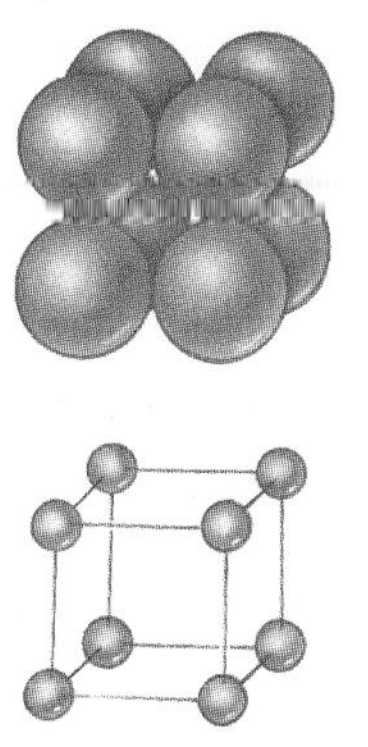

In a **simple cubic** unit cell the atoms or ions are arranged at the corners of an imaginary cube.

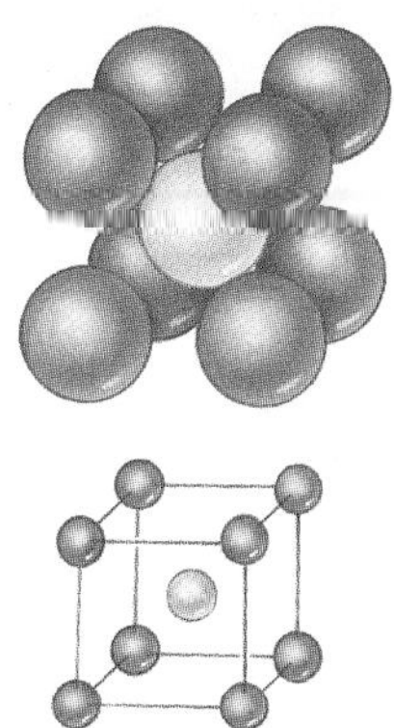

In a **body-centered cubic** unit cell the atoms or ions are at the corners and in the center of an imaginary cube.

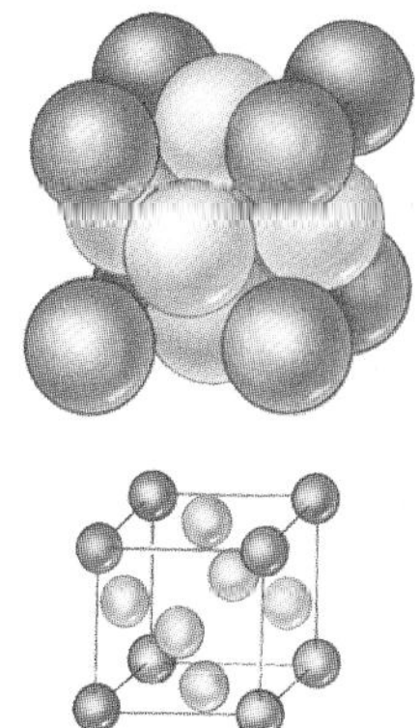

In a **face-centered cubic** unit cell the atoms or ions are also in the center of each face of the imaginary cube.

Figure 9.17 The top row shows the larger spheres representing the atoms or ions of three different cubic lattices. The same cubic unit cells are illustrated in the bottom row.

Some substances can exist in more than one type of solid state. A good example is the element carbon. Diamond is one crystalline form of carbon. It forms when carbon crystallizes under tremendous pressure (thousands of atmospheres). The other crystalline form of carbon is graphite. The "lead" in a pencil is actually graphite. In graphite, the carbon atoms are packed more loosely than in diamond. Figure 9.18 shows the arrangement of carbon atoms in diamond and graphite. The physical properties of diamond and graphite are quite different. Diamond has a high density and is very hard; graphite has a low density and is soft. Diamond and graphite are allotropes of carbon. **Allotropes** *are two or more different molecular forms of the same element in the same physical state.* Until recently, diamond and graphite were thought to be the only two allotropes of carbon. However, this picture changed in

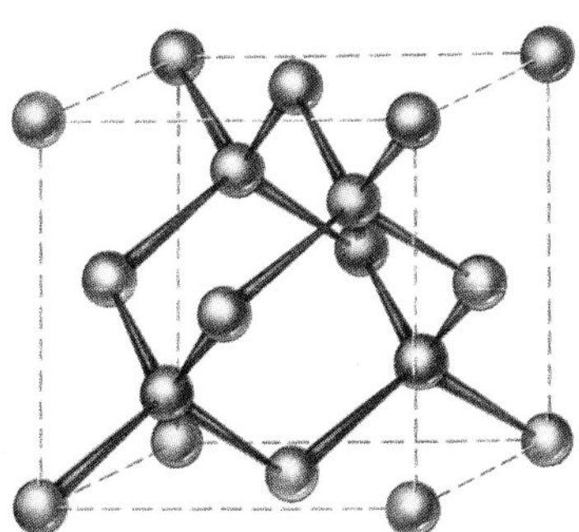

In **diamond**, each carbon atom is strongly bonded to four others, creating a rigid compact array. Diamond is the hardest known material.

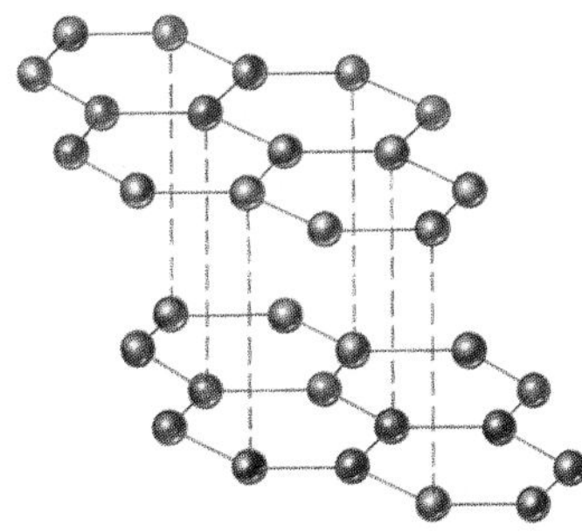

In **graphite**, the carbon atoms are linked in widely spaced layers of hexagonal (six-sided) arrays. Weak bonds between these layers allow them to slide over one another, making graphite very soft.

Figure 9.18 The arrangement of carbon atoms dramatically affects the properties of diamond and graphite, its two most common forms.

Figure 9.19 Glass does not have a definite melting point because it is an amorphous solid.

1985 with the discovery of carbon allotropes called buckminsterfullerenes, which contain 60 carbons. The Materials Science section at the end of this chapter discusses these fascinating molecules.

Not all solids are crystalline in form; some solids are amorphous. **Amorphous solids** *lack an ordered internal structure.* Rubber, plastic, and asphalt are amorphous solids. Their atoms are randomly arranged.

Glasses *are amorphous solids that are sometimes called supercooled liquids.* They are transparent fusion products of inorganic substances that have cooled to a rigid state without crystallizing. The irregular internal structures of glasses are intermediate between those of a crystalline solid and a free-flowing liquid. Glasses do not melt at a definite temperature but gradually soften when heated. This softening with temperature is critical to the glassblower's art, as shown in Figure 9.19.

When a crystalline solid is shattered, the fragments have the same surface angles as the original solid. By contrast, when an amorphous solid such as glass is shattered, the fragments have irregular angles and jagged edges.

Roots of Words

amorphos: (Greek) without shape or form
amorphous describes a solid that lacks an ordered internal structure

One of the forms of elemental sulfur is amorphous.

Concept Practice

17. Briefly, use kinetic theory to explain the nature of solids and why they differ from liquids.

18. Name at least one physical property that would permit you to distinguish a molecular solid from an ionic solid.

9.B Science, Technology, and Society

Liquid Crystals

Not all substances change sharply from orderly solids to disorganized liquids when they melt. Some substances flow like liquids even though their molecules are still ordered. These materials are called liquid crystals.

The molecules in liquid crystals are shaped like rods. The three types of liquid crystals differ in the way the rodlike molecules are organized. In *nematic* substances, the rods remain parallel to each other as they move back and forth in the liquid. In *smectic* liquid crystals, the rods are not only parallel but also arranged in layers. The layers can move, but individual molecules remain fixed within a layer. In a *cholesteric* liquid crystal, the molecules are also in layers. Within a layer, the molecules are free to move back and forth, remaining parallel to each other, as they do in nematic crystals. In contrast to the smectic crystal, the molecules in one layer of a cholesteric crystal are not parallel to those in another layer. These layers are aligned in a spiral shape.

When light strikes a smectic or cholesteric liquid crystal, it is reflected by the layers of molecules within the crystal. The color of light that is reflected depends on the distance between layers. The distance between layers changes as the temperature changes. Thus a temperature change in the crystal will show up as a color change. Liquid crystal thermometers can be placed on the skin to take body temperature or to locate a "hot spot," such as an artery or a vein.

In a digital wristwatch or calculator, a nematic liquid crystal is contained between two layers of glass. The surface of the top layer of glass can be electrically charged in segments that can be grouped to create numbers. Under the influence of these charged segments, the molecules of the liquid crystal orient themselves in a way that prevents light from passing through. This is the reason that the numbers appear black.

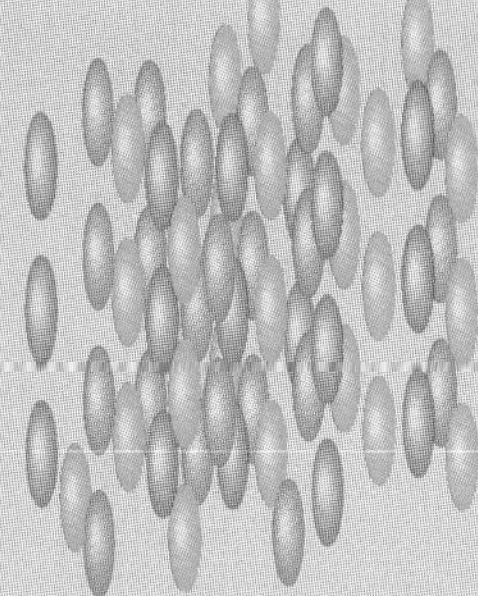

In nematic crystals the molecules are all parallel.

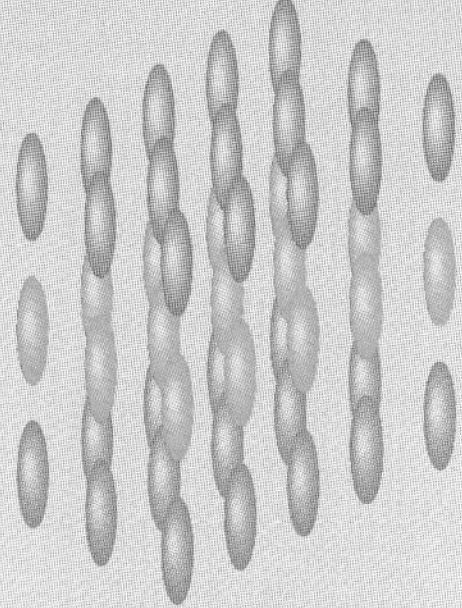

In smectic crystals the molecules are parallel within layers.

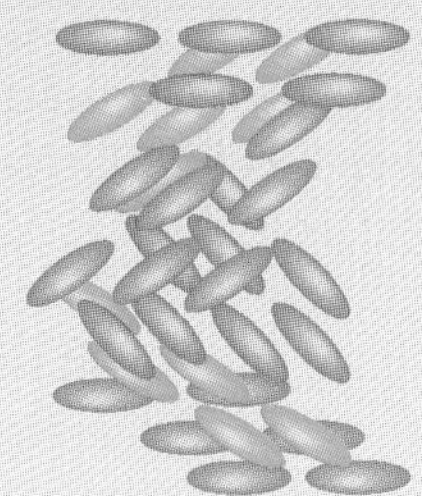

In cholesteric crystals the molecules are parallel within each layer, but the layers are aligned in a spiral shape.

Figure 9.20 Three types of liquid crystals.

Think About It

19. Describe What are some of the physical properties of liquid crystals that permit them to produce digital displays?

Objective

Describe the behavior of solids that go into the vapor state and condense back to solids without passing through the liquid state.

9.8 Sublimation

If you hang wet laundry on a clothesline to dry on a very cold day, the water in the clothes quickly freezes to ice. After several hours, however, the clothes are dry although the ice never thaws. The ice goes to water vapor without melting and passing through the liquid state. Melting, freezing, evaporation, and condensation all involve changes of physical states of matter. Many substances undergo the physical change from solid to liquid and from liquid to gas as the temperature is raised. Like liquids, however, solids have a vapor pressure. The vapor pressure of some solids is high enough that they pass from a solid to a gas or vapor without becoming liquid. *The change of a substance from a solid to a gas or vapor without passing through the liquid state is called* **sublimation**.

Another example of sublimation is iodine. This violet-black solid ordinarily changes into a purple vapor without passing through a liquid state. Notice in Figure 9.21 how violet-black crystals of iodine deposit on the cooled lid of a beaker when iodine vapor sublimes from iodine crystals in the bottom of the beaker.

Figure 9.21 When solid iodine is heated, the crystals sublime, going directly from the solid to a purple vapor. When the vapor cools, solid crystals form without passing through the liquid state.

Freeze-dried coffee is made by freezing freshly brewed coffee and removing the water vapor of the ice with a vacuum pump. Solid carbon dioxide ("dry ice") is another compound that sublimes. Nobody has ever seen a puddle of liquid carbon dioxide at ordinary conditions of temperature and pressure. With its low temperature of –78°C and because there is no melted liquid to dispose of, dry ice is very useful for keeping frozen foods like ice cream solid during shipping. Solid air fresheners and mothballs often contain camphor that sublimes at room temperature. It is the camphor vapor that keeps away the moths. Have you ever noticed that ice cubes left in your freezer for a time get smaller? The ice sublimes to water vapor in the air inside the freezer. Sublimation can be used to separate substances. Chinese alchemists knew the art of purification of substances by sublimation many centuries ago.

Concept Practice

20. A container of food has been left at the bottom of the freezer for several months. When you remove the lid you discover a large collection of ice crystals on the underside of the lid and on top of the food. Explain what has happened. How might this affect the taste of the food?

21. Why do some substances pass from a solid to a gas without becoming liquid?

Activity 9
Sublimation

Purpose

To observe the sublimation of air freshener.

Materials

small pieces of solid air freshener
small shallow container
two 8-oz clear plastic cups
hot water (from a faucet)
ice
three strips of thick cardboard

Procedure

1. Place a few pieces of air freshener in one of the cups.

2. Bend the cardboard strips and place them over the rim of the cup with the air freshener pieces at the bottom.

3. Insert the second cup inside the first. *Note: The base of the second cup should not touch the air freshener.* Adjust the cardboard as necessary. This assembly is your sublimator.

4. Fill the top cup with ice. *Note: It is important that you do not get any ice or water in the bottom cup.*

5. Fill the shallow container about one-third full with hot water from a faucet.

6. Carefully place your sublimator in the hot water.

7. Observe what happens.

Analysis and Conclusions

1. Define the term *sublimation.*

2. Predict what would happen if the water in the shallow container was (a) at room temperature and (b) boiling.

3. Why is it possible to separate the substances in some mixtures by sublimation?

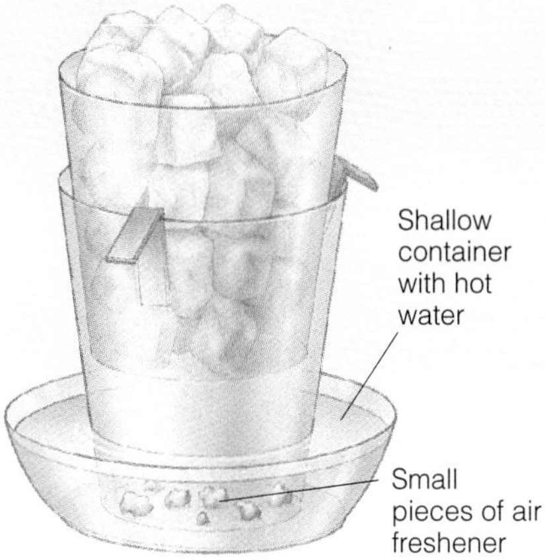

9.9 Phase Diagrams

Objective

Interpret the phase diagram of water at any given temperature and pressure.

The relationships among the solid, liquid, and vapor states or phases of a substance in a sealed container are best represented in a single graph called a **phase diagram.** A phase diagram gives the conditions of temperature and pressure at which a substance exists as a solid, liquid, and gas (vapor). Figure 9.22 shows the phase diagram for water. Each of the three regions represents a pure phase of water. A line that separates any two regions gives the conditions at which those two phases exist in equilibrium. The line that separates the water vapor phase from the liquid water phase shows how the vapor pressure of water varies with temperature. Similarly, the other two lines give the conditions for equilibrium between liquid water and ice and water vapor and ice. A unique feature of the diagram is the point at which all three curves meet. *This is the* **triple point,** *which describes the only conditions at which all three phases can exist in equilibrium with one another.* For water the triple point is a temperature of 0.01°C and a pressure of 0.61 kPa (0.0060 atm).

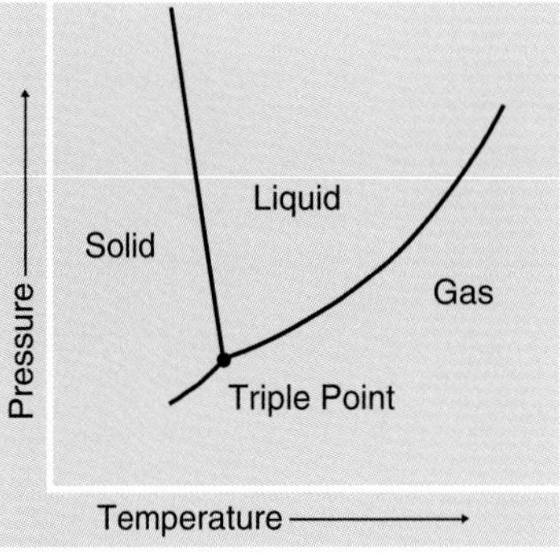

Figure 9.22 Phase diagram of water.

Using a phase diagram, you can determine the changes in the melting point and boiling point of a substance with changes in

Integrating Food Science

Freeze-Drying

Astronauts and backpackers have both enjoyed the benefits of foods preserved by freeze-drying. Freeze-dried foods are lightweight and conveniently reconstituted by adding water. Freeze-dried foods need no refrigeration because bacteria cannot multiply in the absence of moisture. The ready sublimation of ice at low pressure makes freeze-drying possible. Food is frozen and then placed in a chamber attached to a vacuum pump. When the pressure in the chamber is lowered below the vapor pressure of ice, the ice crystals sublime and the food is dried.

external pressure. As shown in Figure 9.23, at 101.3 kPa (1 atm) pressure the normal boiling point and melting point of water are 100°C and 0°C, respectively. What happens if boiling and melting are carried out at pressures higher and lower than 101.3 kPa? A decrease in pressure lowers the boiling point and raises the melting point. Conversely, an increase in pressure raises the boiling point and lowers the melting point.

Ice skaters depend on the result of an increase of pressure on the solid/liquid line of the phase diagram of water. The pressure exerted on ice by a skater lowers its melting point. Consequently, the ice melts and a film of water forms under the blades of the skates. This film acts as a lubricant, enabling skaters to glide gracefully over the ice. While ice skaters depend on this phenomenon, it makes for hazardous winter driving in some climates.

You may recall that ice sublimes during freezing weather. However, if you look at the phase diagram of water you will see that the pressures along the solid/vapor line are much lower than atmospheric pressure on earth. It appears that the sublimation of ice from frozen laundry is impossible, yet it happens. This inconsistency exists because phase diagrams refer to substances in sealed containers, but the sublimation of ice in winter occurs in the open. Many factors are at work in the open, and ice does sublime at conditions found on earth.

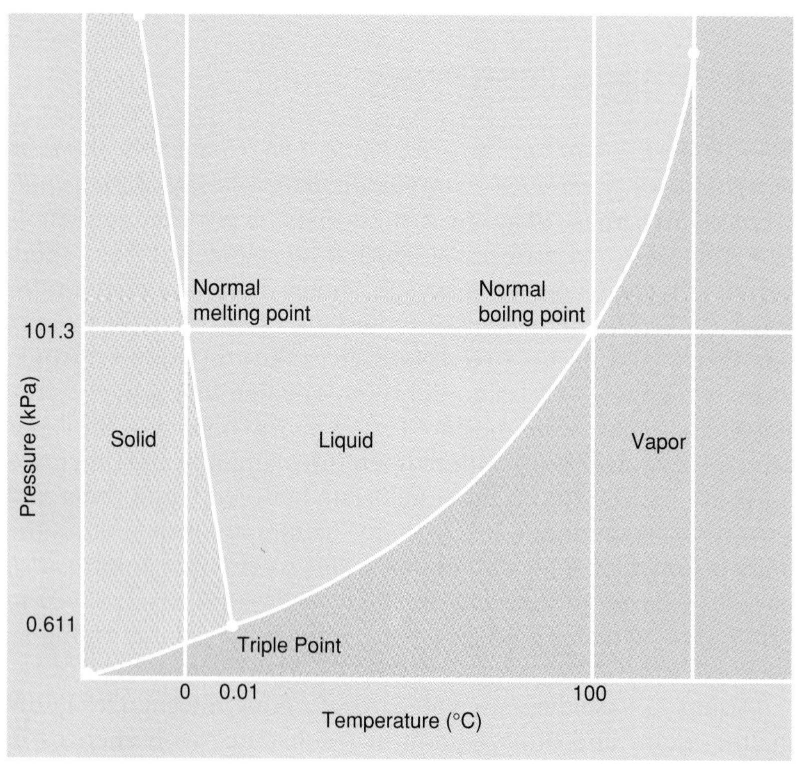

Figure 9.23 The phase diagram for water shows the relationship among pressure, temperature, and physical state. Note that the scales are distorted to emphasize some of the graph's features.

Concept Practice

22. What general information can you get from a phase diagram? Explain what the regions represent.

23. Explain the term *triple point.*

9.10 Plasma: The Fourth State of Matter

Objective

Describe the formation and properties of plasma.

What happens if you heat a gas to a very high temperature? First, the kinetic energy of the molecules becomes great enough to separate molecules into atoms. Then at an even higher temperature, the electrons are stripped off the gaseous atoms. Positive ions and free electrons are the result. *This gaseous mixture of electrons and positive ions is a fourth state of matter, called* **plasma.** Plasma behaves like an ordinary gas in some ways, but it also has some very peculiar properties.

A gas can be partially ionized at low temperatures by common events. Partial plasmas are created in fluorescent lights, neon signs, lightning bolts, and even in flames. The aurora borealis or "northern lights" of Figure 9.24 are atmospheric disturbances caused by low-density plasma. In all of these examples, only a few of the atoms present are ionized at any moment. Even these atoms will not remain ionized for any length of time. A free electron will lose energy when it collides with anything, including other particles or the walls of its container. When it has lost enough energy, it can be recaptured by a gaseous ion. Because of this, plasmas in the atmosphere or those created in neon lights and flames are only weakly ionized.

Figure 9.24 The aurora borealis is caused by the presence of low-density plasma in the upper atmosphere.

A tremendous amount of energy is required to create highly ionized plasmas. Some gases can be mostly converted into plasmas between temperatures of 50 000 K and 100 000 K. These are called "cold plasmas." By contrast, some plasmas require temperatures between 10 000 000 K and 1000 000 000 K and even higher. These "hot plasmas" are the material of the stars.

Concept Practice

24. Based on the properties of plasmas and gases, explain how a plasma differs from an ordinary gas.

Buckyballs

New Allotropes of Carbon

The centuries-old idea that carbon exists in only two allotropes—hard, shiny diamond and soft, slippery graphite—was recently shattered. Ordinary soot has been found to contain small, variable amounts of other molecular forms of carbon. One of these forms has the carbon atoms organized into a spherical molecular structure.

This newly discovered carbon allotrope, called buckminsterfullerene, is a molecule with 60 carbon atoms arranged in regular pentagons (five-sided figures) and hexagons (six-sided figures) to form a hollow cage. Because of this shape, the molecule was named for Buckminster Fuller, the designer of the geodesic dome. A soccer ball has the same pattern of pentagons and hexagons. Therefore many people call the buckminsterfullerene molecule a "buckyball." The pattern of pentagons and hexagons, which imparts great strength and rigidity to geodesic domes and soccer balls, makes buckyballs strong and rigid as well. The great stability of this arrangement is probably the reason that buckyballs are formed.

Buckyballs behave a lot like ordinary soccer balls. They spin madly at room temperature. When they are shot at a surface at speeds of 15 000 miles per hour they rebound without being damaged. They are somewhat mushy at atmospheric pressure but resist collapse at very high pressures.

The discovery of the buckyball opened the door to exciting possibilities for many new applications. Replacement of some of the buckyball carbon atoms with silicon produces a semiconductor. By contrast, when a potassium atom is trapped inside the hollow cage of the buckyball, the material becomes a superconductor at 54 K (–219°C). Because of their rigidity at high pressures, buckyballs might replace diamonds in some industrial applications. So-called diamond anvils are now used to squeeze materials together at pressures of up to 4 million atmospheres. Buckyball materials used similarly could make it possible to achieve even higher pressures. Finally, buckyballs could serve as molecular "Christmas trees" on which all kinds of chemical "ornaments" could be hung. Designed properly, these new materials might be used as lubricants, plastics, and medicines.

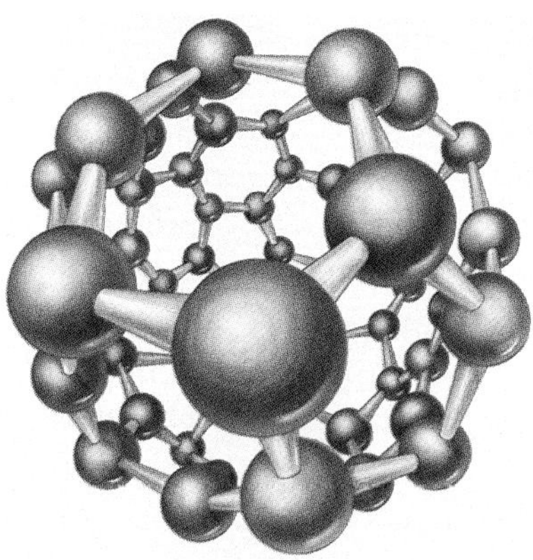

Think About It

25. Summarize What is the new allotrope of carbon and why is it an exciting discovery?

Chapter 9 Review
The States of Matter

Key Terms

allotrope 9.7
amorphous solid 9.7
atmospheric pressure 9.2
barometer 9.2
boiling point (bp) 9.6
crystal 9.7
evaporation 9.5
gas pressure 9.2
glass 9.7
kinetic energy 9.1
kinetic theory 9.1
melting point (mp) 9.7
normal boiling point 9.6
pascal (Pa) 9.2
phase diagram 9.9
plasma 9.10
standard atmosphere (atm) 9.2
sublimation 9.8
triple point 9.9
unit cell 9.7
vacuum 9.2
vapor pressure 9.5
vaporization 9.5

Chapter Summary

The kinetic theory describes the motion of particles in matter and the forces of attraction between them. The theory assumes that the volume occupied by a gas is mostly empty space and that the particles of a gas are far apart, move rapidly, and have chaotic motion. The pressure of a gas results from the collisions of the gas particles with an object. Barometers are used to measure atmospheric pressure.

Standard conditions when working with gases are a temperature of 0°C and a pressure of 101.3 kPa. The temperature of a gas is directly proportional to the average kinetic energy of the particles. When the temperature of a gas is lowered, the particles slow down, and the gas condenses to a liquid. As the temperature is lowered further, the liquid solidifies. Solids are rigid and have fixed volumes. In a solid, the movement of particles is restricted to vibrations about fixed points. Liquids have a fixed volume and characteristic vapor pressure. A liquid boils when its vapor pressure equals the external pressure. The normal boiling point of a liquid is the temperature at which the vapor pressure is equal to 1 atm.

Most substances change their physical state and melt or vaporize as the temperature is raised. They condense or freeze as the temperature is lowered. When the physical state of a substance changes, a phase change occurs. During a phase change, the temperature of the system remains constant.

The particles in a solid vibrate more rapidly when the solid is heated. Solids melt when the vibrations are greater than the forces holding the particles together. Most solids are crystalline. The particles are arranged in a repeating three-dimensional pattern known as a crystal lattice. Some solids have a disordered array of particles and are amorphous.

Practice Questions and Problems

26. What is meant by the term *elastic collision*? *9.1.*

27. Change 1656 km/h to m/s. *9.1*

28. How can you raise the average kinetic energy of the water molecules in a glass of water? *9.2*

29. What pressure in kilopascals and atmospheres does a gas exert at 385 mm Hg? *9.2*

30. How many millimeters of mercury pressure does a gas exert at 3.1 atm? *9.2*

31. Express 545 mm Hg in kilopascals. *9.2*

32. What does the abbreviation STP represent? *9.2*

33. Express standard temperature in kelvins and standard pressure in millimeters of mercury. *9.2*

34. What is significant about the temperature absolute zero? *9.3*

35. A cylinder of oxygen gas is cooled from 300 K (27°C) to 150 K (–123°C). By what factor does the average kinetic energy of the oxygen molecules in the cylinder decrease? *9.3*

36. Explain why liquids and gases differ. *9.4*

a. in physical state

b. in compressibility

37. Why does evaporation lower the temperature of a liquid? *9.5*

38. Explain why increasing the temperature of a liquid increases its rate of evaporation. *9.5*
39. Would you expect an equilibrium vapor pressure to be reached above a liquid in an open container? Why? *9.5*
40. Describe the effect that increasing temperature has on the vapor pressure of a liquid. *9.5*
41. Distinguish between the boiling point and the normal boiling point of a liquid. *9.6*
42. Use Figure 9.12 to determine the boiling point of each of these liquids. *9.6*
    a. ethanoic acid at 27 kPa
    b. chloroform at 80 kPa
    c. ethanol at 53 kPa
43. At the top of Mt. Everest, water boils at only 60°C. Use Figure 9.12 to estimate the atmospheric pressure at the top of this mountain. *9.6*
44. Explain how boiling is a cooling process. *9.6*
45. Describe what happens when a solid is at its melting point. *9.7*
46. In general, molecular solids have lower melting points than ionic solids. Why? *9.7*
47. What is the crystal lattice of a solid? *9.7*
48. What is the difference between nematic, smectic, and cholesteric liquid crystals? *9.B*
49. Any liquid stays at a constant temperature while it is boiling. Why? *9.8*
50. Describe the process of sublimation. What practical use can be made of this process? *9.8*
51. Define the terms. *9.9*
    a. phase diagram **b.** triple point
52. How is the fourth state of matter produced and what are its properties? *9.10*

Mastery Questions and Problems

53. Make a concept map using states of matter as the main concept. Use the chapter key terms and the following: solid, liquid, gas, freezes, condenses, and boils.
54. Describe evaporation, vapor pressure, and boiling point.
55. The temperature of the gas in an aerosol container is 0°C (273 K). To what new temperature must the gas be raised to increase the average kinetic energy of its molecules by a factor of 3?

56. If liquid nitrogen is poured onto a balloon, the volume of the balloon decreases dramatically as shown above. When no more liquid nitrogen is poured on the balloon, it "reinflates." Use kinetic theory to explain this. The temperature of liquid nitrogen is –196°C.
57. What causes atmospheric pressure, and why is it much lower on the top of a mountain than at sea level?
58. Why do we call the equilibrium that exists between a liquid and its vapor in a closed container a dynamic equilibrium?
59. What happens to the average kinetic energy of all the water molecules in your body when you get a fever?
60. Explain what happens at the melting point of a substance.

Critical Thinking Questions

61. Choose the term that best completes the second relationship.
    a. temperature:thermometer
    atmospheric pressure: _____
    (1) valve (3) volume
    (2) barometer (4) gauge
    b. education:knowledge
    vaporization: _____
    (1) evaporation (3) gas (vapor)
    (2) water (4) condensation
    c. evolution:organisms
    kinetic theory: _____
    (1) particles (3) heat
    (2) temperature (4) pressure

62. What everyday evidence suggests that all matter is in constant motion?
63. Are perfectly elastic collisions possible between objects we can see?
64. How does perspiration help cool your body on a hot day?
65. Why do different liquids have different boiling points?
66. Is the average kinetic energy of the particles in a block of ice at 0°C the same as or different from the average kinetic energy of the particles in a gas-filled dirigible at 0°C? Explain.
67. Your car needs new tires. As a concerned citizen, would you consider buying a set of remanufactured tires? Explain your decision.

Cumulative Review

68. Balance these equations.
   a. $V_2O_5 + H_2 \rightarrow V_2O_3 + H_2O$
   b. $(NH_4)_2Cr_2O_7 \rightarrow Cr_2O_3 + N_2 + H_2O$
   c. $NH_3 + O_2 \rightarrow NO + H_2O$
   d. $C_6H_{14} + O_2 \rightarrow CO + H_2O$
69. What is the density of krypton gas at STP?
70. Hydrogen reacts with ethene (C_2H_4) to form ethane (C_2H_6).
$$C_2H_4 + H_2 \rightarrow C_2H_6$$
What is the limiting reagent when 40g of C_2H_4 reacts with 3.0 g of H_2?
71. How many moles are there of each substance?
   a. 888 g of sulfur dioxide
   b. 2.84×10^{22} molecules of ammonia
   c. 0.47 L of carbon dioxide (at STP)
72. Perchloric acid is formed by the reaction of water with dichlorine heptoxide.
$$Cl_2O_7 + H_2O \rightarrow HClO_4$$
   a. How many grams of Cl_2O_7 must be reacted with an excess of H_2O to form 56.2 g of $HClO_4$?
   b. How many mL of water are needed to form 3.40 mol of $HClO_4$?

Challenge Questions and Problems

73. If the volume of the container in which there is a liquid-vapor equilibrium is changed, the vapor pressure is not affected. Why?
74. The ions in sodium chloride are arranged in a face-centered cubic pattern. Sketch a layer of the ions in a crystal of sodium chloride.

Connections Questions

75. Describe what further experiment Torricelli could have done to show the existence of a vacuum above the level of mercury in his barometer.
76. How would the agricultural industry use cryogenics to its benefit?
77. What phase change is linked with the process of freeze-drying?

Write About Chemistry

78. Imagine that you are a water molecule in a crystal of ice. Describe your ability to move around as the temperature around you is gradually increased first above 0°C and then above 100°C.
79. Write a short story revolving around cryobiology—the study of the preservation of living things at very cold temperatures.

Readings and References

Davenport, Derek A. "Burning Diamonds and Squeezing Peanuts." *ChemMatters* (April 1990), pp. 14–15.

"Liquid Crystal Displays." *ChemMatters* (April 1984), pp. 10–11.

Wood, Clair. "Buckyballs." *ChemMatters* (December 1992), pp. 7–9.

10 Thermochemistry

Goals

- Describe heat changes in physical and chemical processes as exothermic or endothermic.
- List the steps needed to measure heats of chemical and physical processes by calorimetry.
- Explain the meaning of enthalpy.
- Construct thermochemical equations.
- Calculate heats of reaction.

Striking a match provides the energy necessary for a chemical reaction to take place. Carbon subnitride (C_4N_2) makes the hottest flame possible at a temperature of 5261 K.

Concept Overview

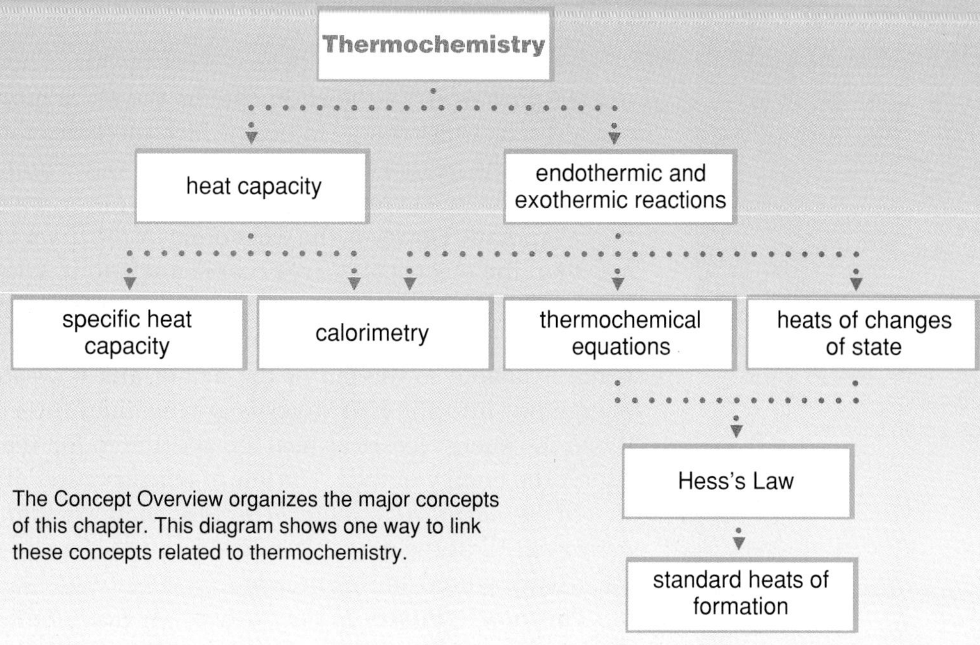

The Concept Overview organizes the major concepts of this chapter. This diagram shows one way to link these concepts related to thermochemistry.

Glowing campfires, the sun's rays, and rubbing your hands together all produce heat. However, it takes heat to melt ice or to boil water. Some processes produce heat, while others require heat. In this chapter, you will examine the heat changes that take place in a number of chemical and physical processes.

10.1 Energy

Objective

Distinguish among various forms of energy: stored energy, work, and heat.

When you buy gasoline you are buying the potential energy stored in the fuel to do work. You commonly buy gasoline to put in an engine to do the work of propelling a car, for example. Explosions of the gasoline in the engine of the car accomplish the transformation of potential energy into work. Unlike matter, energy is weightless, odorless, and tasteless. Energy is detected only because of its effects. **Energy** *is the capacity to do work or to supply heat.* **Chemical potential energy** *is energy stored in chemicals because of their compositions.* Different substances store different amounts of energy. The kinds of atoms and the arrangement of the atoms in the substance determine the amount of energy stored in the substance.

Figure 10.1 Chemical potential energy is determined by the chemical composition. Gasoline has a very high potential energy content.

On a summer day, cool air absorbs the radiant energy of the sun, and the temperature of the air is increased. **Heat**, *represented by q, is a form of energy that always flows from a warmer object to a cooler object.* One of the observable effects of adding heat is a change in temperature.

Consider a hair dryer with an electric fan and a heater. The electric fan does work on the air by forcing the air to move. The heater converts electrical energy to heat, which increases the temperature of the air. The heated air does work on the water molecules in your hair. The kinetic energy of the water molecules is increased so that they evaporate. However, the work done by the dryer is considerably less than the electrical energy that is put into it. Like all electrical motors, the electric fan motor converts some of the electrical energy it uses into unusable heat. The energy converted into unusable heat is not available to the fan or the heater and is wasted. Thus, the energy put into the hair dryer is greater than the energy output. When the energy losses as heat are accounted for, the energy input equals the energy output. *The* **law of conservation of energy** *states that in any chemical or physical process, energy is neither created nor destroyed.* All of the energy involved in a process can be accounted for as work, stored energy, or heat.

Thermochemistry *is the study of the heat changes that occur during chemical reactions and physical changes of state.* Essentially all chemical reactions and changes in the physical state of substances involve either the release or the absorption of heat.

Roots of Words

thermos: (Greek) hot
thermochemistry the study of the heat changes that accompany chemical reactions

Concept Practice

1. Explain the law of conservation of energy.

2. What always happens when two objects at different temperatures come in contact? Give an example from your own experience.

Objective

Explain the heat capacity of objects and express it in standard units of heat.

10.2 Heat Capacity

What does it mean to "burn Calories" when you exercise? During exercise your body generates a certain amount of heat, measured in units called Calories. The heat comes from the chemical breakdown of sugars and fats into carbon dioxide and water. In breaking down 10 g of sugar, your body generates a certain amount of heat. The same amount of heat would be produced if 10 g of sugar were burned completely in a fire to produce carbon dioxide and water.

Although there is a more precise definition, one **calorie** *is the quantity of heat that raises the temperature of 1 g of pure water 1°C.* Notice that there is an important difference between a Calorie and a calorie. The dietary Calorie, written with a capital C, always refers to food. The calorie, written with a small c, is defined above and is usually used except when referring to food. One dietary Calorie is actually equal to one kilocalorie, or 1000 calories (1 Calorie = 1 kcal = 1000 cal). The statement "10 g of sugar has 41 Calories" means that 10 g of sugar releases 41 kilocalories of heat when it burns completely to produce carbon dioxide and water.

The calorie is also related to the **joule**, *the SI unit of heat and energy (1 kcal = 4186 J and 1 J = 0.239 cal).* The joule is named after the English physicist James Prescott Joule (1818–1889). One joule of heat will raise the temperature of 1 g of pure water 0.239°C.

You can convert between Calories, calories, and joules with the following relationships.

$$1 \text{ Calorie} = 1000 \text{ cal} = 1 \text{ kcal} = 4186 \text{ J} \quad \text{and} \quad 1 \text{ J} = 0.239 \text{ cal}$$

The amount of heat it takes to change an object's temperature by exactly 1°C is the **heat capacity** *of that object.* Heat capacity depends partly on mass. The greater the mass of the object, the greater its heat capacity. A massive steel girder, for example, has a much larger heat capacity than a small steel nail. A cup of water has a much greater heat capacity than a drop of water. Besides varying with mass, the heat capacity of an object also depends on its chemical composition. For this reason, different substances of the same mass may have different heat capacities. Which of the foods in Figure 10.2 has the highest heat capacity?

Integrating Physical Education

Exertion and Energy

Your proper caloric intake depends on your level of physical activity. In an 8-hour day at your school desk, you burn about 800 Calories. This is about the number of Calories in two helpings of spaghetti. However, when exercising you become a relative biochemical blast furnace. In vigorous activities like running and jumping, you expend 7–10 Calories per *minute*, or 420–600 Calories per hour. At these rates, a runner who covers a 26-mile marathon course in 3 hours might expend 1800 Calories, or the equivalent of 4.5 helpings of spaghetti.

Concept Practice

3. What factors determine the heat capacity of an object?

4. What is the relationship between a calorie and a Calorie?

5. A label on a granola bar says "175 Calories." Explain.

Practice Problems

6. How many joules of energy can you expect a 175-Calorie granola bar to release?

7. Using the definition of a calorie, find how much heat 32.0 g of water absorbs when it is heated from 25.0°C to 80.0°C. How many joules is this?

Figure 10.2 Which would you rather eat to warm up on a cold day: warm soup or hot toast? Why?

Objective

Identify different substances using specific heat capacities.

10.3 Specific Heat Capacity

On a sunny day, a 20-kg puddle of water may be cool. A nearby 20-kg iron sewer cover may be too hot to touch. Suppose that both the water and the iron absorb the same amount of radiant energy from the sun. In this situation, the temperature of the water changes less than the temperature of the iron because of the high *specific heat capacity* of water.

The **specific heat capacity**, *or simply the* **specific heat**, *represented by* C, *of a substance is the amount of heat it takes to raise the temperature of 1 g of the substance 1°C and is measured in J/(g × °C).* Table 10.1 gives specific heats for some common substances. Water has the highest specific heat of almost all substances. You can see from the table that 1 calorie of heat raises the temperature of 1 g of water by 1°C. Metals have low specific heats. One calorie of heat raises the temperature of 1 g of iron by 9°C. Therefore water has a specific heat nine times that of iron. Heat affects the temperature of objects with a high specific heat much less than the temperature of those with a low specific heat. Since it takes a lot of heat energy to raise the temperature of water, water releases a lot of heat energy as it cools. Therefore, the water cools slowly. This property of water affects the climate in coastal areas.

Specific heat helps you find out how many joules or calories it takes to heat a known mass of a substance from one temperature to another. To figure out the specific heat of a substance, you divide the heat generated by the temperature change and by the mass of the substance.

Table 10.1 Specific Heat Capacities of Some Common Substances

Substance	Specific heat capacity [J/(g × °C)]	Specific heat capacity [cal/(g × °C)]
Water	4.18	1.00
Grain alcohol	2.4	0.58
Ice	2.1	0.50
Wood	1.8	0.42
Steam	1.7	0.40
Chloroform	0.96	0.23
Aluminum	0.90	0.21
Glass	0.50	0.12
Iron	0.46	0.11
Silver	0.24	0.057
Mercury	0.14	0.033

Table 10.2 Heat Measurements	
Quantity	**Unit and abbreviation**
Heat, energy (q)	joule, J
Heat capacity	joule/degree celsius, J/°C
Specific heat capacity (C)	joule/gram times degree celsius, J/(g × °C)

$$\text{Specific heat } \frac{\text{J}}{\text{g} \times {}^\circ\text{C}} = \frac{\text{heat (J)}}{\text{mass (g)} \times \text{change in temperature (°C)}}$$

The equation follows.

$$C = \frac{q}{m \Delta T} = \frac{\text{heat (J)}}{\text{mass (g)} \times \text{change in temperature (°C)}}$$

In this equation, specific heat may be expressed in terms of joules or calories.

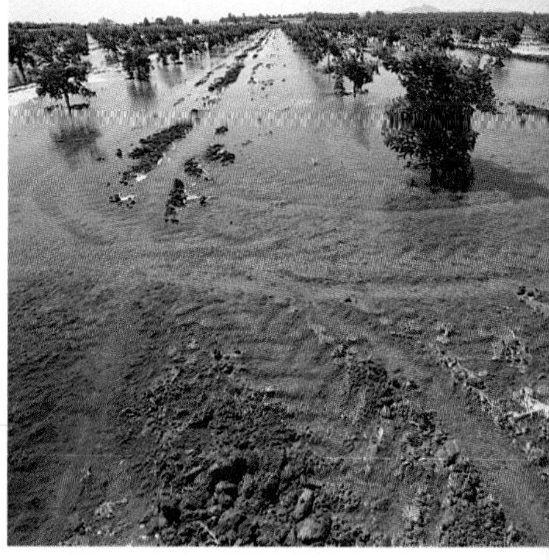

Figure 10.3 Water gives off a lot of heat in order to freeze. Sometimes farmers use water's high specific heat capacity to their advantage. Here, an orchard has been intentionally flooded with water in order to prevent it from freezing and damaging the trees on a cold winter night.

Example 1 Calculating the Specific Heat of a Metal

The temperature of a piece of copper with a mass of 95.4 g changes from 25.0°C to 48.0°C when the metal absorbs 849 J of heat. What is the specific heat of copper?

Solution

Use the equation for the specific heat capacity and substitute the given values. The change in temperature, $T_f - T_i$, is 48.0°C – 25.0°C = 23.0°C.

$$\text{Specific heat } \frac{\text{J}}{\text{g} \times {}^\circ\text{C}} = \frac{\text{heat (J)}}{\text{mass (g)} \times \text{change in temperature (°C)}}$$

$$= \frac{849 \text{ J}}{95.4 \text{ g} \times 23.0^\circ\text{C}}$$

$$= 0.387 \frac{\text{J}}{\text{g} \times {}^\circ\text{C}}$$

Concept Practice

8. Give the units for specific heat. How are the units related to the definition of specific heat? Explain.

9. Will the specific heat of 50.0 g of a substance be the same as or greater than the specific heat of 10 g of the same substance?

Practice Problems

10. A chunk of silver has a heat capacity of 42.8 J/°C. If the silver has a mass of 181 g, calculate the specific heat of silver.

11. When 435 J of heat is added to 3.4 g of olive oil at 21°C, the temperature increases to 85°C. What is the specific heat of olive oil?

Objective

Describe heat changes in terms of a system and its surroundings.

10.4 Exothermic and Endothermic Processes

Thermochemistry is concerned with the flow of heat between a chemical system (reaction) and its surroundings. A typical system might be the chemicals that will undergo a reaction. The surroundings might be a water bath that surrounds the flask holding the chemicals. *A* **system** *is the specific part of the universe on which you focus your attention. The* **surroundings** *include everything outside the system. Together, the system and surroundings constitute the* **universe**. Ordinarily, you can consider the surroundings to be only the region in the immediate vicinity of the system.

Roots of Words

exo: (Greek) outside of
therme: (Greek) heat
exothermic reaction a chemical change in which energy is released in the form of heat

The burning of gasoline is an exothermic reaction.

endon: (Greek) within
therme: (Greek) heat
endothermic reaction a chemical change in which heat is absorbed

During an endothermic reaction the surroundings cool down.

In thermochemical calculations the direction of the heat flow is given from the point of view of the system. In Figure 10.4a, the system (the human bodies) gain heat from the fire. Thus, heat flows into the system from the surroundings. This heat is given a positive value because the system is gaining heat. *A process that absorbs heat from the surroundings is called an* **endothermic process**. In an endothermic process, the surroundings cool down. In Figure 10.4b, consider the body as the system. As sweat evaporates from the skin, the system cools and heat flows to the surroundings. Heat that flows from the system to the surroundings is given a negative value because the system is losing heat. *A process that loses heat to the surroundings is called an* **exothermic process**. In an exothermic process, the surroundings heat up.

Table 10.3 Heat Change Sign Convention

Direction of heat flow	Sign	Reaction type
Heat flows out of the system	Heat change<0 (negative)	Exothermic
Heat flows into the system	Heat change>0 (positive)	Endothermic

(a) Endothermic

(b) Exothermic

Figure 10.4 **(a)** A fire helps you keep warm when you're out in the cold. If your body is the system, what is the fire? **(b)** The human body cools itself by giving off heat when perspiration evaporates. What is the system here?

Concept Practice

12. Why do you think it is important to define the *system* and the *surroundings*?

10.5 Calorimetry

Objective

Calculate the heat changes that occur in chemical and physical processes.

Plastic foam cups are used to keep hot drinks hot and cold drinks cold because plastic foam is an excellent heat insulator. Since the plastic foam doesn't let much heat into or out, plastic foam cups are often used as *calorimeters.* **Calorimeters** *are devices used to measure the amount of heat absorbed or released during chemical or physical processes.* **Calorimetry** *is the accurate and precise measurement of the heat change for chemical and physical processes.* To measure heat change, reactions or changes of state must be carried out in insulated containers.

The heat changes for many chemical reactions have been measured in the open atmosphere in calorimeters similar to nested plastic foam cups. Most chemical reactions carried out in the laboratory are open to the atmosphere, at constant pressure. *For systems at constant pressure, the heat content is the same as a property called the* **enthalpy**, ***H***, *of the system.* Heat changes for reactions carried out at constant pressure are the same as changes in enthalpy, symbolized as ΔH (read "delta H"). The reactions presented in this text occur at constant pressure, so the terms *heat* and *enthalpy* are used interchangeably. Thus, $q=\Delta H$. The sign of ΔH is negative for an exothermic reaction and positive for an endothermic reaction.

Roots of Words

enthalpein: (Greek) to warm in **enthalpy** the amount of heat a substance has at a given temperature and pressure

The enthalpy change, ΔH, is the heat change for a process at constant pressure.

Figure 10.5 In a plastic-cup calorimeter, the thermometer measures the temperature change of the chemicals as they react in the water. The stirrer is used to keep the water at a uniform temperature.

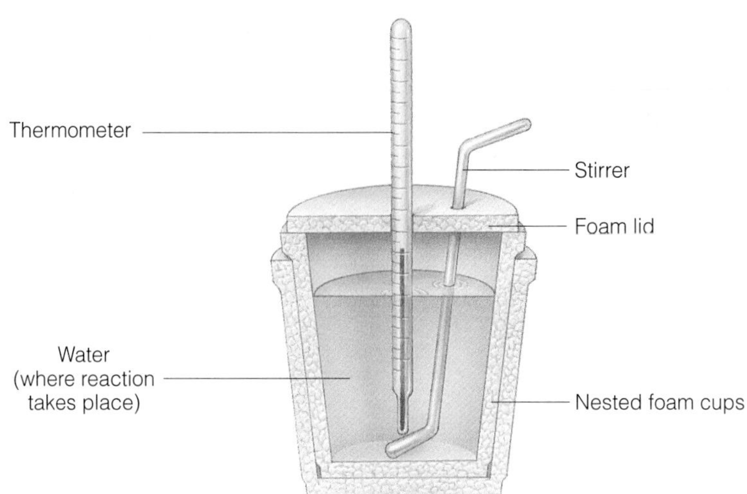

Table 10.4 Enthalpy Sign Convention	
Reaction type	**Sign**
Exothermic	$\Delta H<0$, negative
Endothermic	$\Delta H>0$, positive

In order to measure the heat change for a reaction in aqueous solution in a plastic-cup calorimeter, you dissolve the reacting chemicals (the system) in known volumes of water (the surroundings). You measure the initial temperature of the solutions and then mix them in the cup. You then measure the final temperature of the mixed solutions after the reaction is complete. Since you know the initial and final temperatures and the heat capacity of water, you can calculate the heat released or absorbed in the reaction from the following equation.

$$q = \Delta H = m \times C \times \Delta T$$

The heat is equal to ΔH; m is the mass of the water; C is the specific heat capacity of the water; and ΔT (read "delta T") is the change in temperature, $T_{\text{final}} - T_{\text{initial}}$.

Figure 10.6 In a bomb calorimeter, the sample is burned in pure oxygen in a constant-volume chamber under high pressure. The heat generated warms the water surrounding the bomb. By measuring the temperature increase of the water, you can determine the heat given off by the reaction.

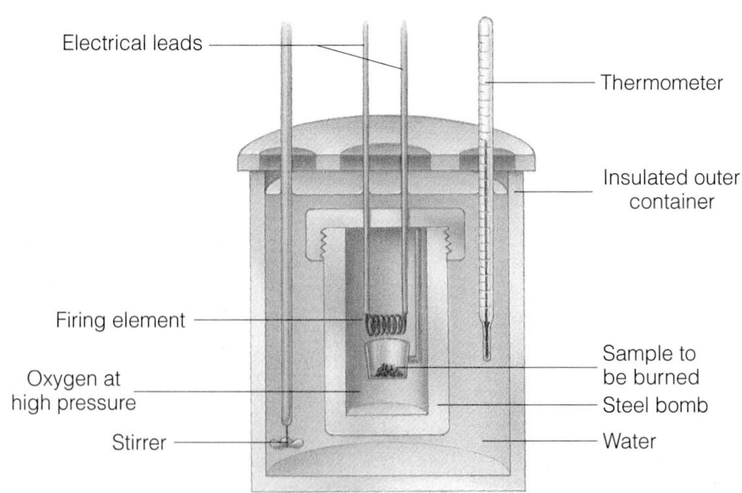

Example 2 Calculating the Heat Change for a Reaction

Suppose you added 25.0 mL of water containing 0.025 mol HCl to 25.0 mL of water containing 0.025 mol NaOH in a plastic-cup calorimeter. At the start, the solutions and the calorimeter were all at 25.0°C. During the reaction, the highest temperature observed was 32.0°C. Calculate the heat released in this reaction. Assume the densities of the solutions are 1.00 g/mL.

Solution

Use the equation $\Delta H = m \times C \times \Delta T$.

$$\begin{aligned}\Delta H &= (50.0\ \text{mL} \times 1.00\ \text{g/mL}) \times [4.18\ \text{J/(g} \times {}^\circ\text{C)}] \times (32.0^\circ\text{C} - 25.0^\circ\text{C}) \\ &= 50.0\ \text{g} \times 4.18\ \text{J/(g} \times {}^\circ\text{C)} \times 7.0^\circ\text{C} \\ &= 1463\ \text{J} = 1.5 \times 10^3\ \text{J} = 1.5\ \text{kJ}\end{aligned}$$

Concept Practice

13. What is the system in a plastic-cup calorimeter? What are the surroundings?

14. What is the name for a heat change associated with a chemical or physical process carried out at constant pressure?

Practice Problem

15. A student mixed 50.0 mL of water containing 0.025 mol HCl at 22.5°C with 50.0 mL of water containing 0.025 mol NaOH at 22.5°C in a plastic-cup calorimeter. The temperature of the resulting solution increased to 26.0°C. What is the heat change (kJ) in this reaction?

Chemistry in Careers

Calorimetrist

A package of cereal says that a 1-ounce serving contains 100 Calories, or 144 Calories with 1/2 cup of skim milk fortified with vitamins A and D. Have you ever wondered who determines these numbers? Calorimetrists measure the caloric content of various foods by burning them in combustion calorimeters. They work in government laboratories or for food companies. A calorimetrist must make careful, accurate measurements with high precision because many people such as nutritionists and dieticians rely on the results. A calorimetrist usually has a degree in chemistry and may be knowledgeable about food science.

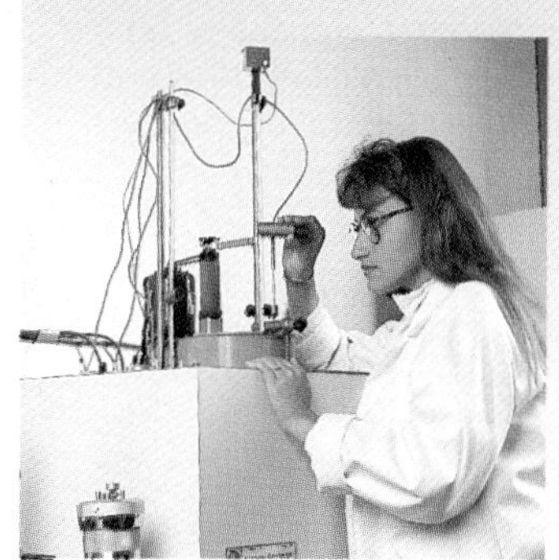

10.6 Thermochemical Equations

Objective

Construct equations that show the heat changes for chemical and physical processes.

If you mix calcium oxide with water, an exothermic reaction takes place. The water in the mixture gets hot. This occurs when cement is mixed to make concrete. When one mole of calcium oxide reacts with one mole of water, one mole of calcium hydroxide forms and 65.2 kJ of heat evolves. You can show this in the chemical equation by including a heat term as a product of the reaction.

$$CaO(s) + H_2O(l) \rightarrow Ca(OH)_2(s) + 65.2\ \text{kJ}$$

You can treat heat change in a chemical reaction like any other reactant or product in a chemical equation. *An equation that includes the heat change is a* **thermochemical equation**. *A* **heat of reaction** *is the heat change for the equation exactly as it is written.* You will usually see heats of reaction reported as the enthalpy change, ΔH, at a set of standard conditions. The standard conditions are that (1) the reaction is carried out in the open at 1 atmosphere of pressure and (2) the reactants and products are in their usual physical states at 25°C.

The heat of reaction or ΔH above is –65.2 kJ. Each mole of calcium oxide and water that react to form calcium hydroxide produce 65.2 kJ of heat. Remember that ΔH is negative for an exothermic reaction.

$$CaO(s) + H_2O(l) \rightarrow Ca(OH)_2(s) \qquad \Delta H = -65.2 \text{ kJ}$$

The diagram in Figure 10.7a shows the heat change that occurs in this exothermic reaction.

Endothermic reactions absorb heat from the surroundings. For example, baking soda (sodium hydrogen carbonate) decomposes when it is heated. The released carbon dioxide causes a cake to rise. The heat of reaction is 129 kJ.

$$2NaHCO_3(s) + 129 \text{ kJ} \rightarrow Na_2CO_3(s) + H_2O(g) + CO_2(g)$$

Remember that ΔH is positive for endothermic reactions.

$$2NaHCO_3(s) \rightarrow Na_2CO_3(s) + H_2O(g) + CO_2(g) \qquad \Delta H = +129 \text{ kJ}$$

To decompose 2 mol of sodium hydrogen carbonate requires the absorption of 129 kJ of heat. Figure 10.7 shows the heat changes for this reaction.

Figure 10.7 These enthalpy diagrams show exothermic and endothermic processes: **(a)** the reaction of calcium oxide and water and **(b)** the decomposition of sodium hydrogen carbonate.

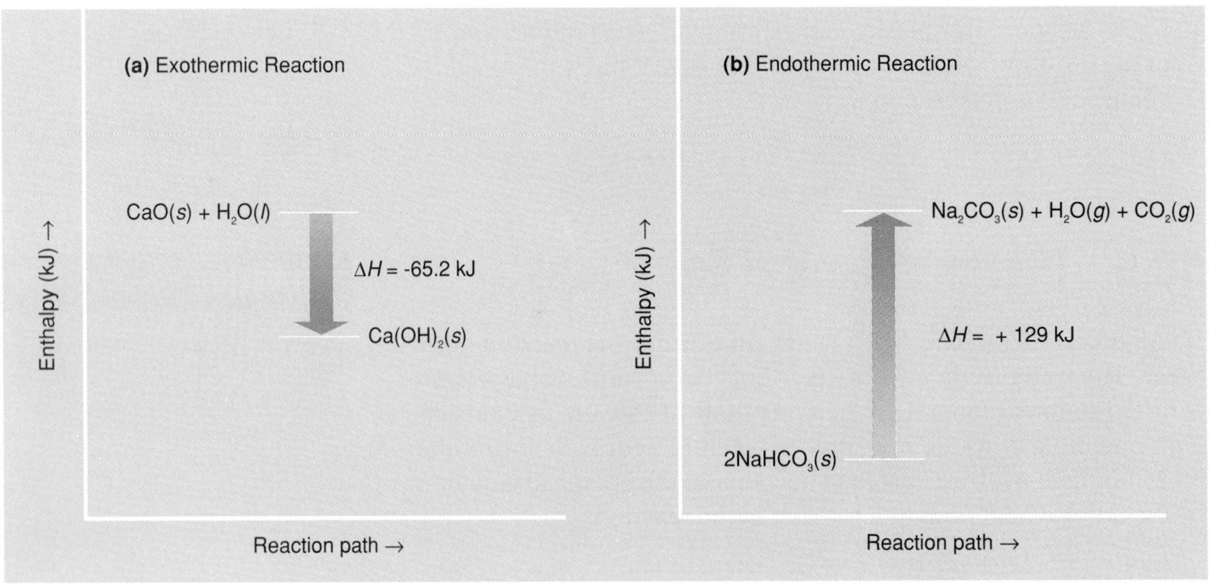

Example 3 Calculating the Heat of Reaction

Using the equation just given, calculate the kilojoules of heat required to decompose 2.24 mol of $NaHCO_3(s)$.

Solution

The equation indicates that it takes 129 kJ to decompose 2 mol of $NaHCO_3(s)$. Use this to write a conversion factor.

$$2.24\ \text{mol NaHCO}_3(s) \times \frac{129\ \text{kJ}}{2\ \text{mol NaHCO}_3(s)} = 145\ \text{kJ}$$

The physical state of the reactants and products in a thermochemical reaction must be stated. To see why, compare the following two equations for the decomposition of water.

$$H_2O(l) \rightarrow H_2(g) + \tfrac{1}{2}O_2(g) \qquad \Delta H = +285.8\ \text{kJ}$$

$$H_2O(g) \rightarrow H_2(g) + \tfrac{1}{2}O_2(g) \qquad \Delta H = +241.8\ \text{kJ}$$

$$\text{difference} = 44.0\ \text{kJ}$$

(Fraction coefficients are needed here because you are dealing with the decomposition of 1 mol of water.) In one case the reactant, water, is a gas. In the other case the reactant is a liquid. The vaporization of the liquid water to water vapor at 25°C requires an extra 44.0 kJ of heat.

Table 10.5 Standard Heats of Combustion at 25°C

Substance	Formula	ΔH^0_{rxn} (kJ/mol)
Hydrogen	$H_2(g)$	–286
Carbon	$C(s)$, graphite	–394
Carbon monoxide	$CO(g)$	–283
Methane	$CH_4(g)$	–890
Methanol	$CH_3OH(l)$	–726
Acetylene	$C_2H_2(g)$	–1300
Ethanol	$C_2H_5OH(l)$	–1368
Propane	$C_3H_8(g)$	–2220
Benzene	$C_6H_6(l)$	–3268
Glucose	$C_6H_{12}O_6(s)$	–2808
Octane	$C_8H_{18}(l)$	–5471
Sucrose	$C_{12}H_{22}O_{11}(s)$	–5645

Integrating Biology

Warmth from Fat

How do animals such as polar bears and seals survive the cold land and water temperatures they live in? A good coat of fur helps, but it is not enough to keep them cozy. These animals also have special fat cells that generate heat to keep them warm. These special cells are in tissue called brown fat. The cells of brown fat are unlike other fat cells in the animal's body. Most other cells trap the chemical energy from the breakdown of carbohydrates and fatty acids in adenosine triphosphate (ATP). ATP acts as the central source of energy for activities and growth of all animals. Heat is mostly a waste product in ATP-producing cells. Brown fat cells, however, are designed to convert the energy from the breakdown of fats into heat instead of ATP. The heat generated by the brown fat tissue helps the animal keep relatively comfortable even in severe cold.

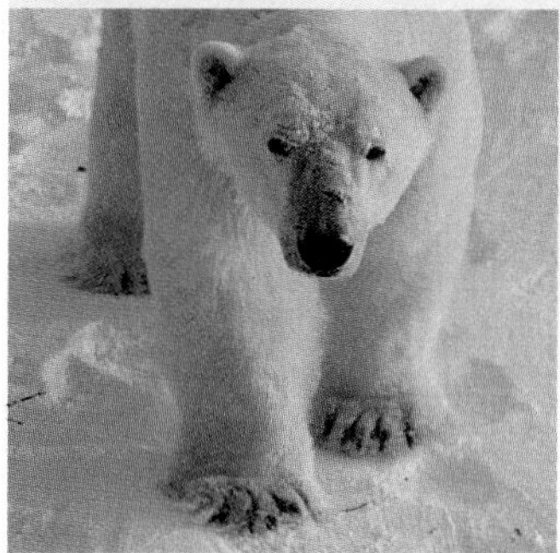

Table 10.5 lists heats of reaction for the combustion of some common substances. This kind of heat of reaction is the heat of combustion. *The* **heat of combustion** *is the heat of reaction for the complete burning of one mole of a substance.*

The combustion of natural gas, which is mostly methane, is an exothermic reaction that heats many homes around the country.

$$CH_4(g) + 2O_2(g) \rightarrow CO_2(g) + 2H_2O(l) + 890.4 \text{ kJ}$$

This can also be written as follows.

$$CH_4(g) + 2O_2(g) \rightarrow CO_2(g) + 2H_2O(l) \qquad \Delta H = -890.4 \text{ kJ}$$

Burning 1 mol of methane completely releases 890.4 kJ of heat. The heat of combustion, ΔH, for this reaction is –890.4 kJ per mole of carbon burned.

Like other heats of reaction, heats of combustion are reported as the enthalpy changes when the reactions are carried out in the open at 1 atmosphere of pressure and the reactants and products are in their usual physical states at 25°C. Therefore you can compare heats of combustion directly with other heats of reaction.

Concept Practice

16. Give the standard conditions for heat of combustion.

17. Explain what heat of reaction is.

Practice Problems

18. Gasohol contains ethanol, $C_2H_5OH(l)$, which reacts with oxygen when burned to produce $CO_2(g)$ and $H_2O(g)$. The equation for the complete combustion of ethanol is as follows:

$$C_2H_5OH(l) + 3O_2(g) \rightarrow 2CO_2(g) + 3H_2O(g) \quad \Delta H = -1235 \text{ kJ}$$

How much heat is produced when 12.5 g of ethanol burns?

19. When carbon disulfide forms from its elements, heat is absorbed.

$$C(s) + 2S(s) \rightarrow CS_2(l) \quad \Delta H = +89.3 \text{ kJ}$$

Calculate the amount of heat (in kilojoules) absorbed when 5.66 g of carbon disulfide forms.

20. How much energy is produced when 0.58 mol methane is burned completely? (Hint: Use equations in this section to solve this problem.)

10.A Environmental Awareness

The Greenhouse Effect

Have you ever noticed how warm it gets inside a car that has been parked in the sun? Like a greenhouse, the interior of a car stays warm even on a cold, sunny day. The source of heat is the visible light from the sun, which penetrates your car windows. The interior of the car absorbs and converts the light into heat or infrared radiation. Glass is opaque to infrared, and the heat does not escape.

In a similar process, the atmosphere of Earth keeps the planet warm. Because the atmosphere prevents heat from escaping just as the glass walls of a greenhouse do, the warming process is called the greenhouse effect. Mars, frozen and barren, has no such effect. Venus swelters under too much of it. A delicate balance of gases in the atmosphere keeps the greenhouse effect on Earth stable.

Earth's atmosphere surrounds the planet like a blanket. Within the atmosphere are several trace gases. Solar energy passes through these gases easily, reaching Earth's surface. Some of this energy is absorbed by the surface and reradiated as infrared heat waves. These heat waves do not pass through the gases easily, but are absorbed and radiated back to Earth. Thus, these greenhouse gases keep Earth's surface about 33°C warmer than it would be otherwise.

Carbon dioxide (CO_2) is the most prevalent greenhouse gas. Normally, interactions between the atmosphere, the oceans, and organisms keep the atmospheric CO_2 at a constant level. Living plants remove CO_2 from the air through photosynthesis. When plants are burned, however, CO_2 is released into the air. Experts estimate that by burning forests and fossil fuels, more than 8 billion metric tons of CO_2 are being pumped into the atmosphere every year! Carbon dioxide is not the only culprit. Other gases, such as methane (CH_4), nitrous oxide (N_2O), and chlorofluorocarbons (CFCs), contribute to the greenhouse effect as well.

According to current scientific models, a rise of only a few degrees in Earth's temperature could cause global problems. In the worst case, farmlands would become deserts and coastal cities would be under water. Solving the greenhouse problem will require international cooperation. Nonpolluting energy sources must be developed. Destruction of the world's forests must end. People must realize that the atmosphere is intricately tied to life on Earth.

Figure 10.8 Earth's atmosphere works much like this greenhouse.

Figure 10.9 An important CO_2 removal system is being destroyed as forests are cleared for agriculture.

Think About It

21. Analyze In what ways does burning the world's rain forests contribute to the greenhouse problems?

Objective

Describe in words and with diagrams the heat changes that occur in melting, freezing, boiling, and condensing.

10.7 Heat and Changes of State

What happens when you drop an ice cube on the floor of a warm room? The ice cube is the system, and it is at 0°C. The floor and air surrounding it are the surroundings. The ice absorbs heat from the surroundings and begins to melt. The mixture of ice and water is at 0°C. The temperature of the ice and the water produced remains at 0°C until all of the ice is melted. The temperature of the water begins to increase only after all of the ice is melted.

Like ice cubes, all solids absorb heat in melting to liquids. *The heat absorbed by one mole of a substance in melting from a solid to a liquid at a constant temperature is the* **molar heat of fusion**, ΔH_{fus}. *The heat lost when one mole of a liquid changes to a solid at a constant temperature is the* **molar heat of solidification**, ΔH_{solid}. Because energy is conserved in all physical and chemical changes, the quantity of heat absorbed by a melting solid is exactly the same as the quantity of heat lost when the liquid solidifies. That is, $\Delta H_{\text{fus}} = -\Delta H_{\text{solid}}$, as shown in Figure 10.10. Table 10.6 gives heats of fusion of some substances.

The melting of 1 mol of ice at 0°C to 1 mol of water at 0°C requires the absorption of 6.01 kJ of heat, ΔH_{fus}. Conversion of 1 mol of water at 0°C to 1 mol of ice at 0°C releases –6.01 kJ, ΔH_{solid}.

$$H_2O(s) \rightarrow H_2O(l) \qquad \Delta H_{\text{fus}} = 6.01 \text{ kJ/mol}$$

$$H_2O(l) \rightarrow H_2O(s) \qquad \Delta H_{278} = -6.01 \text{ kJ/mol}$$

Table 10.6 Standard Heats of Physical Change

Substance	Formula	Freezing point (K)	ΔH^0_{fus} (kJ/mol)	Boiling point (K)	ΔH^0_{vap} (kJ/mol)
Acetone	CH_3COCH_3	177.8	5.72	329.4	29.1
Ammonia	NH_3	195.3	5.65	239.7	23.4
Argon	Ar	83.8	1.2	87.3	6.5
Benzene	C_6H_6	278.7	9.87	353.3	30.8
Ethanol	C_2H_5OH	158.7	4.60	351.5	43.5
Helium	He	3.5	0.02	4.22	0.08
Hydrogen	H_2	14.0	0.12	20.3	0.90
Methane	CH_4	90.7	0.94	111.7	8.2
Methanol	CH_3OH	175.5	3.16	337.2	35.3
Neon	Ne	24.5	0.33	27.1	1.76
Nitrogen	N_2	63.3	0.72	77.4	5.58
Oxygen	O_2	54.8	0.44	90.2	6.82
Water	H_2O	273.2	6.01	373.2	40.7

Example 4 Calculating the Energy Involved in a Phase Change

How many grams of ice at 0°C could be melted by the addition of 2.25 kJ of heat?

Solution

The molar heat of fusion of water is 6.01 kJ/mol. Find the amount of ice (in mol) that can be melted; then convert moles of ice to grams of ice.

$$2.25\ \cancel{kJ} \times \frac{1\ \cancel{mol\ ice}}{6.01\ \cancel{kJ}} \times \frac{18.0\ g\ ice}{1\ \cancel{mol\ ice}} = 6.74\ g\ ice$$

Practice Problem

22. Heavy water, in which the hydrogens are hydrogen-2 instead of the more common hydrogen-1, is called deuterium oxide (D_2O). Solid D_2O melts at 3.78°C. The molar heat of fusion of $D_2O(s)$ is 6.34 kJ/mol. How much heat is released when 8.46 g of $D_2O(l)$ solidifies at its melting point?

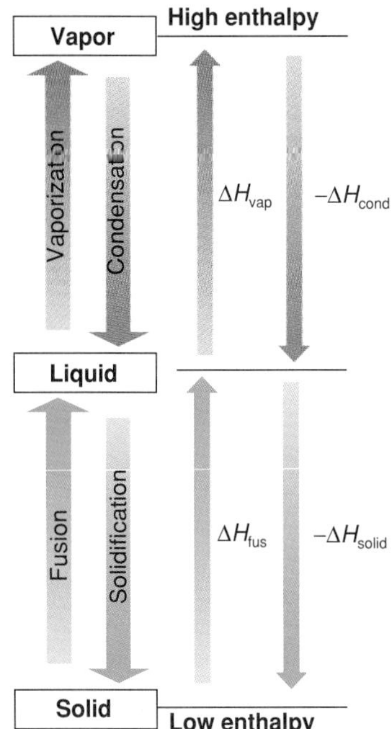

Figure 10.10 The enthalpy changes that accompany changes in state. Fusion and vaporization are endothermic processes. Solidification and condensation are exothermic processes.

When liquids absorb heat at their boiling points, they become vapors. Vaporization of a liquid, through boiling or evaporation, cools the environment around the liquid as heat flows from the surroundings to the liquid. The effect of cooling the surroundings can be dramatic. Diethyl ether ($C_4H_{10}O$) is a low-boiling-point liquid (boiling point 34.6°C) that is a good solvent. When diethyl ether is poured into a beaker on a warm, humid day, the ether absorbs heat from the beaker walls and evaporates very rapidly. The beaker may lose enough heat that the water vapor in the air condenses and freezes on the beaker walls. A coating of frost may form on the outside of the beaker. *The evaporation of diethyl ether is an endothermic process with a* **molar heat of vaporization**, ΔH_{vap}, *of 15.7 kJ/mol.* Table 10.6 gives some values of molar heats of vaporization for various compounds.

$$C_4H_{10}O(l) \rightarrow C_4H_{10}O(g) \qquad \Delta H_{vap} = +15.7\ kJ/mol$$

Conversely, the condensation of 1 mol of vapor releases heat as the **molar heat of condensation**, ΔH_{cond}. You can receive a scalding burn from steam when the heat of condensation is released as the steam touches your skin.

$$H_2O(g) \rightarrow H_2O(l) \qquad \Delta H_{cond} = -40.7\ kJ/mol$$

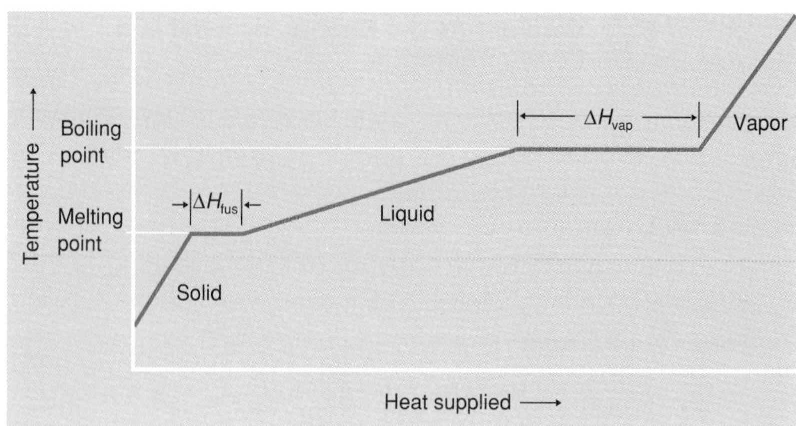

Figure 10.11 The heating curve for water. Notice that the temperature remains constant during melting and vaporization. Notice also that it requires much more energy to vaporize the substance than it does to melt it.

Notice in Figure 10.10 that the heats of vaporization and condensation of a substance are exactly the same magnitude or size, but of different sign. Figure 10.11 summarizes the heat changes that occur as a solid is heated to a liquid and then to a gas.

Example 5 Using the Heat of Vaporization

How much heat is absorbed when 24.8 g of $H_2O(l)$ at 100°C is converted to steam at 100°C?

Solution

For water, $\Delta H_{vap} = -\Delta H_{cond} = 40.7$ kJ/mol.

First find out how many moles of water are converted to steam; then use ΔH_{vap} to calculate the heat absorbed.

$$24.8 \text{ g } H_2O(l) \times \frac{1 \text{ mol } H_2O(l)}{18.0 \text{ g } H_2O(l)} \times \frac{40.7 \text{ kJ}}{1 \text{ mol } H_2O(l)} = 56.1 \text{ kJ}$$

Concept Practice

23. Why is a burn from steam potentially far more serious than a burn from very hot water?

Practice Problem

24. How many kilojoules of heat are absorbed when 0.46 g of chloroethane (C_2H_5Cl, boiling point 12.3°C) vaporizes at its boiling point? For chloroethane, $\Delta H_{vap} = 26.4$ kJ/mol.

Heat changes can occur when a substance is dissolved in a solvent. *The heat change caused by dissolution of one mole of substance is the* **molar heat of solution**, ΔH_{soln}. In a handwarmer, one substance dissolves in another and gives off heat, ΔH_{soln}. When 1 mol of sodium hydroxide, $NaOH(s)$, is dissolved in water, the solution can become so hot that it steams. The heat of solution is released as the sodium ions and the hydroxide ions separate and interact with water. The heat is transferred to the water in this very exothermic physical process. The temperature of the solution increases, releasing 445.1 kJ of heat as the molar heat of solution, ΔH_{soln}.

$$NaOH(s) \xrightarrow{H_2O(l)} Na^+(aq) + OH^-(aq) \qquad \Delta H_{soln} = -445.1 \text{ kJ/mol}$$

The dissolution of ammonium nitrate, $NH_4NO_3(s)$, is an endothermic process. When ammonium nitrate dissolves in water the solution becomes so cold that frost may form on the outside of the container. Heat is absorbed as the ammonium and chloride ions separate and interact with water. Heat is drawn from the water and the temperature of the solution decreases. Figure 10.12 illustrates practical applications of heats of solution. The hot pack mixes calcium chloride, $CaCl_2$, and water. The cold pack allows water and ammonium nitrate, NH_4NO_3, to mix when a seal separating the chemicals is broken.

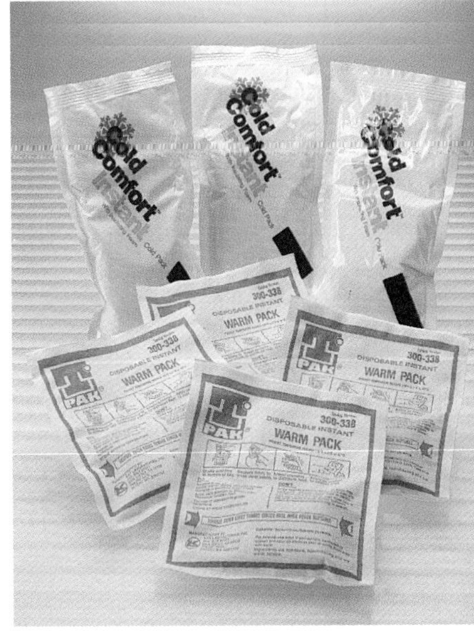

Figure 10.12 Cold and hot packs are available for a variety of medical uses.

$$NH_4NO_3(s) \xrightarrow{H_2O(l)} NH_4^+(aq) + NO_3^-(aq) \qquad \Delta H_{soln} = 25.7 \text{ kJ/mol}$$

Example 6 Using the Heat of Solution

How much heat is released when 2.500 mol of $NaOH(s)$ is dissolved in water?

Solution

The molar heat of solution of $NaOH(s)$ is –445.1 kJ. Multiply the number of moles times the molar heat of solution.

$$2.500 \cancel{\text{mol NaOH}(s)} \times \frac{-445.1 \text{ kJ}}{1 \cancel{\text{mol NaOH}(aq)}} = -1113 \text{ kJ}$$

This means that 1113 kJ of heat is released during the dissolution.

Practice Problem

25. How many moles of $NH_4NO_3(s)$ must be dissolved in water so that 88.0 kJ of energy is absorbed from the water?

10.B Science, Technology, and Society

Food As Your Fuel

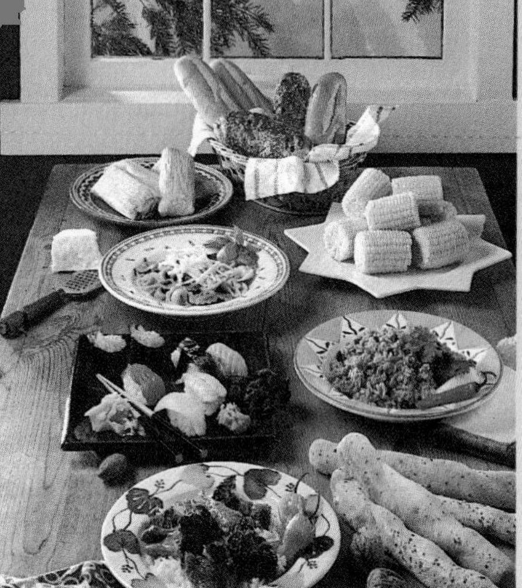

Figure 10.13 You have a tremendous variety of fuel sources (foods) to choose from.

Your body needs energy to produce heat and to do work. You use the food you eat for these purposes, similar to burning fuel in an internal combustion engine. Which of the items in Figure 10.13 are part of your daily fuel? An internal combustion engine releases the energy from combustion of fuel in a rapid burst. Some of the energy does the work of running the engine, and a substantial amount is lost as heat. The energy release from your body's fuel is more controlled. Your body breaks down its fuel in a large number of chemical reactions called metabolism. Many of the reactions of metabolism release small amounts of energy. This is in contrast to having all of the energy released in one reaction, as in an internal combustion engine. The overall amount of energy produced by your body's metabolism is large, but releasing the energy in small increments makes it easier for your body to use the energy productively. The energy of metabolism is used for heat to keep your body temperature at 37°C, for building new molecules your body needs, and for the mechanical work of your muscles.

Like a gasoline engine, your body meets its energy requirements with compounds of carbon. Instead of gasoline, your body uses the carbon-containing carbohydrates, fats, and proteins as its fuels. Carbohydrates typically yield about 17 kJ/g upon combustion to carbon dioxide and water in your body. Dietary fats yield about 84 kJ/g. Proteins are less important than carbohydrates and fats as a source of energy. They produce about 17 kJ/g. Table 10.7 lists heats of combustion of some common foods.

Table 10.7 Heats of Combustion for Certain Foodstuffs

Item	ΔH (kJ/g)
Apple	−2
Beef	−8
Bread	−11
Butter	−34
Cheese	−18
Eggs	−6
Milk	−3
Potatoes	−3

When you are at rest, your body cells are using energy at a level near the minimum needed to sustain life. Because you are active during a typical day, you need additional energy beyond the minimum. A typical teen-age male requires a total of about 12 000 kJ/day (2900 C/day), and a typical teen-age female requires about 9000 kJ/day (2200 C/day). When you eat less food than your daily requirement, your body calls on storage reserves of fat to supply energy and you lose weight. Of course, eating too little food when dieting is dangerous for your health. When you eat more than you need, energy reserves are stored as fat and you gain weight. Only when your fuel intake equals your energy output do you stay the same weight.

Think About It

26. Infer What factors might affect your daily intake of Calories necessary to your body?

10.8 Hess's Law

Objective

Apply Hess's law of heat summation to find heat changes for chemical and physical processes.

You can find elemental carbon both as graphite and as diamond at 25°C. Because graphite is more stable than diamond, you expect the following process to take place.

$$C(\text{diamond}) \rightarrow C(\text{graphite})$$

Fortunately for people who own diamonds, the conversion of diamonds to graphite takes millions and millions of years. This reaction is far too slow for the enthalpy change to be measured. Hess's law, however, provides a way to calculate the heat change. Hess's law is expressed by a simple rule: *If you add two or more thermochemical equations to give a final equation, then you can also add the heat changes to give the final heat change.* This rule is **Hess's law of heat summation**.

You can use Hess's law to find the enthalpy changes for the conversion of diamond to graphite by using the following combustion reactions.

a. $C(s, \text{graphite}) + O_2(g) \rightarrow CO_2(g) \qquad \Delta H = -393.5 \text{ kJ}$

b. $C(s, \text{diamond}) + O_2(g) \rightarrow CO_2(g) \qquad \Delta H = -395.4 \text{ kJ}$

Write the reverse of equation (a) to give:

c. $CO_2(g) \rightarrow C(s, \text{graphite}) + O_2(g) \qquad \Delta H = +393.5 \text{ kJ}$

When you write a reverse reaction, you must also change the sign of ΔH. If you now add equations (b) and (c), you get the equation for the conversion of diamond to graphite. Note that the $CO_2(g)$ and $O_2(g)$ terms on both sides of the summed equations cancel, just as in algebra. Now if you also add the values of ΔH for equations (b) and (c), you get the ΔH for this conversion.

$$C(s, \text{diamond}) + O_2(g) \rightarrow CO_2(g) \qquad \Delta H = -395.4 \text{ kJ}$$

$$CO_2(g) \rightarrow C(s, \text{graphite}) + O_2(g) \qquad \Delta H = +393.5 \text{ kJ}$$

$$C(s, \text{diamond}) \rightarrow C(s, \text{graphite}) \qquad \Delta H = -1.9 \text{ kJ}$$

Thus, the conversion of diamond to graphite is an exothermic process. Conversely, the change of graphite to diamond is an endothermic process.

Some reactions give products besides the compound of interest. Suppose you want to find the enthalpy change for the formation of carbon monoxide from its elements. The reaction is:

$$C(s, \text{graphite}) + \tfrac{1}{2}O_2(g) \rightarrow CO(g) \qquad \Delta H = ?$$

Although it is easy to write the equation, carrying out the reaction in the laboratory as written is virtually impossible. Carbon

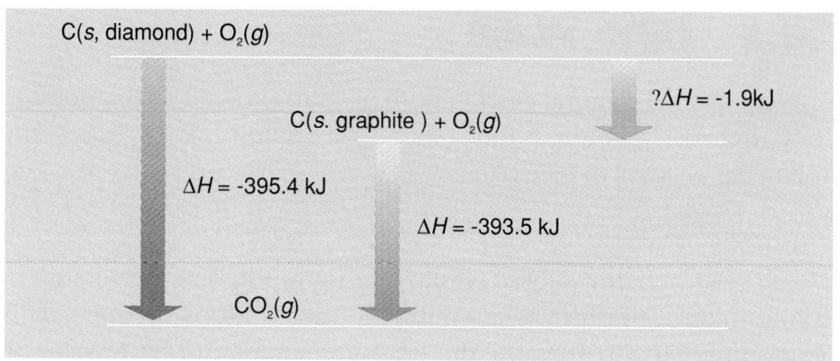

Figure 10.14 Hess's law is used to determine the enthalpy change of a very slow chemical process, C(*s*, diamond) → C(*s*, graphite).

dioxide (a "side product") is produced along with carbon monoxide (the "desired product"). Thus any measured enthalpy change is related to the formation of both $CO(g)$ and $CO_2(g)$, and not $CO(g)$ alone. You can solve the problem by using Hess's law and two reactions that can be carried out in the laboratory. The reactions are:

a. $C(s, \text{graphite}) + O_2(g) \rightarrow CO_2(g) \qquad \Delta H = -393.5 \text{ kJ}$

b. $CO(g) + \frac{1}{2}O_2(g) \rightarrow CO_2(g) \qquad \Delta H = -283.0 \text{ kJ}$

Write the revcrse of equation (b) and be sure to change the sign of ΔH.

c. $CO_2(g) \rightarrow CO(g) + \frac{1}{2}O_2(g) \qquad \Delta H = +283.0 \text{ kJ}$

Add equations (a) and (c) to obtain the expression for the formation of $CO(g)$ from its elements. Notice that only $\frac{1}{2}O_2(g)$ cancels in the final equation.

$$C(s, \text{graphite}) + O_2(g) \rightarrow CO_2(g) \qquad \Delta H = -393.5 \text{ kJ}$$
$$CO_2(g) \rightarrow CO(g) + \frac{1}{2}O_2(g) \qquad \Delta H = +283.0 \text{ kJ}$$
$$C(s, \text{graphite}) + \frac{1}{2}O_2(g) \rightarrow CO(g) \qquad \Delta H = -110.5 \text{ kJ}$$

The formation of $CO(g)$ is exothermic; 110.5 kJ of heat is given off when 1 mol of $CO(g)$ is formed from its elements. Figure 10.15 shows the enthalpy diagram for this reaction.

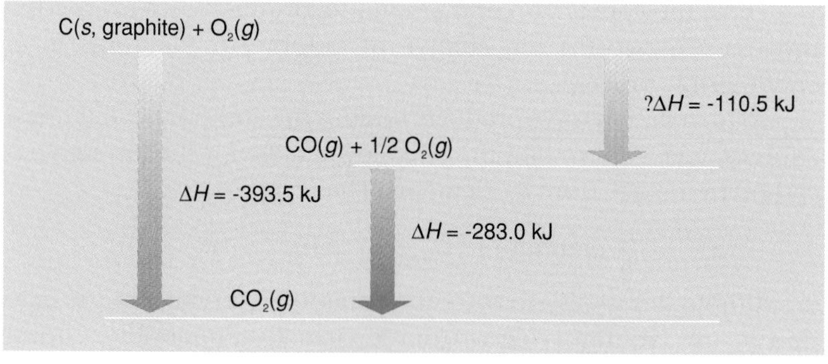

Figure 10.15 Hess's law is used to determine the enthalpy change for C(*s*, graphite) + $\frac{1}{2}O_2(g) \rightarrow$ $CO(g)$.

Concept Practice

27. State Hess's law of heat summation in your own words. Explain its usefulness.

28. When the reverse of a chemical reaction is written, what happens to the sign of ΔH? Why?

Practice Problems

29. Calculate the enthalpy change, ΔH (in kJ), for the reaction

$2Al(s) + Fe_2O_3(s) \rightarrow 2Fe(s) + Al_2O_3(s) \quad \Delta H = ?$

Use the enthalpy changes for the combustion of aluminum and iron:

$2Al(s) + \frac{3}{2}O_2(g) \rightarrow Al_2O_3(s) \qquad \Delta H = -1669.8 \text{ kJ}$

$2Fe(s) + \frac{3}{2}O_2(g) \rightarrow Fe_2O_3(s) \qquad \Delta H = -824.2 \text{ kJ}$

30. What is the enthalpy change, ΔH, for the decomposition of hydrogen peroxide?

$2H_2O_2(l) \rightarrow 2H_2O(l) + O_2(g)$

Use the enthalpy change, ΔH, for the combination of hydrogen with oxygen to make two different compounds.

$H_2(g) + O_2(g) \rightarrow H_2O_2(l) \qquad \Delta H = -187.9 \text{ kJ}$

$H_2(g) + \frac{1}{2}O_2(g) \rightarrow H_2O(l) \qquad \Delta H = -285.8 \text{ kJ}$

10.9 Standard Heats of Formation

Objective

Calculate heat changes, using standard heats of formation.

Sometimes it is hard to measure the heat change for a reaction. Materials may not be available, or perhaps the reaction is too slow for an enthalpy change to be measured. The chemicals involved may be too expensive to buy. In these cases you can calculate the enthalpy change of the reaction from standard heats of formation. *The* **standard heat of formation** (ΔH_f^0) *of a compound is the change in enthalpy that accompanies the formation of one mole of the compound from its elements with all substances in their standard states at 25°C.*

The ΔH_f^0 of the free element in its standard state is arbitrarily set at zero. For example, for the diatomic molecules—$H_2(g)$, $N_2(g)$, $O_2(g)$, $F_2(g)$, $Cl_2(g)$, $Br_2(l)$, and $I_2(s)$—the $\Delta H_f^0 = 0.0$. Similarly, the ΔH_f^0 for carbon in the form of graphite, C(*s*, graphite), is 0.0.

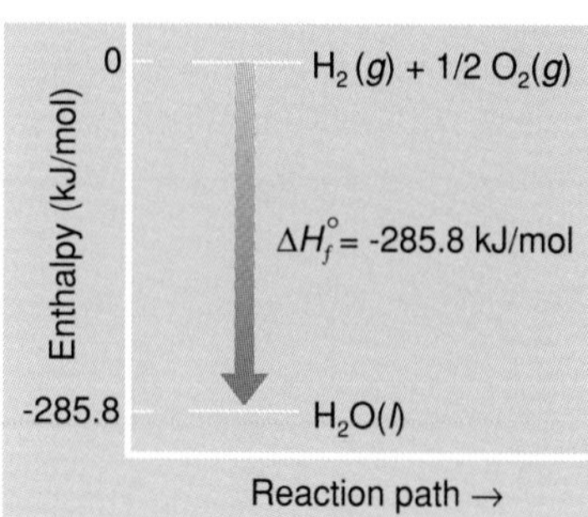

Figure 10.16 The enthalpy diagram shows the standard heat of formation of water. Water has a lower enthalpy than the elements from which it is formed.

Many values of ΔH_f^0 have been measured. They are compiled in Appendix A, Table A.6, for some common substances. Standard heats of formation of compounds are handy for calculating heats of reaction at standard conditions. The ΔH^0 for the reaction is the difference between the standard heats of formation of all the reactants and products.

$$\Delta H^0 = \Delta H_f^0(\text{products}) - \Delta H_f^0(\text{reactants})$$

Figure 10.16 is a diagram similar to others you have seen, but notice that it displays the *standard heats* of formation of the reactants hydrogen and oxygen and the product water. The heat difference between the reactants and products, –285.8 kJ/mol, is the standard heat of formation of liquid water from the gases hydrogen and oxygen.

Example 7 Calculating Standard Heats of Reaction

What is the standard heat of reaction (ΔH^0) for the reaction of carbon monoxide gas with oxygen to form carbon dioxide gas?

Solution

First, write a balanced equation,

$$2CO(g) + O_2(g) \rightarrow 2CO_2(g)$$

Then use Table A.6 in Appendix A to find the standard heats of formation.

$$\Delta H_f^0\ O_2(g) \quad = 0.0 \text{ kJ/mol (free element)}$$

$$\Delta H_f^0\ CO(g) \quad = -110.5 \text{ kJ/mol}$$

$$\Delta H_f^0\ CO_2(g) \quad = -393.5 \text{ kJ/mol}$$

Sum the ΔH_f^0 values of the reactants and then the products, taking into account the number of moles of each.

$$2\ \cancel{\text{mol CO}(g)} \times \frac{-110.5 \text{ kJ}}{1\ \cancel{\text{mol CO}(g)}} + 1\ \cancel{\text{mol O}_2(g)} \times \frac{0.0 \text{ kJ}}{1\ \cancel{\text{mol O}_2(g)}} = -221.0 \text{ kJ}$$

$$2\ \cancel{\text{mol CO}_2(g)} \times \frac{-393.5 \text{ kJ}}{1\ \cancel{\text{mol CO}_2(g)}} = -787.0 \text{ kJ}$$

Since $\Delta H^0 = \Delta H_f^0$ (products) – ΔH_f^0 (reactants),

$$\Delta H^0 = (-787.0 \text{ kJ}) - (-221.0 \text{ kJ}) = -566.0 \text{ kJ}$$

ΔH^0 is negative. Therefore the reaction is exothermic, as shown in Figure 10.17.

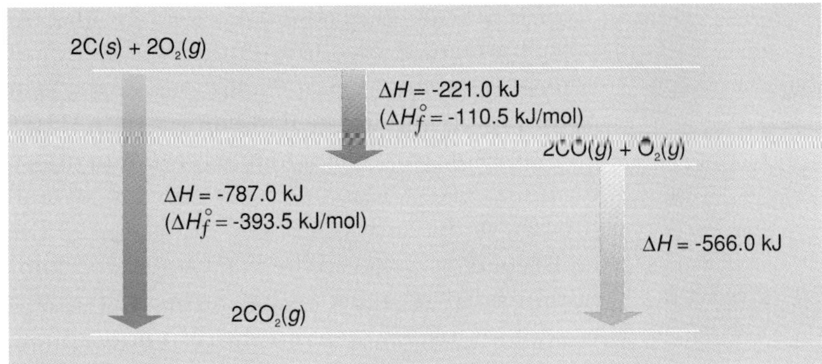

Figure 10.17 Hess's law is used to determine the enthalpy change for the reaction $2CO(g) + O_2(g) \rightarrow 2CO_2(g)$.

Concept Practice

31. What is the standard heat of formation of a free element?

Practice Problem

32. Calculate the change in enthalpy (in kJ) for these reactions.
a. $CH_4(g) + 2O_2(g) \rightarrow CO_2(g) + 2H_2O(l)$
b. $2SO_2(g) + O_2(g) \rightarrow 2SO_3(g)$

Activity 10
Heat of Fusion of Ice

Purpose

To estimate the heat of fusion of ice.

Materials

ice
plastic foam cup
graduated cylinder
thermometer
hot water

Procedure

1. Fill a 100-mL graduated cylinder with hot tap water. Allow the filled cylinder to stand 1 minute. Pour the water into the sink.

2. Use the graduated cylinder to measure 70 mL of hot water. Pour it into the plastic cup. Measure the temperature of the water.

3. Add a small ice cube to the cup of water and gently swirl the cup. Measure the temperature of the water immediately after the ice cube has completely melted.

4. Pour the water from the cup into the graduated cylinder and measure the volume.

5. Calculate the heat of fusion of ice (kJ/mol) by dividing the heat given up by the water by the moles of ice melted. (Hint: The mass of ice melted is the same as the increase in the volume of the water—1 g H_2O = 1 mL H_2O.)

Analysis and Conclusions

1. Compare your experimental value for the heat of fusion of ice with the accepted value of 6 kJ/mol or 80 cal/g. How do you account for error in your value?

2. Suggest some changes in this procedure that would improve the accuracy of the results.

Chapter 10 Review
Thermochemistry

Key Terms

calorie *10.2*
calorimeter *10.5*
calorimetry *10.5*
chemical potential energy *10.1*
energy *10.1*
endothermic process *10.4*
enthalpy *10.5*
exothermic process *10.4*
heat *10.1*
heat capacity *10.2*
heat of combustion *10.6*
heat of reaction *10.6*
Hess's law of heat summation *10.8*
joule *10.2*
law of conservation of energy *10.1*
molar heat *10.7*
specific heat capacity *10.3*
standard heat of formation *10.9*
surroundings *10.4*
system *10.4*
thermochemical equation *10.6*
thermochemistry *10.1*
universe *10.4*

Chapter Summary

Energy is the capacity to do work or to supply heat. Heat always flows from a warmer body to a colder body, and heat flow can be detected by a change in temperature. Thermochemistry is the study of heat changes that take place, during reactions, between a system and its surroundings.

The heat changes that occur in chemical reactions and changes of physical state can be measured. A process is exothermic if heat flows from the system to the surroundings and endothermic if heat flows to the system from the surroundings.

Calorimetry is used to measure the heat change associated with a chemical reaction or change of state. For a process carried out at constant pressure the heat change is equal to the change in enthalpy, ΔH.

Thermochemical equations show the accompanying heat of reaction (enthalpy change) at constant pressure. Two specific cases are the heat of formation and the heat of combustion. Hess's law states that in a reaction that is the sum of two or more other reactions, ΔH for the overall process is the sum of the ΔH values for all the constituent reactions. When an element or compound is in its most stable form at standard conditions, usually at a pressure of 1 atmosphere and 25°C, it is in its standard state. The enthalpy change for a reaction when all the reactants and products are in their standard states is the standard enthalpy change, ΔH^0. Specifically, the enthalpy for the formation of one mole of a compound from its elements, is the enthalpy of formation, ΔH_f^0. By definition, ΔH_f^0 of an element is zero. Using Hess's law you can calculate ΔH_f^0 for a product or to determine ΔH^0 for a reaction.

Heat changes that occur in physical processes are also important. The heat of fusion or the heat of vaporization may be used to determine the quantity of heat transferred to or from a system when it undergoes a change of state at constant temperature. This heat change can be measured, for example, when a solid substance melts to a liquid at its melting point.

Practice Questions and Problems

33. Define *chemical potential energy. 10.1*

34. One fan motor may be more energy efficient than another. Explain the phrase *energy efficient. 10.1*

35. Make the following conversions. *10.2*
a. 850 cal to Calories
b. 444 cal to joules
c. 1.8 kJ to joules
d. 0.45 kJ to calories

36. Why does the concrete deck around an outdoor swimming pool become too hot to walk on barefoot, while the water stays cool? *10.3*

37. How many kilojoules of heat is absorbed when 1.00 L of water is heated from 18°C to 85°C? *10.3*

38. A piece of stainless steel weighing 1.55 g absorbs 141 J of heat energy when its temperature increases by 178°C. What is the specific heat of stainless steel? *10.3*

39. Describe the *sign convention* that is used when you do thermochemical calculations. *10.4*

40. Two substances in a glass beaker react chemically and the glass beaker becomes too hot to touch. *10.4*

a. Is this an exothermic reaction or an endothermic reaction?

b. If the two substances are defined as the system, what constitutes the surroundings?

41. Classify these processes as exothermic or endothermic. *10.4*

a. discharging a battery **c.** burning alcohol

b. photosynthesis **d.** baking a potato

42. What is the purpose of a calorimeter? *10.5*

43. There are some obvious sources of error in experiments in which plastic foam cups are used as calorimeters. Name at least three. *10.5*

44. Why is it important to give the physical state of a substance in a thermochemical reaction? *10.6*

45. What information is given in a thermochemical equation? *10.6*

46. The production of iron and carbon dioxide from iron(II) oxide and carbon monoxide is an exothermic reaction. *10.6*

$Fe_2O_3(s) + 3CO(g) \rightarrow 2Fe(s) + 3CO_2(g) + 26.3\ kJ$

How many kilojoules of heat are produced when 3.40 mol of Fe_2O_3 reacts with an excess of CO?

47. The burning of magnesium in oxygen is a very exothermic reaction. *10.6*

$2Mg(s) + O_2(g) \rightarrow 2MgO(s) + 1204\ kJ$

How many kilojoules are given off when 6.55 g of Mg reacts with an excess of oxygen?

48. Identify each heat change by name: *10.7*

a. 1 mol $C_3H_8(l) \rightarrow$ 1 mol $C_3H_8(g)$

b. 1 mol $NaCl(s) \rightarrow$ 1 mol $NaCl(aq)$

$\Delta H_{soln} = +3.88\ kJ/mol$

c. 1 mol $NaCl(s) \rightarrow$ 1 mol $NaCl(l)$

d. 1 mol $NH_3(g) \rightarrow$ 1 mol $NH_3(l)$

e. 1 mol $Hg(l) \rightarrow$ 1 mol $Hg(s)$

49. Classify each change in the previous problem as exothermic or endothermic. *10.7*

50. Explain why ice melts at 0°C without an increase of temperature even though heat is flowing into the system (the ice). *10.7*

51. Calculate the quantity of heat gained or lost in the following changes. *10.7*

a. 3.50 mol water freezes at 0°C.

b. 0.44 mol steam condenses at 100°C.

c. 1.25 mol $NaOH(s)$ dissolves in water.

d. 0.15 mol $C_2H_5Cl(l)$ vaporizes at 12.3°C.

52. Sodium acetate dissolves readily in water. *10.7*

$NaC_2H_3O_2(s) \rightarrow NaC_2H_3O_2(aq)$

$\Delta H = -17.3\ kJ/mol$

Would this process increase or decrease the temperature of the water?

53. Explain the usefulness of Hess's law of heat summation in thermochemistry. *10.8*

54. A considerable amount of heat is required for the decomposition of aluminum oxide. *10.8*

$2Al_2O_3(s) \rightarrow 4Al(s) + 3O_2(g)$

$\Delta H = +3352\ kJ$

a. What is the heat change for the formation of one mole of aluminum oxide from aluminum and oxygen?

b. Is the reaction exothermic or endothermic?

55. Calculate the heat change for the formation of lead(IV) chloride by the reaction of lead(II) chloride with chlorine. *10.8*

$PbCl_2(s) + Cl_2(g) \rightarrow PbCl_4(l) \quad \Delta H = ?$

Use the following thermochemical equations.

$Pb(s) + 2Cl_2(g) \rightarrow PbCl_4(l) \quad \Delta H = -329.2\ kJ$

$Pb(s) + Cl_2(g) \rightarrow PbCl_2(s) \quad \Delta H = -359.4\ kJ$

56. From the following reactions: *10.8*

$\frac{1}{2}N_2(g) + \frac{1}{2}O_2(g) \rightarrow NO(g)$

$\Delta H = +90.4\ kJ/mol$

$\frac{1}{2}N_2(g) + O_2(g) \rightarrow NO_2(g)$

$\Delta H = +33.6\ kJ/mol$

determine the heat of reaction for

$NO(g) + \frac{1}{2}O_2(g) \rightarrow NO_2(g) \quad \Delta H = ?$

57. Calculate the heat change for the formation of copper(I) oxide from the elements. *10.8*

$Cu(s) + \frac{1}{2}O_2(g) \rightarrow CuO(s)$

Use the following two thermochemical equations to make the calculation.

$CuO(s) + Cu(s) \rightarrow Cu_2O(s) \quad \Delta H = -11.3\ kJ$

$Cu_2O(s) + \frac{1}{2}O_2(g) \rightarrow 2CuO(s) \quad \Delta H = -114.6\ kJ$

58. What is the standard heat of formation of a compound? *10.9*

59. Use standard heats of formation to calculate the heat change (ΔH) for these reactions. *10.9*

a. $Br_2(g) \rightarrow Br_2(l)$

b. $CaCO_3(s) \rightarrow CaO(s) + CO_2(g)$

c. $2NO(g) + O_2(g) \rightarrow 2NO_2(g)$

Mastery Questions and Problems

60. Use the key terms to construct a concept map with *thermochemical equation* as the central concept term.

61. With one exception, the standard heats of formation of all the following substances are identical: $Na(s)$, $O_2(g)$, $Br_2(l)$, $CO(g)$, $Fe(s)$, $He(g)$. What is the standard heat of fusion for all but one? What is the exception? Explain the difference.

62. Equal masses of two substances absorb the same amount of heat. The temperature of substance A increases twice as much as the temperature of substance B. Which substance has the higher specific heat? Explain.

63. Calculate the heat required, in joules and in calories, to change 15.00 g of ice at –10°C to 15.00 g of water at 15°C.

64. If 3.20 kcal of heat is added to 1.00 kg of ice at 0°C, how much water, at 0°C, is produced and how much ice is left?

65. The amounts of energy required to change different quantities of carbon tetrachloride, $CCl_4(l)$, into vapor are given in the following table.

a. Graph the data, using energy as the dependent variable.

b. What is the slope of the line?

c. The heat of vaporization of $CCl_4(l)$ is 53.8 cal/g. How does this value compare with the slope of the line?

Mass of $CCl_4(l)$ (g)	Energy (J)	(cal)
2.90	652	156
7.50	1689	404
17.0	3825	915
26.2	5894	1410
39.8	8945	2140
51.0	11 453	2740

66. Calculate the heat change in calories when 45.2 g of steam at 100°C condenses to water at the same temperature. What is the heat change in joules?

67. Find the enthalpy change for the formation of phosphorus pentachloride from its elements.
$2P(s) + 5Cl_2(g) \rightarrow 2PCl_5(s)$
Use the following thermochemical equations.
$PCl_5(s) \rightarrow PCl_3(g) + Cl_2(g)$ $\Delta H = +87.9$ kJ
$2P(s) + 3Cl_2(g) \rightarrow 2PCl_3(g)$ $\Delta H = -574$ kJ

68. Use standard heats of formation, ΔH_f^0, to calculate the change in enthalpy for these reactions.

a. $2C(s, \text{graphite}) + O_2(g) \rightarrow 2CO(g)$

b. $2H_2O_2(l) \rightarrow 2H_2O(l) + O_2(g)$

c. $4NH_3(g) + 5O_2(g) \rightarrow 4NO(g) + 6H_2O(g)$

69. An ice cube with a mass of 40.0 g melts in water originally at 25.0°C.

a. How much heat does the ice cube absorb from the water when it melts? Report your answer in calories, kilocalories, and joules.

b. Calculate the number of grams of water that can be cooled to 0°C by the melting ice cube.

70. The molar heat of vaporization of ethanol, $C_2H_5OH(l)$, is 39.3 kJ/mol. Calculate the heat required to vaporize 25.0 g of ethanol at its boiling point.

71. When metabolized, an orange provides 445 kJ of energy. What mass of water could this amount of energy raise from 25.0°C to the boiling point?

72. The combustion of ethene, C_2H_4, is an exothermic reaction.
$C_2H_4(g) + 3O_2(g) \rightarrow 2CO_2(g) + 2H_2O(l)$
$\Delta H = -1.39 \times 10^3$ kJ
Calculate the amount of heat liberated when 4.79 g of C_2H_4 reacts with excess oxygen.

73. Calculate the heat change, ΔH, for the formation of nitrogen monoxide from its elements.
$N_2(g) + O_2(g) \rightarrow 2NO(g)$
Use these thermochemical equations.
$4NH_3(g) + 3O_2(g) \rightarrow 2N_2(g) + 6H_2O(l)$
$\Delta H = -1530$ kJ
$4NH_3(g) + 5O_2(g) \rightarrow 4NO(g) + 6H_2O(l)$
$\Delta H = -1170$ kJ

74. How much heat (energy) must be removed from a 45.0-g sample of naphthalene, $C_{10}H_8$, at its freezing point to bring about solidification? The heat of fusion of naphthalene is 191.2 kJ/mol.

Critical Thinking Questions

75. Choose the term that best completes the second relationship.

a. kilojoules:heat cm^3: _____

(1) mass   (3) energy
(2) volume   (4) weight

b. right:left   exothermic: _____

(1) combustion   (3) endothermic
(2) heat   (4) joule

c. thermometer:temperature
calorimeter: _____

(1) constant pressure   (3) endothermic
(2) reactants   (4) heat

76. At what conditions of temperature and pressure are standard heats of formation typically measured? Why are these conditions chosen?

77. How is the chemical potential energy of the food you eat like the chemical potential energy of the gasoline that fuels a car?

Cumulative Review

78. What fraction of the average kinetic energy of hydrogen gas at 100 K does hydrogen gas have at 40 K?

79. How many hydrogen molecules are in 44.8 L of $H_2(g)$ at STP?

80. Write the net ionic equation for the reaction of aqueous solutions of sodium chloride and silver acetate.

81. How many grams of oxygen are formed by the decomposition of 25.0 g of hydrogen peroxide?
$2H_2O_2(l) \rightarrow 2H_2O(l) + O_2(g)$

Challenge Questions and Problems

82. Ethane, $C_2H_6(g)$, can be formed by the reaction of ethene, $C_2H_4(g)$, with hydrogen gas.

$$C_2H_4(g) + H_2(g) \rightarrow C_2H_6(g)$$

Use the heats of combustion for the following reactions to calculate the heat change for the formation of ethane from ethene and hydrogen gas.

$2H_2(g) + O_2(g) \rightarrow 2H_2O(l)$
$\Delta H = -572$ kJ
$C_2H_4(l) + 3O_2(g) \rightarrow 2H_2O(l) + 2CO_2(g)$
$\Delta H = 1401$ kJ
$2C_2H_6(l) + 7O_2(g) \rightarrow 6H_2O(l) + 4CO_2(g)$
$\Delta H = -3100$ kJ

83. An ice cube at 0.0°C was dropped into 30.0 g of water in a cup at 45.0°C. At the instant that all the ice was melted, the temperature of the water in the cup was 19.5°C. What did the ice cube weigh?

84. 41.0 g of glass at 95°C is placed in 175 g of water at 21°C in an insulated container and both are allowed to come to the same temperature. What is the final temperature of the glass-water mixture? The specific heat of glass is 2.1 $cal/(g \times °C)$.

Connections Questions

85. Approximately how many Calories might you burn in jogging for one-half hour?

86. How would a calorimetrist determine the energy content of an apple?

87. What is the function of brown fat cells in animals that live in cold climates?

Write About Chemistry

88. Write an editorial, discussing evidence that supports the theory that the earth is entering a period of global warming. Explore the social implications of global warming.

89. Heat was once thought to be an invisible fluid, called *caloric*. Write a paragraph defining some properties of heat that could be explained by the existence of caloric.

Readings and References

Barnwell, George. "Your Personal Greenhouse." *ChemMatters* (December 1990), pp. 8–10.

Gardner, Robert. *Energy Projects for Young Scientists.* New York: Watts, 1987.

11 The Behavior of Gases

Goals

- Describe in qualitative terms the effects of changes in pressure, volume, and temperature on contained gases.
- Define and calculate the quantitative effects of changes in pressure, volume, and temperature on contained gases.
- Combine the laws of Boyle, Charles, and Gay-Lussac into the combined gas law.
- Apply Dalton's law to calculate the total pressure of a mixture of gases from the partial pressures of the gases in the mixture.

The largest container of popcorn on record was about 106 m^3. What made all that popcorn pop? The complex process hinges on the expansion of water vapor inside each kernel. The expansion of gases is one topic of this chapter.

Concept Overview

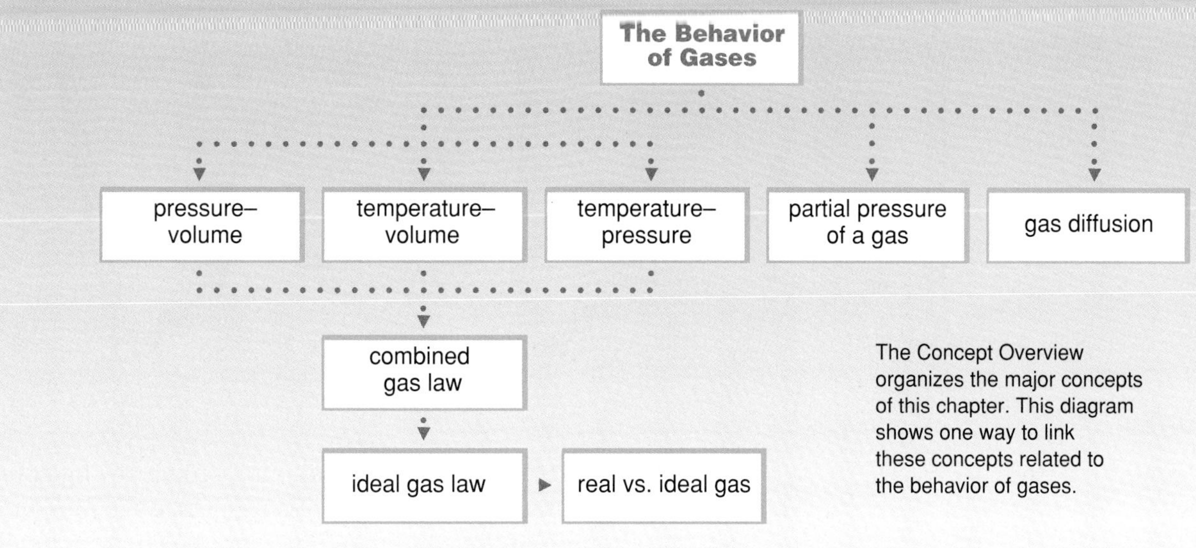

This chapter examines the work of such eminent scientists as Robert Boyle and Jacques Charles. These scientists studied the effects of changes in the pressure, volume, and temperature of contained gases. From their results they proposed a set of mathematical relationships that together are known as the gas laws. Using the kinetic theory, however, you can often explain how gases will respond to a change of conditions without resorting to formal mathematical expressions. This chapter begins by showing how simple kinetic theory is used to explain gas behavior. The emphasis will be on gas pressure.

11.1 The Effect of Adding or Removing Gas

Objective

Infer from observation the effect of changing the amount of gas in a container.

When you pump up a tire, the pressure inside it increases. The pressure exerted by an enclosed gas is caused by collisions of gas particles with the walls of the container. By adding gas you increase the number of gas particles. This increases the number of collisions and therefore the gas pressure. Doubling the number of gas particles in an inflated tire, for example, doubles the pressure as long as the temperature of the gas does not change. Tripling the number of gas particles triples the pressure and so forth.

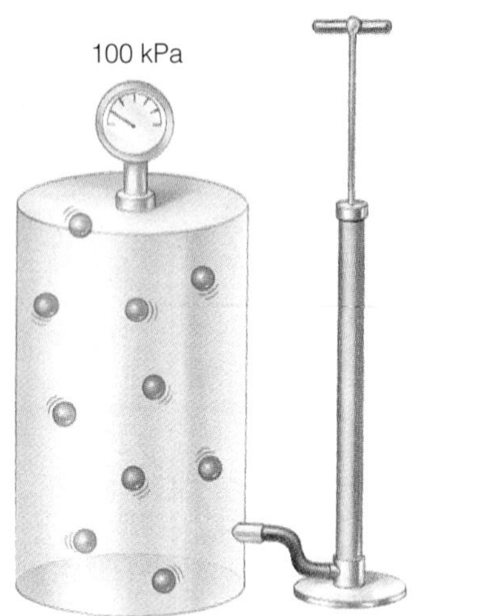

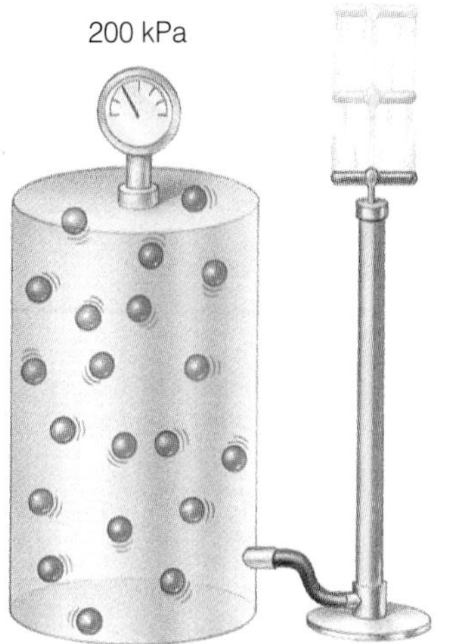

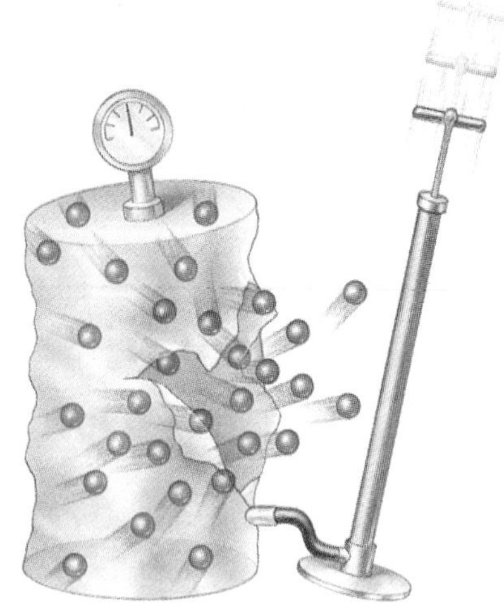

Figure 11.1 When gas is pumped into a closed rigid container, the pressure increases in proportion to the number of particles added. If the number of particles doubles, the pressure doubles. If the pressure exceeds the strength of the container, the container explodes.

Look at Figure 11.1. With a powerful pump and a strong container you can generate very high gas pressures. Once the pressure exceeds the strength of the container, however, the container will burst. Overinflated balloons pop for this reason.

Letting the air out of a tire or the gas out of a storage cylinder decreases the pressure in the container. Fewer particles are left inside. As you have probably already guessed, halving the number of particles in a given volume of gas decreases the pressure by one-half, as illustrated in Figure 11.2. When a sealed container of gas under pressure is opened, the gas always moves from the region of higher pressure to the region of lower pressure. This is the principle used in aerosol cans, as Figure 11.3 shows. The propellant in an aerosol container is a gas at high pressure. The air outside the container is a gas at a lower pressure. The movement of gases from higher to lower pressure occurs because there is more empty space

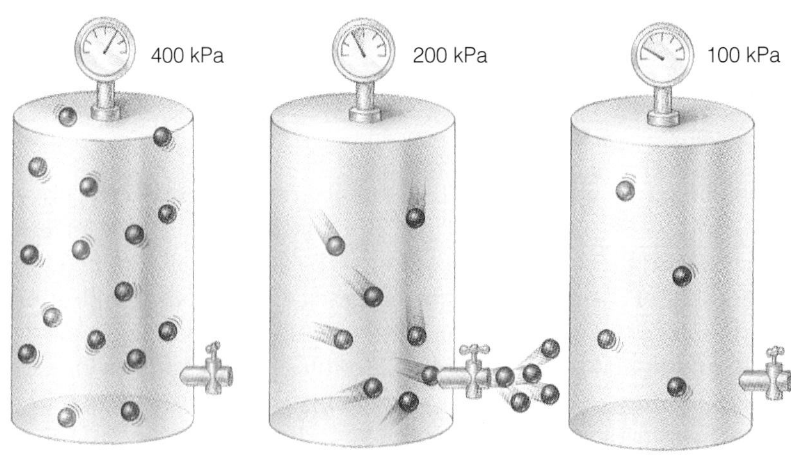

Figure 11.2 A gas under pressure in a sealed rigid container rushes into the atmosphere if the container is opened. The pressure in the container decreases in proportion to the number of gas particles released. If the number of particles decreases by one-half, the pressure also decreases by one-half.

for the gas particles to occupy in the region of lower pressure. Gas particles increase their randomness by moving into the empty space, which is always a favorable process. Eventually the gas pressures inside and outside the container will be equal.

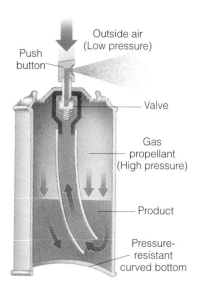

Figure 11.3 When the push-button is pressed, high pressure inside the container forces the product out through the opening in the valve.

Concept Practice

1. Keeping temperature constant, how could you increase the pressure in a container 100 times?

Practice Problem

2. The manufacturer of an aerosol deodorant wishes to produce a family-size package that will hold twice as much gas in the same 150-mL regular size container. How will the pressure of the new product compare to that of the original product?

11.2 The Effect of Changing the Size of the Container

Objective

Infer from observation the effect of changing the dimensions of the container.

You can increase the pressure exerted by a contained gas by reducing its volume. The more the gas is compressed, the greater the pressure it exerts inside the container. Reducing the volume of the contained gas by one-half leads to a doubling of the pressure, as Figure 11.4 shows. The effect on pressure is the same as doubling

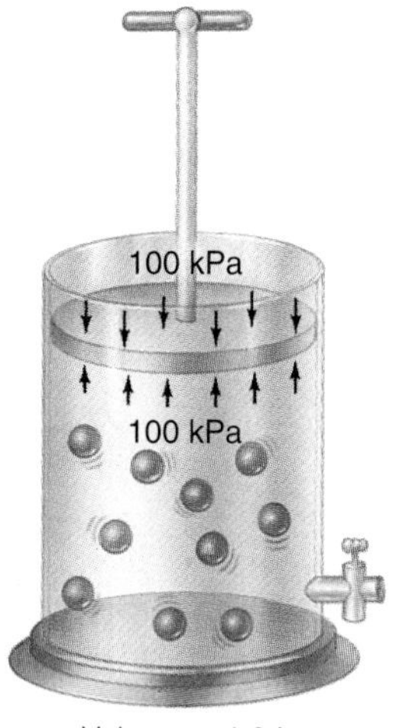

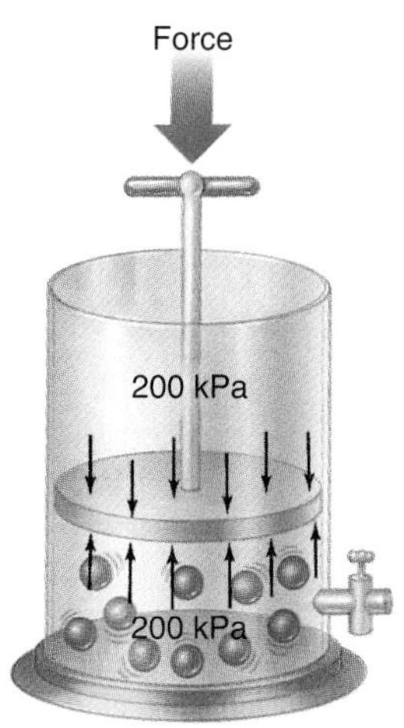

Figure 11.4 Doubling the force on a gas reduces the volume of the gas by one-half and doubles the pressure the gas exerts.

Safety

Always open a bottle of liquid slowly and cautiously to release any built-up pressure.

the quantity of gas while keeping the volume constant. Increasing the volume of the container has just the opposite effect. By doubling the volume you halve the gas pressure. There are now one-half as many gas particles in a given volume.

Concept Practice

3. What would you have to do to the volume of a gas to reduce its pressure to one-quarter of the original value?

Objective

Calculate pressure or volume from the pressure–volume relationship of a contained gas at constant temperature.

11.3 Boyle's Law for Pressure–Volume Changes

Consider the effect of pressure on the volume of a contained gas while the temperature is held constant. When the pressure goes up, the volume goes down. Similarly, when the pressure goes down, the volume goes up. The first person to do a systematic and quantitative study of this pressure–volume relationship was the Anglo-Irish chemist Robert Boyle (1627–1691). In 1662 he proposed a law to describe this behavior of gases. **Boyle's law** *states that for a given mass of gas at constant temperature, the volume of the gas varies inversely with pressure.* In an inverse relationship, the product of the two quantities that change is always constant.

Look at Figure 11.5. In the figure, a volume of 1 L (V_1) is at a pressure of 100 kPa (P_1). If you increase the volume to 2 L (V_2), the pressure decreases to 50 kPa (P_2). Observe that the product $P_1 \times V_1$ (100 kPa × 1 L = 100 L × kPa) is the same as the product $P_2 \times V_2$ (50 kPa × 2 L = 100 L × kPa). If you decrease the volume to 0.5 L, the

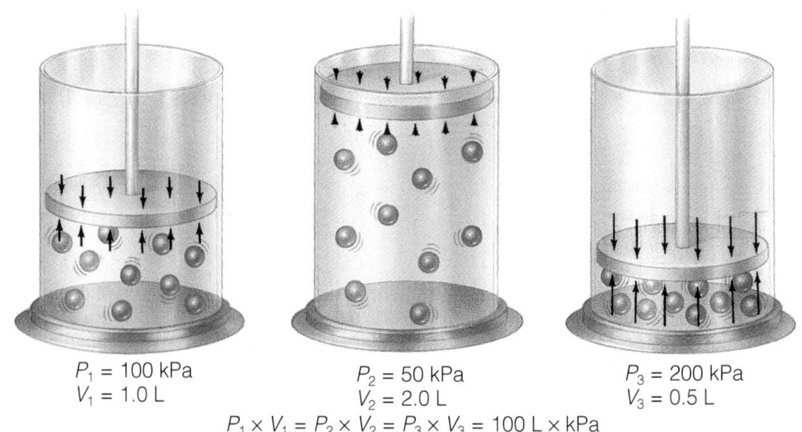

Figure 11.5 Boyle's law and pressure–volume relationships are studied by using a cylindrical container fitted with a frictionless, weightless piston. When the pressure of a gas at constant temperature decreases (P_2), the volume increases (V_2). When the pressure increases (P_3), the volume decreases (V_3).

gas pressure increases to 200 kPa. Once again, the product of pressure times volume equals 100 L × kPa. When you graph an inverse relationship the result is a curved line, as shown in Figure 11.6. The product of pressure and volume at any two sets of conditions is always constant at a given temperature. You can write Boyle's law as a mathematical equation as follows.

$$P_1 \times V_1 = P_2 \times V_2$$

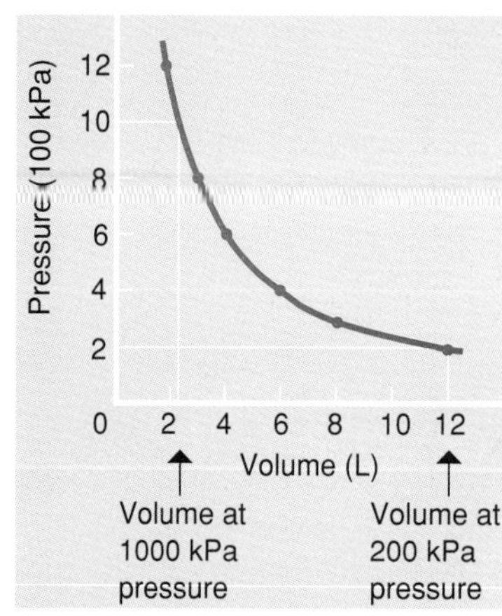

Figure 11.6 This graph illustrates Boyle's law. When the pressure of a gas decreases at constant temperature, the volume increases. At any point on this curve the product of pressure (P) and volume (V) is a constant.

Example 1 Pressure–Volume Calculations

A balloon contains 30 L of helium gas at 100 kPa. What is the volume when the balloon rises to an altitude where the pressure is only 25 kPa? (Assume that the temperature remains constant.)

Solution *(algebraic)*

You know that $P_1 = 100$ kPa, $V_1 = 30$ L, and $P_2 = 25$ kPa. You need to solve for V_2. Rearrange the expression for Boyle's law to obtain V_2.

$$P_1 \times V_1 = P_2 \times V_2$$

Therefore: $$V_2 = \frac{P_1 \times V_1}{P_2}$$

Substitute values for P_1, V_1, and P_2.

$$V_2 = \frac{30\text{ L} \times 100\text{ kPa}}{25\text{ kPa}} = 120\text{ L}$$

Solution *(kinetic theory/dimensional analysis)*

Using kinetic theory, you know that at constant temperature a decrease in pressure must correspond to a proportional increase in volume. Therefore multiply the given volume by a ratio of pressures (larger pressure over smaller pressure) so that the resulting volume will be larger.

$$\frac{30\text{ L} \times 100\text{ kPa}}{25\text{ kPa}} = 120\text{ L}$$

Concept Practice

4. Write the mathematical equation for Boyle's law and explain the symbols. What can you say about the temperature?

Biographical Note

Robert Boyle
(1627–1691)

Robert Boyle was the youngest of 14 children. Boyle was sent away to school at the age of 8. When he returned home in 1643 his interests turned to medicine. He progressed from preparing drugs to experimental chemistry. Boyle viewed chemistry as an important physical science. His aim as stated in his book *The Sceptical Chymist* (1661) was to establish an empirically based theory of matter. Boyle's contribution to the scientific method must rank as his greatest achievement.

Practice Problem

5. The pressure on 2.50 L of gas changes from 100 kPa to 40 kPa. What is the new volume if the temperature is constant?

Objective

Infer from kinetic theory the effect of temperature changes on a contained gas.

11.4 The Effect of Heating or Cooling a Gas

Raising the temperature of an enclosed gas increases the gas pressure. The kinetic energy of gas particles increases as they absorb thermal energy. Naturally, fast-moving particles bombard the walls of their container with more energy than slow-moving particles. For this reason an aerosol can, carelessly thrown onto a fire, is an explosion hazard. Look at Figure 11.7. The average kinetic energy of gas particles in a system doubles with a doubling of the Kelvin temperature. Hence doubling the Kelvin temperature of an enclosed gas doubles the gas pressure.

By contrast, as the temperature of an enclosed gas decreases, the particles move more slowly and strike the container walls with less force. Halving the Kelvin temperature of a gas in a rigid container decreases the gas pressure by one-half.

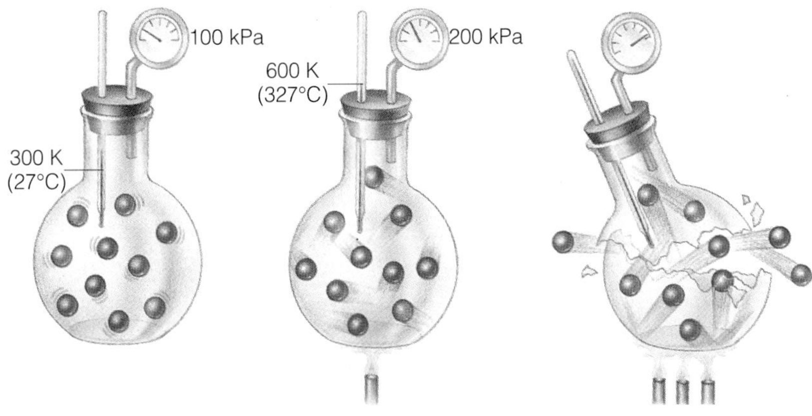

Figure 11.7 When a gas in a container is heated from 300 K (27°C) to 600 K (327°C), the kinetic energy of the gas particles doubles. The particles strike the sides of the container with greater force at 600 K than they do at 300 K. The pressure exerted by the gas therefore doubles. The pressure buildup at high temperatures may cause the container to explode.

Concept Practice

6. What happens to the volume of a balloon when it is taken outside on a cold winter day? Why?

11.5 Charles's Law for Temperature–Volume Changes

Objective

Calculate temperature or volume from the temperature–volume relationship of a contained gas at constant pressure.

In 1787 the French physicist and balloonist Jacques Charles (1746–1823) investigated the quantitative effect of temperature on the volume of a gas at constant pressure. In every experiment, he observed an increase in the volume of a gas with an increase in temperature and a decrease in volume with a decrease in temperature. In practice, the volume–temperature relationship for any gas can be measured only over a limited range because at low temperatures gases condense to form liquids.

From his quantitative studies Charles observed that for any given pressure, the graph of volume of a gas versus temperature yields a straight line. Figure 11.8 shows this graph. In addition to the straight lines, another important feature emerged. The lines extended (extrapolated) to zero volume ($V = 0$) all intersect the temperature axis at –273°C. William Thompson (Lord Kelvin) realized the significance of this value. He identified the temperature, –273°C, as absolute zero. Absolute zero is the temperature at which the average kinetic energy of gas particles would theoretically be zero. This was the basis for the *absolute temperature* scale set up by Kelvin in 1848. This scale is now called the Kelvin temperature scale. On the Kelvin temperature scale 0 K corresponds to –273.15°C.

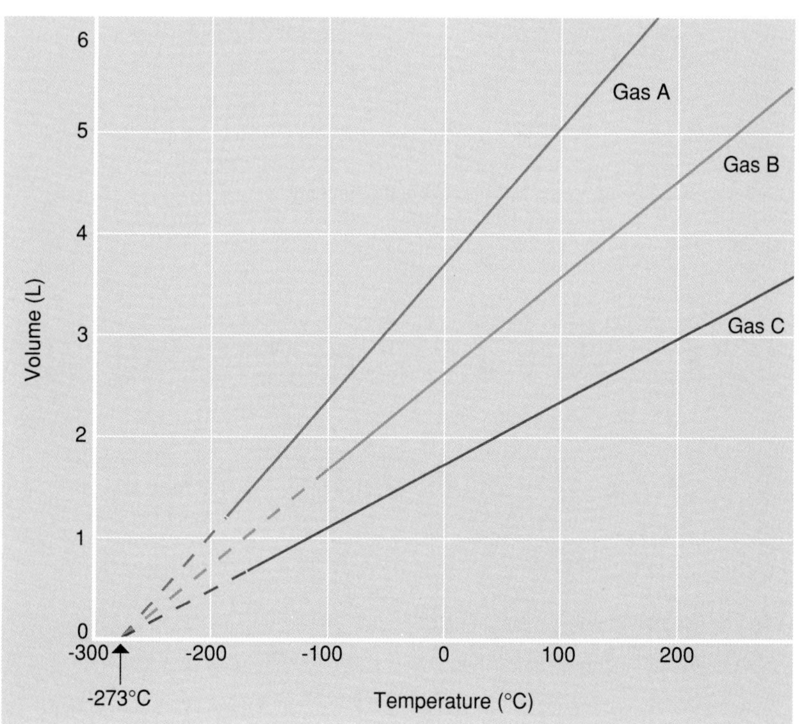

Figure 11.8 Jacques Charles's graphs showed the direct relationship between volume and temperature for a gas at constant pressure.

Charles's observations and the findings of Kelvin can be summarized in a law. **Charles's law** *states that the volume of a fixed mass of gas is directly proportional to its Kelvin temperature if the pressure is kept constant.* In a direct relationship, the ratio of the two quantities that change is a constant. In Figure 11.9, for example, a 1-L sample of gas (V_1) is at a temperature of 300 K (T_1). *(Temperature in gas law problems is always in kelvins.)* When the temperature is increased to 600 K (T_2), the volume increases to 2 L (V_2). Observe that the ratio V_1/T_1 (1 L/300 K = 0.00333 L/K) is equal to the ratio V_2/T_2 (2 L/600 K = 0.00333 L/K). Moreover, the ratio of volume to Kelvin temperature at any two sets of conditions is constant. As long as the pressure is held constant, you can write Charles's law as:

$$\frac{V_1}{T_1} = \frac{V_2}{T_2}$$

The graph of a relationship that is a direct proportion is a straight line, as shown in Figure 11.10.

Integrating Mechanical Engineering

Refrigeration Is Cool

Every day you get food out of your refrigerator, but do you know how refrigerators keep things cold? Refrigerators move heat from inside the refrigerator to the outside. In a refrigerator, a fluid, called a refrigerant, circulates through a cycle. Heat inside the refrigerator causes the refrigerant, a liquid at low pressure, to boil into a vapor, absorbing heat in the process. The low-pressure vapor is then compressed and becomes a high-pressure vapor. This vapor condenses into a liquid at high pressure outside the refrigerator, giving off heat in the process. The refrigerant is then expanded into a low-pressure liquid, and the cycle begins again.

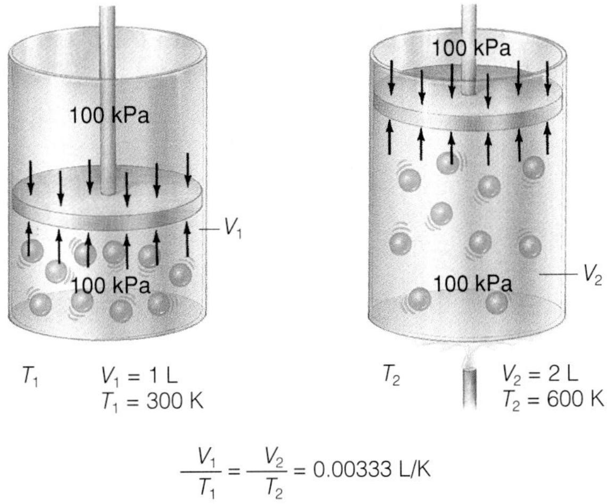

Figure 11.9 This apparatus illustrates Charles's law. When a gas at constant pressure is heated, the volume increases. When a gas at constant pressure is cooled, the volume decreases.

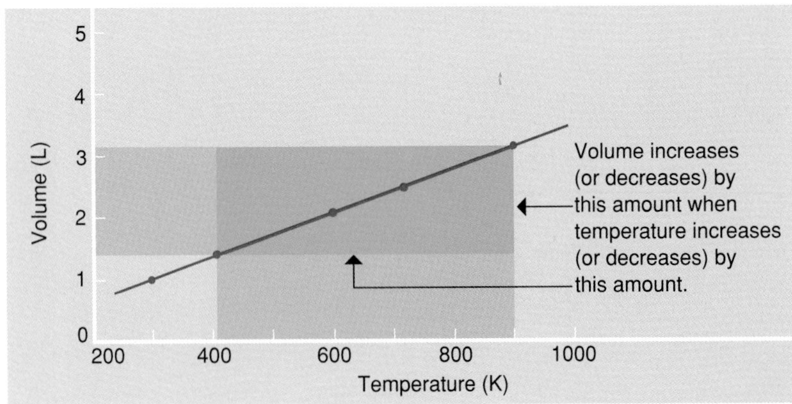

Figure 11.10 This graph illustrates Charles's law. When the temperature of a gas increases, the volume increases if the pressure is held constant. At any point on this curve the ratio of the volume (V) to temperature (T) is a constant; in this case, V/T = 0.00333 L/K.

Example 2 Volume–Temperature Calculations

A balloon, inflated in a air-conditioned room at 27°C, has a volume of 4.0 L. The balloon is then heated to a temperature of 57°C. What is the new volume of the balloon if the pressure remains constant?

Solution *(algebraic)*

Temperature in all gas problems is expressed as kelvins. Therefore you must convert degrees Celsius to kelvins.

$$T_1 = 27°C + 273 = 300 \text{ K}$$

$$T_2 = 57°C + 273 = 330 \text{ K}$$

You know that $V_1 = 4.0$ L, $T_1 = 300$ K, and $T_2 = 330$ K. Therefore you use Charles's law to solve for V_2. First rearrange the expression for Charles's law to obtain V_2.

$$\frac{V_1}{T_1} = \frac{V_2}{T_2}$$

Therefore: $$V_2 = V_1 \times \frac{T_2}{T_1}$$

Then substitute the values for T_1, V_1, and T_2.

$$V_2 = \frac{4.0 \text{ L} \times 330 \cancel{\text{K}}}{300 \cancel{\text{K}}} = 4.4 \text{ L}$$

Solution *(kinetic theory/dimensional analysis)*

Using the kinetic theory, you would predict that the volume would increase with an increase in temperature. Therefore you multiply the given volume by a ratio of Kelvin temperatures greater than one. This will give a larger volume.

$$\frac{4.0 \text{ L} \times 330 \cancel{\text{K}}}{300 \cancel{\text{K}}} = 4.4 \text{ L}$$

The balloon will expand from a volume of 4.0 L at 27°C to a volume of 4.4 L at 57°C.

Practice Problem

7. If a sample of gas occupies 6.8 L at 327°C, what will its volume be at 27°C if the pressure does not change?

Figure 11.11 The volume of a balloon is less in a beaker of ice water than if the same balloon is in a beaker of hot water. Why does this happen?

Objective

Calculate temperature or pressure from the temperature–pressure relationship of a contained gas at constant volume.

11.6 Temperature–Pressure Changes

On a hot summer day the pressure in a car tire increases. This action illustrates the following relationship. *In general, the pressure of a gas is directly proportional to the Kelvin temperature if the volume is kept constant.* If the Kelvin temperature is doubled, for example, the gas pressure is doubled, as in Figure 11.12. Because this relationship involves direct proportions, the ratios P_1/T_1 and P_2/T_2 are constant at constant volume. (Work out these ratios for the quantities shown in Figure 11.12 to assure yourself this is true.) Therefore, assuming the volume is held constant, you can write the following mathematical relationship for temperature–pressure changes:

$$\frac{P_1}{T_1} = \frac{P_2}{T_2}$$

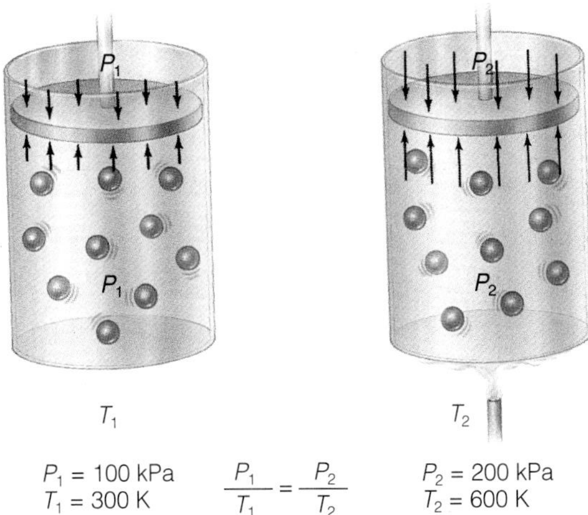

Figure 11.12 When a gas at constant volume is heated, the pressure increases. When a gas at constant volume is cooled, the pressure decreases.

Safety

Never heat a closed container. Make sure there is an opening somewhere.

Example 3 Pressure–Temperature Calculations

The gas left in a used aerosol can is at a pressure of 100 kPa at 27°C (room temperature). If the can is thrown onto a fire, what will the internal pressure of the gas be when its temperature reaches 927°C?

Solution *(algebraic)*

First convert degrees Celsius to kelvins.

$$T_1 = 27°\text{C} + 273 = 300 \text{ K} \qquad T_2 = 927°\text{C} + 273 = 1200 \text{ K}$$

You know that $P_1 = 100$ kPa, $T_1 = 300$ K, and $T_2 = 1200$ K.

Thus, you can solve the temperature–pressure equation for P_2.

$$\frac{P_1}{T_1} = \frac{P_2}{T_2}$$

Therefore: $P_2 = \dfrac{P_1 \times T_2}{T_1}$

Then insert values for P_1, T_2, and T_1 into the equation.

$$P_2 = \frac{100 \text{ kPa} \times 1200 \cancel{\text{K}}}{300 \cancel{\text{K}}} = 400 \text{ kPa}$$

Problem-Solving Tip

Solve the equation for the unknown before you substitute the known quantities.

Solution ***(kinetic theory/dimensional analysis)***

Once again, from the kinetic theory you would expect the increase in temperature of a gas to give an increase in pressure if the volume is held constant. Therefore multiply the given pressure by a temperature ratio larger than one (1200 K/300 K).

$$\frac{100 \text{ kPa} \times 1200 \cancel{\text{K}}}{300 \cancel{\text{K}}} = 400 \text{ kPa}$$

This is the pressure buildup in a can containing 100 kPa of gas when it is heated from 27°C to 927°C.

Concept Practice

8. Why do aerosol containers display the warning "Do not incinerate"? Use the temperature–pressure relationship.

Practice Problem

9. A gas has a pressure of 6.58 kPa at 540 K. What will the pressure be at 210 K if the volume does not change?

11.7 The Combined Gas Law

Objective

Calculate pressure, volume, or temperature from the pressure–volume–temperature relationships of contained gases.

The three gas laws just discussed can be combined into a single expression called the **combined gas law**.

$$\frac{P_1 \times V_1}{T_1} = \frac{P_2 \times V_2}{T_2}$$

If you have been wondering how to remember the expressions for the other gas laws, it turns out that there is really no need. Just

Integrating Physics

Cryostats

A given amount of any substance has a much smaller volume as a liquid than as a gas, even if the gas is under pressure. For this reason, many gases are stored and transported in their liquefied form rather than as gases. The containers in which liquefied gases are stored and transported are called cryostats. They are designed to prevent heat from being transferred from the environment to the very cold liquid inside. The most widely used cryostats are called Dewar flasks after the Scottish scientist Sir James Dewar, who invented them in 1892. Dewar flasks are double-walled vessels with a vacuum between the walls, like the familiar thermos bottle used to carry hot or cold drinks.

remember this one. The other laws can be obtained from the combined gas law by holding one quantity (pressure, volume, or temperature) constant.

To illustrate, suppose you hold *temperature* constant ($T_1 = T_2$).

$$\frac{P_1 \times V_1}{T_1} = \frac{P_2 \times V_2}{T_2}$$

Therefore: $$P_1 \times V_1 = \frac{P_2 \times V_2 \times \cancel{T_1}}{\cancel{T_2}}$$

You see that T_1 and T_2 cancel, and $P_1V_1 = P_2V_2$ (Boyle's law).

In addition to providing a useful means of recall for the three previous gas laws, the combined gas law does much more. It allows you to do calculations involving gases in which none of the variables (P, V, or T) are kept constant. In the example and problem that follow you will use the combined gas law to calculate the new volume of a gas that results from changing the conditions of both the pressure and temperature.

Example 4 Using the Combined Gas Law

The volume of a gas-filled balloon is 30.0 L at 40°C and 150 kPa pressure. What volume will the balloon have at standard temperature and pressure (STP)?

Solution *(algebraic)*

Standard temperature is 0°C (273 K); standard pressure is 100 kPa.

First you convert degrees Celsius to kelvins:

$$40°\text{C} + 273 = 313\ \text{K}$$

You know that $V_1 = 30.0$ L, $T_1 = 313$ K, $T_2 = 273$ K, $P_1 = 150$ kPa, $P_2 = 100$ kPa. You can now rearrange the combined gas law to obtain V_2.

$$\frac{P_1 \times V_1}{T_1} = \frac{P_2 \times V_2}{T_2}$$

Therefore: $$V_2 = \frac{V_1 \times P_1 \times T_2}{P_2 \times T_1}$$

Now you can substitute the known quantities into the expression for the combined gas law.

$$V_2 = \frac{30.0\ \text{L} \times 150\ \cancel{\text{kPa}} \times 273\ \cancel{\text{K}}}{100\ \cancel{\text{kPa}} \times 313\ \cancel{\text{K}}} = 39.2\ \text{L}$$

Solution ***(kinetic theory/dimensional analysis)***

The temperature decreases, so the temperature ratio is less than one (273 K/313 K). The pressure decreases, so the pressure ratio is greater than one (150 kPa/100 kPa). Multiply the initial volume by these two ratios:

$$\frac{30.0\text{ L} \times 150\text{ kPa} \times 273\text{ K}}{100\text{ kPa} \times 313\text{ K}} = 39.2\text{ L}$$

Concept Practice

10. Show how Charles's law can be derived from the combined gas law.

11. Show how the temperature–pressure relationship can be derived from the combined gas law.

Practice Problem

12. A container with an initial volume of 1.0 L is occupied by a gas at a pressure of 150 kPa at 25°C. By changing the volume, the pressure of the gas increases to 600 kPa as the temperature is raised to 100°C. What is the new volume?

11.8 The Ideal Gas Law

Objective

Calculate the amount of gas at any specified conditions of pressure, volume, and temperature.

Up to this point the *amount* of gas in the system has not been considered. The amount of substance, whether it is solid, liquid, or gas, is expressed in moles. Suppose you want to calculate the number of moles of a gas in a fixed volume at a known temperature and pressure. The calculation of moles is possible if the combined gas law is modified. The modification may be understood by recognizing that the volume occupied by a gas at a specified temperature and pressure is directly proportional to the number of particles in the gas. The number of moles, n, of gas is also directly proportional to the number of particles. Hence moles must be directly proportional to volume as well. Therefore you can introduce moles into the combined gas law by dividing each side of the equation by n.

$$\frac{P_1 \times V_1}{T_1 \times n_1} = \frac{P_2 \times V_2}{T_2 \times n_2}$$

This equation says that $(P \times V)/(T \times n)$ is a constant for any ideal gas.

Figure 11.13 When the temperature, pressure, and volume of a gas are measured, you can use the ideal gas law to calculate the number of moles of the gas. If you know the percent composition, you can use the number of moles to find the molecular formula.

Safety

Gas cylinders should always be securely strapped to the wall or to the cart on which they are transported.

If you could evaluate the constant $(P \times V)/(T \times n)$, you could then calculate the number of moles of gas at any specified conditions of P, V, and T.

If you are told that 1 mol of every gas occupies 22.4 L at STP, you have sufficient information to evaluate the constant. Inserting the values of P, V, T, and n into the equation, you obtain a constant.

$$\frac{P_1 \times V_1}{T_1 \times n_1} = \frac{101.3\text{ kPa} \times 22.4\text{ L}}{273\text{ K} \times 1\text{ mol}} = 8.31\text{ (L} \times \text{kPa)/(K} \times \text{mol)}$$

The **ideal gas constant** *(R) is 8.31 (L × kPa)/(K × mol). Rearranging the equation for* R *and dropping the subscripts, you obtain the usual form of the* **ideal gas law**.

$$\frac{P \times V}{T \times n} = R$$

or

$$P \times V = n \times R \times T$$

An obvious advantage of the ideal gas law over the combined gas law is that it permits you to solve for the number of moles of a contained gas when P, V, and T are known.

Example 5 Ideal Gas Law Calculations

You fill a rigid steel cylinder with a volume of 20.0 L with nitrogen gas to a final pressure of 20 000 kPa at 27°C. How many moles of N_2 gas does the cylinder contain?

Solution

First you convert degrees Celsius to kelvins.

$$27°\text{C} + 273 = 300\text{ K}$$

The conditions are $P = 20\,000$ kPa, $V = 20.0$ L, and $T = 300$ K. Because you want to find the number of moles of N_2 gas, you may rearrange the ideal gas law to obtain n.

$$n = \frac{P \times V}{R \times T}$$

Now you can substitute the known quantities into the equation.

$$n = \frac{20\,000\,\cancel{\text{kPa}} \times 20.0\,\cancel{\text{L}}}{8.31\,\frac{\cancel{\text{L}} \times \cancel{\text{kPa}}}{\cancel{\text{K}} \times \text{mol}} \times 300\,\cancel{\text{K}}} = 160\text{ mol}$$

Example 6 Finding Moles of a Gas with the Ideal Gas Law

A deep underground cavern contains 2.24×10^6 L of methane gas at a pressure of 1500 kPa and a temperature of 42°C. How many kilograms of methane does this gas deposit contain?

Solution

The problem calls for an answer in kilograms, but the ideal gas law permits you to obtain the solution only in moles. You must first find the number of moles of methane, then convert to kilograms.

You know that $P = 1500$ kPa, $V = 2.24 \times 10^6$ L, and $T = 315$ K (42°C + 273). As in the previous example, you substitute the known quantities into the equation.

$$n = \frac{P \times V}{R \times T}$$

$$n = \frac{1.5 \times 10^3 \cancel{\text{kPa}} \times (2.24 \times 10^6 \text{ L})}{8.31 \frac{\cancel{\text{L}} \times \cancel{\text{kPa}}}{\cancel{\text{K}} \times \text{mol}} \times 315 \cancel{\text{K}}}$$

The cavern contains 1.28×10^6 mol of methane. One mole of methane has a mass of 16.0 g (C = 12.0 g; 4 H = 4.0 g). A mole–mass conversion gives the number of grams of methane.

$$1.28 \times 10^6 \cancel{\text{mol } CH_4} \times \frac{16.0 \text{ g } CH_4}{1 \cancel{\text{mol } CH_4}} = 20.5 \times 10^6$$

$$= 2.05 \times 10^7 \text{ g } CH_4(g)$$

$$= 2.05 \times 10^4 \text{ kg } CH_4(g)$$

The cavern contains 2.05×10^4 kg of methane gas.

Problem-Solving Tip

Break complex problems down into two simpler parts, and then put together the solutions to the simpler parts.

Practice Problems

13. When a rigid hollow sphere containing 680 L of helium gas is heated from 300 K to 600 K, the pressure of the gas increases to 1800 kPa. How many moles of helium are in the sphere?

14. A child has a lung capacity of 2.2 L. How many grams of air do her lungs hold at a pressure of 100 kPa and a normal body temperature of 37°C? Air is a mixture, but you may assume a molar mass of 29 g/mol for air because air is about 20% oxygen (molar mass of O_2 = 32) and 80% nitrogen (molar mass of N_2 = 28). Thus 0.20×32 g/mol + 0.80×28 g/mol = 29 g/mol.

11.A Science, Technology, and Society

Explosives

The road you take to school or work may have been carved through a rocky hillside by explosives. The coal burned at the power plant that makes your electricity may have been blasted from a seam kilometers below the earth's surface. You have probably enjoyed bright, noisy fireworks on Independence Day or during Chinese New Year.

An explosion is an extremely rapid combustion or decomposition reaction that produces gaseous products and heat. The most forceful explosions occur when liquid or solid reactants are instantaneously converted to gases. The volume of the gases produced will be much larger than the volume of the reactants. If the gases are confined, the resultant pressure will be great. Furthermore, the heat given off will increase this pressure. If the reaction is fast enough, however, the pressure will build up even if the gases are not confined. When the gas expands, the resulting release of pressure causes a shock wave. The kinetic energy of this "wave," the wind that follows it, and the heat from the reaction are the destructive forces of the explosion.

Figure 11.14 Properly sized explosive charges and precise timing are required for the controlled demolition of this building within the confined space of a city block.

An explosion reaction involves a fuel and an oxidizer. If the oxidizer is separate from the fuel, the reaction is called combustion. An example is the combustion of methane.

$$CH_4(g) + 2O_2(g) \longrightarrow CO_2(g) + 2H_2O(g) + \text{heat}$$

Such an explosion could occur if natural gas leaked into a building and was subsequently ignited by a spark or flame. If the fuel is its own oxidizer, a decomposition reaction takes place. An example of this type of explosive is nitroglycerine, $C_3H_5O_9N_3$. This compound is a thick, pale, oily liquid. It decomposes to give a variable mixture of products such as CO, CO_2, H_2O, and nitrogen oxides.

Some highly explosive materials that are fuel and oxidizer in one, like nitroglycerine, are unstable. Even jarring them may be enough to cause detonation. Mixing diatomaceous earth with nitroglycerine helps make it less shock sensitive. However, the mixture of nitroglycerine and diatomaceous earth is as explosive as the pure liquid. Ordinarily the mixture, called dynamite, can be set off only by using a blasting cap. Dynamite is one of the most widely used explosives because it can be handled relatively safely.

Safety

If you notice a strong odor of gas, air out the room and have the gas lines checked for leaks before lighting a flame or using an electrical switch.

Think About It

15. Describe What are the characteristics of a chemical reaction that make it an *explosive* reaction?

11.9 Dalton's Law of Partial Pressures

Objective

Calculate the total pressure of a mixture of gases or the partial pressure of a gas in a mixture of gases.

Many gases, including air, are mixtures. Table 11.1 gives the composition of dry air. The particles in any gas at the same temperature have the same average kinetic energy. Gas pressure depends only on the number of gas particles in a given volume and their average kinetic energy. You can add the individual pressures exerted by each gas in a mixture and get the total gas pressure. *The contribution each gas in a mixture makes to the total pressure is the* **partial pressure** *exerted by that gas.* In a mixture of gases the total pressure is the sum of the partial pressures of the gases. Count the number of particles in the three containers on the left in Figure 11.15. What are the relative partial pressures of the gases in these containers? What must be the total relative pressure in the container on the right?

$$P_{total} = P_1 + P_2 + P_3$$

This equation is one mathematical form of **Dalton's law of partial pressures**: *At constant volume and temperature, the total pressure exerted by a mixture of gases is equal to the sum of the partial pressures of the component gases.*

Table 11.1 Composition of Dry Air

Component	Volume (%)	Partial pressure (kPa)
Nitrogen	78.08	79.11
Oxygen	20.95	21.22
Carbon dioxide	0.04	0.04
Argon and others	0.93	0.95
	100.00	101.32

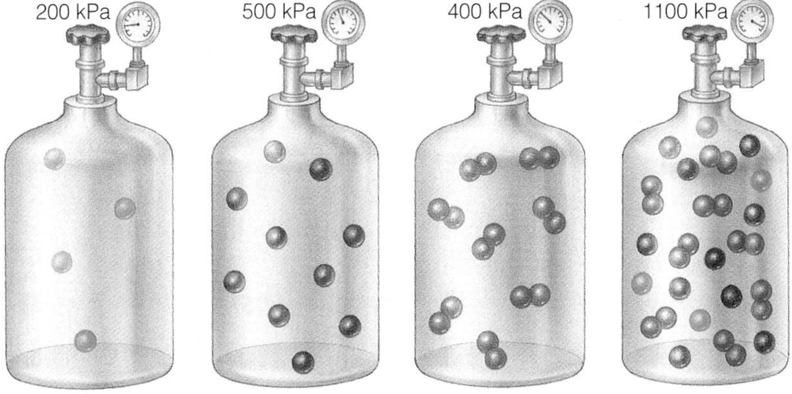

Figure 11.15 The sum of the pressures exerted by the gas in each container is the same as the total pressure exerted by a mixture of the gases in the same volume as long as the temperature stays the same. Dalton's law of partial pressures holds because each gas exerts its own pressure independent of the pressure exerted by other gases.

Figure 11.16 Why must high-altitude pilots have a separate oxygen supply available?

The proportionate pressure exerted by each gas in a mixture does not change as the temperature, pressure, or volume changes. This fact has important implications for airplane pilots and mountain climbers. When the total atmospheric pressure is reduced to 34 kPa, as it is atop Mount Everest, the partial pressure of oxygen is reduced to 7.1 kPa. This is one-third the partial pressure of oxygen at sea level. This reduced oxygen pressure is insufficient for respiration. Breathing air with a P_{O_2} of about 11 kPa supplies the minimum amount of oxygen that you can tolerate. Like the pilot in Figure 11.16, sometimes people in airplanes or on mountaineering expeditions need to supplement their oxygen intake.

Example 7 Using Dalton's Law of Partial Pressures

Air contains oxygen, nitrogen, carbon dioxide, and trace amounts of other gases. What is the partial pressure of oxygen (P_{O_2}) at 101.30 kPa of pressure if P_{N_2} = 79.10 kPa, P_{CO_2} = 0.040 kPa, and P_{others} = 0.94 kPa?

Solution

You know that P_{total} = 101.3 kPa.

$$P_{total} = P_{O_2} + P_{N_2} + P_{CO_2} + P_{others}$$

$$\begin{aligned} P_{O_2} &= P_{total} - (P_{N_2} + P_{CO_2} + P_{others}) \\ &= 101.30 \text{ kPa} - (79.10 \text{ kPa} + 0.040 \text{ kPa} + 0.94 \text{ kPa}) \\ &= 21.22 \text{ kPa} \end{aligned}$$

Concept Practice

16. How would the number of particles of two gases compare if their partial pressures in a container were identical?

Practice Problems

17. Determine the total pressure of a gas mixture that contains oxygen, nitrogen, and helium if the partial pressures of the gases are P_{O_2} = 20.0 kPa, P_{N_2} = 46.7 kPa, and P_{He} = 26.7 kPa.

18. A balloon contains mostly helium and a little methane. The partial pressure of helium is 101.2 kPa. If the pressure inside the balloon is 101.30 kPa, what is the partial pressure of methane?

11.10 Avogadro's Hypothesis

Objective

Explain, using kinetic theory, why equal volumes of gases contain the same number of particles at the same conditions of temperature and pressure.

What would you think of a hypothesis that stated that two rooms of the same size could be filled by the same number of objects, no matter whether the objects were marbles or oranges? You probably wouldn't believe it. Disbelief was the reaction of many scientists to Avogadro's hypothesis in 1811. These scientists knew that particles that make up different gases must have different sizes. For example, chlorine molecules have large numbers of electrons, protons, and neutrons. They must be bigger and occupy more volume than hydrogen molecules, which have only two protons and two electrons. *However, according to* **Avogadro's hypothesis**, *equal volumes of gases at the same temperature and pressure contain equal numbers of particles.* How could this be so?

What Avogadro had in mind is not so mysterious. His idea makes sense if the particles in a gas are very far apart with a lot of space in between. You can suspend ten marbles or ten oranges in a ballroom without decreasing the volume of the room very much. If you put the marbles or oranges into motion, they would occasionally collide with one another or with the walls of the room. On the average, however, there would be large expanses of space between them. The same concept can be applied to gases, as shown in Figure 11.17. This was Avogadro's great insight, and it is easily demonstrated by experiment. At STP, 1 mol (6.02×10^{23} particles) of any gas, regardless of the size of the particles, occupies 22.4 L.

You can also understand Avogadro's hypothesis by thinking of the modern explanation for gas pressure. The same number of particles of different gases in a given volume at the same temperature should exert the same pressure. This is because the particles have the same average kinetic energy and are contained within equal volumes. *Whenever you have equal volumes of gases at the same temperature and pressure, the volumes must contain equal numbers of particles.*

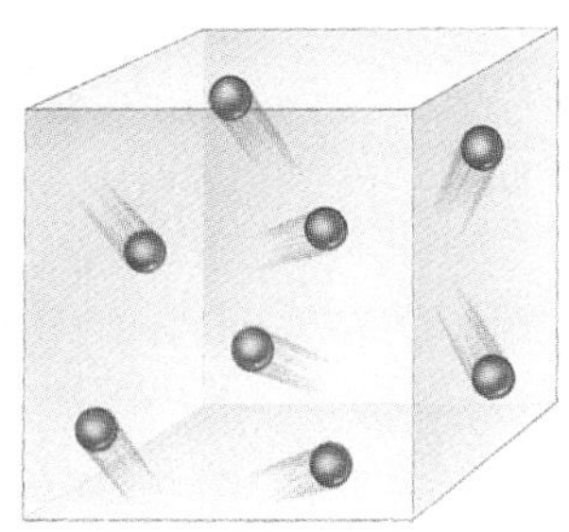

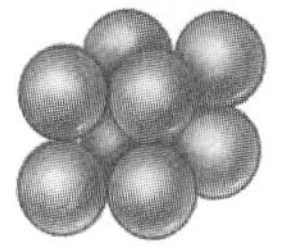

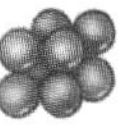

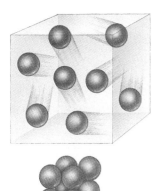

Figure 11.17 The volume of a container easily accommodates the same number of rapidly moving large or small particles as long as the particles are not tightly packed. When the particles are tightly packed, large particles take up more space than small particles.

Example 8 Applying Avogadro's Hypothesis

Determine the volume, in liters, occupied by 0.202 mol of a gas at STP.

Solution

You know that 1 mol of a gas at STP has a volume of 22.4 L. Thus, the problem can be solved by dimensional analysis.

$$0.202\ \cancel{\text{mol}} \times \frac{22.4\ \text{L}}{1\ \cancel{\text{mol}}} = 4.52\ \text{L}$$

Example 9 Calculating Molecules in a Given Volume of a Gas

How many oxygen molecules are in 3.36 L of oxygen gas at STP?

Solution

You use Avogadro's number and Avogadro's hypothesis to solve this problem. At STP, 22.4 L of oxygen contains 1 mol. One mole of oxygen contains 6.02×10^{23} oxygen molecules.

Problem-Solving Tip

Converting the unit of a measurement is conveniently done by dimensional analysis.

$$3.36\ \text{L}\ \cancel{O_2(g)} \times \frac{1\ \cancel{\text{mol}\ O_2(g)}}{22.4\ \cancel{\text{L}\ O_2(g)}} \times \frac{6.02 \times 10^{23}\ \text{molecules}\ O_2(g)}{1\ \cancel{\text{mol}\ O_2(g)}}$$

$$= 9.03 \times 10^{22}\ \text{molecules}\ O_2(g)$$

Example 10 Finding the Volume of a Given Mass of a Gas

Determine the volume of liters occupied by 14.0 g of nitrogen gas at STP.

Solution

Nitrogen is a diatomic molecule (N_2). One mole of nitrogen gas has a mass of 28.0 g and occupies a volume of 22.4 L at STP.

$$14.0\ \text{g}\ \cancel{N_2(g)} \times \frac{1\ \cancel{\text{mol}\ N_2(g)}}{28.0\ \cancel{\text{g}\ N_2(g)}} \times \frac{22.4\ \text{L}\ N_2(g)}{1\ \cancel{\text{mol}\ N_2(g)}} = 11.2\ \text{L}\ N_2(g)$$

Concept Practice

19. Briefly, in your own words, explain Avogadro's hypothesis.

20. What is the significance of the volume 22.4 L at STP?

Practice Problems

21. How many moles does 11.2 L of hydrogen gas contain at STP? How many particles (hydrogen molecules) does it contain?

22. What is the volume occupied by 0.25 mol of a gas at STP?

23. What is the volume of a container if it holds 8.8 g of carbon dioxide at STP?

Activity 11
Carbon Dioxide from Antacid Tablets

Purpose

To measure the amount of carbon dioxide gas given off when antacid tablets dissolve in water.

Materials

3 rubber balloons (round)

6 antacid tablets

tape measure

plastic eyedropper

water

graph paper

clock or watch

Procedure

1. Break an antacid tablet into small pieces and put them into one of the balloons. Put the pieces from two tablets into a second balloon. Repeat the procedure with pieces from three tablets and a third balloon.

2. Use the eyedropper to squirt about 5 mL of cold water into each balloon. Immediately, tie a knot in the neck of the balloon.

3. Shake the balloons to mix the contents and allow the balloons and contents to warm to room temperature.

4. Carefully, measure and record the circumference of each balloon several times during the next 20 minutes.

5. Use the maximum circumference of each balloon to calculate the volume of each balloon. Assume the balloons are spherical. (Tip: volume of a sphere = $\frac{4\pi r^3}{3}$.)

6. Plot a graph with number of tablets along the x axis and the volume on the y axis.

Analysis and Conclusions

1. According to your graph, what is the relationship between the number of tablets used and the volume of the balloon?

2. Assume the balloon is filled with carbon dioxide gas at 20°C and standard pressure. Calculate the mass and the number of moles of CO_2 in each balloon at maximum inflation.

3. If a typical antacid tablet contains 2.0 g of sodium hydrogen carbonate, show how your carbon dioxide result compares with the theoretical value.

Objective

Explain, using kinetic theory, why molecules of small mass diffuse more rapidly than molecules of large mass.

Roots of Words

diffusus: (Latin) spread out
diffusion the tendency of molecules and ions to move toward areas of lower concentration until it is uniform

Aromatic molecules diffuse through the kitchen.

effusus: (Latin) pour out
effusion the process of gas escaping through a small hole

Piercing a basketball with a pin causes the air to effuse.

11.11 Diffusion and Graham's Law

When you open a perfume bottle, perfume molecules eventually diffuse throughout a room. **Diffusion** *is the tendency of molecules and ions to move toward areas of lower concentration until the concentration is uniform throughout the system.* Look at Figure 11.18. Bromine vapor is a reddish color and bromine diffuses readily in air.

Much of the early work on diffusion was done in the 1840s by the Scottish chemist Thomas Graham (1805–1869). Graham actually measured the rates of **effusion**, *which occurs as a gas escapes through a tiny hole in a container of gas.* Graham noticed that lower-molecular-mass gases effuse faster than gases with a higher formula mass. From his observations, he proposed **Graham's law of effusion**: *The rate of effusion of a gas is inversely proportional to the square root of its molar mass.* Subsequently, this relationship was also shown to be true for the diffusion of gases. *The rate of diffusion of a gas is inversely proportional to the square root of its molar mass.*

You can understand Graham's law by examining the relationship of the mass and speed of a moving body to the force the body exerts when it strikes a stationary object. The mathematical expression that relates the mass (m) and the speed or velocity (v) of an object to its kinetic energy (KE) is $KE = \frac{1}{2}mv^2$. The kinetic energy influences the force the body is capable of exerting. Suppose a ball

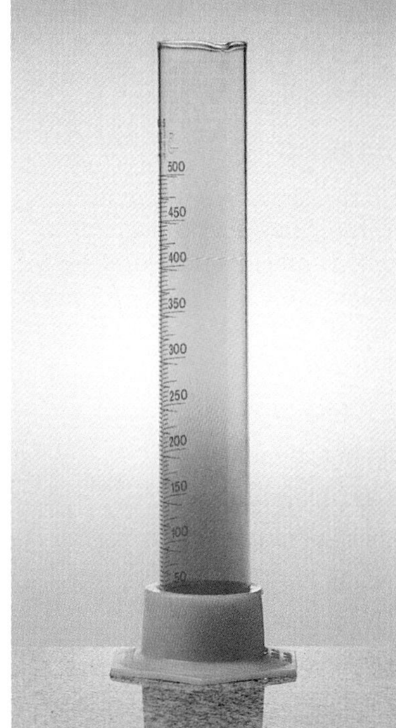

Figure 11.18 The diffusion of one substance through another is a relatively slow process. Here it took two hours for bromine vapors to diffuse into air outside the graduated cylinder.

bearing with a mass of 2 g traveling at 5 m/s has just enough kinetic energy to shatter a pane of glass. A ball bearing with a mass of 1 g would need to travel at slightly more than 7 m/s to have the same kinetic energy. The lighter ball bearing would therefore have to move faster to shatter the same pane of glass.

There is an important principle here. *When two bodies of different mass have the same kinetic energy, the lighter body moves faster.* The particles in two gases at the same temperature have the same average kinetic energy. Thus a gas of low molar mass should diffuse faster than a gas of high molar mass at the same temperature. It is easy to show this is true by comparing two balloons, one filled with helium and the other filled with air. Balloons filled with air stay inflated longer. This is because the main components of air, oxygen molecules and nitrogen molecules, move more slowly and therefore diffuse more slowly than helium atoms. Fast-moving helium atoms, with molar masses of only 4 g, diffuse rapidly through small pores in the balloon. The pores are large enough for both helium atoms and air molecules to pass through freely. Thus the rate of diffusion is related only to the particle's speed.

In a mathematical form Graham's law can be written as follows:

$$\frac{\text{Rate}_A}{\text{Rate}_B} = \frac{\sqrt{\text{molar mass}_B}}{\sqrt{\text{molar mass}_A}}$$

That is, the rates of effusion of two gases are inversely proportional to the square roots of their formula masses. Now compare the rates of effusion of nitrogen (molar mass, 28.0 g) and helium (molar mass, 4.0 g).

$$\frac{\text{Rate}_{He}}{\text{Rate}_{N_2}} = \frac{\sqrt{28.0\text{ g}}}{\sqrt{4.0\text{ g}}} = \frac{5.3\text{ g}}{2.0\text{ g}} = 2.7$$

You see that helium effuses nearly three times faster than nitrogen at the same temperature.

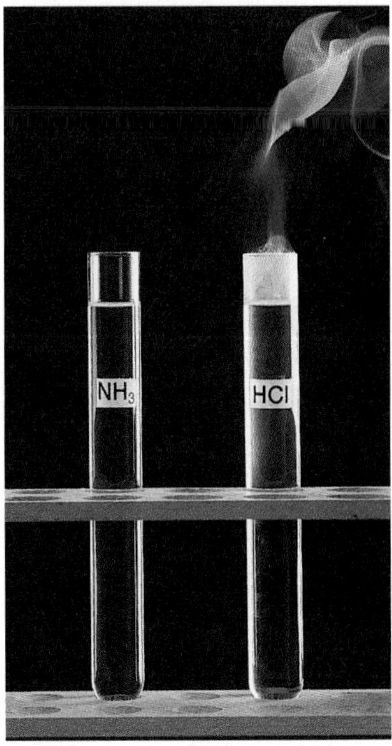

Figure 11.19 White vapors of ammonium chloride form as the vapors from test tubes containing ammonia (NH_3) and hydrochloric acid (HCl) diffuse into the air. Which molecule diffuses more quickly?

Concept Practice

24. At the same temperature the rates of diffusion of carbon monoxide and nitrogen gas are identical. Explain.

Practice Problem

25. Which gas effuses faster, hydrogen or chlorine? How much faster?

Objective

Distinguish between real and ideal gases.

11.12 Real Versus Ideal Gases

The previous discussions of kinetic theory and the gas laws assumed that the gases were ideal gases. An ideal gas is one that follows the gas laws at all conditions of pressure and temperature. With the kinetic theory it was assumed that the particles of a gas have no volume and that they are not attracted to each other at all. There is no gas for which this is true. An ideal gas does not exist. Nevertheless, at many conditions of temperature and pressure real gases behave like an ideal gas.

Real gases can be liquefied and sometimes solidified by cooling and applying pressure. Ideal gases cannot. For example, when water vapor is cooled below 100°C, it condenses to a liquid at atmospheric pressure. The behavior of other real gases is similar, although lower temperatures and greater pressures may be required. You may recall that carbon dioxide goes from a gas to a solid without passing through the liquid state. The product is solid carbon dioxide, or "dry ice." Conversely, upon warming, solid carbon dioxide passes from the solid state to the gaseous state without passing through the liquid state. This by-pass of the liquid state is shown in Figure 11.20 and is an example of sublimation.

Figure 11.20 Solid carbon dioxide is known as dry ice. It can injure the skin because it is much colder (–78.5°C) than frozen water. Why is dry ice not as messy to use as regular ice?

Concept Practice

26. Why is it impossible for an *ideal* gas to exist?

27. Give an example of a real gas and its properties.

Objective

Explain why no gas behaves as an ideal gas at all temperatures and pressures.

11.13 Departures from the Gas Laws

A gas that adheres to the gas laws at some conditions of temperature and pressure is said to exhibit ideal behavior. No gas behaves ideally, however, at all temperatures and pressures.

At any pressure the ideal gas law gives this ratio for an ideal gas: $(P \times V)/(n \times R \times T) = 1$. This constant ratio plotted against pressure gives a horizontal line. For several real gases at high pressures, $(P \times V)/(n \times R \times T)$ departs widely from the ideal. The ratio may be greater or less than one; the deviation may be positive (above the line) or negative (below the line). The explanation for these departures or deviations from ideality is based on two different factors. These are the attractions between molecules and the volume of gas molecules.

Simple kinetic theory assumes that gas particles are not attracted to each other and that gas particles have no volume. These assumptions are incorrect. Gases and vapors could not be liquefied if there were no attractions between molecules. Of course, real gas particles do have a volume and so they must also occupy space, as Figure 11.22 illustrates. Furthermore, intermolecular forces tend to hold the particles in a gas together. This effectively reduces the distance between particles. The gas therefore occupies less volume than is assumed by the kinetic theory, and $(P\times V)/(n\times R\times T)$ tends to be less than one. At the same time, the molecules themselves occupy some volume and $(P \times V)/(n \times R \times T)$ tends to become greater than one. One or the other of these effects will usually dominate. Look at Figure 11.21. In portions of the curves below the line, the intermolecular attractions dominate. In portions of the curves above the line, the effect of volume of the molecules dominates. The temperature of the gas determines which of these two effects is the dominant one.

Compare the curves for $CH_4(g)$ at 0°C and 200°C. At 0°C the methane molecules are moving relatively slowly. The attractions between the molecules are sufficiently strong that, at the lower pressures, the curve is below the $(P \times V)/(n \times R \times T) = 1$ line. At higher pressures, the space between the molecules is reduced. The actual physical volume of the methane molecules now becomes important, and the curve is above the $(P\times V)/(n\times R\times T) = 1$ line. Raising the temperature to 200°C increases the average kinetic energy of the methane molecules sufficiently to overcome weak attractive effects when the molecules collide. Thus $(P\times V)/(n\times R\times T)$ is near one at lower pressures. The ratio increases to greater than one as the volume of the gas particles becomes important.

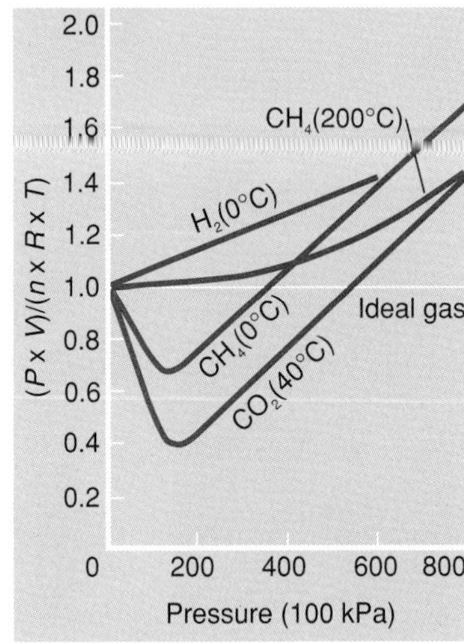

Figure 11.21 For an ideal gas, $(P\times V)/(n\times R\times T)$ always equals 1. By contrast, real gases deviate from ideality. What is the value of $(P\times V)/(n\times R\times T)$ for CO_2 at 40°C and 10 000 kPa?

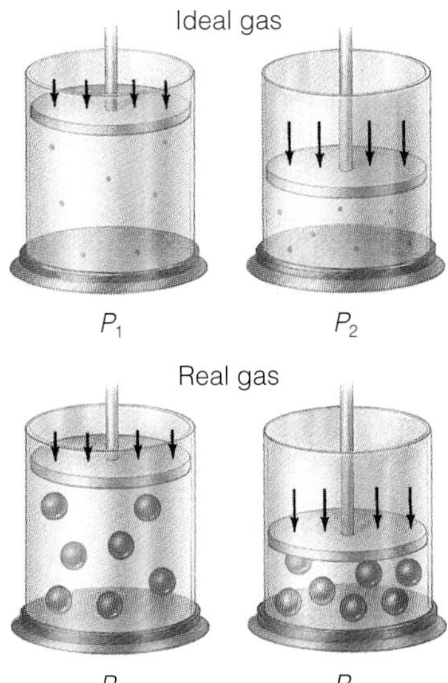

Figure 11.22 As pressure increases, the volume occupied by gas molecules is no longer negligible.

Concept Practice

28. Why do real gases deviate from ideal behavior?

Practice Problem

29. Small gas molecules such as $N_2(g)$ and $O_2(g)$ give the expected molar volumes of 22.41 L at STP. The nonideal behavior of gases is not limited, however, to extreme pressures and temperatures. The molar volumes of $CH_4(g)$, $CO_2(g)$, and $NH_3(g)$ are respectively 22.37 L, 22.26 L, and 22.06 L under the same conditions. Explain the reasons for these departures from ideality.

11.B Science, Technology, and Society

Scuba Diving and the Gas Laws

Figure 11.23 The self-contained underwater breathing apparatus (scuba), also called the aqualung, enables divers to explore freely the depths of the oceans.

In 1943 Jacques Cousteau and Emile Gagnan invented scuba: a self-contained underwater breathing apparatus. No longer did divers need to be tethered to the surface by air hoses. The increased maneuverability and convenience of scuba gear gave rise to the sport of scuba diving. It also greatly increased the use of diving for scientific research.

All divers must have a good understanding of the science involved in order to dive safely. At the water's surface, the pressure on your body due to the mass of air around you is about 100 kPa. Under water, the pressure increases because of the added mass of the water. Every 10 m of depth adds 100 kPa. Thus the total pressure on your body at a depth of 10 m will be 200 kPa, at 20 m it will be 300 kPa, and so on. At around 40 m the pressure on your chest would make it impossible for you to inflate your lungs to breathe. If the pressure in your lungs had also increased as you went down, however, you would be able to breathe normally. Scuba equipment provides air to the lungs at a pressure to match that of the underwater environment. This enables the diver to breathe comfortably.

According to Boyle's law, the 6–7 L of air in the lungs will expand to three times its volume if the pressure is reduced from 300 kPa to 100 kPa. So, if a diver ascends to the surface without exhaling along the way, the air held in the lungs will expand as the external pressure drops. The increase in volume can rupture the lungs.

Decompression sickness, or the "bends," is explained by another important gas law. The solubility of a gas in a liquid is proportional to the pressure of the gas above the liquid. A diver is breathing air at higher than atmospheric pressure. Thus the nitrogen in the air will be more soluble in the diver's blood. When the pressure drops as the diver ascends, the nitrogen again becomes less soluble. If the drop in pressure occurs too rapidly, the nitrogen will come out of the blood in the form of tiny bubbles, just like the bubbles that form when you open a carbonated drink. If nitrogen bubbles form in the joints of muscles, they cause a great deal of pain. They can cause paralysis or death. Decompression sickness can be prevented by ascending from a dive slowly.

Figure 11.24 Scuba divers must be careful not to stay down too long or to ascend too rapidly.

Think About It

30. Interpret How does scuba equipment make it possible for a diver to breathe comfortably under water?

31. Describe Name two dangers of a too-rapid ascent.

Aerogels

Conspicuous by Their Absence

Aerogels are among the lowest-density solids known. What makes aerogels such remarkable materials is that they are almost totally lacking in substance! One type of aerogel called a silica aerogel looks a lot like a puff of smoke hovering above a desk top. But, unlike a puff of smoke, it is surprisingly firm to the touch.

A silica aerogel consists of a spongelike framework of silicon and oxygen atoms joined together to form long, randomly linked strands. The spaces between the strands are filled with air. This makes silica aerogels extremely light and porous. Some silica aerogels are only about four times denser than air, but the molecular framework gives the materials physical substance and makes them visible to the eye. Silica aerogels have remarkable strength, supporting up to 1600 times their own weight.

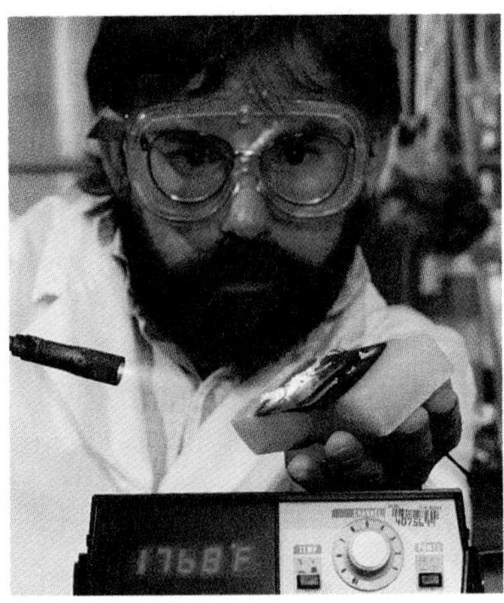

Silica aerogels are amazing insulators! This chemist has only a piece of silica aerogel between his hand and the propane torch.

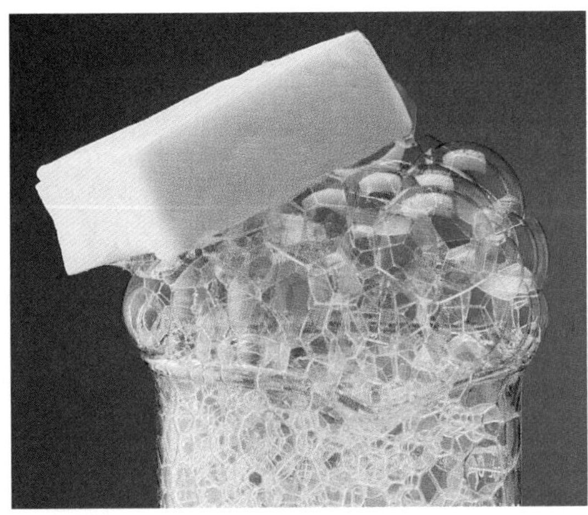

"It's basically like a fog, a heavy air, but yet it has substance to it, so you can stack coins on it."

Thomas Tillotson, Lawrence Livermore National Laboratories, Livermore, CA

Another aerogel that scientists at Lawrence Livermore National Laboratories have developed is the world's least dense material. Called SEAgel (Safe Emulsion Agar Gel), at its lowest density, it is less dense than air. In denser forms, it can be used as an inexpensive replacement for balsa wood, which is becoming scarce. SEAgel is processed from agar, a seaweed derivative used to thicken ice cream. The seaweed extract is dissolved in water, emulsified with an organic solvent, and then frozen and freeze-dried.

Aerogels have many potential commercial applications. They are the world's best insulating solids and have been used as refrigerator insulation. The current cost is about four times the cost of the conventional insulation. Within two years the cost of the energy saved would more than make up for the higher initial expense. Another benefit of aerogels is that they are environmentally benign. Much conventional insulation is made with CFCs (chlorofluorocarbons), compounds that have come under attack because they contribute to the depletion of the ozone layer. Aerogels could help to ease the CFC problem. SEAgel also has major environmental advantages over solid foam insulation materials because it is biodegradable and so nontoxic that you can eat it.

Think About It

32. Identify What is the most striking property of an aerogel?

33. Application What uses can you think of for aerogels?

Chapter 11 Review

The Behavior of Gases

Key Terms

Avogadro's hypothesis *11.10*
Boyle's law *11.3*
Charles's law *11.5*
combined gas law *11.7*
Dalton's law of partial pressures *11.9*
diffusion *11.11*
effusion *11.11*
Graham's law of effusion *11.11*
ideal gas constant (R) *11.8*
ideal gas law *11.8*
partial pressure *11.9*

Chapter Summary

Gases expand to fill any volume available to them. The collision of the particles in a gas with the walls of the container is gas pressure. Gas pressure is measured in kilopascals; at sea level the pressure of the atmosphere is 101.3 kPa.

The pressure and volume of a fixed mass of gas are inversely related. If one decreases, the other increases. This relationship is Boyle's law. The *pressure* of a fixed volume of gas is directly related to its Kelvin temperature; the *volume* of a gas at constant pressure is directly related to its Kelvin temperature (Charles's law). These three separate gas laws can be written as a single expression called the combined gas law. Another expression is the ideal gas law, $PV = nRT$, which relates the moles of a gas to its pressure, temperature, and volume. The letter R represents the ideal gas constant, $8.31(\text{L} \times \text{kPa})/(\text{K} \times \text{mol})$.

Avogadro proposed that there is a lot of space between gas particles. He stated that equal volumes of gases, at the same temperature and pressure, contain equal numbers of particles. At a pressure of 101.3 kPa and a temperature of 273 K (STP), the volume of 1 mol of any gas is 22.4 L. This is called the molar volume. Air is a mixture of gases, approximately 20% oxygen and 80% nitrogen. The total pressure in a mixture of gases is equal to the sum of the partial pressures of each gas present (Dalton's law). Gases diffuse from a region of high gas concentration to a region of lower gas concentration. The smaller the molar mass of a gas, the greater its rate of diffusion (Graham's law).

Practice Questions and Problems

34. A metal cylinder contains 1 mol of nitrogen gas at STP. What will happen to the pressure if another mole of gas is added to the cylinder but the temperature and volume do not change? *11.1*

35. If a gas is compressed from 4 L to 1 L and the temperature remains constant, what happens to the pressure? *11.2*

36. A gas with a volume of 4 L is allowed to expand to a volume of 12 L. What happens to the pressure in the container if the temperature remains constant? *11.2*

37. A gas with a volume of 4.0 L at a pressure of 90 kPa is allowed to expand until the pressure drops to 20 kPa. What is the new volume? *11.3*

38. A given mass of air has a volume of 6.0 L at 100 kPa. What volume will it occupy at a pressure of 25 kPa if the temperature does not change? *11.3*

39. Heating a contained gas at constant volume makes its pressure higher. Why? *11.4*

40. The gas in a container has a pressure of 300 kPa at 27°C (300 K). What will the pressure be if the temperature is lowered to −173°C (100 K)? *11.4*

41. Five liters of air at −50°C is warmed to 100°C. What is the new volume if the pressure remains constant? *11.5*

42. The pressure in an automobile tire is 200 kPa at a temperature of 27°C. At the end of a journey on a hot sunny day the pressure has risen to 223 kPa. What is the temperature of the air in the tire? (Assume that the volume has not changed.) *11.6*

43. State the combined gas law. *11.6*

44. A 5.0-L air sample at a temperature of –50°C has a pressure of 107 kPa. What will the new pressure be if the temperature is raised to 100°C and the volume expands to 7.0 L? *11.7*

45. What volume will 12.0 g of oxygen gas (O_2) occupy at 25°C and a pressure of 52.7 kPa? *11.8*

46. Calculate the number of liters occupied, at STP. *11.8*

  a. 2.5 mol $N_2(g)$

  b. 0.600 g $H_2(g)$

  c. 0.350 mol $O_2(g)$

47. What pressure will be exerted by 0.450 mol of a gas at 25°C if it is contained in a vessel whose volume is 0.65 L? *11.8*

48. What physical changes happen during the chemical reaction of an explosion? *11.A*

49. A gas mixture contains oxygen, nitrogen, and carbon dioxide at 32.9 kPa. If P_{O_2} = 6.6 kPa and P_{N_2} = 23.0 kPa, what is P_{CO_2}? *11.9*

50. What does STP represent? *11.10*

51. A gas has a volume of 2.24 L at STP. How many moles of gas is this? *11.10*

52. Which gas effuses faster at the same temperature: molecular oxygen or atomic argon? *11.11*

53. Calculate the ratio of the velocity of helium atoms to that of neon atoms at the same temperature. *11.11*

54. Calculate the velocity ratio of helium and fluorine molecules at the same temperature. *11.11*

55. Describe an *ideal* gas. *11.12*

56. Determine the volume occupied by 0.582 mol of a gas at 15°C if the pressure is 81.8 kPa. *11.13*

57. No gas exhibits ideal behavior at all temperatures and pressures. Explain the meaning of this statement. *11.13*

58. At a depth of 15 m, what is the external pressure on a scuba diver's body? *11.B*

Mastery Questions and Problems

59. Construct a concept map using the ideal gas law as the central concept. Use the key terms for the chapter and appropriate equations.

60. If 4.50 g of methane gas (CH_4) is introduced into an evacuated 2.00-L container at 35°C, what is the pressure in the container?

61. A gas with a volume of 300 mL at 150°C is heated until its volume is 600 mL. What is the new temperature of the gas if the pressure is unaltered?

62. Under what conditions do real gases behave like ideal gases? Why?

63. A 5.00-L flask, at 25°C, contains 0.200 mol of Cl_2. What is the pressure in the flask?

64. A certain gas effuses four times as fast as oxygen, O_2. What is its molar mass?

65. Calculate the volume of a gas in liters at 100 kPa if its volume at 120 kPa is 1500 mL.

66. A 3.50-L gas sample at 20°C and a pressure of 86.7 kPa is allowed to expand to a volume of 8.00 L. The final pressure of the gas is 56.7 kPa. What is the final temperature of the gas in degrees Celsius?

67. Samples of neon and helium are placed in separate containers connected by a pinched rubber tube as shown below. When the clamp is removed from the rubber tube and the gases are allowed to mix, what are the partial pressure of each gas and the total pressure of the gas mixture? Assume that the volume of the rubber tubing connecting the containers is negligible.

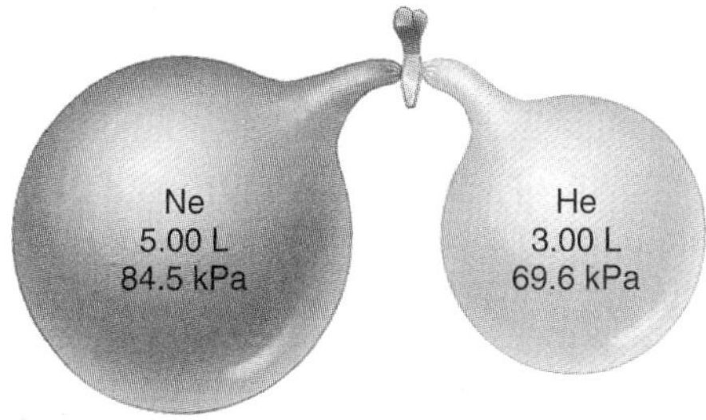

68. A gas cylinder contains nitrogen gas at 1000 kPa pressure and a temperature of 20°C. The cylinder is left in the sun, and the temperature of the gas increases to 50°C. What is the pressure in the cylinder?

69. During an effusion experiment, it took 75 seconds for a certain number of moles of an unknown gas to pass through a tiny hole. Under the same conditions, the same number of moles of oxygen gas passed through the hole in 30 seconds. What is the molar mass of the unknown gas?

Critical Thinking Questions

70. Choose the term that best completes the second relationship.

a. ideal gas:real gas fiction: _____

(1) biography (3) movie

(2) novel (4) nonfiction

b. Charles's law:temperature Boyle's law:_____

(1) pressure (3) ideal mass

(2) volume (4) mass

71. Gases will expand to fill a vacuum. Why do the earth's atmospheric gases not escape into the near-vacuum of space?

72. How does the vacuum used in thermos bottles and Dewar flasks prevent heat transfer?

73. What real gas comes closest to having the characteristics of an ideal gas? Why?

Cumulative Review

74. Calculate the molar mass of each of these substances.

a. $Ca(CH_3CO_2)_2$

b. H_3PO_4

c. $C_{12}H_{22}O_{11}$

d. $Pb(NO_3)_2$

75. Name these compounds.

a. $SnBr_2$ **b.** $BaSO_4$ **c.** $Mg(OH)_2$ **d.** IF_5

76. An atom of lead-206 weighs 17.16 times as much as an atom of carbon.

a. What is the molar mass of this isotope of lead?

b. How many protons, electrons, and neutrons are in this atom of lead?

77. Write a balanced equation for each of these chemical reactions.

a. Calcium reacts with water to form calcium hydroxide and hydrogen gas.

b. Tetraphosphorus decoxide reacts with water to form phosphoric acid.

c. Mercury and oxygen are prepared by heating mercury(II) oxide.

d. Aluminum hydroxide and hydrogen sulfide form when aluminum sulfide reacts with water.

78. How many kilojoules and kcal of heat are required to raise 40.0 g of water from –12°C to 130°C?

79. Classify each of the reactions in Problem 77 as to type.

80. Calculate the molecular formula of each of these compounds.

a. The empirical formula is C_2H_4O and the gmm = 88 g/mol.

b. The empirical formula is CH and the gmm = 104 g/mol.

c. The gmm = 90 g/mol. The percent composition is 26.7% C, 71.1% O, and 2.2% H.

81. A piece of metal has a mass of 9.92 g and measures 4.5 cm × 1.3 cm × 1.6 mm. What is the density of the metal?

82. Calculate the percent composition of 2-propanol, C_3H_7OH.

83. Aluminum oxide is formed from its elements.

$$Al(s) + O_2(g) \longrightarrow Al_2O_3(s)$$

a. Balance the equation.

b. How many grams of each reactant are needed to form 583 g of $Al_2O_3(s)$?

Challenge Questions and Problems

84. A mixture of ethyne, $C_2H_2(g)$, and methane, $CH_4(g)$, occupied a certain volume at a total pressure of 16.8 kPa. Upon burning the sample to form $CO_2(g)$ and $H_2O(g)$, the $CO_2(g)$ was collected and its pressure found to be 25.6 kPa in the same volume and at the same temperature as the original mixture. What percent of the original mixture was methane?

85. A 0.10-L container holds 3.0×10^{20} molecules of H_2 at 100 kPa and 0°C.

a. If the volume of a hydrogen molecule is 6.7×10^{-24} mL, what percent of the volume of the gas is occupied by its molecules?

b. If the pressure is increased to 100 000 kPa, the volume of the gas is 1×10^{-4} L. What fraction of the total volume do the hydrogen molecules now occupy?

86. Oxygen is produced in the laboratory by heating potassium nitrate, KNO_3. Use the data table below, which gives the volume of oxygen produced at STP from varying quantities of KNO_3, to determine the mole ratio by which KNO_3 and O_2 react.

Mass of KNO_3 (g)	Volume of O_2 (cL)
0.84	9.3
1.36	15.1
2.77	30.7
4.82	53.5
6.96	77.3

87. The following reaction takes place in a sealed 40.0-L container at a temperature of 120°C.

$$4NH_3(g) + 5O_2(g) \longrightarrow 4NO(g) + 6H_2O(g)$$

a. When 34.0 g of $NH_3(g)$ reacts with 96.0 g of $O_2(g)$, what is the partial pressure of $NO(g)$ in the container?

b. What is the total pressure in the container?

Connections Questions

88. What was Robert Boyle's greatest contribution to chemistry?

89. What is the purpose of the refrigerant in a refrigerator?

90. What is the function of a cryostat?

Write About Chemistry

91. Imagine taking a ride in a hot-air balloon. Write a letter to a friend describing how the balloon is kept aloft.

92. Suppose you are one of a group of nitrogen molecules, N_2, at 100°C. Describe what happens to you and your companions as the temperature is lowered to near absolute zero.

Readings and References

Linner-Luebe, Marilyn. "Hydrogen and Helium." *ChemMatters* (October 1985), pp. 4–7.

Morris, Daniel Luzon. "Cooking with Steam." *ChemMatters* (February 1987), pp. 17–19.

12 Electrons in Atoms

Goals

- Compare Dalton's, Thomson's, Bohr's, and Schrödinger's models of the atom.
- Apply the Aufbau principle, Pauli exclusion principle, and Hund's rule in writing electron configurations for atoms.
- Describe the contributions of Planck, Einstein, Bohr, de Broglie, and Heisenberg to quantum theory.
- Explain the theory of atomic emission spectra using quantum theory.

The letter *M* shown here on the Great Mississippi River Bridge in Louisiana is comprised of 200 high-intensity sodium vapor lamps. This very long sign takes advantage of the behavior of electrons in sodium atoms.

Concept Overview

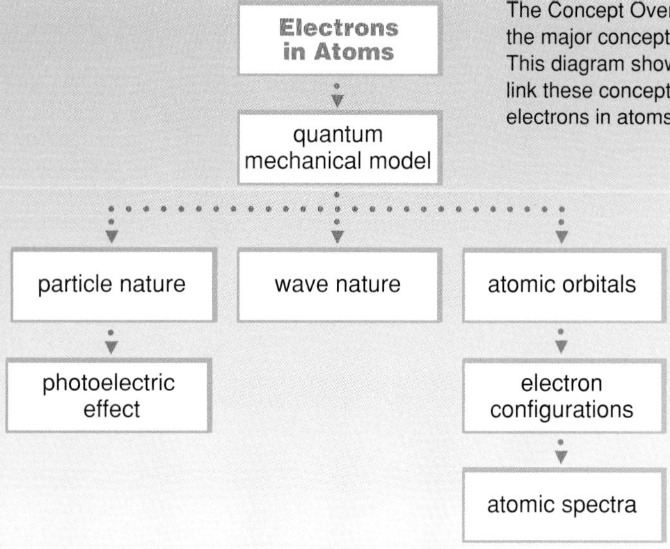

The Concept Overview organizes the major concepts of this chapter. This diagram shows one way to link these concepts related to electrons in atoms.

Thus far, the atomic model presented considered atoms as combinations of protons and neutrons that make up the nucleus. The nucleus is surrounded by electrons. This model has worked very well. However, this model of atomic structure has outlived its usefulness because it explains only a few simple properties of atoms. It does not tell you, for example, why metals or compounds of metals give off characteristic colors when heated in a flame. You need a more sophisticated model. As it turns out, the chemical properties of atoms, ions, and molecules are related to the arrangement of the electrons within them. Therefore, in this chapter you will again take up the subject of models of atomic structure with emphasis on the electrons in atoms.

12.1 The Development of Atomic Models

Objective

Summarize the development of atomic theory.

For about 50 years past the time of John Dalton (1766–1844), the atom was considered to be a solid indestructible mass. Dalton's atomic theory was a great advance in explaining the nature of chemical reactions. Dalton's theory included, however, the idea of indivisible atoms. The discovery of subatomic particles shattered every theory people had about indivisible atoms.

Figure 12.1 These drawings show how the model of the atom has changed as physicists have learned more about its structure.

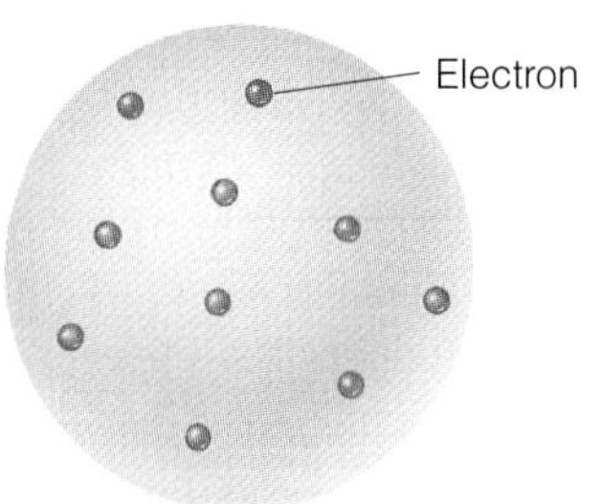

(a) Thomson model
In the nineteenth century, Thomson described the atom as a ball of positive charge containing a number of electrons.

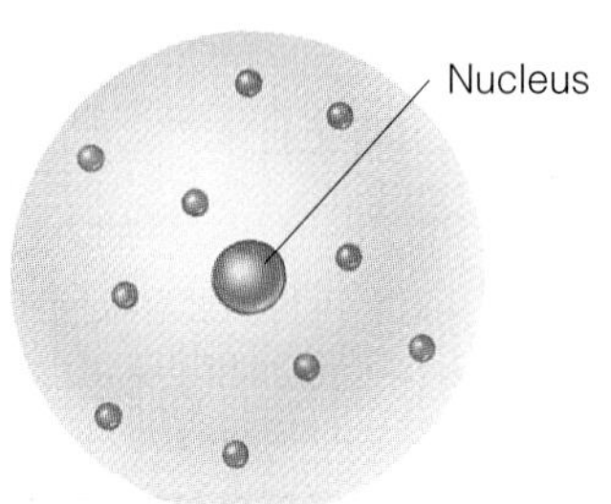

(b) Rutherford model
In the early twentieth century, Rutherford showed that most of an atom's mass is concentrated in a small, positively charged region called the nucleus.

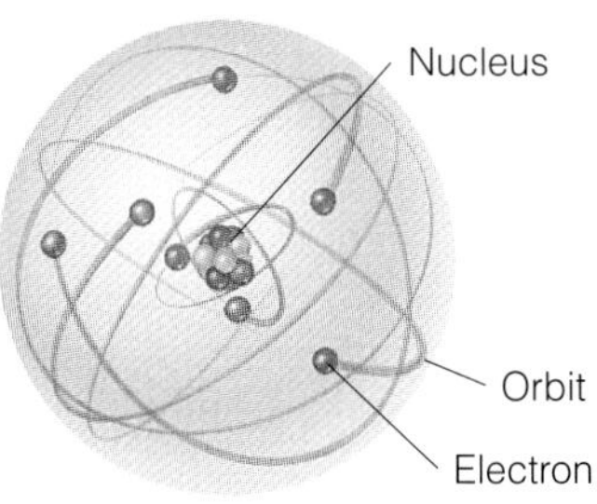

(c) Bohr model
Later, Bohr proposed that electrons travel around the nucleus in definite orbits.

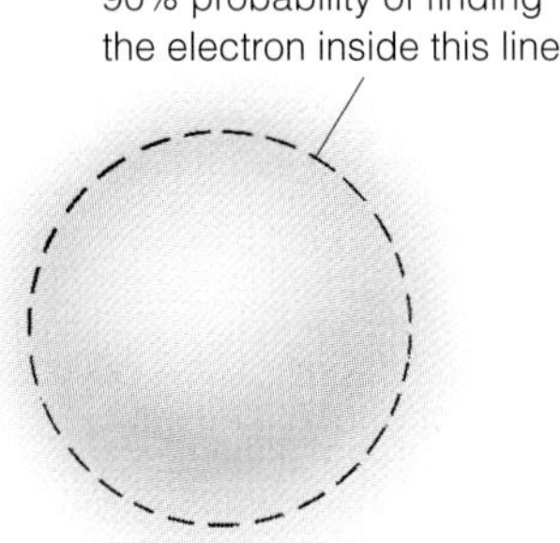

(d) Quantum mechanical model
Modern physicists maintain that the atom has no definite shape and that electrons do not have precise orbits.

The discoverer of the electron, Joseph John Thomson (1856–1940), realized that the accepted model of an indivisible atom did not take electrons and protons into account. Thomson therefore proposed a revised model that was referred to as the "plum pudding atom." Figure 12.1 shows this and other proposed models of the atom. The plum pudding atom had negatively charged electrons (raisins) stuck into a lump of positively charged protons (the dough). The plum pudding model explained some electrical properties of atoms. It said nothing, however, about the number of protons and neutrons, their arrangements in the atom, or the ease with which atoms are stripped of electrons to form ions.

Based on his discovery of the nucleus, Ernest Rutherford proposed the nuclear atom in which electrons surround a dense nucleus. He thought of the rest of the atom as empty space. Later experiments showed that the nuclei of atoms are composed of protons and neutrons.

Oppositely charged particles attract each other. Based on this, the negative electrons should be drawn into a positive nucleus. This would cause the atom to collapse. Given the Rutherford model, what prevents the electrons from falling into the nucleus?

In 1913 Niels Bohr (1885–1962), a young Danish physicist and a student of Rutherford's, came up with a new atomic model. He proposed that electrons are arranged in concentric circular paths, or orbits, around the nucleus. This model was patterned after the motions of the planets around the sun and is often referred to as the planetary model. Bohr answered in a novel way the question of what prevents electrons from falling into the nucleus. He proposed that the electrons in a particular path have a fixed energy. Thus they do not lose energy and fall into the nucleus. *The* **energy level** *of an electron is the region around the nucleus where the electron is likely to be moving.* The rungs of a ladder are analogous to the fixed energy levels of electrons, as Figure 12.2 illustrates. The lowest rung of the ladder corresponds to the lowest energy level. A person can climb up or down a ladder by going from rung to rung. Similarly, an electron can jump from one energy level to another. A person on a ladder cannot stand between the rungs. Similarly, the electrons in an atom cannot exist between energy levels. To move from one energy level to another, an electron must gain or lose just the right amount of energy. To move from one rung to another, a person climbing a ladder must move just the right distance.

A **quantum** *of energy is the amount of energy required to move an electron from its present energy level to the next higher one.* Thus the energies of electrons are said to be *quantized.* The term *quantum leap,* used to describe an abrupt change, comes from this concept. In general, the higher an electron is placed on the energy ladder, the farther from the nucleus it is.

The amount of energy gained or lost by every electron is not always the same. Unlike the rungs of a ladder, the energy levels in an atom are *not* equally spaced. In fact, the energy levels become more closely spaced the greater the distance from the nucleus. Instead of a ladder, you might prefer to think of the spacing of energy levels in terms of an escalator. On an escalator, the steps become closer together as you reach the top. It is easy to step off the escalator at the top. Similarly, the higher the energy level occupied by an electron, the easier it is for the electron to escape from the atom.

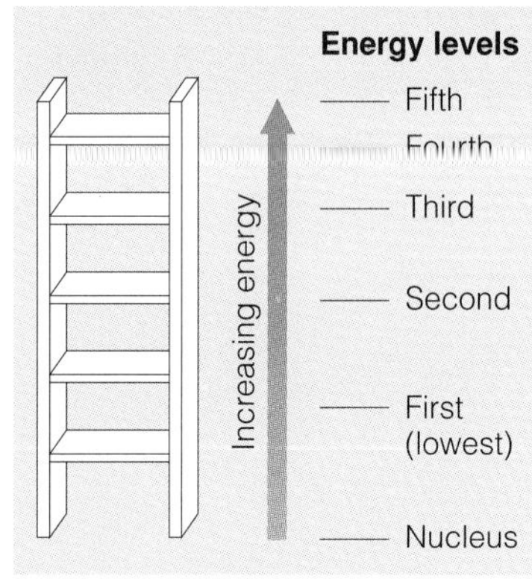

Figure 12.2 The rungs on a ladder are analogous to the energy levels in an atom. The higher the energy level occupied by the electron, the more energetic it is and the farther it usually is from the nucleus.

Concept Practice

1. Which subatomic particles did Thomson include in the "plum pudding" model of the atom?

2. How did Bohr answer the objection that an electron traveling in a circular orbit would radiate energy and fall into the nucleus?

Objective

Explain the significance of quantized energies and the quantum mechanical model of the atom.

12.2 The Quantum Mechanical Model of the Atom

In 1926 the Austrian physicist Erwin Schrödinger (1887–1961) took atomic models one step further. He used the new quantum theory to write and solve a mathematical equation describing the location and energy of an electron in a hydrogen atom. *The modern description of the electrons in atoms, the* **quantum mechanical model**, *comes from the mathematical solution to the Schrödinger equation.* Previous models were physical models based on the motion of large objects. In contrast, the quantum mechanical model is primarily mathematical. It has few analogies in the visible world.

Like the Bohr model, the quantum mechanical model of the atom restricts the energy of electrons to certain values. In a radical departure from the Bohr model, however, the quantum mechanical model does not define the exact path an electron takes around the nucleus. Rather, it estimates the probability of finding an electron in a certain position. Probability is a concept that you may know as chance. If you place three red marbles and one green marble into a box and then draw out one marble, the probability or chance of drawing the green marble is one in four or 25%. The chance of drawing out a red marble is three in four or 75%.

In the quantum mechanical model of the atom, the probability of finding an electron within a certain volume of space surrounding the nucleus can be portrayed as a fuzzy cloud. The cloud is most dense where the probability of finding the electron is high. The cloud is less dense where the probability is low. It is unclear where the cloud ends. There is at least a slight chance of finding the electron a considerable distance from the nucleus. Therefore attempts to show probabilities as a fuzzy cloud are usually limited to the volume in which the electron is found 90% of the time. Suppose you could mold a sack around an electron cloud so that the electron was inside the sack 90% of the time. The shape of the sack now gives you a useful picture of the shape of the cloud. In drawings of electron clouds, only the surface of an electron cloud inside the shape where the electron would be found 90% of the time is shown. This gives you a useful picture of the shape of the cloud.

Concept Practice

3. What is the basis for the quantum mechanical model of the atom?

12.3 Atomic Orbitals

Objective

Distinguish among principal energy level, energy sublevel, and atomic orbital.

As in the Bohr atom, the quantum mechanical model designates energy levels of electrons by *principal quantum numbers* (n). Each principal quantum number refers to a major or *principal energy level* in an atom. These are assigned values in order of increasing energy: $n = 1, 2, 3, 4$, and so forth. The average distance of the electron from the nucleus increases with increasing values of n.

Within each principal energy level, the electrons occupy *energy sublevels,* much as people in theater seats arranged in sections (principal energy levels) occupy rows within sections (energy sublevels). Table 12.1 gives the number of sublevels within each principal energy level. Notice that the number of energy sublevels is the same as the principal quantum number.

You might like to know where the electrons in the various sublevels would be located in relation to the nucleus. You may recall, however, that the quantum mechanical model limits the description of the position of an electron to a probability cloud shape. Because the electron is not confined to a fixed circular path, as it is in the Bohr atom, these cloud shapes cannot be called orbits. *In the quantum mechanical model, the cloud shapes are called* **atomic orbitals**. The atomic orbitals are denoted by letters. As Figure 12.3 shows, *s orbitals* are spherical, and the three kinds of *p orbitals* are dumbbell shaped. The shapes of *d orbitals* and *f orbitals* are far more complex. Notice that in *p* orbitals there are regions close to the nucleus where the probability of finding the electron is very low. These regions are called *nodes.* Four of the five kinds of *d* orbitals are shaped like clover leaves. The shapes of *f* orbitals are very complex and hard to visualize.

The shapes of atomic orbitals depend on the energy sublevel. The lowest principal energy level ($n = 1$) has only one sublevel, called 1*s*. The *s* atomic orbital is spherical. In the s atomic orbital,

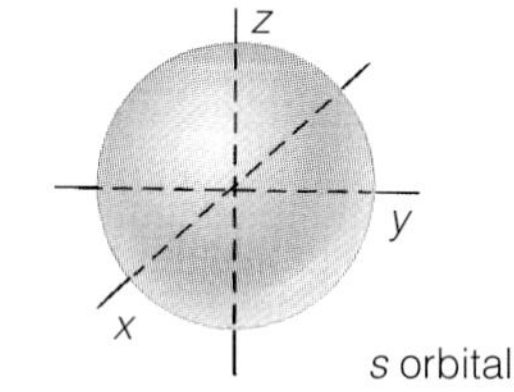

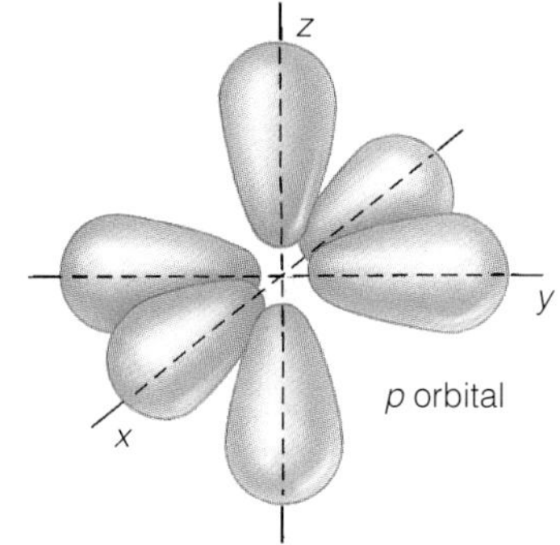

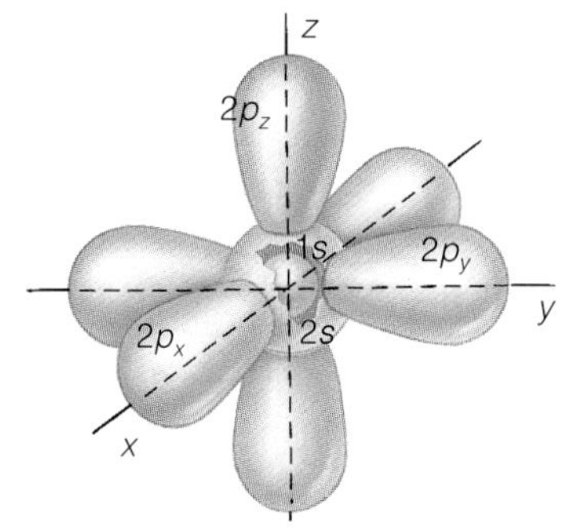

Figure 12.3 The electron probability clouds for the *s* orbital, the *p* orbitals, and a composite of one 1*s*, one 2*s*, and three 2*p* orbitals are shown.

Table 12.1 Summary of Principal Energy Levels, Sublevels, and Orbitals

Principal energy level	Number of sublevels	Type of sublevel
$n = 1$	1	1*s* (1 orbital)
$n = 2$	2	2*s* (1 orbital), 2*p* (3 orbitals)
$n = 3$	3	3*s* (1 orbital), 3*p* (3 orbitals), 3*d* (5 orbitals)
$n = 4$	4	4*s* (1 orbital), 4*p* (3 orbitals), 4*d* (5 orbitals), 4*f* (7 orbitals)

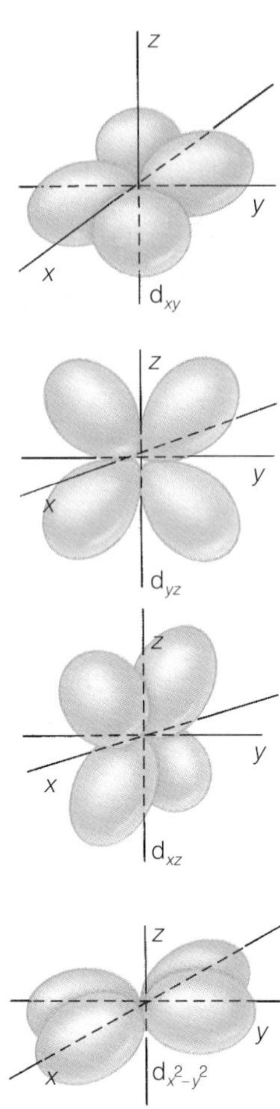

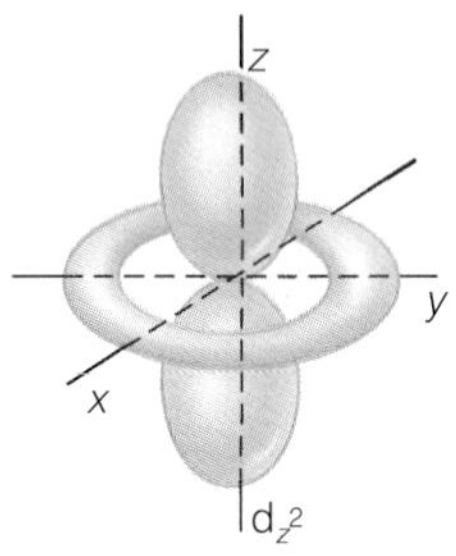

Figure 12.4 Four of the five *d* orbitals have the same shape but different orientations in space.

there is an equal probability of finding the electron in any direction from the nucleus. The second principal energy level ($n = 2$) has two sublevels, $2s$ and $2p$. The $2s$ orbital is spherical, and the $2p$ orbitals are dumbbell shaped. The $2p$ sublevel is of higher energy than the $2s$ and consists of three p orbitals of equal energy. The long axis of each dumbbell-shaped p orbital is perpendicular to the other two. It is convenient to label the axes $2p_x$, $2p_y$, and $2p_z$. Thus the second principal energy level has four orbitals: $2s$, $2p_x$, $2p_y$, and $2p_z$.

The third principal energy level ($n = 3$) has three sublevels, called $3s$, $3p$, and $3d$. The $3d$ sublevel consists of five d orbitals of equal energy. Thus the third principal energy level has nine orbitals (one $3s$, three $3p$, and five $3d$ orbitals). The fourth principal energy level ($n = 4$) has four sublevels, called $4s$, $4p$, $4d$, and $4f$. The $4f$ sublevel consists of seven f orbitals of equal energy. The fourth principal energy level, then, has 16 orbitals (one $4s$, three $4p$, five $4d$, and seven $4f$ orbitals).

As mentioned, the principal quantum number always equals the number of sublevels within that principal energy level. The maximum number of electrons that can occupy a principal energy level is given by the formula $2n^2$. Here n is the principal quantum number. The number of electrons allowed in each of the first four energy levels is as follows.

	Increasing energy (increasing distance from nucleus) →			
Energy level n	1	2	3	4
Maximum number of electrons allowed	2	8	18	32

Concept Practice

4. What is an atomic orbital?

Practice Problem

5. How many orbitals are in the following sublevels?
a. $3p$ sublevel
b. $2s$ sublevel
c. $4f$ sublevel
d. $4p$ sublevel
e. $3d$ sublevel
f. third principal energy level

12.A Science, Technology, and Society

The Chemistry of Lighting

The famous, flashing neon lights of Times Square and Las Vegas shine because of electron orbitals. These lights contain neon gas or other gases at low pressure. When electric current passes through the gas, the atoms absorb some of the electrical energy, causing some of their electrons to move to higher orbitals. While dropping back to lower orbitals, the electrons give off the energy in the form of light. The color of the light is characteristic of the gas in the tube. Figure 12.5 shows some of these colors. Helium produces a yellowish light, and argon produces lavender. Krypton gives a whitish light, xenon gives blue, and neon shines orange-red. By combining neon with other gases, other colors can be obtained. Sodium and mercury vapor lamps work in a similar way except that these metals must first be vaporized.

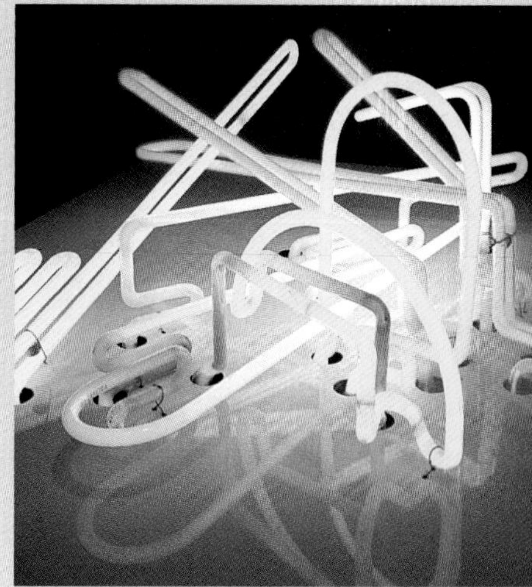

Figure 12.5 Noble gases give off light of characteristic colors.

The light bulbs used in most homes are incandescent lamps. Their light is produced by a white-hot tungsten wire heated by an electric current. At such high temperatures the tungsten atoms give off white light much like sunlight. White light is really a combination of all the colors. This type of light is given off by hot solids and liquids and even by dense gases. The tungsten filament would rapidly burn up in the presence of oxygen. To prevent this, an incandescent bulb is filled with argon or nitrogen.

Figure 12.6 Sodium vapor lamps produce a bright yellowish light. Sodium vapor lamps are used where energy efficiency and low maintenance are more important than realistic color.

Fluorescent lighting is much more efficient than incandescent lighting because no hot filament is involved. The long glass tube of a typical fluorescent bulb contains small amounts of mercury vapor and argon gas. The inside of the bulb is coated with a powder called a phosphor. When current passes through the bulb, electrons in the mercury atoms are excited to higher energy levels. In dropping back to the ground state, they emit ultraviolet (UV) light, which is not visible. The UV light is absorbed by the electrons in the molecules of the phosphor coating of the tube. When the phosphor electrons return to their ground state, they emit visible white light. A 40-watt fluorescent bulb produces as much light as a 150-watt incandescent bulb. It is no wonder that more than 75% of the lighting used in North America is fluorescent.

Think About It

6. Appraise Which of these gives the most "natural" light: tungsten-filament bulb, fluorescent lamp, or neon light? Why?

7. Explain Why would an energy-conscious consumer choose fluorescent lighting over incandescent lighting?

Objective

Apply the Aufbau principle, the Pauli exclusion principle, and Hund's rule to write the electron configurations of the elements.

Roots of Words

aufbauen: (German) to build up

Aufbau principle electrons enter orbitals of lowest energy first.

The Aufbau principle helps you write correct electron configurations of atoms.

12.4 Electron Configurations

In all natural phenomena, change proceeds toward the lowest possible energy state. High-energy systems are unstable. Unstable systems lose energy to become more stable. In the atom, electrons and the nucleus interact to make the most stable arrangement possible. *The ways in which electrons are arranged around the nuclei of atoms are called* **electron configurations.**

Three rules tell you how to find the electron configurations of atoms. Yet, this is *not* the way atoms are formed. These rules are the Aufbau principle, the Pauli exclusion principle, and Hund's rule.

1. Aufbau principle *Electrons enter orbitals of lowest energy first.* The various orbitals within a sublevel of a principal energy level are always of equal energy. Furthermore, within a principal energy level the *s* sublevel is always the lowest energy sublevel. Yet the range of energy levels within a principal energy level can overlap the energy levels of an adjacent principal level. This is shown on the Aufbau diagram of Figure 12.7. A circle (○) is used to represent an atomic orbital. Electrons enter the orbitals of lowest energy first. As a result, the filling of atomic orbitals does not follow a simple pattern

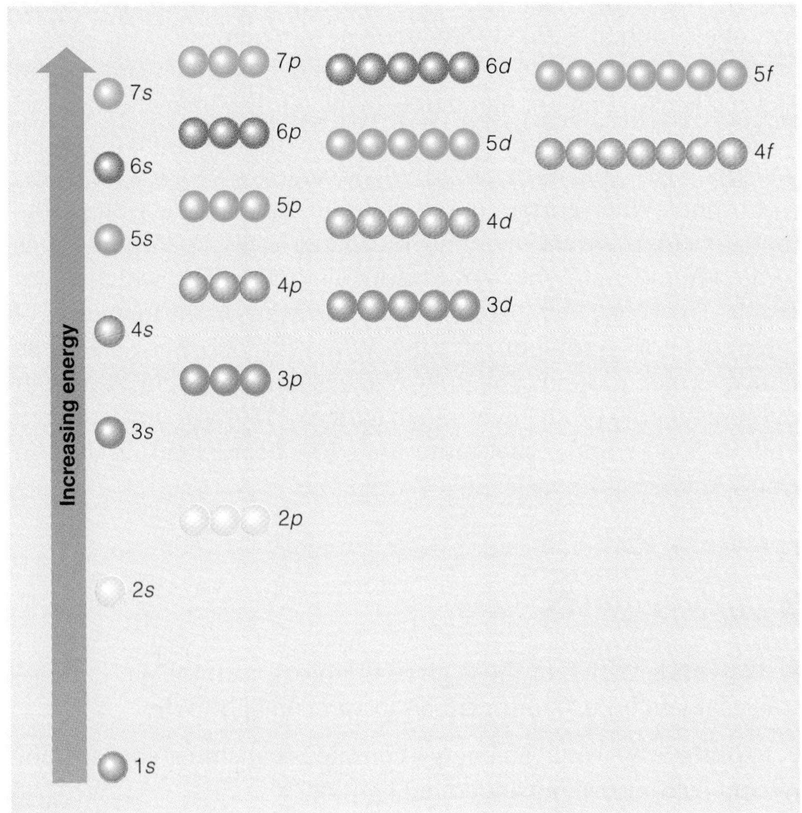

Figure 12.7 The energy levels of the various atomic orbitals are shown in this Aufbau diagram. Orbitals of greater energy are shown higher on the diagram.

beyond the second energy level. For example, the 4*s* orbital is lower in energy than the 3*d*. The 4*f* orbital is also lower in energy than the 5*d*.

2. Pauli exclusion principle *An atomic orbital may describe at most two electrons.* For example, either one or two electrons can occupy an *s* orbital or a *p* orbital. To occupy the same orbital, two electrons must have opposite spins; that is, the electron spins must be paired. Spin is a quantum property of electrons and may be clockwise or counterclockwise. A vertical arrow (ⓘ) is used to indicate an electron and its direction of spin (↑ or ↓). An orbital containing paired electrons is written as ⇅.

3. Hund's rule *When electrons occupy orbitals of equal energy, one electron enters each orbital until all the orbitals contain one electron with spins parallel* (↑↑↑). Second electrons then add to each orbital so that their spins are paired with those of the first electrons in the orbital.

Consider the electron configurations of atoms of the nine elements in Table 12.2. An oxygen atom contains eight electrons. The orbital of lowest energy, 1*s*, gets one electron, then a second of opposite spin. The next orbital to fill is 2*s*. Three electrons then go, one each, into the three 2*p* orbitals, which have equal energy. The remaining electron now pairs with an electron occupying one of the 2*p* orbitals. The other two 2*p* orbitals remain only half filled.

You can use a convenient shorthand method for showing the electron configuration of an atom. This involves writing the energy level and the symbol for every sublevel occupied by an electron. A superscript indicates the number of electrons occupying that sublevel. For hydrogen, with one electron in a 1*s* orbital, the electron configuration is written $1s^1$. For helium, with two electrons in a 1*s*

Table 12.2 Electron Configurations for Some Selected Elements

Element	Orbital filling						Electron configuration
	1*s*	2*s*	$2p_x$	$2p_y$	$2p_z$	3*s*	
H	↑	○	○	○	○	○	$1s^1$
He	⇅	○	○	○	○	○	$1s^2$
Li	⇅	↑	○	○	○	○	$1s^2\,2s^1$
C	⇅	⇅	↑	↑	○	○	$1s^2\,2s^2\,2p^2$
N	⇅	⇅	↑	↑	↑	○	$1s^2\,2s^2\,2p^3$
O	⇅	⇅	⇅	↑	↑	○	$1s^2\,2s^2\,2p^4$
F	⇅	⇅	⇅	⇅	↑	○	$1s^2\,2s^2\,2p^5$
Ne	⇅	⇅	⇅	⇅	⇅	○	$1s^2\,2s^2\,2p^6$
Na	⇅	⇅	⇅	⇅	⇅	↑	$1s^2\,2s^2\,2p^6\,3s^1$

orbital, it is $1s^2$. For oxygen, with two electrons in a $1s$ orbital, two electrons in a $2s$ orbital, and four electrons in $2p$ orbitals, it is $1s^2\,2s^2\,2p^4$. Note that the sum of the superscripts equals the number of electrons in the atom.

Example 1 Writing Electron Configurations of Atoms

Use Figure 12.7 to write electron configurations for these atoms.

a. phosphorus **b.** nickel

Solution

Phosphorus has 15 electrons; nickel has 28 electrons. Using Figure 12.7, start placing electrons in the orbitals with the lowest energy ($1s$). Remember that there is a maximum of 2 electrons in each orbital. Electrons do not pair up in orbitals of equal energy until necessary.

a. phosphorus

○ $4s$

↑ ↑ ↑ $3p$

↑↓ $3s$

↑↓ ↑↓ ↑↓ $2p$

↑↓ $2s$

↑↓ $1s$

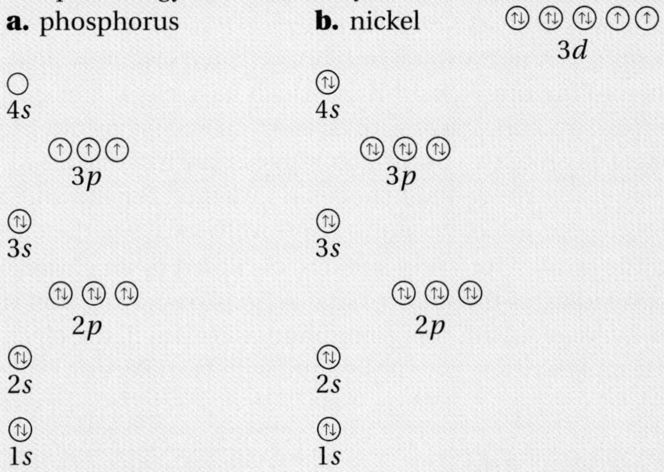

P $1s^2\,2s^2\,2p^6\,3s^2\,3p^3$

b. nickel

↑↓ ↑↓ ↑↓ ↑ ↑ $3d$

↑↓ $4s$

↑↓ ↑↓ ↑↓ $3p$

↑↓ $3s$

↑↓ ↑↓ ↑↓ $2p$

↑↓ $2s$

↑↓ $1s$

Ni $1s^2\,2s^2\,2p^6\,3s^2\,3p^6\,3d^8\,4s^2$

When the configurations are written, the sublevels within the same principal energy level are written together. This is not always the same order as given on the Aufbau diagram.

Practice Problems

8. Arrange the following sublevels in order of decreasing energy: $2p$, $4s$, $3s$, $3d$, and $3p$.

9. Write electron configurations for atoms of the following elements. How many unpaired electrons do these atoms have?

a. boron **b.** fluorine

12.5 Exceptional Electron Configurations

Objective

Explain why the electron configurations of chromium and copper differ from those assigned using the Aufbau diagram.

You can obtain correct electron configurations for the elements up to vanadium (atomic number 23) if you follow the Aufbau diagram for orbital filling. If you were to continue, you would assign chromium and copper the following configurations.

$$\text{Cr } 1s^2\, 2s^2\, 2p^6\, 3s^2\, 3p^6\, 3d^4\, 4s^2$$

$$\text{Cu } 1s^2\, 2s^2\, 2p^6\, 3s^2\, 3p^6\, 3d^9\, 4s^2$$

The correct electron configurations are shown below.

$$\text{Cr } 1s^2\, 2s^2\, 2p^6\, 3s^2\, 3p^6\, 3d^5\, 4s^1$$

$$\text{Cu } 1s^2\, 2s^2\, 2p^6\, 3s^2\, 3p^6\, 3d^{10}\, 4s^1$$

These arrangements give chromium a half-filled *d* sublevel and copper a filled *d* sublevel. However, it has been shown that filled energy sublevels are more stable than partially filled sublevels. Half-filled levels are not as stable as filled levels, but they are more stable than other configurations. With only one electron in the 4*s* sublevel, chromium atoms and copper atoms are more stable.

These unexpected results are worth knowing. It is more important, however, for you to achieve a good understanding of the general procedure for obtaining electron configurations.

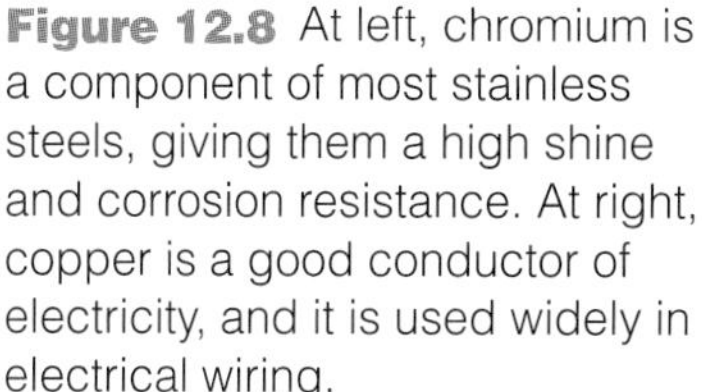

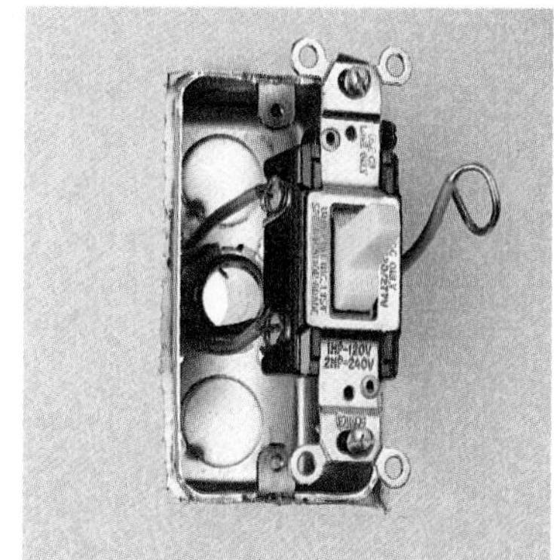

Figure 12.8 At left, chromium is a component of most stainless steels, giving them a high shine and corrosion resistance. At right, copper is a good conductor of electricity, and it is used widely in electrical wiring.

Practice Problem

10. Use the periodic table, pages 354-55, to compare the listed electron configurations of molybdenum and silver with the electron configurations from the Aufbau diagram.

Objective

Calculate the frequency and wavelength of light.

Integrating Astronomy

Helium

Sometimes discoveries in one area of science, like chemistry, become important in solving problems in another, such as astronomy. In 1868, astronomers Pierre Janssen and Joseph Lockyer discovered an emission spectrum from gases on the surface of our sun, which is a star, that was unmatched by any known element on earth. In 1895 William Ramsay discovered the existence of helium on earth. The emission spectrum of helium was found to be identical to the spectrum of the unknown gas observed by Janssen and Lockyer almost thirty years earlier. Thus by combining these two discoveries from different fields of science a new discovery was made, that the earth and the stars have some elements in common.

12.6 Light and Atomic Spectra

The discussion of the previous sections in this chapter introduced some ideas about the history of atomic structure. It also prepared you to write electron configurations of atoms. In the remainder of this chapter, you will backtrack a bit in order to delve further into the work that led to the development of the quantum mechanical model of the atom. Rather curiously, this model grew out of the study of light. Isaac Newton (1642–1727) had thought of light as consisting of particles. By the year 1900, however, the idea that light was a wave phenomenon was firmly ingrained among scientists.

In the wave model, light is considered to consist of electromagnetic waves that travel in a vacuum at a speed of 3.0×10^8 m/s. **Electromagnetic radiation** *includes radio waves, microwaves, visible light, infrared and ultraviolet light, X-rays, and gamma rays.* Figure 12.9 shows the parts of a wave at an instant of time. Each wave cycle begins at the origin, then returns to the origin. *The* **amplitude** *of a wave is the height of the wave from the origin to the crest. The* **wavelength** (λ, the Greek letter lambda) *is the distance between the crests.* This can vary. *In a traveling wave,* **frequency** (ν, the Greek letter nu) *is the number of wave cycles to pass a given point per unit of time.* The frequency and wavelength of all waves, including light, are inversely related.

$$\nu = \frac{c}{\lambda}$$

As the wavelength of light increases, the frequency decreases. Figure 12.10 shows this relationship. The product of frequency and wavelength always equals a constant, *c*, the speed of light. The units of frequency are usually cycles per second. *The SI unit of cycles per second is called a* **hertz**, Hz. Frequency is expressed as reciprocal seconds (s^{-1}); the term "cycles" is assumed to be understood.

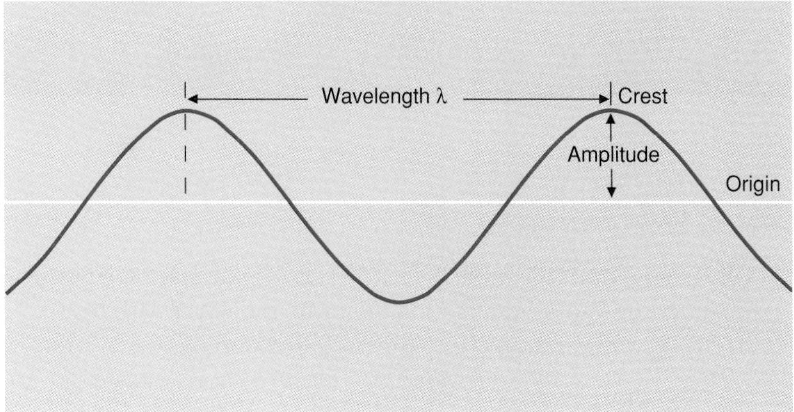

Figure 12.9 The amplitude of a wave is the height of the wave from the origin to the crest. The wavelength is the distance between crests.

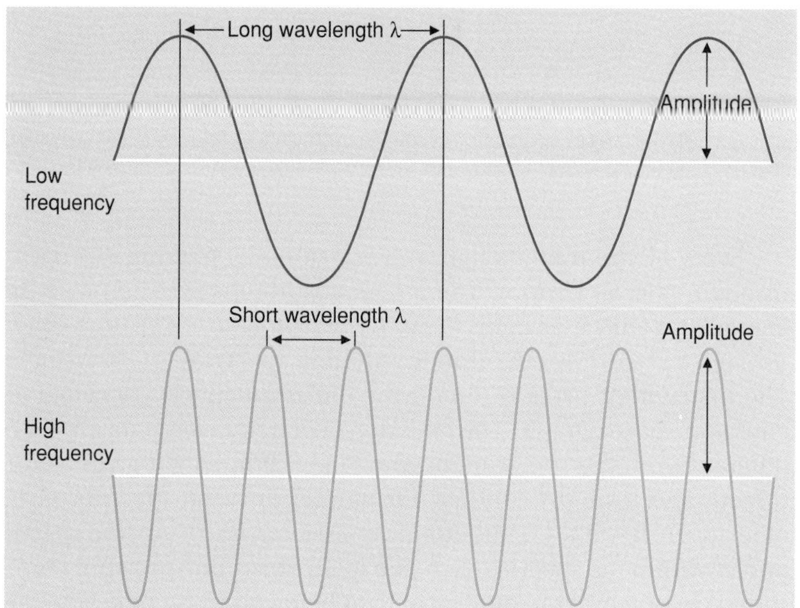

Figure 12.10 The frequency and wavelength of light are inversely related. As the wavelength increases, the frequency decreases. The wavelength and frequency do not affect the amplitude.

Sunlight consists of light with a continuous range of wavelengths and frequencies. The wavelength and frequency of yellow light are different from those of red light. *When sunlight passes through a prism, the light separates into a* **spectrum** *of colors.* Each color blends into the next in order: red, orange, yellow, green, blue, indigo, and violet. In the visible spectrum, red light has the longest wavelength and the lowest frequency. Violet light has the shortest wavelength and highest frequency.

Figure 12.11 The electromagnetic spectrum consists of radiation over a broad band of wavelengths. The visible-light portion is very small. It is in the 10^{-7} m wavelength range and the 10^{15} Hz (s^{-1}) frequency range. What types of nonvisible radiation have wavelengths close to those of red light? To those of blue light?

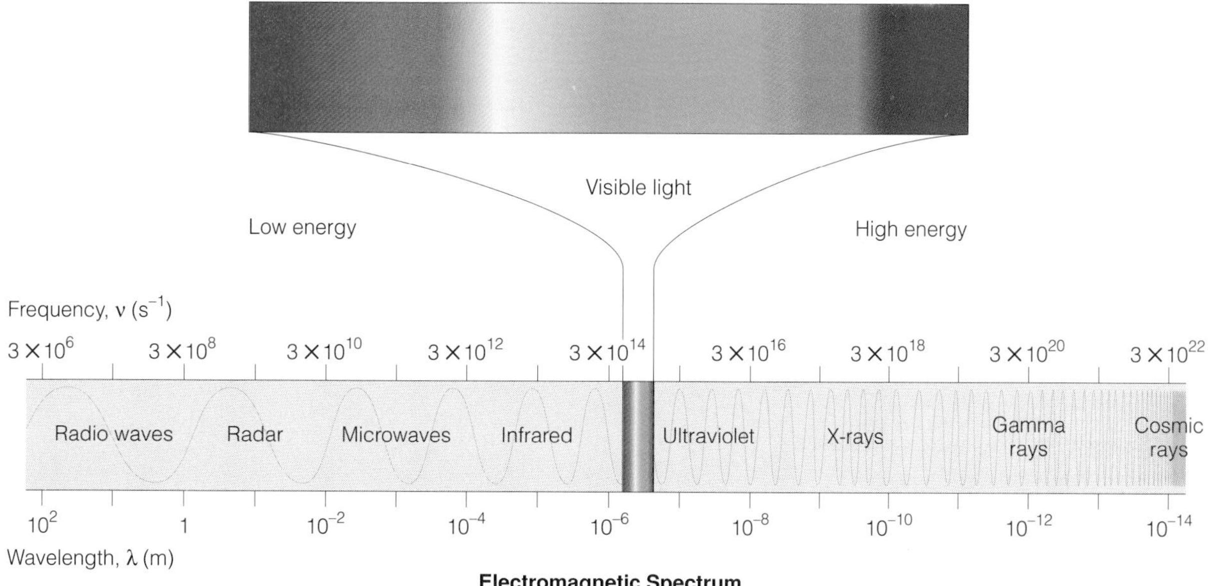

Electromagnetic Spectrum

Figure 12.12 The emission spectrum of an element consists of a series of bands that are characteristic for the element. The emission spectrum of atomic hydrogen consists of a few widely spaced bands.

Every element emits light if it is heated by passing electricity through its gas or vapor. The atoms absorb energy, then lose the energy and emit it as light. *Passing the light emitted by an element through a prism gives the* **atomic emission spectrum** *of the element.* The instrument used to obtain the emission spectra is called an emission spectrograph. The emission spectra of elements are quite different from the spectrum of white light. White light gives a continuous spectrum. By contrast, the atomic emission spectra consist of relatively few lines. Thus atomic emission spectra are line spectra or discontinuous spectra. Each line in an emission spectrum corresponds to one exact frequency of light being given off or emitted by the atom. Therefore each line corresponds to one exact amount of energy being emitted.

The emission spectrum of each element is unique to that element. This makes these spectra extremely useful for identifying unknown and sometimes otherwise inaccessible substances. Much of our knowledge of the composition of the universe, for example, comes from the atomic spectra of the stars, which are hot glowing bodies of gases. A telescope gathers light from the star of interest. This light is then transmitted to an emission spectrograph for recording of the atomic emission spectrum.

Example 2 Calculating the Wavelength of Light

Calculate the wavelength of the yellow light emitted by a sodium lamp if the frequency of the radiation is $5.10 \times 10^{14}\ \text{s}^{-1}$.

Solution

First rearrange the equation $\nu = c/\lambda$ to give $\lambda = c/\nu$. Substitute values for c and ν.

$$\lambda = \frac{3.00 \times 10^{8}\ \text{m/s}}{5.10 \times 10^{14}\ \text{s}^{-1}}$$

$$= \frac{3.00 \times 10^{8}\ \text{m}\ \cancel{\text{s}^{-1}}}{5.10 \times 10^{14}\ \cancel{\text{s}^{-1}}}$$

$$= 5.88 \times 10^{-7}\ \text{m}$$

Problem-Solving Tip

Check that the answer has an appropriate unit after canceling and before doing the calculation.

Concept Practice

11. List the colors of the visible spectrum in order of increasing wavelength.

12. What is meant by the term *frequency* of a wave? What are the units of frequency? Describe the relationship between frequency and wavelength.

Practice Problems

13. What is the frequency of radiation whose wavelength is 5.00×10^{-6} cm? In what region of the electromagnetic spectrum is this radiation?

14. A hydrogen lamp emits several lines in the visible region of the spectrum. One of these lines has a wavelength of 6.56×10^{-5} cm. What are the color and frequency of this radiation?

Activity 12
A Delightful Wintergreen Mint

Purpose

To infer the reason some wintergreen mints emit light when broken.

Materials

pliers

clear transparent tape

3 different brands of wintergreen mints

a dark room

Procedure

1. Break each of the three different mints in half.

2. Wrap the jaws of the pliers with transparent tape.

3. Turn out the lights and allow a minute for your eyes to adjust to the darkness.

4. Watch the exposed edge of the mint as you carefully crush half a mint between the jaws of the pliers. Note the color and brightness of any light emitted.

5. Repeat for all three samples.

Analysis and Conclusions

1. Explain the origin of the light you observed.

2. Did all the mints emit light? If not, explain.

3. How did the color and relative brightness of the emitted light compare? Propose an explanation for any differences.

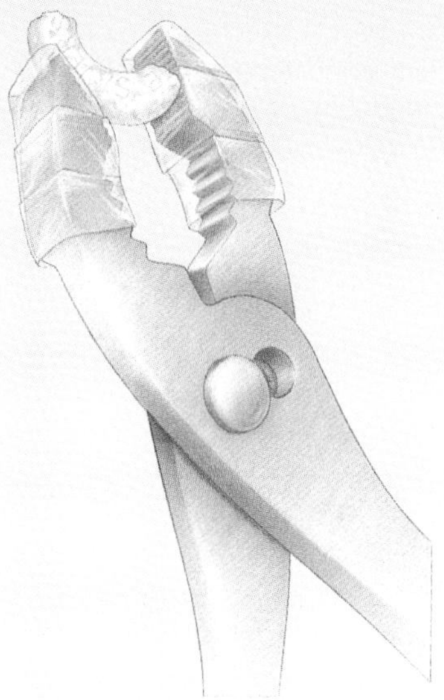

12.B Historical Notebook

Chemical Dyes

Figure 12.13 The deep blue color in the Japanese hanten (a short top worn over a kimono) is indigo dye. The colors in the Navajo rug are from natural dyes.

Dyes are intensely colored organic materials that, in relatively small quantities, change the color of a fiber. Dyeing with natural materials to obtain pleasing colors has been known since the earliest civilizations. Most dyes used by the ancients were obtained from plants or insects. For example, Native Americans of Mexico obtained a vivid red dye from the cochineal insect. The most famous of ancient dyes was used by the Phoenicians. The dye, Tyrian purple, was extracted from a marine snail. Once Tyrian purple was so expensive that it was the mark of royalty.

Before the mid-1800s, the only dyes available were of natural origin. Today, there are thousands of dyes in commercial use that are synthesized from petrochemicals or coal tar. The breakthrough into synthetic dyes came in 1856, when William H. Perkin, a 17-year-old Englishman, made the lilac-colored dye which he called mauveine. He synthesized the dye from aniline, a compound derived from coal tar. This event led to the large-scale dye industry that emerged in the late nineteenth century. Early research was directed toward determining the structures of important natural dyes and then synthesizing them. The first natural dye to be reproduced in the laboratory was alizarin, a dark red dye, in 1868. Alizarin was produced from anthracene, a compound obtained from coal tar. Indigo blue dye was first synthesized in 1880 but was not produced economically until 20 years later.

indigo

Congo red dye, synthesized in 1884, was the first direct cotton dye that required no mordanting. A mordant is a chemical, such as potassium aluminum sulfate, that improves the fastness, or permanence, of the dye. Acetate dyes, made in 1922–1923, were capable of penetrating new synthetic acetate fibers. Among the more recent advances in textile coloring are fiber-reactive dyes that form a strong covalent bond with the fiber that they color.

Think About It

15. List Name some sources of early natural dyes.

12.7 The Quantum Concept

The laws of classical physics hold that there is no limit to how small the energy gained or lost by an object may be. According to these laws, the emission spectrum of an element should be continuous. Thus classical physics is no help in explaining the emission spectra of atoms, which consist of lines. The seed of an idea that explained atomic spectra came in 1900 from the German physicist Max Planck (1858–1947).

Planck was trying to describe quantitatively why a body like a chunk of iron appears to change color as it is heated. First it appears black, then red, yellow, white, and blue as its temperature increases. Planck found he could explain the color changes if he assumed that the energy of a body changes only in small discrete units. By analogy, a brick wall can be increased or decreased in size only by units of one or more bricks.

Planck showed mathematically that the amount of radiant energy, E, absorbed or emitted by a body is proportional to the frequency of the radiation, v.

$$E \propto v \text{ or } E = h \times v$$

Here h *is a constant now called* **Planck's constant**, *which has a value of* 6.6262×10^{-34} *J s (J is the joule, the SI unit of energy).* The energy of a quantum equals $h \times v$. Any attempt to increase or decrease the energy of a system by a fraction of $h \times v$ must fail. The size of an emitted or absorbed quantum depends on the size of the energy change. A small energy change involves the emission or absorption of low-frequency radiation. A large energy change involves the emission or absorption of high-frequency radiation.

Figure 12.14 All objects change colors when they are heated. Although this looks like a continuous process, the atoms in the iron are giving off energy in small discrete units.

Objective

Calculate the energy of a photon associated with a given wavelength or frequency of light.

Integrating Printing Technology

Inks and Color

Your eyes detect the various wavelengths of light reflected by the inks in a photograph. The photographs in this book closely resemble the original photographs even though they are produced using only four colors of ink: yellow, cyan (blue-green), magenta (red-blue), and black. In order to make the printing plates, the colors on the original color photo are separated into yellow, cyan, magenta, and black components. A plate is made from each separation and inked for printing. The paper receiving the photograph is then overprinted with each color to reproduce the original color photograph.

Planck's proposal of absorption or emission of quanta of energy was revolutionary. Everyday experience had led people to believe that there was no limitation to the smallness of permissible energy changes in a system. It appears, for example, that thermal energy may be continuously supplied to heat liquid water to any temperature between 0°C and 100°C. Actually, the water temperature increases by infinitesimally small steps. This occurs as individual molecules absorb quanta of energy. Your eyes are unable, however, to detect such small changes in temperature. Thus your everyday experience gives you no clue to the fact that energy is quantized.

Concept Practice

16. Explain the difference between the laws of classical physics and the quantum concept—for example, when describing the energy lost or gained by an object.

Practice Problem

17. What is the energy of a photon of green light whose frequency is $5.80 \times 10^{14}\ s^{-1}$?

Objective

Apply quantum theory to explain the photoelectric effect.

12.8 Light as Particles: The Photoelectric Effect

In 1905 Albert Einstein, then a patent examiner in Zurich, Switzerland, returned to Newton's idea of particles of light. Einstein proposed that light could be described as quanta of energy that behave as particles. *Light quanta are called* **photons**. The energy of photons is quantized according to the equation $E = h \times \nu$.

The dual wave-particle behavior of light was difficult for scientists trained in classical physics to accept. It was even more difficult to dispute because it provided an explanation for the previously mysterious photoelectric effect.

In the **photoelectric effect**, *electrons called photoelectrons are ejected by metals when light shines on them.* The alkali metals (Li, Na, K, Cs, and Rb) are particularly subject to the effect. Not just any light will do. Red light ($\nu = 4.3 \times 10^{14}\ s^{-1}$ to $4.6 \times 10^{14}\ s^{-1}$) will not cause the ejection of photoelectrons from potassium no matter how intense the light. Yet even a very weak yellow light ($\nu = 5.1 \times 10^{14}\ s^{-1}$ to $5.2 \times 10^{14}\ s^{-1}$) shining on potassium begins the effect.

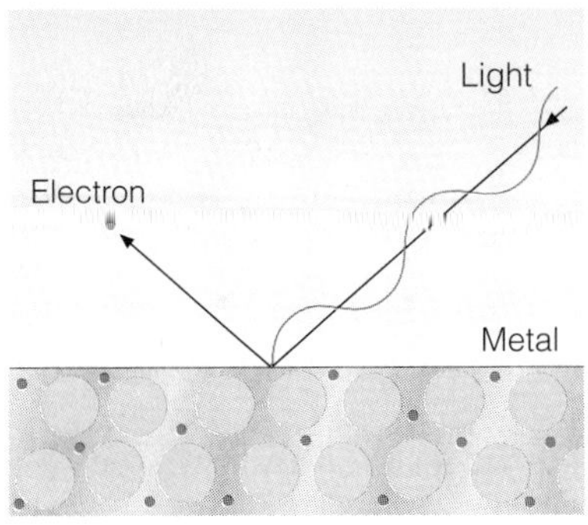

(a) When light strikes a metal surface, electrons are ejected.

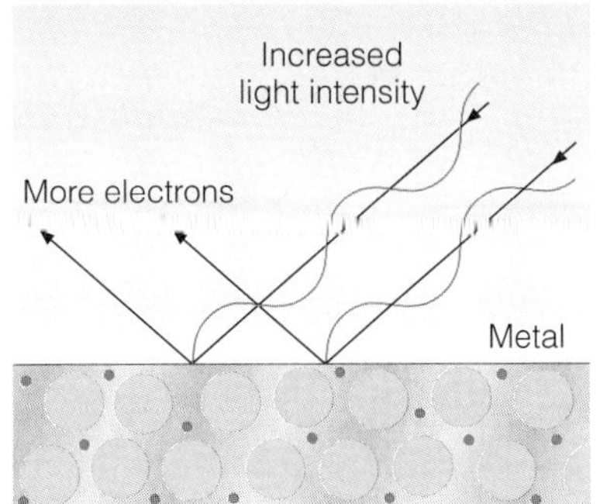

(b) If the threshold frequency has been reached, increasing the intensity only increases the number of electrons ejected.

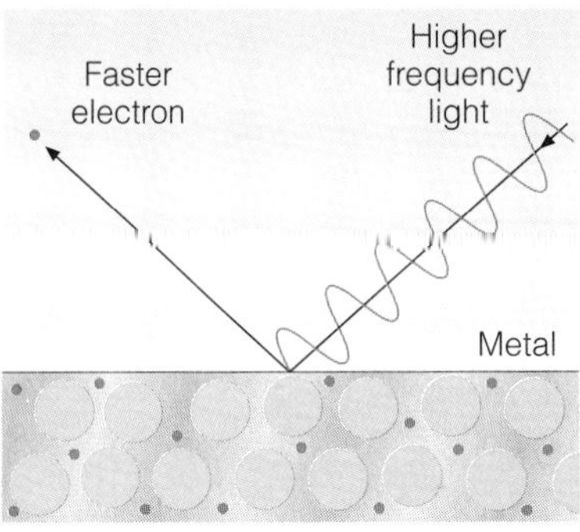

(c) If the frequency is increased, the ejected electrons will travel faster.

Figure 12.15 The photoelectric effect.

The photoelectric effect could not be explained by classical physics, which had no quantum concept. Classical physics correctly viewed light as a form of energy. It assumed, however, that under weak light of any wavelength, an electron in a metal should eventually collect enough energy to be ejected. Obviously, the photoelectric effect presented a serious problem for the classical wave theory of light.

Einstein used his particle theory of light to explain the photoelectric effect as demonstrated in Figure 12.15. He recognized that there is a threshold value of energy below which the photoelectric effect does not occur. Because $E = h \times v$, all the photons in a beam of light of only one frequency (monochromatic light) have the same energy. If the frequency and therefore the energy of the light are too low, no photoelectron will be ejected. It does not matter whether a single photon or a steady stream of low-energy photons strike an electron in the metal. Only if the frequency of light is above the threshold frequency will the photoelectric effect occur. The photoelectric effect has practical applications in photoelectric cells such as that in the calculator of Figure 12.16, which use the energy of light to generate electricity.

Figure 12.16 Photoelectric cells convert light energy into electrical energy.

An analogous situation occurs with a table-tennis ball that strikes a billiard ball. A table tennis ball is not energetic enough to budge the stationary billiard ball, no matter how many times a ball collides with it. By contrast, one golf ball moving at the same speed as the table tennis ball sets the target ball in motion. The golf ball is above the energy threshold. With the photoelectric effect, any excess energy of a photon beyond that needed to eject a photoelectron causes the ejected electron to travel faster. Increasing the intensity of light, however, only increases the number of photons striking the metal. Above the threshold frequency, increasing the intensity increases the number of electrons ejected. It does not, however, make them travel faster.

Example 3 Finding the Energy of a Photon of Light

Calculate the energy, in joules, of a quantum of radiant energy (the energy of a photon) whose frequency is $5.00 \times 10^{15}\ s^{-1}$.

Solution

Use the equation $E = h \times v$. Substitute values for h and v to give E.

$$E = 6.62 \times 10^{-34}\ J\cancel{s} \times 5.00 \times 10^{15}\ \cancel{s}^{-1} = 3.31 \times 10^{-18}\ J$$

Concept Practice

18. Briefly describe the photoelectric effect and explain why it could not be explained by classical physics.

Practice Problem

19. What is the energy of a photon of microwave radiation whose frequency is $3.20 \times 10^{11}\ s^{-1}$?

Objective

Explain the origin of the atomic emission spectrum of an element.

12.9 An Explanation of Atomic Spectra

Bohr's application of quantum theory to the energy levels of the electrons in atoms resulted in an explanation of the hydrogen spectrum. The lines observed in the spectrum are consistent with the idea that quantization limits the possible energies that an electron in a hydrogen atom can attain. *Consider the lone electron of the hydrogen atom in the lowest energy level, or* **ground state**. This energy level is designated by a quantum number, n. For the ground state, $n = 1$. Excitation of the electron raises it to an excited state so that $n = 2, 3, 4, 5$, or 6, and so forth. If the energy levels are quantized, it takes a quantum of energy, $h \times v$, to raise the electron from the ground state to an excited state. The same amount of energy is emitted as a photon when the electron drops from the excited state to the ground state. Only electrons in transition from higher to lower energy levels lose energy and emit light.

Figure 12.17 shows the explanation for the three groups of lines observed in the emission spectrum of hydrogen atoms. The lines at the ultraviolet end of the hydrogen spectrum are the Lyman series. These match expected values for the emission due to transitions

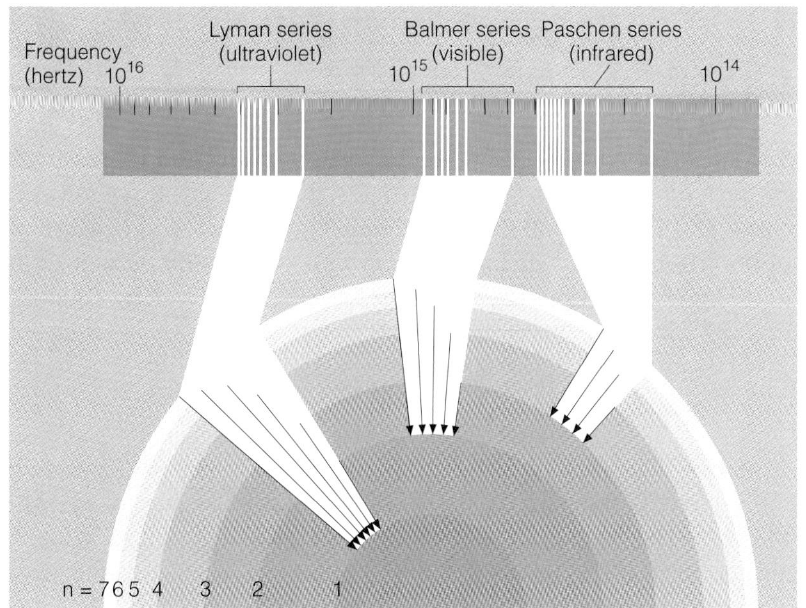

Figure 12.17 The three groups of lines in the hydrogen spectrum correspond to transitions from higher to lower energy levels

from higher energy levels to $n = 1$. The lines in the visible spectrum are the Balmer series. They are the result of transitions from higher energy levels to $n = 2$. Those in the infrared spectrum are the Paschen series. They correspond to transitions from higher energy levels to $n = 3$. Lines for the transitions from higher energy levels to $n = 4$ and $n = 5$ also exist. Note that the spectral lines in each group become more closely spaced at increased values of n. This means that the energy differences between higher energy levels are smaller than those between lower levels. There is an upper limit to the frequency of emitted light for each set of lines. This is because a very excited electron completely escapes the atom.

Bohr's theory of the atom was only partially satisfactory. It explained only the emission spectra of atoms and ions containing one electron. Moreover, it was of no help in understanding how atoms bond to form molecules. Eventually the Bohr model of the atom was displaced by a new and better model. The latter is based on the description of the motion of material objects as waves.

Concept Practice

20. What happens when a hydrogen atom absorbs a quantum of energy?

21. Distinguish between the ground state and the excited state of an electron.

Chemistry in Careers

Spectroscopist

A spectroscopist uses various spectroscopic instruments to identify and quantify substances. For example, emission spectra of mixtures of substances can give both qualitative and quantitative information. The wavelengths detected tell the spectroscopist what is in the sample. The intensity of the light at different wavelengths tells how much of each component of the mixture is present. Spectroscopy is not limited to atomic emission spectra. The spectroscopist may also use such spectroscopic instruments as nuclear magnetic resonance spectrometers, infrared spectrometers, or atomic absorption spectrometers in his or her work.

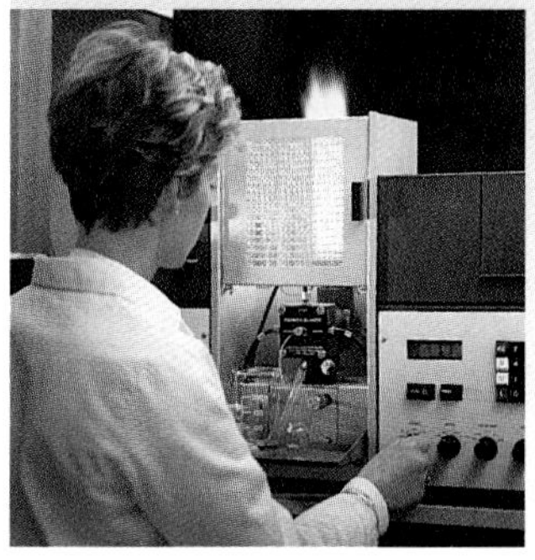

Objective

Explain the wave-particle duality of matter.

12.10 The Wave Motion of Matter and Quantum Mechanics

Such strange goings on! Energy absorbed or emitted in packages. Light behaving as waves *and* particles. Stranger things were yet to come. In 1924 Louis de Broglie, a French graduate student, asked an important question. Since light behaves as waves and particles, can particles of matter behave as waves? De Broglie derived an equation that described the wavelength, λ, of a moving particle.

$$\lambda = \frac{h}{mv}$$

Here h is Planck's constant, m is the mass of the particle, and v is the velocity of the particle. From this equation it is easy to calculate the wavelength of a moving electron. With a mass of 9.11×10^{-28} g and moving at the speed of light, an electron has a wavelength of about 2×10^{-10} cm. This is about the diameter of an atom.

Indeed, **de Broglie's equation** *predicts that all matter exhibits wavelike motions.* Why then are people generally unaware of this wave motion? As with quanta, the answer is concerned with the size of the object in motion. Objects that are visible to the naked eye have wavelengths too small to measure. Objects with measureable wavelengths cannot be seen by the naked eye. A 200-g baseball moving at 30 m/s has a wavelength of approximately 10^{-32} cm. This is too small to detect by any experiment that you could perform. By contrast, an electron moving at the same speed has a wavelength of about 2×10^{-3} cm. This is easily measured with appropriate scientific instruments.

De Broglie's proposal of matter waves set the stage for an entirely new method of describing the motions of subatomic particles, atoms, and molecules. Since mechanics is the study of the motion of bodies, the new method is called quantum mechanics. Here is a summary of the most important differences between classical mechanics and quantum mechanics.

Figure 12.18 De Broglie said all matter exhibits wavelike motions. This phenomenon is more apparent in some forms of matter than in others.

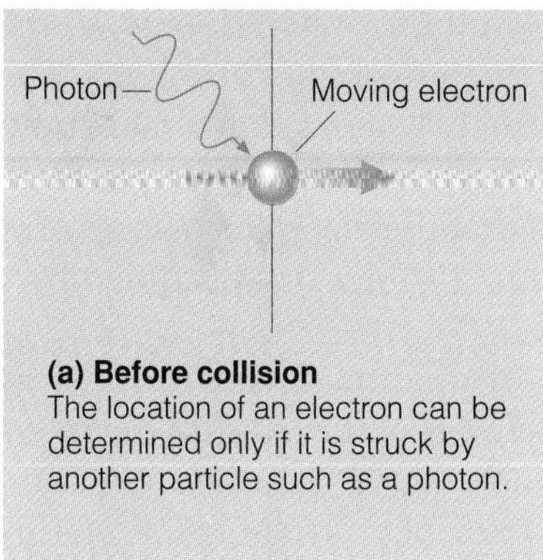

Photon
Moving electron
(a) Before collision
The location of an electron can be determined only if it is struck by another particle such as a photon.

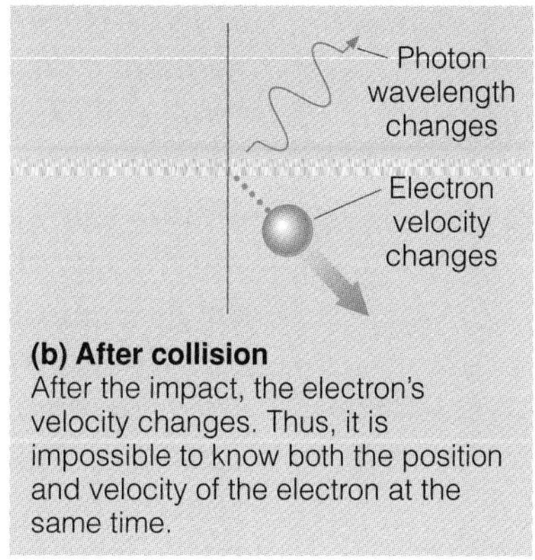

Photon wavelength changes
Electron velocity changes
(b) After collision
After the impact, the electron's velocity changes. Thus, it is impossible to know both the position and velocity of the electron at the same time.

Figure 12.19 The Heisenberg uncertainty principle.

1. Classical mechanics adequately describes the motions of bodies much larger than the atoms of which they are composed. It appears that such a body gains or loses energy in any amount.

2. Quantum mechanics describes the motions of subatomic particles and atoms as waves. These particles gain or lose energy in packages called quanta.

Another feature of quantum mechanics that is not found in classical mechanics is the uncertainty principle. This was derived by the German physicist Werner Heisenberg (1901–1976) in 1927. *The* **Heisenberg uncertainty principle** *states that it is impossible to know exactly both the velocity and the position of a particle at the same time.* As the measurement of velocity is made more accurately, the measurement of the position must become less accurate. Conversely, if the position of a moving particle is known accurately, the velocity is less well known. Figure 12.19 illustrates this point.

The uncertainty principle is much more obvious with small bodies like electrons than with large objects like baseballs. The uncertainty in the position of a baseball traveling at 30 m/s is only about 10^{-21} cm, which is not measurable. The uncertainty in the position of an electron with a mass of 9.11×10^{-28} g moving at the same speed is nearly a billion centimeters! Schrödinger's quantum mechanical description of the electrons in atoms shaped the concept of electron orbitals and configurations. It incorporates both the wave properties of bodies in motion and the uncertainty principle.

Concept Practice

22. Use de Broglie's equation to show why the wavelength of a photon decreases with increasing mass.

Chapter 12 Review

Electrons in Atoms

Key Terms

amplitude *12.6*
atomic emission spectrum *12.6*
atomic orbital *12.3*
Aufbau principle *12.4*
de Broglie's equation *12.10*
electromagnetic radiation *12.6*
electron configuration *12.4*
energy level *12.1*
frequency (ν) *12.6*
ground state *12.9*
Heisenberg uncertainty principle *12.10*
hertz (Hz) *12.6*
Hund's rule *12.4*
Pauli exclusion principle *12.4*
photoelectric effect *12.8*
photon *12.8*
Planck's constant (h) *12.7*
quantum *12.1*
quantum mechanical model *12.2*
spectrum *12.6*
wavelength (λ) *12.6*

Chapter Summary

Rutherford pictured the atom as a dense nucleus surrounded by electrons. Rutherford's model was refined by Niels Bohr. In the Bohr model of the atom, the electrons move in fixed circular paths around a dense, positively charged nucleus.

The energies of electrons in an atom are quantized. The quantum mechanical model is the modern description of the electrons in atoms. This model does not define the exact path of an electron. It does show the probability of finding an electron as a cloud of negative charge. Each cloud shape can be calculated from a mathematical expression called an atomic orbital.

The ways in which electrons are arranged around the nuclei of atoms are called electron configurations. Correct electron configurations for atoms may be written by using the Aufbau principle, the Pauli exclusion principle, and Hund's rule. The Aufbau principle tells us the sequence in which the orbitals are filled. The Pauli exclusion principle states that a maximum of only two electrons can occupy each orbital. Hund's rule states that the electrons pair up only after each orbital in a sublevel is occupied by a single electron.

The concept of quantized electron energy levels in atoms grew out of the study of the interaction of light and matter. The line emission spectra of atoms are best explained if energy levels are quantized. The quantum concept developed in part from Planck's studies of light radiation from heated objects and Einstein's explanation of the photoelectric effect. De Broglie's proposal that all matter in motion has wavelike properties further stimulated the development of a new mathematical description of electron configuration. Erwin Schrödinger devised the most successful of these early quantum mechanical models. It also incorporates the Heisenberg uncertainty principle.

Practice Questions and Problems

23. Describe Rutherford's model of the atom and compare it with the model proposed by his student Niels Bohr. *12.1*

24. The energies of electrons are said to be *quantized.* Explain. *12.1*

25. In general terms, explain how the quantum mechanical model of the atom describes the electron structure of an atom. *12.2*

26. Sketch 1*s*, 2*s*, and 2*p* orbitals using the same scale for each. *12.3*

27. What are the three rules that govern the filling of atomic orbitals by electrons? *12.4*

28. Write electron configurations for the elements that are identified only by these atomic numbers. *12.4*

a. 15 **b.** 12 **c.** 9 **d.** 18

29. What is meant by $3p^3$? *12.4*

30. Write complete electron configurations for each of the following kinds of atoms. *12.4*

a. carbon **c.** fluorine
b. argon **d.** rubidium

31. Indicate which of these orbital designations is incorrect. *12.4*

a. 4*s** **c.** 2*d*
b. 3*f* **d.** 3*d*

32. How many electrons are in the second energy level of an atom of these elements? *12.4*

a. chlorine **b.** phosphorus **c.** potassium

33. How many electrons are in the highest occupied energy level of these atoms? *12.4*

a. barium **b.** sodium **c.** aluminum

34. What is the maximum number of electrons that can go into each of the following sublevels? *12.4*

a. 2*s* **c.** 4*s* **e.** 4*p* **g.** 4*f*
b. 3*p* **d.** 3*d* **f.** 5*s* **h.** 5*p*

35. Write electron configurations for atoms of these elements. *12.4*

a. selenium
b. vanadium
c. nickel
d. calcium
e. oxygen

36. Why does one electron in a potassium atom go into the fourth energy level instead of squeezing into the third energy level along with the eight already there? *12.5*

37. Arrange the following electromagnetic radiations in order of decreasing wavelength. *12.6*

a. infrared radiation from a heat lamp
b. ultraviolet light from the sun
c. dental X-rays
d. the signal from a short-wave radio station
e. green light

38. Use a diagram to illustrate the following terms. *12.6*

a. wavelength **b.** amplitude **c.** wave cycle

39. What is the wavelength of a radiation whose frequency is $1.50 \times 10^{13}\ s^{-1}$? Does this radiation have a longer or shorter wavelength than red light? *12.6*

40. Suppose that your favorite AM radio station broadcasts at a frequency of 1150 kHz. What is the wavelength in centimeters of the radiation from the station? *12.6*

41. How did Planck influence the development of modern atomic theory? *12.7*

42. What will happen if the following occur? *12.8*

a. Monochromatic light shining on the alkali metal cesium is just above the threshold frequency.
b. The intensity of light increases, but the frequency remains the same.
c. Monochromatic light of a shorter wavelength is used.

43. Explain the difference between a photon and a quantum. *12.8*

44. When white light is viewed through sodium vapor in a spectroscope, the spectrum is continuous except for a dark line at 589 nm. How can you explain this observation? *12.9*

45. What is the wavelength of a 2500-kg truck traveling at a rate of 75 km/h? *12.10*

Mastery Questions and Problems

46. Construct a concept map using the key terms in this chapter with light as the key concept.

47. Give the symbol for the atom whose electron configuration corresponds to each of the following electron configurations.

a. $1s^2\,2s^2\,2p^6\,3s^2\,3p^6$
b. $1s^2\,2s^2\,2p^6\,3s^2\,3p^6\,3d^{10}\,4s^2\,4p^6\,4d^7\,5s^1$
c. $1s^2\,2s^2\,2p^6\,3s^2\,3p^6\,3d^{10}\,4s^2\,4p^6\,4d^{10}\,4f^7\,5s^2\,5p^6\,5d^1\,6s^2$

48. Write the electron configuration for an arsenic atom. Calculate the total number of electrons in each level and state which levels are not full.

49. How many paired electrons are there in an atom of each of these elements?

a. helium **c.** sodium
b. boron **d.** oxygen

50. An atom of an element has two electrons in the first energy level and five electrons in the second energy level. Write the electron configuration and name the element. How many unpaired electrons does an atom of this element have?

51. The threshold photoelectric effect in tungsten is produced by light of wavelength 260 nm. Give the energy of a photon of this light in joules.

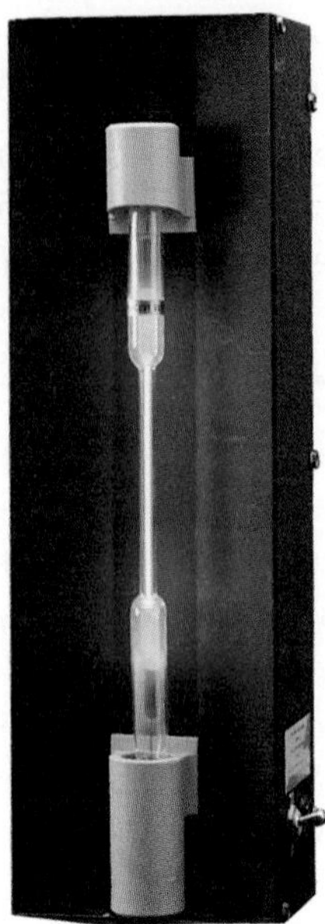

52. A mercury lamp like that shown above emits radiation with a wavelength of 4.36×10^{-7} m.
    a. What is this wavelength in centimeters?
    b. In what region of the electromagnetic spectrum is this radiation?
    c. Calculate the frequency of this radiation.
53. Calculate the energy of a photon of red light whose wavelength is 6.45×10^{-5} cm. Compare your answer with the answer of Problem 52 and say whether red light is of higher or lower energy than blue light.
54. Give the symbols and names of the elements whose atoms have these configurations.
    a. $1s^2\,2s^2\,2p^6\,3s^1$
    b. $1s^2\,2s^2\,2p^3$
    c. $1s^2\,2s^2\,2p^6\,3s^2\,3p^2$
    d. $1s^2\,2s^2\,2p^4$
    e. $1s^2\,2s^2\,2p^6\,3s^2\,3p^6\,4s^1$
    f. $1s^2\,2s^2\,2p^6\,3s^2\,3p^6\,3d^2\,4s^2$

Critical Thinking Questions

55. Choose the term that best completes the second relationship.
    a. orbital:energy level apartment: ——
    (1) floor (3) building
    (2) room (4) stairway
    b. water:container electrons: ——
    (1) frequency (3) nuclei
    (2) sublevel (4) orbitals
    c. electromagnetic radiation:visible light
    student body: ——
    (1) eleventh graders (3) teachers
    (2) principal (4) textbooks
56. Traditional cooking methods make use of infrared radiation (heat). Microwave radiation cooks food faster. Could radio waves be used for cooking? Explain.
57. Think about the currently accepted models of the atom and of light. In what ways do these models seem strange to you? Why are these models not exact or definite?

Cumulative Review

58. A potassium atom has a diameter of about 0.406 nm. Express this in meters and micrometers. If the measurement is always the same, why are the two numbers different?
59. Calculate the percent composition of each compound.
    a. SiO_2 **b.** $FeCl_3$ **c.** H_2O **d.** H_2SO_4
60. Balance the following chemical equations.
    a. $KNO_3 + H_2SO_4 \longrightarrow K_2SO_4 + HNO_3$
    b. $Cu_2O + H_2 \longrightarrow Cu + H_2O$
    c. $NO + Br_2 \longrightarrow NOBr$
61. Calculate the volume of O_2 at STP required for the complete combustion of 5.00 L of acetylene (C_2H_2) at STP.

$$2C_2H_2(g) + 5O_2(g) \longrightarrow 4CO_2(g) + 2H_2O(l)$$

62. Write symbols for the following ions.
    a. iron(III) c. hydrogen carbonate
    b. mercury(II) d. oxide
63. Give the number of protons and electrons in each of the following.
    a. Cs **b.** Ag^+ **c.** Cd^{2+} **d.** Se^{2-}
64. The temperature of a gas at STP is changed to 125°C at constant volume. Calculate the final pressure of the gas in atmospheres.
65. The density of gold is 19.3 g/cm^3. What is the mass in grams of a cube of gold 2.00 cm on each edge? In kilograms?

Challenge Questions and Problems

66. The average distance between Earth and Mars is about 2.08×10^8 km. How long does it take to transmit television pictures from the *Mariner* spacecraft to Earth from Mars?

67. The energy of a photon is related to its wavelength and its frequency.

a. Complete the table below.

b. Plot the energy of the photon (y axis) versus the frequency (x axis).

c. Determine the slope of the line.

d. What is the significance of this slope?

Energy of photon (J)	Wavelength (m)	Frequency (s^{-1})
3.45×10^{-21}	5.77×10^{-5}	———
2.92×10^{-20}	6.82×10^{-6}	———
6.29×10^{-20}	3.16×10^{-6}	———
1.13×10^{-19}	1.76×10^{-6}	———
1.46×10^{-19}	1.36×10^{-6}	———
3.11×10^{-19}	6.38×10^{-5}	———

68. In a photoelectric experiment a student shines light of greater than the threshold frequency on the surface of a metal. She observes that after a long time the maximum energy of the ejected electrons begins to decrease. Can you explain why?

69. Bohr's atomic theory can be used to calculate the energy required to remove an electron from an orbit of a hydrogen atom or an ion containing only one electron. This is the *ionization energy* of that atom or ion. The formula for determining the ionization energy E is

$$E = \frac{Z^2 \times k}{n^2}$$

where Z is the atomic number, k is 1312 kJ per mole, and n is the energy level. What is the energy required to eject an electron from a hydrogen atom when the electron is in the ground state ($n = 1$)? In the second energy level? How much energy is required to eject a ground state electron from the species Li^{2+}?

Connections Questions

70. How are the elements in a star identified?

71. This book is an example of a four-color book. Explain what *four-color* means.

72. What do the various spectroscopic techniques have in common?

Write About Chemistry

73. Imagine that you are an electron in the outer energy level of an atom of the phosphor coating of a fluorescent light bulb. Describe your "travels" when the light is turned on.

74. Describe how you have used or encountered electromagnetic radiation, other than visible light, in the following activities: audio entertainment (other than radio), medicine, visual entertainment, working in the kitchen, at the dentist's office, in a safety device in your home, and on a warm day at the pool.

75. Use personal experiences to support the idea that there is a relationship between the color of an object and the amount of solar energy it absorbs. Describe a controlled experiment that would test this hypothesis.

Readings and References

Blaedel, Niels. *Harmony and Unity: The Life of Niels Bohr.* Madison, WI: Science Tech, 1988.

Holzman, David. "Superconductivity." *ChemMatters* (October 1987), pp. 18–21.

Soloman, Burt. "Will Solar Sell?" *Science 84* (April 1984), pp. 70–76.

Sweeting, Linda. "Light Your Candy." *ChemMatters* (October 1990), pp. 10–12.

Townes, Charles H. "Harnessing Light." *Science 84* (November 1984), pp. 153–155.

von Baeyer, Hans Christian. *Taming the Atom: The Emergence of the Visible Microworld.* New York: Random, 1992.

13 Chemical Periodicity

Goals

- Summarize the development of the modern periodic table of the elements.
- Categorize the elements into four classifications based on their outer electron structure.
- Interpret periodic trends based on atomic structure.

The periodic table could be thought of as a puzzle put together in the most logical way. The largest jigsaw puzzle on record had 15,520 pieces.

Concept Overview

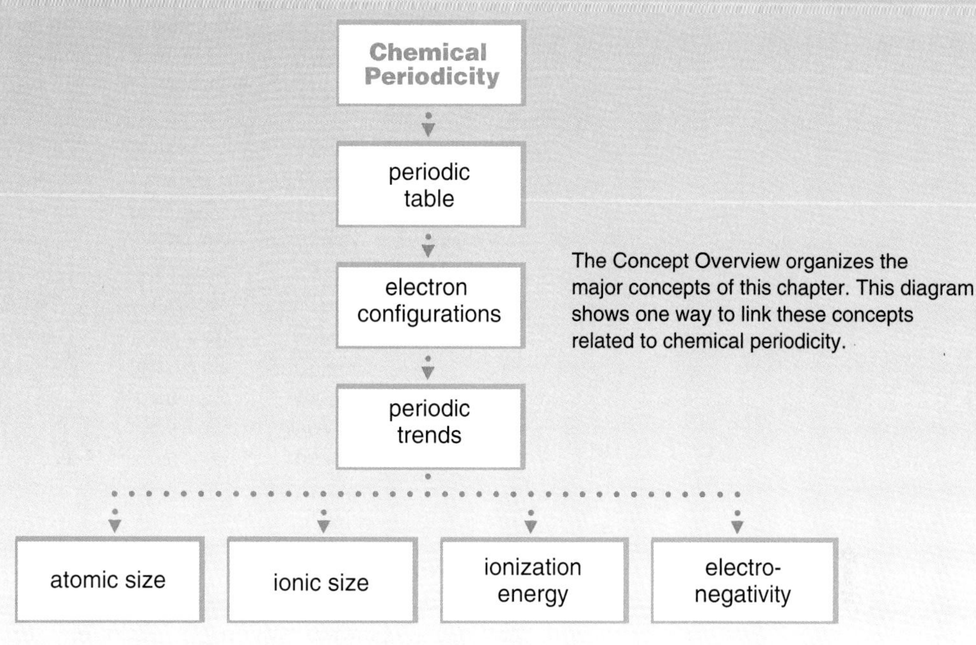

During the nineteenth century, chemists began to categorize the elements according to similarities in their physical and chemical properties. The end result of these studies was the modern periodic table. The periodic table is very useful for understanding and predicting the properties of the elements. In this chapter you will learn how the periodic table is organized and its relationship to the atomic structure and properties of the elements.

13.1 Development of the Periodic Table

Objective

Describe the origin of the periodic table.

About 70 elements had been described by the mid-1800s, but no one had found a common feature that would relate them. Dmitri Mendeleev (1834–1907), a Russian chemist, had more success than most. Mendeleev listed the elements in several vertical columns in order of increasing atomic mass. He noticed a regular (periodic) recurrence of their physical and chemical properties. This led him to arrange the columns so that elements with the most similar properties were side by side. Mendeleev thus constructed the first

Figure 13.1 Mendeleev designed his periodic table by grouping elements with similar properties in rows and ordering these rows according to the atomic masses.

			Ti=50	Zr=90	?=180.
			V=51	Nb=94	Ta=182.
			Cr=52	Mo=96	W=186.
			Mn=55	Rh=104,4	Pt=197,4
			Fe=56	Ru=104,4	Ir=198.
			Ni=Co=59	Pl=106,6	Os=199.
H=1			Cu=63,4	Ag=108	Hg=200.
	Be=9,4	Mg=24	Zn=65,2	Cd=112	
	B=11	Al=27,4	?=68	Ur=116	Au=197?
	C=12	Si=28	?=70	Sn=118	
	N=14	P=31	As=75	Sb=122	Bi=210
	O=16	S=32	Se=79,4	Te=128?	
	F=19	Cl=35,5	Br=80	I=127	
Li=7	Na=23	K=39	Rb=85,4	Cs=133	Tl=204
		Ca=40	Sr=87,6	Ba=137	Pb=207.
		?=45	Ce=92		
		?Er=56	La=94		
		?Yt=60	Di=95		
		?In=75,6	Th=118?		

Biographical Note

Henry Moseley
(1887–1915)

Henry Moseley was educated at Oxford University, England. He was appointed lecturer in physics at Ernest Rutherford's laboratory at the University of Manchester in 1910. Moseley's experimental work proved that the properties of the elements are related to the atomic number instead of the atomic mass. As a result of his studies, Moseley predicted the existence of three as yet unknown elements between aluminum and gold, which were later found. Unfortunately for science, Moseley was killed during World War I. He was only 28 years old.

periodic table. This is an arrangement of the elements according to similarities in their properties. As you can see in Figure 13.1, numerous blank spaces had to be left in the table because there were no known elements with the appropriate properties.

Mendeleev noted the properties of the elements adjacent to the blank spaces. Then he and others were able to predict the physical and chemical properties of the missing elements. Eventually these missing elements were discovered and found to have properties similar to those predicted.

In 1913 Henry Moseley (1887–1915), a young British physicist, determined the nuclear charge, also called the atomic number, of the atoms of the elements. Moseley arranged the elements in a table by order of atomic number. This is the way the periodic table is arranged today.

Concept Practice

1. What criteria did Mendeleev use to construct his periodic table of the elements?

2. Use a modern periodic table to determine the identity of elements with masses of 68 and 70 on Mendeleev's periodic table in Figure 13.1.

13.2 The Modern Periodic Table

Objective

Distinguish between a group and a period in the periodic table.

The most commonly used form of the modern periodic table, sometimes called the long form, is shown in Figure 13.2 on the following two pages. In this figure the elements are arranged in seven horizontal rows in order of increasing atomic number. Each element is identified by its symbol placed in a colored square. The atomic number of the element is shown above the symbol. The atomic mass and the name of the element are shown below the symbol. The circled letter in the upper left corner indicates the physical state of the element at 25°C.

The horizontal rows of the periodic table are called **periods**. There are seven periods. The number of elements in a period increases from 2 in Period 1 to 32 in Period 6. *The vertical columns are called* **groups**, *or families.* Each group is identified by a numeral and the letter A or B. Groups 1A through 7A and Group 0 make up the *representative elements.* They exhibit a wide variety of both physical and chemical properties. The Group B elements are the transition metals. Below the main periodic table appear two rows of elements, the lanthanides and actinides. The elements in any group of the periodic table have similar physical and chemical properties. The properties of the elements in the periods change from group to group. The sequence of change is the same, however, in all the periods. *This gives rise to the* **periodic law**: *When the elements are arranged in order of increasing atomic number, there is a periodic pattern in their physical and chemical properties.* Without the periodic table, you would find it difficult to learn and remember the chemical and physical properties of over 100 individual elements. Instead, you need only learn the general behavior and trends within the major groups to have a useful working knowledge of the properties of most of the elements.

Concept Practice

3. Name two elements that have properties similar to those of the element calcium.

4. Relate the terms *group* and *period* to the periodic table.

5. Look up the word *periodic* in the dictionary. Propose a reason for the naming of the periodic table.

6. If you know how to use the periodic table, you don't have to memorize the chemical and physical properties of 100 elements. Explain why.

Figure 13.2

Periodic Table of the Elements

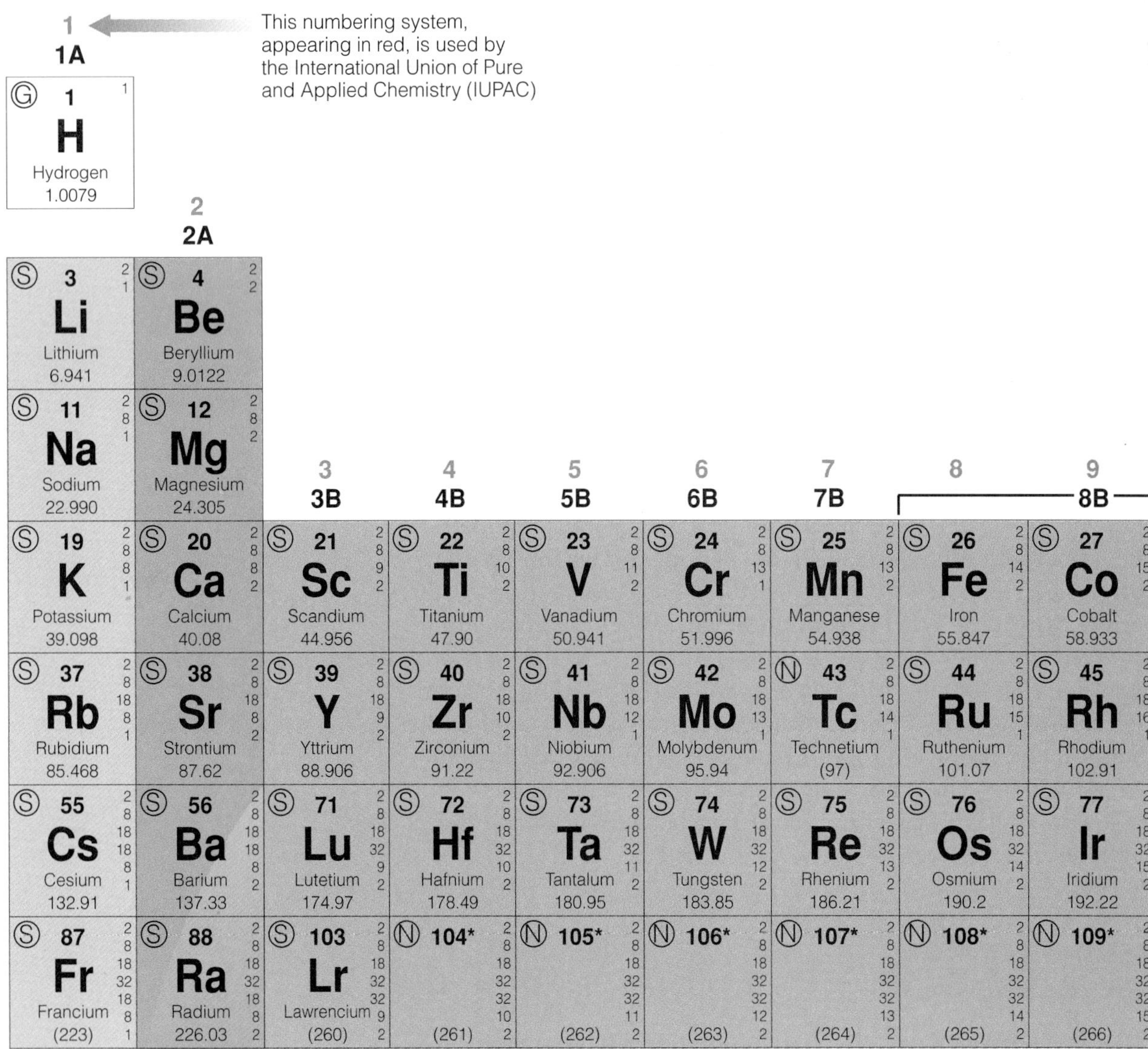

Lanthanide Series

S 57 La Lanthanum 138.91 2 8 18 18 9 2
S 58 Ce Cerium 140.12 2 8 18 20 8 2
S 59 Pr Praseodymium 140.91 2 8 18 21 8 2
S 60 Nd Neodymium 144.24 2 8 18 22 8 2
N 61 Pm Promethium (145) 2 8 18 23 8 2
S 62 Sm Samarium 150.4 2 8 18 24 8 2

Actinide Series

S 89 Ac Actinium (227) 2 8 18 32 18 9 2
S 90 Th Thorium 232.04 2 8 18 32 18 10 2
S 91 Pa Protactinium 231.04 2 8 18 32 20 9 2
S 92 U Uranium 238.03 2 8 18 32 21 9 2
N 93 Np Neptunium 237.05 2 8 18 32 22 9 2
N 94 Pu Plutonium (244) 2 8 18 32 24 8 2

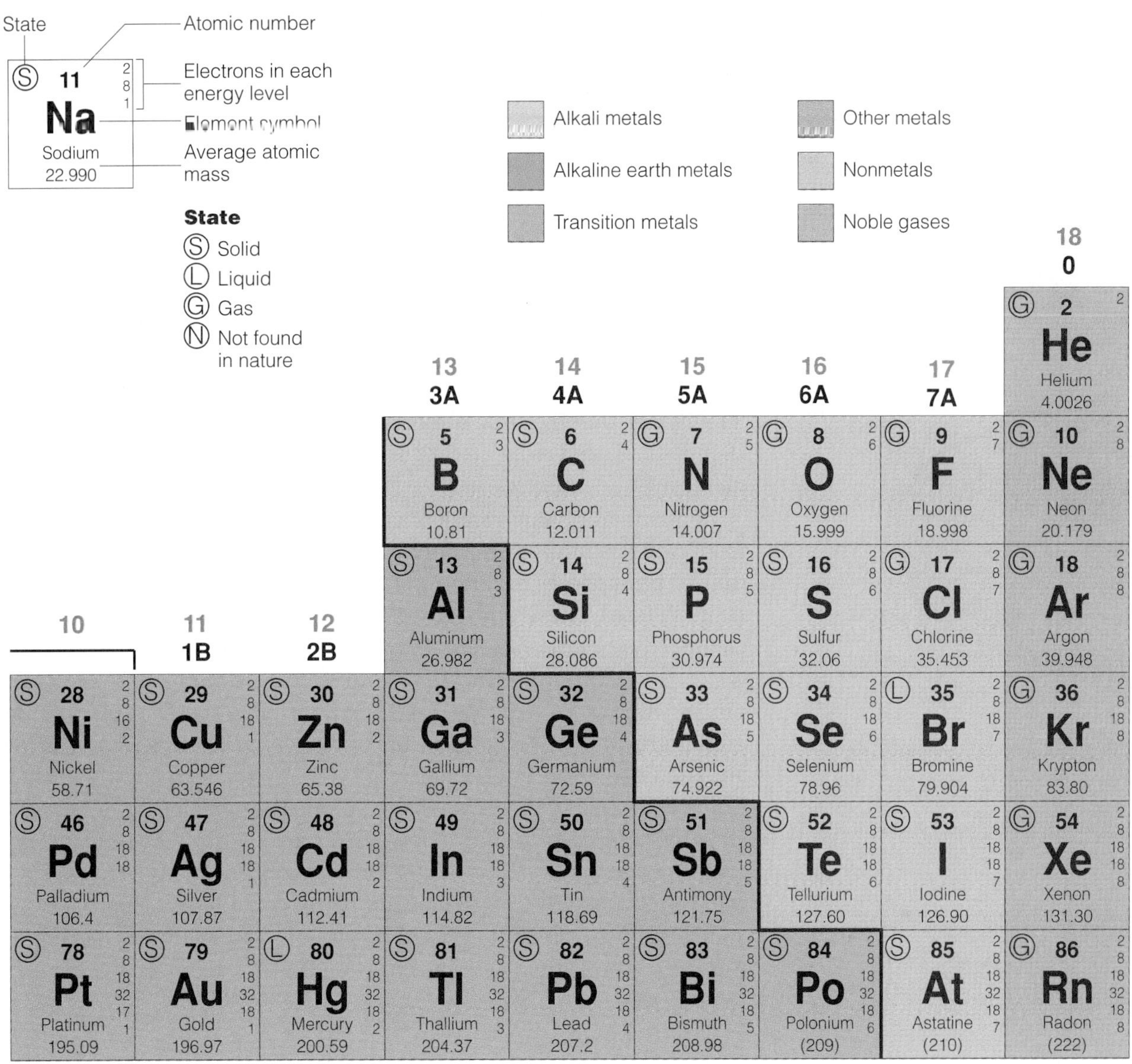

10	11 1B	12 2B	13 3A	14 4A	15 5A	16 6A	17 7A	18 0
								Ⓖ 2 He Helium 4.0026 (2)
			Ⓢ 5 B Boron 10.81 (2 3)	Ⓢ 6 C Carbon 12.011 (2 4)	Ⓖ 7 N Nitrogen 14.007 (2 5)	Ⓖ 8 O Oxygen 15.999 (2 6)	Ⓖ 9 F Fluorine 18.998 (2 7)	Ⓖ 10 Ne Neon 20.179 (2 8)
			Ⓢ 13 Al Aluminum 26.982 (2 8 3)	Ⓢ 14 Si Silicon 28.086 (2 8 4)	Ⓢ 15 P Phosphorus 30.974 (2 8 5)	Ⓢ 16 S Sulfur 32.06 (2 8 6)	Ⓖ 17 Cl Chlorine 35.453 (2 8 7)	Ⓖ 18 Ar Argon 39.948 (2 8 8)
Ⓢ 28 Ni Nickel 58.71 (2 8 16 2)	Ⓢ 29 Cu Copper 63.546 (2 8 18 1)	Ⓢ 30 Zn Zinc 65.38 (2 8 18 2)	Ⓢ 31 Ga Gallium 69.72 (2 8 18 3)	Ⓢ 32 Ge Germanium 72.59 (2 8 18 4)	Ⓢ 33 As Arsenic 74.922 (2 8 18 5)	Ⓢ 34 Se Selenium 78.96 (2 8 18 6)	Ⓛ 35 Br Bromine 79.904 (2 8 18 7)	Ⓖ 36 Kr Krypton 83.80 (2 8 18 8)
Ⓢ 46 Pd Palladium 106.4 (2 8 18 18)	Ⓢ 47 Ag Silver 107.87 (2 8 18 18 1)	Ⓢ 48 Cd Cadmium 112.41 (2 8 18 18 2)	Ⓢ 49 In Indium 114.82 (2 8 18 18 3)	Ⓢ 50 Sn Tin 118.69 (2 8 18 18 4)	Ⓢ 51 Sb Antimony 121.75 (2 8 18 18 5)	Ⓢ 52 Te Tellurium 127.60 (2 8 18 18 6)	Ⓢ 53 I Iodine 126.90 (2 8 18 18 7)	Ⓖ 54 Xe Xenon 131.30 (2 8 18 18 8)
Ⓢ 78 Pt Platinum 195.09 (2 8 18 32 17 1)	Ⓢ 79 Au Gold 196.97 (2 8 18 32 18 1)	Ⓛ 80 Hg Mercury 200.59 (2 8 18 32 18 2)	Ⓢ 81 Tl Thallium 204.37 (2 8 18 32 18 3)	Ⓢ 82 Pb Lead 207.2 (2 8 18 32 18 4)	Ⓢ 83 Bi Bismuth 208.98 (2 8 18 32 18 5)	Ⓢ 84 Po Polonium (209) (2 8 18 32 18 6)	Ⓢ 85 At Astatine (210) (2 8 18 32 18 7)	Ⓖ 86 Rn Radon (222) (2 8 18 32 18 8)

Ⓢ 63 Eu Europium 151.96 (2 8 18 25 8 2)	Ⓢ 64 Gd Gadolinium 157.25 (2 8 18 25 9 2)	Ⓢ 65 Tb Terbium 158.93 (2 8 18 27 8 2)	Ⓢ 66 Dy Dysprosium 162.50 (2 8 18 28 8 2)	Ⓢ 67 Ho Holmium 164.93 (2 8 18 29 8 2)	Ⓢ 68 Er Erbium 167.26 (2 8 18 30 8 2)	Ⓢ 69 Tm Thulium 168.93 (2 8 18 31 8 2)	Ⓢ 70 Yb Ytterbium 173.04 (2 8 18 32 8 2)
Ⓝ 95 Am Americium (243) (2 8 18 32 25 8 2)	Ⓝ 96 Cm Curium (247) (2 8 18 32 25 9 2)	Ⓝ 97 Bk Berkelium (247) (2 8 18 32 27 8 2)	Ⓝ 98 Cf Californium (251) (2 8 18 32 28 8 2)	Ⓝ 99 Es Einsteinium (254) (2 8 18 32 29 8 2)	Ⓝ 100 Fm Fermium (257) (2 8 18 32 30 8 2)	Ⓝ 101 Md Mendelevium (258) (2 8 18 32 31 8 2)	Ⓝ 102 No Nobelium (259) (2 8 18 32 32 8 2)

13.A Consumer Chemistry

Detergents

Figure 13.3 Detergents are common household chemicals.

You probably clean your clothes and dishes with synthetic detergents designed for such tasks. Detergents have largely replaced soaps for clothes- and dish-washing. The reason is that soaps form "soap scum" when used in water that contains calcium, magnesium, or iron ions. This makes clothes look gray. However, you pay an environmental price for having whiter whites!

Modern detergent formulations usually contain biodegradable detergents such as linear alkylsulfonates (LAS) as well as other substances used to bleach, brighten, or improve the detergency. Substances that increase the detergent action by making the water slightly basic and tying up Ca^{2+} and Mg^{2+} ions as water-soluble complexes are called *builders.*

Phosphates, which were once widely used as builders, are now restricted or banned in many areas. Still, an estimated 2 million tons of phosphates are used in detergent products annually in the United States. These phosphates eventually enter river systems and create a major environmental problem. Once phosphates are in the water they act as a nutrient source for algae and other aquatic plants. As the phosphate concentration increases, rapid plant growth results in "algal blooms"—dense growths of algae and aquatic vegetation. Algal blooms deplete the oxygen supply in the water, leading to the death of fish and other organisms.

The detergent industry is working on a variety of phosphate replacements. Sodium silicate, sodium carbonate, and complex aluminosilicates known as *zeolites* are being considered. The first two soften water by precipitating the calcium ions. Zeolites are perhaps the most promising. They trap calcium ions by exchanging them for their own sodium ions.

$$Ca^{2+} + Na_2Al_2Si_2O_7 \longrightarrow 2Na^+ + CaAl_2Si_2O_7$$

The calcium ions are held in suspension rather than being precipitated, and the water is only mildly basic and therefore will not irritate the eyes and skin.

What you use to do your laundry may affect the environment. How will you choose a detergent the next time you have to do the laundry? Can you live with a little soap scum? Will you opt for whiter whites? Or will you wait for zeolites?

Think About It

7. Infer What is the purpose of phosphates in detergents? Why would you want to limit the use of phosphates?

13.3 Electron Configurations and Periodicity

Objective

Categorize the elements as representative elements, noble gases, transition metals, or inner transition metals.

Of the three subatomic particles, the electron plays the greatest part in determining the physical and chemical properties of an element. The arrangement of elements in the periodic table depends on these properties. Thus there should be some relationship between the electron configuration of elements and their arrangement in the table. Elements can be classified into four different categories according to their electron configuration.

1. *The* **noble gases** *are elements in which the outermost s and p sublevels are filled.* The noble gases belong to Group 0. The elements in this group are sometimes called the *inert gases* because they do not participate in many chemical reactions. The electron configurations of the first four noble gas elements are shown below. These elements have filled outermost *s* and *p* levels.

Helium $1s^2$

Neon $1s^2 2s^2 2p^6$

Argon $1s^2 2s^2 2p^6 3s^2 3p^6$

Krypton $1s^2 2s^2 2p^6 3s^2 3p^6 3d^{10} 4s^2 4p^6$

2. *The* **representative elements** *are elements whose outermost s or p sublevels are only partially filled.* The representative elements are usually called the Group A elements. Some definitions of the representative elements may include the noble gases. Besides the noble gases, three groups of representative elements have been given names. *Group 1A elements are called the* **alkali metals** *and Group 2A elements are called the* **alkaline earth metals**. *The nonmetallic elements of Group 7A are called the* **halogens**. For any representative element the group number is equal to the number of electrons in the outermost occupied energy level. For example, the elements in Group 1A (lithium, sodium, potassium, rubidium, and cesium) have one electron in the outermost energy level.

Lithium $1s^2 2s^1$

Sodium $1s^2 2s^2 2p^6 3s^1$

Potassium $1s^2 2s^2 2p^6 3s^2 3p^6 4s^1$

Carbon, silicon, and germanium, in Group 4A, have four electrons in the outermost energy level.

Carbon $1s^2 2s^2 2p^2$

Silicon $1s^2 2s^2 2p^6 3s^2 3p^2$

Germanium $1s^2 2s^2 2p^6 3s^2 3p^6 3d^{10} 4s^2 4p^2$

Roots of Words

al aqali: (Arabic) the ashes
alkali metal any metal of Group 1A of the periodic table

Wood ashes are rich in the salts of the alkali metals sodium and potassium.

hals: (Greek) salt
genesis: (Latin) to be born
halogen any member of the nonmetallic elements from Group 7A

The halogens chlorine, bromine, and iodine may be prepared from their salts.

Figure 13.4 This block diagram identifies groups of elements according to the sublevels that are filled with electrons.

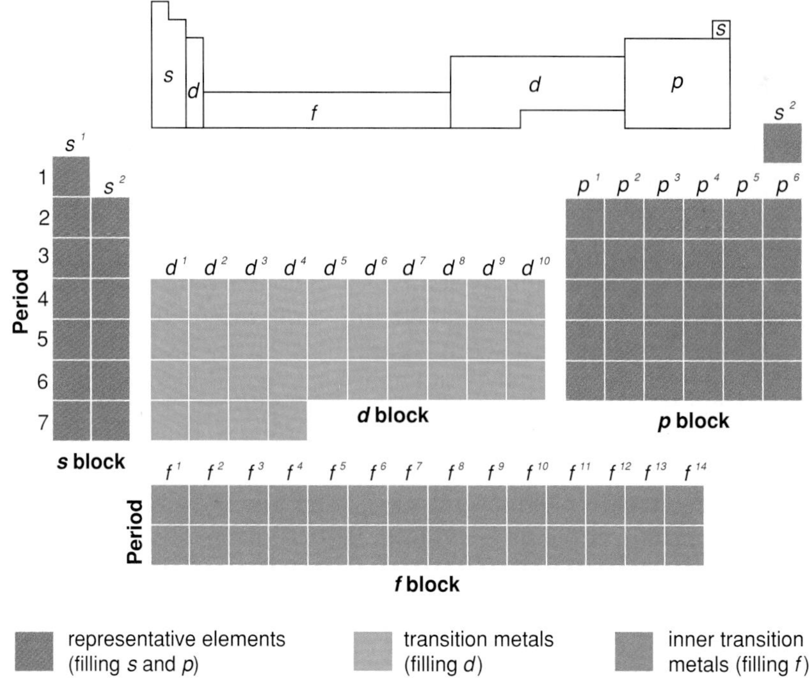

3. *The* **transition metals** *are elements whose outermost s sublevel and the nearby d sublevel contain electrons.* The transition elements are called the Group B elements. They are characterized by having electrons added to the *d* orbitals.

4. *The* **inner transition metals** *are elements whose outermost s sublevel and the nearby f sublevel generally contain electrons.* The inner transition metals are characterized by the filling of *f* orbitals.

If you consider both the electron configurations and the positions of the elements in the periodic table, another pattern emerges. As shown in Figure 13.4, the periodic table can be divided into sections, or blocks, which correspond to the sublevels that are filled with electrons.

The *s* block is the part of the periodic table that contains the elements with s^1 and s^2 electron configurations. It is composed of the elements in Groups 1A and 2A and the noble gas helium.

The *p* block is composed of elements in Groups 3A, 4A, 5A, 6A, 7A, and 0 with the exception of helium.

The transition metals belong to the *d* block, and the inner transition metals belong to the *f* block.

The electron configurations of elements can be determined by using the periodic table in Figure 13.4. Simply read the periodic table like a book from left to right and top to bottom until the element of interest is reached. Each period number on the periodic table corresponds to the principal energy level. The number of electrons in a partially filled sublevel is determined by counting over to the element, starting at the left side of the sublevel. For the transition elements, electrons are added to a *d* sublevel with a principal energy level that is one less than the period number. For the inner transition metals, the principal energy level is two less than the period number.

Example 1 Writing Electron Configurations

Refer to Figure 13.4 and write the electron configurations for these elements.

a. nitrogen **b.** nickel **c.** iodine

Solution

a. Nitrogen has seven electrons. From the periodic table in Figure 13.4 the first period is $1s^2$ and the second period is $2s^22p^3$. There are three electrons in the $2p$ sublevel because nitrogen is the third element in the $2p$ block.

b. Nickel has 28 electrons. From Figure 13.4 the first three periods are $1s^22s^22p^63s^23p^6$. Next is $4s^2$ and finally $3d^8$. Remember that the principal energy level number for the *d* block is always one less than the period number. The complete configuration is $1s^22s^22p^63s^23p^63d^84s^2$.

c. Iodine has 53 electrons. Using Figure 13.4 you find the electron configuration to be $1s^22s^22p^63s^23p^63d^{10}4s^24p^64d^{10}5s^25p^5$.

Concept Practice

8. What are the representative elements, the transition elements, and the inner transition elements?

9. Which of the following are representative elements? Na, Mg, Fe, Ni, Cl

Practice Problems

10. Use Figure 13.4 to write the electron configuration for these elements.

a. boron **b.** magnesium **c.** vanadium **d.** strontium

11. Write the electron configuration of these elements.

a. the inert gas in period 3 **b.** the element in Group 4A, period 4 **c.** the element in Group 2A, period 6

Integrating Astronomy

The Big Bang

Astronomers theorize that the material universe began with an explosion of indescribable energy, the Big Bang. At the moment of this explosion the temperature was many billions of degrees. The elements were formed as a result of the Big Bang. Neutrons, protons, and electrons may have formed within 10^{-4} s after the Big Bang, and the lightest nuclei formed within 3 minutes. At this time, the temperature was still probably 70 times the temperature of the sun. Matter was in the form of plasma, a sea of positive nuclei and negative electrons. It probably took 500 000 years for electrons and nuclei to cool enough to form atoms. Astronomers and physicists are continuing to look for evidence to prove or disprove the Big Bang theory of the origin of the universe.

Objective

Interpret the trend shown by atomic radii within the periodic table.

13.4 Periodic Trends in Atomic Size

You know from the quantum mechanical model that an atom does not have a sharply defined boundary to set the limit of its size. Therefore the radius of an atom cannot be measured directly. There are, however, several ways to estimate the relative sizes of atoms. If the atoms are in a solid crystalline structure, a technique called X-ray diffraction can give an estimate of the distance between the nuclei. For elements that exist as diatomic molecules, the distance between the nuclei of the atoms bonded in the molecule can be estimated. *Half the distance between the nuclei of two like atoms is the* **atomic radius**. For example, the separation between the nuclei in a diatomic bromine molecule (Br_2) is 0.228 nm. Thus a value of 0.114 nm (0.228 ÷ 2) is assigned as the radius of the bromine atom. Figure 13.5 shows atomic radii of the elements.

Group Trends Atomic size generally increases as you move down a group of the periodic table. As you descend, electrons are added to successively higher principal energy levels, and the nuclear charge increases. The outermost orbital is larger as you move downward. The shielding of the nucleus by electrons also increases with the additional number of occupied orbitals between the outermost orbital and the nucleus. You might expect the increase in charge on

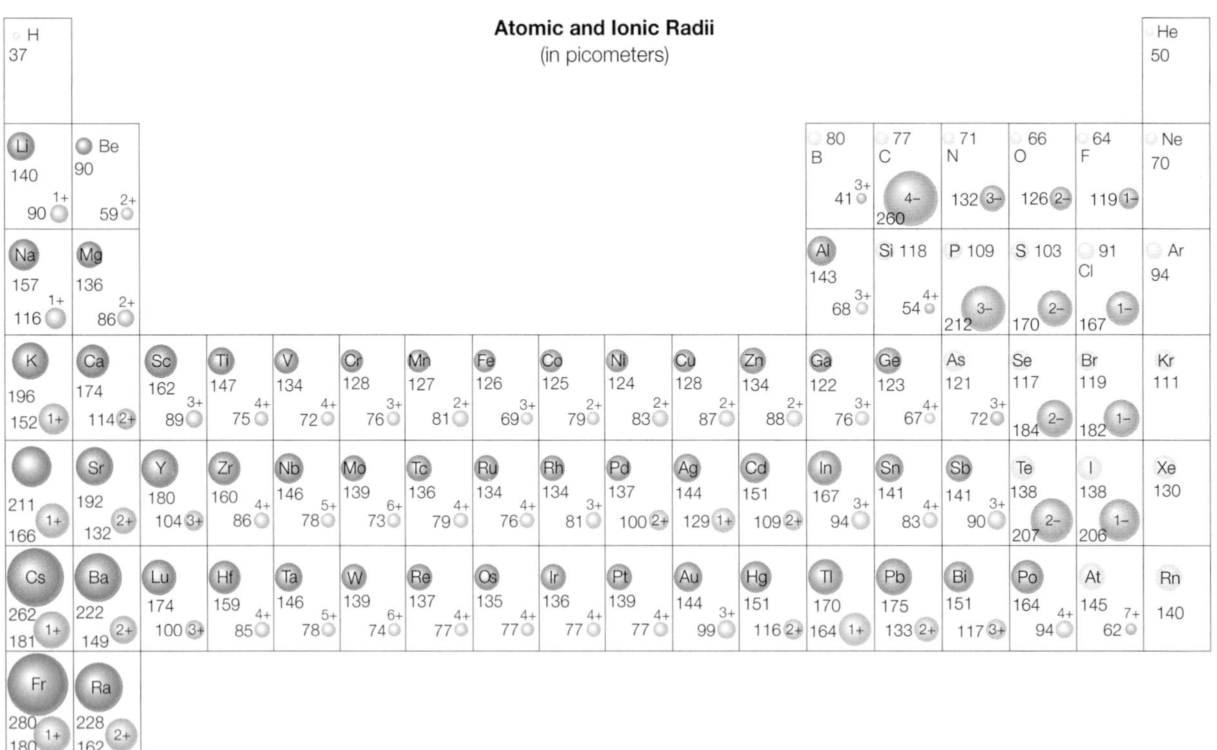

Figure 13.5 Atomic and ionic radii of most of the elements.

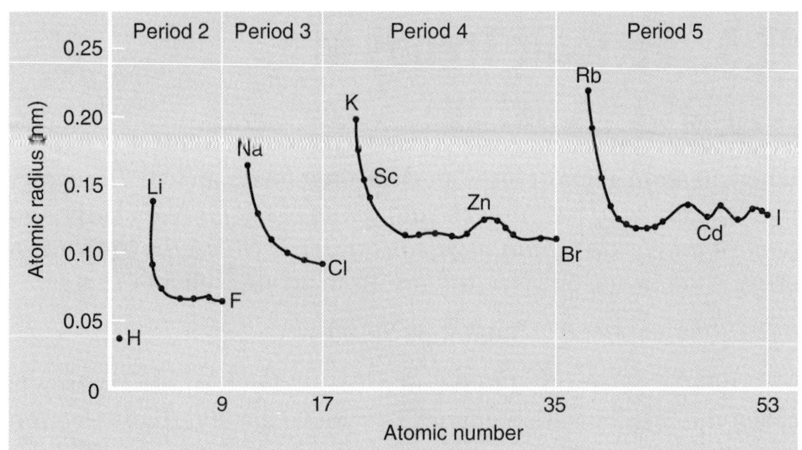

Figure 13.6 This plot of atomic radius versus atomic number shows a periodic variation.

the nucleus to attract the outer electrons and shrink the size of the atom. However, the enlarging effect of the longer distance overcomes the shrinking effect caused by the increasing charge of the nucleus. Therefore the atomic size increases.

Periodic Trends Atomic size generally decreases as you move from left to right across a period. As you go across a period you remain in the same principal energy level. Each element has one proton and one electron more than the preceding element. The electrons are being added to the same principal energy level. The effect of the increasing nuclear charge on the outermost electrons is to pull them closer to the nucleus. Atomic size therefore decreases. If atomic radii are plotted against atomic numbers, as in Figure 13.6, a periodic trend becomes obvious. The trend is less pronounced in periods where there are more electrons in the occupied principal energy levels between the nucleus and the outermost electrons. This is because these inner electrons help shield the outermost electrons and the nucleus from each other. In any period the number of electrons between the nucleus and the outermost electrons is the same for all the elements. Consequently, the *shielding effect* of these electrons on the nucleus is constant within a period.

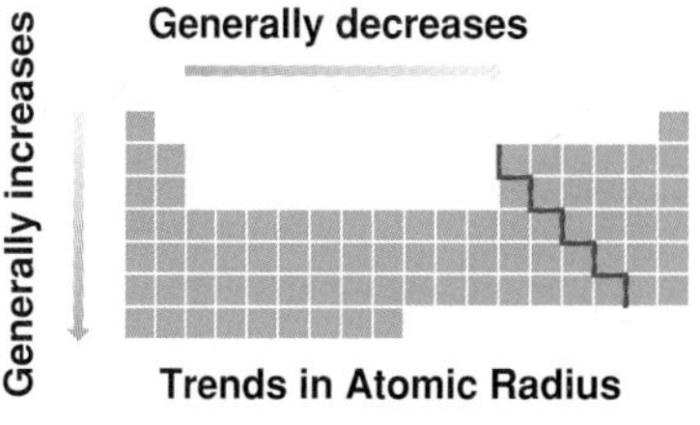

Concept Practice

12. Explain why fluorine has a smaller atomic radius than both oxygen and chlorine.

13. Arrange these elements in order of decreasing atomic size: sulfur, chlorine, aluminum, and sodium. Does your arrangement demonstrate a periodic or a group trend?

Objective

Explain the variation in ionization energies within the periodic table.

13.5 Periodic Trends in Ionization Energy

When an atom gains or loses an electron it forms an ion. *The energy that is required to overcome the attraction of the nuclear charge and remove an electron from a gaseous atom is called the* **ionization energy**. Removing one electron results in an ion with a 1+ charge.

$$\text{Na}(g) \longrightarrow \text{Na}^+(g) + e^-$$

The energy required to remove this first outermost electron is called the first ionization energy. To remove the outermost electron from the gaseous 1+ ion requires an amount of energy called the second ionization energy, and so forth. Table 13.1 gives the first three ionization energies of the first 20 elements.

You can use the concept of ionization energy to predict ionic charges. Look at the three Group 1A metals in Table 13.1. You will see a large increase in energy between the first and second ioniza-

Integrating Music

Newlands's Octaves

Mendeleev's publication of his first periodic table in 1869 was far from the first attempt to organize the elements according to their properties. In 1863, John Newlands (1838–1898), an English chemist, arranged the elements in order of increasing atomic masses. He noted that the properties of the elements repeated when the elements were arranged by increasing atomic mass in groups of eight. For example, the chemical properties of lithium and sodium are very similar. Newlands referred to his arrangement as the law of octaves. This is similar to the musical scale, which repeats every eighth tone. Although the law of octaves fails for elements beyond calcium, Newlands's work was a step in the right direction in the classification of the elements.

Table 13.1 Ionization Energies of the First 20 Elements (in kilojoules per mole)

Symbol of element	Ionization Energy (kJ/mol) First	Second	Third
H	1312		
He (noble gas)	2371	5247	
Li	520	7297	11810
Be	900	1757	14840
B	800	2430	3659
C	1086	2352	4619
N	1402	2857	4577
O	1314	3391	5301
F	1681	3375	6045
Ne (noble gas)	2080	3963	6276
Na	495.8	4565	6912
Mg	737.6	1450	7732
Al	577.4	1816	2744
Si	786.2	1577	3229
P	1012	1896	2910
S	999.6	2260	3380
Cl	1255	2297	3850
Ar (noble gas)	1520	2665	3947
K	418.8	3069	4600
Ca	589.5	1146	4941

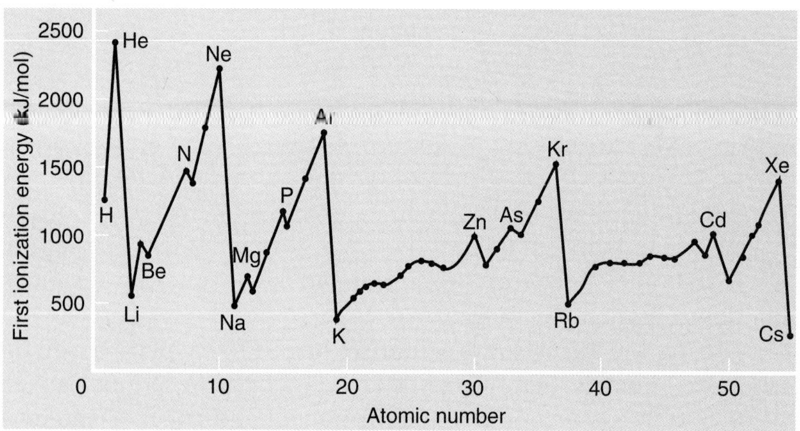

Figure 13.7 Here the first ionization energy is graphed versus the atomic number. Notice the ease with which Group 1A elements are ionized and the difficulty of ionizing noble gases.

tion energies. It is relatively easy to remove one electron from a Group 1A metal to form an ion with a 1+ charge. It is very difficult, however, to remove an additional electron. For the three Group 2A metals, the large increase in ionization energy occurs between the second and third ionization energies. You know that aluminum, in Group 3A, forms a 3+ ion. The large increase in ionization energy for aluminum occurs after the third electron is removed.

Group Trends Table 13.1 shows that in general the first ionization energy decreases as you move down a group of the periodic table. The size of the atoms increases as you descend. Thus the outermost electron is farther from the nucleus. It should be removed more easily and therefore have a lower ionization energy.

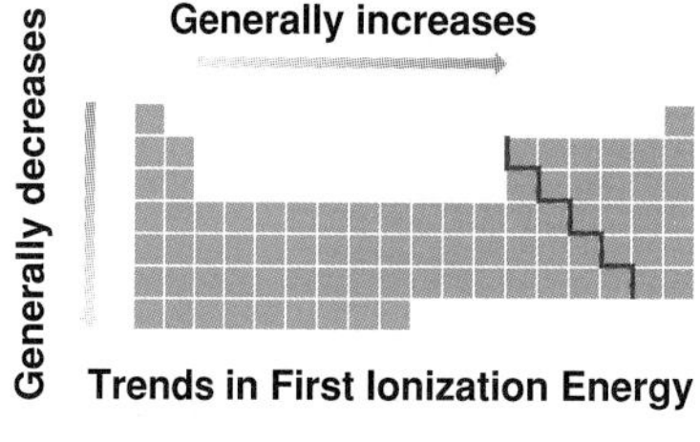

Trends in First Ionization Energy

Periodic Trends For the representative elements the first ionization energy generally increases as you move from left to right across a period. The nuclear charge is increasing, and the shielding effect is constant as you move across. A greater attraction of the nucleus for the electron therefore leads to the increase in ionization energy. The periodic trends of first ionization energies are shown in Figure 13.7.

Concept Practice

14. Distinguish between the first and second ionization energies of an atom.

15. Indicate which element in each of the following pairs has the greater first ionization energy.

a. lithium, boron
b. magnesium, strontium
c. cesium, aluminum

13.B Environmental Awareness

The Ozone Hole

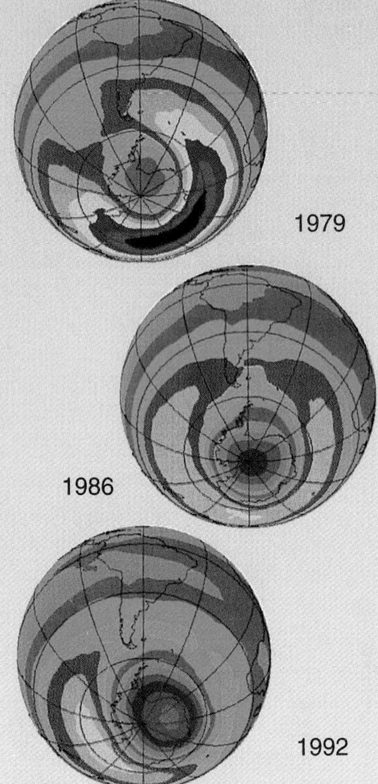

Figure 13.8 These photographs show the progression of the ozone hole in recent years. Ozone levels in the atmosphere are represented from high to low by the colors yellow, green, blue, purple, and pink. The lowest levels of ozone, shown in pink, are located over the polar regions.

The earth is surrounded by a layer of ozone in the upper atmosphere. Ozone (O_3) is the form of oxygen produced when a single oxygen atom joins a molecule of O_2. The ozone layer is important because it screens out 99% of the sun's ultraviolet (UV) radiation. UV radiation is dangerous because it can cause mutations, cancer, blindness, and crop damage.

During the 1970s some scientists began to suspect, based on laboratory models, that the ozone layer might be in serious danger. In 1985 their suspicions were confirmed when British researchers discovered that an ozone "hole" was forming over Antarctica every spring. The amount of ozone in the area of the hole had been reduced by as much as 50%. A similar thin spot has also been identified over the Arctic.

The destruction of the ozone layer is being caused by a category of molecules called chlorofluorocarbons (CFCs). Once used primarily as propellants in aerosol spray cans, CFCs were banned from that use in the United States. However, CFCs are still used in refrigerators, in air conditioners, and in the manufacture of some products. CFCs are highly stable and inert in the lower atmosphere, but they eventually drift up into the stratosphere. Once in the stratosphere, CFCs are broken down by solar radiation, releasing chlorine atoms. These chlorine atoms react with and destroy ozone molecules in their path. A single chlorine atom can destroy as many as 100 000 molecules of ozone. Ice crystals in clouds enhance the ozone-destroying reaction. Therefore, ozone depletion is most evident at the poles during the coldest time of the year when the number of ice crystals is greatest.

The good news is that ozone depletion is a reversible process. If CFC production were reduced by 85%, ozone depletion could be reversed in the next century. Delegates at a United Nations conference in Copenhagen agreed to the elimination of CFCs and carbon tetrachloride by 1996. Hopefully, with the invention of safe substitutes for CFCs and the cooperation of the global community, the world will restore its ozone-depleted stratosphere.

Think About It

16. Describe What are the uses of CFCs? How do CFCs affect the ozone layer?

17. Deduce What are some of the possible harmful effects of the depletion of the ozone layer in the stratosphere?

13.6 Periodic Trends in Ionic Size

The atoms of metallic elements have low ionization energies. They form positive ions easily. By contrast, the atoms of nonmetallic elements readily form negative ions. How does the gain or the loss of electrons affect the size of the ion produced? Positive ions (cations) are always *smaller* than the atoms from which they are formed. This is because the loss of outer shell electrons results in increased attraction by the nucleus for the fewer remaining electrons. As you can see in Figure 13.9, the radius of the Na^+ ion, 0.116 nm, is only about one-half that of the Na atom, 0.186 nm. In contrast, negative ions (anions) are always *larger* than the atoms from which they are formed. This is because the effective nuclear attraction is less for an increased number of electrons. The radius of the Cl^- ion, 0.167 nm, is about twice that of the Cl atom, 0.091nm.

A periodic relationship for the ionic radii of the elements can be seen in Figure 13.5. Going from left to right, across a row, there is a gradual decrease in the size of positive ions. Then, beginning with Group 4, the negative ions (which are much larger) gradually decrease in size as you continue to move right. The ionic radius of both anions and cations increases as you go down each group.

Objective

Interpret the trend shown by ionic sizes within the periodic table.

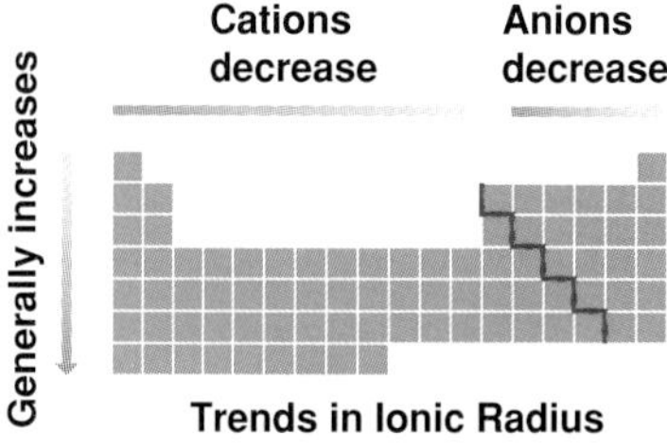

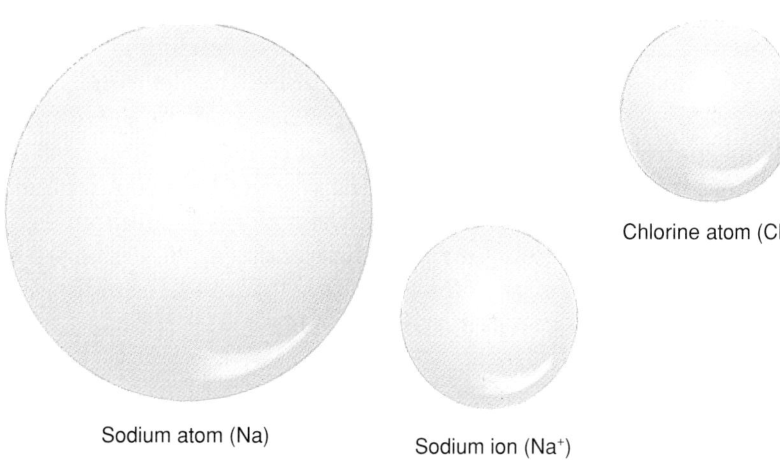

Figure 13.9 The relative sizes of sodium and chlorine atoms and their ions.

Concept Practice

18. Which particle has the largest radius in each atom/ion pair? **a.** Na, Na^+ **b.** S, S^{2-} **c.** I, I^- **d.** Al, Al^{3+}

Objective

Interpret the trend shown by electronegativities within the periodic table.

13.7 Periodic Trends in Electronegativity

The **electronegativity** *of an element is the tendency for the atoms of the element to attract electrons when they are chemically combined with another element.* Electronegativities have been calculated for the elements. They are expressed in arbitrary units on the *Pauling electronegativity scale.* This scale is based on a number of factors, including the ionization energies and electron affinities of the elements.

The electronegativities, arranged in the form of the periodic table, are presented in Table 13.2. Note that the noble gases are omitted because they do not form many compounds. Otherwise, each element is assigned an electronegativity number. Cesium, the least electronegative element, is 0.7 and fluorine, the most electronegative element, is 4.0. When fluorine is chemically bonded to any other element, it attracts the shared electrons, or it tends to form a negative ion. In contrast, cesium, with the lowest electronegativity, has the least tendency to attract electrons. It loses the electron tug-of-war and forms a positive ion.

As you go across a period from left to right, the electronegativity of the representative elements *increases.* The metallic elements at the far left of the periodic table have low electronegativities. By contrast, the nonmetallic elements at the far right (excluding the noble gases) have high electronegativities. Ordinarily, electronegativity decreases as you move down a group. The trends in electronegativity among the transition metals are not so regular. As you will see in Chapters 14 and 15, electronegativity values help you to predict the type of bonding that can exist between atoms in compounds.

You have seen how four periodic trends can be explained by looking at variations in atomic structure. Figure 13.10 summarizes the general trends seen in the periodic table.

Table 13.2 Electronegativity Values for Atoms of Selected Elements

H 2.1						
Li 1.0	Be 1.5	B 2.0	C 2.5	N 3.0	O 3.5	F 4.0
Na 0.9	Mg 1.2	Al 1.5	Si 1.8	P 2.1	S 2.5	Cl 3.0
K 0.8	Ca 1.0	Ga 1.6	Ge 1.8	As 2.0	Se 2.4	Br 2.8

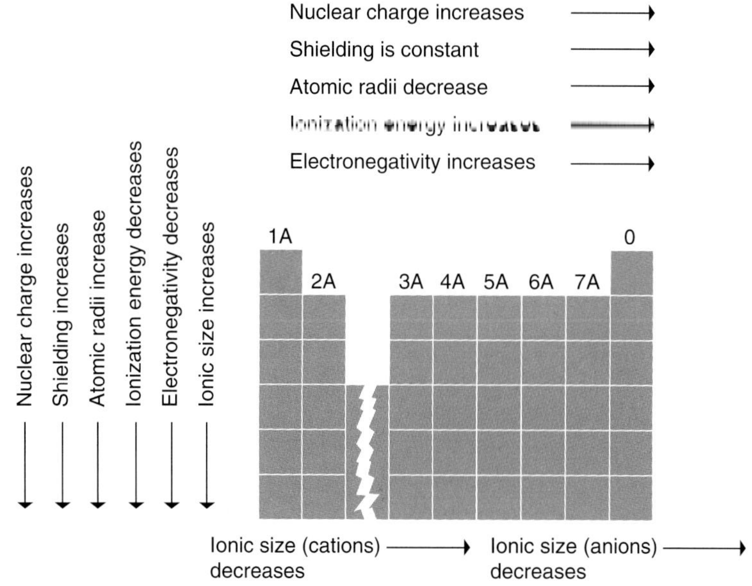

Figure 13.10 Periodic trends are those that vary as you move across and down the periodic table. These properties include the atomic radius, ionization energy, nuclear charge, shielding effect, and electronegativity of the elements.

Concept Practice

19. Why don't the noble gases appear in Table 13.2?

20. Which of these elements has a larger ionization energy?
a. sodium or potassium **b.** magnesium or phosphorus

Activity 13 Periodic Trends

Purpose

To make a graph of ionic radius versus atomic number for each period and examine the graph for periodic and group trends.

Materials

graph paper
pencil

Procedure

1. Use the information presented in Figure 13.5 to make graphs of ionic radius versus atomic number.

2. Make a separate graph for each of the periods. You might want to refer to Figure 13.6.

Analysis and Conclusions

1. Comment on the sizes of cations compared to the sizes of anions. How do these sizes compare with those of the atoms?

2. Are the general trends shown for periods 1, 2, 3, and 4 similar or different?

3. Describe and explain the shapes of the graphs for the periodic trends.

4. How does the ionic radius for anions and cations change as you go down a group? Explain.

Semiconductors

Big Jobs for Little Devices

In 1946 at the University of Pennsylvania, a team of engineers built the Electronic Numerical Integrator And Calculator (ENIAC). The ENIAC was a machine designed to perform high-speed calculations for the government. The machine occupied 2000 square feet of floor space, almost half the size of a basketball court. The ENIAC was a mass of wires and vacuum tubes that processed electricity into complex circuits. Today the calculations performed by the university's giant computer can be done by credit card–sized calculators. The invention of the transistor made this possible. The transistor, a device that amplifies an electrical signal, was the first practical use of semiconductor technology.

Semiconductors are elements that conduct electricity better than insulators but less well than conductors. Silicon (Si), germanium (Ge), and gallium (Ga) are semiconductors. The value of semiconductors lies in their dramatic increase in conductivity when they are mixed with tiny amounts of other atoms. Adding other atoms, usually arsenic (As) or boron (B), to the semiconductor is called doping. In a pure silicon crystal, each atom contains four electrons in the outer shell. In a donor or *n*-type semiconductor, some silicon atoms are replaced with arsenic, which contains five electrons in the outer shell. The extra electrons can move and thus conduct. In an acceptor, or *p*-type semiconductor, some silicon is replaced with boron. Because boron has only three electrons in the outer shell, the acceptor has positive "holes." These holes can move and thus conduct. By selectively doping sections of a semiconductor, miniature electronic components are fabricated. Transistors are just one of the components that are made from semiconductors. Different components are joined to create miniature integrated circuits. Integrated circuits containing millions of components are then placed on a semiconductor wafer in a space smaller than your fingernail! The wafer is then sliced into "chips."

A scanning electron microscope photograph of a semiconducting chip.

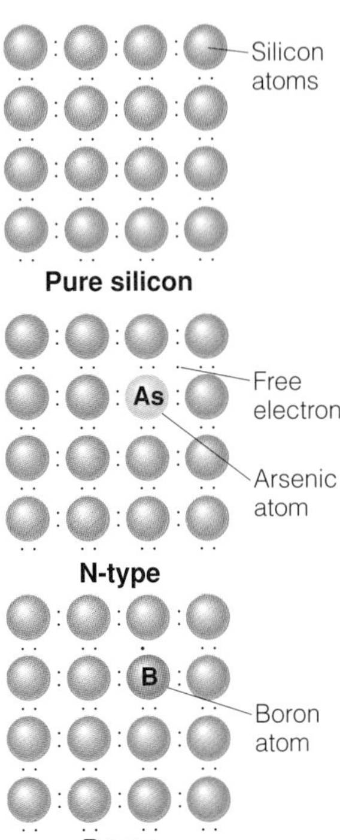

Miniature electronic circuits have revolutionized the electronics and computer industries. Electronic equipment is now smaller, more complex and less expensive than it could ever have been using vacuum tubes and conventional wires. Also, many items that are available today could not have been bought years ago at any price.

Think About It

21. List What elements are used in integrated circuit chips?

22. Give examples Name five items that you use in a typical day that contain electronic chips.

Chapter 13 Review
Chemical Periodicity

Key Terms

alkali metal *13.3*
alkaline earth metal *13.3*
atomic radius *13.4*
electronegativity *13.7*
group *13.2*
halogen *13.3*
inner transition metal *13.3*
ionization energy *13.5*
noble gas *13.3*
period *13.2*
periodic law *13.2*
representative element *13.3*
transition metal *13.3*

Chapter Summary

In the periodic table the elements are organized into groups (vertical columns) and periods (horizontal rows) in order of increasing atomic number. Most of the elements in the periodic table are metals. The nonmetals are confined to a triangular area on the upper right-hand side of the table. Elements that have similar chemical properties are in the same group. The properties of any element are generally intermediate between those of its neighbors on either side in the same period and similar to those of elements above and below it in the same group.

Elements with similar properties have similar electron configurations and are members of the same group. The atoms of the noble gas elements have their outermost *s* and *p* sublevels filled. The outermost *s* and *p* sublevels of the representative elements are only partially filled. The outermost *s* and nearby *d* sublevels of transition metals contain electrons. The outermost *s* and nearby *f* sublevels of inner transition metals generally contain electrons.

The regular changes in the electron configuration of the elements cause gradual changes in both the physical and the chemical properties of the elements within a group and within a period. Atomic radii generally decrease as you move from left to right in a given period of the periodic table because there is an increase in the nuclear charge while the number of inner electrons, and hence the shielding effect, remains constant. Atomic size generally increases within a given group because the outer electrons are farther from the nucleus as you go down the group. The attractive effect of the increased nuclear charge is unable to overcome the effect of the greater distance, which works in opposition. The ionization energy, the energy required to remove an electron from an atom, generally increases as you move from left to right across a period. It decreases as you move down a group. Electronegativity is a measure of the ability of a bonded atom to attract electrons to itself. It generally increases as you move from left to right across a period.

Practice Questions and Problems

23. The graph below shows how many elements were discovered before 1750 and in each 50-year period since then. *13.1*

a. In which 50-year period were the most elements discovered?

b. How did Mendeleev's work contribute to the discovery of so many elements during this time?

c. What characteristic do all the elements discovered since 1950 have in common?

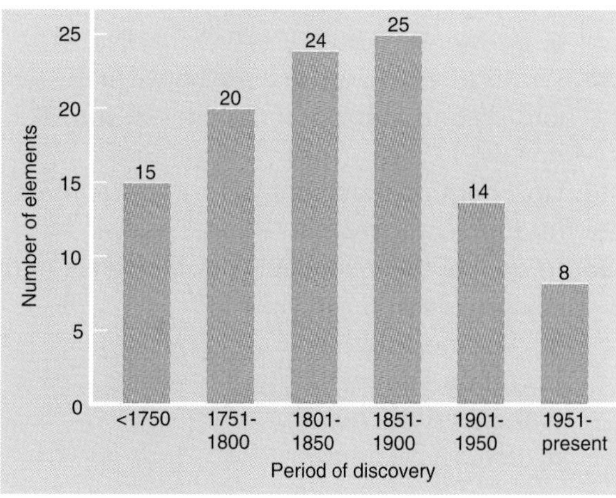

24. What criterion did Mendeleev use in arranging his periodic table? What criterion was used in constructing the modern periodic table? *13.1*

25. What is the periodic law? *13.2*

26. Use Figure 13.2 to complete this table. *13.2*

Element Symbol	Element Name	State	Atomic Number
Hg	_____	_____	_____
_____	silicon	_____	_____
_____	_____	_____	86

27. How is an element's outer electron configuration related to its position in the periodic table? *13.3*

28. Use Figure 13.4 to write the electron configuration of these atoms. *13.3*

a. fluorine **c.** aluminum
b. zinc **d.** tin

29. What are the symbols for all the elements that have the following outer configurations? *13.3*

a. s^1 **b.** s^2p^2 **c.** s^2d^{10}

30. Indicate which element in each of the following pairs has the greater atomic radius. *13.4*

a. sodium, lithium
b. strontium, magnesium
c. carbon, germanium
d. selenium, oxygen

31. In general, would you expect metals or nonmetals to have higher ionization energies? Why? *13.5*

32. Arrange the following elements in order of increasing ionization energy. *13.5*

a. Be, Mg, Sr **b.** Bi, Cs, Ba **c.** Na, Al, S

33. Why is there a large increase between the first and second ionization energies of the alkali metals? *13.5*

34. How does the ionic radius of a typical metallic atom compare to its atomic radius? *13.6*

35. In each of the following pairs, which element is more electronegative? *13.7*

a. chlorine, fluorine
b. carbon, nitrogen
c. magnesium, neon
d. arsenic, calcium

Mastery Questions and Problems

36. Construct a concept map using the key terms with *periodic table* as the central concept.

37. The Mg^{2+} and Na^+ ions each have ten electrons surrounding the nucleus. Which ion would you expect to have the smaller radius? Why?

38. Explain why it takes more energy to remove a 4*s* electron from an atom of zinc than from an atom of calcium.

39. Give the name and symbol of the element found at each of the following locations in the periodic table.

a. Group 1A, period 4
b. Group 3A, period 3
c. Group 6A, period 3
d. Group 2A, period 6
e. Group 3A, period 4

40. Give the symbols of the elements in these groups.

a. alkali metals
b. alkaline earth metals
c. halogens
d. noble gases

41. Give the names, symbols, and electron configurations of the ten first-row transition metals.

Critical Thinking Questions

42. Choose the term that best completes the second relationship.

a. sister:brother oxygen: _____
(1) hydrogen (3) silicon
(2) sulfur (4) Group 6A

b. Mendeleev:atomic mass Moseley: _____
(1) atomic number (3) atomic radius
(2) periodicity (4) neutrons

c. magnesium:*s* orbital zinc: _____
(1) *s* orbital (3) *d* orbital
(2) *p* orbital (4) *f* orbital

43. Why did Mendeleev and later scientists classify the elements into groups?

44. Do you think there are more elements left to be discovered? Explain your answer.

Cumulative Review

45. A 2.00-L flask at 27°C contains 4.40 g of carbon dioxide and 2.00 g of nitrogen gas. What is the pressure, in atmospheres, of each of the two components?

46. Balance the following chemical equations.

a. $Ag + S \longrightarrow Ag_2S$

b. $Na_2SO_4 + Ba(OH)_2 \longrightarrow BaSO_4 + NaOH$

c. $Zn + HNO_3 \longrightarrow Zn(NO_3)_2 + H_2$

d. $H_2O + SO_2 + O_2 \longrightarrow H_2SO_4$

47. The smelting of iron ore consists of heating the ore with carbon.

$2Fe_2O_3 + 3C \longrightarrow 4Fe + 3CO_2$

What mass of iron can be obtained from 100 g of the ore?

48. Write chemical formulas for the following compounds.

a. lithium sulfate

b. zinc phosphate

c. potassium permanganate

d. strontium carbonate

49. If a gas sample at 25°C occupies a volume of 2.93 L, what will the volume be at 500°C if the pressure is unchanged?

Challenge Questions and Problems

50. The ions S^{2-}, Cl^-, K^+, Ca^{2+}, and Sc^{3+} have the same *total* number of electrons as the noble gas argon. How would you expect the radii of these ions to vary? Would you expect to see the same variation in the series O^{2-}, F^-, Na^+, Mg^{2+}, and Al^{3+}, in which each ion has the same total number of electrons as the noble gas neon? Why or why not?

51. Using a chemistry reference book, make a table for the Group 2A elements. Include densities, atomic masses, formulas of the chlorides and oxides, and first ionization energies. Can you justify placing these elements in one group on the basis of these data?

52. The elements are arranged in the periodic table in order of increasing atomic number. You might logically expect that they would also be arranged in order of increasing atomic mass. For the most part this is true, but there are a number of exceptions. Can you find them? Can you explain them?

Connections Questions

53. How did Moseley improve on Mendeleev's periodic table?

54. Describe Newlands's law of octaves.

55. According to the Big Bang theory, which state of matter existed right after the "big bang"?

Write About Chemistry

56. Many designs, including some in three dimensions, have been proposed for the periodic table. Create a unique representation of the periodic table, and explain how it is consistent with the periodic law.

57. Imagine that you are a contemporary of Mendeleev and Moseley interested in discovering new elements. Describe how Mendeleev's newly published periodic table would guide your work.

Readings and References

Emsley, John. *The Elements*, 2nd ed. New York: Oxford University Press, 1991.

Heiserman, David L. *Exploring Chemical Elements and Their Compounds.* Blue Ridge Summit, PA: TAB, 1992.

Sandage, Allan. "Inventing the Beginning." *Science 84* (November 1984), pp. 111–113.

14 Ionic Bonds

Goals

- Apply the octet rule and its exceptions to predict the charges on the cations and anions in ionic compounds.
- Predict the ratio of cations to anions in ionic compounds.
- Explain why ionic compounds have high melting points and high electrical conductivity in the molten state and in water solutions.
- Compare ionic bonding and metallic bonding.

Over three hundred salt domes rise out of the earth along a 2800 km stretch of the Gulf of Mexico. Some of these domes are over 18 000 m deep. However, each individual salt crystal has a cubic structure related to its ionic bonding.

Concept Overview

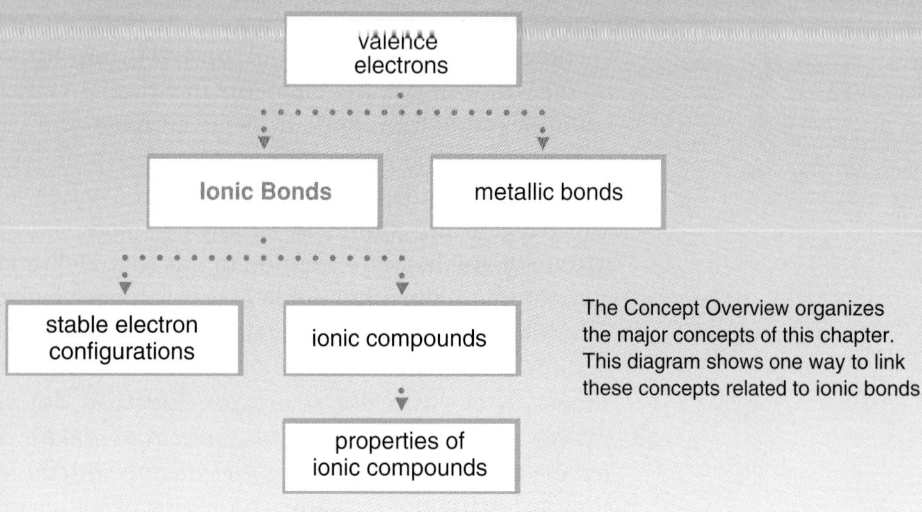

The Concept Overview organizes the major concepts of this chapter. This diagram shows one way to link these concepts related to ionic bonds.

In Chapters 12 and 13 you learned about the electron structure of atoms and the organization of the periodic table. Now you will put this knowledge to work. It will help you understand the chemical bonding that occurs between atoms. For example, the electron configurations of the sodium and chlorine atoms will tell you why these atoms combine to make sodium chloride. They also explain why the formula unit for sodium chloride is NaCl and not Na_2Cl, $NaCl_2$, or Na_2Cl_2. The properties of many compounds can also be explained by their electronic structure. Why does melted sodium chloride conduct electricity? Why is sodium chloride a solid with a terrifically high melting point of 800°C? Questions like these will be answered in this chapter.

14.1 Valence Electrons

Objective

Infer the number of valence electrons in an atom of a representative element using the periodic table, and then construct its electron dot formula.

You may recall that Mendeleev used the properties of the elements to organize his periodic table. Later scientists learned that all the elements in a particular group of the periodic table have the same number of valence electrons. **Valence electrons** *are the electrons in the highest occupied energy level of an element's atoms.* You can figure out the number of valence electrons from an element's electron configuration. Knowing electron configurations is important

Roots of Words

valere: (Latin) to be powerful
valence electron an electron in the highest occupied orbital of an atom

The combining power of an element is determined by the number of its valence electrons.

because *the number of valence electrons largely determines the chemical properties of an element.* The number of valence electrons is also related to the group numbers in the periodic table. For the representative elements it is easy to find an atom's number of valence electrons. Simply look up the group number of that element. For example, the elements in Group 1A (hydrogen, lithium, sodium, potassium, and so forth) all have one valence electron. Carbon and silicon, in Group 4A, have four valence electrons. Nitrogen and phosphorus, in Group 5A, have five valence electrons; and oxygen and sulfur, in Group 6A, have six. The noble gases (Group 0) are the one exception to this rule. Helium has two valence electrons, and the other noble gases each have eight.

Valence electrons are usually the only electrons used in the formation of chemical bonds. Often only the valence electrons are shown in electron dot structures. **Electron dot structures** *show valence electrons as dots. The inner electrons and the atomic nuclei are represented by the symbol for the element being considered.* Table 14.1 shows electron dot structures for atoms of some Group A elements. Notice that all of the elements in a given group, with the exception of helium, have the same number of electron dots in their structures.

Figure 14.1 All of the elements in Group 4A have the same number of valence electrons. How many do they have?

Table 14.1 Electron Dot Structures of Some Group A Elements

Period	Group 1A	2A	3A	4A	5A	6A	7A	0
1	H·						H·	He:
2	Li·	·Be·	·Ḃ·	·Ċ·	·N̈·	:Ö·	:F̈·	:N̈e:
3	Na·	·Mg·	·Al·	·Si·	·P̈·	:S̈·	:C̈l·	:Är:
4	K·	·Ca·	·Ga·	·Ge·	·Äs·	:S̈e·	:B̈r·	:K̈r:

Practice Problems

1. How many valence electrons does each of the following atoms have?
a. potassium **c.** magnesium
b. carbon **d.** oxygen

2. Write the electron dot structure for each element in Problem 1.

14.2 Electron Configurations for Cations

Objective

Describe the formation of a cation from an atom of a metallic element, using the octet rule and the importance of noble-gas electron configurations.

You have seen that noble gases such as neon and argon are quite inert in chemical reactions. In 1916 Gilbert Lewis thought of a reason that atoms form certain kinds of ions and molecules. He gave the world this reason as the **octet rule**: *Atoms in compounds tend to have the electron configuration of a noble gas.* Recall that each noble gas, except helium, has eight electrons (ns^2np^6) in its highest energy level. The octet rule takes its name from this fact. Atoms of the metallic elements obey the octet rule by losing electrons. Atoms of some nonmetallic elements obey the rule by gaining electrons or by sharing electrons with another nonmetallic element. Although exceptions are known, the octet rule applies to most atoms in compounds.

Roots of Words

okto: (Greek) eight
octet eight electrons in the highest occupied orbital of the noble gases, except helium

Atoms in compounds have usually gained or lost enough electrons to acquire the octet of a noble gas.

You may recall that a *cation* is any atom or group of atoms with a positive charge. *The loss of valence electrons from an atom produces a cation.* The most common cations are those produced by the loss of valence electrons from metal atoms. These atoms usually have up to three valence electrons that are easily removed. Sodium, in Group 1A of the periodic table, is typical. Sodium atoms have a total of 11 electrons, including 1 valence electron. When forming a compound, a sodium atom loses its 1 valence electron. In Figure 14.2, you can see that the sodium *ion* has the same electron configuration as neon, a noble gas. The sodium ion has an octet (eight electrons) in its highest energy level. Because the number of protons in the sodium nucleus is still 11, the lack of one unit of negative charge produces a sodium ion with a charge of 1+. You can show the electron loss, or ionization, of the sodium atom by drawing the complete electron configuration of the atom and the ion formed.

$$\text{Na} \quad 1s^2 2s^2 2p^6 3s^1$$
$$\text{Na}^+ \quad 1s^2 \underbrace{2s^2 2p^6}_{\text{octet}}$$

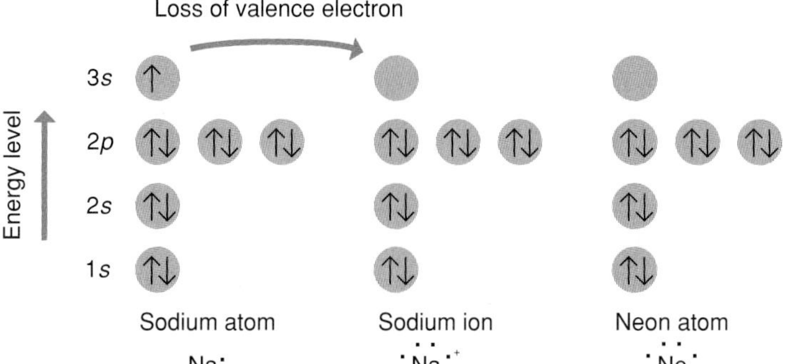

Figure 14.2 A sodium atom loses an electron to become a positively charged sodium ion. The sodium ion has an electron configuration that is like the electron configuration of neon. Neon is a noble gas. In both Na^+ and Ne, there are eight electrons (an octet) in the highest energy levels.

Biographical Note

Percy Julian
(1899–1975)

Percy Julian was an important contributor to natural products chemistry. Natural products are organic substances derived from plants and animals. These organic substances are used in the preparation of flavors, fragrances, resins, and pharmaceuticals. Julian, an industrial chemist, was awarded over 100 patents, many of them for substances he extracted from soybeans. Perhaps Julian's most important contribution was the inexpensive method he developed for isolating sterols from soybeans. Cortisone, a sterol derivative, is prescribed to relieve arthritis pain. As a result of Julian's research, cortisone became more widely available. In 1947, Julian received the NAACP Spingarn Award for outstanding achievement by an African American.

The electron configuration of the sodium ion is the same as that of the neon atom. Both have an octet of outer electrons.

$$\text{Ne} \quad 1s^2\underbrace{2s^2 2p^6}_{\text{octet}}$$

The ionization can be shown more simply by using an electron dot structure for the atom.

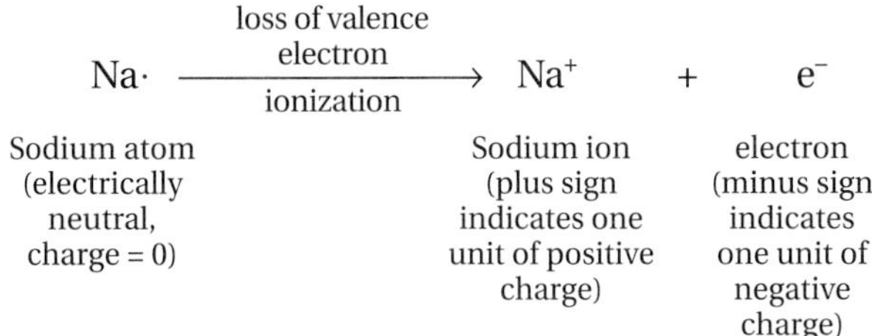

Magnesium (atomic number 12) belongs to Group 2A of the periodic table and therefore has two valence electrons. Magnesium atoms attain the electron configuration of neon by losing both valence electrons. The loss of the valence electrons produces a magnesium ion, a cation with twice the positive charge of a sodium ion.

$$\underset{\text{Magnesium atom}}{\cdot\text{Mg}\cdot} \longrightarrow \underset{\text{Magnesium ion}}{\text{Mg}^{2+}} + 2\text{e}^-$$

You have seen that the cations of Group 1A elements always have a charge of 1+. Similarly, the cations of Group 2A elements always have a charge of 2+. You can now explain this constancy in terms of the loss of valence electrons by metal atoms: the atoms lose enough electrons to attain the electron configuration of a noble gas. The elements in Group 2A all have two valence electrons. In losing these two electrons they form 2+ cations. The charge of transition metal cations may vary. An atom of iron loses two electrons to form the iron(II), or ferrous, ion, Fe^{2+}. An atom of iron loses three electrons in forming the iron(III), or ferric, ion, Fe^{3+}.

Some ions do not have noble-gas electron configurations (ns^2np^6). These ions are exceptions to the octet rule. Take silver with the electron configuration of $1s^22s^22p^63s^23p^63d^{10}4s^24p^64d^{10}5s^1$ as an example. To achieve the structure of the noble gas krypton, a silver atom would have to lose 11 electrons. Alternatively, it could gain 7 electrons to acquire the electron configuration of the noble gas xenon. Since ions with a charge greater than three are uncommon, neither of these possibilities is likely.

Silver does not acquire a noble-gas configuration. Yet its outer electron configuration will be $4s^24p^64d^{10}$ if it loses its $5s^1$ electron. This configuration, with 18 electrons in the outer energy level and all orbitals filled, is relatively favorable in compounds of silver. It is known as the *pseudo noble-gas* electron configuration. Silver forms a positive ion (Ag^+) in this way. Other elements that behave similarly to silver are at the right of the transition metal series. Another example is shown in Figure 14.3. Copper (Cu^+), gold (I) (Au^+), cadmium (Cd^{2+}), and mercury(II) (Hg^{2+}) ions have pseudo noble-gas electron configurations.

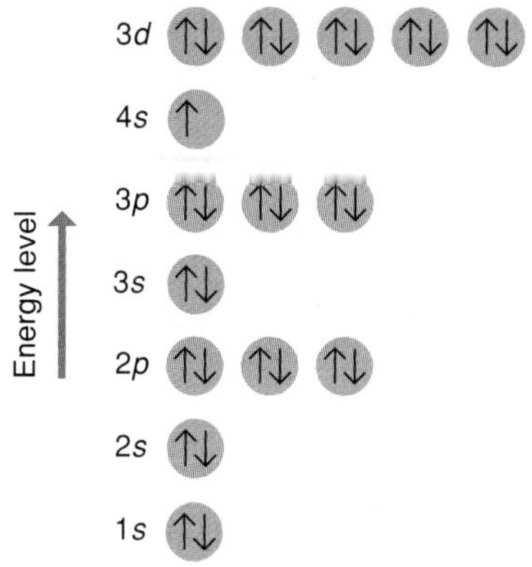

Figure 14.3 By losing the 4*s* electron, copper attains a pseudo noble-gas electron configuration. Thus, a copper atom can become a copper(I) ion, Cu^+.

Concept Practice

3. Why do metals tend to form cations when they react to form compounds?

Practice Problem

4. Write electron configurations for the following transition metal ions: copper(I) (Cu^+), gold(I) (Au^+), cadmium (Cd^{2+}), and mercury(II) (Hg^{2+}).

14.3 Electron Configurations for Anions

Objective

Describe the formation of an anion from an atom of a nonmetallic element.

An anion is an atom or a grouping of atoms with a negative charge. *The gain of valence electrons produces an anion.* Atoms of nonmetallic elements attain noble-gas electron configurations more easily by gaining electrons than by losing them. For example, chlorine belongs to Group 7A, the halogen family, of the periodic table. A gain of one electron converts a chlorine atom into a chloride ion. It is an anion with a single negative charge. Chlorine atoms therefore need one more valence electron to achieve the electron configuration of the nearest noble gas, argon.

$$\text{Cl} \quad 1s^2 2s^2 2p^6 3s^2 3p^5 \qquad \text{Cl}^- \quad 1s^2 2s^2 2p^6 \underbrace{3s^2 3p^6}_{\text{octet}}$$

The chloride ion has eight electrons (an octet) in its highest energy level, as shown in Figure 14.4. The chloride ion has the same electron configuration as the noble gas argon.

$$\text{Ar} \quad 1s^2 2s^2 2p^6 3s^2 3p^6$$

Electron configuration diagrams can also be used to write an equation showing the formation of a chloride ion from a chlorine atom. Compare these diagrams in Figure 14.4 on the next page with the electron dot structures.

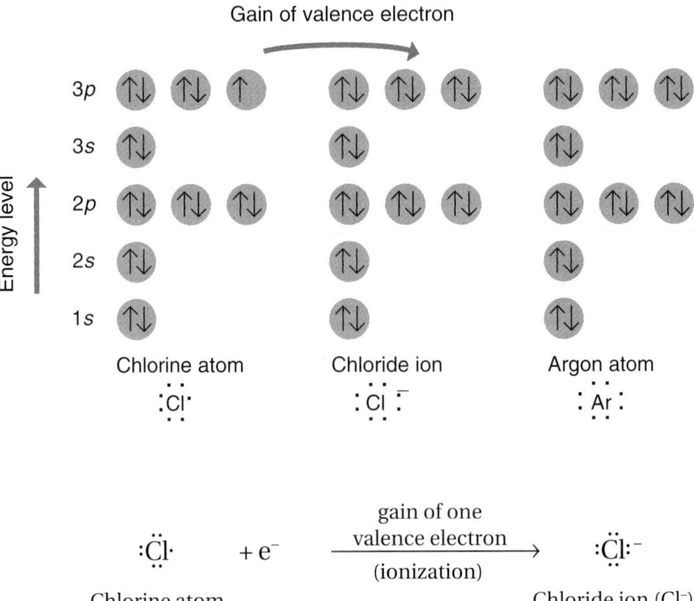

Figure 14.4 A chlorine atom gains an electron to become a negatively charged chloride ion. The chloride ion has an electron configuration like the electron configuration of argon. Argon is a noble gas. Both the chloride ion and the argon atom have an octet of electrons.

$$:\ddot{\underset{..}{Cl}}\cdot \quad + e^- \xrightarrow[\text{(ionization)}]{\text{gain of one valence electron}} :\ddot{\underset{..}{Cl}}:^-$$

Chlorine atom — Chloride ion (Cl^-)

Atoms of chlorine and the other halogens gain electrons to form **halide ions**. Any halogen atom has seven valence electrons. A halogen atom needs to gain one electron to achieve the electron configuration of a noble gas. Therefore, as you have seen, all halide ions have a charge of 1^-: F^-, Cl^-, Br^-, and I^-.

Oxygen atoms each have six valence electrons. Oxygen atoms attain the electron configuration of neon by gaining two electrons. The resulting oxide ions have charges of 2– and are written as O^{2-}.

$$:\ddot{\underset{\cdot}{O}}\cdot \quad + 2e^- \longrightarrow :\ddot{\underset{..}{O}}:^{2-}$$

Oxygen atom — Oxide ion

Concept Practice

5. Why do nonmetals tend to form anions when they react to form compounds?

6. How many electrons do the following elements gain or lose in forming an ion?

a. calcium (Ca) **c.** aluminum (Al)
b. fluorine (F) **d.** oxygen (O)

7. What is the formula of the ion formed when the following elements gain or lose valence electrons and attain noble-gas configurations?

a. sulfur (S) **b.** sodium (Na) **c.** fluorine (F) **d.** barium (Ba)

Integrating Food Science

Sulfur Dioxide and Sulfites

Sulfur dioxide (SO_2) has been used as a food additive since the time of the ancient Egyptians and Romans. Sulfur dioxide reacts with water to make hydrogen sulfite ions (HSO_3^-) and sulfite ions (SO_3^{2-}). The mixture of these ions and sulfur dioxide is usually referred to simply as "sulfites." Sulfites are especially effective in preventing the deterioration of dried fruits and fruit juices. Spraying fresh lettuce and other produce with water containing low concentrations of sulfites keeps them from turning brown. The use of sulfites was once so common that they were often not labeled as an ingredient in foods. However, sulfur dioxide is a choking gas that plays a role in air pollution. Also, there is evidence that sulfites can trigger episodes of asthma in people who suffer from the illness. Thus, the use of sulfites to preserve foods is discouraged.

14.A Historical Notebook

Damascus Steel

About 2000 years ago Middle Eastern blacksmiths forged steel into scimitars and armor. They used a secret process to produce an extremely durable steel that could be stretched and forged into complex shapes. The scimitar blades made from this steel were razor sharp and retained their strength after many battles. The weaponry came to be known as Damascus steel, after the ancient Syrian capital where Westerners first encountered it. Knowledge of how to make this special steel was presumably passed on by word of mouth, and the secret was eventually lost. Not until the nineteenth century did several leading scientists attempt to rediscover the process of making Damascus steel. These scientists failed in their attempts.

Attempts to create a steel like Damascus steel have continued to the present day with some recent success. Scientists have developed steels, called superplastic steels, that are very similar to Damascus steel. The secret to making superplastic steels is to double, roughly, the amount of carbon used in making conventional steels. Where conventional steels are less than 1% carbon, superplastic steels are as much as 2% carbon. Superplastic steel is also subjected to the right combination of heating, cooling, and forming. The extra carbon keeps the grain size of the steel extremely fine. The fine grain size gives the superplastic steel its pliability at high temperatures.

The development of superplastic steel promises to have a major impact on the steel industry. Superplastic steels, also known as ultra-high-carbon steel (UHCS) alloys, are stronger, more malleable, and more ductile than conventional steels. Whereas most metals can be stretched up to 50% before breaking, superplastic steels can be stretched 1000% or more in many instances. This malleability means that instead of machining steel and having leftover metal shavings, workers can form superplastic steel into complex shapes directly. The conservation of material and energy would mean a real economic savings for industries that use steel. Thus, Damascus steel, although an old technology, continues to contribute to new technologies.

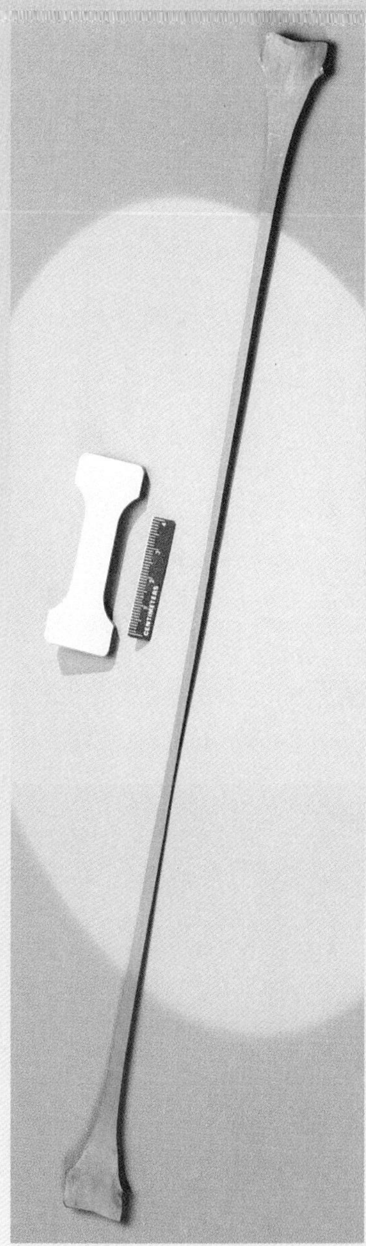

Figure 14.5 The original size of each piece of steel was 2.54 centimeters. The piece at the left, a conventional steel, stretched to about 4 centimeters. The superplastic steel stretched to about 35.6 centimeters.

Think About It

8. Contrast What are the advantages of superplastic steel over conventional steels?

Objective

List the characteristics of an ionic bond.

14.4 Ionic Compounds

Anions and cations have opposite charges. They attract one another by electrostatic forces. *The forces of attraction that bind oppositely charged ions together are called* **ionic bonds**. Ionic compounds are electrically neutral groups of ions joined by electrostatic forces. Ionic compounds are also called *salts.* In any sample of an ionic compound, the positive charges of the cations must equal the negative charges of the anions.

Sodium chloride provides a simple example of how ionic bonds are formed. Consider the reaction between a sodium atom and a chlorine atom. Sodium has a single valence electron that it can easily lose. The sodium atom loses its valence electron to gain the stable electron configuration of neon. Chlorine has seven valence electrons and can easily gain one. The chlorine atom gains a valence electron to have the stable electron configuration of argon. When sodium and chlorine react to form a compound, the sodium atom gives its one valence electron to a chlorine atom. Thus sodium and chlorine atoms combine in a one-to-one ratio, and both ions have stable octets.

$$\mathrm{Na\cdot} + \mathrm{\cdot\ddot{\underset{..}{Cl}}:} \longrightarrow \mathrm{Na^+} \quad \mathrm{:\ddot{\underset{..}{Cl}}:^-} \quad \text{or} \quad \mathrm{NaCl}$$

$$1s^22s^22p^6(3s^1) \quad 1s^22s^22p^63s^23p^5 \qquad \underbrace{1s^22s^22p^6}_{\text{octet}} \qquad 1s^22s^22p^6\underbrace{3s^23p^6}_{\text{octet}}$$

$$\text{Ne} \qquad\qquad \text{Ar}$$

$$\underbrace{1s^22s^22p^6}_{\text{octet}} \qquad 1s^22s^22p^6\underbrace{3s^23p^6}_{\text{octet}}$$

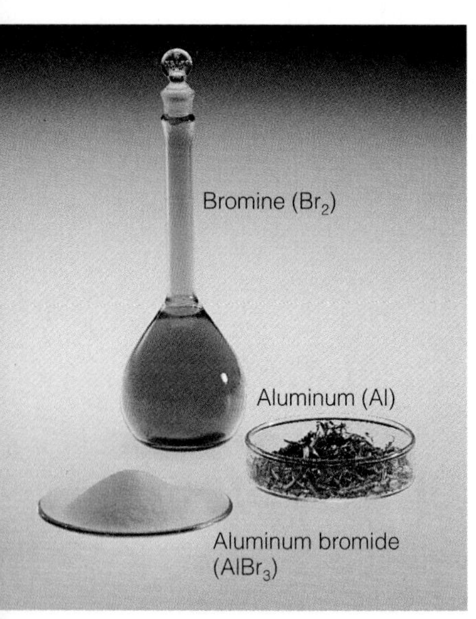

Figure 14.6 Aluminum and bromine combine to form aluminum bromide. Why do three bromine atoms combine with each aluminum atom?

The chemical formula, NaCl, is a *formula unit.* It represents the smallest sample of an ionic compound that has the composition of the compound. The formula NaCl shows that one formula unit of sodium chloride contains one sodium ion and one chloride ion.

In Figure 14.6, aluminum and bromine, the reactants, form the compound aluminum bromide, the product. Each aluminum atom has three valence electrons to lose. A bromine atom has seven valence electrons. Each bromine easily gains an additional electron. When aluminum and bromine react, three bromine atoms react with each aluminum atom.

$$\mathrm{\dot{A}l\cdot} + 3\,\mathrm{\cdot\ddot{\underset{..}{Br}}:} \longrightarrow \mathrm{Al^{3+}} \quad 3\,\mathrm{:\ddot{\underset{..}{Br}}:^-} \quad \text{or} \quad \mathrm{AlBr_3}$$

The formula for aluminum bromide is therefore $AlBr_3$.

Example 1 Predicting Formulas of Ionic Compounds

Use electron dot formulas to predict the formulas of the ionic compounds formed from these elements.

a. potassium and oxygen **b.** magnesium and nitrogen

Solution

Write the correct electron dot formula of each atom in the compound. Enough atoms of each element must be used in the formula so that electrons lost equal electrons gained.

a. Start with the atoms: K· and ·Ö:

Oxygen needs two electrons. These electrons can come from two potassium atoms.

$$\begin{matrix} K\cdot \\ K\cdot \end{matrix} + \cdot\ddot{O}: \longrightarrow \begin{matrix} K^{+} \\ K^{+} \end{matrix} \; :\ddot{O}:^{2-}$$

Electrons *lost* now equal electrons *gained*. The formula of potassium oxide is K_2O.

b. Start with the atoms: Mg and ·N:

Nitrogen needs three electrons, but each magnesium atom can lose only two. Thus you need three magnesium atoms for every two nitrogen atoms.

$$\begin{matrix} Mg \\ Mg \\ Mg \end{matrix} + \begin{matrix} \cdot N: \\ \cdot N: \end{matrix} \longrightarrow \begin{matrix} Mg^{2+} \\ Mg^{2+} \\ Mg^{2+} \end{matrix} \; \begin{matrix} :\ddot{N}:^{3-} \\ :\ddot{N}:^{3-} \end{matrix}$$

The formula of magnesium nitride is Mg_3N_2.

Practice Problems

9. Use electron dot formulas to determine chemical formulas of the ionic compounds formed when the following elements combine.

a. potassium and iodine
b. calcium and sulfur
c. aluminum and oxygen
d. sodium and phosphorus

10. Name the compounds formed in Problem 9.

11. Use ionic charges to write chemical formulas of the compounds named in Problem 9.

Integrating Geochemistry

Mineral Salts

Many ionic substances appear as minerals in the Earth's crust. A mineral is a naturally occurring solid of more or less specific composition that generally occurs in crystalline form and is usually inorganic in nature. Minerals are often found incorporated into rocks. Geochemistry is concerned in part with the composition of minerals and the processes by which minerals were formed. Geochemists believe that, under favorable conditions of temperature and pressure, silicon dioxide, SiO_2, grew into clear crystals of the mineral quartz. Iron sulfide formed perfect cubes of pyrite, also known as "fool's gold" because its golden color has fooled many amateur gold prospectors. Limestone consists of either the mineral calcite or the mineral dolomite, two different crystalline forms of calcium carbonate, $CaCO_3$. Because there are at least 3000 different kinds of rocks, geochemists can expect to be busy for a very long time!

Objective

Explain the electrical conductivity of melted and of aqueous solutions of ionic compounds, using the characteristics of ionic compounds.

14.5 Properties of Ionic Compounds

Most ionic compounds are crystalline solids at room temperature. *The component molecules, atoms, or ions of a crystal are arranged in repeating three-dimensional patterns.* The composition of a crystal of sodium chloride is typical. In solid NaCl each sodium ion is surrounded by six chloride ions and each chloride ion is surrounded by six sodium ions. In this arrangement each ion is attracted strongly to each of its neighbors and repulsions are minimized. The large attractive forces result in a very stable structure. This is reflected in the fact that NaCl and ionic compounds in general have very high melting points.

Figure 14.7 shows the three-dimensional arrangement of ions in NaCl. Because each Na^+ ion is surrounded by six Cl^- ions, it has a coordination number of 6. *The* **coordination number** *gives the number of ions of opposite charge that surround each ion in a crystal.* Each Cl^- ion is surrounded by six Na^+ ions and also has a coordination number of 6.

Cesium chloride (CsCl) has a formula unit that is similar to NaCl. Both compounds have cubic crystals but their internal crystal structures are different. Each Cs^+ ion is surrounded by eight Cl^- ions, and each Cl^- ion is surrounded by eight Cs^+ ions. The anion and cation in cesium chloride each have a coordination number of 8.

The crystalline form of titanium dioxide (TiO_2) is rutile. A diagram of the crystal is shown in Figure 14.8. In this compound the coordination number for the cation (Ti^{4+}) is 6. Each Ti^{4+} ion is surrounded by six O^{2-} ions. The coordination number of the anion (O^{2-}) is 3. Each O^{2-} ion is surrounded by three Ti^{4+} ions. The internal structures of crystals are determined using a technique known as X-ray diffraction crystallography. Patterns are formed when X-rays pass through a crystal onto X-ray film. These patterns are used to calculate the positions of ions in the crystal and to define the structure of the crystal.

Figure 14.7 Both cesium chloride and sodium chloride form clear, cubic crystals. The unit cells of these cubic materials differ. While sodium chloride is face-centered cubic, cesium chloride is body-centered cubic. A photograph of magnified sodium chloride crystals appears below.

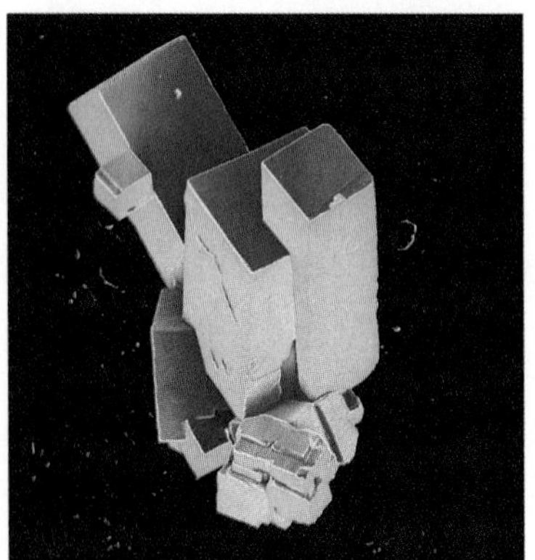

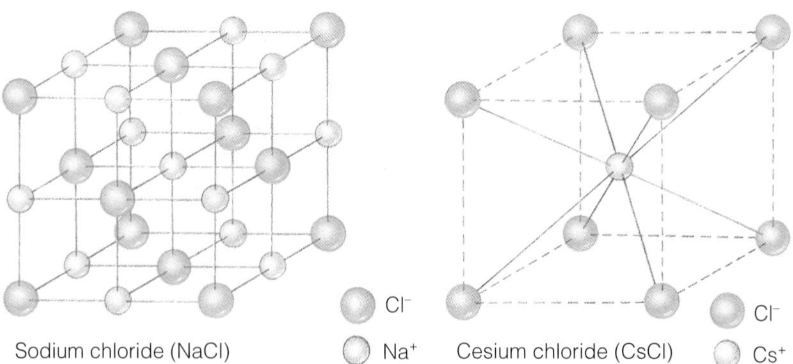

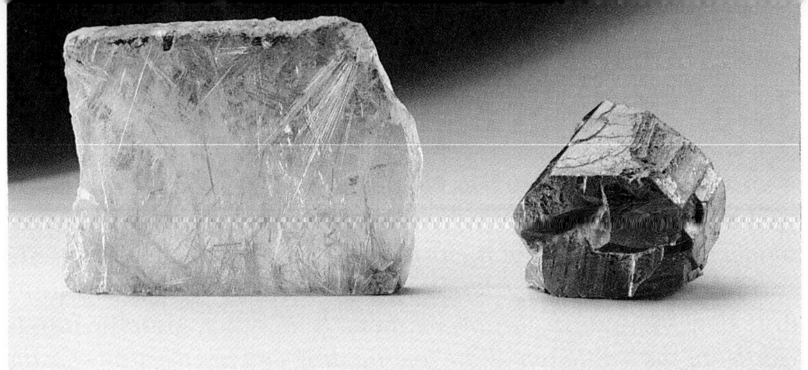

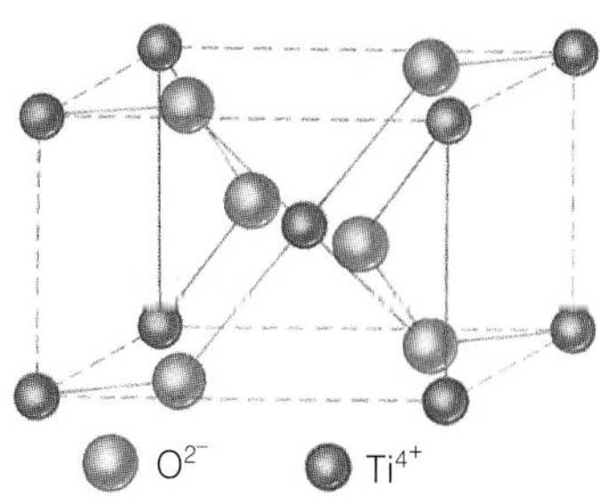

Figure 14.8 The shape of a crystal depends on its unit cell structure. Crystals of the mineral rutile (titanium dioxide) are tetragonal. Quartz that has rutile running through it is shown at left. Rutile is shown at right.

Ionic compounds conduct an electric current in the molten state. When sodium chloride melts (melting point 800°C) the orderly crystal structure breaks down, as in Figure 14.9. If a voltage is applied across this melt, cations migrate freely to one electrode and anions migrate to the other. This movement of ions means that there is a flow of electricity between the two electrodes. Ionic compounds also conduct electricity if they are dissolved in water. When such compounds dissolve, their ions are free to move about.

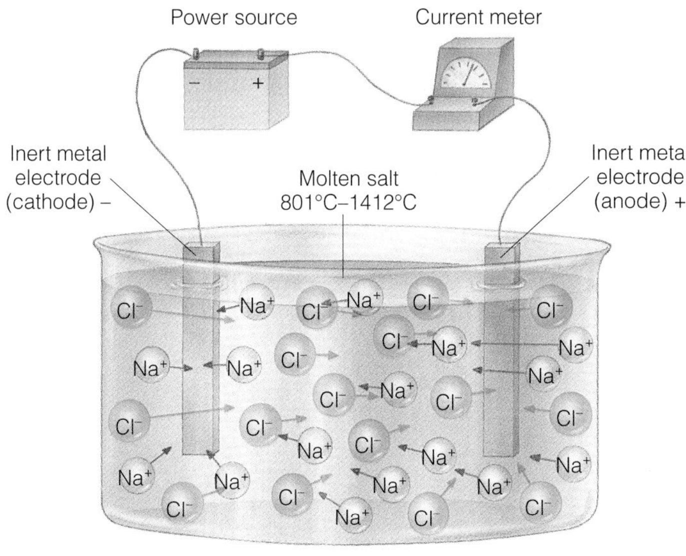

Figure 14.9 When sodium chloride melts, the sodium and chloride ions are free to move about. If a voltage is applied, positive sodium ions move to the negative electrode, the cathode. At the same time, negative chloride ions move to the positive electrode, the anode.

Concept Practice

12. In your own words describe a crystal.

13. Can you predict the coordination number of an ion from the formula of a compound? Explain.

Objective

Explain the physical properties of metals, using the theory of metallic bonding.

Safety

Metals are excellent conductors of heat. When heating glassware, position clamps or iron rings so that they will not be heated by the flame. Be careful not to burn yourself when disassembling the equipment.

14.6 Metallic Bonds

A piece of pure metal such as copper or iron is probably not closely packed metal atoms. The properties of metals suggest that a better model of metal structure is closely packed cations. The cations are surrounded by mobile valence electrons. These valence electrons drift freely from one part of the metal to another. **Metallic bonds** *consist of the attraction of the free-floating valence electrons for the positively charged metal ions.* These are the forces of attraction that hold metals together.

This model of metallic bonding explains many physical properties of metals. For example, *metals are good conductors of electrical current (flow of electrons) because as electrons enter one end of a bar of metal, an equal number leave the other end.* Metals are *ductile* in that they can be drawn into wires, shown in Figure 14.10. Metals are also *malleable* in that they can be hammered into shapes like the item shown in Figure 14.11. Both the ductility and malleability of metals can be explained by the mobility of valence electrons. The metal cations are insulated from one another by a sea of drifting valence electrons. When a metal is subjected to pressure, the metal cations easily slide past one another like ball bearings immersed in oil. In contrast, if an ionic crystal is struck with a hammer, the blow tends to push ions of like charge into contact. The ions repel one another, and the crystal shatters.

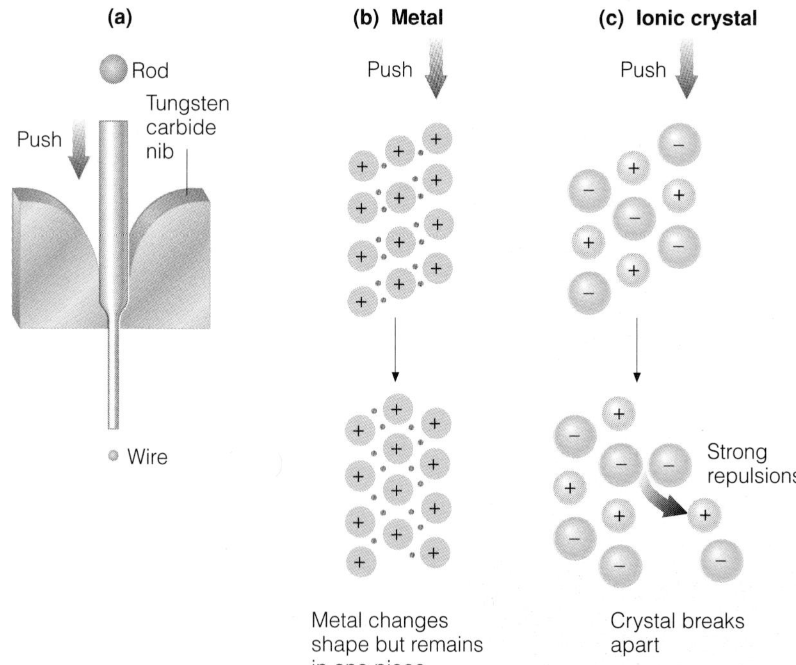

Figure 14.10 **(a)** A metal rod can be forced through a narrow opening in a die to produce wire. **(b)** As this occurs, the metal changes shape but remains in one piece. **(c)** If an ionic crystal were forced through the die, it would shatter. Why is this so?

Metals are among the simplest crystalline solids. Each metal contains just one kind of atom. Metal atoms are arranged in a very compact and orderly pattern, just as you might pack tennis balls in a box. Several arrangements give the closest packing possible for spheres of identical size, like metal atoms. Figure 14.12 shows body-centered cubic, face-centered cubic, and hexagonal close-packed arrangements in that order.

In a *body-centered cubic* structure, every atom (except those on the surface) has 8 neighbors. The metallic elements sodium, potassium, iron, chromium, and tungsten crystallize in the body-centered cubic pattern.

In a *face-centered cubic* arrangement, every atom has 12 neighbors. Among the metals that form a face-centered cubic lattice are copper, silver, gold, aluminum, and lead.

In a *hexagonal close-packed* arrangement, every atom has 12 neighbors. The pattern is different, however, from the face-centered cubic. Metals that have this crystal structure include magnesium, zinc, and cadmium.

Figure 14.11 Because they are malleable, metals can be hammered into different shapes.

Chromium

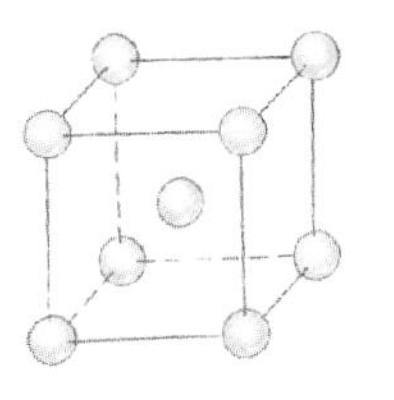
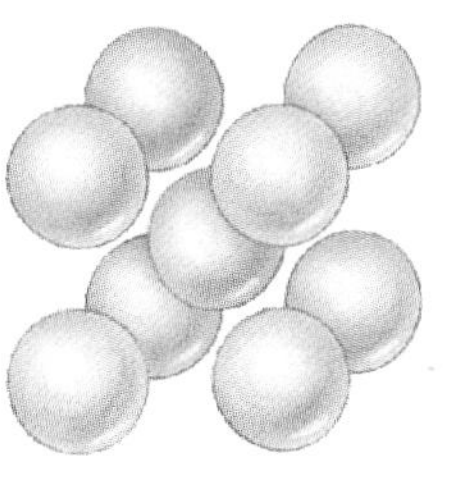

Gold

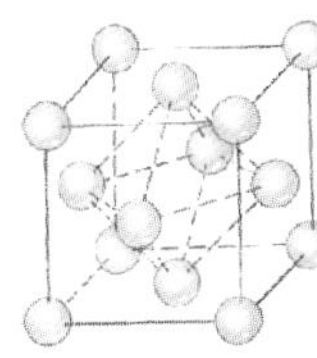
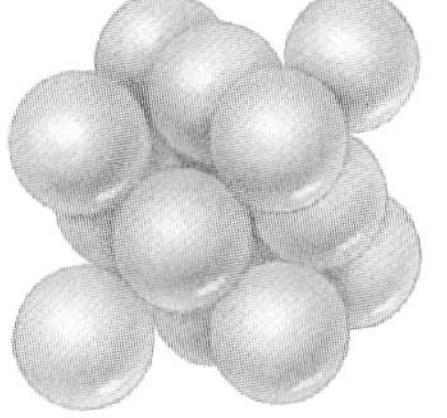

Zinc

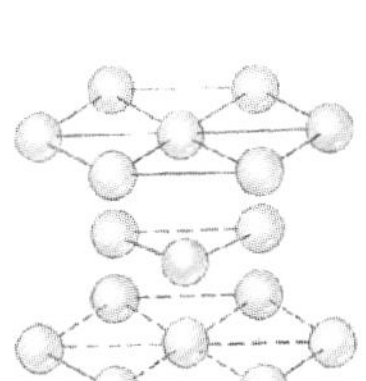
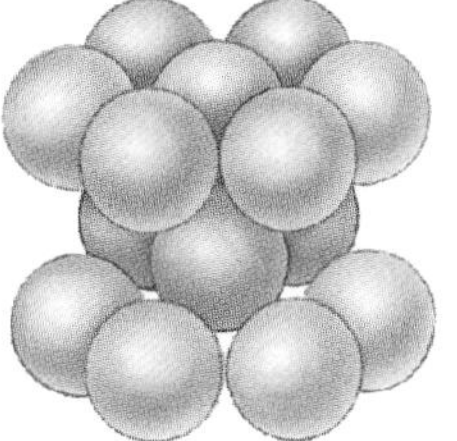

Figure 14.12 The atoms of chromium (top) have a body-centered cubic arrangement. The atoms of gold (center) have a face-centered cubic arrangement. The atoms of zinc (bottom) have a hexagonal close-packed arrangement.

Concept Practice

14. Describe what is meant by the terms *ductile* and *malleable.*

Practice Problem

15. Write electron configurations for the ions of these elements with a 3+ charge.

a. chromium **b.** manganese **c.** iron

Activity 14 Solutions Containing Ions

Purpose

To demonstrate that solutions containing ions conduct an electric current.

Materials

sodium chloride

sodium hydrogen carbonate

vinegar (a solution of acetic acid)

sucrose (sugar)

distilled water

two 12-inch lengths of bell wire with ends scraped bare

masking tape

3 new flashlight batteries

clear plastic cup

Procedure

1. Tape the batteries together so that the positive end of one is in contact with the negative end of another. Tape the bare end of one piece of bell wire to the positive terminal and the bare end of the other piece of bell wire to the negative terminal of the battery assembly.

2. Fill the plastic cup halfway with distilled water and hold the bare ends of the wires close together in the water. Look for the production of gas bubbles. (The bubbles are a sign that the solution conducts electricity.)

3. Repeat step 2 with: tap water, a concentrated solution of sugar, vinegar, a concentrated solution of sodium chloride, and a concentrated solution of sodium hydrogen carbonate.

Analysis and Conclusions

1. Which solutions produced bubbles of gas? Explain.

2. Which samples did not produce bubbles of gas? Explain.

3. Would you expect the same results if you used (a) only one battery and (b) six batteries? Explain your answer.

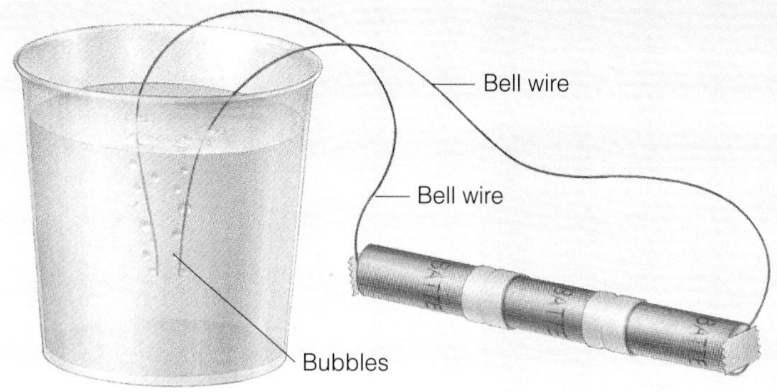

14.B Science, Technology, and Society

Alloys

Although you use metallic items such as spoons or the kitchen faucet, very few of these substances are pure metals. Rather, most metals you use are actually alloys. Alloys are metallic substances composed of two or more elements, at least one of which is a metal. Alloys are prepared by melting a mixture of the ingredients and cooling the mixture. Brass is an alloy of copper and zinc.

The reason alloys are important is that their properties are often much superior to those of their component elements. Sterling silver (92.5% silver and 7.5% copper) is harder and more durable than pure silver but still soft enough to be made into jewelry and flatware. Bronze is an alloy containing 7 parts of copper and 1 part of tin. Bronze is more easily cast, and it is a harder material than copper. Nonferrous alloys, such as bronze, copper-nickel, and aluminum alloys, are commonly used in coinage.

The most important alloys today are steels. The principal alloying elements, in addition to iron and carbon, are boron, chromium, manganese, molybdenum, nickel, tungsten, and vanadium. Alloy steels have a wide range of useful properties, such as corrosion resistance, ductility, hardness, and toughness. Table 14.2 gives the composition and uses of some common alloys.

Amalgams are alloys of mercury. They may be liquids or solids. Dental amalgam, used for filling cavities in teeth, is an alloy of mercury, silver, and zinc. Dental amalgam is a liquid when first prepared but hardens quickly as shown in Figure 14.13.

Fusible alloys have melting points below 232°C. They are used as solder, in electrical fuses, and in safety sprinklers that automatically spray water when the heat from a fire melts the alloy. Wood's metal, which melts at 70°C, is an alloy of 50 parts bismuth, 25 parts lead, 12.5 parts tin, and 12.5 parts cadmium.

If the atoms of the components in an alloy are about the same size, they can replace each other in the crystal. This type of alloy is called a substitutional alloy. Sometimes, however, the atomic sizes are quite different. Then the smaller atoms can fit into the interstices, the spaces between the larger atoms. This is called an interstitial alloy. In the various types of steel, for example, carbon atoms occupy the spaces between the iron atoms.

Table 14.2 Composition of Some Common Alloys

Name	Composition (by mass)
Sterling silver	Ag 92.5%; Cu 7.5%
Coinage silver	Ag 90%; Cu 10%
Cast iron	Fe 96%; C 4%
Stainless steel	Fe 80.6%; Cr 18%; C 0.4%; Ni 1%
Spring steel	Fe 98.6%; Cr 1%; C 0.4%
Surgical steel	Fe 67%; Cr 18%; Ni 12%; Mo 3%

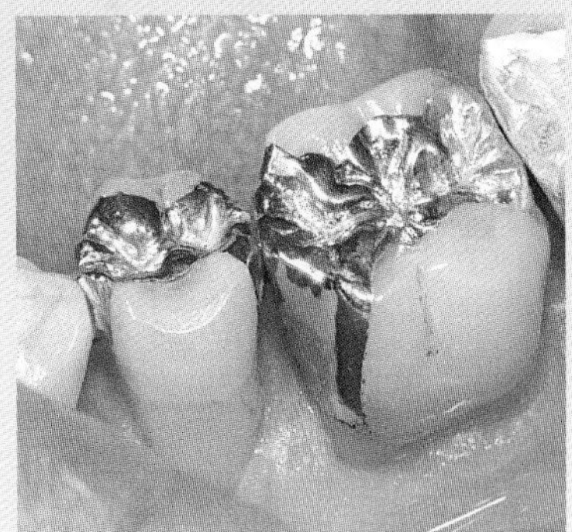

Figure 14.13 Dental amalgam expands as it hardens to fill the cavity in your tooth.

Think About It

16. List Name some alloys that you have used today.

17. Explain Why aren't the properties of all steels identical?

Chapter 14 Review
Ionic Bonds

Key Terms

coordination number *14.5*
electron dot structure *14.1*
halide ion *14.3*
ionic bond *14.4*
metallic bond *14.6*
octet rule *14.2*
valence electron *14.1*

Chapter Summary

Atoms are held together in compounds by chemical bonds. Chemical bonds result from the sharing or transfer of valence electrons between pairs of atoms. Many bonded atoms attain the stable electron configuration of a noble gas. The noble gases themselves exist as isolated atoms because that is their most stable condition. The transfer of one or more valence electrons between atoms produces positively and negatively charged ions: cations and anions.

The attraction between an anion and a cation is an ionic bond. A substance with ionic bonds is an ionic compound. Nearly all ionic compounds are crystalline solids at room temperature. They generally have high melting points. These solids consist of positive and negative ions packed in an orderly arrangement. The total positive charge is balanced by the total negative charge. Ionic compounds, also known as salts, are electrically neutral. Many ionic compounds contain polyatomic ions. The coordination number indicates the number of ions of opposite charge that surround each ion in a crystal.

Metals are like ionic compounds in some ways. They consist of positive metal ions packed together and surrounded by a sea of their valence electrons. This arrangement constitutes the metallic bond. The valence electrons are mobile and can travel from one end of a piece of metal to the other. This electron mobility accounts for the excellent electrical conductivity of metals and helps explain why metals are malleable and ductile. Metals are among the simplest crystalline solids. The metal atoms are commonly packed in a body-centered cubic, a face-centered cubic, or a hexagonal close-packed arrangement.

Practice Questions and Problems

18. Define the term *valence electrons. 14.1*

19. Name the first four halogens. What group are they in, and how many valence electrons does each of them have? *14.1*

20. How many electrons does each of the following atoms have? What groups are they in? *14.1*
a. nitrogen **c.** phosphorus
b. lithium **d.** barium

21. Write electron dot structures for each of the following elements. *14.1*
a. Cl **b.** S **c.** Al **d.** Li

22. How many electrons must be lost by each of the following atoms to attain a noble gas electron configuration? *14.1*
a. Ca **b.** Al **c.** Li **d.** Ba

23. The atoms of the noble gas elements are stable. Explain. *14.2*

24. Write the formula for the ion you get when the following elements lose their valence electrons. *14.2*
a. aluminum **d.** potassium
b. lithium **e.** calcium
c. barium **f.** strontium

25. Write complete electron configurations for the following atoms and ions. For each group, comment on the results. *14.2*
a. Ar, K^+, Ca^{2+}
b. Ne, Na^+, Mg^{2+}, Al^{3+}

26. How many electrons must be gained by each of the following atoms to achieve a stable electron configuration? *14.3*
a. N **b.** S **c.** Cl **d.** P

27. Write electron configurations for the following and comment on the result. *14.3*
a. N^{3-} **b.** O^{2-} **c.** F^- **d.** Ne

28. Write the formula for the ion you get when each of the following elements gains electrons and attains a noble gas configuration. *14.3*
   a. Br **b.** H **c.** As **d.** Se
29. What element in its formulation makes superplastic steel different from conventional steels? *14.A*
30. Why are ionic compounds electrically neutral? *14.4*
31. Which of the following pairs of elements are most likely to form ionic compounds? *14.4*
   a. chlorine and bromine
   b. potassium and helium
   c. lithium and fluorine
   d. iodine and sodium
32. Which pairs of elements will not form ionic compounds? *14.4*
   a. sulfur and oxygen
   b. sodium and calcium
   c. sodium and sulfur
   d. oxygen and chlorine
33. Write the correct chemical formula, the formula unit, for the following pairs of ions. *14.4*
   a. K^+, S^{2-} **c.** Na^+, SO_4^{2-}
   b. Ca^{2+}, O^{2-} **d.** Al^{3+}, PO_4^{3-}
34. Write the formula for the ions in the following compounds. *14.4*
   a. KCl **c.** $MgBr_2$
   b. $BaSO_4$ **d.** Li_2CO_3
35. Write formulas for the following compounds. *14.4*
   a. potassium nitrate
   b. barium chloride
   c. magnesium sulfate
   d. lithium oxide
   e. ammonium carbonate
   f. calcium phosphate
36. What determines the crystal structure of an ionic compound? *14.5*
37. Most ionic substances are brittle. Why? *14.5*
38. Why does molten $MgCl_2$ conduct an electric current although crystalline $MgCl_2$ does not? *14.5*
39. In your own words define a *metallic bond*. *14.6*
40. Why is it possible to bend metals but not ionic crystals? *14.6*
41. Explain briefly why metals are good conductors of electricity. *14.6*
42. Name the three crystal arrangements that give close packing of metal atoms. Give an example of a metal that crystallizes in each arrangement. *14.6*
43. What is the difference between coinage silver and sterling silver? Contrast the properties of these two kinds of silver and the ways they are used. *14.B*

Mastery Questions and Problems

44. Construct a concept map with *ionic bond* as the central concept.
45. Which of the following substances are most probably not ionic?
   a. H_2O **c.** CO_2 **e.** NH_3
   b. Na_2O **d.** CaS **f.** SO_2
46. Construct a table that shows the relationship among the group number, valence electrons lost or gained, and the formula of the cation or anion produced for the following metallic and nonmetallic elements. Na, Ca, Al, N, S, Br.
47. Write electron dot formulas for the following atoms.
   a. C **c.** O **e.** Na
   b. Be **d.** F **f.** P
48. Why does a cation have a positive charge?
49. Metallic cobalt crystallizes in a hexagonal close-packed structure. How many neighbors will a cobalt atom have?
50. Write electron configurations for the ions of these elements that have a 2+ charge.
   a. Fe **b.** Co **c.** Ni
51. Why does an anion have a negative charge?
52. Write electron configurations for these atoms and ions, and comment on the result.
   a. Ar **b.** Cl^- **c.** S^{2-} **d.** P^{3-}
53. Show the relationship between the electron dot structure of an element and the location of the element in the periodic table.
54. Explain how hexagonal close-packed, face-centered cubic, and body-centered cubic unit cells are different.

55. The spheres below represent the relative diameters of atoms or ions. Rearrange each of the following sequences so that the relative sizes of the particles in the sequence correspond to the increasing size of the particles in the illustration.

   a. oxygen atom, oxide ion, sulfur atom, sulfide ion

   b. sodium atom, sodium ion, potassium atom, potassium ion

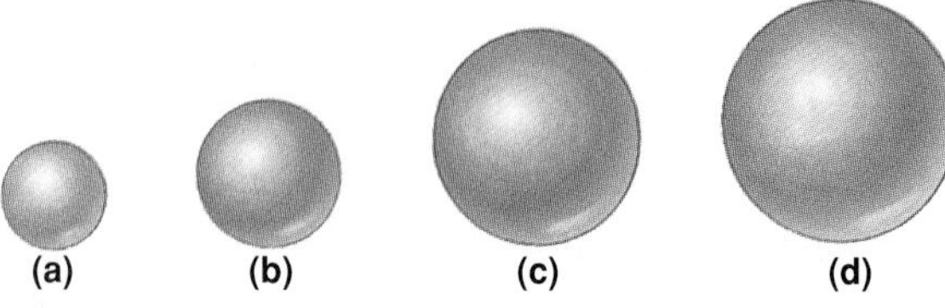

Critical Thinking Questions

56. Choose the term that best completes the second relationship.

a. cow:horse	ionic bond: _____
(1) metallic bond	(3) chemical bond
(2) cation	(4) covalent bond
b. Cl:Cl^-	Mg: _____
(1) Mg^{2+}	(3) Al^{3+}
(2) Mg^{2-}	(4) Mn
c. pipe:water	metal: _____
(1) ions	
(2) ionic bond	
(3) electricity	
(4) conductor	

57. Compare the physical and chemical characteristics of metals and ionic compounds.

Cumulative Review

58. Hydrogen and oxygen react to give water according to this equation.

   $2H_2 + O_2 \longrightarrow 2H_2O$

   How many liters of hydrogen at STP are needed to produce 0.50 mol of water?

59. Distinguish among gases, liquids, and solids with respect to shape, volume, relative density, and motion of particles.

60. What is the volume in liters occupied by 8.0 g of oxygen gas at STP?

61. If you raise the temperature of a gas, what actually happens to the gas particles?

62. A gas occupies 750 cm^3 at 27°C and 1.6 kPa. Find its volume at STP.

63. Explain each of these observations on the basis of the kinetic theory and the forces of attraction that exist between the particles in matter.

   a. Water evaporates faster at 40°C than 20°C.

   b. A burn from steam at 100°C is worse than a burn from water at 100°C.

   c. A cap "pops" off a bottle of root beer that has been kept in a car trunk on a hot day.

   d. Diethyl ether, $C_4H_{10}O$, has a vapor pressure of 58.9 kPa at 20°C, whereas the vapor pressure of water at 20°C is only 2.3 kPa.

   e. A melting ice cube cools a glass of tea.

   f. Foods are dehydrated (water is removed) by using low pressures rather than high heat.

64. Use the gas laws and the kinetic theory to complete these statements. Unless otherwise stated, assume a constant amount of gas.

   a. As the volume of a gas increases at constant temperature, its pressure _____.

   b. As the temperature of a gas increases and its pressure decreases, its volume _____.

   c. At constant pressure, a decrease in the volume of a gas is caused by a/an _____ in its temperature.

   d. An increase in the volume and pressure of a gas is caused by a/an _____ in its temperature.

   e. At constant volume, a decrease in the temperature of a gas causes the pressure to _____.

   f. If the volume of a gas is increased while its temperature is increased, the pressure will _____.

65. A gas mixture contains 1.50 g of O_2 and 1.50 g of N_2. If the partial pressure of O_2 is 63.3 kPa, what is the total pressure of the mixture?

66. At what temperature will the average kinetic energy of a nitrogen molecule be twice the average kinetic energy of a nitrogen molecule at 25°C?

67. The reaction of zinc with an acid produces hydrogen gas. The table below gives the amount of hydrogen gas produced at STP when various amounts of zinc are reacted with an excess of hydrochloric acid.

a. Calculate the moles of zinc used.

b. Make a graph of the volume of hydrogen produced (y axis) versus the moles of zinc reacting (x axis).

c. Determine the slope of the line. Include units on the slope.

d. Based on the value of the slope, what can you surmise about the moles of hydrogen produced per mole of zinc that reacts?

Mass of Zn (g)	Moles of Zn	Volume of H_2 (L)
0.960	____	0.329
2.44	____	0.835
4.18	____	1.43
5.75	____	1.96

Challenge Questions and Problems

68. The chemically similar alkali metal chlorides NaCl and CsCl have different crystal structures, whereas the chemically different NaCl and MnS have the same crystal structure. Why?

69. Silver crystallizes in a face-centered cubic unit cell. A silver atom is at the edge of each lattice point. The length of the edge of the unit cell is 0.4086 nm. What is the atomic radius of silver?

Connections Questions

70. List some accomplishments of Percy Julian.

71. Give an advantage and a disadvantage of using sulfites in the food industry.

72. The marble in a statue has different properties from chalk, yet both are calcium carbonate. Explain.

Write About Chemistry

73. Imagine that you are a chloride ion in an electrolytic cell like the one shown in Figure 14.9. Describe your movement and what your eventual chemical identity will be.

74. Write a recipe for an alloy as if the alloy were food. Give step-by-step directions for creating the alloy.

Readings and References

Daintith, John (Ed.). *The Facts on File Dictionary of Chemistry*, revised and expanded ed. New York: Facts on File, 1988.

Smith, Trevor. "Salt." *ChemMatters* (December 1992), pp. 4–6.

15 Covalent Bonds

Goals

- Show how electron sharing between atoms can produce covalent bonds.
- Explain the bonding in molecules using the concept of resonance.
- Give examples of elements that violate the octet rule in covalent bonding.
- Predict the polarities of covalent bonds using atomic electronegativities.
- Give examples of how the bonding in molecules affects the shape and physical properties of compounds.

The most abundant component of air is nitrogen, at about 78%. Oxygen, though essential to life, makes up only about 21% of air. Carbon dioxide is a mere 0.033% of air. All of these important molecules have covalent bonds.

Concept Overview

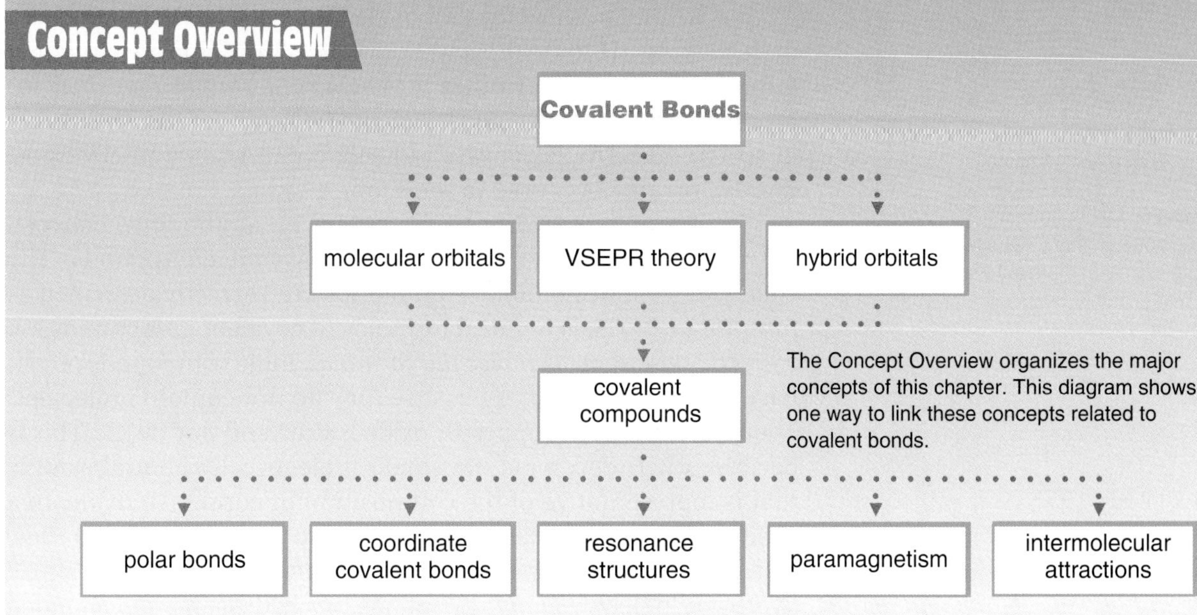

Salts such as sodium chloride are crystalline solids with high melting points. However, hydrogen chloride, HCl, is a gas. Water, H_2O, is a liquid. These compounds are so different from salts that you might suspect that electrostatic attraction between ions fails to explain their bonding. Your suspicions would be correct. Many atoms do not give up an electron as readily as sodium does. In such cases a kind of tug-of-war for electrons takes place between atoms, ending in a standoff, more or less. In this chapter you will learn about atoms that share electrons to form a different kind of bond, the covalent bond.

15.1 Single Covalent Bonds

Objective

Describe the formation of a covalent bond between two nonmetallic elements.

To begin your study of covalent bonding, consider hydrogen, H_2, the simplest molecule. A hydrogen atom has a single valence electron. Pairs of hydrogen atoms share electrons to form diatomic hydrogen molecules.

$$\underset{\text{Hydrogen atom}}{\mathrm{H}\cdot} + \underset{\text{Hydrogen atom}}{\cdot\mathrm{H}} \longrightarrow \underset{\text{Hydrogen molecule}}{\mathrm{H}:\mathrm{H}} \quad \text{shared pair of electrons}$$

Each hydrogen gets the electron configuration of helium, which has two valence electrons. *A* **single covalent bond** *is formed when a pair of electrons is shared between two atoms.* The chemical formula for the hydrogen molecule is therefore H_2.

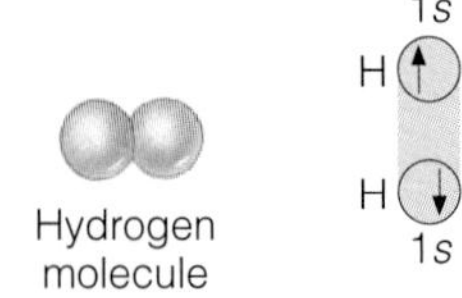

Figure 15.1 The two bonding electrons in the hydrogen molecule come from the 1*s* atomic orbitals of the hydrogen atoms.

It is helpful to show the pair of electrons in a covalent bond as a dash, as in H—H for hydrogen. Notations of this type are structural formulas. **Structural formulas** *are chemical formulas that show the arrangement of atoms in molecules and polyatomic ions.* The dashes in structural formulas always indicate a pair of shared electrons. The dashes are never used to show ionic bonds.

The formula of hydrogen, H_2, brings up a difference between the chemical formulas of ionic and covalent compounds. The chemical formulas of ionic compounds are correctly described as *formula units.* The chemical formulas of covalent compounds are correctly described as *molecular formulas.* Ionic compounds do not have molecular formulas because they do not contain molecules. The formula unit of copper(II) oxide is CuO and not Cu_2O_2. This is because CuO represents the smallest electrically neutral sample that is representative of the composition of copper(II) oxide. In a similar way, only one pair of shoes, not two pairs, is needed to show someone what a pair of shoes is. On the other hand, a single hydrogen molecule actually contains two hydrogen atoms bonded together. Writing the molecular formula of hydrogen as H would be similar to showing one shoe to someone who asks to see a pair. Sometimes the correct formulas of molecular compounds have subscripts that are multiples of the lowest whole-number ratio, as in C_3H_6 (not CH_2) or C_4H_{10} (not C_2H_5). This is uncommon in ionic compounds. Figure 15.2 illustrates the essential difference between ionic compounds and covalent compounds.

Figure 15.2 Sodium chloride, an ionic compound, and water, a molecular compound, are compared here. How do molecular compounds differ from ionic compounds?

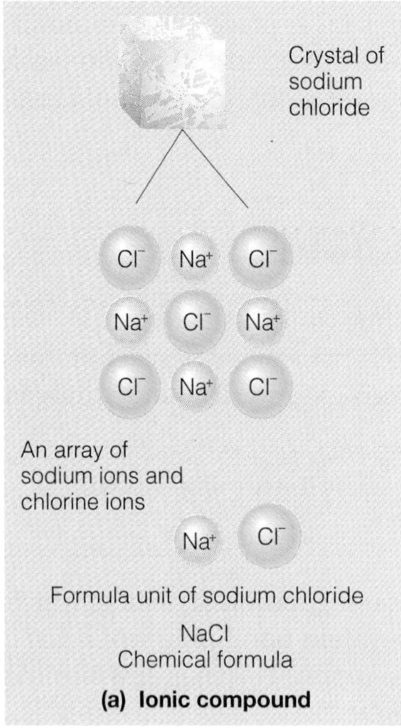

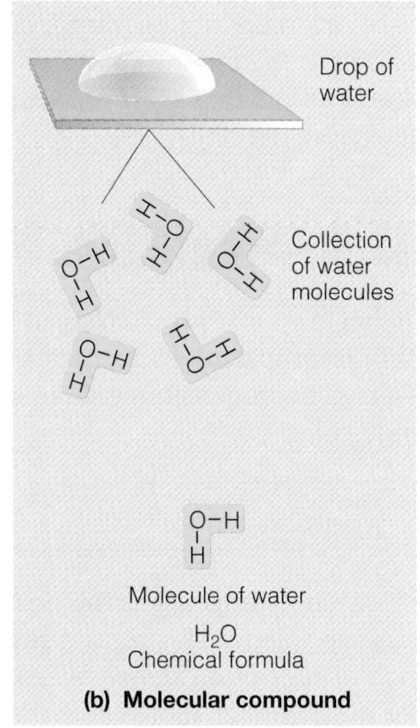

In addition to hydrogen, atoms of the nonmetallic elements in Groups 4A, 5A, 6A, and 7A of the periodic table are particularly prone to form covalent bonds. Gilbert Lewis summarized this tendency in the octet rule for covalent bonding: *Sharing of electrons occurs if the atoms involved acquire the electron configurations of noble gases.* Often the configurations contain eight valence electrons (an octet). You have already seen the most notable exception to this rule, hydrogen. When hydrogen shares two electrons it acquires the electron configuration of helium.

The halogens also form single covalent bonds in their diatomic molecules. Fluorine is one example, and the other halogens are similar. Because a fluorine atom has seven valence electrons, it needs one more to attain the electron configuration of neon. By electron sharing, two fluorine atoms gain the electron configuration of neon and form a single covalent bond. Figure 15.3 shows the same process in terms of atomic orbitals.

$$:\ddot{\underset{..}{F}}\cdot \quad + \quad \cdot\ddot{\underset{..}{F}}: \quad \longrightarrow \quad :\ddot{\underset{..}{F}}:\ddot{\underset{..}{F}}: \quad \textit{or} \quad :\ddot{\underset{..}{F}}-\ddot{\underset{..}{F}}:$$

Fluorine atom	Fluorine atom	Fluorine molecule

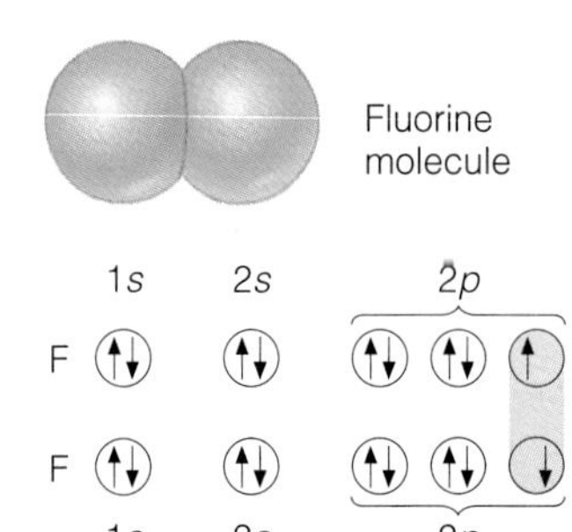

Figure 15.3 The bonding electrons in the fluorine molecule come from the 2*p* atomic orbitals of the fluorine atoms.

Each fluorine atom contributes one electron to complete the octet. Notice that each fluorine nucleus shares only that pair of valence electrons. *The pairs of valence electrons that are not shared between atoms are called unshared pairs of electrons, or* **unshared pairs**. They are also called *lone pairs* or *nonbonding pairs*.

Concept Practice

1. What kinds of information about a compound can you get from its structural formula?

2. Explain why chemical formulas of compounds with ionic bonds are called formula units. Compare formula units with molecular formulas.

Practice Problems

3. Draw electron dot structures for these diatomic halogen molecules.
a. chlorine
b. bromine
c. iodine

4. How many unshared pairs are in each halogen molecule in Problem 3? In fluorine?

Objective

Describe double and triple covalent bonds.

15.2 Double and Triple Covalent Bonds

Atoms sometimes share more than one pair of electrons to attain stable, noble-gas electron configurations. **Double covalent bonds** *involve two shared pairs of electrons.* **Triple covalent bonds** *include three shared pairs of electrons.*

Oxygen, O_2, is an example of a molecule that should have a double covalent bond according to the octet rule. You might assume that an oxygen atom, with six valence electrons, would share two of these electrons with another oxygen atom to form the double bond.

:Ȯ:	+	:Ȯ:	⟶	:O::O: *or* :O=O:
Oxygen atom		Oxygen atom		Oxygen molecule

Experimental evidence indicates, however, that the electrons in the oxygen molecule are not all paired. Look at Figure 15.4a and take special note when you read Section 15.6. The oxygen molecule represents an exception to the octet rule.

In contrast to the exceptional bonding in the oxygen molecule, the nitrogen molecule bonds according to the octet rule. The nitrogen molecule (N_2) in Figure 15.4b contains a triple covalent bond. A nitrogen atom has five valence electrons. Each nitrogen atom in the nitrogen molecule needs three more electrons to attain the electron configuration of neon. In the nitrogen molecule each nitrogen has one unshared pair of electrons.

:Ṅ·	+	·Ṅ:	⟶	:N⋮⋮N: *or* :N≡N:
Nitrogen atom		Nitrogen atom		Nitrogen molecule

Up to this point, the examples of covalent bonds have all been molecules of diatomic elements. Table 15.1 lists all of the elements that exist as diatomic molecules along with their properties and uses.

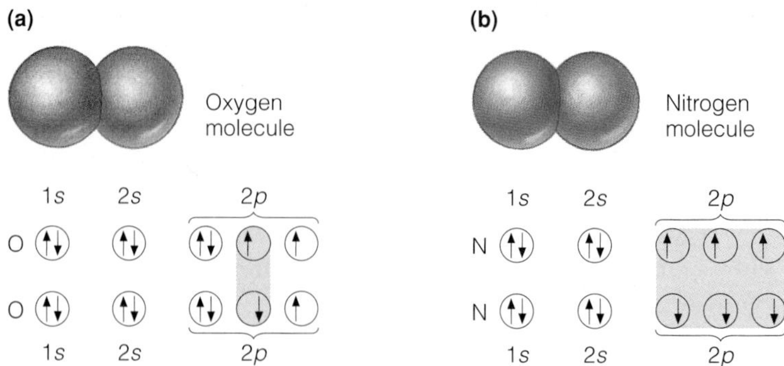

Figure 15.4 The oxygen molecule is an exception to the octet rule. It forms only a single bond, and it has two unpaired electrons. Three pairs of electrons are shared in a nitrogen molecule.

Table 15.1 The Diatomic Elements			
Name	**Chemical formula**	**Structure**	**Properties and uses**
Fluorine	F_2	$:\ddot{\underset{..}{F}}-\ddot{\underset{..}{F}}:$	Greenish-yellow reactive toxic gas. Compounds of fluorine, a halogen, are added to drinking water and toothpaste to promote healthy teeth.
Chlorine	Cl_2	$:\ddot{\underset{..}{Cl}}-\ddot{\underset{..}{Cl}}:$	Greenish-yellow reactive toxic gas. Chlorine is a halogen used in household bleaching agents.
Bromine	Br_2	$:\ddot{\underset{..}{Br}}-\ddot{\underset{..}{Br}}:$	Dense red-brown liquid with pungent odor. Compounds of bromine are used in the preparation of photographic emulsions.
Iodine	I_2	$:\ddot{\underset{..}{I}}-\ddot{\underset{..}{I}}:$	Dense gray-black solid that produces purple vapors; a halogen. A solution of iodine in alcohol (tincture of iodine) is used as an antiseptic.
Hydrogen	H_2	$H-H$	Colorless, odorless, tasteless gas. Hydrogen is the lightest known element.
Nitrogen	N_2	$:N\equiv N:$	Colorless, odorless, tasteless gas. Air is 80% nitrogen by volume.
Oxygen	O_2	$:\ddot{\underset{\cdot}{O}}-\ddot{\underset{\cdot}{O}}:$	Colorless, odorless, tasteless gas that is vital for life. Air is 20% oxygen by volume.

Concept Practice

5. Why is it necessary for some atoms to form double or triple bonds when forming compounds?

6. How many electrons does each atom contribute in a double bond? How many in a triple bond?

15.3 Covalent Compounds

Objective

Create electron dot diagrams for covalent molecules containing single, double, and triple bonds.

You can write electron dot formulas for molecules of compounds in much the same way as for molecules of the diatomic elements. Start with these four examples: water, ammonia, methane, and carbon dioxide.

Water, H_2O, is a triatomic molecule. Two hydrogen atoms share electrons with one oxygen atom. The hydrogen and oxygen atoms attain noble-gas configurations by electron sharing. The oxygen atom in water has two unshared pairs of valence electrons.

$$\underset{\text{Hydrogen atoms}}{2H\cdot} + \underset{\text{Oxygen atom}}{:\ddot{\underset{\cdot}{O}}\cdot} \longrightarrow \underset{\text{Water molecule}}{:\ddot{\underset{\cdot\cdot}{O}}:H \;\; \textit{or} \;\; :\ddot{O}-H}$$

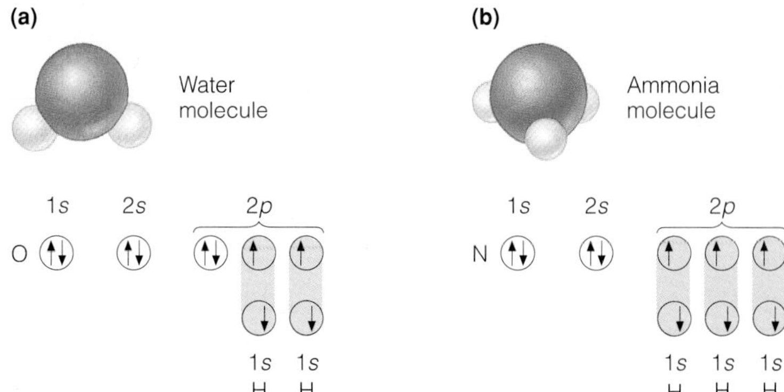

Figure 15.5 **(a)** In the water molecule two hydrogen atoms form single covalent bonds with an oxygen atom. **(b)** In the ammonia molecule three hydrogen atoms form single covalent bonds with a nitrogen atom.

You can write the electron dot formula for ammonia, NH_3, a suffocating gas, in a similar way. The ammonia molecule has one unshared pair of electrons as shown in Figure 15.5b.

$$3\text{H}\cdot \; + \; :\dot{\text{N}}\cdot \; \longrightarrow \; \text{H}:\ddot{\text{N}}:\text{H (with H below) } \quad or \quad :\text{N}-\text{H (with H above and below)}$$

Hydrogen atoms   Nitrogen atom   Ammonia molecule

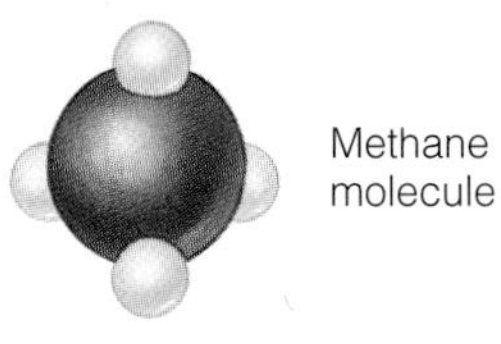

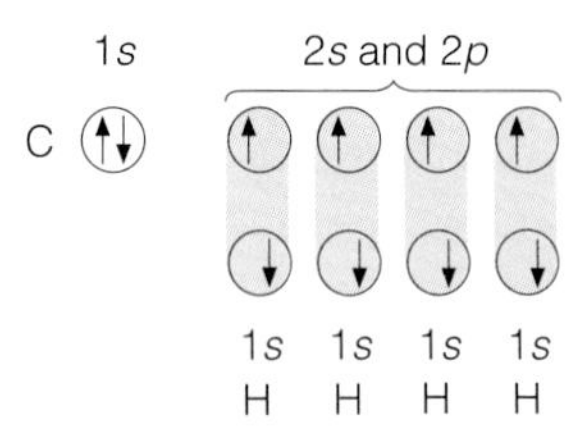

Figure 15.6 The methane molecule has four carbon–hydrogen bonds. In each bond the carbon and hydrogen share a 1*s* electron from hydrogen and an electron from carbon.

Methane, CH_4, contains four single covalent bonds. The carbon atom has four valence electrons and needs four more to attain a noble-gas configuration. Four hydrogen atoms each share one electron with carbon. This forms four identical carbon-hydrogen bonds.

$$4\text{H}\cdot \; + \; \cdot\dot{\underset{\cdot}{\text{C}}}\cdot \; \longrightarrow \; \text{H}:\underset{\text{H}}{\overset{\text{H}}{\ddot{\text{C}}}}:\text{H} \quad or \quad \text{H}-\underset{\text{H}}{\overset{\text{H}}{\text{C}}}-\text{H}$$

Hydrogen atoms   Carbon atom   Methane molecule

When carbon bonds with other atoms it usually forms four bonds. You might not have predicted this from the electron configuration of atomic carbon.

(↑↓) (↑↓) (↑) (↑) ( )

$1s^2 \; 2s^2 \; 2p^2$

If you tried to make covalent C—H bonds for methane by combining the two 2*p* electrons of the carbon with two 1*s* electrons of hydrogen atoms you would predict a molecule with the formula CH_2. Yet carbon tends to form four bonds to other atoms. This can be simply explained for methane. One of the 2*s* electrons is promoted to the vacant 2*p* orbital, as follows.

(↑↓) (↑) (↑) (↑) (↑)

$1s^2$ 2*s* and 2*p*

The electron promotion needs only a small amount of energy. Look at Figure 15.6. This promotion provides four electrons of carbon capable of entering into covalent bonds with four hydrogen atoms. Methane, the compound formed by electron sharing with four hydrogens, is much more stable than CH_2. The small energy cost of the electron promotion is more than paid back by the stability of methane. Therefore, the formation of methane is much preferred to formation of CH_2.

The carbon dioxide molecule contains two oxygens that each share two electrons with carbon to form two carbon-oxygen double bonds, as shown in Figure 15.7.

$$:\dot{\underset{\cdot}{O}}\cdot \quad + \quad \cdot\dot{\underset{\cdot}{C}}\cdot \quad + \quad \cdot\dot{\underset{\cdot}{O}}: \longrightarrow \; \ddot{O}::C::\ddot{O} \quad or \quad \ddot{O}=C=\ddot{O}$$

Oxygen atom	Carbon atom	Oxygen atom	Carbon dioxide molecule

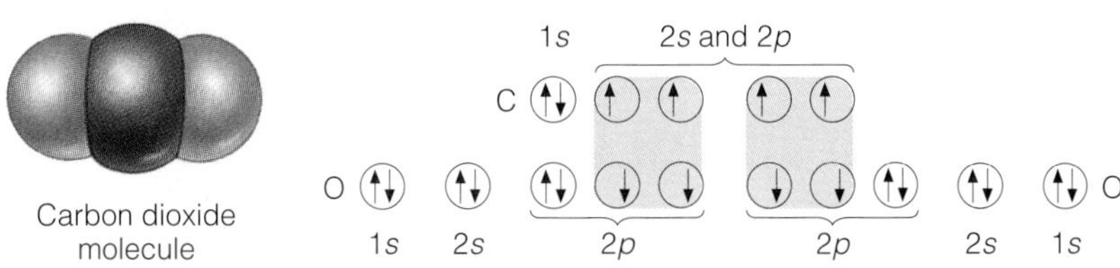

Figure 15.7 The carbon dioxide molecule has two carbon–oxygen double bonds.

Example 1 Drawing an Electron Dot Formula

Aqueous solutions of hydrogen chloride (HCl) produce a common laboratory acid. Hydrogen chloride is a diatomic molecule with a single covalent bond. Draw the electron dot structure for HCl.

Solution

In a single covalent bond, the hydrogen atom and the chlorine atom must share a pair of electrons. This means that they must each contribute one electron. First, write electron dot structures for the two atoms. Then show the electron sharing.

$$H\cdot \quad + \quad \cdot\ddot{\underset{\cdot\cdot}{Cl}}: \longrightarrow \quad H:\ddot{\underset{\cdot\cdot}{Cl}}:$$

Hydrogen atom	Chlorine atom	Hydrogen chloride molecule

As is obvious in the electron dot structures, each atom has an unpaired electron. Through electron sharing, hydrogen and chlorine atoms attain the electron configurations of the noble gases helium and argon.

Concept Practice

7. Based on the examples given in this section, state a general rule for determining the arrangement of atoms in a simple binary molecular compound.

Practice Problem

8. Draw electron dot structures for the following covalent molecules, which have only single covalent bonds.

a. H_2S

b. PH_3

c. ClF

Objective

Explain the formation of a coordinate covalent bond.

15.4 Coordinate Covalent Bonds

Carbon monoxide (CO) is an example of a different kind of covalent bonding than you have seen in water, ammonia, methane, and carbon dioxide. A carbon atom is four electrons short of the electron configuration of neon. An oxygen atom is two electrons short. Yet it is possible for both atoms to achieve noble-gas electron configurations by *coordinate covalent bonding.* To see how, begin by making a double covalent bond between carbon and oxygen.

$$\dot{\text{C}}: + \ddot{\text{O}}: \longrightarrow :\text{C}::\ddot{\text{O}}:$$

Carbon atom   Oxygen atom

With the double bond in place, the oxygen has a stable configuration but the carbon does not. The dilemma is solved if the oxygen also donates one of its unshared pairs of electrons to make a *coordinate covalent bond,* shown in Figure 15.8.

$$:\text{C}::\ddot{\text{O}}: \longrightarrow :\text{C}:::\text{O}:$$

Carbon monoxide molecule

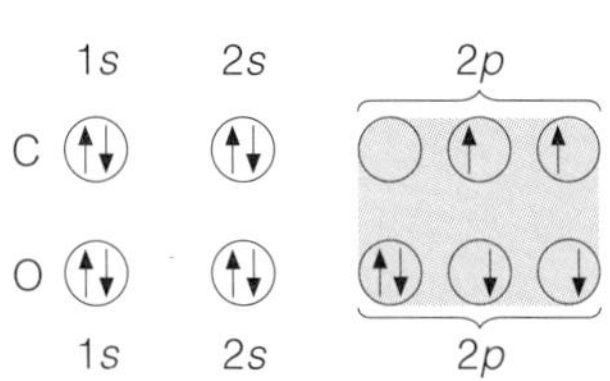

Figure 15.8 In a coordinate covalent compound, one atom contributes both electrons of a bonding pair. In carbon monoxide, oxygen gives two electrons to bond.

A **coordinate covalent bond** *is formed when one atom contributes both bonding electrons in a covalent bond.* You can show coordinate covalent bonds in structural formulas as arrows. They point from the atom donating the pair of electrons to the atom receiving them. The structural formula of carbon monoxide, with two covalent bonds and one coordinate covalent bond, is $C \leftleftharpoons O$. Once formed, a coordinate covalent bond is like any other covalent bond. The only difference is the source of the bonding electrons.

The polyatomic ammonium ion (NH_4^+) has a coordinate covalent bond. It is formed when a positively charged hydrogen ion (H^+) is attracted to the unshared electron pair of an ammonia molecule. Figure 15.9 shows that the ammonium ion is an important component of some nitrogen fertilizers.

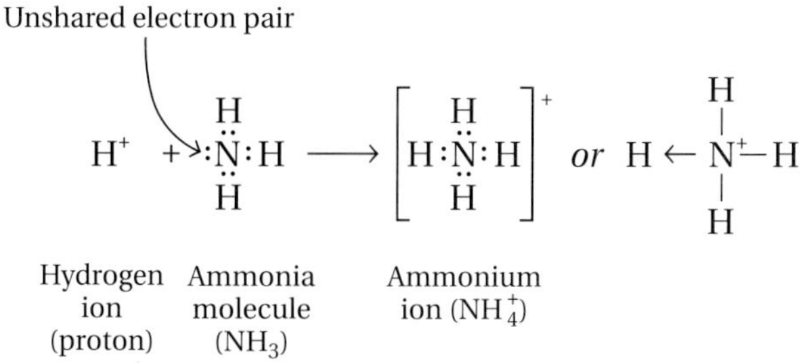

Unshared electron pair

$$H^+ + :\underset{\cdot\cdot}{\overset{\cdot\cdot}{N}}\!:\!H \longrightarrow \left[H:\overset{H}{\underset{H}{\ddot{N}}}:H\right]^+ \quad or \quad H \leftarrow \overset{H}{\underset{H}{N^+}}-H$$

Hydrogen ion (proton) — Ammonia molecule (NH_3) — Ammonium ion (NH_4^+)

Most polyatomic cations and anions contain covalent and coordinate covalent bonds. Table 15.2 lists some common covalent compounds.

Example 2 Drawing the Electron Dot Formula of a Polyatomic Cation

The polyatomic hydronium ion (H_3O^+) contains a coordinate covalent bond. It forms when a hydrogen ion is attracted to an unshared electron pair of a water molecule. Write the electron dot structure for the hydronium ion.

Solution

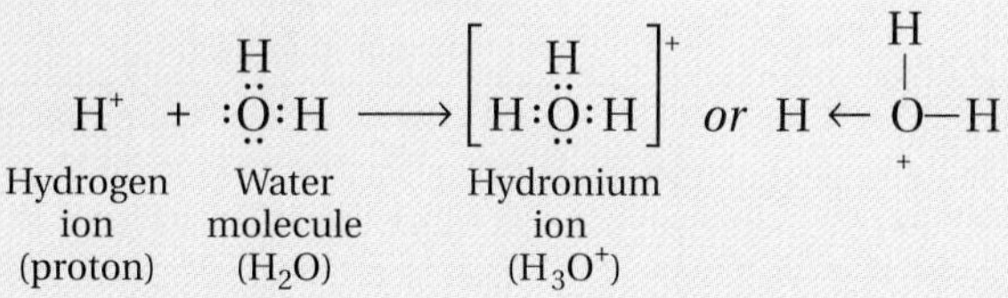

$$H^+ + :\overset{H}{\ddot{O}}:H \longrightarrow \left[H:\overset{H}{\ddot{O}}:H\right]^+ \quad or \quad H \leftarrow \overset{H}{\underset{+}{O}}-H$$

Hydrogen ion (proton) — Water molecule (H_2O) — Hydronium ion (H_3O^+)

Figure 15.9 The polyatomic ammonium ion is an important component of fertilizer.

Many polyatomic ions have a negative charge. Because the atoms in polyatomic ions are covalently bonded, you can write electron dot structures for these ions. The negative charge of a polyatomic ion shows the number of electrons *in addition* to the valence electrons of the atoms present. Because a polyatomic ion is found as part of an ionic compound, these additional electrons are balanced by the positive charge of the cation of the compound.

The hydroxide ion is OH^-. The components of this ion are $H\cdot$, $\cdot\ddot{\underset{\cdot\cdot}{O}}\cdot$, and an electron (.). The additional electron is signified by the 1– charge. The stable electron dot formula is $[H:\ddot{\underset{\cdot\cdot}{O}}:]^{1-}$.

Table 15.2 Some Common Covalent Compounds

Name	Chemical formula	Structure	Properties and uses
Carbon monoxide	CO	$:C\equiv O:$	Colorless, highly toxic gas. It is a major air pollutant present in cigarette smoke and automobile exhaust.
Carbon dioxide	CO_2	$\ddot{O}=C=\ddot{O}$	Colorless unreactive gas. This normal component of the atmosphere is exhaled in the breath of animals and is essential for plant growth.
Water	H_2O	$H-\ddot{O}:-H$	Colorless, odorless, tasteless liquid with melting point of 0°C and boiling point of 100°C. The human body is approximately 60% water.
Hydrogen peroxide	H_2O_2	$H-\ddot{O}-\ddot{O}-H$	Colorless, unstable liquid when pure. It is used as rocket fuel. A 3% solution is used as a bleach and antiseptic.
Sulfur dioxide	SO_2	$\ddot{O}=\dot{S}\rightarrow\ddot{O}:$	Oxides of sulfur are produced in combustion of petroleum products and coal. They are major air pollutants in industrial areas. Oxides of sulfur can lead to respiratory problems.
Sulfur trioxide	SO_3	$\ddot{O}=S(\rightarrow\ddot{O}:)_2$	
Ammonia	NH_3	$H-\ddot{N}(-H)-H$	Colorless gas with pungent odor; extremely soluble in water. Household ammonia is a solution of ammonia in water.
Nitric oxide	NO	$\ddot{O}=\ddot{N}\cdot$	Oxides of nitrogen are major air pollutants produced by the combustion of fossil fuels in automobile engines. They irritate the eyes, throat, and lungs. Nitrogen dioxide, a dark brown gas, readily converts to colorless dinitrogen tetroxide.
Nitrogen dioxide	NO_2	$\ddot{O}=\dot{N}\rightarrow\ddot{O}$	
Dinitrogen tetroxide	N_2O_4	$(O=)(O\leftarrow)N-N(\rightarrow O)(=O)$	
Nitrous oxide	N_2O	$:\ddot{O}\leftarrow N\equiv N:$	Colorless sweet-smelling gas. It is used as an anesthetic commonly called laughing gas.
Hydrogen cyanide	HCN	$H-C\equiv N:$	Colorless toxic gas with the smell of almonds.
Hydrogen fluoride	HF	$H-\ddot{F}:$	Four hydrogen halides, all extremely soluble in water. Hydrogen chloride, a colorless gas with pungent odor, readily dissolves in water to give a solution called hydrochloric acid.
Hydrogen chloride	HCl	$H-\ddot{Cl}:$	
Hydrogen bromide	HBr	$H-\ddot{Br}:$	
Hydrogen iodide	HI	$H-\ddot{I}:$	

Example 3 Drawing the Electron Dot Formula of a Polyatomic Anion

Draw the electron dot structure for sulfite, SO_3^{2-}, where sulfur is the central atom.

Solution

Start with the atoms and their valence electrons and the two "extra" electrons indicated by the charge.

:Ö· ·S̈: ·Ö: + ··
·Ö:

Join two of the oxygens to sulfur by single covalent bonds.

:Ö:S̈: ·Ö:
·Ö:

Join the remaining oxygen by a coordinate covalent bond, and add the extra two electrons.

:Ö:S̈:Ö: + ·· → [:Ö:S̈:Ö: / :Ö:]$^{2-}$
·Ö:

Concept Practice

9. Characterize a coordinate covalent bond.

Practice Problem

10. Draw the electron dot structures for sulfate, SO_4^{2-}, and carbonate, CO_3^{2-}. Sulfur and carbon are the central atoms, respectively.

Safety

Some people have an asthmatic allergic reaction to sulfites.

15.5 Resonance

Objective

Explain the modern interpretation of resonance bonding.

Consider the two electron dot structures for ozone shown below. Notice that the structure on the left can be converted to the one on the right by shifting electron pairs *without changing the positions of the oxygen atoms.*

:Ö:Ö::Ö: ⟷ :Ö::Ö:Ö:

The structures suggest that the bonding in ozone consists of one coordinate covalent bond and one double covalent bond. Double covalent bonds are usually shorter than single covalent

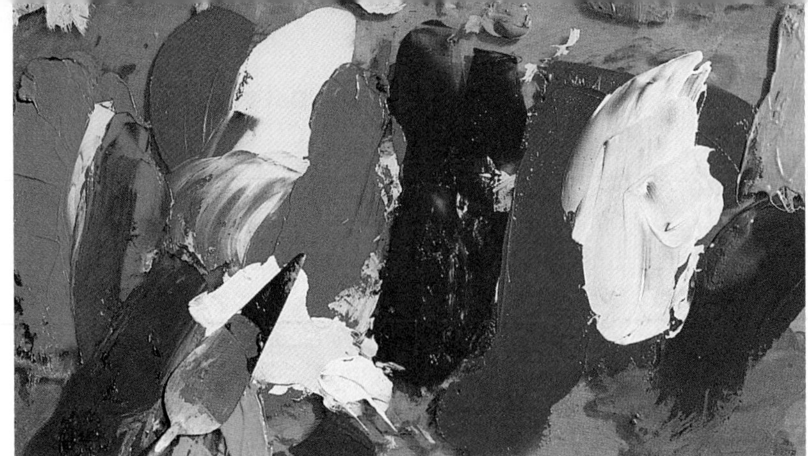

Figure 15.10 Resonance is similar to the mixing of two colors. The result is a color that is different from each of the starting colors.

bonds. Earlier chemists imagined that the electron pairs rapidly flip back and forth, or resonate, between the various electron dot structures. Thus double-headed arrows are used to indicate that two or more structures are in resonance.

Experimental measurements show that the two bonds in ozone are the same length. This result can be explained if the actual bonding in the ozone molecule is the average of the two electron dot structures. A more modern interpretation of resonance structures is that electron pairs do not resonate. The actual bonding is considered to be a hybrid, or mixture, of the extremes represented by the resonance forms. The offspring of a donkey and a horse, a mule has some characteristics of both parents. It is neither half-donkey nor half-horse, nor does it change continually between donkey and horse. Likewise, a resonance hybrid has some characteristics of its resonance forms, but it is a distinct species. The more resonance structures that can be drawn, the more stable is the ion or molecule.

Thus, the two electron dot formulas for ozone are examples of resonance structures. **Resonance** *structures occur when two or more valid electron dot formulas can be written for a molecule.* Resonance structures are simply a way to envision the bonding in certain molecules.

Concept Practice

11. What is true for the electron dot structures of all compounds that exhibit resonance?

Practice Problem

12. Draw resonance structures for the carbonate ion, CO_3^{2-}. Each oxygen is attached to the carbon.

15.A Environmental Awareness

Sunlight

Since you were very small you have probably heard that sunlight is good for you. Indeed, sunlight provides you with many benefits. When sunlight strikes your skin it generates vitamin D, a substance that is necessary for the formation of healthy bones and teeth. At the same time, however, sunlight can harm you. Excessive exposure to ultraviolet (UV) radiation from the sun can cause damage ranging from mild sunburn to skin cancer.

A suntan is visible evidence that your body is trying to protect itself from harm. Your skin responds to exposure to UV light by making more of the dark pigment melanin. The melanin screens out some of the damaging radiation and thus protects the molecular structure of your skin. However, even with this protective mechanism, damage to your skin can occur. UV light can lead to skin cancer. UV light can also damage your connective tissue, eventually producing the wrinkles of prematurely aged skin. Sunlight damage to your skin takes longer to occur if you have dark hair and dark skin because you have larger amounts of melanin.

Figure 15.11 To avoid the effects of overexposure to the sun's harmful UV radiation, you might wear a hat, sunglasses, a shirt, and sunscreen.

The incidence of skin cancers is on the increase due to the depletion of the protective layer of ozone in the stratosphere. The ozone layer helps block the harmful UV rays of the sun. Because this layer is being diminished by the presence of chlorofluorocarbons (CFCs), less UV radiation is being blocked. Today, the UV radiation of the sun must be considered an environmental hazard. Just as you would be wise not to drink polluted water, you would also be wise to protect yourself from the UV radiation of the sun.

The best way to protect yourself from the harmful effects of the sun is to keep out of the sun as much as possible. The next best way is to regularly use a sunscreen product to block out the sun that strikes your skin. Certain chemicals absorb specific wavelengths of light. You can shield your skin from harmful UV radiation by applying a lotion that contains a light-absorbing chemical. The chemical functions as a sunscreen in a similar way to melanin. All sunscreens are given a sun protection factor (SPF) value as a measure of effectiveness. For example, an SPF of 6 would provide six times the skin's natural sunburn protection.

Think About It

13. Explain Why does your skin darken when exposed to sunlight?

14. Describe How does a sunscreen work? What can you apply to your skin that will block out all of the sun's harmful radiation?

Show why some molecules that contain exceptions to the octet rule may exhibit paramagnetism.

15.6 Exceptions to the Octet Rule

Sometimes it is impossible to write electron dot structures that fulfill the octet rule. This happens whenever the total number of valence electrons in the species is an odd number. The NO_2 molecule contains a total of 17 valence electrons. Each oxygen contributes six electrons and the nitrogen contributes five. Two plausible resonance structures can be written for the NO_2 molecule.

:Ö=N̈—Ö̤· ⟷ ·Ö̤—N̈=Ö:

An unpaired electron is present in each of these structures. You cannot write a Lewis structure for NO_2 in which all of the atoms achieve an octet.

You can consider electrons as small, spinning, electric charges. These electric charges create magnetic fields, much as the current in an electric motor creates a magnetic field. You can think of paired electrons as having spins in opposite directions. The magnetic effects of paired electrons essentially cancel. Substances in which all of the electrons are paired are said to be *diamagnetic.* Diamagnetic substances are weakly repelled by an external magnetic field. *In contrast,* **paramagnetic** *substances show a relatively strong attraction to an external magnetic field.* These substances have molecules containing one or more unpaired electrons. Paramagnetism can be detected by measuring the mass of a substance in the absence and then in the presence of a magnetic field. The mass of the substance will appear to be greater in the magnetic field if the substance is paramagnetic.

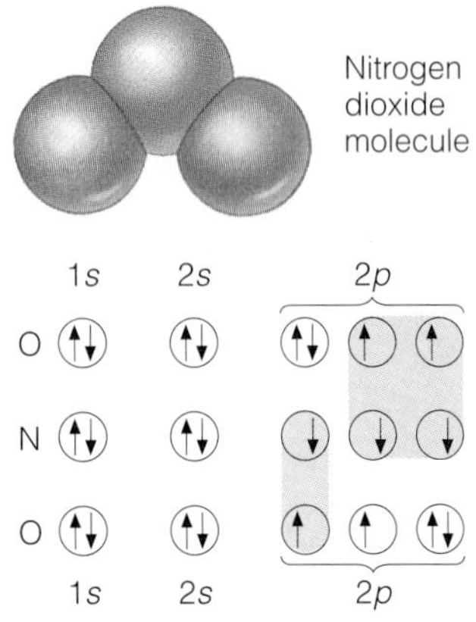

Figure 15.12 The nitrogen dioxide molecule is unusual in that it contains an unpaired electron.

Paramagnetism should not be confused with ferromagnetism. The latter is the much stronger attraction of iron, cobalt, and nickel for magnetic fields. The ions Fe^{2+}, Co^{2+}, and Ni^{2+} all have unpaired electrons. Large groups of ions are randomly dispersed throughout the metals. In a magnetic field these groups of ions line up in an orderly fashion with the field. This creates a strong magnetic attraction. The order remains even when the magnetic field is removed, leading to permanent magnetism.

A structure can be written for the oxygen molecule in which both oxygen atoms are surrounded by eight electrons. In this structure all the electrons are paired. You read in Section 15.2, however, that this structure is incorrect. The experimental evidence for this statement is that oxygen is paramagnetic. This property can be explained only if the oxygen molecule contains unpaired electrons. The measured distance between the oxygen atoms indicates that the oxygen molecule has some multiple bond character. This information suggests that oxygen is a resonance hybrid of these structures.

:Ö̤—Ö̤: ⟷ :Ö=Ö:

Several other molecules, such as some compounds of boron, also fail to follow the octet rule. The boron atom of boron trifluoride (BF_3), for example, is deficient by two electrons. Boron trifluoride readily reacts with ammonia to make the compound $BF_3{\cdot}NH_3$. By doing so, the boron atom accepts the unshared electron pair from ammonia and completes the octet.

```
      ..                           ..
     :F:       H                  :F:  H
      |        |                   |   |
  ..  |        |               ..  |   |
 :F — B   +  :N — H  ——→  :F — B ← N — H
  ..  |        |               ..  |   |
      |        |                   |   |
     :F:       H                  :F:  H
      ..                           ..
```

A few elements, especially phosphorus and sulfur, sometimes expand the octet to include 10 or 12 electrons. Phosphorus trichloride (PCl_3) and phosphorus pentachloride (PCl_5) are stable compounds. In both compounds all of the chlorines are bonded to the phosphorus. Covalent bonding in PCl_3 follows the octet rule because all the atoms acquire eight electrons. An electron dot structure for PCl_5 can be written only if phosphorus has 10 valence electrons. In sulfur hexafluoride (SF_6) the sulfur atom must have 12 valence electrons.

```
 ..   ..                                  ..
:Cl  :Cl:                                :F:  ..
 ..  \ |                                  |  / F:
       P — Cl:                        ..  | /  ..
 ..  / |    ..                       :F — S — F:
:Cl  :Cl:                             .. /|    ..
 ..   ..                             :F  :F:
                                      ..  ..
```

Phosphorus pentachloride

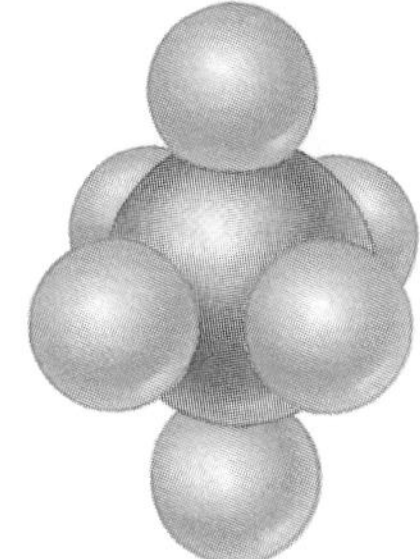

Sulfur hexafluoride

Figure 15.13 Phosphorus pentachloride and sulfur hexafluoride are exceptions to the octet rule.

Concept Practice

15. How can you determine experimentally whether a substance is paramagnetic?

16. Predict the magnetism of the following species.

a. BF_3 **b.** O_2^- **c.** NO_2 **d.** F_2

Objective

Describe the molecular orbital theory of covalent bonding.

15.7 Molecular Orbitals

There are models for covalent bonding besides the one you have seen. Just as there is a quantum mechanical model of the atom, there is also a quantum mechanical model of bonding. The quantum mechanical model describes the electrons in atoms by means of atomic orbitals. Similarly, quantum mechanics describes the electrons in molecules by *molecular orbitals. When two atoms combine, their atomic orbitals overlap to produce* **molecular orbitals**.

Some important parallels exist between atomic orbitals and molecular orbitals. Just as an atomic orbital belongs to a particular atom in the molecule, a molecular orbital belongs to the molecule as a whole. Each atomic orbital describes at most two electrons. Thus an atomic orbital is half-filled if it contains one electron. An atomic orbital is filled if it contains two electrons. Similarly, two electrons are required to fill a molecular orbital. Thus the overlap of two half-filled atomic orbitals can produce a typical two-electron single covalent bond. However, the molecular orbital model of bonding requires that the number of molecular orbitals equal the number of atomic orbitals that overlap. For example, *two* atomic orbitals overlap to create *two* molecular orbitals. This seems odd, since only one bond is formed when the atomic orbitals overlap. Nevertheless, the combination of two atomic orbitals does produce two molecular orbitals. One is a **bonding orbital**, *a molecular orbital whose energy is lower than that of the atomic orbitals from which it is formed.* The other is an **antibonding orbital**, *a molecular orbital whose energy is higher than that of the atomic orbitals from which it is formed.* The following illustration shows the relationship between atomic orbitals and molecular orbitals.

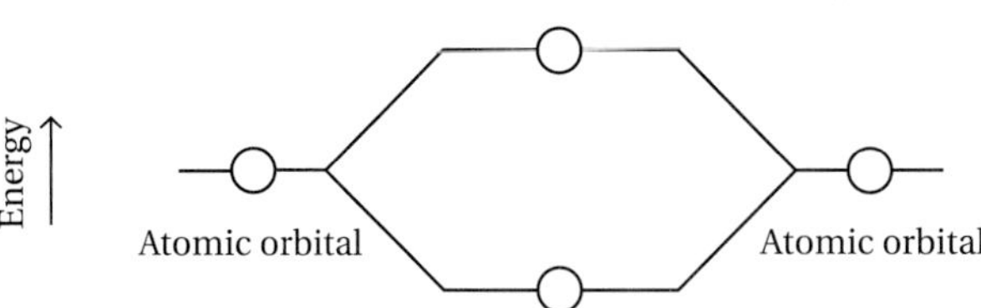

You can use the molecular orbital model of bonding concept to explain the bonding in the hydrogen molecule, H_2. The 1*s* atomic orbitals of each of the two hydrogen atoms overlap in the formation of a hydrogen molecule. Two electrons, one from each hydrogen atom, are available for bonding.

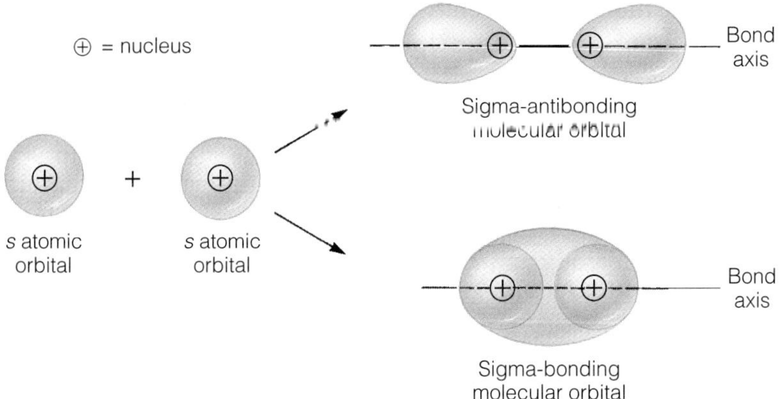

Figure 15.14 In a bonding molecular orbital, the electron density between the nuclei is high. In an antibonding orbital the electron density between the nuclei is extremely low. In the hydrogen molecule the two electrons occupy the bonding orbital.

The energy of the electrons in the bonding orbital is lower than the energy of the electrons in separate hydrogen atoms. Because electrons seek the lowest energy, they fill the bonding molecular energy level. This makes a stable covalent bond between the hydrogens. Figure 15.14 shows the formation of the bonding and antibonding molecular orbitals in the hydrogen molecule.

Energy

$1s^1$ H   H $1s^1$

H_2

In the bonding molecular orbital there is a high probability of finding the electrons between the nuclei of the combining atoms. This orbital is symmetrical along the axis between the hydrogen atoms. *A* **sigma bond** *is formed when two atomic orbitals combine to form a molecular orbital that is symmetrical along the axis connecting two atomic nuclei.* The symbol for the Greek letter sigma is σ.

According to the quantum mechanical model of covalent bonding, you may consider that covalent bonding results from a kind of imbalance. The imbalance is between the attractions and repulsions of the nuclei and electrons involved in the bonding. Being oppositely charged, nuclei and electrons attract each other. Being similarly charged, nuclei repel other nuclei and electrons repel other electrons. In the hydrogen molecule the nuclei repel each other, as do the electrons. There is, however, attraction of the hydrogen nuclei to the electrons between them in a bonding molecular orbital. As it turns out, the balance of all the interactions between hydrogen atoms is tipped in favor of the attractions. The result is the diatomic molecule H_2. In other cases, attempts to combine two atoms could lead to electron pairs in higher-energy, antibonding, molecular orbitals. These electrons are *not* between the nuclei. Thus the balance between attractions and repulsions could favor the repulsions. Electron repulsions would occur if two helium atoms were to combine into an He_2 molecule. Each atom has two 1*s* electrons. Two of these electrons can go into the low-energy bonding orbital, but the other two must go into the high-energy antibonding level.

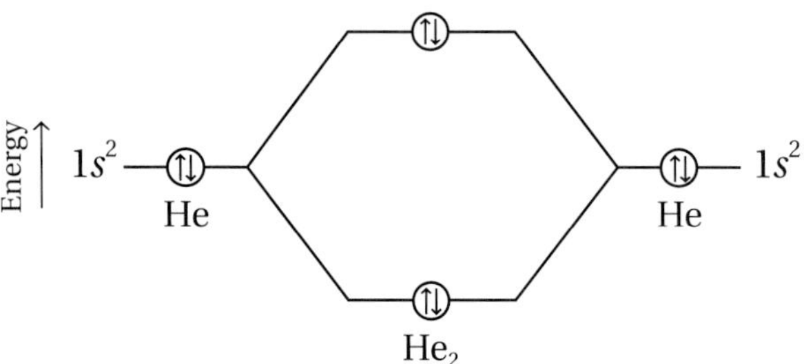

In this case the repulsions are larger than the attractions. Hence a theoretical He_2 molecule is unstable compared with two separate helium atoms, and helium exists only as atoms.

Atomic *p* orbitals also overlap to form molecular orbitals. For example, a fluorine atom has a half-filled 2*p* orbital. As shown in Figure 15.15, when two fluorine atoms combine, these orbitals overlap to make a filled bonding molecular orbital. There is a high probability of finding a pair of electrons in the bonding molecular orbital between the positively charged nuclei of the two fluorines. The fluorine nuclei are attracted to this region of high electron density. This attraction holds the atoms together in the fluorine molecule, F_2. The overlap of the 2*p* orbitals produces a symmetrical bonding molecular orbital when viewed along the F—F bond axis. Therefore the F—F bond is a sigma bond.

In the fluorine molecule the *p* atomic orbitals overlap end-to-end. In some molecules these orbitals can also overlap side-by-side. As shown in Figure 15.16, the side-by-side overlap of atomic *p* orbitals produces pi molecular orbitals. A pi bond results when a pi molecular orbital is filled with two electrons. The symbol for the Greek letter pi is π. *In a* **pi bond**, *the bonding electrons are most likely*

Figure 15.15 Two *p* atomic orbitals can combine to form a sigma-bonding molecular orbital.

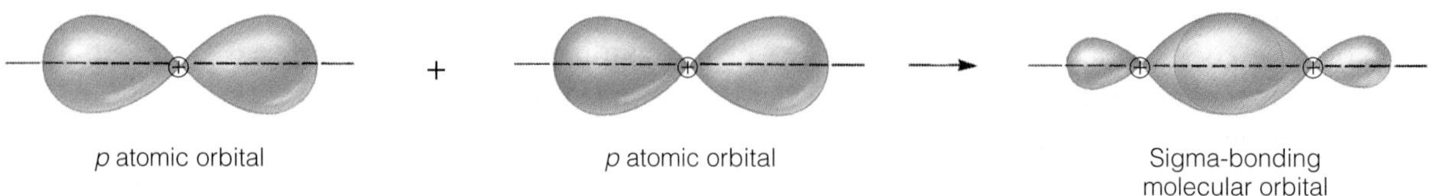

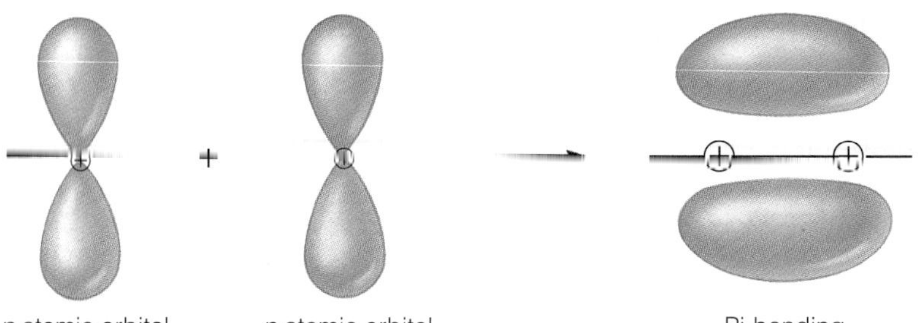

Figure 15.16 The side-by-side overlap of two *p* atomic orbitals produces a pi-bonding molecular orbital. The two sausage-shaped regions in which a bonding electron pair is most likely to be found constitute one pi-bonding molecular orbital.

to be found in sausage-shaped regions above and below the bond axis of the bonded atoms. Orbital overlap in pi bonding is not as extensive as it is in sigma bonding. Therefore pi bonds tend to be weaker than sigma bonds. You will return to pi bonding in the discussion of the shapes of molecules in Section 15.9.

Concept Practice

17. What is a sigma bond? Describe, with the aid of a diagram, how the overlap of two half-filled 1*s* orbitals produces a sigma bond. Use H_2 as your model.

18. How many sigma and pi bonds are in the ethyne, C_2H_2, molecule?

15.8 VSEPR Theory

Objective

Describe the shapes of simple covalently bonded molecules using VSEPR theory.

A photograph or sketch may fail to do justice to your appearance. Similarly, electron dot structures and structural formulas fail to reflect the three-dimensional shapes of molecules. For example, the electron dot structure and structural formula of methane (CH_4) show the molecule in only two dimensions.

```
    H              H
   ..              |
  H:C:H          H—C—H
   ..              |
    H              H
```

Methane (electron dot structure) Methane (structural formula)

In reality, methane molecules exist in three dimensions. Figure 15.17 shows the hydrogens in the methane molecule at the four corners of a geometric solid, the regular tetrahedron. *In this arrangement, all the H—C—H angles are 109.5°, the* **tetrahedral**

Roots of Words

tetra: (Greek) four
hedra: (Greek) face
tetrahedron solid object with four faces

The methane molecule, CH_4, is a tetrahedron.

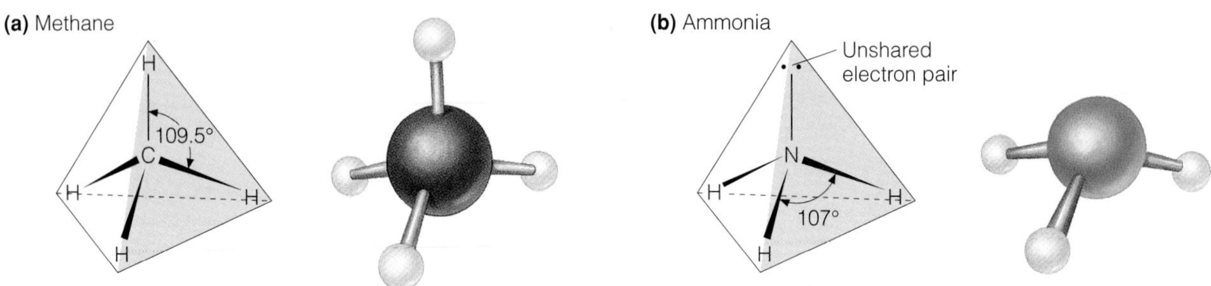

Figure 15.17 (a) Methane is a good example of a tetrahedral molecule. The hydrogens in methane are at the four corners of a regular tetrahedron. **(b)** An ammonia molecule is pyramidal. The unshared pair of electrons repels the bonding pairs, causing the bond angle to be about 107°.

angle. The *v*alence-*s*hell *e*lectron-*p*air *r*epulsion theory, or VSEPR theory, explains this shape. **VSEPR theory** *states that because electron pairs repel, molecules adjust their shapes so that the valence-electron pairs are as far apart as possible.* The methane molecule has four bonding electron pairs and no unshared pairs. The bond pairs are farthest apart when the angle between the central carbon and its attached hydrogens is 109.5°. This is the H—C—H bond angle found by experiment. Any other arrangement tends to bring two bonding pairs of electrons closer together.

Unshared pairs of electrons are important when you are trying to predict the shapes of molecules. The nitrogen in ammonia (NH_3) is surrounded by four pairs of valence electrons, but one of these is an unshared pair. No bonding atom is vying for the unshared electrons. Thus they are held closer to the nitrogen than are the bonding pairs. The unshared pair strongly repels the bonding pairs, pushing them closer together. The experimentally measured H—N—H bond angle is only 107°. Thus, the shape of the ammonia molecule is *pyramidal.*

In a water molecule, oxygen forms single covalent bonds with two hydrogen atoms. The two bonding pairs and two unshared pairs of electrons form a tetrahedral arrangement around the central oxygen. Thus the water molecule is planar (flat) but *bent.* With two unshared pairs repelling the bonding pairs, the H—O—H bond angle is compressed compared to the H—C—H bond angle in methane. The experimentally measured bond angle is about 105°, as shown in Figure 15.18.

Figure 15.18 (a) The water molecule is bent because the bonding electrons are repelled by the unshared pairs. **(b)** By contrast, the carbon dioxide molecule is linear. The carbon atom has no unshared pairs of electrons.

(a) Water

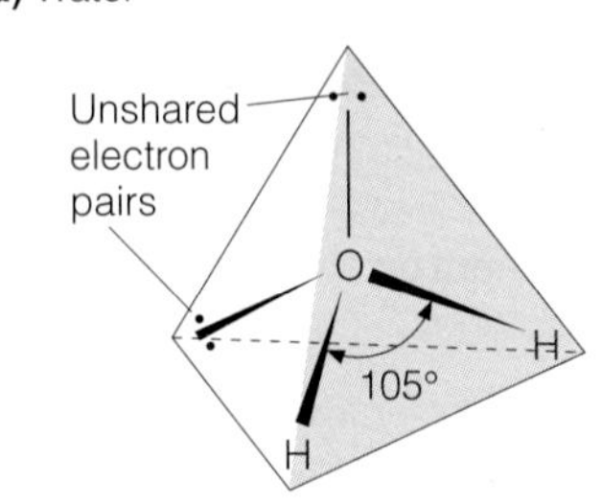

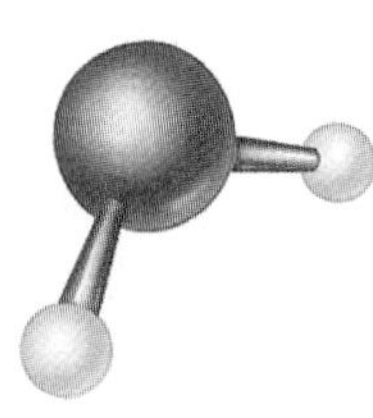

(b) Carbon dioxide

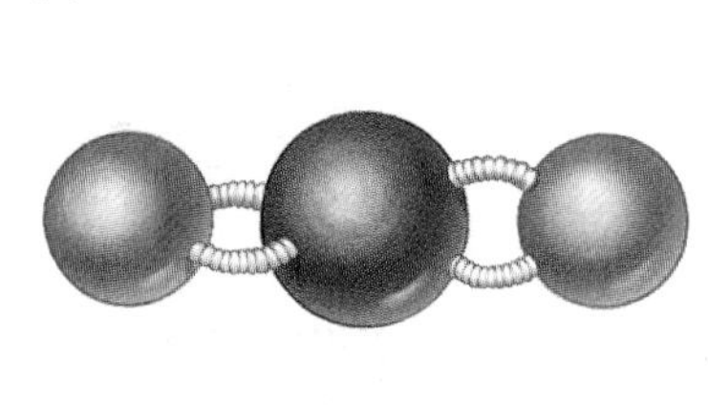

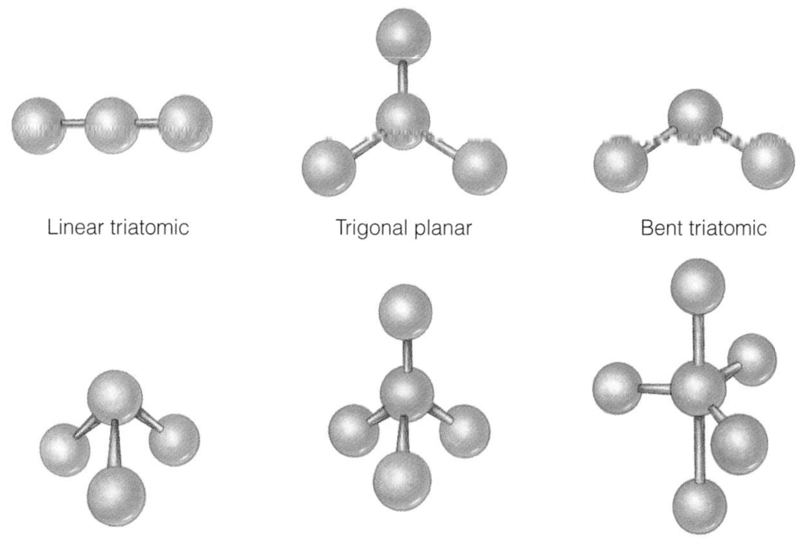

Linear triatomic | Trigonal planar | Bent triatomic

Pyramidal | Tetrahedral | Trigonal bipyramidal

Figure 15.19 Some of the commonly occurring molecular shapes.

The carbon in CO_2 has no unshared pairs. The double bonds joining the oxygens to the carbon are farthest apart when the O=C=O bond angle is 180°. Thus CO_2 is a *linear* molecule. Figure 15.19 shows some common molecular shapes with which you should be familiar.

Concept Practice

19. The BF_3 molecule is planar. Attachment of a fluorine ion to the boron in BF_3 through a coordinate covalent bond creates the BF_4^- ion. What is the geometric shape of this ion?

20. Explain how the VSEPR theory can be used to predict bond angles in these molecules.
a. methane **b.** ammonia **c.** water

15.9 Hybrid Orbitals

Objective

Describe the shapes of simple molecules using orbital hybridization.

Electron dot structures and the combination of unpaired electrons in boxes representing orbitals are two ways of describing covalent bonding. The VSEPR theory does a good job of describing molecular shapes. Another way to describe molecules that is informative about *both* bonding and shape is orbital hybridization. *With* **hybridization** *several atomic orbitals mix to form the same number of equivalent hybrid orbitals.*

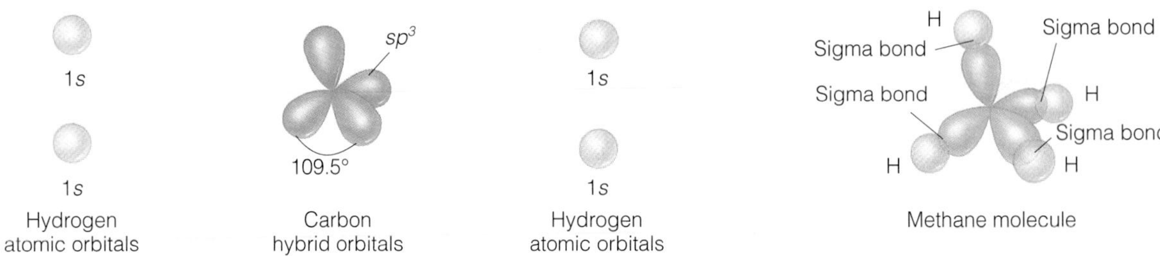

Figure 15.20 In methane, each of the four sp^3 hybrid orbitals of carbon overlaps with a 1*s* orbital of hydrogen. The result of each overlap is a sigma bond.

Orbital hybridization can be used to describe the methane molecule. One 2*s* orbital and three 2*p* orbitals of a carbon atom mix to form four sp^3 hybrid orbitals. These are at the tetrahedral angle of 109.5°. As you can see in Figure 15.20, the four sp^3 orbitals of carbon overlap with the 1*s* orbitals of the four hydrogen atoms. The sp^3 orbitals extend farther into space than either *s* or *p* orbitals. Thus the overlap with a hydrogen 1*s* orbital can be greater. The eight available valence electrons fill the molecules' orbitals to form four C—H sigma bonds. The greater overlap results in an unusually strong covalent bond.

Hybridization is also useful in describing double covalent bonds. Ethene is a relatively simple molecule. It has one carbon–carbon double bond and four carbon–hydrogen single bonds.

```
H       H
 \     /
  C = C
 /     \
H       H
```

Ethene

Figure 15.21 In ethene, two sp^2 hybrid orbitals from each carbon overlap with a 1*s* orbital of hydrogen to form a sigma bond. The other sp^2 orbitals overlap to form a carbon–carbon sigma bond. The *p* atomic orbitals overlap to form a pi bond, which occupies regions above and below the carbons.

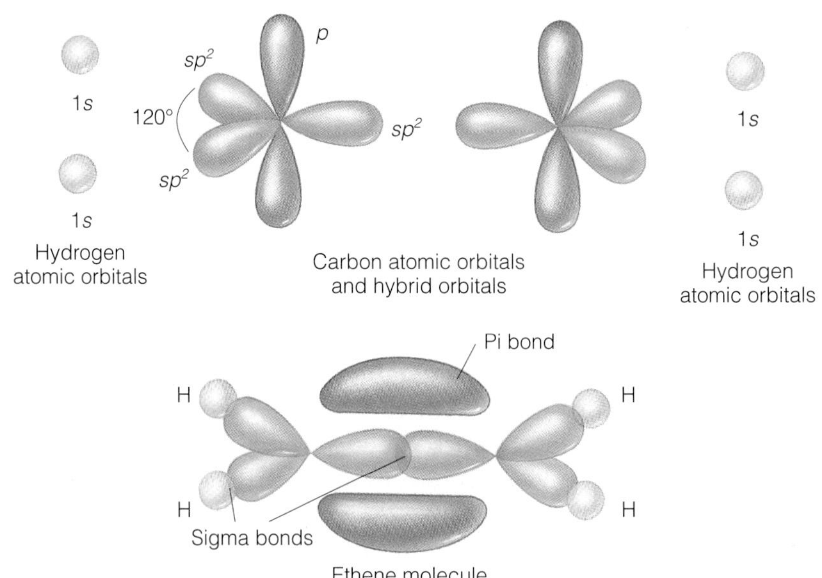

Experimental evidence indicates that the H—C—H bond angles are 120°. In ethene, sp^2 hybrid orbitals form from the combination of one 2*s* and two 2*p* atomic orbitals of carbon. As you can see in Figure 15.21, each hybrid orbital is separated from the other two by 120°. Two sp^2 hybrid orbitals of each carbon form sigma-bonding molecular orbitals with the four available hydrogen 1*s* orbitals. The third sp^2 orbitals of each of the two carbons overlap to form a carbon–carbon sigma-bonding orbital. The nonhybridized 2*p* (carbon) orbitals overlap side-by-side to form a pi-bonding orbital. A total of 12 electrons fill the six bonding orbitals. Thus the ethene molecule is held together by five sigma bonds and one pi bond.

Both sigma and pi bonds are two-electron covalent bonds. These bonds are drawn alike in structural formulas. Pi bonds are weaker than sigma bonds. In chemical reactions of carbon–carbon double bonds, the pi bond breaks in preference to the sigma bond.

A third type of covalent bond is a triple bond such as is found in ethyne, C_2H_2. Another name for this compound is acetylene.

$$H-C\equiv C-H$$

As with other molecules, the hybrid orbital description of ethyne is guided by the properties of the molecule. Ethyne is a linear molecule. The best hybrid orbital description is obtained if a 2*s* atomic orbital of carbon mixes with only one of the three 2*p* atomic orbitals. The result is two *sp* hybrid orbitals for each carbon. A carbon–carbon sigma-bonding molecular orbital forms from the overlap of one *sp* orbital from each carbon. The other *sp* orbital of each carbon overlaps with the 1*s* orbital of each hydrogen. Sigma-bonding molecular orbitals are formed. The remaining pair of *p*

Integrating Geography

Topographic Maps

Topographic maps are usually drawn as a series of lines tracing the elevations of the terrain of a particular region. For example, a line might be drawn for every increase of ten feet in elevation. Thus, the more closely spaced the lines, the steeper the terrain. Scientists who wish to know the positions of atoms in crystals of molecules may use electron densities that are plotted as a kind of topographic map. From X-ray diffraction data, they can find the electron density at any position in a crystal of interest and make a "map." The closer the lines are in the electron density map, the greater is the electron density of the molecule at that spot. Since the greatest electron densities in a molecule are found at the nuclei, the positions of the atoms in the molecule can be pinpointed with great accuracy.

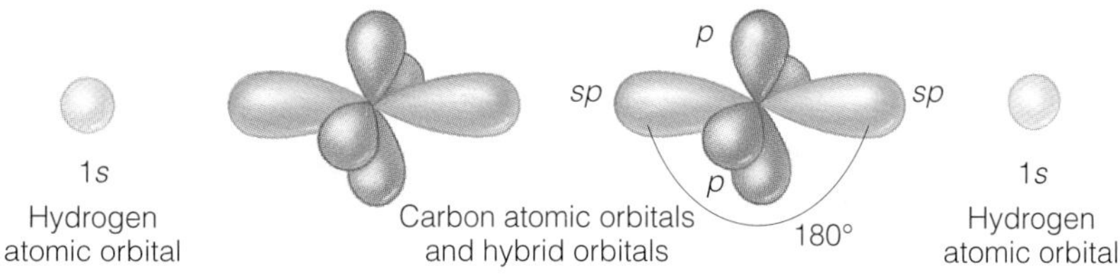

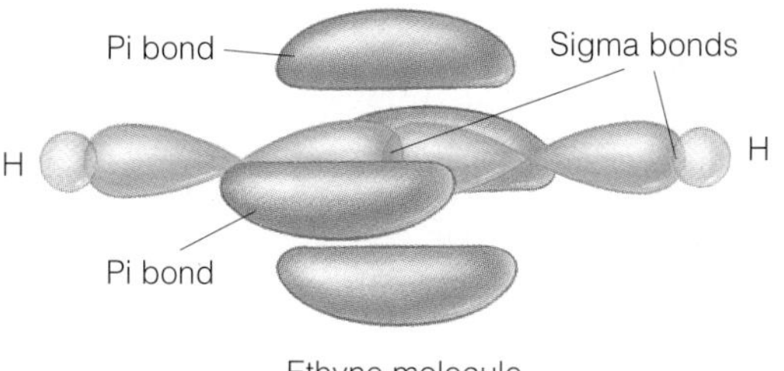

Figure 15.22 In ethyne, one *sp* hybrid orbital from each carbon overlaps with a 1*s* orbital of hydrogen to form a sigma bond. The other*sp* hybrid orbital of each carbon overlaps to form a carbon–carbon sigma bond. The two *p* atomic orbitals from each carbon overlap to form two pi bonds.

atomic orbitals on each carbon overlap side-by-side. They form two pi-bonding molecular orbitals. These surround the central carbons. The ten available electrons completely fill the five bonding molecular orbitals. Thus the bonding of ethyne consists of three sigma bonds and two pi bonds.

Concept Practice

21. What shape would you expect a simple carbon-containing compound to have when the carbon atom has the following hybridization?

a. sp^2 **b.** sp^3 **c.** sp

Practice Problem

22. The molecule CO_2 has two carbon–oxygen double bonds. Draw the bonding in the CO_2 molecule using hybridized orbitals for carbon and oxygen.

Objective

Categorize a bond as nonpolar covalent, polar covalent, or ionic using electronegativity values.

15.10 Polar Bonds

Covalent bonds have electron sharing between atoms. Not all covalent bonds are the same. The character of these bonds in a given molecule depends on the kind and number of atoms joined together. These features in turn determine the properties of the molecules.

Figure 15.23 The nuclei of atoms pull the bonding electrons as in a tug-of-war between two groups.

The bonding pairs of electrons in covalent bonds are pulled, as in a tug-of-war, between the nuclei of the atoms sharing the electrons. *When the atoms in a bond are the same, the bonding electrons are shared equally and the bond is a* **nonpolar covalent bond**. Hydrogen (H_2), oxygen (O_2), and nitrogen (N_2) have nonpolar covalent bonds. *When two different atoms are joined by a covalent bond and the bonding electrons are shared unequally, the bond is a* **polar covalent bond**, *or simply a* **polar bond**. The atom with stronger electron attraction (the more electronegative atom) in a polar bond acquires a slightly negative charge. The less electronegative atom acquires a slightly positive charge. Table 13.2 on page 366 gives electronegativities of some common elements. The higher the electronegativity value, the greater is the ability of an atom to attract electrons to itself.

Consider the hydrogen chloride molecule (HCl) in Figure 15.24. Hydrogen has an electronegativity value of 2.1, and chlorine has an electronegativity value of 3.0. The covalent bond in hydrogen chloride is polar. The chlorine atom acquires a slightly negative charge. The hydrogen atom acquires a slightly positive charge. The Greek letter delta (δ) is used to show that atoms involved in the covalent bond acquire only partial charges, much less than 1+ or 1–.

$$\overset{\delta+}{\mathrm{H}}-\overset{\delta-}{\mathrm{Cl}}$$

The minus sign shows that chlorine has acquired a slightly negative charge. The plus sign shows that hydrogen has acquired a slightly positive charge. These partial charges can be shown as clouds of electron density. The polarity of the bond may also be represented with an arrow pointing to the more electronegative atom, as shown here.

$$\overset{\longmapsto}{\mathrm{H}-\mathrm{Cl}}$$

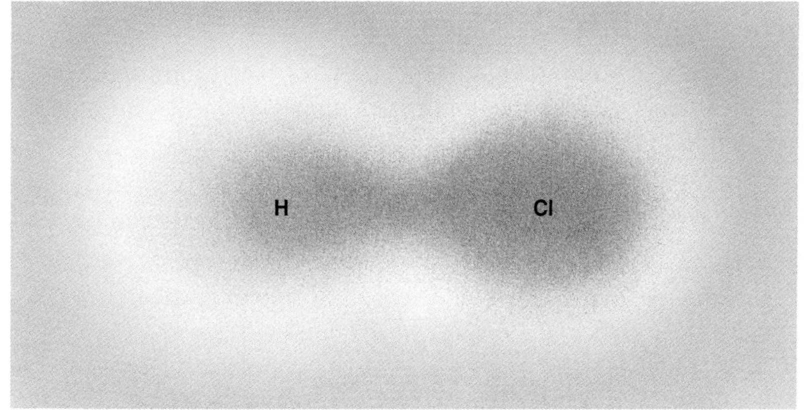

Figure 15.24 This electron cloud picture for hydrogen chloride shows that the chlorine atom attracts more of the electron cloud than does the hydrogen atom. Chlorine is more electronegative than hydrogen.

Integrating Computer Science

Molecular Modeling

The widespread availability of fast computers has greatly benefited chemists who are interested in the shapes of molecules and the interactions between molecules. For example, molecular modeling on computers is becoming an important tool in the pharmaceutical industry for the design of drugs. Computer scientists, in cooperation with chemists, have written many programs especially for chemists. These programs make possible the creation of models of molecules composed of up to thousands of atoms. Using a special viewing apparatus, chemists can see three-dimensional representations of complex molecules on the computer monitor. It is possible to turn the molecule over to see the other side, to shrink it, or to cut it in pieces on the monitor. In the future, through a computer technology called "virtual reality," it is likely that a chemist will even be able to "get inside" a molecular structure in order to examine it from every possible angle.

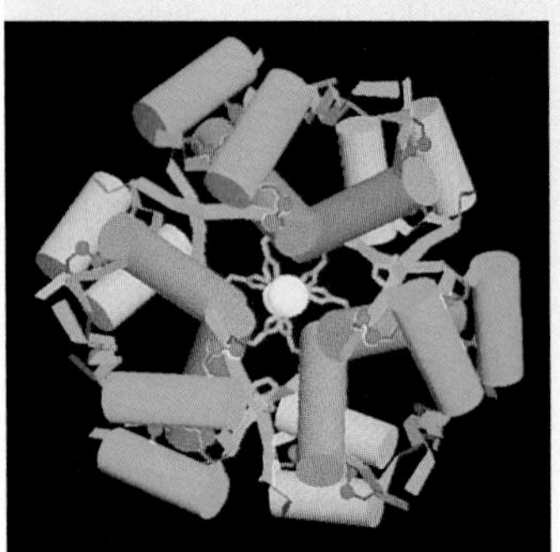

The O—H bonds in the water molecule are also polar. The very electronegative oxygen pulls the bonding electrons away from hydrogen. The oxygen acquires a slightly negative charge. The hydrogens acquire a slightly positive charge.

$$\overset{\delta-}{O} \text{ bonded to } {}_{\delta+}H \text{ and } H_{\delta+} \quad \textit{or} \quad H \leftarrow O \rightarrow H$$

Electronegativities also indicate the type of bond that two atoms will tend to form. For example, if the electronegativity difference between two atoms is greater than 2.0, a bond is ionic. Table 15.3 relates the electronegativity difference and the type of bond formed.

Table 15.3 Electronegativity Differences and Bond

Electronegativity difference (approx.)	Type of bond	Example
0.0–0.4	Covalent (nonpolar)	H—H (0.0)
0.4–1.0	Covalent (moderately polar)	$\overset{\delta+}{H}$—$\overset{\delta-}{Cl}$ (0.9)
1.0–2.0	Covalent (very polar)	$\overset{\delta+}{H}$—$\overset{\delta-}{F}$ (1.9)
≥2.0	Ionic	Na^+Cl^- (2.1)

Example 4 Identifying Bond Type

What type of bond (polar covalent, nonpolar covalent, or ionic) will form between atoms of the following pairs of elements?

a. N and H **b.** F and F **c.** Ca and O **d.** Al and Cl

Solution

The types of bonds formed depend on the electronegativity differences between the bonding elements. The rules are given in Table 15.3.

Elements (electronegativities)	Electronegativity difference	Type of bond
a. N (3.0), H (2.1)	0.9	Moderately polar covalent
b. F (4.0), F (4.0)	0.0	Nonpolar covalent
c. Ca (1.0), O (3.5)	2.5	Ionic
d. Al (1.5), Cl (3.0)	1.5	Very polar covalent

Concept Practice

23. What must always be true if a covalent bond is to be polar?

Practice Problems

24. Identify the bonds between atoms of the following pairs of elements as ionic, nonpolar covalent, or polar covalent.

a. H and Br
b. K and Cl
c. C and O
d. Cl and F
e. Li and O
f. Br and Br

25. Which covalent bond is the most polar?

a. H—Cl
b. H—Br
c. H—S
d. H—C
e. F—F

15.11 Polar Molecules

Objective

Show the relationship between polar covalent bonds and polar molecules.

The presence of a polar bond in a molecule often makes the entire molecule polar. *In a* **polar molecule** *one end of the molecule is slightly negative, and one end is slightly positive.* For example, in the hydrogen chloride molecule the partial charges on the hydrogen and chlorine atoms are electrically charged regions, or poles. *A molecule that has two poles is called a dipolar molecule, or* **dipole**. The hydrogen chloride molecule is a dipole.

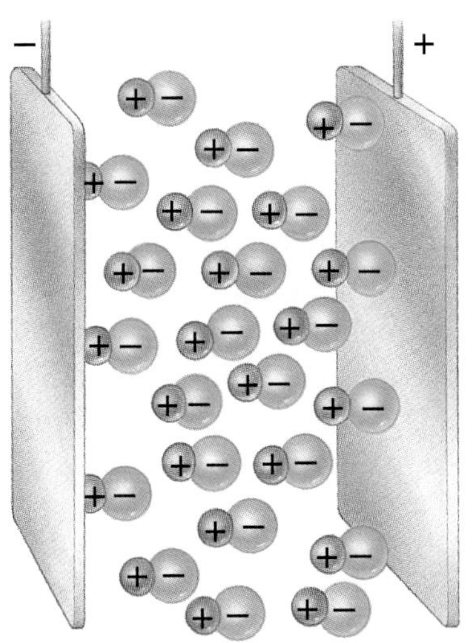

Figure 15.25 When polar molecules are placed in an electric field, the negative ends of the molecules orient toward the positively charged plate and the positive ends of the molecules orient toward the negatively charged plate. What would happen if carbon dioxide molecules were placed in this field? Why?

The effect of polar bonds on the polarity of an entire molecule depends on the shape of the molecule and the orientation of the polar bonds. A carbon dioxide molecule, for example, has two polar bonds and is linear.

$$\overleftarrow{O{=}}C\overrightarrow{{=}O}$$

The carbon and oxygens lie along the same axis. Therefore the bond polarities cancel because they are in opposite directions. Carbon dioxide is a nonpolar molecule.

The water molecule has two polar bonds, but the molecule is bent. Hence the bond polarities do not cancel, and a water molecule is polar.

Concept Practice

26. Not every molecule with polar bonds is itself polar. Explain this statement using CCl_4 and HF as examples.

Practice Problem

27. Draw the electron dot structure for each of the following molecules. Then identify polar covalent bonds by assigning $\delta+$ and $\delta-$ to the appropriate atoms.

a. HOOH
b. BrCl
c. HBr
d. H_2O

Objective

Define bond dissociation energy.

15.12 Bond Dissociation Energies

A large quantity of heat is liberated when hydrogen atoms combine to form hydrogen molecules. This is evidence that the product is more stable than the reactants. Indeed, the covalent bond in the hydrogen molecule is so strong that 435 kJ of energy is required to dissociate 1 mol of hydrogen molecules to hydrogen atoms. *The energy required to break a single bond is known as the* **bond dissociation energy**. Hydrogen molecules have a bond dissociation energy of 435 kJ/mol.

$$H{-}H + 435\text{ kJ} \longrightarrow H\cdot + \cdot H$$

The bond dissociation energy for a carbon–hydrogen bond in a given molecule is 393 kJ/mol.

Table 15.4 Bond Dissociation Energies and Bond Lengths for Covalent Bonds

Bond	Bond energy (kJ/mol)	Bond length (pm)
H—H	435	74
C—H	393	109
C—O	356	143
C=O	736	121
C≡O	1074	113
C—C	347	154
C=C	657	133
C≡C	908	121
C—N	305	147
S—S	259	208
Cl—Cl	243	199
N—N	209	140
Br—Br	192	228
I—I	151	267
O—O	142	132
O—H	464	96

The carbon–carbon single covalent bond has a bond dissociation energy of about 347 kJ. The ability of carbon to form strong carbon–carbon bonds helps explain the stability of carbon compounds. Table 15.4 gives bond dissociation energies of several representative covalent bonds. Compounds with only C—C and C—H single covalent bonds are quite unreactive chemically. In part this is because of the high dissociation energies of these bonds.

Concept Practice

28. What is the relationship between the magnitude of the bond dissociation energy of a molecule and the expected chemical reactivity of the molecule?

Practice Problem

29. How many kilojoules would be required to dissociate all the C—H single bonds in 0.1 mol of methane? Assume that the bond dissociation energy is the same for each bond.

Biographical Note

Ellen Richards
(1842–1911)

Ellen Richards was America's first formally educated female chemist. In 1873, she received a B.S. degree in chemistry from the Massachusetts Institute of Technology (M.I.T.). She soon decided to devote her time to applying chemical knowledge to the public health problems of the day. She focused her attention on water quality and sanitation and helped establish a Department of Sanitary Chemistry at M.I.T., where she was an instructor until her retirement in 1911. Richards was concerned that drinking water was often contaminated by sewage and other harmful substances. She became a strong advocate for establishing public health standards and also initiated significant advances in water treatment. During her career, Richards trained many men and women in sanitary chemistry. These people helped make water and sewage treatment commonplace by the middle of the twentieth century.

Objective

Describe and name the weak attractive forces that hold molecules together.

15.13 Intermolecular Attractions

In addition to covalent bonds in molecules, there are attractions between molecules, or intermolecular attractions. These attractions are weaker than either an ionic or covalent bond. Nevertheless, do not underestimate the power of these forces. Among other things, they are responsible for whether a molecular compound is a gas, liquid, or solid.

The weakest attractions between molecules are collectively called **van der Waals forces**. They are named after the Dutch chemist Johannes van der Waals (1837–1923). Two major van der Waals forces are dispersion forces and dipole interactions.

Dispersion forces, *the weakest of all molecular interactions, are thought to be caused by the motion of electrons.* Generally speaking, the strength of dispersion forces increases as the number of electrons in a molecule increases. The halogens are an example of molecules whose major attraction for one another is caused by dispersion forces. Fluorine and chlorine, with relatively few electrons, are gases at STP. The larger number of electrons in bromine generate larger dispersion forces. Bromine molecules are, therefore, sufficiently attracted to each other to make bromine a liquid at STP. Iodine, with a still larger number of electrons, is a solid at STP.

Dipole interactions *occur when polar molecules are attracted to one another.* Electrostatic attractions occur between the oppositely charged regions of dipolar molecules. Dipole interactions are similar to but much weaker than ionic bonds. Dipole interactions in water, for example, result in a weak attraction of water molecules for one another. Each O—H bond in the water molecule is highly polar. The oxygens in water acquire a slightly negative charge because of oxygen's greater electronegativity. The hydrogens in water acquire a slightly positive charge. Polar molecules attract one another. Hence the positive region of one water molecule attracts the negative region of another. The dipolar attraction between the hydrogen of one water molecule and the oxygen of another water molecule is strong relative to other dipolar interactions. This relatively strong interaction, which is also found in some molecules besides water, is given the special name *hydrogen bond.*

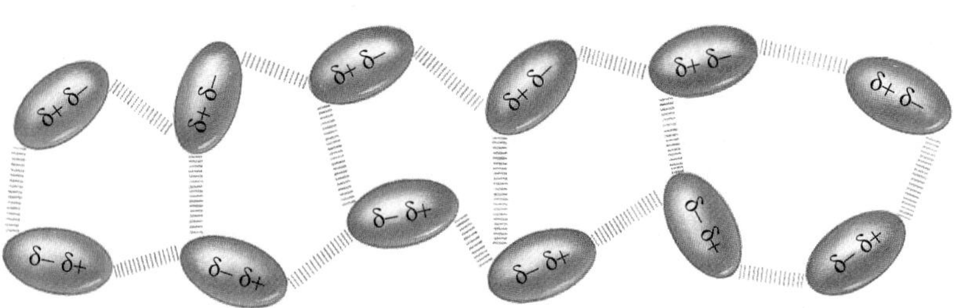

Figure 15.26 Polar molecules are attracted to one another by van der Waals forces called dipole interactions.

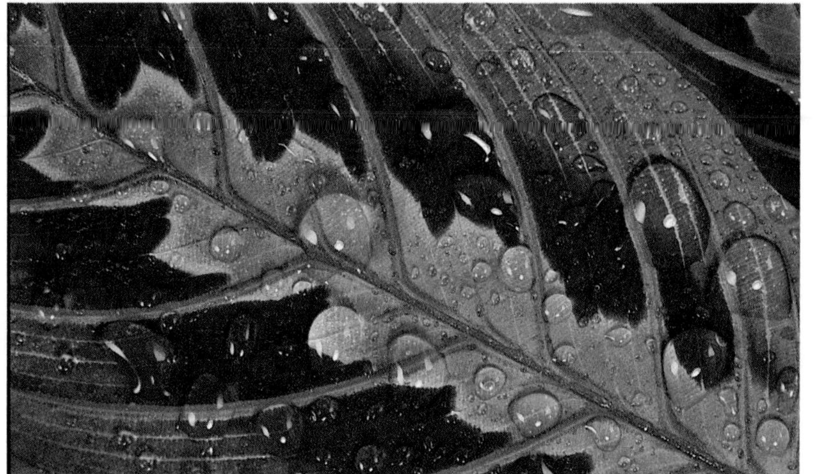

Figure 15.27 Liquids tend to form drops because of intermolecular attractions. Molecular substances with weak intermolecular attractions are gases at room temperature. Molecular substances with very strong intermolecular attractions are solids.

Hydrogen bonds *are attractive forces in which hydrogen that is covalently bonded to a very electronegative atom is also weakly bonded to an unshared electron pair of an electronegative atom in the same molecule or in a nearby molecule.* Hydrogen bonding always involves hydrogen. It is the only chemically reactive element whose valence electrons are not shielded from the nucleus by a layer of underlying electrons. A very polar covalent bond is formed when hydrogen bonds to an electronegative atom like oxygen, nitrogen, or fluorine. This leaves the hydrogen nucleus quite electron deficient. The hydrogen makes up for its deficiency by sharing a nonbonding electron pair on a nearby electronegative atom. The resulting hydrogen bond has about 5% of the strength of an average covalent bond. Hydrogen bonds are the strongest of the intermolecular forces. They are extremely important in determining the properties of water and biological molecules like proteins. Figure 15.28 shows hydrogen bonding between water molecules.

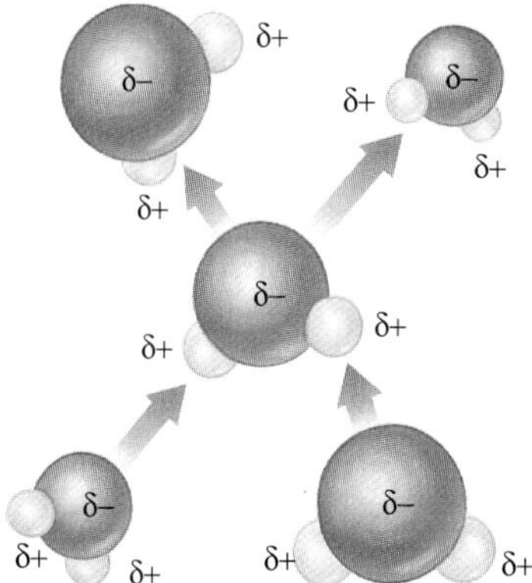

Figure 15.28 Hydrogen bonding between water molecules accounts for many properties of water. The hydrogen bond has about 5% the strength of an average covalent bond.

Concept Practice

30. Depict the hydrogen bonding between two ammonia molecules and between one ammonia molecule and one water molecule.

31. Rank these intermolecular attractive forces from strongest to weakest.
a. dipole interactions
b. dispersion forces
c. hydrogen bonds

Objective

Identify the characteristics of molecular substances.

15.14 Properties of Molecular Substances

The physical properties of a compound depend on the type of bonding it displays. Some covalent compounds are gases, some are liquids, and some are solids at room temperature. We have already touched on this point by noting that most ionic compounds are crystalline solids. Table 15.5 summarizes some of the differences between ionic and molecular substances. A great variety of physical properties occurs among covalent compounds. This is in large part because of intermolecular attractions.

The melting and boiling points of most molecular compounds are low compared with those of ionic compounds. A few molecular solids resist melting, until the temperature reaches 1000°C to 3000°C. Some decompose without melting at all. *Most of these very stable substances are* **network solids** *(or network crystals) in which all of the atoms are covalently bonded to each other.* Diamond is a network solid because each carbon in a diamond is covalently bonded to four other carbons. Diamond cutting requires breaking a multitude of these bonds. Diamond does not melt, but vaporizes to

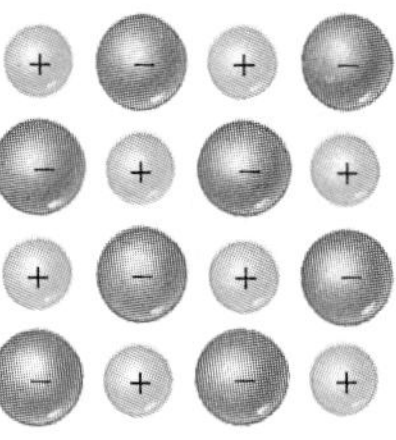

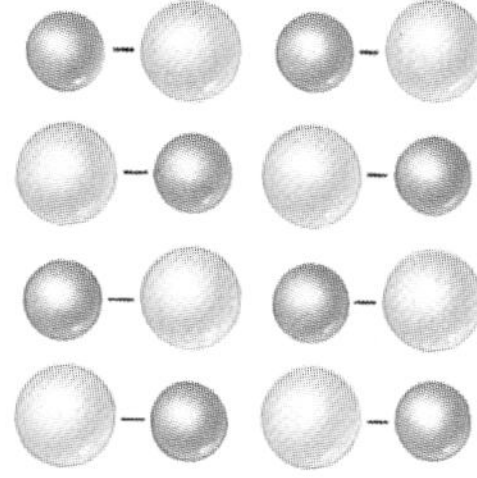

Figure 15.29 Ionic compounds have high melting points. Each ion in the crystal lattice is held firmly in place by electrostatic forces of attraction. By contrast, molecular crystals generally have low melting points. Even strong intermolecular bonds are much weaker than ionic bonds.

Table 15.5 Characteristics of Ionic and Covalent Compounds

Characteristic	Ionic compound	Covalent compound
Representative unit	Formula unit	Molecule
Bond formation	Transfer of one or more electrons between atoms	Sharing of electron pairs between atoms
Type of elements	Metallic and nonmetallic	Nonmetallic
Physical state	Solid	Solid, liquid, or gas
Melting point	High (usually above 300°C)	Low (usually below 300°C)
Solubility in water	Usually high	High to low
Electrical conductivity of aqueous solution	Good conductor	Poor to nonconducting

a gas at 3500°C and above. Silicon carbide, with the formula unit SiC and a melting point of about 2700°C, is also a network solid. Silicon carbide is so hard that it is used in grindstones and as an abrasive. The molecular structure of silicon carbide is like that of diamond except that every other carbon is replaced by silicon. Samples of diamond or silicon carbide can be thought of as single molecules. The melting of silicon carbide requires that covalent bonds be broken. To melt other molecular solids we need only break the weak attractions between molecules.

Concept Practice

32. How does a network solid differ from most covalent compounds?

33. Which of these is characteristic of most covalent compounds?

a. High melting point
b. Sharing bonding electrons
c. Low water solubility
d. Exist as molecules
e. Composed of a metal and a nonmetal

Activity 15 Making a Polymer

Purpose

To create a new substance and observe its properties.

Materials

measuring teaspoon (tsp) and tablespoon (tbsp)

small paper or plastic cup

white glue

2% borax (sodium borate, $Na_2B_4O_7$) solution

water

stirring rod

small plastic bag

Procedure

1. In the small cup, add 2 tbsp of white glue to 1 tbsp of water and stir.

2. Add 2 tsp of borax solution to the cup and stir.

3. Carefully pour off and discard the excess liquid.

4. Explore the properties of the solid material. Try to shape it, stretch it (slowly and rapidly), and bounce it.

5. If you wish to save your sample, store it in the plastic bag.

Analysis and Conclusions

1. Compare the properties of your solid with those of the materials you started with.

2. Propose an explanation for what may have happened at the molecular level to account for the new properties of your solid.

15.B Consumer Chemistry

Adhesives

Figure 15.30 Traditional methods of fastening, such as welding, riveting, and bolting, are being replaced by adhesives in many manufacturing industries.

Modern manufacturing and repair work depend to an enormous extent on the use of adhesives. Your local hardware store probably carries a bewildering array of adhesives designed for specific applications. There, you may discover that an epoxy resin or a cyanoacrylate adhesive is the best choice.

Epoxy resins are a group of very strong synthetic adhesives. These adhesives usually come in two parts, which must be mixed. One part contains an epoxy prepolymer. The other part is a chemical curing agent. The epoxy prepolymer combines chemically with the curing agent to form an interlocking polymer. The end result of this kind of chemical reaction is that the glue layer is essentially one big molecule. The polar OH^- groups in the final polymer are strongly attracted to the surface to which the resin is applied. The attractions between the resin and the surface are extremely strong. So are the attractions within the resin itself. When an object glued with epoxy is subjected to stress, other parts of the object will often break before the glued surface breaks!

The cyanoacrylates are another class of adhesives. These adhesives are thin and free-flowing. This makes cyanoacrylates suitable for bonding smooth, relatively nonporous materials such as glass and plastics. Like epoxies, cyanoacrylate adhesives require a curing agent. Cyanoacrylate adhesives polymerize upon contact with water vapor in the air. The resulting polymer network makes strong adhesive bonds to the materials with which it comes in contact. Because the polymerization of cyanoacrylates is very rapid, these superadhesives are completely cured only a few seconds after being exposed to air. The rapid-curing property of cyanoacrylate adhesives is convenient because it generally eliminates the need to clamp the pieces being glued. However, the quick curing of cyanoacrylates upon contact with traces of water can also present an unusual hazard. Your skin, eyes, and mouth are always somewhat moist. If you are careless with cyanoacrylate adhesives, you can glue your fingers, eyelids, or lips together in an instant!

Safety

The solvents used in many adhesives are toxic. Inhaling the fumes is dangerous. Work in a well-ventilated area.

Think About It

34. Explain What is the function of the curing agent in an epoxy adhesive?

35. Explain When two pieces of wood that are glued together with epoxy are bent, the wood often breaks before the epoxy joint. Explain in molecular terms the reason that this happens.

Nanostructured Materials

Layer by Layer

More than 30 years ago, Richard P. Feynman, a Nobel Prize–winning physicist, suggested that when scientists were able to manipulate matter on an exceedingly small scale the materials produced would exhibit a variety of improved properties. Today, scientists are doing just what Feynman envisioned. New materials are being created by combining metals and other materials in many fine layers, each only a few atoms thick!

The design of these new materials is called nanoengineering. These multilayer materials are called "nanostructured materials," because the thickness of the layers is about 1 to 100 nm (nanometers). Multilayer materials have fewer defects in their structure than metals. Consequently, they are stronger and less likely to fail under stress. The thinnest multilayers have the most uniform structure and produce the strongest materials.

Multilayer materials can be formed from materials that have very different properties. For example, a hard but brittle material can be combined with a tough material to produce a new material that is both hard and tough. An example of this is a multilayer of copper and Monel metal (an alloy of copper and nickel), which has a tensile strength 10 times greater than copper itself. Other multilayers include tungsten with tungsten carbide, which can withstand very high temperatures, and stainless steel with Monel metal, which is very corrosion resistant.

Multilayers are made by a technique called sputtering. In sputtering, solid materials are first vaporized in a vacuum chamber at temperatures near 90 000°C. Ions are then fired at the vaporized material which is to be deposited. The impact of the ions blasts atoms from the vaporized material. These atoms are then attracted by an electrical charge to the surface to be layered. The resulting layer of atoms on the surface is incredibly thin.

Unfortunately, these supertough and superhard materials rapidly wear out cutting tools and are therefore difficult to fabricate into useful parts. Thus, one of the next goals is to make objects close to their final size so that they require little or no machining. The ultimate goal is to rapidly produce components using multilayer materials that have designer properties and practical shapes.

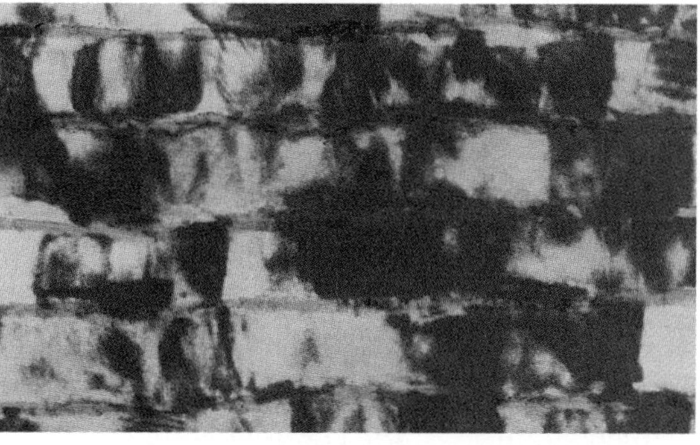

The reflective surface of a multilayer foil consists of 1750 layers of copper and copper/zirconium alloy. A cross-section is shown at left.

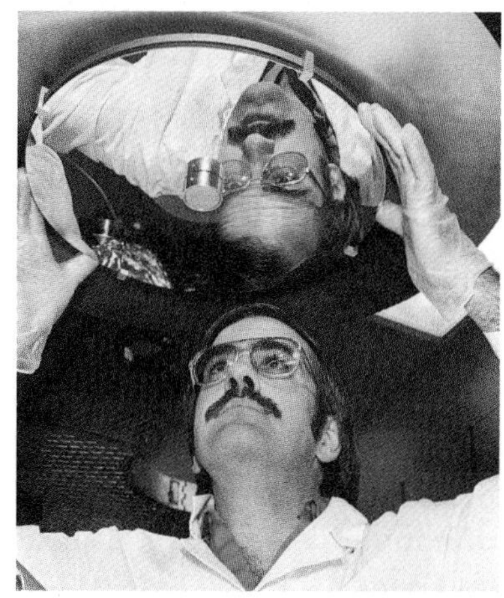

A multilayer sample 1 mm thick would consist of about 200,000 separate layers!

Think About It

36. Explain What characterizes "nanostructured materials"?

37. Suppose Think of some additional applications for multilayer materials.

Chapter 15 Review
Covalent Bonds

Key Terms

antibonding orbital *15.7*
bond dissociation energy *15.12*
bonding orbital *15.7*
coordinate covalent bond *15.4*
dipole *15.11*
dipole interaction *15.13*
dispersion force *15.13*
double covalent bond *15.2*
hybridization *15.9*
hydrogen bond *15.13*
molecular orbital *15.7*
network solid *15.14*
nonpolar covalent bond *15.10*
paramagnetic *15.6*
pi bond (π bond) *15.7*
polar bond *15.10*
polar covalent bond *15.10*
polar molecule *15.11*
resonance *15.5*
sigma bond (σ bond) *15.7*
single covalent bond *15.1*
structural formula *15.1*
tetrahedral angle *15.8*
triple covalent bond *15.2*
unshared pair *15.1*
van der Waals force *15.13*
VSEPR theory *15.8*

Chapter Summary

When atoms share electrons to gain the electron configuration of a noble gas, they form covalent bonds. A shared pair of valence electrons constitutes a single covalent bond. Sometimes two or three pairs of electrons may be shared to give double or triple covalent bonds. In some cases only one of the atoms in a bond provides the pair of bonding electrons; this is a coordinate covalent bond.

When like atoms are joined by a covalent bond, the bonding electrons are shared equally and the bond is nonpolar. When the atoms in a bond are not the same, the bonding electrons are shared unequally and the bond is polar. The degree of polarity of a bond between any two atoms is determined by consulting a table of electronegativities. Some molecules are polar because they contain polar covalent bonds. Bond dissociation energies are affected by bond polarity and the electronegativity of the joined atoms. The attractions between opposite poles of polar molecules constitute dipole interactions. The dipole interaction is one of several weak attractions between molecules. Another weak attractive force is the hydrogen bond. These weak forces determine whether a covalent compound is a solid, liquid, or gas.

As a rule, molecules adjust their three-dimensional shapes so that the valence-electron pairs around a central atom are as far apart as possible. This is the guiding principle in the valence-shell electron-pair repulsion, or VSEPR, theory of molecular geometries. Molecular orbital theory is a logical extension of the quantum mechanical description of the electron structure of atoms. Covalent bonding is described in terms of sigma and pi bonds. In some instances molecular geometry is adequately described by simple overlap of atomic orbitals. In others a description of molecular shape that better fits experimental results is obtained from hybridized atomic orbitals.

Practice Questions and Problems

38. Explain why neon is monatomic but chlorine exists as diatomic molecules. *15.1*

39. The following covalent molecules have only single covalent bonds. Draw an electron dot structure for each. *15.1*
a. H_2O **b.** H_2O_2 **c.** PCl_3 **d.** NH_3

40. Classify the following compounds as ionic or covalent. *15.1*
a. $MgCl_2$ **b.** Na_2S **c.** H_2O **d.** H_2S

41. Describe the difference between an ionic and a covalent bond. *15.1*

42. How many electrons are shared by two atoms in a double covalent bond? In a triple covalent bond? *15.2*

43. Write plausible electron dot structures for the following substances. Each substance contains only single covalent bonds. *15.3*
a. I_2 **b.** OF_2 **c.** H_2S **d.** NI_3

44. Draw the electron dot structures of these molecules. *15.3*

a. F_2 **b.** HCl **c.** HCCH **d.** HCN

45. What are the benefits and the risks of exposure to sunlight? *15.A*

46. Explain why compounds containing C—N and C—O single bonds can form coordinate covalent bonds with H^+ but compounds containing only C—H and C—C single bonds cannot. *15.4*

47. Draw all resonance forms for sulfur dioxide, SO_2. The oxygens in SO_2 are attached to the sulfur. *15.5*

48. Using electron dot structures, draw at least two resonance structures for the nitrite ion, NO_2^-. The oxygens in NO_2^- are attached to the nitrogen. *15.5*

49. Can you suggest a reason why phosphorus and sulfur expand octets in many of their compounds but nitrogen and oxygen never do? *15.6*

50. Which of the following species would you predict to be diamagnetic? Paramagnetic? *15.6*

a. NO_3^- **b.** OH^- **c.** H_2O **d.** SO_3

51. Draw molecular orbital diagrams for the possible diatomic molecule Li_2. Would you expect Li_2 to exist as a stable molecule? *15.7*

52. What is the total number of sigma bonds and pi bonds in each of the following molecules? *15.7*

a. H—C≡N **b.** H—C(H)(H)—N=C=O

53. Use VSEPR theory to predict the shapes of the following species. *15.8*

a. CO_2 **c.** SO_3 **e.** CO

b. $SiCl_4$ **d.** SCl_2 **f.** I_3^-

54. What types of hybrid orbitals are involved in bonding of each atom in the following molecules? *15.9*

a. CO **c.** $H_2C{=}O$

b. H_2O **d.** N≡C—C≡N

55. Arrange the following bonds in order of increasing ionic character. *15.10*

a. Cl—F **c.** K—O **e.** S—O

b. N—N **d.** C—H **f.** Li—F

56. The bonds between the following pairs of elements are covalent. Arrange them according to polarity, naming the most polar bond first. *15.10*

a. H—Cl **c.** H—F **e.** H—H

b. H—C **d.** H—O **f.** S—Cl

57. Based on the information about molecular shapes in Section 15.8, which of these molecules would you expect to be polar? *15.11*

a. SO_2 **c.** CO_2

b. H_2S **d.** BF_3

58. Explain what is meant by the term *bond dissociation energy. 15.12*

59. Assume that the total bond energy in a molecule is the sum of the individual bond energies. Calculate the total bond energy in a mole of ethyne, C_2H_2. (*Hint:* Write the electron dot structure to determine the kinds of bonds. Then refer to Table 15.4.) *15.12*

60. Which compound in each pair exhibits the stronger intermolecular hydrogen bonding? *15.13*

a. H_2S and H_2O **c.** HBr and HCl

b. HCl and HF **d.** NH_3 and H_2O

61. What is a hydrogen bond? *15.13*

62. List some of the properties of epoxy adhesives. *15.B*

63. Why do compounds with strong intermolecular attractive forces have higher boiling points than compounds with weak intermolecular attractive forces? *15.14*

Mastery Questions and Problems

64. Construct a concept map using *molecular compound* as the central concept.

65. Devise a hybridization scheme and predict the shape of PCl_3 based on this scheme.

66. Write two electron dot structures for the molecule N_2O. Predict the magnetic properties and shape of this molecule.

67. The chlorines and oxygen in thionyl chloride, $SOCl_2$, are bonded directly to the sulfur. Write an acceptable electron dot structure for thionyl chloride.

68. Explain why each of the following electron dot structures is incorrect. Replace each structure with one that is more acceptable.

```
                              :Cl:
                               ::
a. [:C::N̈:]⁻             c.  H:C̈::O

      ..     ..                  ..
b. :F:P::F:              d.    :F:
    ..  ..  ..              ..  ..  ..
       :F:                 :F:B:F:
        ..                  ..  ..  ..
```

69. Use VSEPR theory to predict the geometry of each of the following:

a. $SeCl_4$ **c.** CCl_4
b. CO_3^{2-} **d.** $SnCl_2$

70. The graph below shows how the percent ionic character of a single bond varies according to the difference in electronegativity between the two elements forming the bond. Answer the following questions using this graph and Table 13.2 on page 366.

a. What is the relationship between the percent ionic character of single bonds and the electronegativity difference between their elements?

b. What electronegativity difference will result in a bond with a 50% ionic character?

c. Estimate the percent ionic character of the bonds formed between (1) lithium and oxygen, (2) nitrogen and oxygen, (3) magnesium and chlorine, (4) nitrogen and fluorine.

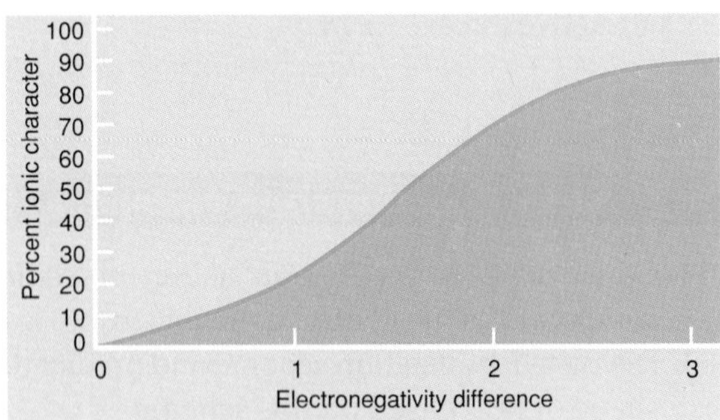

71. Using bond dissociation energies, estimate ΔH for the following reaction.

$CO(g) + 2H_2(g) \longrightarrow CH_3OH(g)$

72. Describe the difference between a bonding molecular orbital and an antibonding molecular orbital. How do their energies compare?

73. Give the angles between the orbitals of each of the following hybrids.

a. sp^3 hybrids
b. sp^2 hybrids
c. sp hybrids

Critical Thinking Questions

74. Choose the term that best completes the second relationship.

a. house:lumber bond: _____
(1) atoms (3) valence electrons
(2) molecules (4) octet rule

b. globe:earth
electron dot formula: _____
(1) atoms (3) valence electrons
(2) molecules (4) octet rule

75. Make a list of the elements found in Table 15.2. What do the elements that form covalent bonds have in common?

76. Is there a clear difference between a *very* polar covalent bond and an ionic bond? If so, what criteria would you use to tell the difference?

Cumulative Review

77. Which of the following ions have the same number of electrons as a noble gas?

a. Al^{3+} **b.** O^{2-} **c.** Br^- **d.** N^{3-}

78. A solution containing 0.10 mol of $BaCl_2$ is mixed with a solution containing 0.20 mol of Na_2SO_4 to give a precipitate of $BaSO_4$. What is the maximum yield in moles of $BaSO_4$? In grams?

79. Write correct electron configurations for atoms of the following elements.

a. sodium **c.** phosphorus
b. sulfur **d.** nitrogen

80. Calculate the gram formula mass of each of the following substances.

a. $CaSO_4$ **b.** H_2SO_4 **c.** NI_3 **d.** $FeCl_3$

81. Give the number of representative particles in the following molar quantities.

a. 2.00 centimole **c.** 8.73 nanomole
b. 1.54 millimole **d.** 3.00 micromole

82. Name and give the symbol for the element in the following position in the periodic table.
a. Group 7B, period 4 **c.** Group 1A, period 7
b. Group 3A, period 5 **d.** Group 6A, period 6

Challenge Questions and Problems

83. The electron structure and geometry of the methane molecule, CH_4, can be described by a variety of models. These include the electron dot structure, simple overlap of atomic orbitals, and orbital hybridization of carbon. Write the electron dot structure of CH_4. Sketch two molecular orbital pictures of the CH_4 molecule. For your first sketch assume that one of the paired $2s^2$ electrons of carbon has been "promoted" to the empty $2p$ orbital. Overlap each half-filled atomic orbital of carbon to a half-filled $2s$ orbital of hydrogen. What is the predicted geometry of the CH_4 molecule using this simple overlap method? In your second sketch assume hybridization of the $2s$ and $2p$ orbitals of carbon. Now what geometry would you predict for CH_4? Which picture is preferable based on the facts that all H—C—H bond angles in CH_4 are 109.5° and all C—H bond distances are identical?

84. There are some compounds in which one atom has more electrons than the corresponding noble gas. Examples are PCl_5, SF_6, and IF_7. Write the electron dot formulas of P, S, and I, and then draw the electron dot structures for these compounds. Looking at the outer shell configuration of P, S, and I, develop an orbital hybridization scheme to explain the existence of these compounds.

Connections Questions

85. You may have made models of simple molecules using a "ball-and-stick" model kit. What are some advantages of molecular modeling on a computer?

86. Describe how the work of Ellen Richards contributed to a safer, healthier society in this century.

87. What can chemists determine from X-ray diffraction studies of a crystal of a substance?

Write About Chemistry

88. Hair consists of chains of amino acids (proteins) held in place chiefly by hydrogen bonds and covalent disulfide linkages. Interview a hair stylist and write a short description of the chemistry of hair styling.

89. Nitrogen molecules are very stable. Nitrogen molecules are products of the reaction of explosives such as TNT and nitroglycerine that contain nitrogen atoms. Write a paragraph that links the chemistry of the first statement with the chemistry of the second statement.

Readings and References

Gordon, J. E. *The New Science of Strong Materials or Why You Don't Fall Through the Floor*, 2nd ed. Princeton, NJ: Princeton University Press, 1984.

Salem, Lionel. *Marvels of the Molecule.* New York: VCH Publishers, 1987.

Wood, Clair G. "Dissolving Plastic." *ChemMatters* (October 1987), pp. 12–14.

16 Water and Aqueous Systems

Goals

- Describe how hydrogen bonding influences various properties of water.
- Explain the tendency of ionic solids to dissolve in water and to form hydrates.
- Explain why some ionic compounds act as strong electrolytes and others act as weak electrolytes.
- Distinguish among solutions, suspensions, colloids, and emulsions.

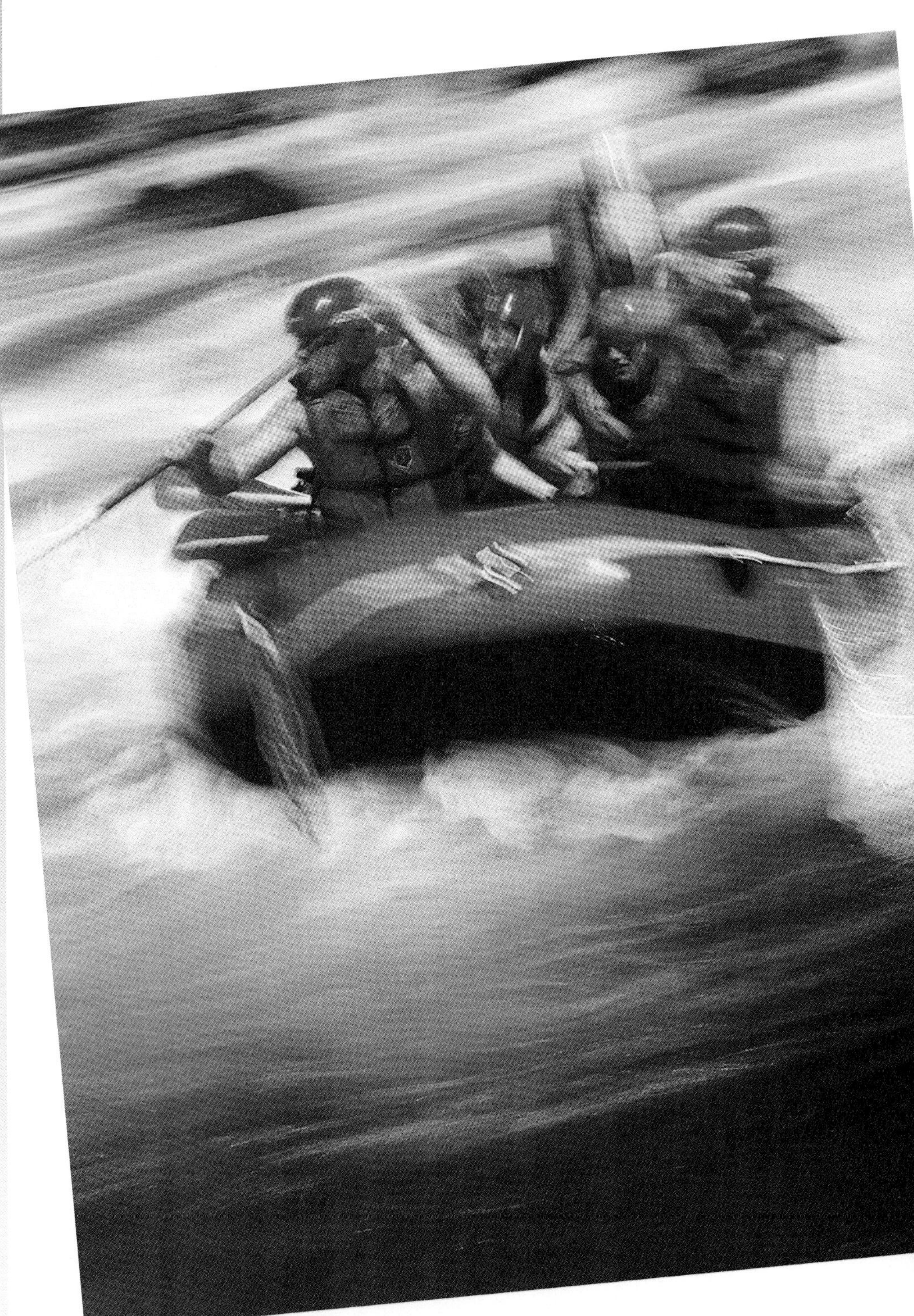

The average flow rate of the water in the Amazon River is about 1.027×10^{13} liters per day. Although these rafters are miles from the Amazon, they feel the thrill of rushing water. In this chapter, you will discover the basis for some of the amazing properties of water.

Concept Overview

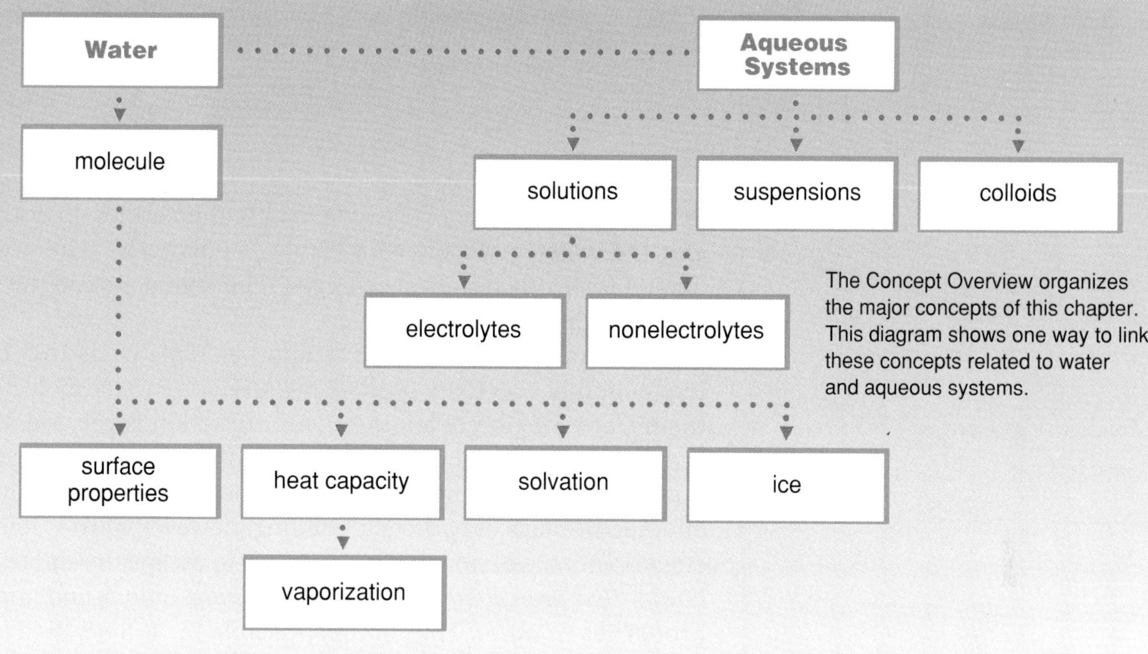

The Concept Overview organizes the major concepts of this chapter. This diagram shows one way to link these concepts related to water and aqueous systems.

Water has a unique story because it is a unique compound. Liquid water covers about three-quarters of the surface of the earth, as oceans, lakes, and rivers. Immense aquifers store water deep underground. Ice dominates the vast polar regions of the globe. Water appears as icebergs in the oceans, and it whitens the temperate zones as snow in winter. Water vapor from the evaporation of surface water and from steam spouted from geysers and volcanoes is ever-present in the earth's atmosphere. Water is the foundation of everything that lives. Without it neither plant nor animal life as you know it could exist.

16.1 The Water Molecule

Objective

Describe the hydrogen bonding that occurs in water due to the structure of the polar water molecule.

Water is a simple triatomic molecule. Each O—H covalent bond in the water molecule is highly polar. Because of its greater electronegativity, oxygen attracts the electron pair of the covalent O—H bond and acquires a slightly negative charge. The less electronegative hydrogen atoms acquire a slightly positive charge. The water molecule has an H—O—H bond angle of 105°. Because of the water

Figure 16.1 The water molecule is bent. The bond polarities are equal, but the two dipoles do not cancel each other. There is a net polarity, and the molecule as a whole is polar.

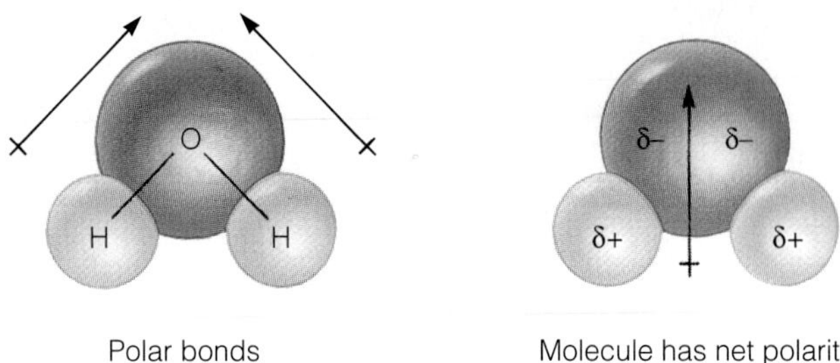

molecule's bent shape, the two O—H bond polarities do not cancel, and the water molecule as a whole is polar. The region around oxygen is slightly negatively charged. The region around the hydrogens is slightly positively charged.

Polar molecules attract one another. This leads to a dipolar interaction between the positive region of one water molecule and the negative region of another. This attraction is very weak, however, when compared with the strength of intermolecular hydrogen bonds. In water the molecules change position by sliding over one another. Because of hydrogen bonding, however, most water molecules do not have enough kinetic energy to escape the surface of the liquid. *Hydrogen bonds* are the cause of many unique and important properties of water. They are responsible for water's high surface tension, low vapor pressure, high specific heat capacity, high heat of vaporization, and high boiling point.

Figure 16.2 Due to their polarity, shown in **(a)**, water molecules are attracted to each other. They participate in hydrogen bonding **(b)**.

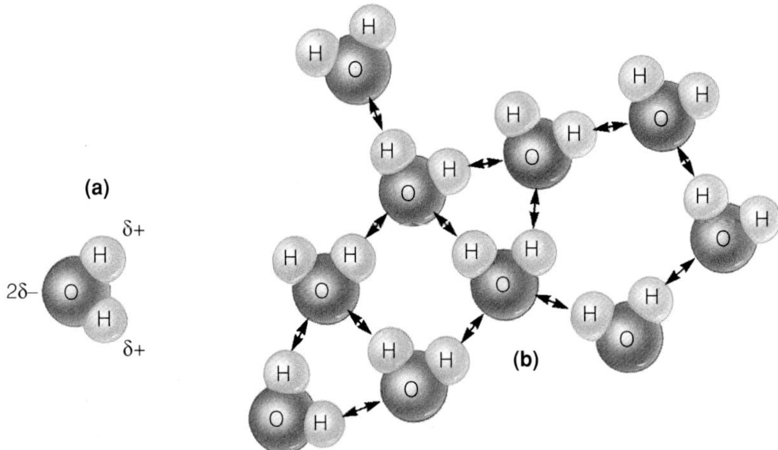

Concept Practice

1. Describe the hydrogen bonding among molecules in water.

16.2 Surface Properties of Water

Objective

Explain the high surface tension and low vapor pressure of water using the concept of hydrogen bonding.

You have probably seen a glass so filled with water that the water surface bulges above the rim. You may also have noticed that water forms nearly spherical droplets at the end of a medicine dropper or when sprayed on a greasy surface. A needle floats if placed on the surface of water, but it sinks immediately if it breaks through the surface. The surface of water acts like a skin. This phenomenon, called *surface tension,* is explained by the ability of water to form hydrogen bonds. The molecules within the liquid are completely surrounded by, and hydrogen bonded to, adjacent water molecules. At the surface of the liquid, however, water molecules experience an uneven attraction. Look at Figure 16.3. The water molecules are hydrogen bonded on only one side of the drop. They are not attracted to the air because they cannot form hydrogen bonds with air molecules. As a result, water molecules at the surface tend to be drawn into the body of the liquid. *This inward force or pull which tends to minimize the surface area of any liquid is* **surface tension**.

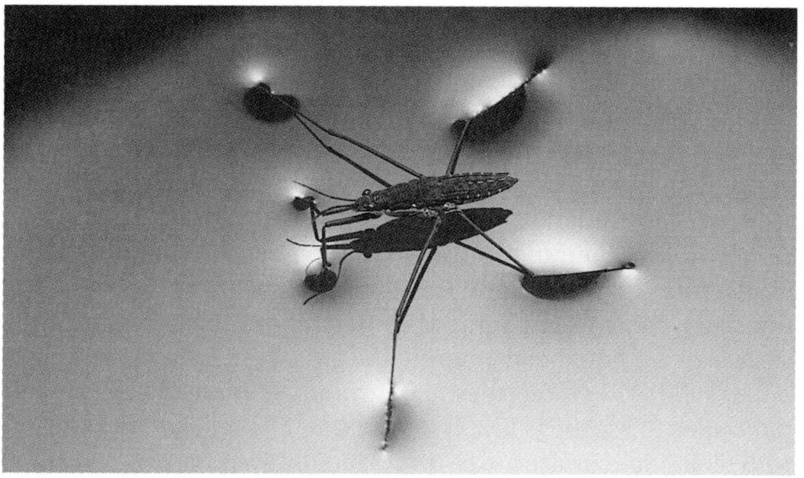

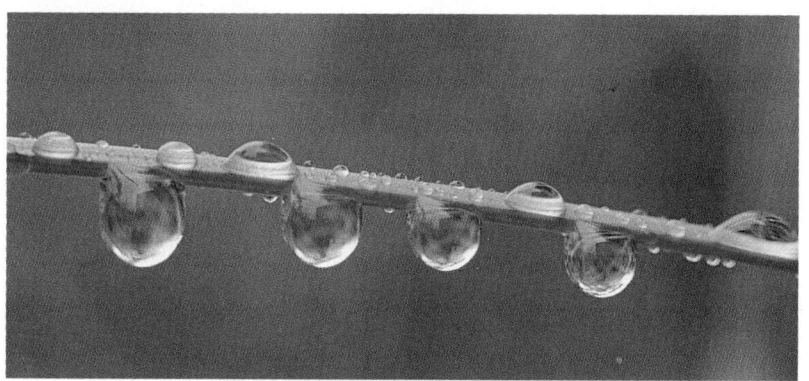

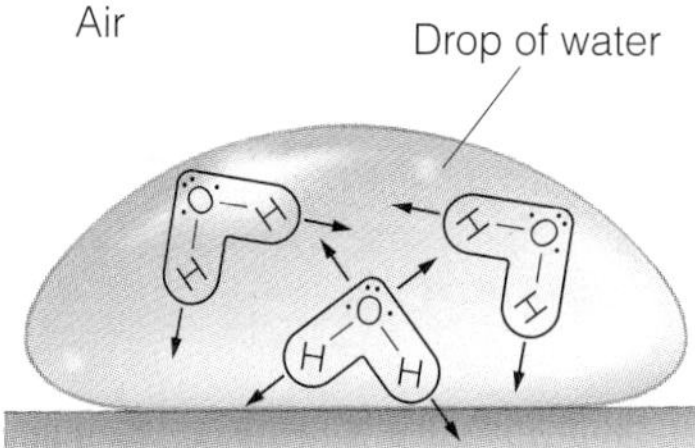

Figure 16.3 Surface tension makes it possible for some insects such as this water strider to "walk" on water. The force of gravity pulling the insect downward is less than the forces of attraction between the water molecules. Water molecules at the surface experience an uneven attraction because they cannot hydrogen-bond with air molecules. Thus, the surface water molecules tend to be drawn into the body of the liquid, producing surface tension.

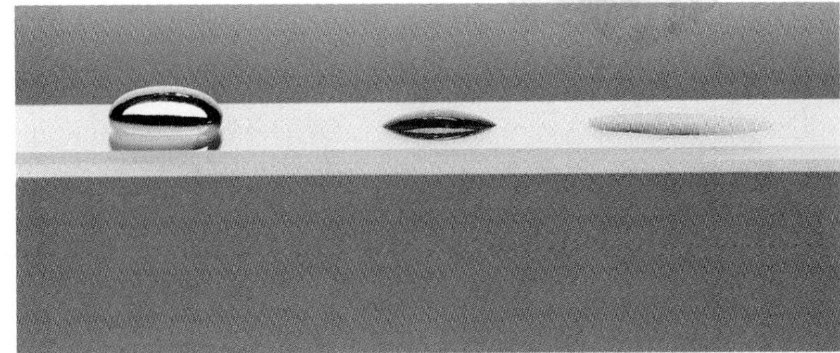

Figure 16.4 All of the drops shown are of equal volume. From left to right they are mercury, water, and water with detergent.

A sphere has the smallest surface area for a given volume. The surface tension of a liquid tends to hold a drop of liquid in a spherical shape. At the same time the force of gravity tends to flatten the drops. A liquid that has strong intermolecular attractions has a high surface tension. Look at Figure 16.4. The higher the surface tension, the more nearly spherical the drop of that particular liquid.

All liquids have a surface tension, but water's surface tension is higher than most. This is why water has a tendency to bead up on some surfaces rather than wet them down. The surface tension of water may be decreased by adding a *wetting agent* such as soap or detergent. Soaps and detergents are **surfactants** (*surf*ace-*act*ive *ag*e*nts*). When a detergent is added to beads of water on a greasy surface, the detergent molecules interfere with the hydrogen bonding between water molecules. As a result, surface tension is reduced. The beads collapse, and the water spreads out.

Hydrogen bonding between water molecules also explains water's unusually low vapor pressure. As you learned in Section 9.5, the *vapor pressure* of a liquid is caused by molecules escaping the surface of the liquid and entering the gas phase. Because hydrogen bonds hold water molecules to one another, the tendency of these molecules to escape is low. If it were not, all the lakes and oceans, with their large surface areas, would rapidly evaporate!

Chemistry in Careers

Water Quality Technicians and Chemists

The first people involved in testing the quality of the treated water are laboratory technicians. They perform routine chemical analyses of stream samples, raw and treated wastewater, sludge, and other products of the treatment process. Water quality chemists take the testing phase a step further. They carry out specialized and complex chemical and bacteriological analyses of the wastewater. These tests guarantee that the wastewater treatment plant is operating efficiently and meets all government regulatory requirements.

Concept Practice

2. What is surface tension? Why do the particles at the surface of a liquid behave differently from those in the bulk of the liquid?

3. Describe the origin of the vapor pressure of water.

4. Explain why it is easier to wash a car with water that has soap in it than with water alone.

16.A Environmental Awareness

Wastewater Treatment

Cleaning used water is one of the most important functions a society can perform for its survival. Wastewater treatment protects the environment from harmful substances carried by the used water. Wastewater treatment also helps to recycle water, a resource in increasingly short supply.

Wastewater treatment begins with the water from your home, your school, or industry that collects in underground pipes called sewers. Gravity moves the wastewater through the sewers to the wastewater treatment plant. Once at the plant, the wastewater moves through a number of purification stages. The primary treatment stage is mostly a physical process. A coarse screen traps large debris. Then the water enters a grit chamber where sand and gravel fall to the bottom. The water flows from the grit chamber into settling tanks where sedimentation occurs. Most of the suspended organic matter settles out in the settling tanks. The more modern treatment plants process the water further by means of secondary treatment. Secondary treatment is a federal requirement.

In secondary treatment large populations of microorganisms convert the remaining dissolved organic matter into solids that separate as a sludge. Air is bubbled into the water to provide life-sustaining oxygen for the microorganisms as they oxidize the organic matter. This oxidation produces the sludge. The sludge can produce offensive odors if not handled properly. The sludge is treated in digesters with anaerobic bacteria. The sludge becomes harmless organic matter which can be applied to the land as a fertilizer or soil conditioner. The effluent water from secondary treatment is generally pure enough to release to a receiving stream or river.

Primary and secondary treatments remove about 90% of the organic matter from wastewater. Sometimes additional processing, tertiary treatment, is needed. At this level of treatment, nutrients such as nitrogen and phosphorus compounds that produce unwanted growth of algae are removed. Tertiary treatment is not a federal requirement. Some states, however, require tertiary treatment if the effluent is to be discharged into a lake or stream. The effluent from a wastewater treatment plant can enter another water treatment facility and be processed to yield drinking water.

Figure 16.5 Two aspects of wastewater treatment are shown. In a settling tank (top) suspended solids sink to the bottom and are periodically removed as sludge. Air can be added in an aeration tank (bottom) to allow bacteria to break down organic materials.

Think About It

5. Debate State an argument for and an argument against the tertiary treatment of all wastewater.

Objective

Contrast the high specific heat of water with that of most other substances.

16.3 The Heat Capacity of Water

You may recall that it takes 4.18 J (1 cal) of heat energy to raise the temperature of 1 g of water 1°C. The specific heat capacity of water is nearly constant at 4.18 J/g°C at temperatures between 0°C and 100°C. The specific heat capacity of water is higher than that of most other substances. Iron has a specific heat capacity of only 0.447 J/g°C. For the same increase in temperature, iron requires only about one-tenth as much heat as does an equal mass of water. On a sunny day a puddle of water remains relatively cool. Meanwhile, a nearby manhole cover gets hot enough, so it is said, to fry an egg.

Water's high specific heat capacity helps moderate daily air temperatures around large bodies of water. On a warm day, water absorbs heat from its warmer environment, lowering the air temperature. On a cool night the transfer of heat is from the water to its cooler environment, raising the air temperature. Thus water is a storage medium for solar energy.

Figure 16.6 People flock to the beach in hot weather because the shore is cooler than inland areas. Can you explain this phenomenon in terms of water's heat capacity?

Concept Practice

6. What three quantities must you know in order to calculate the specific heat capacity of a sample of water?

7. Does the specific heat capacity of water vary depending on the quantity of water? Explain.

16.4 The Evaporation of Water

Because of hydrogen bonding, water absorbs a large amount of heat before it evaporates or vaporizes. The heat of vaporization is the amount of energy needed to convert 1 g of a substance from a liquid to a gas at the boiling point. It takes 2.26 kJ to convert 1 g of water at 100°C to 1 g of steam at 100°C. The extensive network of hydrogen bonds holds the molecules in water tightly together. These bonds have to be broken before water changes from the liquid to the vapor state. The heat of vaporization of liquid ammonia, which is less hydrogen bonded than water, is 1.37 kJ/g. Liquid methane, which has no hydrogen bonding, has a heat of vaporization of only 0.510 kJ/g.

The reverse of vaporization is condensation. When 1 g of steam at 100°C condenses to 1 g of water at 100°C, 2.26 kJ of heat is liberated. The heat of condensation of water is, therefore, 2.26 kJ/g. As expected, this heat is numerically equal to the heat of vaporization. You can get a severe burn if you allow steam to condense on your hand. Not only is the temperature of steam 100°C, but the additional heat of condensation is also absorbed by your skin.

The evaporation and condensation of water are also important to geographic temperatures. Temperatures in the tropics would be much higher if water did not absorb heat while evaporating from the surface of the surrounding oceans. Temperatures in the polar regions would be much lower if water vapor did not release its heat while condensing out of the air.

Compounds of low molar mass are usually gases or low-boiling liquids at normal atmospheric pressure. In Table 16.1, you can see that ammonia is a typical example. Ammonia has a molar mass of 17 g and boils at −33°C. Water, with a molar mass of 18 g, is an important exception. It has a boiling point of 100°C. The reason is again hydrogen bonding. Hydrogen bonding is more extensive in water

Table 16.1 Melting Points and Boiling Points of Some Substances with Low Molecular Mass

Name of substance	Formula	Formula mass (amu)	Melting point (°C)	Boiling point (°C)
Methane	CH_4	16	−183	−164
Ammonia	NH_3	17	−77.7	−33.3
Water	H_2O	18	0	100
Neon	Ne	20	−249	−246
Methanol	CH_3OH	32	−93.9	64.9
Hydrogen sulfide	H_2S	34	−85.5	−60.7

Objective

Explain the high heat of vaporization and the high boiling point of water using the concept of hydrogen bonding.

Integrating Geology

Hydrologic Sciences

Hydrologists are scientists whose main concern is with the Earth's water in all of its forms: solid ice, liquid water, and water vapor. They study the complex relationships between these various forms of water, from underground water to the polar icecaps, in the enormously complex water cycle. The water cycle begins when precipitation falls on the earth. Some of the water is absorbed; some runs off into rivers and eventually reaches the oceans. Water from all of these sources continually evaporates. Eventually this water vapor will form clouds and fall on the earth as precipitation, thereby continuing the water cycle. In the long run, the hydrologists' work may provide an understanding of how to ensure sufficient water to meet the world's needs.

than in ammonia. It takes much more heat to disrupt the attractions between water molecules than between ammonia molecules. If the hydrogen bonding in water were as weak as it is in ammonia, water would be a gas at the usual temperatures found on Earth.

Concept Practice

8. Explain why water has a relatively high boiling point.

Practice Problem

9. How many joules are required to vaporize 5.0 mg of water at its boiling point?

Objective

Explain the low density and high heat of fusion of ice.

16.5 Ice

As a typical liquid is cooled, it contracts slightly. Its density increases because its mass stays constant. If the cooling continues, the liquid eventually solidifies. Because the density of a typical solid is greater than that of the liquid, the solid sinks in its own liquid. For example, lead shot sinks in molten lead. As water is cooled, it first behaves like a typical liquid. Its density gradually increases *until* the temperature reaches 4°C. However, in Table 16.2 you can see that below 4°C, the density of water starts to *decrease.* At 0°C, ice begins to form. Ice, which forms at 0°C, has about 10% greater volume and therefore a lower density than water. As a result, ice floats on water. This is certainly unusual behavior for a solid. Ice is one of the very few solids that float in their own liquids.

Table 16.2 Density of Water and Ice

Temperature (°C)	Density (g/cm^3)
100 (water)	0.9584
50	0.9881
25	0.9971
10	0.9997
4	1.0000*
0 (water)	0.9998
0 (ice)	0.9168

*Most dense.

Why does ice behave so differently? As Figure 16.7 shows, the structure of ice is a very regular open framework of water molecules arranged like a honeycomb. Hydrogen bonding holds the water molecules in place. At low temperatures the molecules do not have sufficient kinetic energy to break out of this rigid framework. When ice melts, the framework collapses. Consequently, the water molecules can pack more closely together, making water more dense than ice.

The fact that ice floats has important consequences for living organisms. A layer of ice on the top of a pond acts as an insulator for the water beneath, preventing it from freezing except under extreme conditions. Since the water at the bottom of a frozen pond is warmer than 0°C, aquatic life is able to survive. If ice were more dense than water, all bodies of water would tend to freeze solid during the winter months, destroying many types of aquatic life.

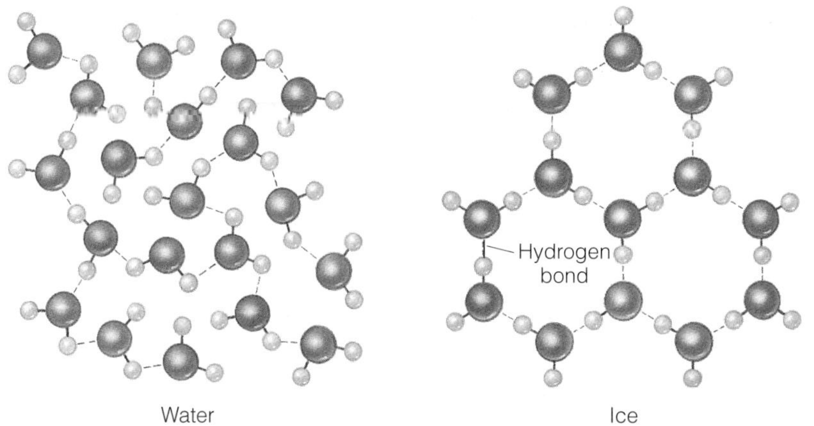

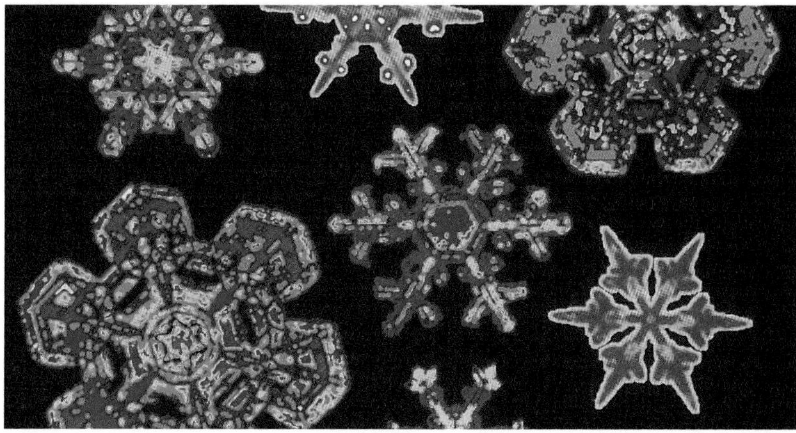

Figure 16.7 Top left: The molecules in liquid water are hydrogen bonded but free to move about. Top right: Extensive hydrogen bonding in ice causes the water molecules to be held farther apart and in a more ordered arrangement than in liquid water. Bottom: The hexagonal symmetry of snowflakes results from the hydrogen bonding of water molecules in ice.

Water molecules require a considerable amount of kinetic energy to return to a liquid state from a frozen state. Ice melts at 0°C, a high temperature for such a small molecule. The heat absorbed when 1 g of water changes from a solid to a liquid is 334 J/g. This amount of energy could also raise the temperature of 1 g of water from 0°C to 80°C!

Concept Practice

10. What unique characteristic of ice distinguishes it from other solid substances?

Practice Problem

11. How many kilojoules are required to melt 24 g of ice at 0°C?

Objective

Define the terms *solution, aqueous solution, solute,* and *solvent* and give an example of each.

16.6 Aqueous Solutions

Chemically pure water never exists in nature because water dissolves so many substances. Tap water contains varying amounts of dissolved minerals and gases. *Water samples containing dissolved substances are* **aqueous solutions**. *In a solution, the dissolving medium is the* **solvent** *and the dissolved particles are the* **solute**. If sodium chloride is dissolved in water, water is the solvent and sodium chloride is the solute.

You may recall that solutions are homogeneous mixtures. They are also stable. For example, sodium chloride does not settle out when its solutions are allowed to stand, as long as other conditions such as temperature remain constant. Solute particles can be either ionic or molecular. Their average diameters are usually less than 1.0 nm (10^{-9} m). If a solution is filtered, both the solute and the solvent pass through the filter. Solvents and solutes may be gases, liquids, or solids. In Chapter 1, Table 1.4 lists some common types of solutions.

Substances that dissolve most readily in water include ionic compounds and polar covalent molecules. Nonpolar covalent molecules like methane and like those in grease and gasoline do not dissolve in water. Nevertheless, grease will dissolve in gasoline. Why the difference? To answer this question, the structural features of the solvent and the solute and the attractions between them must be discussed.

Figure 16.8 The small size of solute particles allows them to pass through filter paper.

Concept Practice

12. Distinguish between a solution and an aqueous solution.

13. Identify the solvent and the solute in vinegar, a dilute aqueous solution of acetic acid.

Objective

Describe the role of solvation in the dissolving process and use the rule "like dissolves like" to predict the solubility of one substance in another.

16.7 Solvation

Water molecules are in continuous motion because of their kinetic energy. When a crystal of sodium chloride is placed in water, the water molecules collide with it. The solvent molecules (H_2O) attract the solute (Na^+, Cl^-) ions. As individual sodium ions and chloride ions break away from the crystal, the sodium chloride dissolves. **Solvation** *occurs when a solute dissolves.* The negatively and positively charged ions become solvated, that is, surrounded by solvent molecules. Figure 16.9 shows a model of the solvation of an ionic solid.

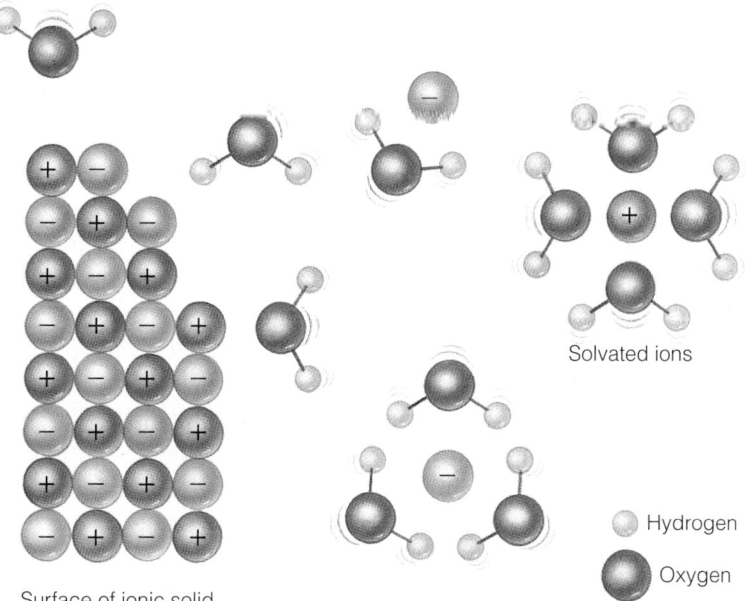

Figure 16.9 When an ionic solid dissolves, the ions become solvated and are surrounded by solvent molecules.

In some ionic compounds the attractions between the ions in the crystals are stronger than the attractions exerted by water. These compounds cannot be solvated and are therefore insoluble. Barium sulfate ($BaSO_4$) and calcium carbonate ($CaCO_3$) are examples of nearly insoluble ionic compounds.

What about dissolving grease in gasoline? Both grease and gasoline are composed of nonpolar molecules. They mix to form a solution, but not because the solute and solvent are favorably attracted. Rather, it is because there are no repulsive forces between the two. As a rule, polar solvents dissolve ionic and polar compounds. Similarly, nonpolar solvents dissolve nonpolar compounds. This relationship can be summed up in the expression "like dissolves like."

Safety

Many solutions are odor free and have the appearance of water. Always label prepared solutions. Never taste a liquid to determine its identity.

Concept Practice

14. In your own words, describe how an ionic compound dissolves in water.

15. Which of the following substances dissolve in water? Give reasons for your choices.

a. HCl
b. NaI
c. NH_3
d. $MgSO_4$
e. CH_4
f. $CaCO_3$
g. gasoline

Objective

Distinguish among strong electrolytes, weak electrolytes, and nonelectrolytes, and give examples of each.

Integrating Health

Water and Exercise

The normal human body contains about 60% by mass of water. You lose water by perspiration, as water vapor from breathing, and in your body's waste products, mainly urine. The loss of water during periods of inactivity is probably 75–300 mL per hour. Obviously, you must replace this water in order to avoid dehydration. Medical experts recommend that you drink at least eight glasses of water every day. When you endure prolonged periods of heavy exercise your loss of water through perspiration may increase to as much as 3000 mL/hour, which increases your risk of dehydration. The drinking of water by athletes during athletic events has been the subject of much controversy. Today, most sports physiologists agree that athletes should be permitted to drink water at room temperature as necessary in order to maintain good health and maximize performance.

16.8 Electrolytes and Nonelectrolytes

Compounds that conduct an electric current in aqueous solution or the molten state are **electrolytes**. All ionic compounds are electrolytes. Sodium chloride, copper(II) sulfate, and sodium hydroxide are typical water-soluble electrolytes. They conduct electricity in solution and in the molten state. Barium sulfate is an example of an ionic compound that conducts electricity in the molten state but not in aqueous solution because it is insoluble.

Compounds that do not conduct an electric current in either aqueous solution or the molten state are **nonelectrolytes**. Many molecular compounds are nonelectrolytes because they are not composed of ions. Most compounds of carbon, such as cane sugar and rubbing alcohol, are nonelectrolytes.

Some very polar molecular compounds are nonelectrolytes in the pure state, but they become electrolytes when they dissolve in water. This is because they ionize in solution. For example, neither ammonia, $NH_3(g)$, nor hydrogen chloride, $HCl(g)$, is an electrolyte. Yet an aqueous solution of ammonia conducts electricity. This is because ammonium ions (NH_4^+) and hydroxide ions (OH^-) are formed when ammonia dissolves in water.

$$NH_3(g) + H_2O(l) \longrightarrow NH_4^+(aq) + OH^-(aq)$$

Similarly, hydrogen chloride produces hydronium ions (H_3O^+) and chloride ions (Cl^-). An aqueous solution of hydrogen chloride conducts electricity and is therefore an electrolyte.

$$HCl(g) + H_2O(l) \longrightarrow H_3O^+(aq) + Cl^-(aq)$$

Table 16.3 Some Examples of Strong Electrolytes, Weak Electrolytes, and Nonelectrolytes

Strong electrolyte	Weak electrolyte	Nonelectrolyte
Acids (inorganic) HCl, HBr, HI, HNO_3, H_2SO_4, $HClO_4$	Heavy metal halides $HgCl_2$, $PbCl_2$	Most organic compounds Sucrose (cane sugar) Glycerol
Bases (inorganic) NaOH, KOH	Ammonia Organic acids and bases, acetic acid, aniline	
Soluble salts KCl, $MgSO_4$, $KClO_3$, $CaCl_2$	H_2O (very weak)	

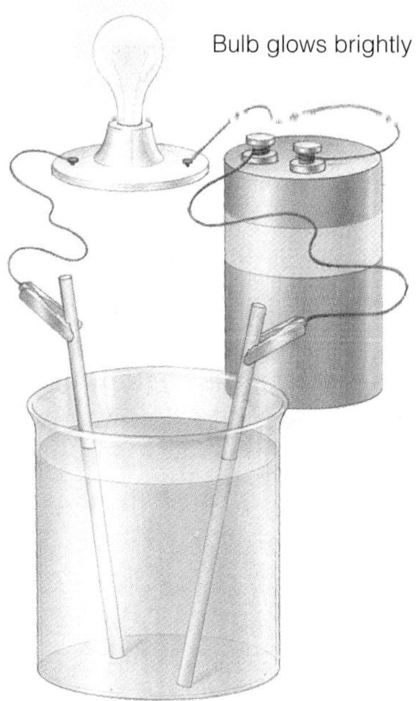

(a) Sodium chloride solution

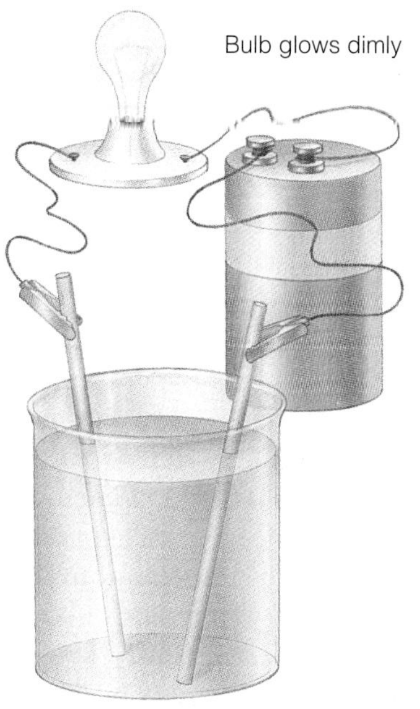

(b) Mercuric chloride solution

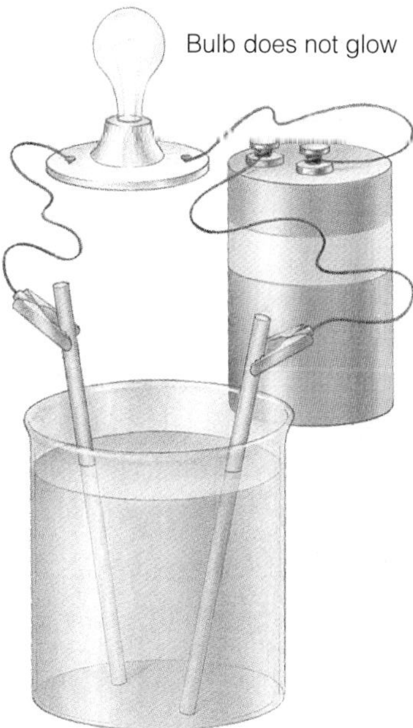

(c) Sucrose solution

Figure 16.10 The presence of an electrolyte in solution can be determined by a conductivity test. **(a)** Sodium chloride is a strong electrolyte. **(b)** Mercuric chloride is a weak electrolyte. **(c)** Sucrose is a nonelectrolyte.

Not all electrolytes conduct an electric current to the same degree. In a simple conductivity test, shown in Figure 16.10, a bulb glows brightly for a sodium chloride solution. By contrast, the bulb glows dimly with the electrodes in a mercuric chloride solution. Mercuric chloride is a weak electrolyte. *When a* **weak electrolyte** *is in solution, only a fraction of the solute exists as ions.* In a solution of mercuric chloride, most of the solute exists as unionized $HgCl_2$. *When a* **strong electrolyte** *is dissolved, almost all of the solute exists as ions.* Sodium chloride is a strong electrolyte. All the dissolved sodium chloride in a solution exists as Na^+ and Cl^- ions. In a solution of sucrose, a nonelectrolyte, the bulb fails to glow. Table 16.3 lists some common electrolytes and nonelectrolytes.

Concept Practice

16. In your own words, distinguish between an electrolyte and a nonelectrolyte.

Practice Problem

17. Write an equation to show how calcium chloride dissociates in water.

16.B Consumer Chemistry

Cosmetics

Figure 16.11 Many cosmetics are solutions, colloids, suspensions, or emulsions. How many of the cosmetics that you use have emulsifiers in them?

Chemistry plays a role in making people look good and smell nice through the use of cosmetics. Cosmetics are preparations which are applied to, or introduced into, the body to beautify, cleanse, disinfect, or alter the appearance or smell. Because of the widespread use of cosmetics, you, as a consumer, may find a discussion of some of the chemistry involved to be helpful.

Your skin is the body organ that is most exposed to the ravages of the elements. The outermost layer of your skin, the corneal layer, is made of dead cells. If the moisture content of the corneal layer is below 10%, your skin becomes dry and flaky. Exposure to sun and wind may leave your skin dry and scaly. Too frequent washing also removes natural oils from the skin and can leave your skin dry. A wide variety of creams and lotions are available to treat dry and flaky skin. The essential ingredient in all these preparations is a fatty or oily substance, such as petroleum jelly or mineral oil, that forms a protective coating on the skin and prevents moisture loss. Other ingredients include water, emulsifiers, perfume, and natural fats and oils such as lanolin (a fat obtained from sheep wool) and olive oil. Emulsifiers keep the incompatible ingredients (water and oils) dispersed in one another.

The composition of lipstick is quite similar to that of skin cream but a high proportion of wax (beeswax or carnauba wax) is used to keep the lipstick firm. Dyes and pigments provide the color. Lipsticks, with or without color, form a protective coat on the lips and prevent them from drying and cracking.

The most widely used and ancient of cosmetics are perfumes. Even today, many perfumes are still extracted from natural sources, such as fruits and flowers, but some of the components have been identified and can be synthesized in the laboratory. A perfume may have more than one hundred components! Colognes are made by diluting perfumes with ethanol to a 1% to 2% solution.

Both deodorants and antiperspirants have cosmetic functions. Deodorants are perfume formulations designed to mask body odor; antiperspirants are designed to slow or stop perspiration. Because they modify a bodily function, antiperspirants are technically drugs. The active ingredient in antiperspirants is aluminum chlorohydrate, an astringent. This compound acts by constricting the openings of sweat glands and thus reduces the perspiration that escapes.

Think About It

18. Describe State, in your own words, the purpose of a cosmetic.

Activity 16
Surface Tension of Water

Purpose

To observe the unusual surface properties of water due to hydrogen bonding.

Materials

paper clip

shallow dish

water

rubber band, approximately 2" long

vegetable oil

dishwashing liquid

Procedure

1. Fill the dish with water and dry your hands.

2. Being careful not to break the surface, gently place the paper clip on the water. Observe what happens.

3. Repeat step 1.

4. Again being careful not to break the surface, gently place the rubber band on the water.

5. Slowly drop oil onto the water inside the rubber band until it is covered with a layer of oil. Observe for 15 seconds.

6. Allow one drop of detergent to fall onto the center of the oil layer. Observe the system for 15 seconds.

Analysis and Conclusions

1. What happened to the paper clip? Explain.

2. If a paper clip becomes wet, does it float? Explain your answer.

3. What shape does the rubber band take when the water inside it is covered with oil? Why does it take the observed shape?

4. Describe what happened when detergent was dropped onto the layer of oil.

16.9 Suspensions and Colloids

Objective

Distinguish colloids and suspensions from solutions by discussing their properties.

The emphasis of the chapter now shifts from homogeneous mixtures with water to heterogeneous mixtures. You will now turn your attention from mixtures that are true solutions to two other mixtures that are not: suspensions and colloids. **Suspensions** *are mixtures from which some of the particles will settle slowly upon standing.* A piece of clay shaken with water forms a suspension. The clay particles become suspended in the water, but they start to settle when shaking stops. A suspension differs from a solution because the component particles are much larger. The particles in a typical suspension have an average diameter greater than 100 nm. By contrast, the particle size in a solution is usually about 1 nm. Suspensions are heterogeneous because at least two substances can be clearly identified. In this example, they are clay and water. If the muddy water is filtered, the suspended clay particles are trapped by the filter and clear water passes through.

Figure 16.12 Suspended particles can be removed by filtration.

Colloids *are mixtures containing particles that are intermediate in size between those of suspensions and true solutions.* Thus the particles range in size from 1 nm to 100 nm. The particles are the *dispersed phase.* They are spread throughout the *dispersion medium.* The first colloids that were identified as such were glues. Many other mixtures such as gelatin desserts, paint, aerosol sprays, and smoke are also colloids.

The properties of colloids differ from those of solutions and suspensions. Many colloids are cloudy or milky in appearance but look clear when they are very dilute. The particles in a colloid cannot be retained by filter paper and do not settle out with time.

Colloidal particles exhibit the **Tyndall effect**, *which is the scattering of visible light in all directions.* You can see a beam of light passed through a colloid just as you see a sunbeam in a dusty room. Light is scattered by the colloidal particles in the same way the sunbeam is scattered by dust particles. Suspensions also exhibit the Tyndall effect, but solutions never do. Figure 16.13 summarizes the Tyndall effect with respect to colloids, suspensions, and solutions.

Flashes of light (scintillations) are seen when colloids are studied under a microscope. Colloids scintillate because the particles reflecting and scattering the light move erratically. *The chaotic movement of colloidal particles is called* **Brownian motion**. It was first observed by the Scottish botanist Robert Brown (1772–1858). Brownian motion is caused by the water molecules of the medium colliding with the small, dispersed colloidal particles. The buffeting action exerts such a force on the particles that they cannot settle.

Roots of Words

kolla: (Greek) glue
colloid liquid mixture containing particles that are intermediate in size between those of a true solution and a suspension

The word colloid, based on the glue-like appearance of many colloids, was coined by the English scientist Thomas Graham in 1861.

Table 16.4 Some Colloidal Systems

System			
Dispersed phase	**Dispersion medium**	**Type**	**Example**
Gas	Liquid	Foam	Whipped cream
Gas	Solid	Foam	Marshmallow
Liquid	Liquid	Emulsion	Milk, mayonnaise
Liquid	Gas	Aerosol	Fog, aerosol sprays
Solid	Gas	Smoke	Dust in air
Solid	Liquid	Sols and gels	Egg white, jellies, paint, colloidal gold, blood, starch in water

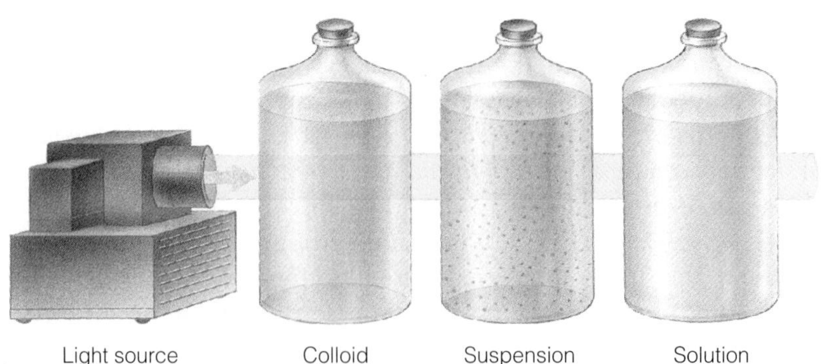

Figure 16.13 Light is reflected in all directions from particles in colloids or in suspensions. This effect, called the Tyndall effect, is not observed with true solutions.

Table 16.5 Properties of Solutions, Colloids, and Suspensions			
	System		
Property	Solution	Colloid	Suspension
Particle type	Ions, atoms, small molecules	Large molecules or particles	Large particles or aggregates
Particle size (approximate)	0.1–1 nm	1–100 nm	100 nm and larger
Effect of light	No scattering	Gives Tyndall effect	Gives Tyndall effect
Effect of gravity	Stable, does not separate	Stable, does not separate	Unstable, sediment forms
Filtration	Particles not retained on filter	Particles not retained on filter	Particles retained on filter
Uniformity	Homogeneous	Borderline	Heterogeneous

Colloidal particles may also absorb charged particles from the surrounding medium onto their surface. Whether or not this occurs depends on the characteristics of the particles. Some colloidal particles can absorb positively charged particles and become positively charged. Other colloidal particles can absorb negatively charged particles and become negatively charged. All the particles in a system will have the same charge. The repulsion of the like-charged particles prevents them from forming aggregates. This keeps them dispersed throughout the medium. Charged colloidal particles form aggregates and precipitate from the dispersion when ions of opposite charge are added. Table 16.5 summarizes the properties of solutions, colloids, and suspensions.

Emulsions *are colloidal dispersions of liquids in liquids.* An emulsifying agent is essential for the formation of an emulsion and for maintaining its stability. For example, oils and greases are not soluble in water. They readily form a colloidal dispersion, however, if soap or detergent is added to the water. Soap and detergents are emulsifying agents. One end of the large soap molecule is polar and is attracted to water molecules. The other end of the soap or detergent molecule is nonpolar and is soluble in oil or grease. Soaps and other emulsifying agents thus allow the formation of colloidal dispersions between liquids that do not ordinarily mix.

Concept Practice

19. Name two ways to distinguish a suspension from a colloid.

20. Define *emulsion* and tell how emulsions are stabilized.

21. Explain why solutions do not exhibit the Tyndall effect.

Objective

Define the term "water of hydration" and calculate the percent of water in a given hydrate.

16.10 Water of Hydration

Water molecules are an integral part of the crystal structure of many substances. *The water in a crystal is called the* **water of hydration**, *or water of crystallization.* When an aqueous solution of copper(II) sulfate is allowed to evaporate, deep blue crystals of copper(II) sulfate pentahydrate are deposited. The chemical formula for this compound is $CuSO_4{\cdot}5H_2O$. In writing the formula of a hydrate a dot is used to connect the formula of the compound and the number of water molecules per formula unit. Crystals of copper sulfate pentahydrate always contain five molecules of water for every copper and sulfate ion pair. The deep blue crystals are dry to the touch. They are unchanged in composition or appearance in normally moist air. When heated above 100°C, however, the crystals lose their water of hydration. They crumble to a white anhydrous powder whose formula is $CuSO_4$. If anhydrous copper sulfate is treated with water, the blue pentahydrate is regenerated.

$$CuSO_4{\cdot}5H_2O(s) \underset{-\text{heat}}{\overset{+\text{heat}}{\rightleftharpoons}} CuSO_4(s) + 5H_2O(g)$$

Table 16.6 lists some familiar hydrates. They all contain a fixed quantity of water and have a definite composition.

The forces holding the water molecules in hydrates are not very strong. This is shown by the ease with which water is lost and regained. Because the water molecules are held by weak forces,

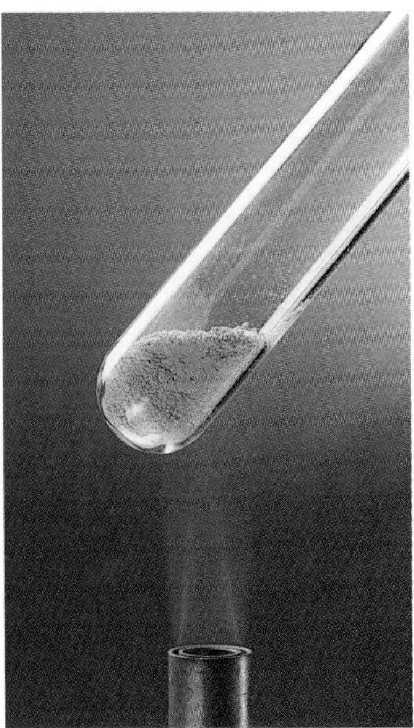

Figure 16.14 When hydrated copper sulfate (left) is heated, the water is driven off, leaving anhydrous copper sulfate (right).

hydrates often have an appreciable vapor pressure. *If a hydrate has a vapor pressure higher than that of the water vapor in air, the hydrate will* **effloresce** *by losing the water of hydration.* For example, $CuSO_4 \cdot 5H_2O$ has a vapor pressure of about 7.8 mm Hg at room temperature. The average pressure of water vapor at room temperature is usually about 10 mm Hg. This hydrate is stable until the humidity decreases. When the vapor pressure drops below 7.8 mm Hg the hydrate will effloresce. Washing soda (sodium carbonate decahydrate, $Na_2CO_3 \cdot 10H_2O$) is efflorescent. As the crystals lose water of hydration they become coated with a white powder of anhydrous sodium carbonate.

Some hydrated salts, with a low vapor pressure, remove water from moist air to form higher hydrates. *Salts and other compounds that remove moisture from air are said to be* **hygroscopic**. Calcium chloride monohydrate is hygroscopic, as are sodium hydroxide and concentrated sulfuric acid.

$$CaCl_2 \cdot H_2O(s) \xrightarrow{\text{moist air}} CaCl_2 \cdot 2H_2O(s)$$

Roots of Words

efflorescere: (Latin) to burst forth as a flower blossoms
effloresce to lose water of hydration

A compound that effloresces blossoms water of hydration, so to speak.

hygros: (Greek) moist, wet
scopein: (Greek) to view
hygroscopic term describing salts and other compounds that remove moisture from the air

Some salts, such as calcium chloride ($CaCl_2$), are so hygroscopic that they go into solution if permitted to stand in humid air; such salts are deliquescent.

Table 16.6 Some Common Hydrates

Formula	Chemical name	Common name
$MgSO_4 \cdot 7H_2O$	Magnesium sulfate heptahydrate	Epsom salts
$Ba(OH)_2 \cdot 8H_2O$	Barium hydroxide octahydrate	
$CaCl_2 \cdot 2H_2O$	Calcium chloride dihydrate	
$CuSO_4 \cdot 5H_2O$	Copper(II) sulfate pentahydrate	Blue vitriol
$Na_2SO_4 \cdot 10H_2O$	Sodium sulfate decahydrate	Glauber's salt
$KAl(SO_4)_2 \cdot 12H_2O$	Potassium aluminum sulfate dodecahydrate	Alum
$Na_2B_4O_7 \cdot 10H_2O$	Sodium tetraborate decahydrate	Borax
$FeSO_4 \cdot 7H_2O$	Iron(II) sulfate heptahydrate	Green vitriol
$H_2SO_4 \cdot H_2O$	Sulfuric acid hydrate (m.p. 8.6°C)	

Figure 16.15 Dry sodium hydroxide pellets exposed to air will, over time, remove water from the air (left). Eventually they will form a solution (right).

Hygroscopic substances are used as drying agents, or **desiccants.** Some compounds are so hygroscopic that they become wet when exposed to normally moist air. *These* **deliquescent** *compounds remove sufficient water from the air to dissolve completely and form solutions.* Deliquescence occurs when the solution formed has a lower vapor pressure than the water in the air.

Example 1 Finding the Percent of Water in a Hydrate

Calculate the percent by mass of water in washing soda, sodium carbonate decahydrate ($Na_2CO_3 \cdot 10H_2O$).

Solution

The gram formula mass of $Na_2CO_3 \cdot 10H_2O$ is 286 g. The mass of water per gram formula mass of $Na_2CO_3 \cdot 10H_2O$ is $10 \times 18\ g = 180\ g$.

$$\text{Percent } H_2O = \frac{\text{mass of water}}{\text{mass of hydrate}} \times 100\%$$

$$= \frac{180\ g}{286\ g} \times 100\%$$

$$= 62.9\%$$

Problem-Solving Tip

Percent is always the part over the whole expressed as parts per 100 parts.

Concept Practice

22. Describe the water of hydration of a substance.

Practice Problems

23. Write formulas for these hydrates.
a. sodium sulfate decahydrate
b. magnesium sulfate heptahydrate
c. barium hydroxide octahydrate

24. Write the formula or the name for these hydrates.
a. $Na_2CO_3 \cdot 10H_2O$
b. magnesium carbonate trihydrate
c. $Mg_3(PO_4)_2 \cdot 4H_2O$
d. calcium nitrate trihydrate
e. $CoCl_2 \cdot 2H_2O$

25. What is the percent by mass of water in $CuSO_4 \cdot 5H_2O$?

Chapter 16 Review
Water and Aqueous Systems

Key Terms

aqueous solution *16.6*
Brownian motion *16.9*
colloid *16.9*
deliquescent *16.10*
desiccant *16.10*
effloresce *16.10*
electrolyte *16.8*
emulsion *16.9*
hygroscopic *16.10*
nonelectrolyte *16.8*
solute *16.6*
solvation *16.7*
solvent *16.6*
strong electrolyte *16.8*
surface tension *16.2*
surfactant *16.2*
suspension *16.9*
Tyndall effect *16.9*
water of hydration *16.10*
weak electrolyte *16.8*

Chapter Summary

Hydrogen bonding between polar water molecules explains the high boiling point (100°C) and freezing point (0°C) of water, and it explains why ice floats in water. Hydrogen bonding is also responsible for the high surface tension of water. Liquids tend to minimize their surface area and form spherical droplets because of their surface tension. Water is a polar liquid and an excellent solvent for many substances. Aqueous solutions are homogeneous mixtures of ions or molecules in water. The solubility of a solute depends on the interactions of the solute and solvent particles. A good rule to remember is that "like dissolves like."

Substances that are in solution as ions are electrolytes. A solute that is completely ionized in solution is a strong electrolyte. A solute that is only partially ionized is a weak electrolyte. A solution of an electrolyte conducts an electric current, whereas a solution of a nonelectrolyte is nonconducting.

True solutions are distinguished from colloidal dispersions and suspensions on the basis of particle size. Particles with an average diameter greater than 100 nm can be kept in suspension if the fluid (water) is kept agitated. Gravity or filtration, however, will separate the suspended particles from the liquid. The particles in a colloidal dispersion range in size from 1 nm to 100 nm. In general, they do not settle under gravity, and they pass through ordinary filter paper unchanged. Colloids and suspensions are good at scattering light, as evidenced by the Tyndall effect. Colloidal dispersions also exhibit Brownian motion. The particles in solutions are ions and small molecules. They cannot be trapped by filter paper, nor do they exhibit the Tyndall effect.

Many crystals are hydrates; they contain water of hydration. If water of hydration is lost from a hydrate when it is exposed to air, the process is called efflorescence. Some substances take up water from moist air and may eventually form a solution. Substances that exhibit this property are deliquescent.

Practice Questions and Problems

26. Explain why water molecules are polar. *16.1*

27. Name four physical properties of water. *16.1*

28. Describe some observable effects that can be produced by the surface tension of a liquid. *16.2*

29. Explain how hydrogen bonding is responsible for the high surface tension of water. *16.2*

30. What is a surfactant? Explain how it works. *16.2*

31. Define the term *vapor pressure* and explain why the vapor pressure of water is unusually low. *16.2*

32. How many joules are required to heat 256 g of water from 20°C to 99°C? How many joules are required to heat the same mass of iron through the same range of temperature? *16.3*

33. How many calories are liberated when 24 g of steam at 100°C condenses to 24 g of water at 100°C? *16.4*

34. Why does ammonia have a much higher boiling point (–33°C) than methane (–164°C) although their molar masses are almost the same? *16.4*

35. Distinguish between the structures of water and ice. Then explain why ice floats on water. *16.5*

36. What would be some of the consequences if ice were denser than water? *16.5*

37. How much energy is required to change 47.6 g of ice at 0°C to 47.6 g of water at the same temperature? *16.5*
    a. kilojoules **b.** kilocalories

38. Why is water an excellent solvent for most ionic compounds and polar covalent molecules but not for nonpolar compounds? *16.6*

39. Give a familiar example of solutions of each of these types. *16.6*
    a. gas in liquid **c.** solid in liquid
    b. liquid in liquid **d.** gas in gas

40. Suppose an aqueous solution contains both sugar and salt. Can you separate either of these solutes from the water by filtration? Explain. *16.6*

41. What is the significance of the statement "like dissolves like"? What does "like" refer to? *16.6*

42. Which of the following substances dissolve in water? Why? *16.7*
    a. CH_4 **c.** He **e.** cane sugar
    b. KCl **d.** $MgSO_4$ **f.** $NaHCO_3$

43. Contrast the characteristics of strong and weak electrolytes. *16.8*

44. Why does molten sodium chloride conduct electricity? *16.8*

45. What is the main distinction between an aqueous solution of a strong electrolyte and an aqueous solution of a weak electrolyte? *16.8*

46. What is the basis for distinguishing among solutions, colloids, and suspensions? *16.9*

47. Explain the Tyndall effect. *16.9*

48. Suspensions do give the Tyndall effect. Why? *16.9*

49. What makes a colloidal dispersion stable? *16.9*

50. Define Brownian motion. *16.9*

51. Mayonnaise is an example of what kind of colloidal dispersion? *16.9*

52. Name each of these hydrates. *16.10*
    a. $SnCl_4 \cdot 5H_2O$ **c.** $BaBr_2 \cdot 4H_2O$
    b. $FeSO_4 \cdot 7H_2O$ **d.** $FePO_4 \cdot 4H_2O$

53. Calcium chloride forms a hexahydrate. Write the equation for the formation of this hydrate from the anhydrous salt. *16.10*

54. Epsom salt ($MgSO_4 \cdot 7H_2O$) changes to the monohydrate form at 150°C. Write an equation for this change. *16.10*

Mastery Questions and Problems

55. Construct a concept map using the key terms in this chapter with *solute* as the central concept.

56. Water has its maximum density at 4°C. Explain why this is so, and discuss the consequences of this fact.

57. From your knowledge of intermolecular forces, arrange these liquids in order of increasing surface tension: water, H_2O; hexane, C_6H_{14}; ethanol, C_2H_5OH; chloroform, $CHCl_3$.

58. Name these hydrates and determine the percent by mass of water in each.
    a. $Na_2B_4O_7 \cdot 10H_2O$ **c.** $MgSO_4 \cdot 7H_2O$
    b. $Na_2CO_3 \cdot H_2O$ **d.** $(CaSO_4)_2 \cdot H_2O$

59. If 5.0 g of steam, $H_2O(g)$, at 100°C condenses to 5.0 g of water, $H_2O(l)$, at 50°C, how much heat is liberated?
    a. calories **b.** kilocalories

60. Explain why ions become solvated in aqueous solution.

61. A block of ice at 0°C has a mass of 176.0 g. How much heat must be added to change 25% of this mass of ice to water at 0°C? (Express your answer in calories, kilocalories, joules, and kilojoules.) What is the mass of ice remaining?

62. You are given a solution containing either sugar or salt dissolved in water.
    a. Can you tell which it is by visual inspection?
    b. Give two ways in which you could easily tell which it is.

63. Explain why ethyl alcohol (C_2H_6O) will dissolve in both gasoline and water.

64. Water is a polar solvent; gasoline is a nonpolar solvent. Decide which of the following compounds are more likely to dissolve in water and which are more likely to dissolve in gasoline.
   a. sugar ($C_{12}H_{22}O_{11}$)
   b. chloroform ($CHCl_3$)
   c. Na_2SO_4
   d. methane (CH_4)
   e. KCl
   f. $BaSO_4$

65. Match each of the descriptions with the following terms. A description may apply to more than one term.
   1. true solution
   2. colloidal dispersion
   3. suspension
   a. Does not settle out on standing: _____
   b. Heterogeneous mixture: _____
   c. Particle size less than 1.0 nm: _____
   d. Particles can be filtered out: _____
   e. Gives Tyndall effect: _____
   f. Particles are invisible to the naked eye: _____
   g. Milk: _____
   h. Salt water: _____
   i. Jelly: _____

66. Explain which unique properties of water are responsible for these occurrences.
   a. Water in tiny cracks in rocks helps break up the rocks when it freezes.
   b. Water beads up on a newly waxed car.
   c. As you exercise and your body temperature increases, your body produces sweat.
   d. Grape vines are damaged at temperatures below 28°F. When severe frost is predicted, grape growers spray a mist of water on their vines.
   e. An efficient way to heat a large building is to generate steam in a boiler and circulate it through pipes to radiators throughout the entire building.

67. A 25.0 m × 10.0 m swimming pool is filled with fresh water to a depth of 1.7 m. The water temperature is initially at 25°C. How much heat must be removed from the water to change it all to ice at 0°C? Express your answer in kilocalories and kilojoules.

68. Are all liquids soluble in each other? Explain your answer.

69. Write equations to show how these substances ionize or dissociate in water.
   a. NH_4Cl
   b. $Cu(NO_3)_2$
   c. $HC_2H_3O_2$
   d. $HgCl_2$

70. The graph below shows the variation in the density of water over the temperature range 0°C to 20°C.
   a. What is the maximum density of water?
   b. At what temperature does the maximum density of water occur?
   c. Would it be correct to extend the smooth curve of the graph back below 0°C?

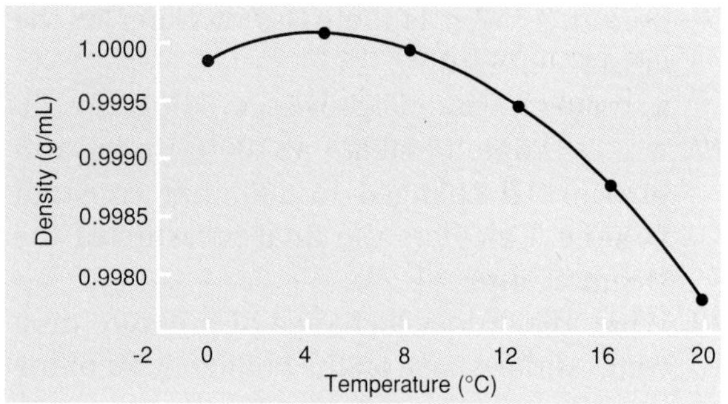

Critical Thinking Questions

71. Choose the term that best completes the second relationship.
   a. plant:green   water molecule: _____
      (1) polar   (3) frozen
      (2) ionic   (4) vapor
   b. east:west   condensation: _____
      (1) boiling   (3) vaporization
      (2) vapor pressure   (4) freezing
   c. colloid:emulsion   cat: _____
      (1) dog   (3) lion
      (2) Siamese   (4) fox

72. When the humidity is low and the temperature high, human beings must take in large quantities of water or face serious dehydration. Why do you think water is so important for the proper functioning of your body?

73. Describe as specifically as possible what would happen if a nonpolar molecular liquid were added to water. What would be formed if you shook this mixture?

74. Why must bacteria be present in a wastewater treatment process?

75. List the ingredients from several brands of face, hand, or body creams and lotions. Identify the function of as many ingredients as possible.

Cumulative Review

76. A cylindrical vessel, 28.0 cm in height and 3.00 cm in diameter, is filled with water at 50°C. The density of water is 0.988 g/cm^3 at this temperature. What is the mass of water in the vessel?
   a. grams **b.** milligrams **c.** kilograms

77. A 1-L sample of steam at 100°C and 1 atm pressure is changed to 200°C at constant volume. Calculate the final pressure of the steam in atm.

78. What effect does a change in pressure on a water surface have on the boiling point of the water?
   a. an increase **b.** a decrease

79. The decomposition of hydrogen peroxide is given by this equation.
   $2H_2O_2(l) \longrightarrow 2H_2O(l) + O_2\ (g)$
   Calculate the mass of water in grams and the volume of oxygen at STP when 2.00×10^{-3} mol of hydrogen peroxide is decomposed.

80. How many grams each of hydrogen and oxygen are required to produce 4.50 mol of water?

81. Calculate the mass of water produced in the complete combustion of 8.00 L of propane (C_3H_8) at STP.
   $C_3H_8 + O_2 \longrightarrow CO_2 + H_2O$

82. Acetaldehyde, C_2H_4O, is produced commercially by the reaction of acetylene with water.
   $C_2H_2 + H_2O \longrightarrow C_2H_4O$
   How many grams of C_2H_4O can be produced from 260 g of H_2O, assuming sufficient C_2H_2 is present?

83. Write the correct electron configuration for the oxide ion. Which noble gas has the same electron configuration?

84. Hydrogen reacts with oxygen to form water.
   $2H_2 + O_2 \longrightarrow 2H_2O$
   How many moles of oxygen are required to produce 10.8 g of H_2O? How many liters of oxygen is this at STP?

85. Balance these equations.
   a. $CO_2 + H_2O \longrightarrow C_6H_{12}O_6 + O_2$
   b. $Na + H_2O \longrightarrow Na^+ + OH^- + H_2$
   c. $C_6H_6 + O_2 \longrightarrow CO_2 + H_2O$
   d. $NaHCO_3 \longrightarrow Na_2CO_3 + H_2O + CO_2$

86. Calculate the number of molecules in 4.5×10^{-3} g of H_2O.

87. The normal boiling point of a substance depends on both the molecular mass and the intermolecular interactions. Considering these, arrange the following in order of decreasing boiling points and explain your answers.
   a. HBr, HCl, H_2O
   b. NH_3, H_2O, CH_4

88. If 20.0 g steam, $H_2O(g)$, occupies 6.25 L at 120°C, what is the pressure in atmospheres?

89. Calculate the percent composition.
   a. H_2O **c.** H_2Se
   b. H_2S **d.** H_2Te

90. What is the mass, in milligrams and in kilograms, of 2.7×10^3 mol H_2O?

91. When a proton is attracted to the unshared electron pair of a water molecule, the polyatomic hydronium ion (H_3O^+) is formed. Write electron dot structures to show the formation of this ion.

Challenge Questions and Problems

92. Deuterium oxide is often described as "heavy water." Why? List the differences in physical and chemical properties you would expect to exist between water and deuterium oxide. Give some uses for deuterium oxide.

93. What relationships exist between the following volumes?
   a. 1 g of ice at 0°C and 1 g of water at 0°C
   b. 1 g of water at 100°C and 1 g of steam at 100°C

94. A mixture of 40 cm^3 of oxygen gas and 60 cm^3 of hydrogen gas, at STP, is ignited. Determine the following.
   a. which gas is the limiting reagent
   b. the mass of water produced
   c. which gas remains after reaction
   d. the volume of the remaining gas

95. When ethyl alcohol (C_2H_6O) dissolves in water, the volume of the final solution is less than the separate volumes of the water and alcohol added together. Can you explain this result? Do you think it might be possible to mix two different liquids and get a mixture volume that is larger than the sum of the volumes of the two components? Explain.

96. When an aqueous solution of sodium chloride starts to freeze, the ice that forms does not contain ions of the salt. Why?

97. Why is the midday sky blue and the early evening western sky often an orange or red color? (*Hint:* There are colloidal-size particles in the atmosphere.)

98. Cobalt chloride test paper is blue. This paper is made by soaking strips of paper in an aqueous solution of $CoCl_2 \cdot 6H_2O$. These paper strips are then dried in an oven.

$$\underset{\text{pink}}{CoCl_2 \cdot 6H_2O} + \text{heat} \longrightarrow \underset{\text{blue}}{CoCl_2 \cdot 4H_2O} + 2H_2O$$

   a. What is the color of the aqueous cobalt(II) chloride hexahydrate?
   b. What is the color of wet cobalt chloride paper?
   c. What is the color of dry cobalt chloride paper?
   d. What is the percent of water in each of these compounds?
   e. What is cobalt chloride test paper used for?

99. An iceberg with a mass of 3.50×10^6 kg is floating in fresh water at a temperature of 0°C. Calculate the mass and volume of the iceberg above the water level. How would this mass and volume change if the temperature of the water was raised to 4°C? (Use Table 16.2 and assume no melting of ice occurs.)

Connections Questions

100. What kinds of samples might a water quality technician analyze?

101. Briefly describe the water cycle.

102. How should you adjust your water intake during moderate to heavy exercise?

Write About Chemistry

103. Write a poem describing a blue sky or a red sunset that incorporates a scientific explanation of the color.

104. Write a short essay describing how your life would be different if water did not have a relatively high heat of vaporization, high specific heat, or high boiling point.

Readings and References

Alper, Joseph. "Survival at Sea." *ChemMatters* (October 1992), pp. 4–7.

Garber, Charri Lou. "Wastewater." *ChemMatters* (April 1992), pp. 12–15.

Maranto, Gina. "The Creeping Poison Underground." *Discover* (March 1985), pp. 83–85.

Smith, Wesley D. "Skin Deep." *ChemMatters* (December 1987), pp. 4–7.

17 Properties of Solutions

Goals

- Describe the factors that determine the rate at which a solute dissolves.
- Show concentrations of solutions given in molarity, percent by volume, percent, molality, and mole fraction.
- Explain what is meant by a colligative property.
- Calculate the molar mass of a molecular compound from the freezing point depression and boiling point elevation of a solution of the compound.

Oil and water do not mix to make a solution. Thus, when an oil tanker, the Exxon *Valdez*, spilled 41 800 m^3 of oil in Alaska's Prince William Sound, the oil did not dissolve. It spread to create a very thin layer of oil 6733 km^2 in area. The spill devastated the surrounding environment.

Concept Overview

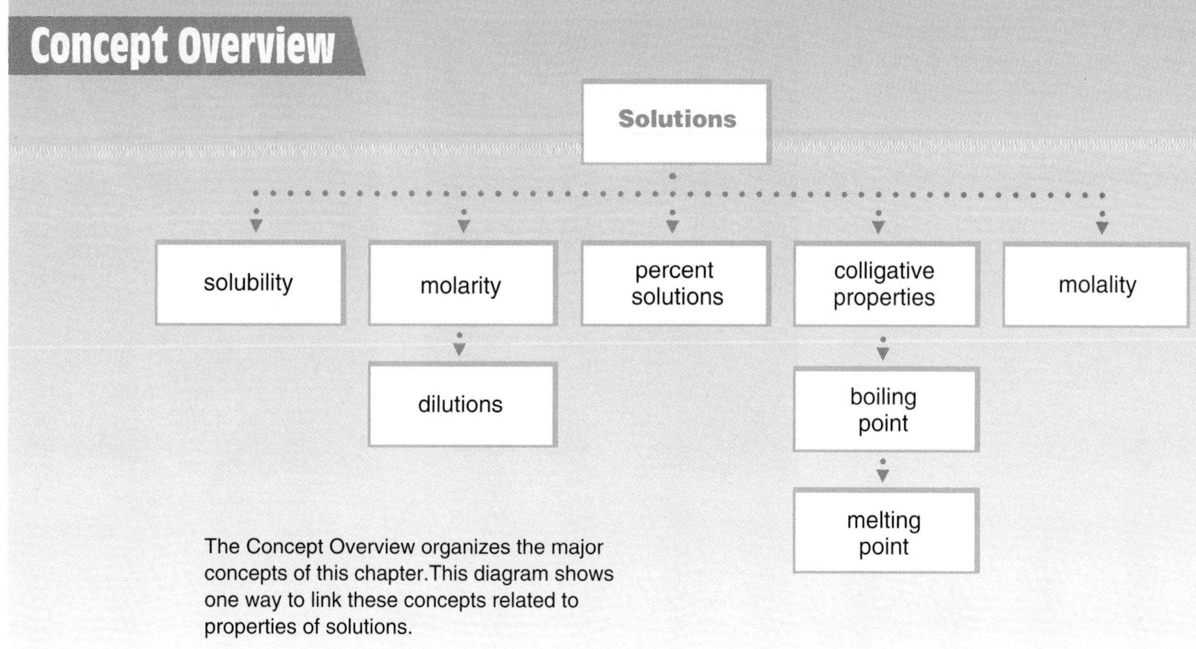

The Concept Overview organizes the major concepts of this chapter. This diagram shows one way to link these concepts related to properties of solutions.

If you have ever helped make home-made ice cream, you know that you add salt to the ice-water mixture surrounding the ice cream container. Do you know why you need salt to get the ice cream to freeze? A teaspoonful of granular sugar dissolves faster than a cube of sugar in a glass of iced tea. Both will dissolve faster with stirring or in a cup of hot tea rather than in the iced tea. Can you account for these observations? You will be able to explain each of these occurrences after you gain an understanding of properties of solutions.

Solutions are homogeneous mixtures that can be grouped according to their physical state. Solid, liquid, and gaseous solutions exist. In this chapter you will study the formation of solutions and ways to express the concentration of solutions. You will also examine how the properties of solutions are changed when the numbers of particles dissolved in them are changed.

17.1 Solution Formation

Objective

List three factors that determine how fast a soluble substance dissolves.

The nature of the solvent and solute affects *whether* a substance will dissolve. Several other factors determine *how fast* a soluble substance dissolves. If sodium chloride crystals are placed in a flask containing water, the crystals eventually dissolve. If the flask and its contents are shaken, the crystals dissolve more quickly than if the flask is not shaken. Agitation makes the solute dissolve more rapidly

Figure 17.1 Heat and agitation increase the rate at which a solute dissolves. Sugar dissolves faster in hot tea (left) than it does in iced tea (right). Stirring also makes the sugar dissolve faster.

because it brings fresh solvent into contact with the surface of the solute. You can see that solvation is a surface phenomenon. This is why people stir coffee after they have added sugar. It is important to realize, however, that agitation affects only the *rate* at which a solute dissolves. It cannot influence the *amount* of solute that dissolves. An insoluble substance remains undissolved no matter how much the system is agitated.

Temperature also influences the rate at which solutes dissolve. A salt crystal dissolves much more rapidly in hot water than in cold water. The kinetic energy of the water molecules is greater at the higher temperature. This leads to increased frequency and force of the collisions of water molecules with the crystal surfaces.

A third factor that determines the rate of dissolution of a solute is its particle size. A powder dissolves more rapidly than a single crystal. This is because a greater surface area of ions or molecules is exposed to the colliding water molecules. Solvation, however, is a surface phenomenon.

Concept Practice

1. Name and distinguish between the two components of a solution.

2. Name three factors that influence the rate at which a solute dissolves in a solvent.

17.2 Solubility

Objective

Explain the difference among saturated, unsaturated, and supersaturated solutions.

When 36.0 g of sodium chloride is added to 100 g of water at 25°C, all the salt dissolves. Yet if you add one more gram of salt and stir, no matter how vigorously or for how long, only 0.2 g of the last portion goes into solution. Why? After all, the kinetic theory says that water molecules are in continuous motion. They must continue to bombard the excess solid, removing and solvating the ions. As ions are solvated they dissolve in the water. Seemingly, all the sodium chloride should eventually dissolve, but that does not happen. What does take place is an exchange. New particles from the solid are solvated and enter into solution. At the same time an equal number of particles come out of solution. They become desolvated and are deposited as a solid. As ions in solution are desolvated they crystallize. The undissolved crystals of sodium chloride change their shape over time, but their mass remains constant.

The particles move from the solid to the solvated state and back to the solid again. Yet there is no net change in the overall system. As shown in Figure 17.2, a state of dynamic equilibrium exists between the solution and the undissolved solute, provided that the temperature remains constant. The sodium chloride solution is saturated. *A* **saturated solution** *contains the maximum amount of solute for a given amount of solvent at a constant temperature.* For example, 36.2 g of sodium chloride in 100 g of water is a saturated solution at 25°C. *The* **solubility** *of a substance is the amount of substance that dissolves in a given quantity of a solvent at a given temperature to produce a saturated solution.* Solubility is usually expressed in grams of solute per 100 g of solvent. *A solution that contains less solute than a saturated solution is* **unsaturated**.

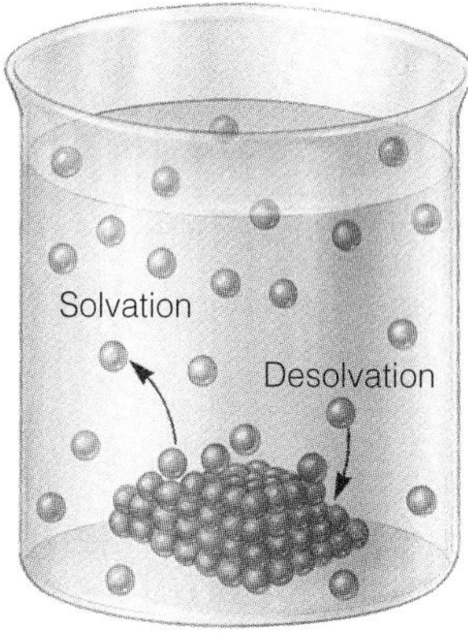

Figure 17.2 A state of dynamic equilibrium exists in a saturated solution. Under these conditions the rate of solvation (dissolving) equals the rate of desolvation (crystallization).

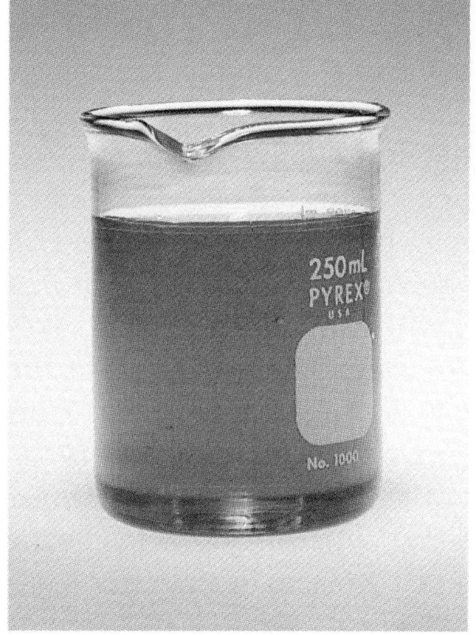

Figure 17.3 Which of these two beakers contains a saturated solution?

Roots of Words

miscere: (Latin) to mix
miscible liquids that dissolve in each other

Completely miscible liquids dissolve in each other in all proportions.

Two liquids are said to be **miscible** *if they dissolve in each other.* For example, water and ethanol are infinitely soluble in one another. Any amount of ethanol will dissolve in a given volume of water and vice versa. Such a pair of liquids is said to be completely miscible. Liquids that are slightly soluble in one another—for example, water and diethyl ether—are partially miscible. *Liquids that are insoluble in one another are* **immiscible**.

Concept Practice

3. What could you do to change:
a. a saturated solution into an unsaturated solution?
b. an unsaturated solution into a saturated solution?

4. Explain the terms *miscible* and *immiscible.*

Practice Problem

5. How much NaCl can be dissolved in 750 g of water at 25°C?

Objective

Apply Henry's law to solve gas solubility problems.

17.3 Factors Affecting Solubility

At 25°C the solubility of sodium chloride in water is 36.2 g per 100 g of water. At 100°C, the solubility increases to 39.2 g of NaCl per 100 g of water. As shown in Figure 17.4, the solubility of most substances increases as the temperature of the solvent is increased. For some substances, however, the reverse occurs. The solubility of sodium sulfate in water drops from 50 g per 100 g at 40°C to 41 g per 100 g at 100°C. Table 17.1 lists the solubilities of some common substances at various temperatures.

The solubilities of gases are greater in cold water than in hot water. Bubbles that form in water when it is heated below its boiling point are the dissolved gases escaping from solution. Figure 17.5 shows that all the components of air become less soluble in water as the temperature of the solution rises. When an industrial plant takes cool water from a lake and dumps hot water back into the lake, the temperature of the lake water rises. This change in temperature is known as thermal pollution. The temperature increase lowers the concentration of dissolved oxygen in the lake water. As a consequence, aquatic animal and plant life can be severely affected by the lack of oxygen. Can you use the kinetic theory to explain this solubility behavior of gases?

Table 17.1 Solubilities of Some Substances in Water at Various Temperatures

Substance	Formula	Solubility (g/100 g of H_2O) 0°C	20°C	50°C	100°C
Barium hydroxide	$Ba(OH)_2$	1.67	31.89	—	—
Barium sulfate	$BaSO_4$	0.00019	0.00025	0.00034	—
Calcium hydroxide	$Ca(OH)_2$	0.189	0.173	—	0.07
Lead(II) chloride	$PbCl_2$	0.60	0.99	1.70	—
Lithium carbonate	Li_2CO_3	1.5	1.3	1.1	0.70
Potassium chlorate	$KClO_3$	4.0	7.4	19.3	56.0
Potassium chloride	KCl	27.6	34.0	42.6	57.6
Sodium chloride	NaCl	35.7	36.0	37.0	39.2
Sodium nitrate	$NaNO_3$	74	88.0	114.0	182
Sodium sulfate	Na_2SO_4	4.76	62	50.0	41.0
Silver nitrate	$AgNO_3$	122	222.0	455.0	733
Lithium bromide	LiBr	143.0	166	203	266.0
Cane sugar	$C_{12}H_{22}O_{11}$	179	203.9	260.4	487
Hydrogen*	H_2	0.00019	0.00016	0.00013	0.0
Oxygen*	O_2	0.0070	0.0043	0.0026	0.0
Carbon dioxide*	CO_2	0.335	0.169	0.076	0.0

*Gas at 101 kPa total pressure

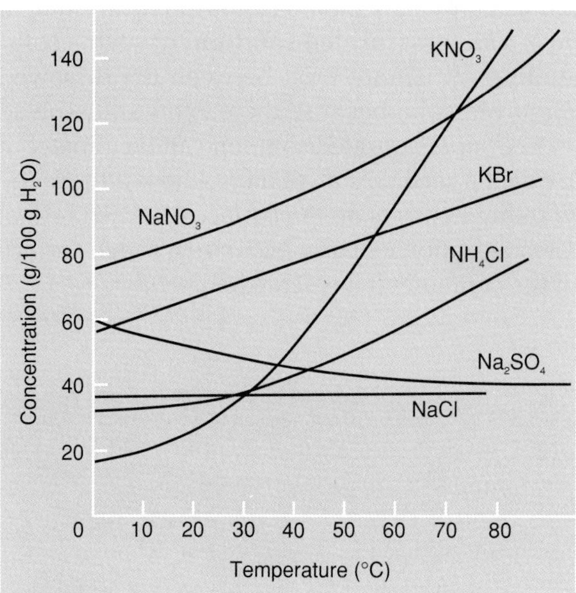

Figure 17.4 Changing the temperature may affect the solubility of a substance. Notice that increasing the temperature greatly increases the solubility of KNO_3 but decreases the solubility of Na_2SO_4.

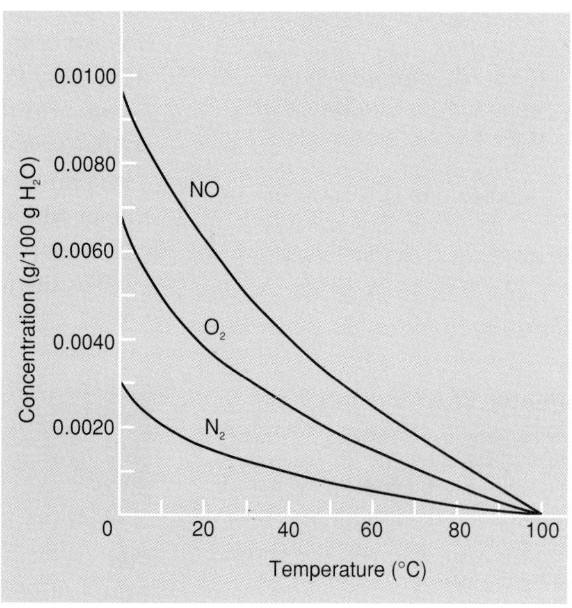

Figure 17.5 Gases have different solubilities in water at different temperatures. Generally, as the temperature increases, the solubilities of gases decrease. Notice that nitrogen, oxygen, and nitric oxide are insoluble at 100°C.

Integrating Agricultural Science

Fertilizer Runoff

Most farmers use fertilizers that contain salts of one or more of the three elements essential to grow plants: potassium, nitrogen, and phosphorus. When more fertilizer is applied than the land can absorb, rains wash off the excess salts. Not only is this economically wasteful, but also the water containing these dissolved salts ends up in streams and rivers. The dissolved nutrients contribute to the eutrophication of these waters. Eutrophied waters are rich in nutrients but deficient in dissolved oxygen. An overgrowth of water plants, algal blooms, and bad odors due to the growth of oxygen-hating bacteria are signs of eutrophication. In recent years the problem of fertilizer runoff has improved somewhat with the introduction of slow-release nitrogenous fertilizers. Many farmers have adopted new fertilizer application cycles and cultivation methods to reduce runoff.

The solubility of a gas increases as the partial pressure of the gas *above* the solution is increased. Carbonated beverages are a good example of this principle. These drinks contain large amounts of carbon dioxide (CO_2) dissolved in water. It is the dissolved CO_2 that makes your mouth tingle. The drinks are bottled under a high pressure of CO_2 gas. This forces large amounts of CO_2 into solution. When a carbonated beverage bottle is opened, the partial pressure of CO_2 above the liquid decreases and the concentration of dissolved CO_2 decreases. Bubbles of CO_2 form in the liquid and escape from the open bottle. If the bottle is left open, the drink becomes flat as the solution loses its CO_2. **Henry's law** *states that at a given temperature the solubility of a gas in a liquid (S) is directly proportional to the pressure of the gas above the liquid (P).* In other words, as the pressure of the gas above the liquid increases, the solubility of the gas increases. Similarly, as the pressure of the gas decreases, the solubility of the gas decreases. You can write this relationship in mathematical form.

$$\frac{S_1}{P_1} = \frac{S_2}{P_2}$$

When the temperature of a saturated solution in the presence of some excess solute is raised, the excess solid usually dissolves. If the system then cools slowly and undisturbed to its original temperature, the excess solute does not always immediately crystallize. *A solution which contains more solute than it can theoretically hold at a given temperature is a* **supersaturated solution**. In such a solution, a dynamic equilibrium cannot exist between the dissolved solute and the undissolved solid because there is no undissolved solid. Crystallization in a supersaturated solution can be initiated if a very small crystal, called a seed crystal, of the solute is added. The rate at which excess solute deposits on the surface of a seed crystal can be very rapid. Crystallization can also occur on a rough surface such as the inside of the container if it is scratched.

Figure 17.6 Mineral deposits form around the edges of this hot spring because the hot water is saturated with minerals. As the water cools at the surface, the minerals crystallize because they are less soluble at a lower temperature.

Figure 17.7 At left is a supersaturated solution before a seed crystal has been added. At right is the same solution after a seed crystal has been added. The seed crystal causes the excess solute to crystallize rapidly.

Scientific rainmaking is done by seeding clouds, which are masses of air supersaturated with water vapor. Tiny silver iodide (AgI) crystals are dusted on a cloud. Water molecules that are attracted to the ionic particles come together and form droplets that act as seeds for other water molecules. The water droplets grow and eventually fall as rain when they are large enough.

Example 1 Calculating the Solubility of a Gas

If the solubility of a gas in water is 0.77 g/L at 350 kPa of pressure, what is its solubility, in grams per liter at 100 kPa of pressure? (The temperature is held constant at 25°C.)

Solution

You can use the same general method that you used for solving gas law problems. The knowns are $P_1 = 350$ kPa, $S_1 = 0.77$ g/L, and $P_2 = 100$ kPa. To find S_2, begin by rearranging Henry's law to give S_2.

$$S_2 = \frac{S_1 \times P_2}{P_1}$$

Then substitute values for the other variables in the equation.

$$S_2 = \frac{0.77\ \text{g/L} \times 100\ \cancel{\text{kPa}}}{350\ \cancel{\text{kPa}}} = 0.22\ \text{g/L}$$

When the pressure is reduced to 100 kPa, the solubility of the gas decreases to 0.22 g/L.

Problem-Solving Tip

Check that the answer has an appropriate unit after canceling and before doing the calculations.

Concept Practice

6. Based on the solid substances listed in Table 17.1, make a general statement relating change in solubility to a change in temperature.

7. Can a solution with undissolved solute be supersaturated? Explain.

Practice Problem

8. A gas has a solubility in water at 0°C of 3.6 g/L at a pressure of 100 kPa. What pressure is needed to produce an aqueous solution containing 9.5 g/L of the same gas at 0°C?

Activity 17
Solutions and Colloids

Purpose

To classify mixtures as solutions or colloids (Section 16.9) using the Tyndall effect.

Materials

sodium hydrogen carbonate
cornstarch
water (distilled if possible)
flashlight
black construction paper
masking tape
jars with parallel sides
teaspoon
cup

Procedure

1. Make a cone with the black construction paper and tape to fit over the lens of the flashlight. Tape the cone in place over the lens.

2. In a cup, make a paste by mixing 1/4 teaspoon of cornstarch with 4 teaspoons of water.

3. Fill one of the jars with water. Add 1/4 teaspoon sodium hydrogen carbonate to a second jar and fill with water. Stir to mix. Add the cornstarch paste to the third jar and fill with water. Stir to mix.

4. Turn out the lights in the room. Shine the narrow beam of light from the flashlight at each of the jars and record your observations.

Analysis and Conclusions

1. In which of the jars was it possible to see the path of the beam of light?

2. Explain what made the light beam visible.

3. If a system that made the light beam visible was filtered, would the light beam be visible in the filtrate? Explain your answer.

4. Predict what you would observe if you were to replace the sodium hydrogen carbonate with sucrose (cane sugar) or sodium chloride (table salt).

5. Predict what you would observe if you were to replace the cornstarch with flour or diluted milk.

6. Explain how you could use this method to distinguish a colloid from a suspension.

17.A Consumer Chemistry

Food Labels

As a consumer, you have an interest in knowing the ingredients and nutritional value of the food you buy. You have probably read the information on the side of a cereal box. Most packaged foods are labeled with information about the vitamins and minerals, fats, carbohydrates, proteins, and calories they contain. However, you may have found the information on the package confusing or incomplete. Moreover, fresh fruits and vegetables generally have not been labeled with much, if any, information about their food value.

An example will demonstrate some of the problems that have been faced by consumers. First, consider the salt contents of canned green beans. At present, the contents of the package are listed in decreasing order of the amount in the package. A can of green beans lists green beans, water, and salt in that order. The manufacturer reveals elsewhere on the label that the amount of salt, given as the sodium content, is 340 mg per serving. This is useful information, especially for someone on a restricted salt diet. One serving of the canned green beans provides about 14% of the recommended daily value of about 2500 mg per day of salt for a normal, healthy individual. However, the recommended daily allowance is *not* given on the package.

In the future, more consistent and informative labeling on food packages could greatly benefit consumers. As a result of voluntary decisions by food distributors and new government regulations, the information on food labels is being improved. Some supermarkets are now displaying the nutritional values of fresh fruits and vegetables on a voluntary basis. Labels on food packages are changing as well. New labels will include the serving size in grams as well as in household units. The amounts of carbohydrates, sugars, cholesterol, proteins, and fats will appear in metric units of milligrams or grams. New labels will also state the contents as percentages of the recommended daily values of these ingredients. While not perfect, the new labels should help you make informed decisions about what foods to buy for the maximum nutritional benefit.

Nutrition Facts

Serving Size 1/2 cup (114g)
Servings Per Container 4

Amount Per Serving	
Calories 260	Calories from Fat 120
	% Daily Value*
Total Fat 13g	**20%**
Saturated Fat 5g	**25%**
Cholesterol 30mg	**10%**
Sodium 660mg	**28%**
Total Carbohydrate 31g	**11%**
Sugars 5g	
Dietary Fiber 0g	**0%**
Protein 5g	

Vitamin A 4% Vitamin C 2%
Calcium 15% Iron 4%

*Percent (%) of daily value is based on a 2,000 calorie diet. Your daily values may be higher or lower depending on your calorie needs.

Figure 17.8 New food labels will include the % Daily Value for fat, cholesterol, sodium, carbohydrates, and dietary fiber that the food contains.

Think About It

9. Appraise Many prepackaged food items are touted as containing *all natural ingredients.* Does this necessarily make the item a wise nutritional choice? Explain.

10. Suppose What additional information would you like to see on the labels of food packages? Why?

Objective

Define and work problems involving the molarity of a solution.

17.4 Molarity

So far you have seen that a particular substance does or does not dissolve in a particular solvent to form a solution. This section focuses on ways to express the concentrations of solutions. *The* **concentration** *of a solution is a measure of the amount of solute that is dissolved in a given quantity of solvent.* The terms *concentrated* and *dilute* are qualitative descriptions of the amount of a solute in solution. *A* **dilute solution** *contains only a small amount of solute.* By contrast, *a* **concentrated solution** *contains a large amount of solute.* An aqueous solution of sodium chloride containing 1 g of NaCl per 100 g of H_2O might be described as dilute compared with another solution containing 30 g per 100 g. The first solution might be described as concentrated if it were compared with another solution containing only 1×10^{-2} g of NaCl per 100 g of H_2O. For this reason, you do not really express the concentration of the solution when you describe it as concentrated or dilute.

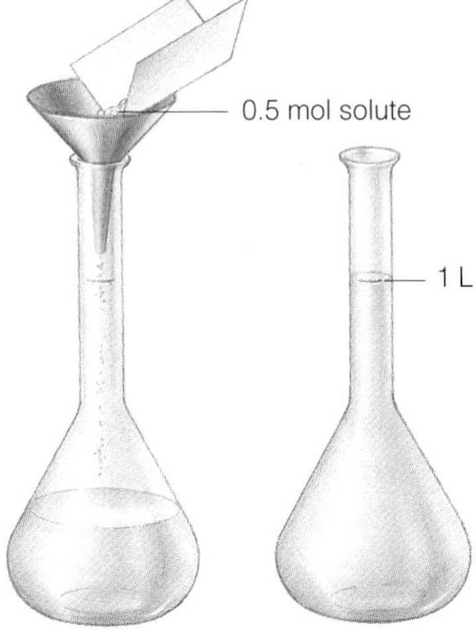

Figure 17.9 To make a 0.5 mol solution, add 0.5 mol of solute to a 1-L volumetric flask half filled with water. Swirl the flask carefully to make the solute dissolve. Then fill the flask with water exactly to the 1-L mark.

Just as the mole is the most important unit of amount of substance in chemistry, the most important unit of concentration is molarity (abbreviated *M*). **Molarity** *is the number of moles of a solute dissolved in 1 L of solution.* Molarity is also known as molar concentration. Note that the volume is the volume of the *solution,* not the volume of the solvent. To determine the molarity of any solution, you calculate the number of moles in 1 L of the solution using the following equation.

$$\text{Molarity } (M) = \frac{\text{number of moles of solute}}{\text{number of liters of solution}}$$

For example, calculate the molarity if water is added to 2 mol of glucose to give 5 L of solution. To get this answer, divide the number of moles by the volume in liters.

$$\frac{2 \text{ mol of glucose}}{5 \text{ L of solution}} = 0.4 \text{ mol/L}$$

The solution is $0.4M$, or 0.4 molar in glucose.

Figure 17.10 One mole of any compound can be dissolved in 1 L of water to make a 1*M* solution.

Example 2 Calculating the Molarity of a Solution

A saline solution contains 0.90 g of NaCl per 100.0 mL of solution. What is its molarity?

Solution

Molarity is moles per liter. You must convert the concentration from grams per 100.00 mL to moles per liter. To do this, start with the gram formula mass of sodium chloride.

$$\text{gfm NaCl} = 23.0\text{ g} + 35.5\text{ g} = 58.5\text{ g}$$

Use a conversion factor based on the gram formula mass to calculate the moles of NaCl in 100.0 mL of saline.

$$\text{Moles} = 0.90\,\cancel{\text{g}} \times \frac{1.0\text{ mol}}{58.5\,\cancel{\text{g}}} = 0.015\text{ mol}$$

Now convert mol per 100.0 mL to mol per L (100.0 mL = 0.1000 L).

$$\text{Molarity} = \frac{\text{moles}}{\text{liter}} = \frac{0.015\text{ mol}}{0.1000\text{ L}} = 0.15M\text{ solution}$$

Example 3 Finding Grams of Solute in a Solution of Known Molarity

How many grams of solute are present in 1.5 L of 0.20*M* Na_2SO_4?

Solution

Rearrange the expression for molarity to give moles of solute.
Liters of solution × molarity (*M*) = moles of solute
Substitute in the known information, stating the molarity in mol/L.

$$1.5\,\cancel{\text{L}} \times \frac{0.20\text{ mol}}{1.0\,\cancel{\text{L}}} = 0.30\text{ mol}$$

To determine the weight of solute, multiply the number of moles of Na_2SO_4 by a conversion factor based on the gram formula mass.

$$0.30\,\cancel{\text{mol}} \times \frac{142.1\text{ g}}{1.0\,\cancel{\text{mol}}} = 42.6\text{ g} = 43\text{ g (to two significant figures)}$$

Problem-Solving Tip

Break complex problems down into two simpler parts.

Concept Practice

11. A measure of the molarity of a solution is more meaningful than knowing whether a solution is dilute or concentrated. Explain.

Practice Problems

12. A salt solution has a volume of 250 mL and contains 0.70 mol of NaCl. What is the molarity of the solution?

13. You have an aqueous solution that has a volume of 2.0 L and contains 36.0 g of glucose. If the gram formula mass of glucose is 180 g, what is the molarity of your solution?

14. How many moles of solute are in 250 mL of 2.0*M* $CaCl_2$? How many grams of $CaCl_2$ is this?

Objective

Describe how to prepare dilute solutions from concentrated solutions of known molarity.

17.5 Making Dilutions

Solutions of known molarity are usually available in the laboratory. You may need dilute solutions of different known concentrations. You can make a solution less concentrated by diluting it with solvent. *The number of moles of solute does not change when a solution is diluted.*

Number of moles of solute *before* dilution = number of moles of solute *after* dilution

Now rearrange the definition of molarity to give an expression for moles of solute in terms of molarity and volume.

$$\text{Molarity } (M) = \frac{\text{number of moles of solute}}{\text{number of liters of solution}}$$

$$\text{Moles of solute} = \text{molarity } (M) \times \text{liters of solution } (V)$$

Since the total number of moles of solute remains unchanged upon dilution, you can write

$$\text{moles of solute} = M_1 \times V_1 = M_2 \times V_2$$

In this equation M_1 and V_1 are the initial solution's molarity and volume, and M_2 and V_2 are the final solution's molarity and volume. Volumes can be in liters or milliliters as long as the same units are used for both V_1 and V_2.

To dilute an acid, always add the acid, while stirring, to the required amount of water. Never add water to the acid. The heat generated may splash the solution out of the container.

Figure 17.11 To prepare 100 mL of $0.40M$ $MgSO_4$ from a stock solution of $2.0M$ $MgSO_4$, transfer 20 mL of the stock solution to a 100-mL volumetric flask. Carefully add water to make 100 mL of solution.

You may have a variety of volume-measuring devices available to you in the laboratory. Your choice of what to use depends on how accurate the concentration of the solution you are making must be. The following example shows how a dilute solution is prepared.

Example 4 Preparing a Dilute Solution

How would you prepare 100 mL of $0.40M$ $MgSO_4$ from a stock solution of $2.0M$ $MgSO_4$?

Solution

Use the last equation to calculate the volume of $2.0M$ $MgSO_4$ required and then describe the procedure for making the solution. The knowns are $M_1 = 2.0M$, $M_2 = 0.40M$, and $V_2 = 100$ mL. V_1 is the unknown. Rearrange the equation to give V_1.

$$M_1 \times V_1 = M_2 \times V_2, \textit{ therefore } V_1 = \frac{M_2 \times V_2}{M_1}$$

Now substitute values into the equation.

$$V_1 = \frac{0.40\cancel{M} \times 100 \text{ mL}}{2.0\cancel{M}} = 20 \text{ mL}$$

Suppose the dilute solution must be very accurate. Measure 20 mL of the $2.0M$ $MgSO_4$ with a 20-mL volumetric pipet and transfer the solution to a 100-mL volumetric flask. (You can also use a buret to measure volumes accurately.) Next add distilled water to the flask up to the etched line. This dilutes the contents to exactly 100 mL. Then shake the flask. This produces 100 mL of $0.40M$ $MgSO_4$.

Safety

Never pipet a solution by mouth. Use a suction bulb.

Concept Practice

15. Your experiment requires 5 mL of 1.0*M* KOH. However, you have 1 L of 0.5*M* KOH. Can you prepare the required solution by diluting what you have? Explain.

Practice Problem

16. You need 250 mL of 0.20*M* NaCl, but the only supply of sodium chloride you have is a solution of 1.0*M* NaCl. How do you prepare the required solution? Assume that you have the appropriate volume-measuring devices on hand.

Objective

Calculate percent by volume and percent by mass for solutions.

17.6 Percent Solutions

If both the solute and the solvent are liquids, a convenient way to make a solution is by measuring volumes. You can then express the concentration of the solute as a percent of the solution by volume. Percent means "parts per hundred." If 20 mL of rubbing alcohol is diluted with water to a total volume of 100 mL, the final solution is 20% alcohol by volume. The concentration can be written as 20 percent (volume/volume), or in shorthand, 20% (v/v).

$$\text{Percent by volume} = \frac{\text{volume of solute}}{\text{volume of solution}} \times 100\%$$

Figure 17.12 Many products give the amounts of their ingredients by percent. Without units, however, you cannot be certain how the percent composition was determined.

In contrast, a commonly used relationship for solutions of solids dissolved in liquids is percent (mass/volume). It is usually convenient to weigh the solute in grams and to measure the volume of the resulting solution in milliliters. Percent (mass/volume) is the number of grams of solute per 100 mL of solution. A solution containing 7 g of sodium chloride in 100 mL of solution is 7 percent (mass/volume) or 7% (m/v).

$$\text{Percent (mass/volume)} = \frac{\text{mass of solute (g)}}{\text{solution volume (mL)}} \times 100\%$$

Because there are two kinds of percent solution, percent composition can often be misleading. When a label says a product contains 5% glucose, what does it mean? If you know that glucose is usually a solid, you would conclude that it is probably specifying percent (mass/volume). However, you cannot be certain unless the units are given. When using percentages to express concentration, be sure to state the units.

Example 5 Calculating Percent by Volume

What is the percent by volume of ethanol (ethyl alcohol, C_2H_6O) in the final solution when 75 mL of ethanol is diluted to a volume of 250 mL with water?

Solution

$$\text{Percent by volume} = \frac{75\ \text{mL}}{250\ \text{mL}} \times 100\% = 0.30 \times 100\%$$

$$= 30\%\ \text{ethanol (v/v)}$$

Example 6 Preparing a Percent (m/v) Solution

How many grams of glucose ($C_6H_{12}O_6$) would you need to prepare 2.0 L of 2.0% glucose (m/v) solution?

Solution

A 2.0% glucose (m/v) solution means that 100 mL of the solution contains 2.0 g of glucose. Use a conversion factor to determine the number of grams per liter.

$$\frac{2.0\ \text{g}}{100\ \text{mL}} \times \frac{1000\ \text{mL}}{1.0\ \text{L}} = 20\ \text{g/L}$$

Multiply the number of grams of solute per liter by the number of liters required.

$$2.0\ \text{L} \times \frac{20\ \text{g}}{1\ \text{L}} = 40\ \text{g glucose}$$

Concept Practice

17. A bottle of hydrogen peroxide antiseptic is labeled 3%. How could this label be improved?

Practice Problem

18. A solution contains 2.7 g of $CuSO_4$ in 75 mL of solution. What is the percent (mass/volume) of the solution?

Integrating Nursing

Intravenous Solutions

A patient in a hospital is often given an intravenous (IV) drip bag containing an aqueous solution. The solution may be necessary to prevent dehydration or to administer nutrition or medicines to the patient. Great care must be taken when fluids are introduced into the blood stream. Otherwise the balance of dissolved electrolytes inside and outside the tissues could be disturbed. The effects of an imbalance in electrolytes and water can be harmful or even cause the death of the patient. Aqueous solutions containing 0.85 to 0.9 percent (weight/volume) sodium chloride or 5 percent (weight/volume) glucose prevent undesired changes in the blood or tissues.

17.B Science, Technology, and Society

Water Softeners

Have you ever found it difficult to get soap to lather? If so, you may have been trying to wash in hard water. Hard water causes people to spend enormous amounts of money to replace corroded and plugged plumbing. Hard water can deposit a rock-hard "scale" of calcium carbonate in industrial boilers, hot-water pipes, and tea kettles. You may spend money for excess amounts of soaps and detergents in order to overcome the effects of hard water.

Hard water contains appreciable amounts of the cations Ca^{2+}, Mg^{2+}, and Fe^{2+}. These ions get into the ground water by reactions of water containing dissolved CO_2 with minerals such as limestone ($CaCO_3$) in the ground.

$$CaCO_3(s) + CO_2(aq) + H_2O(l) \longrightarrow Ca^{2+}(aq) + 2HCO_3^-(aq)$$

The major anions in hard water are usually hydrogen carbonate (HCO_3^-) and sulfate (SO_4^{2-}).

Hard water in the home is often treated with commercial water softeners by ion exchange. In ion exchange an undesirable ion in solution is exchanged for an ion, usually sodium, that is bound to a solid, insoluble material. The material used in ion-exchange water softeners is usually a natural mineral such as zeolite (aluminum silicate) or a synthetic resin. As the hard water passes through the water softener, the metal ions that cause the hardness displace the bound sodium ions. The sodium ions enter the water, but they do not cause hardness. After a time, the ion-exchange material becomes saturated with the hard-water metal ions. The minerals or resins are then regenerated by pouring strong sodium chloride solution (brine) through them to displace the exchanged calcium and magnesium ions. The hard-water cations are replaced with a new stock of sodium ions on the matrix.

Softened water may contain a substantial concentration of sodium ions, which are implicated in some forms of high blood pressure. Health experts recommend that drinking water be taken from a separate tap that is not hooked up to the home water softener.

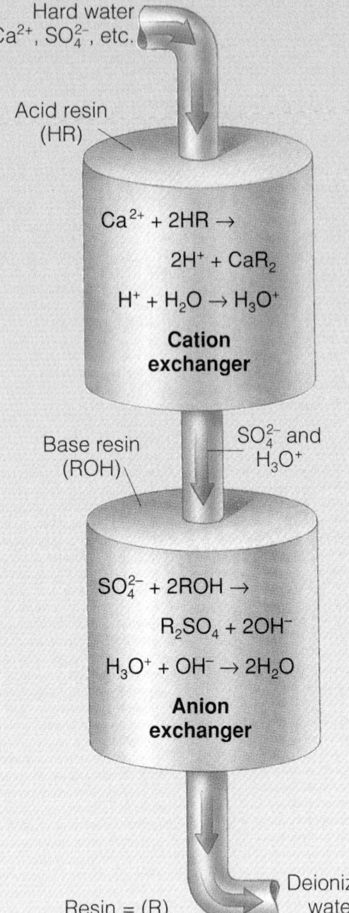

Figure 17.13 Ion-exchange resins are also used to exchange positive and negative ions in the formation of "deionized" water. Deionized water is particularly important for use in the laboratory, where high concentrations of ions in the water may interfere with an analysis.

Think About It

19. List Identify the ions typically found in hard water.

20. Describe Name some advantages and disadvantages of softening water in the home.

17.7 Colligative Properties of Solutions

Objective

Explain on a particle basis why a solution has a lower vapor pressure, a higher boiling point, and a lower freezing point than the pure solvent of that solution.

The physical properties of a solution are different from those of the pure solvent. Some of these differences are due to the mere presence of solute particles in the solution. **Colligative properties** *depend on the number of particles dissolved in a given mass of solvent.* Three important colligative properties of solutions are vapor pressure lowering, boiling point elevation, and freezing point depression.

Vapor pressure is the pressure exerted by a vapor that is in dynamic equilibrium with its liquid in a closed system. A solution that contains a nonvolatile solute always has a lower vapor pressure than the pure solvent. A nonvolatile solute is one that does not vaporize. Glucose, a molecular compound, and sodium chloride, an ionic compound, are examples of nonvolatile solutes. Both glucose and sodium chloride would lower the vapor pressure of a pure solvent. Consider an aqueous sodium chloride solution as an example. Sodium ions and chloride ions are dispersed throughout the liquid. Both within the liquid and at the surface, the ions are surrounded by shells of water of solvation. The formation of these shells occupies much of the surface water. This reduces the number of solvent molecules that have enough kinetic energy to escape as vapor. As a result, the solution has a lower vapor pressure than the pure solvent.

The decrease in the vapor pressure is proportional *to the number of particles the solute makes in solution.* A solute that dissociates into particles, like sodium chloride, has a greater effect on the vapor pressure than the same concentration of a nondissociating solute like glucose. For example, the vapor pressure lowering caused by 0.1 mol of sodium chloride in 1000 g of water is twice the vapor pressure lowering of 0.1 mol of glucose in 1000 g of water. Each formula unit of the ionic compound sodium chloride produces two

Roots of Words

colligatus: (Latin) grouped together
colligative group of properties affected by the number of particles

Boiling point elevation, freezing point lowering, and vapor pressure lowering are colligative properties of solutions.

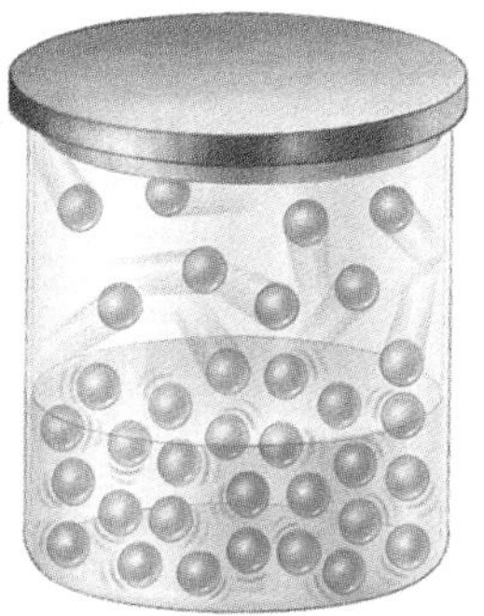

(a) Higher vapor pressure

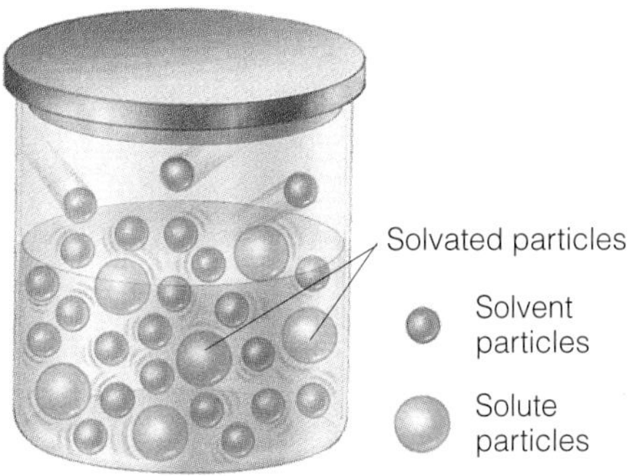

(b) Lower vapor pressure

Figure 17.14 **(a)** Equilibrium is established between the pure solvent liquid and its vapor. **(b)** The equilibrium is disrupted when solute is added. Solvent particles form shells around the solute particles. This reduces the number of free solvent particles able to escape the liquid. Equilibrium is reestablished at a lower vapor pressure.

particles in solution: a sodium ion and a chloride ion. When glucose dissolves, each molecule exists as only one particle, the molecule itself. Similarly, 0.1 mol of $CaCl_2$ in 1000 mL of water produces three times the vapor pressure lowering of a 0.1 mol glucose solution. Each formula unit of calcium chloride produces three particles in solution.

The boiling point of a substance is the temperature at which the vapor pressure of the liquid phase equals the atmospheric pressure. Adding a nonvolatile solute to a liquid solvent decreases the vapor pressure of the solvent. Because of the decrease in vapor pressure, additional kinetic energy must be added to raise the vapor pressure of the liquid phase to atmospheric pressure. Thus the boiling point of the solution is higher than the boiling point of the pure solvent. *The* **boiling point elevation** *is the difference in temperature between the boiling points of a solution and of the pure solvent.*

Another way for you to think about the reason for a boiling point elevation is in terms of particles. Attractive forces exist between the solvent and solute particles. Therefore, it takes additional kinetic energy for the solvent particles to overcome the attractive forces that keep them in the liquid at the boiling point. Thus, the presence of a solute elevates the boiling point of the solvent. The magnitude of the boiling point elevation is proportional to the number of solute particles dissolved in the solvent. For example, the boiling point of water increases by 0.512°C for every mole of *particles* that the solute forms when dissolved in 1000 g of water. Thus boiling point elevation is a colligative property.

When a substance freezes, the particles in the solid take on an orderly pattern. The presence of a solute in water disrupts this pattern due to the shells of water of hydration. As a result, more kinetic energy must be withdrawn from a solution than from pure solvent for it to solidify. *The* **freezing point depression** *is the difference in*

Figure 17.15 Temperatures below 0°C are needed to make ice cream. Thus rock salt is added to ice in an ice cream maker. A freezing point depression occurs and the temperature of the ice-water mixture decreases a few degrees below 0°C.

temperature between the freezing points of a solution and of the pure solvent. The magnitude of the freezing point depression is proportional to the number of solute particles dissolved in the solvent. Thus it is a colligative property.

The addition of 1 mol of particles of solute to 1000 g of water lowers the freezing point by 1.86°C. If you add 1 mol (180 g) of glucose to 1000 g of water, the solution freezes at –1.86°C. If you add 1 mol (58.5 g) of sodium chloride to 1000 g of water, however, the solution freezes at –3.72°C. This is because 1 mol of NaCl produces 2 mol of particles. You may take advantage of the freezing point depression of aqueous solutions to melt ice on sidewalks. Ice sprinkled with salt melts and forms a solution with a lower freezing point than that of pure water.

Concept Practice

21. Would a dilute or concentrated sodium fluoride solution have a higher boiling point? Explain.

22. If equal numbers of moles of KI and MgF_2 are dissolved in equal volumes of water, state which solution has the highest:
a. boiling point
b. vapor pressure
c. freezing point

17.8 Molality and Mole Fraction

Objective

Calculate the molality and mole fraction of a solution.

The colligative properties depend only on the ratio of the number of solute particles to solvent particles. There are two convenient ways of expressing this ratio: in molality units and in mole fractions. **Molality** *(m) is the number of moles of solute dissolved in 1 kilogram (1000 g) of solvent.* Molality is also known as molal concentration.

$$\text{Molality} = \frac{\text{moles of solute}}{\text{kilogram of solvent}} = \frac{\text{moles of solute}}{1000 \text{ g of solvent}}$$

Note that *molality* is not the same as *molarity.* Molality refers to moles per kilogram of *solvent.* Molarity refers to moles per liter of *solution.* In the case of water as the solvent, 1000 g is equal to 1000 mL or 1 L.

You can prepare a solution that is 1.00 molal in glucose by adding 1000 g of water to 1.00 mol (180 g) of glucose. A solution prepared by dissolving 0.500 mol (29.25 g) of sodium chloride in 1.000 kg (1000 g) of water is 0.500 molal (0.500 *m*) in NaCl.

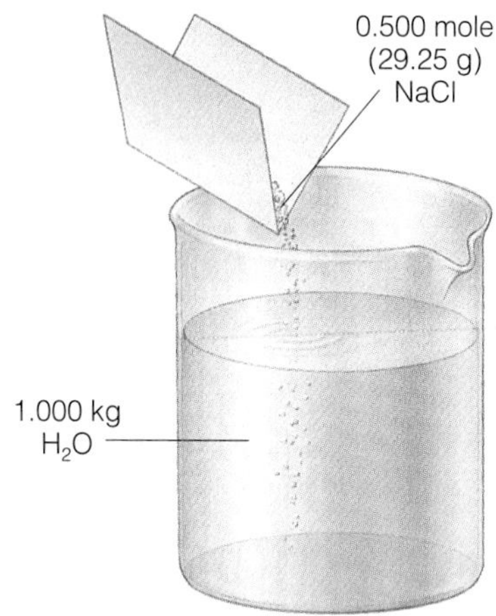

Figure 17.16 To make a 0.500 *m* solution of NaCl, use a balance to measure 1.000 kg of water and add 29.25 g of NaCl to it.

Example 7 Using Solution Molality

How many grams of potassium iodide must you dissolve in 500.0 g of water to produce a 0.060 molal KI solution?

Solution

According to the definition of *molal*, the final solution must contain 0.060 mol KI per 1000 g H_2O. Use this as a conversion factor.

$$500.0\ \text{g}\ \cancel{H_2O} \times \frac{0.060\ \text{mol KI}}{1000\ \text{g}\ \cancel{H_2O}} = 0.030\ \text{mol KI}$$

Then convert 0.030 mol of KI to grams.

$$\text{gfm KI} = 39.1 + 126.9 = 166.0\ \text{g}$$

$$0.030\ \cancel{\text{mol KI}} \times \frac{166.0\ \text{g KI}}{1\ \cancel{\text{mol KI}}} = 5.0\ \text{g KI}$$

You must dissolve 5.0 g KI in 500.0 g of H_2O to get 0.060 molal KI.

The ratio of the moles of solute in solution to the total number of moles of both solvent and solute is the **mole fraction** *of that solute.* In a solution containing n_A moles of solute and n_B moles of solvent, the mole fraction of solute, X_A, and mole fraction of solvent, X_B, can be expressed mathematically.

$$X_A = \frac{n_A}{n_A + n_B} \qquad X_B = \frac{n_B}{n_A + n_B}$$

Example 8 Calculating Mole Fractions

Compute the mole fraction of each component in a solution of 1.25 mol ethylene glycol (EG) and 4.00 mol water.

Solution

The mole fraction of ethylene glycol, X_{EG}, in the solution is the number of moles of ethylene glycol divided by the total number of moles in solution.

$$X_{EG} = \frac{n_{EG}}{n_{EG} + n_{H_2O}} = \frac{1.25\ \text{mol}}{1.25\ \text{mol} + 4.00\ \text{mol}} = 0.238$$

The mole fraction of water, X_{H_2O}, is the number of moles of water divided by the total number of moles in solution.

$$X_{H_2O} = \frac{n_{H_2O}}{n_{EG} + n_{H_2O}} = \frac{4.00 \text{ mol}}{1.25 \text{ mol} + 4.00 \text{ mol}} = 0.762$$

$$\text{Total} = 1.000$$

Note that mole fraction is a dimensionless quantity. *The sum of the mole fractions of all the components in a solution must equal unity.*

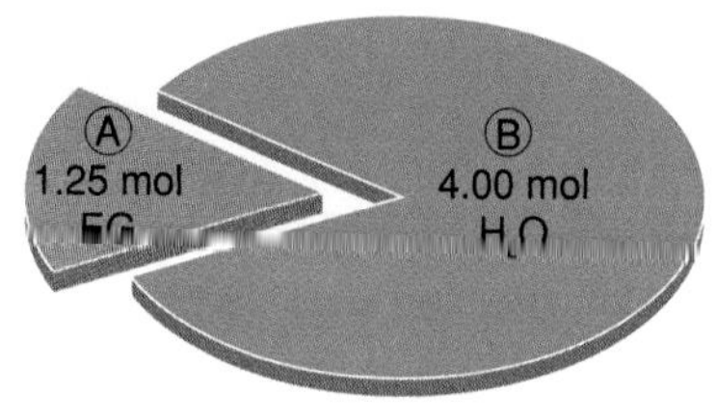

Total moles = Ⓐ + Ⓑ = 5.25 moles

Mole fraction EG = $\frac{Ⓐ}{Ⓐ + Ⓑ} = \frac{1.25}{5.25}$

Mole fraction H_2O = $\frac{Ⓑ}{Ⓐ + Ⓑ} = \frac{4.00}{5.25}$

Figure 17.17 The mole fraction is the ratio of the number of moles of one substance to the total number of moles of all substances in the solution.

Concept Practice

23. Distinguish between a 1 *M* solution and a 1 *m* solution.

Practice Problems

24. Calculate the molality of a solution prepared by dissolving 10.0 g of NaCl in 600.0 g of water.

25. What is the mole fraction of each component in a solution made by mixing 300.0 g of ethanol (C_2H_5OH) and 500.0 g of water?

17.9 Calculating Boiling and Freezing Point Changes

Objective

Calculate the freezing point depression and the boiling point elevation of aqueous solutions.

Elevations of boiling points and depressions of freezing points are usually quite small. They can be measured accurately only with thermometers that can measure temperature changes as small as 0.001°C.

The boiling point of a solvent is raised by the addition of a nonvolatile solute. The magnitude of the boiling point elevation is directly proportional to the molal concentration when the solute is molecular (not ionic).

$$\Delta T_b \propto m$$

The change in the boiling temperature, ΔT_b, is the elevation of the boiling point of the solvent. It is the boiling point of the solution minus the boiling point of the solvent. The term *m* is the molal concentration of the solution. Adding a proportionality constant makes an equality.

$$\Delta T_b = K_b\, m$$

Table 17.2 K_b Values for Some Common Solvents	
Solvent	**K_b (°C/m)**
Water	0.512
Ethanol	1.19
Benzene	2.53
Cyclohexane	2.79
Acetic acid	3.07
Phenol	3.56
Nitrobenzene	5.24
Camphor	5.95

Table 17.3 K_f Values for Some Common Solvents	
Solvent	**K_f (°C/m)**
Water	1.86
Acetic acid	3.90
Benzene	5.12
Nitrobenzene	7.00
Phenol	7.40
Cyclohexane	20.2
Camphor	37.7

The constant K_b, the **molal boiling point elevation constant,** *is equal to the change in boiling point for a 1 molal solution of a nonvolatile molecular solute.* Values of the constant K_b for water and some other solvents are given in Table 17.2. The units of K_b are °C/m.

Example 9 Calculating the Boiling Point Elevation of a Solution

What is the boiling point of a solution that contains 1.20 mol of sodium chloride in 800.0 g of water?

Solution

First determine the molality of the solution.

$$\frac{\text{mol NaCl}}{1000\text{ g H}_2\text{O}} = \frac{1.20\text{ mol NaCl}}{800.0\text{ g}} \times \frac{1000\text{ g}}{1\text{ kg}}$$

$$= 1.50\ m$$

Each formula unit of NaCl is ionized into two particles.

$$\text{NaCl}(s) \longrightarrow \text{Na}^+(aq) + \text{Cl}^-(aq)$$

The molality of *total* particles is $2 \times 1.50\ m = 3.00\ m$. Now determine the boiling point elevation. From Table 17.2, K_b for H_2O is 0.512°C/m.

$$\Delta T_b = K_b \times m$$

$$= 0.512°\text{C}/m \times 3.00\ m$$

$$= 1.54°\text{C}$$

The boiling point of this solution is 100°C + 1.54°C = 101.54°C. (Because the boiling point of water is *defined* as exactly 100°C, this value does not limit the number of significant figures in the solution of the problem.)

You can also calculate the freezing point depression of a solution.

$$\Delta T_f = K_f \times m$$

The change in the freezing temperature, ΔT_f, represents the freezing point depression. The molality is m. *The* **molal freezing point depression constant,** K_f, *is equal to the change in the freezing point for a 1 molal solution of a nonvolatile molecular solute.* Values of the constant K_f for water and some other solvents are given in Table 17.3. The units of K_f are °C/m.

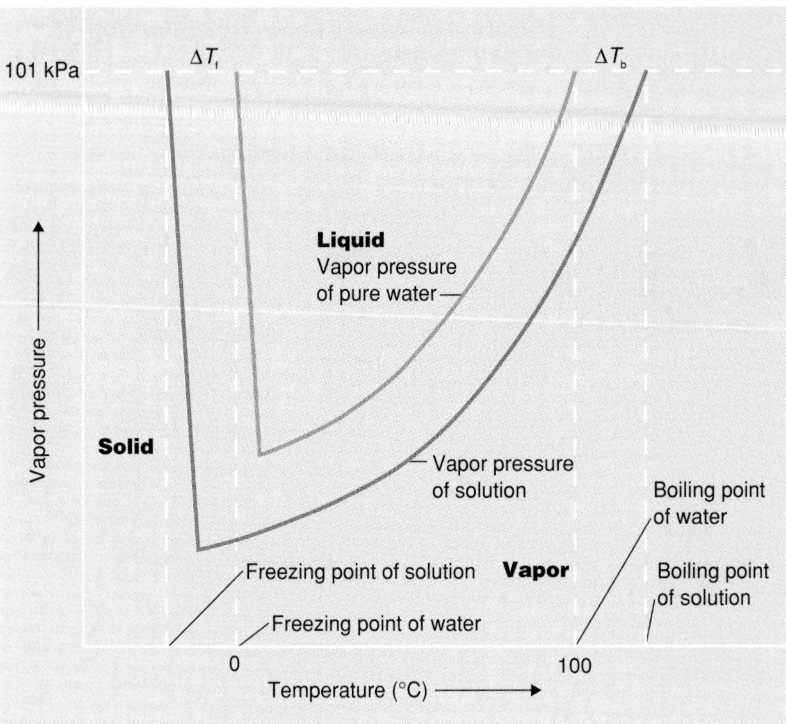

Figure 17.18 The addition of a nonvolatile solute to water lowers its vapor pressure. This results in an increase in the normal boiling point of water and a decrease in the normal freezing point of water.

Practice Problems

26. What is the freezing point of these solutions?

a. 1.40 mol of Na_2SO_4 in 1750 g of H_2O

b. 0.60 mol of $MgSO_4$ in 1300 g of H_2O

27. One mole of a compound of iron and chlorine is dissolved in 1 kg of water. The boiling point of this aqueous solution is 102.05°C; the freezing point is –7.44°C. What is the formula of this compound?

17.10 Molecular Mass Determination

Objective

Calculate the molecular mass of an unknown from experimental freezing point depression or boiling point elevation measurements.

You could use the changes in boiling and freezing points to determine the molecular mass of a substance. You would add a known amount of solute to a known amount of solvent and measure the change in the boiling or freezing point. A solvent with a known molal freezing point depression constant (K_f) or molal boiling point elevation constant (K_b) must be used. Then you would calculate the molecular mass for the solute.

Biographical Note

Mary Swartz Rose
(1874–1941)

When Mary Swartz Rose enrolled at Columbia University in 1905, no curriculum was available in the study of nutrition. Her desire to study the chemistry of food and nutrition led her to Yale University. There she obtained a Ph.D. in physiological chemistry. She returned to Columbia and was largely responsible for establishing a Department of Nutrition. Rose was a brilliant and talented educator. Her department became a leading university center for the study of nutrition. She taught for 31 years and published over 40 scholarly papers on such topics as energy metabolism and the nutritive value of food proteins. She served on many national and international advisory councils concerned with diet and nutrition.

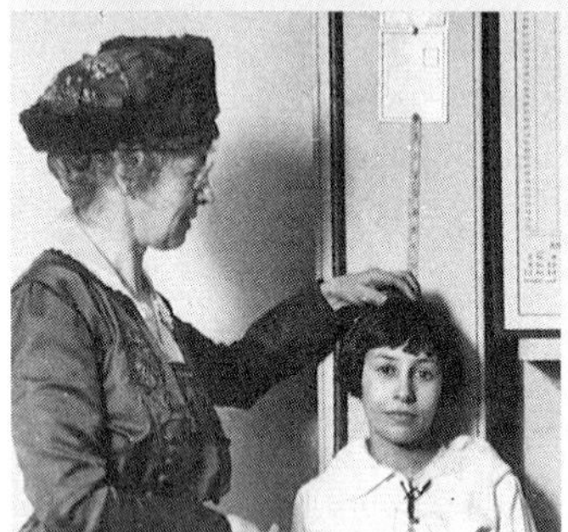

Example 10 Finding the Molar Mass from Boiling Point Elevation

A solution of 7.50 g of a nonvolatile compound in 22.60 g of water boils at 100.78°C at 760 mm Hg. What is the molecular mass of the solute? (Assume the solute exists as molecules.)

Solution

First use the boiling point elevation to calculate the molality of the solution. The observed boiling point elevation is:

$$100.78°\text{C} - 100.00°\text{C} = 0.78°\text{C} = \Delta T_b$$

$$K_b \text{ for water} = 0.512 \frac{°\text{C} \times \text{kg of water}}{\text{mol of solute}}$$

$$m = \frac{0.78°\cancel{\text{C}}}{0.512 \dfrac{°\cancel{\text{C}} \times \text{kg of water}}{\text{mol of solute}}}$$

$$m = 1.5 \frac{\text{mol of solute}}{\text{kg of water}}$$

Now calculate moles of solute in solution.

$$1.5 \frac{\text{mol of solute}}{\cancel{\text{kg of water}}} \times \frac{1\,\cancel{\text{kg}}}{1000\,\cancel{\text{g}}} \times 22.6\ \cancel{\text{g of water}} = 0.034 \text{ mol solute}$$

Finally use the number of moles of solute and its mass to determine the molecular mass of the solute.

$$\text{Molecular mass of solute} = \frac{\text{mass of solute}}{\text{moles of solute}}$$

$$= \frac{7.50 \text{ g}}{0.034 \text{ mol}} = 2.2 \times 10^2 \text{ g/mol}$$

Concept Practice

28. What laboratory measurements must you make to find the molar mass of a solute in a boiling point elevation experiment?

Practice Problem

29. The freezing point of water is lowered to –0.390°C when 3.90 g of a nonvolatile molecular solute is dissolved in 475 g of water. Calculate the molecular mass of the solute.

Thermal-Spray Coatings

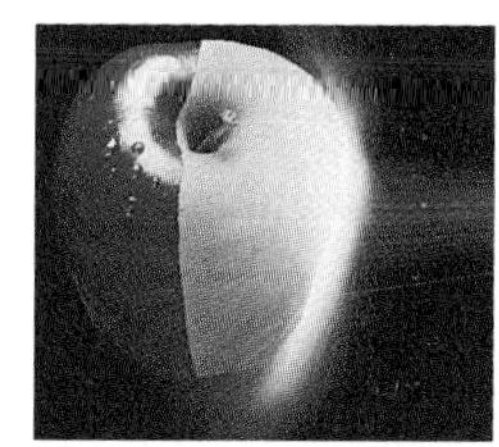

A Hot Topic

Thermal-spray coatings, formed when a material is melted at high temperature and sprayed onto a surface, have been around for decades. Yet only recently, with improvements in thermal-spray equipment, has the process become popular for use by industry. Thermal-spray coatings are now used in the manufacture of new parts and the repair of old worn-out parts.

The crucial piece of equipment used in creating thermal-spray coatings is the thermal-spray gun. The thermal-spray gun heats, melts, and propels the atomized particles of the coating material onto the prepared surface. The coating materials can be metals, alloys, ceramics, carbides, or special plastics. As the technology to apply thermal-spray coatings has improved, the new coating materials promise to outperform traditional polymer paints and coatings. Thermal-spray coatings have superior characteristics compared with traditional polymer paints and coatings; they are stronger, harder, more dense, thicker, and very corrosion and wear resistant.

Thermal-spray coatings have many applications and can provide unusual coatings not achievable in any other way. For

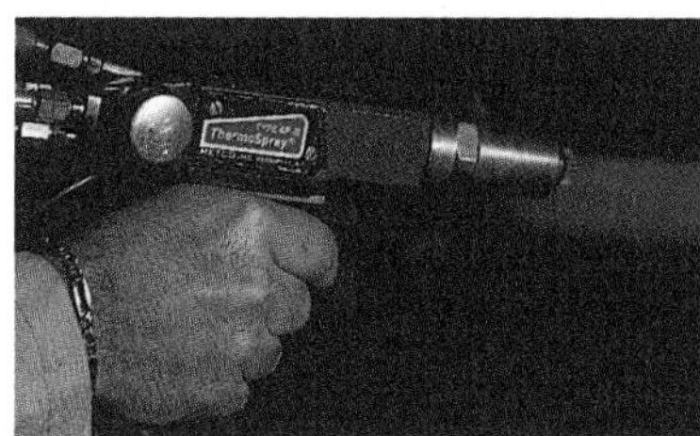

example, you could coat an apple with thermal-sprayed zinc without destroying the apple!

Other large potential markets include the use of aluminum and zinc as coatings on bridges and other outdoor structures. A coat of paint over galvanized steel may protect a bridge from corrosion for up to eight years. However, a 1.5-mm-thick coating of thermally sprayed zinc could protect the bridge up to 25 years or longer! Thermal-spray materials also show great promise for use in the manufacture of medical implants. For human tissue to adhere properly to the metallic medical implants used in bone and joint replacements, a coating must cover the implant. Thermal spray–applied hydroxyapatite forms a porous bioceramic that adheres well and promotes good tissue adhesion.

The application of thermal-spray technology to replace metal-plating operations also has the potential for great environmental benefits. Currently, many metal-plating operations are under regulatory pressure to reduce or eliminate disposal of toxic used metal-plating baths. Plating companies could substantially reduce costly toxic disposals by switching to thermal-spray coating technology.

Hip-joint replacement

Think About It

30. Analyze What are some advantages of replacing traditional metal plating with thermal-spray coatings?

31. Explain Thermal-spray coating a bridge superstructure would protect it for 25 years, yet this technology is not used widely for this purpose. Propose an explanation.

Chapter 17 Review

Properties of Solutions

Key Terms

boiling point elevation *17.7*
colligative property *17.7*
concentrated solution *17.4*
concentration *17.4*
dilute solution *17.4*
freezing point depression *17.7*
Henry's law *17.3*
immiscible *17.2*
miscible *17.2*
molal boiling point elevation constant (K_b) *17.9*
molal freezing point depression constant (K_f) *17.9*
molality (m) *17.8*
molarity (M) *17.4*
mole fraction *17.8*
saturated solution *17.2*
solubility *17.2*
supersaturated solution *17.3*
unsaturated *17.2*

Chapter Summary

Changes in temperature and pressure of a system affect the solubility of a solute. The extent to which a gas dissolves in a liquid is proportional to the pressure of the gas in accordance with Henry's law. The solubility of a gas decreases with increasing temperature. Polar liquids tend to be soluble (miscible) in water, whereas nonpolar liquids tend to be insoluble (immiscible). The solubility of a solid in water increases with increasing temperature, but there are exceptions. The rate at which a solute dissolves is influenced by factors including the solvent temperature and the solute particle size.

The relative amounts of solute and solvent in a solution are best described by using quantitative units. These units include molar concentration, percent composition, molal concentration, and mole fraction.

The effects of a nonvolatile solute on the properties of the solvent are called colligative properties. Colligative properties include freezing point, vapor pressure lowering, and boiling point elevation. In each case, the magnitude of the effect is directly proportional to the number of solute molecules or ions present and is independent of the type of particle. Each solvent has a molal boiling point elevation constant and molal freezing point depression constant. The colligative properties are useful for demonstrating dissociation of solutes in solution and in determining molecular masses.

Practice Questions and Problems

32. Explain why the dissolved component does not settle out of a solution. *17.1*

33. Define the terms solubility, saturated solution, and unsaturated solution. *17.2*

34. What mass of $AgNO_3$ can be dissolved in 250 g of water at 20°C? *17.2*

35. If a clear saturated solution of sodium nitrate is cooled, what change(s) might you observe? *17.2*

36. State Henry's law. *17.3*

37. What is the effect of pressure on the solubility of gases in liquids? *17.3*

38. The solubility of methane, the major component of natural gas, in water at 20°C and 100 kPa pressure is 0.026 g/L. If the temperature remains constant, what will the solubility of this gas be at the following pressures? *17.3*
a. 60 kPa **b.** 180 kPa

39. A label tells you a food contains 5 grams of fat. If you are on a fat-restricted diet, explain why this information alone is not sufficient in determining whether or not this food is a good dietary choice. *17.A*

40. Calculate the molarity of each of the following solutions. *17.4*
a. 1.0 mol of KCl in 750 mL of solution
b. 0.50 mol of $MgCl_2$ in 1.5 L of solution
c. 400 g of $CuSO_4$ in 4.00 L of solution
d. 0.060 mol of $NaHCO_3$ in 1500 mL of solution

41. Define the term *molarity.* *17.4*

42. Calculate the number of moles and the number of grams of solute in each solution. *17.4*
   a. 1.0 L of 0.50M NaCl
   b. 500 mL of 2.0M KNO_3
   c. 250 mL of 0.10M $CaCl_2$
   d. 2.0 L of 0.30M Na_2SO_4

43. You have the following stock solutions available: 2.0M NaCl, 4.0M KNO_3, and 0.50M $MgSO_4$. Calculate the volumes you must dilute to make the following solutions. *17.5*
   a. 500 mL of 0.50M NaCl
   b. 2.0 L of 0.20M $MgSO_4$
   c. 50 mL of 0.20M KNO_3

44. Calculate the number of grams of solute required to make the following: *17.6*
   a. 2.5 L of normal saline solution [0.90% NaCl (m/v)]
   b. 50 mL of 4.0% $MgCl_2$ (m/v)
   c. 250 mL of 0.10% $MgSO_4$ (m/v)

45. What is the concentration in percent (m/v) of the following solutions? *17.6*
   a. 20 g KCl in 600 mL of solution
   b. 32 g $NaNO_3$ in 2.0 L of solution
   c. 75 g K_2SO_4 in 1500 mL of solution

46. What is the boiling point of each solution? *17.9*
   a. 0.50 mol of glucose in 1000 g of H_2O
   b. 1.50 mol of NaCl in 1000 g of H_2O

47. How much NaCl would have to be dissolved in 1000 g of water to raise the boiling point 2.00°C? *17.9*

48. Describe how the ion-exchange process works. *17.B*

49. How many kilograms of water must be added to 9.0 g of oxalic acid, $H_2C_2O_4$, to prepare a 0.025 m solution? *17.8*

50. A solution contains 50.0 g of carbon tetrachloride (CCl_4) and 50.0 g of chloroform ($CHCl_3$). Calculate the mole fraction of each component in the solution. *17.8*

51. Determine the freezing points of these 0.20 m aqueous solutions. *17.9*
   a. K_2SO_4 **b.** $CsNO_3$ **c.** $Al(NO_3)_3$

52. Estimate the freezing point of a solution of 12.0 g of carbon tetrachloride dissolved in 750 g of benzene (which has a freezing point of 5.48°C). *17.9*

53. A solution containing 16.9 g of a nonvolatile molecular compound in 250 g of water has a freezing point of –0.744°C. What is the molecular mass of the substance? *17.10*

Mastery Questions and Problems

54. Construct a concept map using the chapter key terms with *solution concentration* as the central concept.

55. A solution is labeled 0.150 molal NaCl. What are the mole fractions of the solute and solvent in this solution?

56. You are given a clear water solution containing KNO_3. How would you determine experimentally whether the solution is unsaturated, saturated, or supersaturated?

57. A mixture of glycerol and water is used as antifreeze in automobile engines. The freezing point and specific gravity of the glycerol-water mixture vary with the percent by mass of glycerol in the mixture. On the graph below, point A represents 20% glycerol by mass, point B 40%, and point C 60%.
   a. What is the specific gravity of the antifreeze mixture that freezes at –25°C?
   b. What is the freezing point of a mixture that has a specific gravity of 1.06?
   c. Estimate the freezing point of a mixture that is 30% by mass glycerol.

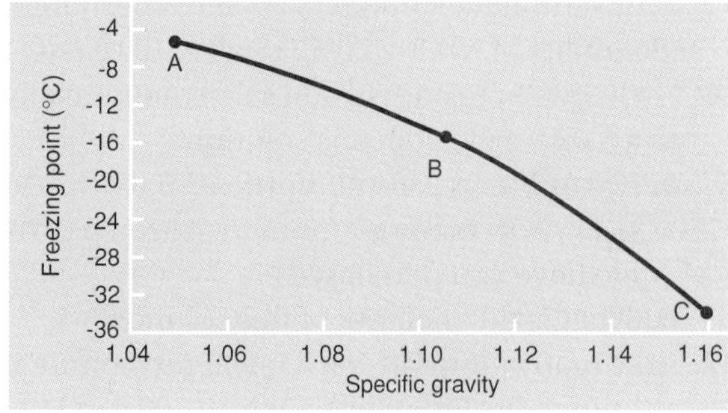

58. Calculate the freezing point and the boiling point of a solution that contains 15.0 g of urea, CH_4N_2O, in 250 g of water. Urea is a covalently bonded compound.

59. Calculate the mole fractions in a solution that is made of 25.0 g of ethyl alcohol, C_2H_5OH, and 40.0 g of water.

60. Estimate the freezing point of an aqueous solution of 20.0 g of glucose, $C_6H_{12}O_6$, dissolved in 500.0 g of water.

61. Plot a graph of solubility versus temperature for the three gases listed in Table 17.1.

62. The solubility of KCl in water is 34.0 g of KCl/100 g of H_2O at 20°C. A warm solution containing 50.0 g of KCl in 130 g of H_2O is cooled to 20°C.

    a. How many grams of KCl remain dissolved?

    b. How many grams came out of solution?

63. How many moles of ions are present when 0.10 mol of the following compounds is dissolved in water?

    a. K_2SO_4 **c.** $Al_2(SO_4)_3$

    b. $Fe(NO_3)_3$ **d.** $NiSO_4$

64. Complete the following table for aqueous solutions of glucose, $C_6H_{12}O_6$.

Mass Solute	Moles Solute	Volume of Solution	Molarity
12.5	____	219 mL	____
____	1.08	____	0.519
____	____	1.62 L	1.08

65. A solution contains 26.5 g of NaCl in 75.0 g of H_2O at 20°C. Determine whether the solution is unsaturated, saturated, or supersaturated. (Solubility of NaCl at 20°C = 36.0 g/100 g H_2O.)

66. Hydrogen peroxide is often sold commercially as a 3.0% (m/v) aqueous solution.

    a. If you buy a 250-mL bottle of 3.0% (m/v) H_2O_2, how many grams of hydrogen peroxide have you purchased?

    b. What is the molarity of this solution?

67. How many grams of $NaNO_3$ will precipitate if a saturated solution of $NaNO_3$ in 200 g of H_2O at 50°C is cooled to 20°C?

68. What is the molecular mass of a nondissociating compound if 5.76 g of the compound in 750 g of benzene gives a freezing point depression of 0.460°C?

69. The molarity of an aqueous solution of sugar, $C_{12}H_{22}O_{11}$, is 1.62 *m*. Calculate the mole fractions of sugar and water.

70. Calculate the freezing and boiling point changes for a solution containing 12.0 g of naphthalene, $C_{10}H_8$, in 50.0 g of benzene.

71. The solubility of sodium hydrogen carbonate, $NaHCO_3$, in water at 20°C is 9.6 g/100 g of H_2O. What is the mole fraction of $NaHCO_3$ in a saturated solution? What is the molality of the solution?

Critical Thinking Questions

72. Choose the term that best completes the second relationship.

    a. tree:trunk solution: ____
    (1) solubility (3) water
    (2) solvent (4) solute

    b. volume:liter concentration: ____
    (1) moles (3) solution
    (2) volume (4) molarity

    c. molarity:L of solution molality: ____
    (1) kg of solvent (3) concentration
    (2) L of solvent (4) moles of solute

73. Why is molarity measured in moles per liter of solution instead of grams per liter?

74. Why might calcium chloride spread on icy roads be more effective at melting ice than sodium chloride?

Cumulative Review

75. The solubility of hydrogen chloride gas in the polar solvent water is much greater than its solubility in the nonpolar solvent benzene. Why?

76. When soap is shaken with water, do you get a solution, a suspension, or a colloid? Explain.

77. Explain the following terms as they are applied to solutions.

    a. solute **e.** supersaturated

    b. solvent **f.** nonelectrolyte

    c. saturated **g.** weak electrolyte

    d. unsaturated **h.** strong electrolyte

78. Write electron dot structures for the following atoms.

a. I **b.** Sr **c.** Te **d.** Cs **e.** Sb **f.** Xe

79. Indicate by simple equations how the following substances ionize or dissociate in water.

a. NH_4Cl **b.** $Cu(NO_3)_2$ **c.** HNO_3
d. $HC_2H_3O_2$ **e.** Na_2SO_4 **f.** $HgCl_2$

80. What relationship exists between surface tension and intermolecular attractions in a liquid?

Challenge Questions and Problems

81. One way in which the solubility of a compound can be expressed is by moles of compound that will dissolve in 1 kg of water. Solubility depends on temperature. Plot a graph of the solubility of potassium nitrate, KNO_3, from the following data.

Temperature, °C	Solubility, mol/kg
0	1.61
20	2.80
40	5.78
60	11.20
80	16.76
100	24.50

From your graph estimate:

a. the solubility of KNO_3 at 76°C and at 33°C.
b. the temperature at which its solubility is 17.6 mol/kg of water.
c. the temperature at which the solubility is 4.24 mol/kg of water.

82. An excess of zinc added to 800 mL of a hydrochloric acid solution evolves 1.21 L of hydrogen gas measured over water at 21°C and 99.66 kPa. What is the molarity of the acid? The vapor pressure of water at 21°C is 2.48 kPa.

83. How many milliliters of 1.50*M* HNO_3 contain enough nitric acid to dissolve an old copper penny with a mass of 3.94 g?

$$3Cu + 8HNO_3 \longrightarrow 3Cu(NO_3)_2 + 2NO + 4H_2O$$

84. The table below lists the most abundant ions in seawater and their molal concentrations.

Ion	Molality
Chloride	0.568
Sodium	0.482
Magnesium	0.057
Sulfate	0.028
Calcium	0.011
Potassium	0.010
Bicarbonate	0.002

Calculate the mass, in grams, of each component contained in 5.00 L of seawater. The density of seawater is 1.024 g/mL.

Connections Questions

85. List some of the negative effects of fertilizer runoff.

86. What are some typical solutions that are given intravenously in a hospital?

87. List some of the accomplishments of Mary Swartz Rose.

Write About Chemistry

88. Imagine you are a geologist describing the chemistry of the formation of beautiful stalactites found in a cave. Write two paragraphs that would be understood by a typical fourth-grader.

89. In a paragraph, discuss why you think the molal boiling point elevation constants given in Table 17.2 vary over such a wide range.

Readings and References

Eagles, Juanita Archibald, Orrea Florence Pye, and Clara Mae Taylor. *Mary Swartz Rose, 1874–1941: Pioneer in Nutrition.* New York: Teachers College Press, 1979.

18 Reaction Rates and Equilibrium

Goals

- Describe in energy terms the conversion of starting materials to products.
- Apply Le Châtelier's principle in predicting the direction of change in an equilibrium.
- List examples of chemical and physical dynamic equilibria and calculate equilibrium constants.
- Define entropy and free energy and calculate standard entropy changes and free energy changes.
- Interpret experimental rate data in order to deduce the reaction rate laws.

When particles collide, they may or may not react, depending on the energy and orientation of the collision. Similarly in the game of pool, the balls may or may not collide to put one in a pocket. The most pool balls pocketed in 24 hours was 16,125.

Concept Overview

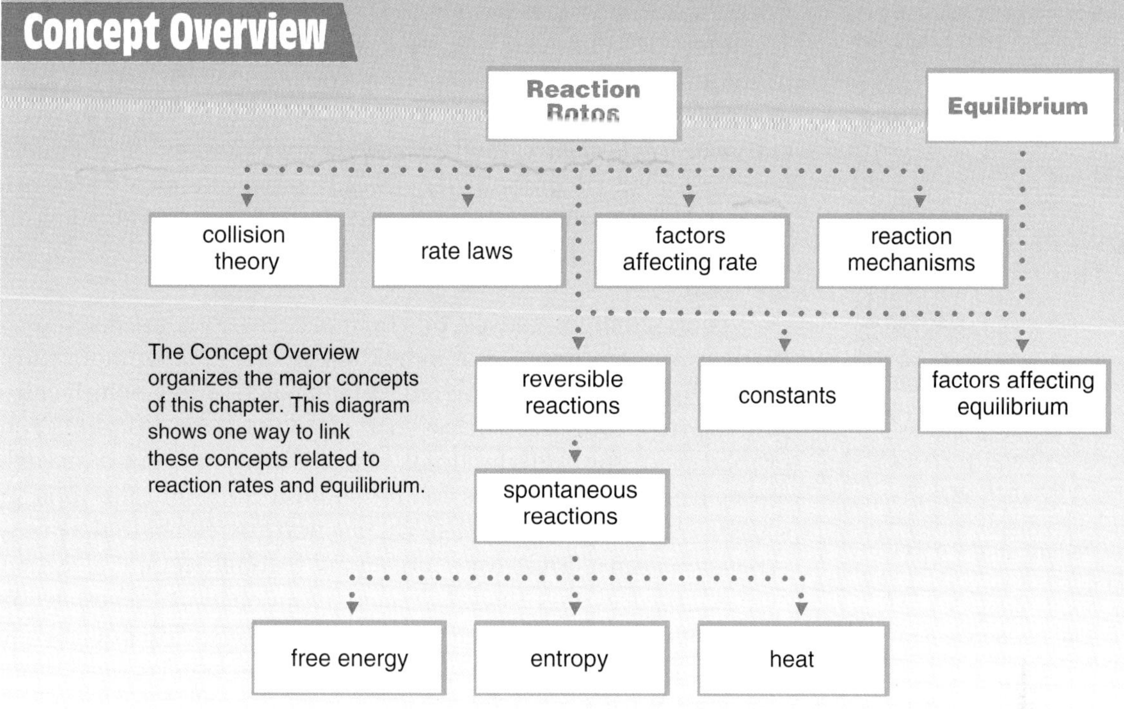

The Concept Overview organizes the major concepts of this chapter. This diagram shows one way to link these concepts related to reaction rates and equilibrium.

When you strike a match it seems to erupt into flame almost instantaneously. However, many other reactions occur much more slowly. Coal was produced from dead plants by a process involving heat and pressure that took millions of years! So the time needed to complete a chemical reaction can vary tremendously. In this chapter you will examine the factors that make chemical reactions proceed at different speeds.

When iron is exposed to damp air it turns to rust. However, you know the reverse is not true. An old rusty iron park bench cannot be made "new" again simply by bringing it in out of the damp weather. In this chapter you will also learn why some substances easily react to form new substances while others seem inert.

18.1 Reaction Rates and Collision Theory

Objective

Interpret and express the meaning of the rate of a chemical reaction.

The concept of speed is one with which you are probably already familiar. A fast sprinter may cover 100 meters in about 11.5 seconds. A slower sprinter may take 15.0 seconds to cover the same distance. On average, the fast sprinter's speed is 100 meters/11.5 seconds, or 8.70 m/s. The slow sprinter's speed is 100 meters/15.0 seconds, or 6.67 m/s. Both 8.70 m/s and 6.67 m/s express speeds or *rates* of

Figure 18.1 The rate tells you how much something changes in a specified amount of time. A male world-class sprinter might cover 100 meters in about 9.8 seconds.

$$\text{Rate} = \frac{100.0 \text{ meters}}{9.80 \text{ seconds}} = 10.2 \text{ m/s}$$

travel. **Rates** *measure changes that occur within intervals of time.* The intervals of time are usually seconds, minutes, or hours. Years or centuries may be convenient units for very slow changes. A snail may move at a rate of 1 m/hour, or a tree might grow at a rate of 30 cm/year. In chemistry, rates or speeds are expressed in chemical terms. Instead of units of length and time, chemical rates are expressed using chemical units and time. Thus a small sheet of metal containing 1 mole of iron might rust at a rate of 0.5 mole of iron/year.

Visible changes caused by chemical reactions are related to changes in the properties of individual atoms, ions, or molecules. For example, shiny silver-colored sodium reacts with greenish chlorine gas to produce colorless crystals of sodium chloride. The properties of the sodium atoms and chlorine molecules are different from the properties of the sodium and chloride ions in sodium chloride. Rates of chemical reaction are related to the properties of atoms, ions, and molecules through a model called *collision theory.* You can explain a lot about chemical reactions by means of a very simple form of collision theory. **Collision theory** *says that atoms, ions, and molecules can form a chemical bond when they collide, provided the particles have enough kinetic energy.* Particles lacking the necessary kinetic energy to react still collide, but simply bounce apart as shown in Figure 18.2. You can use two balls of soft modeling clay to illustrate the point of collision theory. If you throw the balls of clay together gently they bump, but they do not stick together. This corresponds to an absence of reaction between colliding particles. The same balls of clay thrown together with great force stick tightly together. This corresponds to the chemical combination of two particles. In order to combine chemically, the particles of the combining substances must make contact with each other and they must have enough kinetic energy for combination to occur.

Figure 18.2 If colliding particles have enough kinetic energy and collide at the right orientation, they will react to form a new product. If particles lack enough energy or collide at a poor orientation, they will bounce apart without reacting.

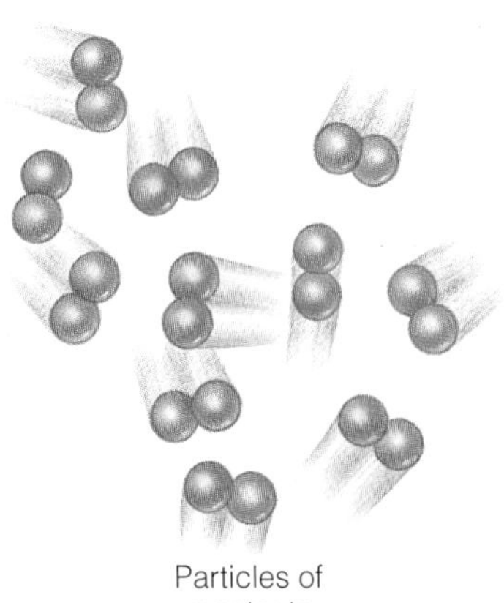

Particles of reactants

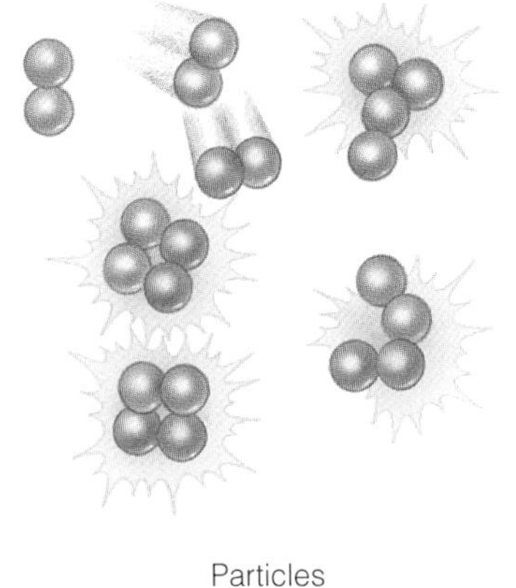

Particles colliding

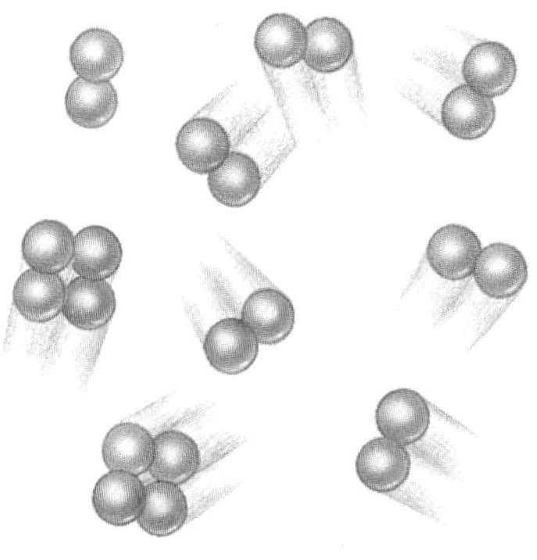

Particles of new products and unchanged reactants

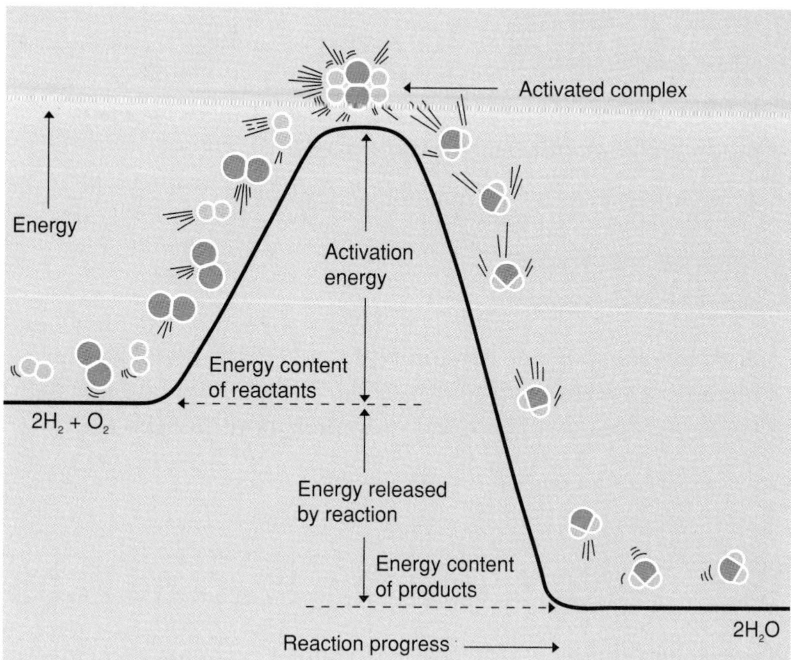

Figure 18.3 The activation energy barrier must be crossed before reactants are converted to products.

You can use modeling clay to illustrate another point about chemical reactions. If you shape the clay into a rope and vigorously shake one end, you will find that the clay rope eventually breaks. Similarly, the bonds holding molecules together can break apart. Substances decompose to simpler substances or reorganize themselves into new substances if they are supplied with enough energy. *The minimum energy colliding particles must have in order to react is the* **activation energy**. In a sense, activation energy is a barrier that the reactants must cross to be converted to products. During a reaction, particles which are neither reactants nor products momentarily form. *An* **activated complex** *is the arrangement of atoms at the peak of the activation energy barrier.* This group of atoms is on its way to becoming an ionic or molecular product. The lifetime of an activated complex is only about 10^{-13} seconds. The very unstable activated complex is as likely to form reactants as it is to form products. For this reason, *the activated complex is sometimes called the* **transition state**.

Collision theory explains why some spontaneous reactions are immeasurably slow at room temperature. The reaction of carbon and oxygen is spontaneous, but it has a high activation energy. At room temperature the collisions of oxygen and carbon molecules are not energetic enough to overcome the activation energy barrier and break the O—O and C—C bonds. These bonds must be broken to form the activated complex. Thus the reaction rate of carbon with oxygen at room temperature is essentially zero.

Concept Practice

1. Does every collision between reacting particles lead to products? What other factor is involved?

2. What is meant by the rate of reaction?

Practice Problem

3. A thin sheet of zinc containing 1.0 mol of the metal is completely converted in air to zinc oxide, ZnO, in 5.3 months. What is the average rate of conversion, in mol/month, of the zinc?

Objective

Explain how the rate of a chemical reaction is influenced by the temperature, concentration, particle size of reactants, and catalysts using collision theory.

18.2 Factors Affecting Reaction Rates

How fast can chemical reactions go? There is no one correct answer to this question. Each reaction proceeds at its own speed. Some reactions are naturally faster or slower than others under the same conditions. However, the rate of almost any reaction can be modified in several ways. Collision theory helps to explain why these rate changes occur.

Effect of Temperature Usually, raising the temperature speeds up a reaction. Lowering the temperature usually slows reactions down. At higher temperatures the motions of the reactant particles are more chaotic and more energetic than at lower temperatures. The main effect of increasing the temperature is to increase the number of particles that have enough kinetic energy to react when they collide. More colliding molecules are energetic enough to slip over the activation energy barrier to become products. The frequency of high-energy collisions between reactants also increases. Therefore products form faster.

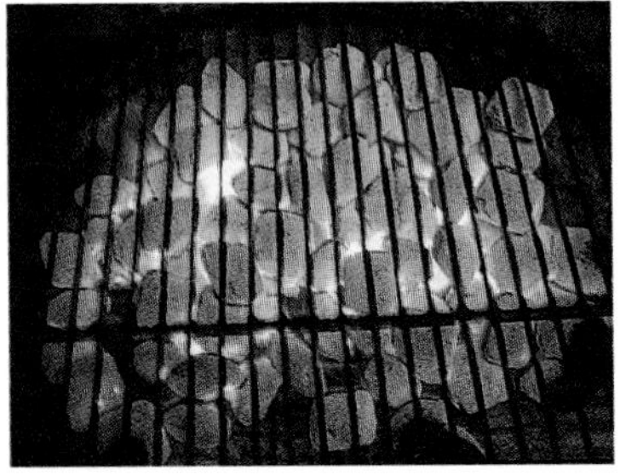

Figure 18.4 A large amount of energy must be added to initiate the reaction of charcoal with oxygen even though the reaction is exothermic. Once the reaction is going, it liberates enough energy to continue to overcome the activation energy barrier.

A familiar example of the effect of temperature on reaction rate is the burning of charcoal. Charcoal does not burn at a measurable rate at room temperature. Figure 18.4 shows, however, that if you supply the charcoal with enough energy in the form of heat, the result is dramatic. When a starter flame touches charcoal, the reactants (carbon and oxygen) collide with higher energy and greater frequency. Some of these collisions are at a high enough energy that the product (carbon dioxide) forms. The heat released by the reaction then supplies enough energy to get more carbon and oxygen over the activation energy barrier. When the starter flame is removed, the reaction continues. The charcoal burns as long as a supply of charcoal and oxygen is available.

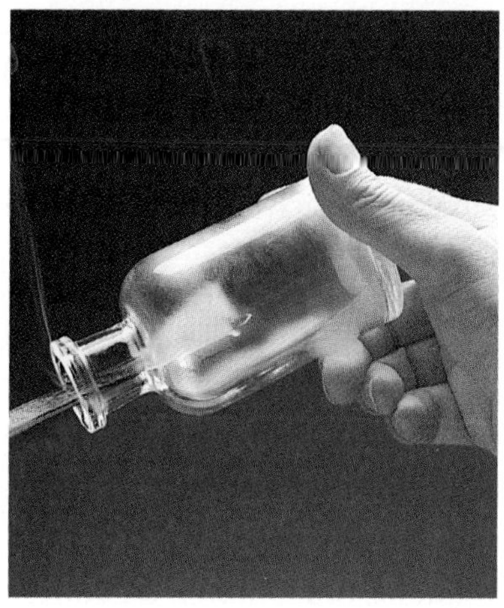

Figure 18.5 Why will a smoldering splint burst into flame if it is placed into a bottle of pure oxygen?

Effect of Concentration The number of reacting particles in a given volume affects the rate at which reactions occur. Cramming more particles into a fixed volume increases the collision frequency. Therefore increasing the concentration of reactants increases the reaction rate. The lighted splint in Figure 18.5 vividly illustrates the effect. A splint glows in air, which is 20% oxygen. However, if a glowing splint is plunged into pure oxygen it immediately bursts into flame because the increased concentration of oxygen greatly speeds up the combustion reaction. This is why smoking is forbidden in hospital areas where oxygen is being used.

Effect of Particle Size The total surface area of a solid or liquid reactant has an important effect on the reaction rate. The smaller the particle size, the larger the surface area for a given mass of particles. An increase in surface area increases the collision frequency and the reaction rate. As you probably know, a bundle of wood kindling burns faster than a single log of equal mass.

One way to increase the surface area of solid reactants is to dissolve them. Dissolving separates the particles. For example, a marble on the floor is more accessible than a marble in the middle of a box of marbles. Homogeneous mixtures of reactants usually

Safety

Finely divided metals such as zinc, aluminum, and magnesium powders are very flammable because of their large surface area. Handle with care.

Figure 18.6 In 1932, this explosion destroyed a Chicago grain elevator. The small size of the reactant particles (grain dust) and the mixture of the grain dust and air caused the reaction to be explosive.

Integrating Auto Shop

Auto Body Repair

Auto body repair technicians often repair rust-damaged automobiles. This damage often occurs where water is able to catalyze the reaction of oxygen with the iron to produce iron(III) oxide, or rust. Slight damage can be repaired by removing the rust and repainting, but extensive damage may require the replacement of body panels. Due to the extensive use of galvanized steel and non-corrosive plastics in new automobiles, body rust is much less common today than in the past.

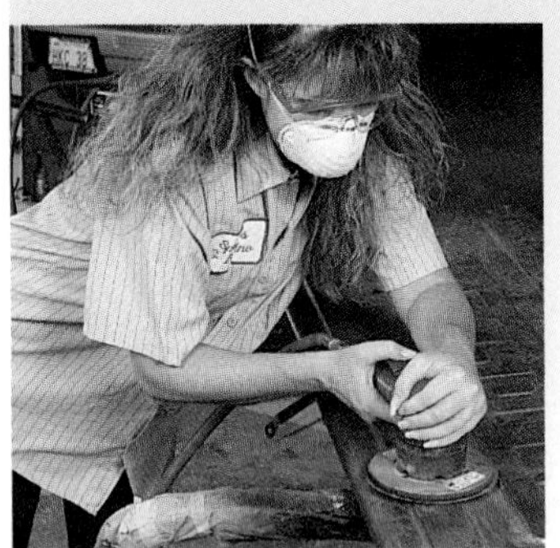

react more rapidly than heterogeneous mixtures. In many reactions, however, it is impossible to obtain homogeneous mixtures, or solutions, of the reactants. *Reactions carried out with heterogeneous mixtures of reactants are called* **heterogeneous reactions**. Since smaller particles are more reactive, if you have to conduct heterogeneous reactions it is usually best to grind solids into a fine powder first. Very small particles like dust can be dangerous for this reason. As coal miners know, coal dust suspended in the air is very reactive and presents an explosion hazard. By contrast, the large chunks of coal on the mine floor present very little hazard.

Effect of Catalysts An increase in temperature is not always the best way to increase the rate of a reaction. A catalyst, if one can be found, is often better. *A* **catalyst** *is a substance that increases the rate of a reaction without being used up itself in the reaction.* Catalysts permit reactions to proceed at a lower energy than is normally required. Figure 18.7 shows how catalysts lower the activation energy barrier. With a lower activation energy barrier, more reactants can form products within a given time. For instance, the reaction of hydrogen and oxygen at room temperature is negligible. With a trace of catalyst, however, the reaction is rapid. Finely divided platinum catalyzes this reaction.

$$2H_2(g) + O_2(g) \xrightarrow{Pt} 2H_2O(l)$$

Remember that catalysts are not used up in a reaction. Thus they do not appear as reactants or products in the equation for the reaction.

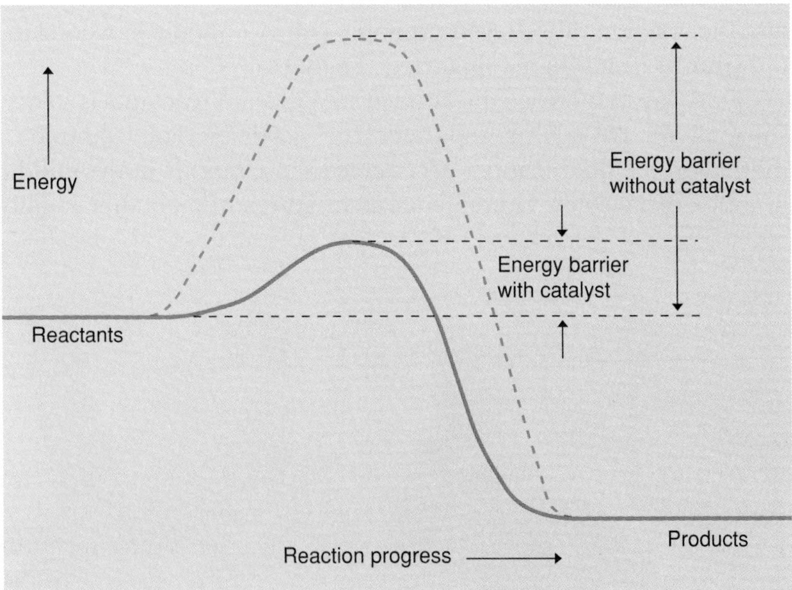

Figure 18.7 A catalyst increases the rate of a reaction by lowering the activation energy barrier.

Your body temperature is approximately 37°C and cannot be raised or lowered significantly without danger to your life. Yet without catalysts, few reactions in the body would proceed fast enough at this temperature. Catalysts called *enzymes* increase the rates of biological reactions. You could not live without enzymes to catalyze these reactions. When you eat a meal containing protein, enzymes in your small intestine break down the protein molecules in a few hours. Without enzymes, the digestion of protein at 37°C would take about fifty years!

An **inhibitor** *is a substance that interferes with the action of a catalyst.* Some inhibitor molecules interfere with the catalytic reaction by reacting with ("poisoning") the catalyst itself. Thus the inhibitor reduces the amount of catalyst available. Reactions are slowed or even stopped when the catalyst is poisoned.

Figure 18.8 Enzymes, like lysozyme shown here, act as catalysts for many important reactions within the body.

Concept Practice

4. Refrigerated food stays fresh for long periods. The same food stored at room temperature quickly spoils. Why?

5. How does each of the following factors affect the rate of a chemical reaction?
a. temperature
b. concentration
c. particle size
d. a catalyst

18.3 Reversible Reactions

Objective

Define chemical equilibrium in terms of a reversible reaction.

In the previous discussions of chemical reactions you may have inferred that chemical reactions go completely to products as written. Some reactions, however, are *reversible.* One example of a reversible reaction is the reaction of sulfur dioxide with oxygen to give sulfur trioxide. The double arrows show that the reaction is reversible.

$$\underset{\text{Sulfur dioxide}}{2SO_2(g)} + \underset{\text{Oxygen}}{O_2(g)} \rightleftharpoons \underset{\text{Sulfur trioxide}}{2SO_3(g)}$$

You see that this reaction is really two reactions. In the first reaction, written in the usual way from left to right, sulfur trioxide is produced from sulfur dioxide and oxygen. In the second reaction, written from right to left, sulfur trioxide decomposes into sulfur

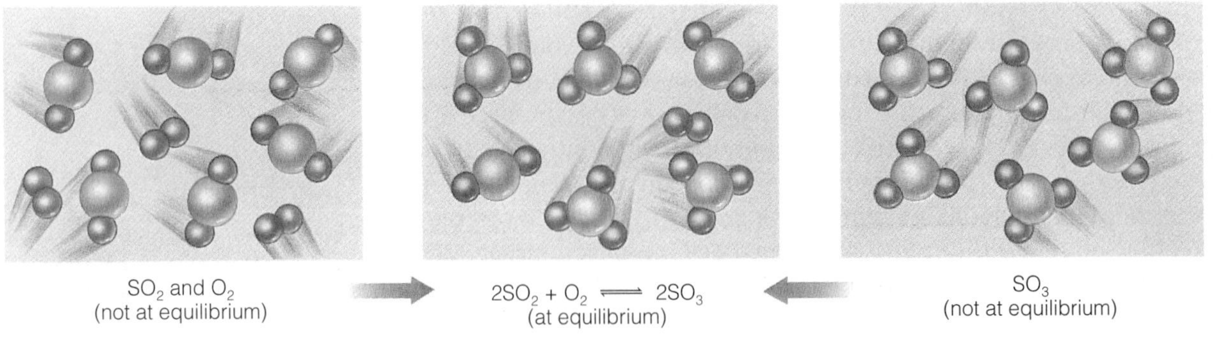

Figure 18.9 Molecules of SO_2 and O_2 react to give SO_3; molecules of SO_3 decompose to give SO_2 and O_2. At equilibrium, all three types of molecules are present in the mixture.

dioxide and oxygen. *In* **reversible reactions** *the reactions in both directions occur simultaneously.* The reaction written in the usual way, from left to right, is called the *forward reaction.* The reaction written from right to left is called the *reverse reaction.*

Consider what happens when sulfur dioxide and oxygen gases are mixed in a sealed chamber. Sulfur trioxide, the product of the forward reaction, begins to form. The rate of the reverse process, formation of sulfur dioxide and oxygen, is zero at first. At this point there is no sulfur trioxide to go back to sulfur dioxide and oxygen. Sulfur trioxide eventually forms, however. As the sulfur trioxide concentration builds up, a small amount slowly reverts to sulfur dioxide and oxygen by the reverse reaction. As the concentration of sulfur trioxide becomes higher and higher, the reverse reaction speeds up. The forward reaction is simultaneously slowing down because sulfur dioxide and oxygen are being used up. As you can see in Figure 18.10, eventually the sulfur trioxide is decomposing into sulfur dioxide and oxygen as fast as sulfur dioxide and oxygen are forming sulfur trioxide. *The reaction has reached* **chemical equilibrium** *when the forward and reverse reactions are taking place at the same rate.* At chemical equilibrium there is no net change in the actual amounts of the components of the system. Chemical equilibrium is similar to the previously described dynamic equilibrium between a saturated solution and a solute.

Roots of Words

aequilibrium: (Latin) in balance
equilibrium a state of balance between opposing forces

A chemical reaction is in equilibrium when the forward and reverse reactions are taking place at the same rate.

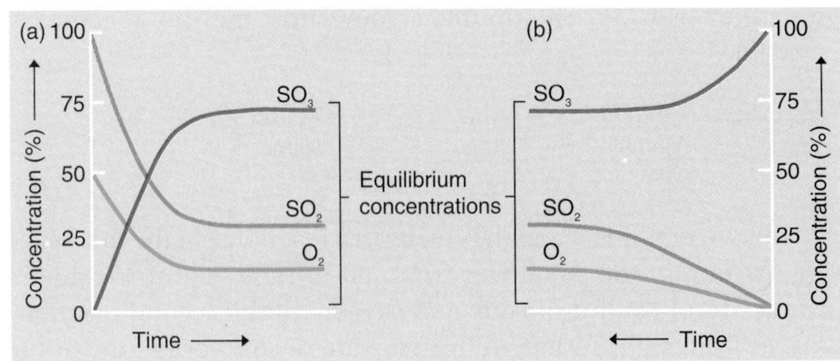

Figure 18.10 These graphs show the variation with time of the concentrations of O_2, SO_2, and SO_3. **(a)** Initially twice as much SO_2 and O_2 is present. At equilibrium, a mixture of all three gases is obtained. **(b)** Initially only SO_3 is present. At equilibrium the amounts of O_2, SO_2, and SO_3 are the same as in **(a)**.

The fact that the rates of forward and reverse reactions are the same in a chemical equilibrium does not mean that the concentrations of the components on both sides of the chemical equation are the same.

In fact the concentrations of the components can be dramatically different. *The* **equilibrium position** *of a reaction is given by the relative concentrations of the components of the system at equilibrium.* The equilibrium position indicates whether the components on the left or right side of a reversible reaction are at higher concentration. If A reacts to give B and the equilibrium mixture contains 1% of A and 99% of B, then the formation of B is *favored.*

$$\underset{1\%}{A} \rightleftharpoons \underset{99\%}{B}$$

If at equilibrium the mixture contains 99% of A and 1% of B, then the formation of A is favored.

$$\underset{99\%}{A} \rightleftharpoons \underset{1\%}{B}$$

The longer arrow indicates the favored direction of the reaction. In principle, all reactions are reversible under the specified conditions. In practice, one set of components is often so favored at equilibrium that the other set cannot be detected. When you start a reaction with one set of components (reactants) that are completely converted to new substances (products), you can say that the reaction has gone to completion or is irreversible. When you mix chemicals expecting to get a reaction, but no products can be detected, you can say there is no reaction. Reversible reactions occupy a middle ground between the theoretical extremes of irreversibility and no reaction.

Catalysts speed up the forward and backward reactions equally. This is because the reverse reaction is *exactly* the opposite of the forward reaction. The energy needed for the reaction is reduced by the same amount for both the forward and reverse directions. Therefore, catalysts do not affect the amounts of reactants and products present at equilibrium. They simply decrease the time it takes for equilibrium to be established.

Concept Practice

6. What is the significance of double arrows in an equation?

7. How do the amounts of reactants and products change once a reaction has achieved chemical equilibrium?

18.A Environmental Awareness

Photochemical Smog

Figure 18.11 Photochemical smog builds up when still air hangs over a city or other pollution source. Persistent smog can pose a health danger.

In large cities such as Los Angeles, you may wake up to disturbing news: the air you will breathe today is dangerous to your health. The brown haze over your city, called photochemical smog, is an example of one of several serious global air pollution problems.

Photochemical smog is mainly produced by the action of sunlight on the chemical compounds in automobile exhaust. Photochemical reactions are initiated when light energy is absorbed by light-sensitive substances. Some photochemical reactions, such as photosynthesis, create beneficial products.

The major pollutants in automobile exhaust are nitrogen monoxide (NO), carbon monoxide (CO), and unburned hydrocarbons from the incomplete combustion of gasoline. Nitrogen monoxide is produced by the direct combination of oxygen and nitrogen in the cylinders of internal combustion engines.

$$N_2(g) + O_2(g) \longrightarrow 2NO(g)$$

The process that forms smog begins when the nitrogen monoxide is oxidized to nitrogen dioxide in the atmosphere.

$$2NO(g) + O_2(g) \longrightarrow 2NO_2(g)$$

Sunlight then causes the photochemical decomposition of nitrogen dioxide into nitrogen monoxide and atomic oxygen.

$$NO_2(g) + \text{light} \longrightarrow NO(g) + O(g)$$

Atomic oxygen is very reactive and initiates further reactions. One of these reactions leads to the production of ozone.

$$O(g) + O_2(g) \longrightarrow O_3(g)$$

Ozone, nitrogen oxides, and unburned hydrocarbons can then combine in a complex series of photochemical reactions. Among the products of these reactions are peroxyacyl nitrates, or PANs. Nitrogen dioxide, ozone, PANs, and carbon monoxide are all extremely toxic. The production of pollutants that contribute to smog formation must be reduced at the source. The most prevalent source is automobile emissions.

Think About It

8. Identify What form of energy drives a photochemical reaction?

9. Suppose How could you change your lifestyle to reduce the possibility of smog formation in your community?

18.4 Factors Affecting Equilibrium

Objective

Predict changes in the equilibrium position due to changes in concentration, temperature, and pressure using Le Châtelier's principle.

A delicate balance exists in a system at equilibrium. Changes of almost any kind disrupt this balance. Systems whose equilibrium has been disturbed make the minimum adjustments needed to restore equilibrium. However, when equilibrium has been restored, the position of equilibrium is different from its original position. That is, the amount of products may have increased and the amount of reactants may have decreased. This difference is called the *shift in the position of equilibrium.* The examples that follow are reversible reactions. Therefore the *product* of the forward reaction is the *reactant* of the reverse reaction and vice versa. For simplicity and clarity, the components on the left side of the reaction arrow are considered reactants and the components on the right side of the reaction arrow are considered products. If you have trouble deciding how the equilibrium shifts, note the colored arrow used to indicate additions to or removals from the system. The arrow always points in the direction that is favored by the shift in the position of equilibrium. Notice that in each case the equilibrium shift compensates for the disturbance that caused it.

Changes in Concentration Changing the amount of any reactant or product in a system at equilibrium disturbs the equilibrium. The system adjusts to minimize the effects of the change. Carbonic acid (H_2CO_3) in aqueous solution decomposes to form carbon dioxide and water. At equilibrium the amount of carbonic acid is less than 1%.

$\longleftarrow$ add CO_2
Direction of shift

$$H_2CO_3(aq) \rightleftharpoons CO_2(aq) + H_2O(l)$$

< 1% | Direction of shift | >99%

$\longrightarrow$ remove CO_2

If more carbon dioxide is added, the equilibrium is disturbed. Say that at the instant of the addition enough carbon dioxide is added to shift the ratio of carbon dioxide to carbonic acid (CO_2/H_2CO_3) from 99:1 to 99.5:0.5. This change in the ratio may look small, but the amount of carbon dioxide has doubled from the original 99:1 ratio to 199:1 (99.5/0.5 = 199:1). As soon as carbon dioxide is added, however, it reacts with water to form more carbonic acid. The ratio shifts back toward the original 99:1. In other words: *Adding a product always pushes a reversible reaction in the direction of reactants.* If carbon dioxide is removed, the CO_2/H_2CO_3 ratio momentarily decreases to less than 99:1. Then carbonic acid decomposes as the system readjusts itself toward a CO_2/H_2CO_3 ratio of 99:1. *Removing a product always pulls a reversible reaction in the direction of products.*

Figure 18.12 The rapid exhalation of CO_2 after exercise helps reestablish the body's H_2CO_3/CO_2 equilibrium. This keeps the pH of the blood within a safe range.

Removal of products is a trick often used to increase the yield of a desired product. As products are removed from a reaction mixture, the system continually changes to restore equilibrium with the products. Because the products are being removed as fast as they are formed, however, the reaction never builds up enough of them to reestablish an equilibrium. The system continues readjusting, and the reactants continue to react to give products until they are completely used up. Farmers use a similar technique to increase the yield of eggs laid by their hens. Hens lay eggs and then proceed to hatch them. When the eggs are removed after they are laid (removing the product), the hen will lay more eggs (increasing the yield).

Your body uses the removal of products to keep carbonic acid at low, safe levels in the blood. Blood contains dissolved carbonic acid in equilibrium with carbon dioxide and water. When you exhale carbon dioxide, the equilibrium shifts toward carbon dioxide and water. This reduces the amount of carbonic acid, keeping the pH of the blood within a safe range. The same principle applies to adding or removing reactants. *When a reactant is added to a system at equilibrium, the reaction shifts in the direction of the formation of products. When a reactant is removed, the reaction shifts in the direction of formation of reactants.*

Changes in Temperature Increasing the temperature causes the equilibrium position of a reaction to shift in the direction that absorbs heat. For example, the production of SO_3 is an exothermic reaction.

$$\overset{\longleftarrow \text{ add heat}}{\text{Direction of shift}}$$

$$2SO_2(g) + O_2(g)) \rightleftharpoons 2SO_3(g) + \text{heat}$$

$$\text{Direction of shift}$$
$$\longrightarrow \text{ remove heat (cool)}$$

Heat can be considered to be a product, just like SO_3. Heating the reaction mixture at equilibrium pushes the equilibrium position to the left. This favors the reactants. As a result, the product yield decreases. Cooling (removing heat) pulls the equilibrium to the right, and the product yield increases.

Changes in Pressure A change in the pressure on a system affects only an equilibrium with an unequal number of moles of *gaseous* reactants and products. For example, an equilibrium is established between ammonia gas and the gaseous elements from which it is formed.

Imagine that the gases are at equilibrium in a cylinder with a piston attached to a plunger, similar to a bicycle pump with the hose sealed. A catalyst has also been included to speed up the reaction. Now increase the pressure by pushing the plunger down. The pressure on the gases momentarily increases.

$$\underset{\underset{\longleftarrow \text{ reduce pressure}}{\text{Direction of shift}}}{N_2(g) + 3H_2(g) \xrightleftharpoons[\hspace{3cm}]{\overset{\text{increase pressure} \longrightarrow}{\text{Direction of shift}}} 2NH_3(g)}$$

This is because the same number of molecules are contained in less than the original volume. The system can relieve some of the pressure increase by reducing the number of gas molecules. Therefore the position of equilibrium shifts to make more ammonia. For every two molecules of ammonia made, four molecules of the reactants are used up (three molecules of hydrogen and one of nitrogen). There are now fewer molecules in the system. The pressure decreases, although it will not decrease to the original pressure. As seen in Figure 18.13, increasing the pressure on the

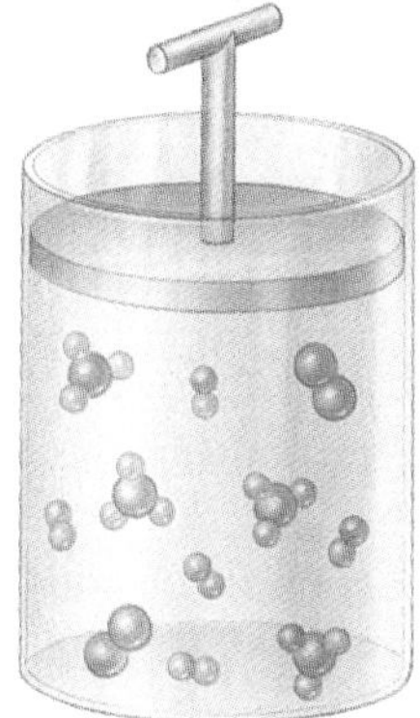

(a) Initial equilibrium condition (11 gas particles)

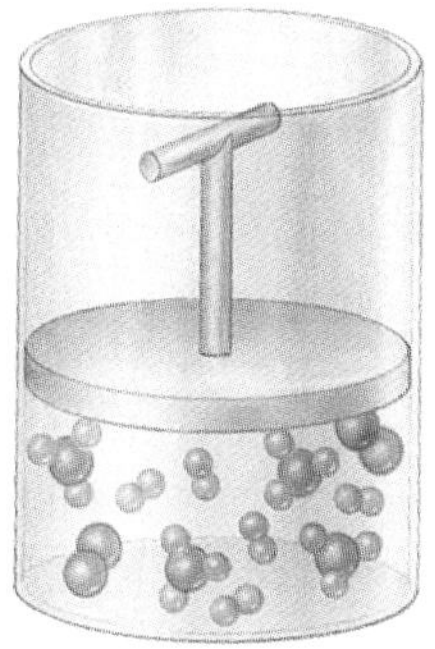

(b) Pressure increased, equilibrium disturbed

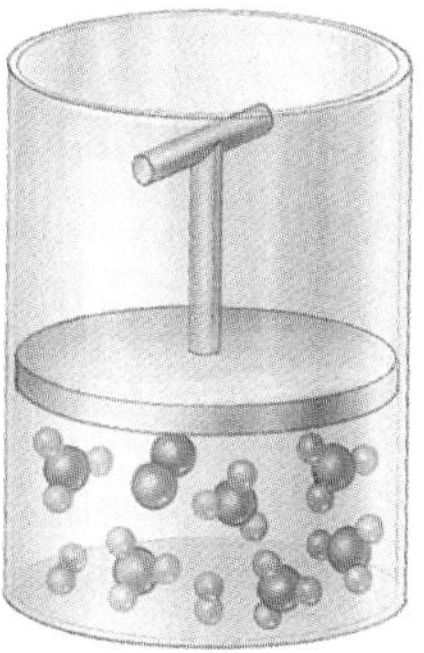

(c) New equilibrium condition at increased pressure (9 gas particles)

Figure 18.13 Effect of pressure on an equilibrium mixture of nitrogen, hydrogen, and ammonia. **(a)** Equilibrium. **(b)** Equilibrium is disturbed. **(c)** New equilibrium condition. More hydrogen and nitrogen have reacted and formed ammonia, reducing the total number of particles and thus the pressure in the cylinder.

Biographical Note

Henri-Louis Le Châtelier
(1850-1936)

Le Châtelier, who today is best known for the principle of equilibrium, was a highly practical industrial chemist. After graduation from the School of Mines in Paris, France, he worked for two years as a mining engineer before returning to the school as a professor of chemistry. He was particularly interested in problems related to metallurgy. He wanted to find ways to promote various reactions useful in industrial processes and to increase yields. This helped lead him to the discovery of the principle that bears his name.

system resulted in a shift in the position of equilibrium that favors the formation of product.

The equilibrium position for this reaction can be made to favor the reactants. Imagine pulling the plunger of your pressure device back up, so that the volume containing the gases increases. Now you have decreased the pressure on the system. To restore the higher starting pressure, the system needs more gas molecules. These are produced by the decomposition of some of the ammonia. Decomposition of two molecules of ammonia produces a total of four molecules of reactants (three molecules of hydrogen and one molecule of nitrogen). Pressure at the new equilibrium is higher than when the pressure was decreased, although it is not as high as it was at the starting equilibrium. Lowering the pressure on the system resulted in a shift of equilibrium to favor the reactants.

The French chemist Henri Le Châtelier (1850–1936) studied the changes in a system that result from changing the conditions. He proposed **Le Châtelier's principle**: *If a stress is applied to a system in a dynamic equilibrium, the system changes to relieve the stress.* Stresses that upset the equilibrium of a chemical system include changes in concentration of reactants and products, changes in temperature, and changes in pressure.

Example 1 Applying Le Châtelier's Principle

What effect do the following changes have on the position of equilibrium for this reversible reaction? How must the reaction shift to relieve the "stress" caused by the change?

$$PCl_5(g) + \text{heat} \rightleftharpoons PCl_3(g) + Cl_2(g)$$

a. addition of Cl_2

b. increase in pressure

c. removal of heat

d. removal of PCl_3 as it is formed

Solution

a. The addition of Cl_2 shifts the equilibrium to the left, ($\longleftarrow$), forming more PCl_5.

b. There are 2 mol of gaseous products and 1 mol of gaseous reactant. The increase in pressure is relieved if the equilibrium shifts to the left ($\longleftarrow$). A decrease in the number of moles of gaseous substances gives a decrease in pressure.

c. Removal of heat causes a shift to the left ($\longleftarrow$) because the reverse reaction produces heat.

d. Removal of PCl_3 causes a shift to the right ($\longrightarrow$) to produce more PCl_3.

Concept Practice

10. Can a pressure change be used to shift the position of equilibrium in every reversible reaction? Explain your answer.

11. How is the equilibrium position of this reaction affected by the following changes?

$$C(s) + H_2O(g) + \text{heat} \rightleftharpoons CO(g) + H_2(g)$$

a. lowering the temperature
b. increasing the pressure
c. removing H_2 from the equilibrium mixture
d. adding H_2O to the equilibrium mixture
e. addition of a catalyst
f. raising the temperature and decreasing the pressure

18.5 Free Energy

Objective

Define free energy.

In many chemical and physical processes, energy is released that can be used to cause other chemical or physical changes. That is, some of the energy liberated in the reaction can be harnessed to do work, such as driving the pistons of an internal combustion engine. **Free energy** *is energy that is available to do work.* Just because the free energy is available for work does not mean that it can be used efficiently. The internal combustion engine in a car is only about 30% efficient. Only about 30% of the free energy released by burning gasoline is used to propel the car. The remaining 70% is lost to friction and as waste heat. Part of today's efforts to conserve energy involves increasing the efficiency of engines and other mechanical devices. There are limits to these efficiency increases, however. No process can be made completely efficient. Living things are some of the most efficient users of free energy. However, even life processes are seldom more than 70% efficient. Your body temperature is maintained at 37°C by the available free energy that is wasted as heat.

Concept Practice

12. Where does "lost" free energy typically end up?

13. Does free energy that is lost as waste heat ever serve a useful function? Explain.

Objective

Contrast spontaneous and nonspontaneous reactions.

18.6 Spontaneous Reactions

Since you know how to write a balanced equation, you can "create" a reaction equation involving many different ions, atoms, and molecules. You can place substances on the left side of the reaction arrow as reactants. You can place other substances on the right side of the arrow as products. Balance both sides, and your equation is finished. It may be, however, that your equation does not represent what will really happen. For example, you can write the reverse of the combustion reaction of carbon: the decomposition of carbon dioxide to carbon and oxygen.

$$CO_2(g) \longrightarrow C(s) + O_2(g)$$

The substances on both sides of the reaction arrow are real. The equation certainly is balanced. The problem is that your experience tells you that the reaction that the equation represents is nonsense. Carbon and oxygen make carbon dioxide upon combustion, not the reverse. So the real world of balanced chemical equations is divided into two groups. One group contains equations that represent reactions that actually give products; the other contains equations that represent reactions that do not work, or at best work very poorly. Chemistry has names for these groups of reactions.

The term *spontaneous* is used in everyday life to mean something that happens naturally. The meaning is similar in chemistry. **Spontaneous reactions** *naturally favor the formation of products at the specified conditions.* In other words, spontaneous reactions are reactions that actually give substantial amounts of products at equilibrium. *All spontaneous reactions release free energy and are said to be* **exergonic**.

Figure 18.14 Fireworks displays are the result of exergonic reactions. A large quantity of free energy is released.

Nonspontaneous reactions *do not favor the formation of products at the specified conditions.* Nonspontaneous reactions do not give substantial amounts of products at equilibrium. What is meant by substantial amounts of products? Generally, you may regard conversion of more than half of the reactants to products as substantial. Consider again the reversible decomposition of carbonic acid in water, as an example.

$$\underset{<1\%}{H_2CO_3(aq)} \rightleftharpoons \underset{>99\%}{CO_2(g) + H_2O(l)}$$

Carbonic acid is the reactant of the forward reaction. If you could start with pure carbonic acid in water and let the system come to equilibrium, more than 99% of the reactant would be converted to the products carbon dioxide and water. These products are highly favored at equilibrium. There is a natural tendency for carbonic acid to decompose to carbon dioxide and water. Thus the forward reaction is spontaneous and ought to release free energy. Carbon dioxide and water are the reactants and carbonic acid is the product in the reverse reaction. If you permit a solution of carbon dioxide in water to come to equilibrium, less than 1% of the reactants combine to form carbonic acid. There is little natural tendency for the reactants to go to products. This reverse reaction is nonspontaneous. In reversible reactions, one of the reactions is always spontaneous and the other is always nonspontaneous. That is, without intervention, one reaction is favored over the other.

Another example, shown in Figure 18.15, is the spontaneous reaction of cadmium nitrate with sodium sulfide in aqueous solutions to produce cadmium sulfide and sodium nitrate. Cadmium sulfide is highly favored in this equilibrium. The reverse reaction, the production of cadmium nitrate and sodium sulfide from cadmium sulfide, is nonspontaneous.

$$Cd(NO_3)_2(aq) + Na_2S(aq) \rightleftharpoons CdS(s) + 2NaNO_3(aq)$$

Do not make the mistake of thinking that the terms spontaneous and nonspontaneous refer to how fast reactants go to products. Some spontaneous reactions go so slowly that they appear to be nonspontaneous. For example, the reaction of sugar and oxygen produces carbon dioxide and water. A small sugar crystal sealed in a can of air on the kitchen table does nothing, and you might assume that the equilibrium between sugar, oxygen, carbon dioxide, and water greatly favors the sugar and oxygen. At room temperature this reaction is so slow, however, that it requires thousands of years to reach equilibrium. Only when you supply energy in the form of heat is the reaction fast. Then you observe that at equilibrium the formation of carbon dioxide and water is highly favored. The combustion of the sugar goes to completion.

Figure 18.15 A yellow precipitate of cadmium sulfide, CdS, forms spontaneously when clear aqueous solutions of sodium sulfide, Na_2S, and cadmium nitrate, $Cd(NO_3)_2$, are mixed.

Figure 18.16 Nonspontaneous reactions can occur when they are coupled with spontaneous reactions.

A reaction that is nonspontaneous under one set of conditions may become spontaneous under other conditions. Changing the temperature or pressure may change whether or not a reaction is spontaneous. A nonspontaneous reaction can sometimes be linked or coupled to a spontaneous reaction. The release of free energy in the spontaneous reaction can then be used to make an ordinarily nonspontaneous reaction into a spontaneous reaction.

Look at Figure 18.16. Coupled reactions occur frequently in living systems.The entropy of the products of photosynthesis (complex sugars such as $C_6H_{12}O_6$) is less than that of the reactants (CO_2 and H_2O). Light energy drives this process. Obviously, your body's energy supply does not come from energy produced by gasoline vapor exploding in cylinders, as in an automobile engine. Nevertheless, your body cells use a number of strategies to use the food you eat to produce free energy. The chemical free energy is used in coupled reactions to drive otherwise nonspontaneous reactions. Many of these reactions are vital to your growth, health, and movement.

Concept Practice

14. What is a spontaneous reaction? Give an example (not given in the text) of a spontaneous reaction.

15. What can you do to change a reaction from nonspontaneous to spontaneous?

Objective

Show how changes in entropy relate to a change of state, a change in temperature, and a change in the number of product particles compared with reactant particles.

18.7 Entropy

You may recall that heat (enthalpy) changes accompany most chemical and physical processes. For example, the combustion of carbon is exothermic. The heat released is 393.5 kJ for each mole of carbon (graphite) burned.

$$C(s, \text{graphite}) + O_2(g) \longrightarrow CO_2(g) + 393.5 \text{ kJ/mol}$$

You might expect that only *exothermic* reactions would be spontaneous. It seems reasonable to assume that any substance that loses heat upon its formation must be of lower energy than the substance from which it is formed. This reasonable assumption sometimes fails. The melting of ice, a physical process, is *endothermic* but spontaneous. One mole of ice at 25°C *absorbs* 6.0 kJ of heat from its surroundings as it melts from a solid to a liquid.

$$H_2O(s) + 6.0 \text{ kJ/mol} \longrightarrow H_2O(l)$$

Ice melts spontaneously at 25°C even though heat is absorbed. The heat change (enthalpy change) is obviously not the only factor in determining whether a reaction will be spontaneous. Another factor, called *entropy*, is also involved.

You are familiar with everyday ideas about order and disorder. A handful of marbles is ordered in the sense that all the marbles are collected in one place. It is highly improbable that, when permitted to fall, the marbles will end up in the same neat arrangement. Instead, the marbles will scatter on the ground. The marbles will become disordered. *The disorder of a system is measured as its* **entropy**. Scattered marbles have a higher entropy than gathered marbles.

The idea that physical and chemical systems attain the lowest possible energy has a companion law. *The* **law of disorder** *states that things move in the direction of maximum disorder or randomness (chaos).* You know about the natural tendency toward disorder. Your bedroom may be neat and clean at the beginning of the week. Unless you clean it regularly, it probably looks messy by the end of the week. The law of disorder also operates at the level of atoms and molecules. On an atomic and molecular scale, the following concepts can be applied.

1. For a given substance, the entropy of the gas is greater than the entropy of the liquid or the solid. Similarly, the entropy of a liquid is usually greater than that of a solid.

2. Entropy often increases in reactions in which solid reactants give liquid or gaseous products. It also increases when liquid reactants give gaseous products.

Roots of Words

tropos: (Greek) direction
en-: (Greek) in
entropy a measure of the disorder of a system

Systems tend to change from a state of order (low entropy) to a state of maximum disorder (high entropy).

Figure 18.17 How does the entropy of your room vary over a week?

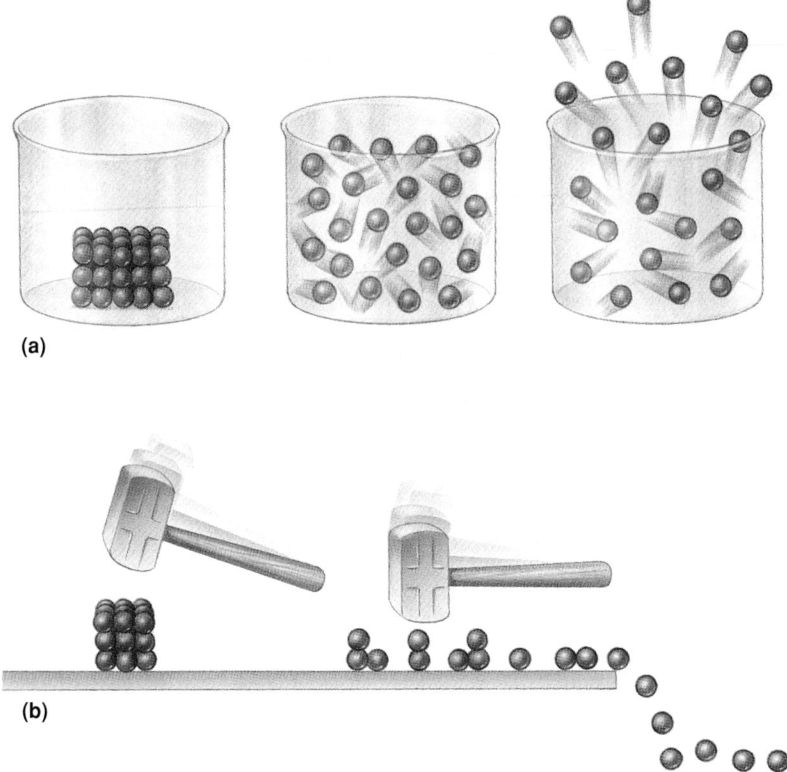

Figure 18.18 Entropy is a measure of the disorder of a system. **(a)** The entropy of a gas is greater than the entropy of a liquid or solid. **(b)** Entropy increases when a substance is divided into parts.

3. Entropy increases when a substance is divided into parts. For instance, entropy increases when a crystalline ionic compound such as sodium chloride is dissolved in water. This is because the solute particles, sodium ions and chloride ions, are more separated in the solvent than they are in the crystal.

4. Entropy tends to increase in chemical reactions in which the total number of product molecules is greater than the total number of reactant molecules. Figure 18.18 illustrates some of these concepts.

Concept Practice

16. The products in a spontaneous process are more ordered than the reactants. Is this entropy change favorable or unfavorable?

17. Which of the following systems has the higher entropy?

a. a new pack of playing cards or playing cards in use?

b. a sugar cube dissolved in water or a cube of sugar?

c. a 1-g salt crystal or 1 g of powdered salt?

18.8 Heat, Entropy, and Free Energy

Objective

Explain how changes in energy and changes in entropy both influence the spontaneity of a reaction.

The size and direction of heat (enthalpy) changes and entropy changes determine whether a reaction is spontaneous (favors products and releases free energy). If a reaction is exothermic (heat is released) and causes an increase in entropy (more disorder), both of these factors are favorable. The reaction is spontaneous. A reaction will also be spontaneous if a decrease in entropy (more order) is offset by a large release of heat. Similarly, an endothermic reaction will be spontaneous if an entropy increase offsets the heat absorbed. Figure 18.19 summarizes the relationship between heat, entropy, and free energy changes for spontaneous reactions.

A nonspontaneous reaction (products not favored) has heat changes or entropy changes, or both, working against it. The desired reaction might not be able to overcome a large decrease in entropy (more order) and might also be highly endothermic (absorb heat). Both of these factors work against formation of products. A reaction may be exothermic, but involve a decrease in entropy large enough to offset the favorable heat change. Alternatively, an increase in entropy might be too small to overcome an endothermic heat

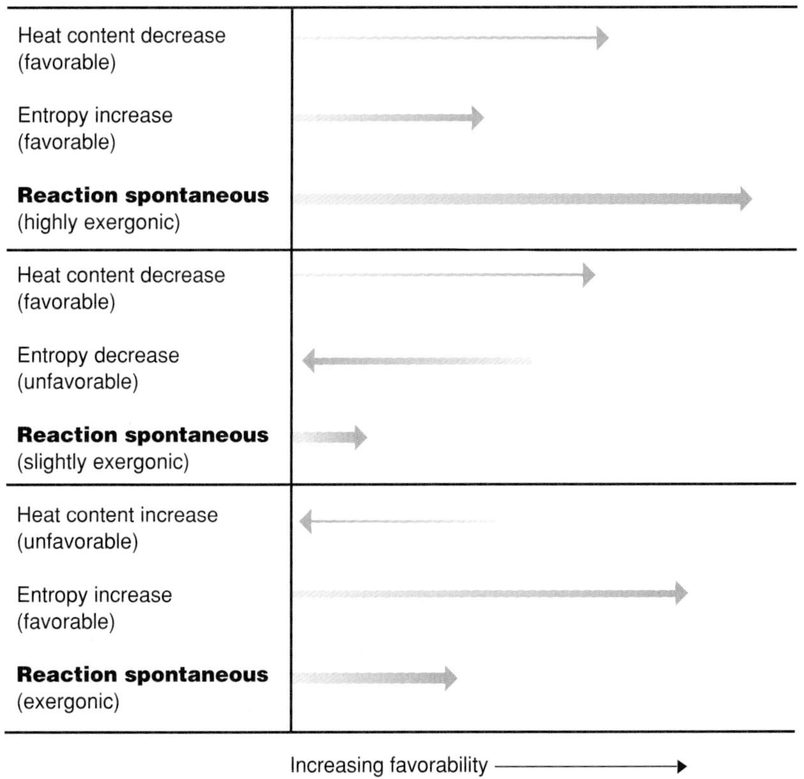

Figure 18.19 Free energy is released in spontaneous reactions. The reaction may be exothermic, the entropy of the system may increase, or both may occur.

change. Figure 18.20 summarizes these relationships for nonspontaneous reactions.

Two examples will enable you to examine these points in real situations. The combustion of carbon has both the heat changes and entropy changes in its favor. The reaction is exothermic. The entropy also increases as *solid* carbon is converted to *gaseous* carbon dioxide. Hence the reaction is spontaneous. The reverse reaction, the production of carbon from carbon dioxide, is nonspontaneous. Because the changes in the reverse direction are *exactly* the opposite of the changes in the forward direction, both the heat and entropy changes are unfavorable.

The heat changes and entropy changes work in opposition when ice melts. Melting of ice is endothermic but still spontaneous above 0°C. The absorption of heat is more than offset by a favorable entropy change. The increase in entropy is large as *solid* water (ice) goes to *liquid* water. Why is the freezing of ice a nonspontaneous process at 0°C?

Table 18.1 summarizes these ideas on how entropy and the heat absorbed or given off affect the spontaneity of chemical reactions. Notice that each of the two variables, heat content and entropy, can be unfavorable for a spontaneous process.

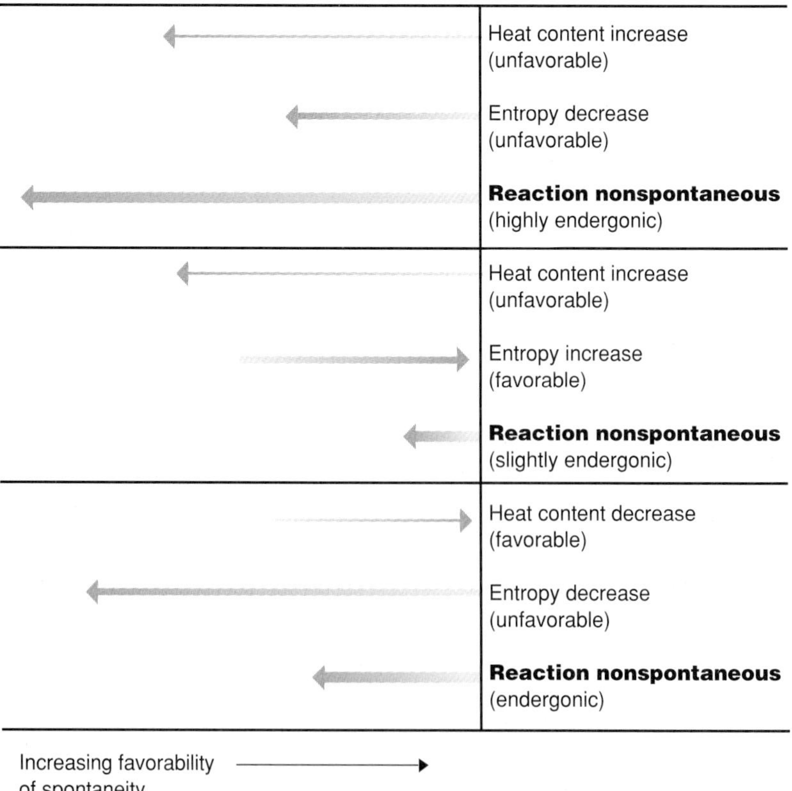

Figure 18.20 A reaction may be nonspontaneous because the reaction is endothermic or the entropy of the system decreases, or both may occur.

Table 18.1 How Changes in Heat Content and Entropy Affect Reaction Spontaneity

Heat content	Entropy	Spontaneous reaction?
Decreases (exothermic)	Increases (more disorder in products than in reactants)	Yes
Increases (endothermic)	Increases	Depends on whether unfavorable heat content change is offset by favorable entropy change
Decreases (exothermic)	Decreases (less disorder in products than in reactants)	Depends on whether unfavorable entropy change is offset by favorable heat content change
Increases (endothermic)	Decreases	No

Concept Practice

18. Is it true that all spontaneous processes are exothermic? Explain your answer.

19. At normal atmospheric pressure, steam condenses to liquid water even though the entropy change is unfavorable. Explain.

18.9 Equilibrium Constants

Objective

Write the equilibrium constant for a reaction and compute its value from experimental data

Chemists seldom use percentages to indicate the position of equilibrium. Rather, they use equilibrium constants. These numbers relate the amounts of reactants to products at equilibrium. Consider the hypothetical reaction in which a mol of reactant A and b mol of reactant B react to give c mol of product C and d mol of product D at equilibrium.

$$aA + bB \rightleftharpoons cC + dD$$

Because the reaction is at equilibrium, there is no *net change* in the amounts of A, B, C, or D at any given instant. *The* **equilibrium constant** K_{eq} *is the ratio of product concentrations to reactant concentrations, with each concentration raised to a power given by the number of moles of that substance in the balanced chemical equation.*

$$K_{eq} = \frac{[C]^c \times [D]^d}{[A]^a \times [B]^b}$$

The exponents in the equilibrium constant expression are the coefficients from the balanced chemical equation. The brackets indicate that the amounts of substances are expressed in moles per liter, as concentration. The value of K_{eq} for a reaction is dependent on the temperature. If the temperature changes, the value of K_{eq} also changes.

Equilibrium constants are valuable chemical information. Among other things, they show whether products or reactants are favored at equilibrium. An equilibrium constant is always written as a ratio of products to reactants. Thus a value of K_{eq} greater than 1 means that products are favored over reactants, and the reaction is spontaneous. Conversely, a value of K_{eq} less than 1 means that reactants are favored over products, and the reaction is nonspontaneous.

$$K_{eq} > 1\text{, products favored at equilibrium}$$

$$K_{eq} < 1\text{, reactants favored at equilibrium}$$

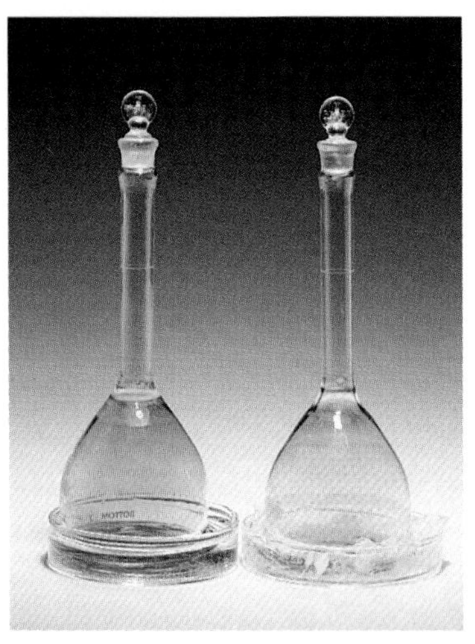

Figure 18.21 Dinitrogen tetroxide is a colorless gas, whereas nitrogen dioxide is brown. The flask on the left is in a dish of hot water, while the flask on the right is in ice. How does temperature affect the equilibrium of a mixture of these gases?

Safety

Any reaction that generates a poisonous gas such as NO_2 should be done only under a fume hood.

Example 2 Expressing and Calculating K_{eq}

Dinitrogen tetroxide (N_2O_4), a colorless gas, and nitrogen dioxide (NO_2), a dark brown gas, exist in equilibrium with each other as shown in Figure 18.21.

$$N_2O_4(g) \rightleftharpoons 2NO_2(g)$$

A liter of a gas mixture at 10°C at equilibrium contains 0.0045 mol of dinitrogen tetroxide and 0.030 mol of nitrogen dioxide.

a. Write the expression for the equilibrium constant.

b. Calculate the equilibrium constant, K_{eq}, for the reaction.

Solution

a. At equilibrium, there is no net change in the amount of N_2O_4 or NO_2 at any given instant. Nitrogen dioxide is the only product of the reaction. It has a coefficient of 2. According to the rule for writing the equilibrium constant, the concentration of nitrogen dioxide, raised to the second power, is in the numerator. The reactant is dinitrogen tetroxide. Its coefficient is 1. Thus the concentration of this substance, raised to the first power, is in the denominator.

$$K_{eq} = \frac{[NO_2]^2}{[N_2O_4]}$$

b. Substitute the given data into the equilibrium constant expression.

$$K_{eq} = \frac{[NO_2]^2}{[N_2O_4]} = \frac{(0.030\text{ mol/L})^2}{0.0045\text{ mol/L}} = \frac{0.030\text{ mol/L} \times 0.030\ \cancel{\text{mol/L}}}{0.0045\ \cancel{\text{mol/L}}}$$

$$= 0.20\text{ mol/L}$$

Example 3 Finding the Equilibrium Constant

One mole of hydrogen gas and 1.00 mol of iodine are sealed in a 1-L flask and allowed to react at 450°C. At equilibrium 1.56 mol of hydrogen iodide is present. Calculate K_{eq} for the reaction.

$$H_2(g) + I_2(g) \rightleftharpoons 2HI(g)$$

Solution

The balanced equation indicates that 1.00 mol of hydrogen and 1.00 mol of iodine form 2.00 mol of hydrogen iodide. To make 1.56 mol of hydrogen iodide therefore consumes 0.78 mol of hydrogen and 0.78 mol of iodine. First you calculate how much of the H_2 and I_2 are left in the flask at equilibrium.

$$\text{mol } H_2 = \text{mol } I_2 = 1.00 \text{ mol} - 0.78 \text{ mol}$$
$$= 0.22 \text{ mol}$$

You can substitute these concentrations in the equation for K_{eq}.

$$K_{eq} = \frac{[HI]^2}{[H_2] \times [I_2]}$$
$$= \frac{(1.56 \text{ mol})^2}{0.22 \text{ mol} \times 0.22 \text{ mol}}$$
$$= \frac{1.56 \cancel{\text{mol}} \times 1.56 \cancel{\text{mol}}}{0.22 \cancel{\text{mol}} \times 0.22 \cancel{\text{mol}}}$$
$$= 50.3 = 5.0 \times 10^1 \text{ (to two significant figures)}$$

Estimate an approximate answer to see if your answer makes sense. At equilibrium the amount of product exceeds the amount of reactants; therefore a $K_{eq} > 1$ should be expected.

Practice Problems

20. Give the equilibrium constant expression for the formation of ammonia from hydrogen and nitrogen.

$$N_2(g) + 3H_2(g) \rightleftharpoons 2NH_3(g)$$

21. Analysis of an equilibrium mixture of nitrogen, hydrogen, and ammonia contained in a 1-L flask at 300°C gives the following results: hydrogen 0.15 mol, nitrogen 0.25 mol, ammonia 0.10 mol. Calculate K_{eq} for the reaction.

$$N_2(g) + 3H_2(g) \rightleftharpoons 2NH_3(g)$$

Example 4 Calculating Equilibrium Concentrations

Bromine chloride, BrCl, decomposes to form chlorine and bromine.

$$2BrCl(g) \rightleftharpoons Cl_2(g)+Br_2(g)$$

At a certain temperature the equilibrium constant for the reaction is 11.1, and the equilibrium mixture contains 4.00 mol Cl_2. How many moles of Br_2 and BrCl are present in the equilibrium mixture?

Solution

$$2BrCl(g) \rightleftharpoons Cl_2(g)+Br_2(g)$$

According to the equation, when BrCl breaks down, equal moles of Cl_2 and Br_2 are formed. The measured equilibrium concentration of Cl_2 was given as 4.00 mol. Thus there must be 4.00 mol Br_2 in the equilibrium mixture. Substitute the known values in the equilibrium expression for the reaction. (K_{eq} was given as 11.1.)

$$K_{eq} = \frac{[Cl_2] \times [Br_2]}{[BrCl]^2} \qquad 11.1 = \frac{(4.00\text{ mol}) \times (4.00\text{ mol})}{[BrCl]^2}$$

Now solve for [BrCl].

$$[BrCl]^2 = \frac{(4.00\text{ mol}) \times (4.00\text{ mol})}{11.1} = \frac{16.0\text{ mol}^2}{11.1} = 1.44\text{ mol}^2$$

$$[BrCl]^2 = \sqrt{1.44\text{ mol}^2} = 1.20\text{ mol}$$

Practice Problems

22. Write the equilibrium constant expression for the decomposition of hydrogen iodide to hydrogen and iodine.

$$2HI(g) \rightleftharpoons H_2(g)+I_2(g)$$

23. Imagine you have determined the equilibrium constants for several reactions. In which of these reactions are the products favored over the reactants?

a. $K_{eq} = 1 \times 20^2$
b. $K_{eq} = 0.003$
c. $K_{eq} = 3.5$
d. $K_{eq} = 6 \times 10^{-4}$

24. The decomposition of hydrogen iodide at 450°C produces an equilibrium mixture that contains 0.50 mol of hydrogen. The equilibrium constant is 0.020 for the reaction. How many moles of iodine and hydrogen iodide are present in the equilibrium mixture?

$$2HI(g) \rightleftharpoons H_2(g) + I_2(g)$$

18.10 Entropy Calculations

Objective

Compute the change in entropy of a reaction using standard entropies.

Entropy is a quantitative measure of the disorder of a system. The symbol for the entropy of a substance is S, with units of J/K. When the entropy (S) is given per mole of substance it has the units of J/(K × mol). These units are also written as J/K•mol. *The* **standard entropy** *of a liquid or solid substance at 25°C and 101.3 kPa is designated S^0.* Table 18.2 gives standard entropies for some common substances. The theoretical entropy of a perfect crystal at 0 K is zero. Other substances have positive entropies, even at absolute zero.

Table 18.2 Standard Entropies (S^0) at 25°C and 101.3 kPa

Substance	S^0 (J/K•mol)	Substance	S^0 (J/K•mol)
$Al_2O_3(s)$	50.99	$HCl(g)$	186.7
$Br_2(g)$	245.3	$H_2S(g)$	205.6
$Br_2(l)$	152.3	$I_2(g)$	260.6
C(*s*, diamond)	2.439	$I_2(s)$	117
C(*s*, graphite)	5.694	$N_2(g)$	191.5
$CH_4(g)$	186.2	$NH_3(g)$	192.5
$CO(g)$	197.9	$NO(g)$	210.6
$CO_2(g)$	213.6	$NO_2(g)$	240.5
$CaCO_3(s)$	88.7	$Na_2CO_3(s)$	136
$CaO(s)$	39.75	$NaCl(s)$	72.4
$Cl_2(g)$	223.0	$O_2(g)$	205.0
$F_2(g)$	203	$O_3(g)$	238
$Fe(s)$	27.2	P(*s*, white)	44.4
$Fe_2O_3(s)$	90.0	P(*s*, red)	29
$H_2(g)$	130.6	S(*s*, rhombic)	31.9
$H_2O(g)$	188.7	S(*s*, monoclinic)	32.6
$H_2O(l)$	69.94	$SO_2(g)$	248.5
$H_2O_2(l)$	92	$SO_3(g)$	256.2

Figure 18.22 What characteristics of an explosion would lead you to think that an increase in entropy is occurring?

Example 5 Calculating the Standard Entropy Change

Calculate the standard entropy change, ΔS^0, that occurs when 1 mol $H_2O(g)$ at 25°C and 101.3 kPa is condensed to 1 mol $H_2O(l)$ at the same temperature.

Solution

You can write the phase change as a reaction.

$$H_2O(g) \longrightarrow H_2O(l)$$

From Table 18.2 find S^0 for $H_2O(g)$ and $H_2O(l)$.

$$S^0 \text{ for } H_2O(g) = 188.7 \text{ J/K·mol}$$

$$S^0 \text{ for } H_2O(l) = 69.94 \text{ J/K·mol}$$

You can calculate the change in entropy ΔS^0 by subtraction.

$$\Delta S^0 = S^0(\text{products}) - S^0(\text{reactants})$$

Only 1 mol of each reactant and product is involved.

$$\Delta S^0 = 69.94 \text{ J/K·mol} - 188.7 \text{ J/K·mol} = -118.8 \text{ J/K·mol}$$

As you might expect, the condensation of 1 mol of water vapor to liquid water at 25°C results in a large decrease in entropy.

Example 6 Finding the ΔS^0 of a Chemical Reaction

What is the standard change in entropy for the following reaction when all reactants and products are in the specified physical states at 101.3 kPa and 25°C?

$$NO(g) + O_2(g) \longrightarrow NO_2(g)$$

Solution

First, you write the balanced equation including all the physical states.

$$2NO(g) + O_2(g) \longrightarrow 2NO_2(g)$$

Then you use Table 18.2 to find the standard entropies.

$$S^0 \text{ for } NO(g) = 210.6 \text{ J/K·mol}$$

$$S^0 \text{ for } O_2(g) = 205.0 \text{ J/K·mol}$$

$$S^0 \text{ for } NO_2(g) = 240.5 \text{ J/K·mol}$$

Sum the S^0 values of the reactants, taking into account the number of moles.

$$S^0 \text{ for NO} = 2 \text{ mol NO} \times 210.6 \text{ J/K·mol NO} = 421.2 \text{ J/K}$$

$$S^0 \text{ for } O_2 = 1 \text{ mol } O_2 \times 205.0 \text{ J/K·mol } O_2 = 205.0 \text{ J/K}$$

$$S^0(\text{reactants}) = 626.2 \text{ J/K}$$

Calculate the S^0 of the products.

$$S^0 \text{ for } NO_2 = 2 \text{ mol } NO_2 \times 240.5 \text{ J/K·mol } NO_2 = 481.0 \text{ J/K}$$

Calculate the change in entropy ΔS^0 by subtraction.

$$\Delta S^0 = S^0(\text{products}) - S^0(\text{reactants})$$

$$\Delta S^0 = (481.0 \text{ J/K}) - (626.2 \text{ J/K}) = -145.2 \text{ J/K}$$

The entropy declines because a total of *three* reactant molecules are reorganized to only *two* product molecules.

Concept Practice

25. How does the magnitude of the standard entropy of an element in the gaseous state compare with the standard entropy of the same element in the liquid state?

Practice Problem

26. Calculate the change in entropy for these reactions.

a. $CaCO_3(s) \longrightarrow CaO(s) + CO_2(g)$
b. $2H_2(g) + O_2(g) \longrightarrow 2H_2O(l)$
c. $H_2(g) + Cl_2(g) \longrightarrow 2HCl(g)$
d. $CH_4(g) + O_2(g) \longrightarrow CO_2(g) + H_2O(g)$
e. $Br_2(l) \longrightarrow Br_2(g)$

18.B Consumer Chemistry

Paint

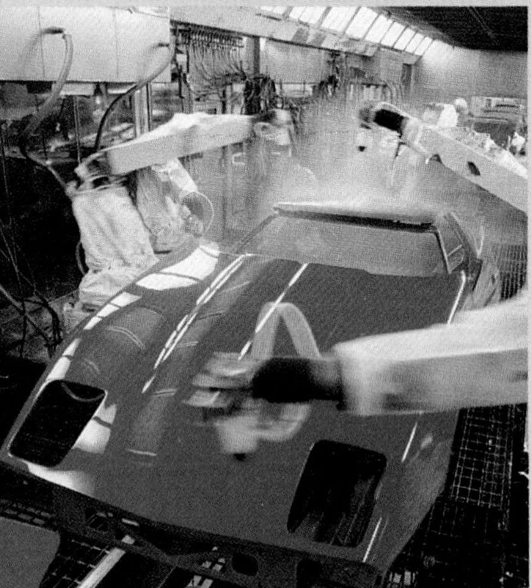

Figure 18.23 While the chemistry involved in making paints has advanced considerably in recent years, so has the technology for applying paint during the manufacturing process. Here computer-controlled robots are applying paint.

Paints save billions of dollars each year by protecting people's furniture, houses, and cars from damage due to wear and weather. The two most common types of paint used today are water-based latex paints and oil-based paints.

Water-based latex and acrylic latex paints are the most popular paints used today. They have the advantages of being nearly odorless and cleaning up in water. These paints are washable and resistant to light damage. Acrylic latex paints are more durable than latex paints and are useful for exterior applications.

All latex paints contain polymers that act as binders and pigments and dyes that produce the desired colors. The binder is emulsified with water to make it easy to spread. Immediately after application, the water begins to evaporate. Soon the emulsion breaks down and the remaining water evaporates quickly, leaving the paint film. The paint pigment becomes trapped in the molecular network of the polymer.

Oil-based paints are often still used for small applications. These odorous paints contain drying oils, resins which act as binders, pigments which provide color, and a thinner. The thinner is a volatile petroleum distillate (mineral spirits) or turpentine. When oil-based paints dry, the thinner evaporates and a chemical reaction between the drying oil and oxygen from the surrounding air creates a tough polymer film. Oil-based paints are used much less often today than previously.

Disadvantages of oil-based paints are that they must be cleaned up with a solvent such as mineral spirits or turpentine, they are flammable, and they are more damaging to the environment than water-based paints. Vapors from the evaporating volatile petroleum distillate, used as a thinner, enter the atmosphere as environmental pollutant. These vapors, or volatile organic compounds (VOCs), are known to contribute to the production of photochemical smog. Paint companies are working to eliminate petroleum distillates from their products. Their ultimate goal is to produce paints that are totally free of VOCs and thus less damaging to the environment.

Think About It

27. List Name at least two advantages of water-based paints over oil-based paints.

28. Analyze What are some criteria that you would use in choosing a paint for your car?

18.11 Free Energy Calculations

Objective

Compute the change in free energy of a reaction in order to determine the spontaneity of the reaction.

You may recall that in every spontaneous process, some energy becomes available to do work. This energy is called the *Gibbs free energy. The* **Gibbs free energy change**, *ΔG, is the maximum amount of energy that can be coupled to another process to do useful work.* The change in Gibbs free energy is related to the change in entropy ΔS and the change in enthalpy ΔH of the system.

$$\Delta G = \Delta H - T\Delta S$$

Temperature (T) in the equation is stated in kelvins. All spontaneous processes release free energy; therefore, they are exergonic. The numerical value of ΔG is negative in spontaneous processes because free energy is lost by the system. By contrast, nonspontaneous processes are endergonic. They require that work be expended to make them go at the specified conditions. The numerical value of ΔG is positive for a nonspontaneous process.

You can use the standard free energy change ΔG^0 to determine whether a chemical reaction is spontaneous when you have the values of ΔH^0 and ΔS^0.

$$\Delta G^0 = \Delta H^0 - T\Delta S^0$$

Alternatively, you can determine ΔH^0 or ΔS^0 for a reaction if the other two quantities in the equation are known. Table 18.3 gives values of ΔG^0 for some common reactions. On the next page, Table 18.4 lists values of ΔG_f^0, the standard free energy change for the formation of substances from their elements. Note that $\Delta G_f^0 = 0$ for elemental substances. You can use ΔG_f^0 to calculate ΔG^0 for a given reaction. This is similar to the way in which ΔH_f^0 is used to calculate

Table 18.3 Free Energy Values (ΔG^0) for Some Spontaneous Processes at 25°C

Reaction	Free energy: Kilocalories	Free energy: Kilojoules
$H_2(g)$ + $Cl_2(g)$ ⟶ $2HCl(g)$ Hydrogen + Chlorine ⟶ Hydrogen chloride	–45.6	–191
$S(s)$ + $O_2(g)$ ⟶ $SO_2(g)$ Sulfur + Oxygen ⟶ Sulfur dioxide	–71.7	–300
$2N_2O_5(s)$ ⟶ $4NO_2(g)$ + $O_2(g)$ Dinitrogen pentoxide ⟶ Nitrogen dioxide + Oxygen	–7.2	–30
$C_6H_{12}O_6(s)$ + $6O_2(g)$ ⟶ $6CO_2(g)$ + $6H_2O(l)$ Glucose + Oxygen ⟶ Carbon dioxide + Water	–686.0	–2868

Table 18.4 Standard Gibbs Free Energies of Formation (ΔG_f^0) at 25°C and 101.3 kPa

Substance	ΔG_f^0 (kJ/mol)	Substance	ΔG_f^0 (kJ/mol)	Substance	ΔG_f^0 (kJ/mol)
$Al_2O_3(s)$	–1576.4	$Fe(s)$	0.0	$NO(g)$	86.69
$Br_2(g)$	3.14	$Fe_2O_3(s)$	–741.0	$NO_2(g)$	51.84
$Br_2(l)$	0.0	$H_2(g)$	0.0	$Na_2CO_3(s)$	–1048
C(*s*, diamond)	2.866	$H_2O(g)$	–228.6	$NaCl(s)$	–384.03
C(*s*, graphite)	0.0	$H_2O(l)$	–237.2	$O_2(g)$	0.0
$CH_4(g)$	–50.79	$H_2O_2(l)$	–114.0	$O_3(g)$	163.4
$CO(g)$	–137.3	$HCl(g)$	–95.27	P(*s*, white)	0.0
$CO_2(g)$	–394.4	$H_2S(g)$	–33.02	P(*s*, red)	–14
$CaCO_3(s)$	–1127.7	$I_2(g)$	19.4	S(*s*, rhombic)	0.0
$CaO(s)$	–604.2	$I_2(s)$	0.0	S(*s*, monoclinic)	0.096
$Cl_2(g)$	0.0	$N_2(g)$	0.0	$SO_2(g)$	–300.4
$F_2(g)$	0.0	$NH_3(g)$	–16.64	$SO_3(g)$	–370.4

the heats of reaction. If you calculate ΔG^0 to see whether a reaction is spontaneous, the result applies only to reactants and products in their standard states. A reaction that is nonspontaneous under one set of conditions such as standard conditions may be spontaneous under another set of conditions.

You can consider a real chemical reaction to show the effect of temperature on the spontaneity of a reaction. Solid calcium carbonate decomposes to give calcium oxide and carbon dioxide. In this reaction the entropy increases because one of the products formed from the *solid* reactant is a *gas*. The entropy increase is not great enough, however, for the reaction to be spontaneous at ordinary temperatures. This is because the reaction is endothermic; the enthalpy of the reactants is lower than that of the products. The effect of an entropy increase is magnified as the temperature is raised. At temperatures above 850°C the favorable entropy-temperature term $T\Delta S^0$ outweighs the unfavorable enthalpy term and the reaction is spontaneous.

Example 7 Calculating the Change in Gibbs Free Energy

Determine whether the following reaction is spontaneous by using the ΔG_f^0 for reactants and products.

$$C(s, \text{graphite}) + O_2(g) \longrightarrow CO_2(g)$$

Solution

Look up the ΔG_f^0 of all reactants and products in Table 18.4.

$$\Delta G_f^0 \text{ for C}(s, \text{graphite}) = 0.0 \text{ kJ/mol}$$

$$\Delta G_f^0 \text{ for O}_2(g) = 0.0 \text{ kJ/mol}$$

$$\Delta G_f^0 \text{ for CO}_2(g) = -394.4 \text{ kJ/mol}$$

Sum the ΔG_f^0 of the reactants and sum the ΔG_f^0 of the products.

$$\Delta G_f^0 \text{ (reactants)} = 0.0 \text{ kJ/mol}$$

$$\Delta G_f^0 \text{ (products)} = -394.4 \text{ kJ/mol}$$

The ΔG^0 for the reaction is the difference between the ΔG_f^0 of the products and the ΔG_f^0 of the reactants.

$$\Delta G^0 = \Delta G_f^0 \text{ (products)} - \Delta G_f^0 \text{ (reactants)}$$

$$\Delta G^0 = -394.4 \text{ kJ/mol} - 0.0 \text{ kJ/mol}$$

$$= -394.4 \text{ kJ/mol}$$

The reaction is spontaneous. You can also determine the spontaneity of the reaction by using the changes in enthalpy and the entropies for the reactants and products, as shown in the next example.

Example 8 Determining Reaction Spontaneity

Using values for ΔH_f^0 and S^0, determine whether the reaction in Example 7 is spontaneous.

Solution

First find the ΔH_f^0 and S^0 of all the reactants and products in Tables A.6 and 18.2. Use dimensional analysis to make the conversions.

Substance	ΔH_f^0 (kJ/mol)	S^0 (J/K•mol)
C(*s*, graphite)	0.0	5.69
$O_2(g)$	0.0	205
$CO_2(g)$	−393.5	214

The S^0 values of Table 18.2 are given in J/K·mol. You must convert them to kJ/K·mol to match the units of ΔH_f^0. Use dimensional analysis to make the conversions.

Problem-Solving Tip

Check that the answer has an appropriate unit after canceling and before doing the numerical calculation.

$$S^0 \text{ for C}(s, \text{graphite}) = 5.7\frac{\cancel{\text{J}}}{\text{K·mol}} \times \frac{1 \text{ kJ}}{1000\cancel{\text{J}}} = 0.0057 \text{ kJ/K·mol}$$

$$S^0 \text{ for O}_2(g) = 205\frac{\cancel{\text{J}}}{\text{K·mol}} \times \frac{1 \text{ kJ}}{1000\cancel{\text{J}}} = 0.205 \text{ kJ/K·mol}$$

$$S^0 \text{ for CO}_2(g) = 214\frac{\cancel{\text{J}}}{\text{K·mol}} \times \frac{1 \text{ kJ}}{1000\cancel{\text{J}}} = 0.214 \text{ kJ/K·mol}$$

Now you know that:

$$\Delta S^0 = S^0(\text{products}) - S^0(\text{reactants})$$

$$\Delta S^0 = 0.214\frac{\text{kJ}}{\text{K·mol}} - \left(0.0057\frac{\text{kJ}}{\text{K·mol}} + 0.205\frac{\text{kJ}}{\text{K·mol}}\right)$$

$$= 0.003 \text{ kJ/K·mol}$$

The standard enthalpy change follows.

$$\Delta H^0 = \Delta H_f^0(\text{products}) - \Delta H_f^0(\text{reactants})$$

$$\Delta H^0 = -393.5 \text{ kJ/mol} - (0.0 \text{ kJ/mol} + 0.0 \text{ kJ/mol}) = -393.5 \text{ kJ/mol}$$

Finally, you can calculate the value of ΔG^0.

$$\Delta G^0 = \Delta H^0 - T\Delta S^0$$

Kelvin temperature $T = 273.15 + 25°\text{C} = 298.15 \text{ K}$

$$\Delta G^0 = -393.5\frac{\text{kJ}}{\text{mol}} - \left(298.15 \cancel{\text{K}} \times 0.003\frac{\text{kJ}}{\cancel{\text{K}}\text{·mol}}\right) = -394.4\frac{\text{kJ}}{\text{mol}}$$

The reaction is spontaneous due to the large decline in ΔH^0 and the increase in entropy when solid graphite is converted to gaseous CO_2.

Practice Problems

29. Determine whether the following reactions are spontaneous. Assume all substances are at 25°C and 101.3 kPa.

a. $2\text{Na}(s) + \text{Cl}_2(g) \longrightarrow 2\text{NaCl}(s)$

b. $4\text{Al}(s) + 3\text{O}_2(g) \longrightarrow 2\text{Al}_2\text{O}_3(s)$

30. When gaseous nitrogen and hydrogen are converted to gaseous ammonia, ΔG^0 equals –16.64 kJ/mol.

$$\text{N}_2(g) + 3\text{H}_2(g) \longrightarrow 2\text{NH}_3(g)$$

Using the S^0 values of Table 18.2, calculate the ΔH_f^0 for the formation of ammonia.

18.12 Rate Laws

Objective

Write the rate law for a reaction given the order of each reactant.

The rate of a reaction depends in part on the concentrations of the reactants. For a reaction in which reactant A reacts to form product B in one step, you can write a simple equation. (A one-step reaction has a reaction with only one activated complex between the reactants and products.)

$$\text{A} \longrightarrow \text{B}$$

The rate at which A is transformed to B is the change in concentration of A (ΔA) with time. Mathematically, you express the rate as the change in A with respect to the change in time (t).

$$\text{Rate} = \frac{\Delta \text{A}}{\Delta t}$$

The rate of disappearance of A is proportional to its molar concentration.

$$\frac{\Delta \text{A}}{\Delta t} \propto [\text{A}]$$

The proportionality can be expressed as a constant multiplied by [A].

$$\text{Rate} = \frac{\Delta \text{A}}{\Delta t} = k \times [\text{A}]$$

This equation is an example of a **rate law**, *an expression relating the rate of a reaction to the concentration of reactants. The* **specific rate constant** *for a reaction (k) is a proportionality constant relating the concentrations of reactants to the rate of the reaction.* The magnitude of the specific rate constant depends on the conditions at which the reaction is conducted. If reactant A reacts to form product B quickly, k will be large. If reactant A reacts to form product B slowly, the value of k will be small.

The conversion of A to B in a one-step reaction is an example of a *first-order reaction.* The order of a reaction is the power to which the concentration of a reactant must be raised to give the *experimentally observed* relationship between concentration and rate. *In a* **first-order reaction** *the reaction rate is directly proportional to the concentration of only one reactant.* The conversion of A to B in the previously discussed reaction is first order because the reaction rate is proportional to the concentration of A raised to the first power: $[\text{A}]^1 = [\text{A}]$. As a first-order reaction progresses, the rate of reaction decreases. This is because the concentration of reactant decreases. On a graph, the rate at any point ($\Delta \text{A}/\Delta t$) equals the slope of the tangent to the curve at that point. For a first-order reaction, a halving of [A] results in a halving of the reaction rate.

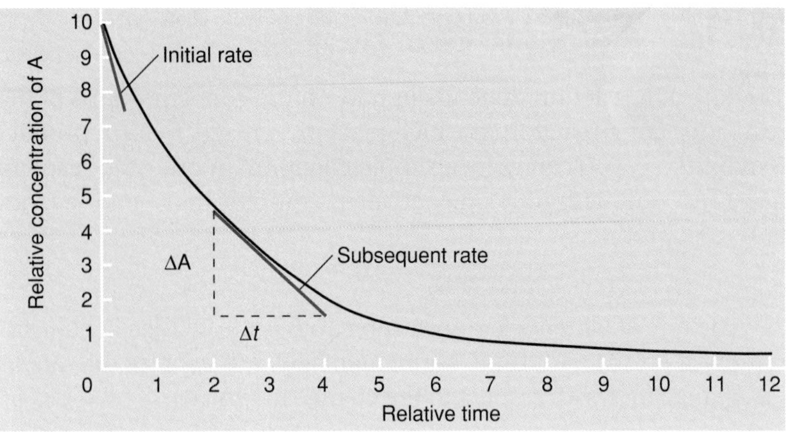

Figure 18.24 The rate of a first-order reaction decreases in direct proportion to the concentration of one reactant. The curved line shows the decrease in concentration of reactant A with time. The short colored lines show the rate at two points in the reaction.

Practice Problem

31. A first-order reaction initially proceeds at a rate of 0.5 mol/(L × s). What will the rate be when half of the starting material remains? When one-fourth of the starting material remains?

In some kinds of reactions, such as double replacement, two substances react to give products. The coefficients in the equation for such a reaction are represented by lowercase letters.

$$a\text{A} + b\text{B} \xrightarrow{k} c\text{C} + d\text{D}$$

For a one-step reaction of A with B the rate of reaction is dependent on the concentrations of both A and B.

$$\text{Rate} = k[\text{A}]^a[\text{B}]^b$$

For any one-step reaction, the experimentally determined exponents in the rate law will turn out to be the same as the coefficients a and b in the chemical equation. However, the exponents in the rate law and the coefficients in the equation seldom correspond in real reactions. This is because most reactions are more complex than the one-step reactions used in the examples. *Remember, the actual kinetic order of a reaction must be determined by experiment. There is no necessary relationship between the kinetic order and the coefficients in the overall chemical equations for complex reactions.* The order of reaction in each reactant is the value of the exponent associated with that reactant. The overall order of the reaction is the sum of the exponents for the individual reactants.

Example 9 Finding the Order of a Reaction from Experimental Data

The rate law for the one-step reaction $a\text{A} \longrightarrow \text{B}$ is of the form: Rate = $k[\text{A}]^a$. From the data in the following table, find the kinetic order of the reaction with respect to A and the overall order of the reaction.

Initial concentration of A (mol/L)	Initial rate (mol/L-s)
0.05	3×10^{-4}
0.10	12×10^{-4}
0.20	48×10^{-4}

Solution

If a reaction is first order in A, then $a = 1$. The initial rate would be directly proportional to the initial [A]. The reaction cannot be first order in A because a doubling of A causes the rate to increase by four times. This suggests that $a = 2$, since $2^2 = 4$. Increasing [A] by four times should, therefore, increase the rate 16-fold ($4^2 = 16$). When the initial concentration of A is increased from 0.05 mol/L to 0.20 mol/L, the initial rate increases from 3×10^{-4} mol/L-s to 48×10^{-4} mol/L-s, a 16-fold increase. The reaction is second order in A and second order overall.

Practice Problem

32. Ammonium ions and nitrite ions react in water to form nitrogen gas.

$$NH_4^+(aq) + NO_2^-(aq) \longrightarrow N_2(g) + 2H_2O(l)$$

From the following data, give the order of the reaction with respect to NH_4^+ and NO_2^-, and the overall order of the reaction.

Initial $[NO_2^-]$ (mol/L)	Initial $[NH_4^+]$ (mol/L)	Initial rate (mol/L-s)
0.0100	0.200	5.4×10^{-7}
0.0200	0.200	10.8×10^{-7}
0.0400	0.200	21.5×10^{-7}
0.0600	0.200	32.3×10^{-7}
0.200	0.0202	10.8×10^{-7}
0.200	0.0404	21.6×10^{-7}
0.200	0.0606	32.4×10^{-7}
0.200	0.0808	43.3×10^{-7}

Integrating Geology

Weathering of Rocks

The process of rock weathering occurs so slowly that it is imperceptible over a span of many human lifetimes. In spite of its slow rate, the weathering of rocks has shaped, and continues to shape, the surface of the Earth. Chemical and physical processes induced by water produce much of the weathering. Some mountains in the United States show the effects of weathering over long periods of time. The relatively young Rocky Mountains (100 million years) are high and craggy. By contrast, the old southern Appalachians (345 million years) are low and smooth due to weathering.

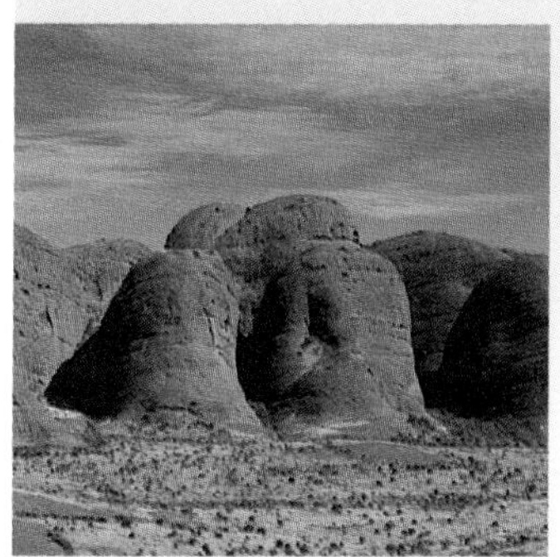

Activity 18
Temperature and Reaction Rates

Purpose

To observe the effect of temperature on chemical reaction rates.

Materials

4 plastic cups

4 effervescent tablets

clock or watch with seconds hand

thermometer (optional)

hot water (from tap)

cold water (from tap)

ice

graph paper

masking tape

pen or pencil

Procedure

1. Mark the letters A, B, C, and D on four separate pieces of masking tape. Label each of the plastic cups with one of the letters.

2. Arrange the cups in alphabetical order and fill each three-quarters full as follows: (cup A) cold water from tap plus some ice, (cup B) cold tap water, (cup C) a mixture of half cold tap water and half hot tap water, (cup D) hot tap water.

3. If you have a thermometer, record the temperature of the water in each cup.

4. Drop an effervescent tablet into each cup and begin timing each reaction.

5. Record the time it takes for the reaction in each cup to go to completion.

6. Draw a line or bar graph of temperature versus reaction time.

Analysis and Conclusions

1. Do the tablets react faster as the temperature of the water increases? Explain.

2. What results would you expect if you crushed the tablets to a powder before adding them to the water? Explain your prediction. (If time permits, check this prediction experimentally.)

Objective

Analyze the reaction mechanism for a reaction given a potential energy diagram.

18.13 Reaction Mechanisms

If enough information were available, you could graph all of the energy changes that occur as reactants are converted to products in a chemical reaction. Such a graph would constitute a *reaction progress curve* for the reaction. The simplest reaction progress curve would be obtained for an *elementary reaction. In an* **elementary reaction** *reactants are converted to products in a single step (a "one-step" reaction).* Such a reaction has only one intervening activated complex between reactants and products. Most chemical reactions consist of a number of elementary reactions. *A* **reaction mechanism** *includes all of the elementary reactions of a complex reaction.* For a complex reaction, the reaction progress curve resembles a number of hills and valleys. Look at Figure 18.25. The hills correspond to the energies of the activated complexes. The valleys correspond to the energies of the intermediate products.

An **intermediate** *is a product of a reaction that becomes a reactant of another reaction within a reaction mechanism.* Intermediates have a significant lifetime compared with an activated complex. They have real ionic or molecular structures and some stability.

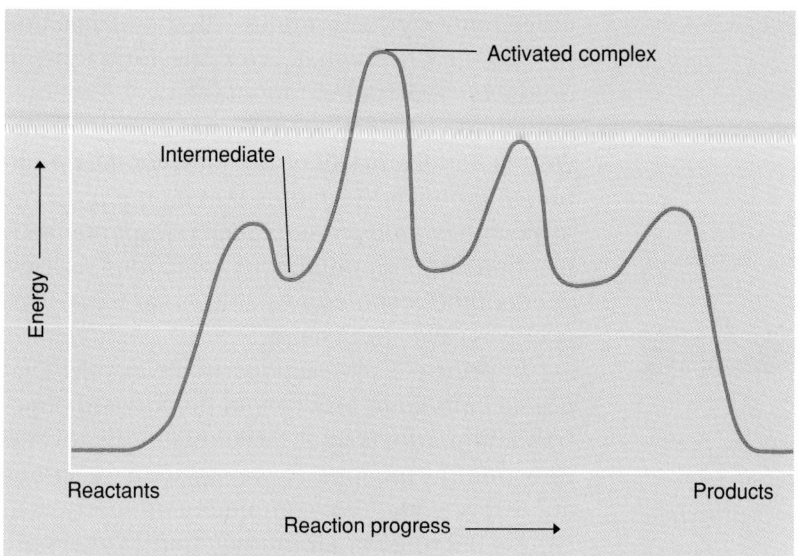

Figure 18.25 A reaction progress curve shows an activation energy peak for each elementary reaction. Valleys indicate the formation of intermediates. How many elementary reactions are part of this reaction? How many intermediates are formed?

They are reactive enough, however, to react further and eventually give the final product of the reaction.

Intermediates do not appear in the chemical equation for a reaction. For example, the decomposition of nitrous oxide (N_2O) is believed to occur in two elementary steps.

$$N_2O(g) \longrightarrow N_2(g) + O(g)$$
$$N_2O(g) + O(g) \longrightarrow N_2(g) + O_2(g)$$
$$2N_2O(g) \longrightarrow 2N_2(g) + O_2(g)$$

Notice that oxygen atoms are intermediates in this reaction. They disappear when the individual reactants are summed to give the final chemical equation. Thus, it is important to note that the overall chemical equation for a complex reaction gives no information about the reaction mechanism.

Concept Practice

33. Define each of the following terms as applied to chemical reactions.

a. elementary reaction
b. intermediate
c. reaction mechanism
d. activation energy

Chapter 18 Review
Reaction Rates and Equilibrium

Key Terms

activated complex *18.1*
activation energy *18.1*
catalyst *18.2*
chemical equilibrium *18.3*
collision theory *18.1*
elementary reaction *18.13*
entropy *18.7*
equilibrium constant *18.9*
equilibrium position *18.3*
exergonic *18.6*
first-order reaction *18.12*
free energy *18.5*
Gibbs free energy change (ΔG) *18.11*
heterogeneous reaction *18.2*
inhibitor *18.2*
intermediate *18.13*
law of disorder *18.7*
Le Châtelier's principle *18.4*
nonspontaneous reaction *18.6*
rate *18.1*
rate law *18.12*
reaction mechanism *18.13*
reversible reaction *18.3*
specific rate constant *18.12*
spontaneous reaction *18.6*
standard entropy (S^0) *18.10*
transition state *18.1*

Chapter Summary

The speed, or rate, at which a chemical reaction goes is determined by the energy with which the particles collide. Reactants must collide with sufficient energy to go to products. The larger the fraction of reactants having the minimum amount of energy needed for the reaction to occur, the faster the reaction. Reactions may be speeded up in a number of ways. The most effective methods are to increase the temperature at which the reaction takes place and to use a catalyst.

The natural tendency for all things to go to lower heat content (enthalpy) and greater disorder (entropy) determines whether a reaction will go. Reactions that favor the formation of products are called spontaneous reactions. Equations for the reverse reactions may be written, but the reactions do not favor the formation of products. Reactions that do not favor the formation of products are called nonspontaneous reactions. All spontaneous reactions release energy that becomes available to do work. This energy is called free energy.

In principle, all reactions are reversible. That is, reactants go to products in the forward direction and products go to reactants in the reverse direction. In practice, however, some reactions are irreversible (go completely to products). Others fail to go at all (no reaction). Others are reversible, with products going to reactants to a certain extent. The point at which the rate of the forward reaction and the rate of the reverse reaction are equal is the position of equilibrium. The relative amounts of reactants and products at equilibrium are useful for determining the position of equilibrium. Le Châtelier's principle can be used to predict how changes in concentration of reactants or products, changes in temperature, or changes in pressure will affect the equilibrium position.

Practice Questions and Problems

34. Explain the collision theory of reactions. *18.1*

35. How is the rate of a spontaneous reaction influenced by a catalyst? How do catalysts make this possible? *18.2*

36. Which of these statements is true? *18.2*
   a. All chemical reactions can be speeded up by increasing the temperature.
   b. Once a chemical reaction gets started, the reacting particles no longer have to collide for products to form.
   c. Enzymes are biological catalysts.

37. When a gas stove is turned on, the gas does not burn unless lit by a flame. Once lit, however, the gas burns until turned off. Explain these observations in terms of the effect of temperature on reaction rate. *18.2*

38. Define a reversible reaction. *18.3*

39. A reversible reaction has reached a state of dynamic chemical equilibrium. What does this information tell you? *18.3*

40. What are some adverse consequences of photochemical smog? *18.A*

41. How do the rates of the forward and reverse reactions compare at a state of dynamic chemical equilibrium? *18.3*

42. What is Le Châtelier's principle? Use it to explain why carbonated drinks go flat when their containers are left open. *18.4*

43. Carbon disulfide can be made by the reaction of carbon dioxide and sulfur trioxide.

$$2SO_3(g) + CO_2(g) + \text{heat} \rightleftharpoons CS_2(g) + 4O_2(g)$$

Assuming that the reaction is at equilibrium, what effect do the following changes have on the equilibrium position? *18.4*

a. addition of CO_2

b. addition of heat

c. decrease in the pressure

d. removal of O_2

e. addition of a catalyst

44. The industrial production of ammonia is described by this reversible reaction.

$$N_2(g) + 3H_2(g) \rightleftharpoons 2NH_3(g) + 92\text{ kJ}$$

What effect do the following changes have on the equilibrium position? *18.4*

a. addition of heat

b. increase in pressure

c. addition of catalyst

d. removal of heat

e. removal of NH_3

45. What is free energy? *18.5*

46. What is meant by the term *exergonic*? *18.6*

47. The reaction of hydrogen and oxygen gas proceeds with a large decrease of free energy. The reaction is very slow at room temperature but occurs with explosive rapidity in the presence of a flame or ignition wire. Explain. *18.6*

48. Which system has the lower entropy? *18.7*

a. a completed jigsaw puzzle *or* puzzle pieces?

b. 50 mL of water *or* 50 mL of ice?

c. 10 g of sodium chloride crystals *or* a solution containing 10 g of sodium chloride?

d. a house *or* a pile of bricks and lumber?

49. What is the meaning of the term *entropy*? *18.7*

50. Predict the direction of the entropy change in each of the following reactions. *18.7*

a. $CaCO_3(s) \longrightarrow CaO(s) + CO_2(g)$

b. $NH_3(g) + HCl(g) \longrightarrow NH_4Cl(s)$

c. $2NaHCO_3(s) \longrightarrow Na_2CO_3(s) + H_2O(g) + CO_2(g)$

d. $CaO(s) + CO_2(g) \longrightarrow CaCO_3(s)$

51. What two factors together determine whether or not a reaction is spontaneous? *18.8*

52. Write the expression for the equilibrium constant for each of the following: *18.9*

a. $2HBr(g) \rightleftharpoons H_2(g) + Br_2(g)$

b. $2SO_3(g) \rightleftharpoons 2SO_2(g) + O_2(g)$

c. $CO_2(g) + H_2(g) \rightleftharpoons CO(g) + H_2O(g)$

d. $4NH_3(g) + 5O_2(g) \rightleftharpoons 6H_2O(g) + 4NO(g)$

53. Write the expression for the equilibrium constant for each of the following. *18.9*

a. $4H_2(g) + CS_2(g) \rightleftharpoons CH_4(g) + 2H_2S(g)$

b. $PCl_5(g) \rightleftharpoons PCl_3(g) + Cl_2(g)$

c. $2NO(g) + O_2(g) \rightleftharpoons 2NO_2(g)$

d. $CO(g) + H_2O(g) \rightleftharpoons H_2(g) + CO_2(g)$

54. At a high temperature the following system reaches equilibrium.

$$N_2(g) + O_2(g) \rightleftharpoons 2NO(g)$$

An analysis of the equilibrium mixture in a 1-L flask gives the following results: nitrogen 0.50 mol; oxygen 0.50 mol; nitrogen monoxide 0.020 mol. Calculate K_{eq} for the reaction. *18.9*

55. At 750°C this reaction reaches an equilibrium in a 1-L container.

$$H_2(g) + CO_2(g) \rightleftharpoons H_2O(g) + CO(g)$$

An analysis of the equilibrium mixture gives the following results: hydrogen 0.053 mol; carbon dioxide 0.053 mol; water 0.047 mol; carbon monoxide 0.047 mol. Calculate K_{eq} for the reaction. *18.9*

56. Comment on the favorability of product formation in each of these reactions. *18.9*

a. $H_2(g) + F_2(g) \rightleftharpoons 2HF(g)$ $K_{eq} = 1 \times 10^{13}$

b. $SO_2(g) + NO_2(g) \rightleftharpoons NO(g) + SO_3(g)$ $K_{eq} = 1 \times 10^{2}$

c. $2H_2O(g) \rightleftharpoons 2H_2(g) + O_2(g)$ $K_{eq} = 6 \times 10^{-28}$

57. Contrast the "drying" process of a water-based latex paint and an oil-based paint. *18.B*

58. The standard entropies are given below for some substances at 25°C.

$$KBrO_3(s),\ S^0 = 149.2\ J/K{\cdot}mol$$

$$KBr(s),\ S^0 = 96.4\ J/K{\cdot}mol$$

$$O_2(g),\ S^0 = 205.0\ J/K{\cdot}mol$$

Calculate ΔS^0 for this reaction. *18.10*

$$KBrO_3(s) \longrightarrow KBr(s) + \frac{3}{2}\ O_2(g)$$

59. Based on the data of Table 18.2, calculate ΔS^0 for conversion of the monoclinic form of sulfur to the rhombic form. *18.10*

60. For the decomposition of $CaCO_3(s)$ to $CaO(s)$ and $CO_2(g)$ at 298 K the ΔH^0 is 178.5 kJ/mol and the ΔS^0 is 161.6 J/K·mol. Is the reaction spontaneous or nonspontaneous at this temperature? *18.11*

61. From the data of Table 18.4, calculate the standard free energy change for each of the following reactions and say whether the reaction is spontaneous or nonspontaneous. *18.11*

a. $Cl_2(g) + H_2O(g) \longrightarrow 2HCl(g) + \frac{1}{2}\ O_2(g)$

b. $4NH_3(g) + 7O_2(g) \longrightarrow 4NO_2(g) + 6H_2O(g)$

c. $2CO_2(g) \longrightarrow 2CO(g) + O_2(g)$

d. $H_2S(g) \longrightarrow H_2(g) + S(s, \text{rhombic})$

62. What is meant by the following terms? *18.12*

a. specific rate constant

b. first-order reaction

c. rate law

63. The rate law for the reaction

$$NO(g) + O_3(g) \longrightarrow NO_2(g) + O_2(g)$$

is first order in NO and O_3 and second order overall. Write the complete rate law for this reaction. *18.12*

64. Sketch a potential energy diagram for the reaction whose mechanism is shown below.

$$2NO(g) \longrightarrow N_2O_2(g)\ \text{(fast)}$$

$$N_2O_2(g) + O_2(g) \longrightarrow 2NO_2(g)\ \text{(slow)}$$

Write the balanced equation for the overall reaction. *18.13*

65. Half of the reactant in a first-order reaction has disappeared in 50 minutes. How many minutes are required for this particular reaction to be 75% complete? *18.12*

Mastery Questions and Problems

66. Construct a concept map with *reversible reaction* as the central concept using the key terms in this chapter.

67. Consider the decomposition of N_2O_5 in carbon tetrachloride (CCl_4) at 45°C.

$$2N_2O_5(soln) \longrightarrow 4NO_2(g) + O_2(g)$$

The reaction is first order in N_2O_5, with the specific rate constant 6.08×10^{-4} per second. Calculate the reaction rate at these conditions.

a. $[N_2O_5] = 0.200$ mol/L

b. $[N_2O_5] = 0.319$ mol/L

68. Which statement or combination of statements is sufficient to determine whether or not a reaction will be spontaneous?

a. The reaction is exothermic.

b. Entropy is increased in the reaction.

c. Free energy is released in the reaction.

69. For the reaction A + B $\longrightarrow$ C, the activation energy of the forward reaction is 5 kJ and the total energy change is –20 kJ. What is the activation energy of the reverse reaction?

70. Explain each of the following.

a. A campfire is "fanned" to help get it going.

b. An explosion at a grain elevator is blamed on dust.

c. A pinch of powdered manganese dioxide causes hydrogen peroxide to explode even though the manganese dioxide is not changed.

71. The entropy decreases in an endothermic reaction. Is the reaction spontaneous?

72. The reaction between diamond (carbon) and oxygen is spontaneous. What can you say about the speed of this reaction?

$$C(s, \text{diamond}) + O_2(g) \longrightarrow CO_2(g)$$

73. Predict what will happen if a catalyst is added to a slow reversible reaction. What happens to the equilibrium position?

74. Write the rate law for each of the elementary rate processes of Problem 64.

75. A large box is divided into two compartments with a door between them. Equal quantities of two different monatomic gases are placed in the two compartments, as shown in the overhead view in **(a)**. The door between the compartments is opened and the gas particles immediately start to mix as shown in **(b)**. Why would it be highly unlikely for the situation in **(b)** to progress to the situation shown in **(c)**?

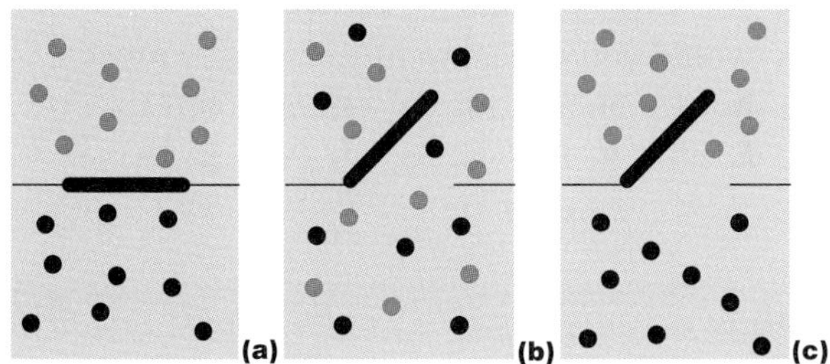

76. Would you expect the entropy to increase in each of the following reactions?

a. $C(s) + O_2(g) \longrightarrow CO_2(g)$

b. $Al_2O_3(s) \longrightarrow 2Al(s) + \frac{3}{2}O_2(g)$

c. $2N(g) \longrightarrow N_2(g)$

d. $N_2(g) \longrightarrow 2N(g)$

77. What would be the effect on the position of equilibrium of decreasing the volume in each of the following reactions?

a. $4HCl(g) + O_2(g) \rightleftharpoons 2Cl_2(g) + 2H_2O(g)$

b. $CO_2(s) \rightleftharpoons CO_2(g)$

c. $CaCO_3(s) \rightleftharpoons CaO(s) + CO_2(g)$

78. Sketch an energy profile curve for this gas-phase reaction.

$$F(g) + H_2(g) \longrightarrow HF(g) + H(g)$$

The reaction has an activation energy of 22 kJ and the total energy change is –103 kJ.

79. By means of a sketch, show that the activation energy of an endothermic reaction must be greater than or equal to the total energy change in the reaction. Does a similar relationship exist for exothermic reactions?

80. A mixture at equilibrium at 827°C contains 0.552 mol CO_2, 0.552 mol H_2, 0.448 mol CO, and 0.448 mol H_2O.

$$CO_2(g) + H_2(g) \rightleftharpoons CO(g) + H_2O(g)$$

What is the value of K_{eq}?

81. Write the equilibrium constant expression for each of the following reactions.

a. $I_2(g) + Cl_2(g) \rightleftharpoons 2ICl(g)$

b. $2NO_2(g) \rightleftharpoons 2NO(g) + O_2(g)$

c. $2SO_2(g) + O_2(g) \rightleftharpoons 2SO_3(g)$

d. $Cl_2(g) + PCl_3(g) \rightleftharpoons PCl_5(g)$

82. The freezing of liquid water at 0°C can be written as follows.

$$H_2O(l,\ d = 1.00\ g/cm^3) \rightleftharpoons H_2O(s,\ d = 0.92\ g/cm^3)$$

Applying pressure causes ice to melt. Why?

83. The decomposition of hydrogen peroxide is catalyzed by iodide ions. The mechanism is thought to be as follows.

$$H_2O_2(aq) + I^-(aq) \rightarrow H_2O(l) + IO^-(aq) \text{ (slow)}$$
$$IO^-(aq) + H_2O_2(aq) \rightarrow H_2O(l) + O_2(g) + I^-(aq) \text{ (fast)}$$

a. What is the reactive intermediate?

b. Does I^- qualify as a catalyst?

c. What is the minimum number of activated complexes needed to describe the reaction?

d. Which of the two reactions has the smallest specific rate constant?

e. Write the balanced equation for the entire reaction.

84. Using the standard entropy data of Table 18.2, calculate the standard entropy change ΔS^0 for this reaction.

$$2NO(g) + 3H_2O(g) \longrightarrow 2NH_3(g) + \frac{5}{2}O_2(g)$$

85. Suppose equilibrium exists for the following reaction at 425 K.

$$Fe_3O_4(s) + 4H_2(g) \rightleftharpoons 3Fe(s) + 4H_2O(g)$$

How would the equilibrium concentration of H_2O be affected by these actions?

a. adding more H_2 to the mixture

b. adding more Fe(*s*)

c. removing $H_2(g)$

d. adding a catalyst

Critical Thinking Questions

86. Choose the term that best completes the second relationship.

a. reaction: intermediate life span: _____

(1) birth (2) products
(3) adolescence (4) 75 years

b. catalyst: inhibitor sunshine: _____

(1) clouds (2) photosynthesis
(3) rain (4) energy

c. temperature: heat entropy: _____

(1) free energy (2) disorder
(3) reaction rate (4) equilibrium

87. An increase in temperature raises the *energy* of the collisions between reactant molecules. An increase in the concentration of reactants increases the *number* of collisions. What is the effect of a catalyst on the collisions between reactant molecules?

88. Make a list of five things you did today that resulted in an increase in entropy.

Cumulative Review

89. Name each of the following ions and identify it as an anion or a cation.

a. F^- **b.** Cu^{2+} **c.** P^{3-} **d.** H^+
e. Na^+ **f.** I^- **g.** O^{2-} **h.** Mg^{2+}

90. Explain how crystalline and amorphous substances differ.

91. What is wrong with saying that solid potassium chloride is composed of KCl molecules?

92. Use ionic charges as a guide to write the formula for each of the following compounds.

a. calcium chloride
b. aluminum sulfide
c. magnesium nitrate
d. aluminum carbonate
e. barium carbonate
f. ammonium nitrate
g. potassium sulfate
h. aluminum phosphate

93. Write electron configurations and draw electron dot structures for the following elements.

a. Ge **b.** Ca **c.** O **d.** Ar **e.** Br **f.** P

94. Name the following compounds and give the charge on the anion for each.

a. $NaClO_4$ **d.** $MgCO_3$
b. $KMnO_4$ **e.** Na_2SO_4
c. $Ca_3(PO_4)_2$ **f.** $K_2Cr_2O_7$

95. List some properties that are typical of ionic compounds.

96. Write the formulas for each of these ionic compounds using electron dot structures.

a. LiBr **b.** $AlCl_3$ **c.** MgF_2 **d.** Na_2S

97. Write the electron configurations and draw electron dot structures for the following:

a. Ca^{2+} **b.** Li^+ **c.** Br^- **d.** S^{2-}

98. Which atoms from the following list would you expect to form positive ions, and which would you expect to form negative ions?

a. Cl **b.** Ca **c.** P **d.** Se **e.** Cu
f. Sn **g.** K **h.** Fe **i.** N **j.** Ni

Challenge Questions and Problems

99. Hemoglobin is a protein molecule in the red blood cell that carries oxygen from the lungs to cells throughout the body. Carbon monoxide poisoning results from formation of a complex of carbon monoxide (CO) with the hemoglobin. This complex is 200 times stronger than the oxygen-hemoglobin complex. This makes it extremely difficult for the oxygen to compete with carbon monoxide in being carried to the cells. When too much hemoglobin is tied up by the carbon monoxide, death occurs by asphyxiation. This is the reaction.

$$\text{Hemoglobin—}O_2 + CO \rightleftharpoons \text{Hemoglobin—}CO + O_2$$

What would be a logical treatment for a person suffering from carbon monoxide poisoning? Using your knowledge of the gas laws, suggest a way to increase the effectiveness of this treatment.

100. Is eating sugar candy really bad for your teeth? Tooth decay is the result of the dissolving of tooth enamel, $Ca_5(PO_4)_3OH$. In the mouth the following equilibrium is established.

$$Ca_5(PO_4)_3OH(s) \rightleftharpoons 5Ca^{2+}(aq) + 3PO_4^{3-}(aq) + OH^-(aq)$$

When sugar ferments on the teeth, H^+ is produced. What effect does this increased H^+ have on tooth enamel?

101. The following data were collected for the decomposition of compound AB into its elements. The reaction is first order in AB.

a. Make a graph of concentration versus time.

b. Using the method shown in Figure 18.24, determine the rate of this reaction at $t = 100$ seconds and $t = 250$ seconds.

[AB] (mol/L)	Time (s)
0.300	0
0.246	50
0.201	100
0.165	150
0.135	200
0.111	250
0.090	300
0.075	350

Connections Questions

102. Why does an auto fender rust where there is a chip in the paint?

103. How was Le Châtelier's work in metallurgy related to the development of his principle of equilibrium?

104. What part does water play in the weathering of rocks?

Write About Chemistry

105. Imagine that you run a videotape of some everyday events "backward." Describe some events you could record that obviously disobey the law of disorder (show a spontaneous decrease in entropy) when run in reverse.

106. Write a paragraph in which you develop an analogy to a system reaching a state of equilibrium.

Readings and References

Davenport, Derek A. "When Push Comes to Shove: Disturbing the Equilibrium." *ChemMatters* (American Chemical Society) (February 1985), p. 14.

Siezen, Roland. "Pumping Oxygen." *ChemMatters* (February 1984), pp. 6–9.

Yohe, Brad. "Toothpaste." *ChemMatters* (February 1986), pp. 12–13.

19 Acids and Bases

Goals

- Distinguish between acidic and basic solutions.
- Convert hydrogen-ion concentrations into values of pH and hydroxide-ion concentrations into values of pOH.
- Compare and contrast acids and bases as defined by the theories of Arrhenius, Brønsted-Lowry, and Lewis.
- Categorize acids and bases by strength according to their dissociation constants.

Nitric acid oxidizes copper metal to produce copper nitrate, the green solution, and nitrogen dioxide, the orange-red gas. One of the strongest acids known is fluoroantimonic acid, HF:SbF_5. A 50% solution of SbF_5 in HF is a quintillion (10^{18}) times stronger than concentrated sulfuric acid.

Concept Overview

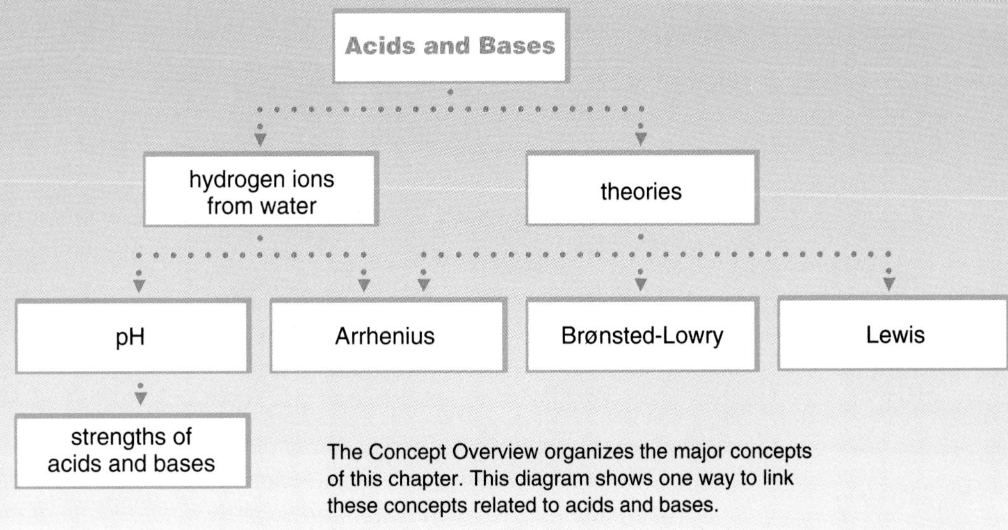

The Concept Overview organizes the major concepts of this chapter. This diagram shows one way to link these concepts related to acids and bases.

Acids and bases play a central role in much of the chemistry that affects your daily life. Many manufacturing processes use acids and bases. Your body needs acids and bases to function properly. For example, foods such as citrus fruits, vinegar, and carbonated beverages contain acids. Bases are present in many commercial products, such as antacid tablets and household cleaning agents.

This chapter explores the qualitative and quantitative aspects of acids and bases. You will see how these two classes of compounds ionize or dissociate in water. You will also see how the concept of pH is used to measure the strength of acidic and basic solutions.

19.1 Properties of Acids and Bases

Objective

List properties of acids and bases.

Many common items contain acids. Acids have many distinctive properties that you are familiar with. Acidic compounds give foods a tart or sour taste. For example, all vinegars contain ethanoic acid, sometimes called acetic acid. Lemons, which taste sour, contain citric acid. Aqueous solutions of acids are electrolytes. Recall that electrolytes conduct electricity. Some acid solutions are strong electrolytes and others are weak electrolytes. Acids cause certain chemical dyes, called indicators, to change color. Many metals, such as zinc and magnesium, react with aqueous solutions of acids to

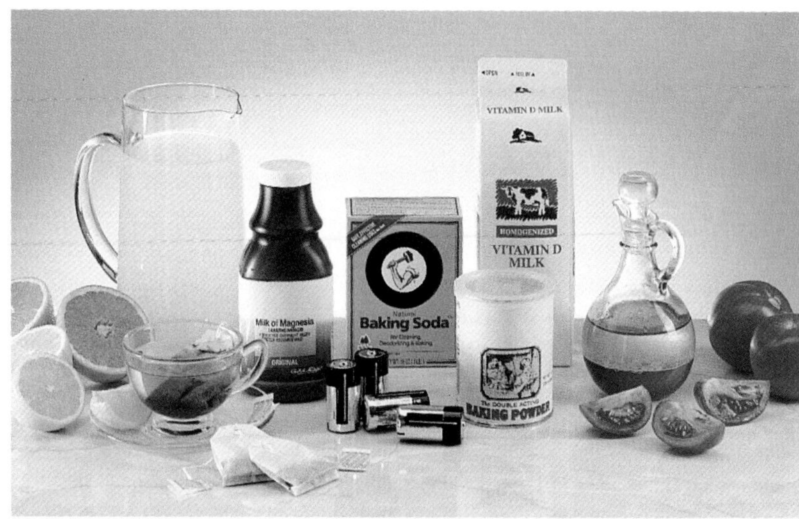

Figure 19.1 All of these items contain acids or bases.

produce hydrogen gas. Acids react with compounds containing hydroxide ions to form water and a salt.

Bases are compounds that react with acids to form water and a salt. Milk of magnesia (magnesium hydroxide) is a base used to treat the problem of excess stomach acid. Aqueous solutions of bases have a bitter taste and feel slippery. Like acids, bases can be strong or weak electrolytes. Like acids, bases change the color of an acid-base indicator.

Safety

Most acids are highly corrosive. Small quantities can be put down the drain with large quantities of water. Large quantities of acid should be neutralized before being discarded.

Concept Practice

1. Identify each property as applying to an acid, a base, or both.

a. bitter taste
b. electrolyte
c. indicator color change
d. sour taste
e. reacts with metal to form $H_2(g)$

Objective

Name an acid or base when given the formula and vice versa.

19.2 Names and Formulas of Acids and Bases

An **acid** *is a compound that produces hydrogen ions when dissolved in water.* The chemical formulas of acids are of the general form HX, where X is a monatomic or polyatomic anion. When the compound $HCl(g)$, hydrogen chloride, is dissolved in water to form $HCl(aq)$, it is named as an acid. Other compounds, such as $HNO_3(aq)$, exist

Table 19.1 Naming Acids

Anion ending	Example	Acid name	Example
-ide	Cl^- chlor*ide*	*hydro*-(stem)-*ic acid*	*hydro*chlor*ic acid*
-ite	SO_3^{2-} sulf*ite*	(stem)-*ous acid*	sulfur*ous acid*
-ate	NO_3^- nitr*ate*	(stem)-*ic acid*	nitr*ic acid*

only in water solution. These compounds are always named as acids. Consider the acid HX dissolved in water. You can name the acid using three rules that focus on the ending of the name of the anion of the acid.

1. When the name of the anion (X) ends in *-ide,* the acid name begins with the prefix *hydro-*. The stem of the anion has the suffix *-ic* and it is followed by the word *acid.* Therefore, $HCl(aq)$ (X = chloride) is named *hydro*chlor*ic acid.* $H_2S(aq)$ (X = sulfide) is *hydro*sulfur*ic acid.* $HF(aq)$ (X = fluoride) is *hydro*fluor*ic acid.*

2. When the anion name ends in *-ite,* the acid name is the stem of the anion with the suffix *-ous,* followed by the word *acid.* $H_2SO_3(aq)$ (X = sulfite) is sulfur*ous acid.* $HNO_2(aq)$ (X = nitrite) is nitr*ous acid.*

3. If the anion name ends in *-ate,* the acid name is the stem of the anion with the suffix *-ic,* followed by the word *acid.* Thus $HNO_3(aq)$ (X = nitrate) is nitr*ic acid.* $H_2CO_3(aq)$ (X = carbonate) is carbon*ic acid.*

Safety

Nitric acid is very reactive and should be stored separately from other acids.

You can also write the formulas of acids by using the preceding three rules in a reverse fashion. For example, what is the formula of chloric acid? As rule 3 shows, chloric acid (*-ic* ending) must be a combination of hydrogen ion (H^+) and chlor*ate* ion (ClO_3^-). The formula of chloric acid is $HClO_3$. According to rule 1, hydrobromic acid (*hydro-* prefix and *-ic* suffix) must be a combination of hydrogen ion and bromide ion (Br^-). The formula of hydrobromic acid is HBr. Hydrogen ion and phosphite ion (PO_3^{3-}) must be the components of phosphorous acid (rule 2). The formula of phosphorous acid is H_3PO_3. (Do not confuse *phosphorous* with *phosphorus,* the element name.)

A **base** *is a compound that produces hydroxide ions when dissolved in water.* Ionic compounds that are bases are named as any other ionic compound: the name of the cation followed by the name of the anion. For example, NaOH is sodium hydroxide and $Ca(OH)_2$ is calcium hydroxide. You write the formulas for bases balancing the ionic charges, just as you write formulas for any ionic compound.

Example 1 Naming Acids

Name these compounds as acids.

a. HClO **b.** HCN **c.** H_3PO_4

Solution

a. hypochlor*ous acid* (rule 2) **c.** phosphor*ic acid* (rule 3)

b. *hydro*cyan*ic acid* (rule 1)

Concept Practice

2. Name these acids and bases.

a. HF **c.** KOH **e.** HNO_2

b. H_3PO_4 **d.** H_2SO_4 **f.** $Mg(OH)_2$

Practice Problem

3. Write formulas for the following acids and bases.

a. chromic acid **d.** lithium hydroxide

b. iron(II) hydroxide **e.** chlorous acid

c. hydroiodic acid **f.** perchloric acid

Objective

Classify a solution as neutral, acidic, or basic, given the hydrogen-ion or hydroxide-ion concentration.

19.3 Hydrogen Ions from Water

Water molecules are highly polar. Even at room temperature they are in continuous motion. Occasionally, the collisions between water molecules are energetic enough that a hydrogen ion transfers from one water molecule to another. *A water molecule that loses a hydrogen ion becomes a negatively charged* **hydroxide ion** (OH^-). *A water molecule that gains a hydrogen ion becomes a positively charged* **hydronium ion** (H_3O^+).

$$H{:}\ddot{\underset{\cdot\cdot}{O}}{:}H + H{:}\ddot{\underset{\cdot\cdot}{O}}{:}H \longrightarrow [H{:}\ddot{\underset{\cdot\cdot}{O}}{:}H\ H]^+ + [H{:}\ddot{\underset{\cdot\cdot}{O}}{:}]^-$$

Water molecules — Hydronium ion — Hydroxide ion

The reaction in which two water molecules react to give ions is the **self-ionization** *of water.* This reaction can also be written as a simple dissociation.

$$H_2O(l) \rightleftharpoons \underset{\text{Hydrogen ion}}{H^+(aq)} + \underset{\text{Hydroxide ion}}{OH^-(aq)}$$

In water or aqueous solution, hydrogen ions (H^+) are always joined to water molecules as hydronium ions (H_3O^+). The hydronium ions are themselves solvated to form species such as $H_9O_4^+$. Hydrogen ions in aqueous solution have several names. Some chemists call them protons. Others prefer to call them hydrogen ions, or hydronium ions, or solvated protons. In this book either H^+ or H_3O^+ is used to represent hydrogen ions in aqueous solution.

The self-ionization of water occurs to a very small extent. In pure water at 25°C the concentration of hydrogen ions, $[H^+]$, and the concentration of hydroxide ions, $[OH^-]$, are each only 1.0×10^{-7} mol/L. Note that the concentrations of H^+ and OH^- must be equal in pure water. These ions are produced in a 1:1 ratio. In fact, *any aqueous solution in which [H⁺] and [OH⁻] are equal is described as a* **neutral solution**. Pure water is a neutral substance.

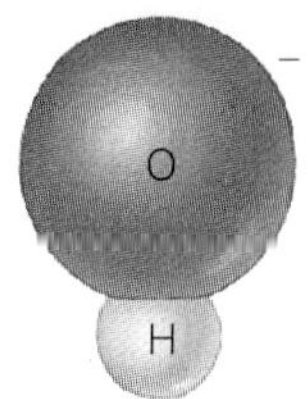

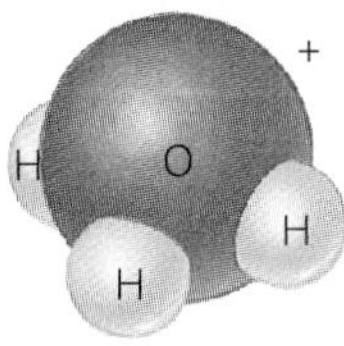

Figure 19.2 Which of these ions is a hydronium ion? Which is a hydroxide ion?

In any aqueous solution $[H^+]$ and $[OH^-]$ are interdependent. If $[H^+]$ increases, then $[OH^-]$ decreases. If $[H^+]$ decreases, then $[OH^-]$ increases. Le Châtelier's principle applies here. If additional ions (either hydrogen ions or hydroxide ions) are added to the solution, the equilibrium shifts. The concentration of the other type of ion decreases. More water molecules form in the process.

$$H^+(aq) + OH^-(aq) \rightleftharpoons H_2O(l)$$

For aqueous solutions the product of the hydrogen-ion concentration, $[H^+]$, and the hydroxide-ion concentration, $[OH^-]$, is equal to $1.0 \times 10^{-14}(\text{mol/L})^2$.

$$[H^+] \times [OH^-] = 1.0 \times 10^{-14}(\text{mol/L})^2$$

The product of the concentrations of the hydrogen ions and hydroxide ions in water is K_w, the **ion-product constant for water**.

$$K_w = [H^+] \times [OH^-] = 1.0 \times 10^{-14}(\text{mol/L})^2$$

Not all solutions are neutral. When some substances dissolve in water they release hydrogen ions. For example, when hydrogen chloride dissolves in water, it forms hydrochloric acid.

$$HCl(g) \xrightarrow{\text{water}} H^+(aq) + Cl^-(aq)$$

In such a solution, the hydrogen-ion concentration, $[H^+]$, is greater than the hydroxide-ion concentration, $[OH^-]$. (The hydroxide ions are present from the self-ionization of water.) *In any* **acidic solution** *the [H⁺] is greater than the [OH⁻].* Therefore, the $[H^+]$ of an acidic solution is always greater than 1.0×10^{-7} mol/L.

Safety

Never taste acids or any other chemical in the laboratory.

When sodium hydroxide dissolves in water it forms hydroxide ions in solution.

$$NaOH(s) \xrightarrow{\text{water}} Na^+(aq) + OH^-(aq)$$

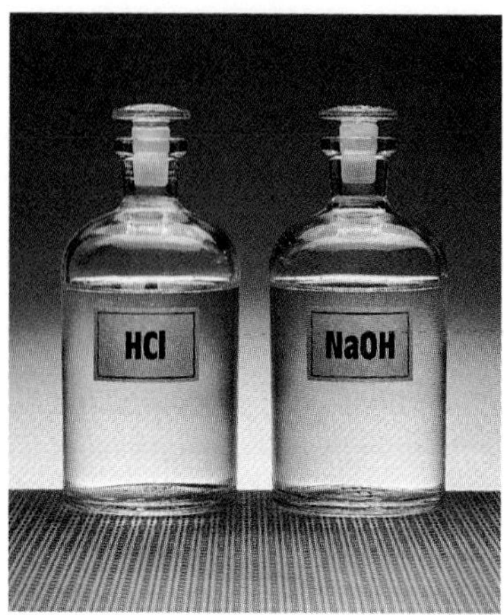

Figure 19.3 These two reagents are an acid and a base. The concentration of hydrogen ions is much greater in HCl(*aq*) than in NaOH (*aq*).

In such a solution, the hydrogen-ion concentration, $[H^+]$, is less than the hydroxide-ion concentration, $[OH^-]$. (The hydrogen ions are present from the self-ionization of water.) *In any* **basic solution** *the* $[H^+]$ *is less than the* $[OH^-]$. Therefore the $[H^+]$ of a basic solution is always less than 1.0×10^{-7} mol/L. *Basic solutions are also known as* **alkaline solutions.**

Example 2 Finding the $[OH^-]$ of a Solution

If $[H^+] = 1.0 \times 10^{-5}$ mol/L, is the solution acidic, basic, or neutral? What is the $[OH^-]$ of this solution?

Solution

The $[H^+]$ is 1.0×10^{-5} mol/L. Because the $[H^+]$ is greater than 1.0×10^{-7} mol/L, the solution is acidic. You know that

$$K_w = [H^+] \times [OH^-]$$

Therefore, the $[OH^-] = K_w / [H^+]$. Substituting the numerical values

$$K_w = 1.0 \times 10^{-14}\ (\text{mol/L})^2$$

and $[H^+] = 1.0 \times 10^{-5}$ mol/L, you can calculate $[OH^-]$.

$$[OH^-] = \frac{1.0 \times 10^{-14}\ (\text{mol/L})^{\cancel{2}}}{1.0 \times 10^{-5}\ \cancel{\text{mol/L}}} = 1.0 \times 10^{-9}\ \text{mol/L}$$

Problem-Solving Tip

Check that the answer has the appropriate unit after canceling and before doing the numerical calculation.

Concept Practice

4. What is true about the relative concentrations of hydrogen ions and hydroxide ions in each of these solutions?
a. basic **b.** acidic **c.** neutral

5. Classify each solution as acidic, basic, or neutral.
a. $[H^+] = 6 \times 10^{-10}$ mol/L
b. $[OH^-] = 3 \times 10^{-2}$ mol/L
c. $[H^+] = 2 \times 10^{-7}$ mol/L
d. $[OH^-] = 1 \times 10^{-7}$ mol/L

Practice Problem

6. If the hydroxide-ion concentration of an aqueous solution is 1.0×10^{-3} mol/L, what is the $[H^+]$ in the solution? Is the solution acidic, basic, or neutral?

19.4 The pH Concept

Objective

Calculate the pH of a solution given the hydrogen-ion or hydroxide-ion concentration.

The written expression for hydrogen-ion concentration in moles per liter is cumbersome. A more widely used system for expressing $[H^+]$ is the pH scale, proposed in 1909 by Danish scientist Søren Sørensen (1868–1939). On the pH scale, neutral solutions have a pH of 7.0. A pH of 0 is strongly acidic. A pH of 14 is strongly basic. Calculating the pH of a solution is straightforward. *The* **pH** *of a solution is the negative logarithm of the hydrogen-ion concentration.*

$$pH = -\log[H^+]$$

In a neutral solution $[H^+] = 1.0 \times 10^{-7}$ mol/L. The pH of a neutral solution is 7.

$$\begin{aligned} pH &= -\log(1.0 \times 10^{-7}\ \text{mol/L}) \\ &= -(\log 1 + \log 10^{-7}) \\ &= -(0.0 + (-7)) = 7.0 \end{aligned}$$

For pH calculations, you should express the hydrogen-ion concentration in scientific notation. For example, you rewrite a hydrogen-ion concentration of 0.001*M* as $1 \times 10^{-3}M$. The pH of this solution is 3.0 as shown in Figure 19.4. A solution with a pH of 3.0 is acidic.

In a similar way, the pOH of a solution equals the negative logarithm of the hydroxide-ion concentration.

$$pOH = -\log[OH^-]$$

A neutral solution has a pOH of 7.0. A solution with a pOH less than 7.0 is basic. A solution with a pOH greater than 7.0 is acidic. A simple relationship between pH and pOH makes it easy to find either pH or pOH when the other is known:

$$pH + pOH = 14$$

$$pH = 14 - pOH$$

$$pOH = 14 - pH$$

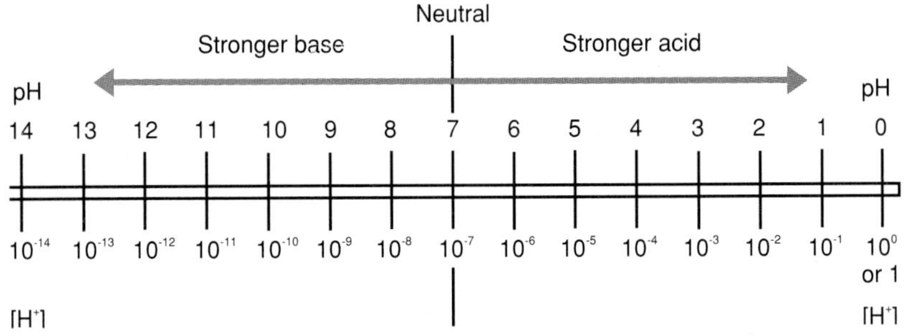

Figure 19.4 The pH scale shows the relationship between pH and the hydrogen-ion concentration. Notice that acids have lower pHs than bases.

Example 3 Calculating pH from $[H^+]$

Problem-Solving Tip

As long as the $[H^+]$ is less than $1.0M$, the pH is always positive.

The hydrogen-ion concentration of a solution is 1×10^{-10} mol/L. What is the pH of the solution?

Solution

You know that the $[H^+] = 1 \times 10^{-10}$ mol/L.

$$pH = -\log[H^+] = -(\log 1 + \log 10^{-10})$$
$$= -(0.0 + (-10)) = 10.0$$

A solution in which the $[H^+]$ is 1×10^{-10} mol/L has a pH of 10.0.

Practice Problem

7. Determine the pH of the following solutions.

a. $[H^+] = 1 \times 10^{-6}$ mol/L

b. $[H^+] = 0.0001M$

c. $[OH^-] = 1 \times 10^{-2}$ mol/L

d. $[OH^-] = 1 \times 10^{-11}$ mol/L

Example 4 Using pH to Find $[H^+]$

Problem-Solving Tip

To solve this problem you can work backward.

The pH of a solution is 6.0. Find $[H^+]$ for this solution.

Solution

$$pH = -\log[H^+]$$
$$6.0 = -\log[H^+]$$
$$-6.0 = \log[H^+]$$

The number whose log is –6.0 is 1×10^{-6}. Therefore the $[H^+] = 1 \times 10^{-6}$ mol/L.

Practice Problems

8. What are the hydrogen-ion concentrations of solutions with the following pH values?

a. 4.0 **b.** 11.0 **c.** 8.0

9. What are the hydroxide-ion concentrations of solutions with the following pH values?

a. 6.0 **b.** 9.0 **c.** 12.0

Table 19.2 Relationship between the $[H^+]$, the $[OH^-]$, and pH

	$[H^+]$ (mol/L)	$[OH^-]$ (mol/L)	pH	Aqueous system
↑ Increasing acidity	1×10^{0}	1×10^{-14}	0.0	1*M* HCl (0.0)
	1×10^{-1}	1×10^{-13}	1.0	0.1*M* HCl (1.0)
	1×10^{-2}	1×10^{-12}	2.0	Gastric juice (1.6–1.8)
	1×10^{-3}	1×10^{-11}	3.0	Lemon juice (2.3), vinegar (2.4–3.4)
	1×10^{-4}	1×10^{-10}	4.0	Soda water (3.8), tomato juice (4.2)
	1×10^{-5}	1×10^{-9}	5.0	Black coffee (5.0)
	1×10^{-6}	1×10^{-8}	6.0	Milk (6.3–6.6), urine (5.5–7.0)
Neutral	1×10^{-7}	1×10^{-7}	7.0	Pure water (7.0), saliva (6.2–7.4)
Increasing basicity ↓	1×10^{-8}	1×10^{-6}	8.0	Blood (7.35–7.45), bile (7.8–8.6)
	1×10^{-9}	1×10^{-5}	9.0	Sodium bicarbonate (8.4), seawater (8.4)
	1×10^{-10}	1×10^{-4}	10.0	Milk of magnesia (10.5)
	1×10^{-11}	1×10^{-3}	11.0	Household ammonia (11.5)
	1×10^{-12}	1×10^{-2}	12.0	Washing soda (12.0)
	1×10^{-13}	1×10^{-1}	13.0	0.1*M* NaOH (13.0)
	1×10^{-14}	1×10^{0}	14.0	1*M* NaOH (14.0)

The pH of pure water or a neutral aqueous solution is 7.0. A solution in which the $[H^+]$ is greater than 1×10^{-7} mol/L has a pH less than 7.0 and is acidic. A solution that has a pH greater than 7.0 is basic and has an $[H^+]$ of less than 1×10^{-7} mol/L.

- *Neutral solution:* pH = 7.0; the $[H^+]$ equals 1×10^{-7} mol/L.
- *Acidic solution:* pH is < 7.0; the $[H^+]$ is greater than 1×10^{-7} mol/L.
- *Basic solution:* pH > 7.0; the $[H^+]$ is less than 1×10^{-7} mol/L.

The pH values of a number of common aqueous solutions are listed in Table 19.2. The table also summarizes the relationship between the $[H^+]$, the $[OH^-]$, and pH. If $[H^+]$ is written in scientific notation and has a coefficient of 1, the pH equals the exponent with the sign changed from minus to plus. For example, a solution with $[H^+] = 1 \times 10^{-2}$ mol/L has a pH of 2.

Practice Problem

10. Give the pH of each of the following solutions.

a. $[H^+] = 1 \times 10^{-4}$

b. $[H^+] = 0.001$

c. $[OH^-] = 0.01$

d. $[OH^-] = 1 \times 10^{-6}$

19.A Environmental Awareness

Acid Rain

Even in a clean, unpolluted environment rain and snow are slightly acidic. Water dissolves small amounts of carbon dioxide gas from the air, forming carbonic acid (H_2CO_3). Normal rainwater is pH 5.6. Gaseous air pollutants can acidify the rain. Thus when you hear the term *acid rain,* it refers to rain with a pH less than 5.6.

A 1981 rainstorm in Baltimore was pH 2.7, about the same as that of vinegar. In 1986, a fog in California was pH 1.7, almost as acidic as stomach acid. Acid rain causes enormous damage to stone structures, paint, metal, and the environment.

The main pollutants responsible for acid rain are sulfur and nitrogen oxides. These pollutants come from automobile exhaust and industrial plants that burn coal and oil. In the atmosphere, these pollutants form sulfuric acid (H_2SO_4) and nitric acid (HNO_3). Eventually, they fall to earth as acid rain.

Figure 19.5 Acid rain can be very damaging to marble masterpieces and to vegetation.

Acid rain damages forests and reduces the pH of many lakes, killing fish. Fish die when lake or stream water drops below pH 4.5–5.0. Evidence also shows that nitric acid is very damaging to pine forests. Many northern regions, which receive the bulk of acid rain, have had their large pine forests drastically affected.

Some attempts are being made to moderate the effects of acid rain by adding limestone to acidic lakes. Limestone contains calcium carbonate ($CaCO_3$), which neutralizes the acid. However, too many lakes are affected by acid rain to make this a practical solution. Some SO_2 from burning coal can be removed by smokestack "scrubbers." In a scrubber, the smoke passes through an aqueous suspension of lime (CaO). The lime reacts with gaseous SO_2 to make calcium sulfite ($CaSO_3$), preventing the sulfur from entering the atmosphere.

$$CaO(s) + SO_2(g) \longrightarrow CaSO_3(s)$$

Unfortunately, the enormous amounts of $CaSO_3$ and other solid wastes that are generated present a serious waste disposal problem. Since the acid rain problem is international, world governments need to cooperate in reducing smokestack and auto emissions.

Think About It

11. Explain How are the compounds that contribute to acid rain produced?

12. Analyze Name some things you could do to reduce the potential for acid rain formation.

19.5 Calculating pH Values

Objective

Calculate the hydrogen-ion or hydroxide-ion concentration given the pH of a solution.

Most pH values are not whole numbers. For example, Table 19.2 shows that milk of magnesia has a pH of 10.5. Using the definition of pH, this means that the $[H^+]$ must equal $1 \times 10^{-10.5}$. Therefore, the $[H^+]$ must be less than 1×10^{-10} (pH 10.0) but greater than 1×10^{-11} (pH 11.0).

If the $[H^+]$ is written in scientific notation but its coefficient is *not* 1, then you need a table of common logarithms or a calculator with a log function key to calculate the pH. A four-place Table of Common Logarithms is provided in Appendix B.5. The following example shows how to make such a pH calculation.

Roots of Words

logo-: (Greek) word or short phrase
arithmos: (Greek) number
logarithm the exponent to which a base number must be raised to obtain a specified number

In logarithms to base 10, the logarithm of 100 is 2, since $100 = 10^2$.

Example 5 Calculating pH from $[H^+]$

What is the pH of a solution if the $[OH^-] = 4.0 \times 10^{-11}$ mol/L?

Solution

To calculate pH, you first calculate the $[H^+]$. Use the definition of K_w.

$$K_w = [OH^-] \times [H^+]$$

$$[H^+] = \frac{K_w}{[OH^-]} = \frac{1.0 \times 10^{-14}}{4.0 \times 10^{-11}} = 0.25 \times 10^{-3}$$

$$= 2.5 \times 10^{-4} \text{ mol/L}$$

Then you solve for the pH using the definition of pH.

$$pH = -\log[H^+]$$

$$= -\log(2.5 \times 10^{-4})$$

$$= -(\log 2.5 + \log 10^{-4})$$

Use the log table to find that $\log 2.5 = 0.40$. From the table, you see that $\log 10^{-4} = -4$.

$$pH = -(0.40) - (-4)$$

$$= -0.40 + 4 = 3.60$$

Practice Problem

13. Calculate the pH for each solution.

a. $[H^+] = 5.0 \times 10^{-6}$

b. $[H^+] = 8.3 \times 10^{-10}$

c. $[OH^-] = 2.0 \times 10^{-5}$

d. $[OH^-] = 4.5 \times 10^{-11}$

Problem-Solving Tip

To find the pH on a calculator, enter $[H^+]$ (use scientific notation if the calculator has an exponential function key), then push the *log* key. The value displayed is the *negative* of the pH.

Integrating Home Economics

Food Canning

Home-canned foods can be tasty and healthy, as long as you take proper precautions in their preparation. Boiling and steaming are necessary to destroy microorganisms. The bacterium *Clostridium botulinum* causes the deadly food-poisoning disease botulism. Because *C. botulinum* cannot grow below pH 4.5, only acidic fruits and vegetables such as tomatoes, pears, apricots, and peaches are recommended for home canning. Nonacidic vegetables such as cucumbers and cabbage are not recommended. However, cucumbers can be preserved by pickling in salt and vinegar (pH 3.0). Cabbage is often preserved by fermenting it to acidic sauerkraut (pH 3.7).

You can calculate the hydrogen-ion concentration of a solution if you know the pH. For example, if the solution has a pH of 3.0, then the $[H^+] = 1.0 \times 10^{-3}$ mol/L. When the pH is not a whole number, you need log tables or a calculator with a Y^x function key to calculate the hydrogen-ion concentration. For example, if the pH is 3.7 the hydrogen-ion concentration must be greater than 1.0×10^{-4} mol/L (pH 4.0) and less than 1.0×10^{-3} mol/L (pH 3.0.) To get an accurate value, use the log tables.

Example 6 Finding $[H^+]$ of a Solution of Known pH

What is the $[H^+]$ of a solution if pH = 3.7?

Solution

You first rearrange the equation: $pH = -\log[H^+]$

$$\log[H^+] = -pH = -3.7$$

You cannot use a log table directly to find a number whose log is negative. To get around this problem, add and subtract the whole number that is closest to and larger than the negative log. In this example, the negative log is 3.7, and the whole number is 4.

$$\log[H^+] = (-3.7 + 4) - 4$$
$$= 0.3 - 4$$
$$[H^+] = 10^{(0.3-4)}$$
$$= 10^{0.3} \times 10^{-4}$$

Use the log table to find the number whose log is 0.3. That number, called the antilog of 0.3, is 2. Then find the number whose log is –4. That number is 10^{-4}. Therefore the $[H^+] = 2 \times 10^{-4}$ mol/L. To use a calculator with a Y^x function key, remember that $[H^+] = 10^{-pH}$. That is, $[H^+]$ is written in the form Y^x. In this example, you would change the sign of the given pH to –3.7. Enter Y = 10, x = –3.7, and press the Y^x key in the order required by your calculator. The readout gives you 1.995×10^{-4}. Rounded to one significant figure, $[H^+] = 2 \times 10^{-4}$ mol/L.

Practice Problem

14. Calculate the $[H^+]$ for each solution.

a. pH = 5.0 **b.** pH = 5.80 **c.** pH = 12.20 **d.** pH = 2.64

19.6 Arrhenius Acids and Bases

Objective

Define and give examples of Arrhenius acids and bases.

In 1887 the Swedish chemist Svante Arrhenius proposed a revolutionary way of thinking about acids and bases. He said that *acids are compounds containing hydrogen that ionize to yield hydrogen ions (H^+) in aqueous solution.* Also, he said that *bases are compounds that ionize to yield hydroxide ions (OH^-) in aqueous solution.*

Table 19.3 lists some important acids. Nitric acid (HNO_3) or *any acid that contains one ionizable hydrogen is called a* **monoprotic acid.** Sulfuric acid (H_2SO_4) or *any acid that contains two ionizable protons is a* **diprotic acid.** Phosphoric acid (H_3PO_4) or *any acid that contains three ionizable protons is a* **triprotic acid**. Do not assume that all compounds containing hydrogen are acids or that all the hydrogens in an acid are released as hydrogen ions. Only the hydrogens in very polar bonds are ionizable. In such a bond, hydrogen is joined to a very electronegative element. A compound that contains such bonds releases hydrogen ions when it dissolves in water. This occurs because the hydrogen ions are stabilized by solvation. An example is the hydrogen chloride molecule shown in Figure 19.6. Hydrogen chloride is a polar covalent molecule. It ionizes to form hydrochloric acid in aqueous solution.

$$\underset{\text{Hydrogen chloride}}{\overset{\delta+}{H}-\overset{\delta-}{Cl}(g)} \xrightarrow{\text{water}} \underset{\substack{\text{Hydrogen}\\\text{ion}}}{H^+(aq)} + \underset{\substack{\text{Chloride}\\\text{ion}}}{Cl^-(aq)}$$

(hydrochloric acid)

Table 19.3 Some Common Acids

Name	Formula
Hydrochloric acid	HCl
Nitric acid	HNO_3
Sulfuric acid	H_2SO_4
Phosphoric acid	H_3PO_4
Ethanoic acid	CH_3COOH
Carbonic acid	H_2CO_3

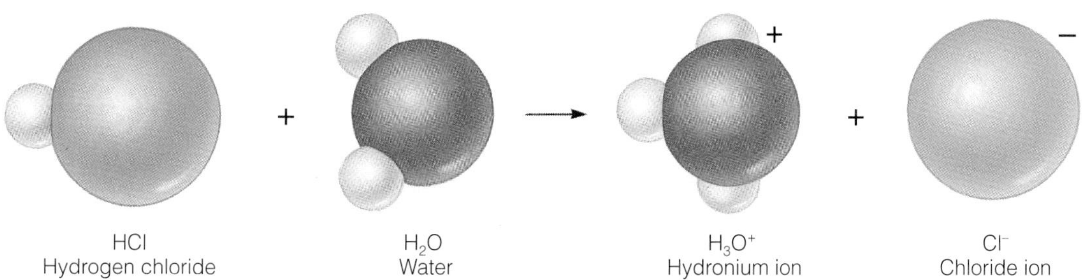

Figure 19.6 Hydrochloric acid is actually hydrogen chloride dissolved in water. The ionized hydrogen forms hydronium ions and makes this compound an acid.

Figure 19.7 Hydrochloric acid, commonly known as muriatic acid, is used to clean stone buildings and swimming pools.

In contrast, the four hydrogens in methane (CH_4) are in weakly polar C—H bonds. Methane has no ionizable hydrogens and is not an acid. Ethanoic acid (CH_3COOH) is different. Although each molecule contains four hydrogens, ethanoic acid is a monoprotic acid. The structural formula shows why.

```
   H  O
   |  ||
H—C—C—O—H
   |
   H
```

Ethanoic acid
(CH_3COOH)

The three hydrogens attached to carbon are in weakly polar bonds. They do not ionize. Only the hydrogen attached to oxygen is ionizable. As you see more written formulas, you will learn to recognize ionizable hydrogens.

Table 19.4 lists some common bases. The base with which you are perhaps most familiar is sodium hydroxide (NaOH). Ordinary lye, shown in Figure 19.8 being used to clean a clogged drain, is sodium hydroxide. Sodium metal reacts with water to form sodium hydroxide.

$$\underset{\text{Sodium metal}}{2Na(s)} + \underset{\text{Water}}{2H_2O(l)} \longrightarrow \underset{\text{Sodium hydroxide}}{2NaOH(aq)} + \underset{\text{Hydrogen}}{H_2(g)}$$

Table 19.4 Some Common Bases

Name	Formula	Solubility in water
Potassium hydroxide	KOH	High
Sodium hydroxide	NaOH	High
Calcium hydroxide	$Ca(OH)_2$	Very low
Magnesium hydroxide	$Mg(OH)_2$	Very low

Figure 19.8 Sodium hydroxide, commonly called lye, is used to clean clogged drains because it is very corrosive.

Potassium reacts vigorously with water to produce potassium hydroxide (KOH). Both sodium hydroxide and potassium hydroxide are ionic solids. They dissociate completely into the metal ions and hydroxide ions when dissolved in water.

$$\underset{\text{Sodium hydroxide}}{NaOH(s)} \xrightarrow{\text{water}} \underset{\text{Sodium ion}}{Na^+(aq)} + \underset{\text{Hydroxide ion}}{OH^-(aq)}$$

Sodium and potassium are Group 1A elements. Elements in Group 1A, the alkali metals, react with water to produce alkaline solutions. Metal oxides also react with water to produce alkaline solutions. Both sodium hydroxide and potassium hydroxide are very soluble in water. Concentrated solutions of these compounds are readily prepared. Such solutions, like other basic solutions, would have a bitter taste and slippery feel. Note, however, that they are extremely corrosive to the skin. They can cause painful, deep, slow-healing wounds if not immediately washed off.

Calcium hydroxide, $Ca(OH)_2$, and magnesium hydroxide, $Mg(OH)_2$, are both hydroxides of Group 2A metals. They are not very soluble in water. Consequently, their solutions are always very dilute, even when saturated. The concentration of hydroxide ions in such solutions is correspondingly low. A saturated solution of calcium hydroxide contains 0.165 g of calcium hydroxide. Magnesium hydroxide is much less soluble than calcium hydroxide. A saturated solution contains only 0.0009 g of $Mg(OH)_2$ per 100 g of water. Suspensions of magnesium hydroxide in water contain low concentrations of hydroxide ion. They are taken internally as "milk of magnesia," an antacid and mild laxative.

Concept Practice

15. Identify the following acids as monoprotic, diprotic, or triprotic.
a. H_2CO_3 **b.** H_3PO_4 **c.** HCl

Practice Problem

16. Write a balanced equation for each reaction. Be sure to show the products!
a. Potassium metal reacts with water.
b. Calcium metal reacts with water.
c. Potassium hydroxide dissolves in water.
d. Magnesium hydroxide dissolves in water.

Biographical Note

Svante Arrhenius
(1859–1927)

The Swedish chemist Svante Arrhenius was educated in the Swedish universities at Uppsala and Stockholm. While working on his Ph.D. dissertation, he devised his theory that some compounds dissociate into ions in aqueous solution. Later he extended this idea to explain certain behaviors of acids and bases. At first, Arrhenius's ideas were not readily accepted. He received the lowest possible passing grade for his Ph.D. defense. However, when Thomson discovered the electrically charged electron in the 1890s, Arrhenius's ideas gained acceptance. In 1903 Arrhenius's work was formally recognized when he received the Nobel Prize in Chemistry.

Objective

Classify substances as acids or bases, and identify conjugate acid-base pairs in acid-base reactions using the Brønsted-Lowry theory.

19.7 Brønsted-Lowry Acids and Bases

One problem with the Arrhenius theory of acids and bases is that it is not comprehensive enough. It does not explain the properties of all compounds that behave as bases. For example, aqueous solutions of ammonia, $NH_3(aq)$, and sodium carbonate, $Na_2CO_3(aq)$, are basic. Neither of these compounds is a hydroxide. In 1923 Johannes Brønsted (Danish, 1879–1947) and Thomas Lowry (English, 1874–1936) independently proposed a new theory. *The Brønsted-Lowry theory defines an acid as a* **hydrogen-ion donor**. Similarly, *a Brønsted-Lowry base is a* **hydrogen-ion acceptor**. All the acids and bases included in the Arrhenius theory are also acids and bases according to the Brønsted-Lowry theory. Some compounds that were not included in the Arrhenius theory are classified as bases by the Brønsted-Lowry theory.

The behavior of ammonia as a base can be understood by the Brønsted-Lowry theory. Ammonia gas is very soluble in water. When ammonia dissolves in water it acts as a base because it accepts a hydrogen ion from water.

Safety

Ammonia is a very irritating gas. Use care when smelling chemicals. Wave your hand over the open container to waft the aroma to your nose.

$NH_3(aq)$	+	$H_2O(l)$	$\rightleftharpoons$	$NH_4^+(aq)$	+	$OH^-(aq)$
Ammonia (hydrogen-ion acceptor, Brønsted-Lowry base)		Water (hydrogen-ion donor, Brønsted-Lowry acid)		Ammonium ion		Hydroxide ion (makes the solution basic)

In this reaction ammonia is the hydrogen-ion acceptor. Therefore it is a Brønsted-Lowry base. Water, the hydrogen-ion donor, is a Brønsted-Lowry acid. Hydrogen ions are transferred from water to ammonia as shown in Figure 19.9. This causes the hydroxide-ion concentration to be greater than it is in pure water. As a result, solutions of ammonia are basic.

Heating an aqueous solution of ammonia drives off ammonia gas. As the ammonia gas moves out of solution, the equilibrium in the ammonia dissolution equation shifts to the left. The ammonium ion, NH_4^+, reacts with OH^- to form NH_3 and H_2O. When the reaction goes from right to left, NH_4^+ gives up a hydrogen ion; it acts as a Brønsted-Lowry acid. The hydroxide ion accepts a H^+; it acts as a

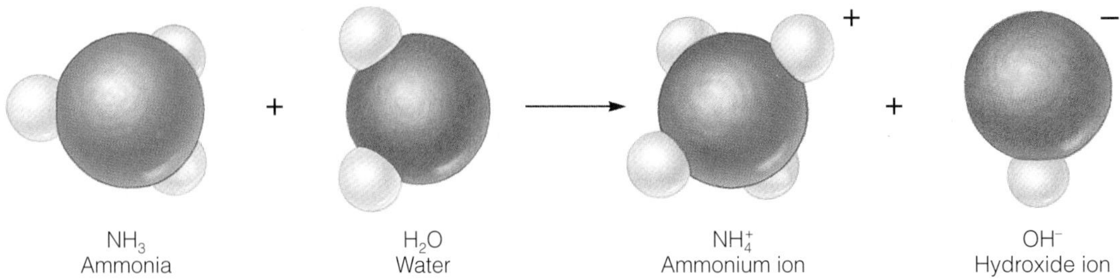

Figure 19.9 Ammonia dissolves in water to form ammonium ions and hydroxide ions. Why isn't ammonia an Arrhenius base?

Brønsted-Lowry base. Overall then, this equilibrium has two acids and two bases.

$$\underset{\text{Base}}{NH_3(aq)} + \underset{\text{Acid}}{H_2O(l)} \rightleftharpoons \underset{\text{Conjugate acid}}{NH_4^+(aq)} + \underset{\text{Conjugate base}}{OH^-(aq)}$$

When ammonia dissolves, NH_4^+ is the *conjugate acid* of the base NH_3. *A* **conjugate acid** *is the particle formed when a base gains a hydrogen ion.* Similarly, OH^- is the *conjugate base* of the acid water. *A* **conjugate base** *is the particle that remains when an acid has donated a hydrogen ion.* Conjugate acids and bases are always paired with an acid and a base. *A* **conjugate acid-base pair** *is two substances that are related by the loss or gain of a single hydrogen ion.* The ammonia molecule and ammonium ion are a conjugate acid-base pair. The water molecule and hydroxide ion are also a conjugate acid-base pair.

$$\underset{\text{Base}}{NH_3(aq)} + \underset{\text{Acid}}{H_2O(l)} \rightleftharpoons \underset{\text{Conjugate acid}}{NH_4^+(aq)} + \underset{\text{Conjugate base}}{OH^-(aq)}$$

The Brønsted-Lowry theory is also applicable to acids. Consider the ionization of hydrogen chloride in water.

$$\underset{\text{Acid}}{HCl(g)} + \underset{\text{Base}}{H_2O(l)} \rightleftharpoons \underset{\text{Conjugate acid}}{H_3O^+(aq)} + \underset{\text{Conjugate base}}{Cl^-(aq)}$$

Hydrogen chloride is the hydrogen-ion donor. It is a Brønsted-Lowry acid. Water is the hydrogen-ion acceptor. It is a Brønsted-Lowry base. The chloride ion is the conjugate base of HCl. The hydronium ion is the conjugate acid of water. Compare this to what happens when sulfuric acid dissolves in water, in Figure 19.10.

Sometimes water receives a hydrogen ion. At other times it donates a hydrogen ion. *A substance that can act as both an acid and a base is termed* **amphoteric**. Water is amphoteric. In the reaction with HCl, water accepts a proton and is therefore a base. In the reaction with NH_3, water donates a proton and is an acid.

Roots of Words

amphoteros: (Greek) partly one and partly the other

amphoteric acting both as an acid and as a base

Water is an amphoteric substance in the Brønsted-Lowry sense because it can act as both a proton donor (acid) and a proton acceptor (base).

Figure 19.10 When sulfuric acid dissolves in water it forms hydronium ions and hydrogen sulfate ions. Which ion is the conjugate acid and which is the conjugate base?

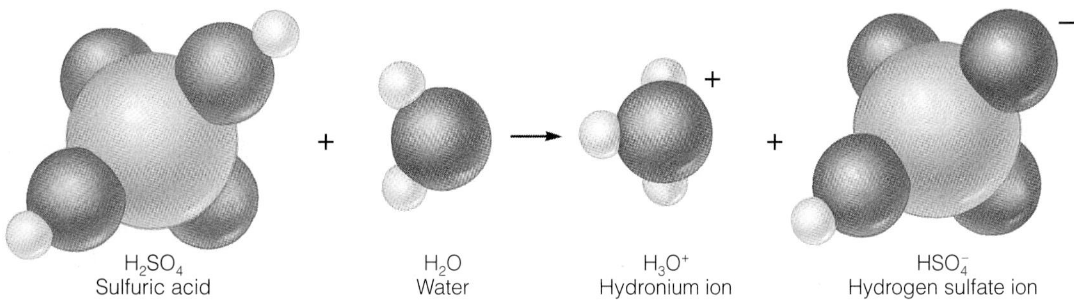

Concept Practice

17. How are acids and bases defined by the Brønsted-Lowry theory? What advantage does this theory have over the theory proposed by Arrhenius?

Practice Problem

18. Write equations for the ionization of HNO_3 and Na_2CO_3 in water.

a. Identify the hydrogen-ion donor and hydrogen-ion acceptor in each case.

b. Label the conjugate acid-base pairs.

Objective

Describe at least two methods used to measure pH.

19.8 Measuring pH

People need to be able to measure the pH of the solutions they use. For preliminary pH measurements and for small-volume samples, indicators like those in Figure 19.11 are often used. For precise and continuous measurements, a pH meter is preferred.

An *indicator* (In) is a weak acid or base that undergoes dissociation in a known pH range. In this range the acid (or base) is a different color from its conjugate base (or acid). The following generalized equation represents this process.

$$\underset{\text{Acid}}{HIn(aq)} \underset{H^+}{\overset{OH^-}{\rightleftharpoons}} \underset{\text{Conjugate base}}{In^-(aq)} + H_2O(l)$$

Figure 19.11 Acid-base indicators respond to pH changes over a specific range. Methyl orange (left group) is shown at pH 2, 4, and 6 (left to right). Bromthymol blue (right group) is shown at pH 5, 7, and 9.

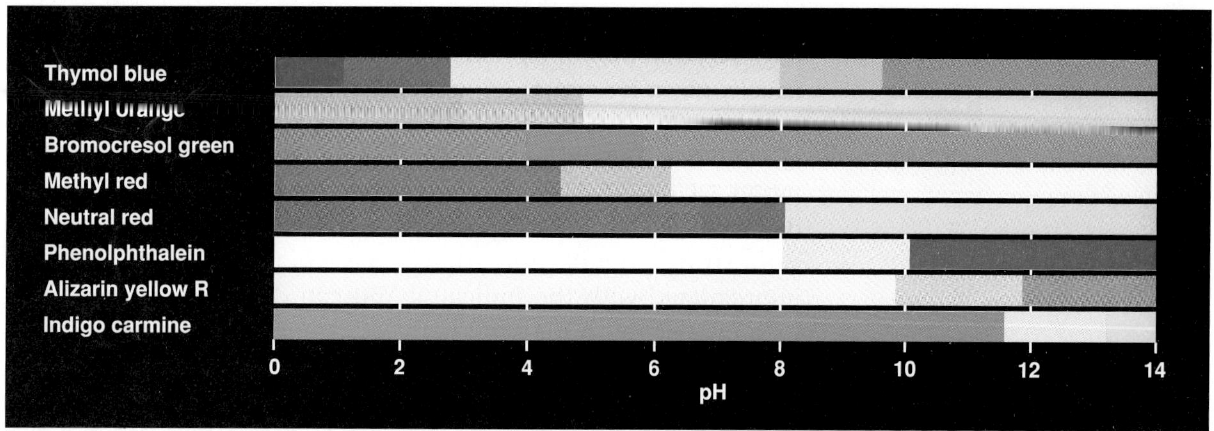

Figure 19.12 Each indicator changes color at a different pH. What indicator would you choose to show that a reaction solution has changed from pH 3 to pH 6?

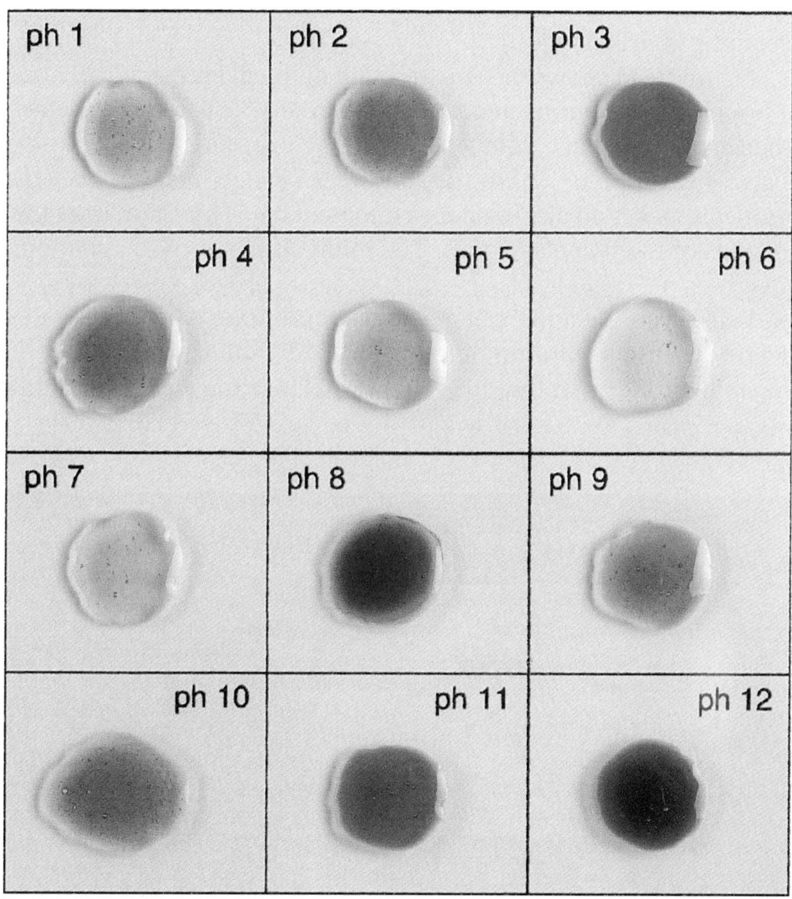

Figure 19.13 You use this colorimetric pH meter similarly to the way you use pH paper. After you have created the meter, you compare the colors of acid or base samples that have been mixed with universal indicator with the colors on the pH meter.

Each indicator is useful only over a pH range of approximately two units. Many different indicators are needed to span the entire pH spectrum. Figure 19.12 shows the pH range of some commonly used indicators.

Indicators are useful tools. They have certain characteristics, however, that limit their use. The listed pH values of indicators are usually given for a temperature of 25°C. At other temperatures, an indicator may change color at a different pH. If the solution being tested has a color of its own, the color of the indicator may be distorted. Dissolved salts in a solution may also change the indicator's dissociation. Often, these problems can be overcome by using indicator strips. An indicator strip is a piece of paper or plastic that is impregnated with the indicator. You can dip the paper into the unknown solution and compare the result with a color chart to measure the pH. Some pH paper contains multiple indicators so that it can indicate pHs from 1 to 14.

Most chemistry laboratories have a pH meter. It is used to make rapid, accurate measurements of pH. If a pH meter is connected to a computer or chart recorder, it can be used to make a continuous recording of pH changes.

Figure 19.14 shows the construction of the pH meter. It consists of two electrodes connected to a millivoltmeter. The reference electrode has a constant voltage. The voltage of the glass electrode changes with the $[H_3O^+]$ in the solution in which it is dipped. The pH meter makes an electrical measurement of pH by comparing the voltages of the two electrodes. The millivoltmeter gives a readout directly as pH.

Before you use a pH meter, you must calibrate it by dipping the electrodes into a solution of known pH. You adjust the readout of the millivoltmeter to that pH. Then, you rinse the electrodes with

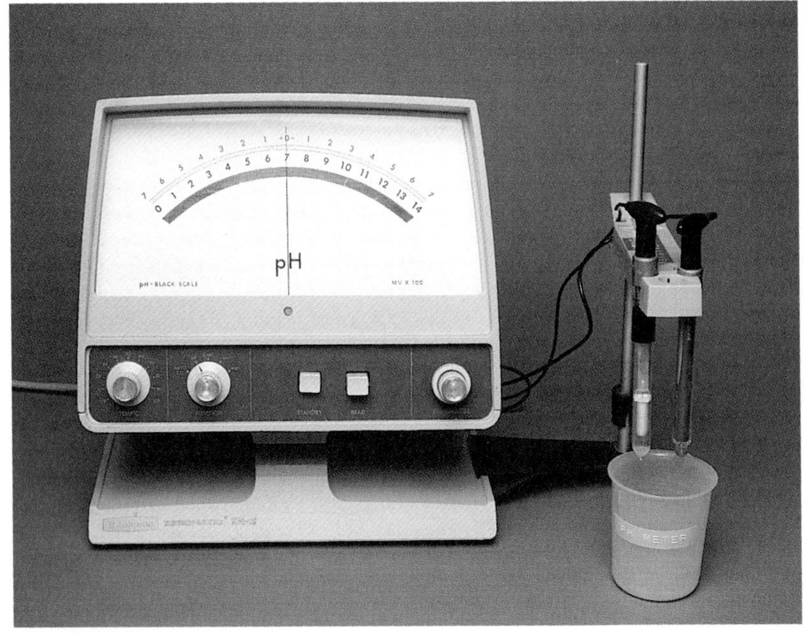

Figure 19.14 A pH meter is used to measure hydrogen-ion concentrations. The instrument consists of two electrodes: a glass electrode and a reference electrode. A meter measures the voltage difference between the two electrodes and gives a pH reading. The meter may be connected to a strip-chart recorder.

Figure 19.15 pH meters are often used in nurseries to monitor soil pH.

distilled water and dip them into the solution of unknown pH. To make continuous readings of pH, you may leave the electrodes in the solution.

A pH meter is a valuable instrument. In many situations it is easier to use than liquid indicators or indicator strips. Measurements of pH obtained with a pH meter are typically accurate to within a 0.01 pH unit of the true pH. The color and cloudiness of the unknown solution do not affect the accuracy of the pH value obtained. Hospitals use pH meters to find small but meaningful changes of pH in blood and other body fluids. Sewage and industrial effluents are also easily monitored with a pH meter.

Concept Practice

19. A green-colored aqueous solution contains the indicator with a general formula, HIn.

$$\underset{\text{yellow}}{\mathrm{HIn}(aq)} \rightleftharpoons \underset{\text{blue}}{\mathrm{In}^-(aq)} + \mathrm{H_2O}(l)$$

Use Le Châtelier's principle to predict the color change that occurs when you add:
a. acid **b.** base

20. A pH meter gives a more precise measurement of $[H^+]$ than an indicator solution. Explain.

Objective

Classify substances as Lewis acids or bases.

Integrating Health

Tooth Decay

The chief cause of tooth decay is lactic acid ($C_3H_6O_3$), K_a 1.4 × 10^{-4}. Lactic acid is formed in the mouth by the action of bacteria, such as *Streptococcus mutans*, on sugars in sticky plaque on tooth surfaces. Normally, saliva keeps plaque at pH 6.8. A pH of 6.0 or higher causes no problem. However, when lactic acid lowers the pH to 5.5 or less, the tooth enamel can break down. Once the enamel is penetrated, dental caries or cavities result. The damage can progress to the underlying dentin and pulp, which contains blood vessels and nerves, causing a toothache.

19.9 Lewis Acids and Bases

A third theory of acids and bases was proposed by Gilbert Lewis (1875–1946). He focused on the donation or acceptance of a pair of electrons during a reaction. This concept is more general than either the Arrhenius theory or the Brønsted-Lowry theory. *A* **Lewis acid** *is a substance that can accept a pair of electrons to form a covalent bond. A* **Lewis base** *is a substance that can donate a pair of electrons to form a covalent bond.* A hydrogen ion (Brønsted-Lowry acid) can accept a pair of electrons in forming a bond. A hydrogen ion, therefore, is also a Lewis acid. A substance that accepts a hydrogen ion (Brønsted-Lowry base) must have a pair of electrons available (Lewis base). Consider the reaction of H^+ and OH^-.

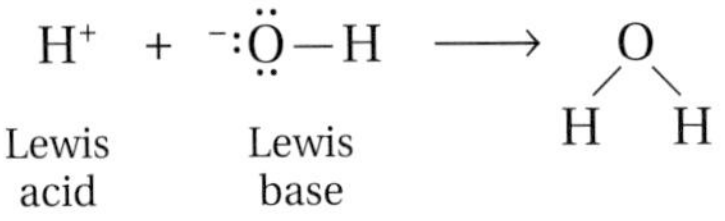

$$\underset{\text{Lewis acid}}{H^+} + \underset{\text{Lewis base}}{^-\!:\ddot{\underset{..}{O}}-H} \longrightarrow \underset{H\quad H}{\overset{O}{/\;\backslash}}$$

A hydroxide ion is a Lewis base. It is also a Brønsted-Lowry base. A hydrogen ion is both a Lewis acid and a Brønsted-Lowry acid. The Lewis theory also includes some compounds that are not classified as Brønsted-Lowry acids or bases.

Example 7 Identifying Lewis Acids and Bases

Identify the Lewis acid and the Lewis base in this reaction.

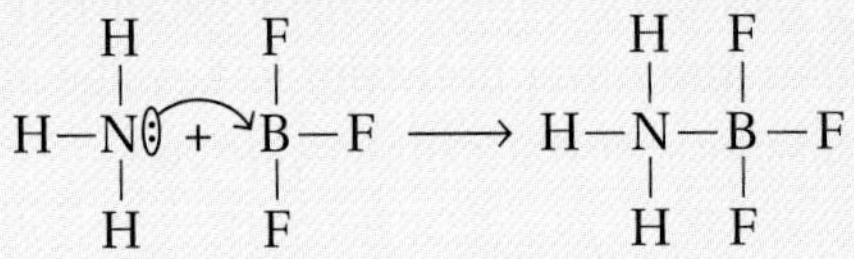

$$H-\underset{H}{\overset{H}{\underset{|}{\overset{|}{N}}}}\!: + \;\underset{F}{\overset{F}{\underset{|}{\overset{|}{B}}}}-F \longrightarrow H-\underset{H}{\overset{H}{\underset{|}{\overset{|}{N}}}}-\underset{F}{\overset{F}{\underset{|}{\overset{|}{B}}}}-F$$

Solution

Ammonia is donating a pair of electrons. Ammonia is a Lewis base. Boron trifluoride is accepting a pair of electrons. It is a Lewis acid.

Concept Practice

21. Is PCl_3 a Lewis acid or a Lewis base? Why?

22. Identify the Lewis acid and Lewis base in each reaction.

a. 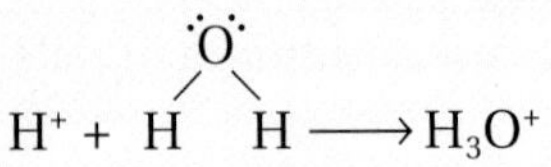 $H^+ + \underset{H\quad H}{\overset{\ddot{O}}{/\;\backslash}} \longrightarrow H_3O^+$ **b.** $AlCl_3 + Cl^- \longrightarrow AlCl_4^-$

19.10 Strengths of Acids and Bases

Objective

Distinguish between strong and weak acids and bases using the extent of ionization and the dissociation constants.

Acids are classified as strong or weak depending on the degree to which they ionize in water. For practical purposes, **strong acids** *are completely ionized in aqueous solution.* Hydrochloric acid and sulfuric acid are examples of strong acids.

$$HCl(g) + H_2O(l) \longrightarrow H_3O^+(aq) + Cl^-(aq) \text{ (100\% dissociated)}$$

Weak acids *ionize only slightly in aqueous solution.* The ionization of ethanoic acid, a typical weak acid, is not complete.

$$\underset{\text{Ethanoic acid}}{CH_3COOH(aq)} + \underset{\text{Water}}{H_2O(l)} \rightleftharpoons \underset{\text{Hydronium ion}}{H_3O^+(aq)} + \underset{\text{Ethanoate ion}}{CH_3COO^-(aq)}$$

Safety

The concentration of a "concentrated" acid is too high to be measured on the pH scale. Concentrated HCl is 12*M*, concentrated HNO_3 is 16*M*, and concentrated H_2SO_4 is 18*M*. Use these materials only with great care.

Fewer than 1% of ethanoic acid molecules are ionized at any instant. Table 19.5 gives the relative strengths of some common acids and bases.

Recall that you can write an equilibrium-constant expression from a chemical equation. You can write the equilibrium-constant expression for the ionization of acetic acid as follows.

$$K_{eq} = \frac{[H_3O^+] \times [CH_3COO^-]}{[CH_3COOH] \times [H_2O]}$$

Table 19.5 Relative Strengths of Common Acids and Bases

Substance	Formula	Relative Strength
Hydrochloric acid	HCl	Strong acids
Nitric acid	HNO_3	Strong acids
Sulfuric acid	H_2SO_4	Strong acids
Phosphoric acid	H_3PO_4	↑ Increasing strength
Ethanoic acid	CH_3COOH	
Carbonic acid	H_2CO_3	
Hydrosulfuric acid	H_2S	
Hypochlorous acid	$HClO$	
Boric acid	H_3BO_3	
		Neutral solution
Sodium cyanide	$NaCN$	↓ Increasing strength
Ammonia	NH_3	
Methylamine	CH_3NH_2	
Sodium silicate	Na_2SiO_3	
Calcium hydroxide	$Ca(OH)_2$	Strong bases
Sodium hydroxide	$NaOH$	Strong bases
Potassium hydroxide	KOH	Strong bases

Table 19.6 Dissociation Constants of Weak Acids

Acid	Ionization	K_a(25°C)
Oxalic acid	$HOOCCOOH(aq) \rightleftharpoons H^+(aq) + HOOCCOO^-(aq)$	5.6×10^{-2}
	$HOOCCOO^-(aq) \rightleftharpoons H^+(aq) + OOCCOO^{2-}(aq)$	5.1×10^{-5}
Phosphoric acid	$H_3PO_4(aq) \rightleftharpoons H^+(aq) + H_2PO_4^-(aq)$	7.5×10^{-3}
	$H_2PO_4^-(aq) \rightleftharpoons H^+(aq) + HPO_4^{2-}(aq)$	6.2×10^{-8}
	$HPO_4^{2-}(aq) \rightleftharpoons H^+(aq) + PO_4^{3-}(aq)$	4.8×10^{-13}
Methanoic acid	$HCOOH(aq) \rightleftharpoons H^+(aq) + HCOO^-(aq)$	1.8×10^{-4}
Benzoic acid	$C_6H_5COOH(aq) \rightleftharpoons H^+(aq) + C_6H_5COO^-(aq)$	6.3×10^{-5}
Ethanoic acid	$CH_3COOH(aq) \rightleftharpoons H^+(aq) + CH_3COO^-(aq)$	1.8×10^{-5}
Carbonic acid	$H_2CO_3(aq) \rightleftharpoons H^+(aq) + HCO_3^-(aq)$	4.3×10^{-7}
	$HCO_3^-(aq) \rightleftharpoons H^+(aq) + CO_3^{2-}(aq)$	4.8×10^{-11}

For dilute solutions the concentration of water is a constant. It can be combined with K_{eq} to give an acid dissociation constant. *An* **acid dissociation constant** (K_a) *is the ratio of the concentration of the dissociated form of an acid to the concentration of the undissociated form.* The dissociated form includes both the H^+ and the anion.

$$K_{eq} \times [H_2O] = K_a = \frac{[H^+] \times [CH_3COO^-]}{[CH_3COOH]}$$

The acid dissociation constant, K_a, reflects the fraction of an acid that is in the ionized form. For this reason dissociation constants are sometimes called ionization constants. If the value of the ionization constant, K_a, is small, then the dissociation of the acid in the solution is small. Weak acids have small K_a values. A larger value of K_a means that the dissociation, or ionization, of the acid is more complete. Strong acids have large K_a values. For example, nitrous acid has a K_a of 4.4×10^{-4} whereas ethanoic acid has a K_a of 1.8×10^{-5}. This means that nitrous acid is more ionized, or dissociated, in solution than ethanoic acid. Nitrous acid is a stronger acid than ethanoic acid.

Glacial ethanoic (acetic) acid is 17*M*. It causes severe chemical burns. A concentrated weak acid can be very corrosive.

Diprotic and triprotic acids lose their hydrogens one at a time. Each ionization reaction has a separate ionization constant, K_a. Thus phosphoric acid, H_3PO_4, has three ionization constants to go with its three ionizable hydrogens. Table 19.6 shows the ionization reactions and ionization constants for some common acids. The acids in Table 19.6 are ranked by the value of the first ionization constant for each acid.

Just as there are strong acids and weak acids, there are also strong bases and weak bases. All of the hydroxides in Table 19.4 are classified as strong bases. **Strong bases** *dissociate completely into metal ions and hydroxide ions in aqueous solution.* Some strong bases, such as calcium hydroxide and magnesium hydroxide, are not very soluble in water. The small amounts of those bases that do dissolve dissociate completely. The relative strengths of some bases are listed in Table 19.5

Weak bases *react with water to form the conjugate acid of the base and the hydroxide ion.* Ammonia is an example of a weak base.

$$\underset{\text{Ammonia}}{NH_3(aq)} + \underset{\text{Water}}{H_2O(l)} \rightleftharpoons \underset{\text{Ammonium ion}}{NH_4^+(aq)} + \underset{\text{Hydroxide ion}}{OH^-(aq)}$$

The equilibrium greatly favors the reverse reaction. Only about 1% of the ammonia is present as NH_4^+, the conjugate acid of NH_3. The concentrations of NH_4^+ and OH^- are low and equal. Interestingly, the compound ammonium hydroxide (NH_4OH) cannot be isolated from solutions of aqueous ammonia. In order to isolate NH_4OH, you would need to remove the NH_3 and H_2O. Suppose you began to remove the ammonia first. According to Le Châtelier's principle, the equilibrium would shift even further in the reverse direction (to the left) to compensate for the loss of NH_3. This cycle of loss of NH_3 and reduction of the amount of NH_4^+ and OH^- would continue until all of the ammonia had gone from the water. An attempt to remove the water first or the ammonia and water together would also fail to isolate any NH_4OH. Bottles of aqueous ammonia used in laboratories are sometimes labeled "ammonium hydroxide" but nobody has ever isolated this compound.

Recall how to write an equilibrium-constant expression from a chemical equation. The equilibrium-constant expression for the reaction of ammonia with water is as follows.

$$K_{eq} = \frac{[NH_4^+] \times [OH^-]}{[NH_3] \times [H_2O]}$$

As previously discussed for K_a, the concentration of water is constant in dilute solutions. It can be combined with K_{eq} to give a base dissociation constant, K_b.

$$K_b = \frac{[NH_4^+] \times [OH^-]}{[NH_3]}$$

In general, the **base dissociation constant**, K_b, *is the ratio of concentrations: [conjugate acid]* × *[OH⁻]/[conjugate base].* The magnitude of K_b indicates the ability of a weak base to compete with the very strong base OH^- for hydrogen ions. Because bases like ammonia are weak relative to the hydroxide ion, K_b is usually small. The K_b of ammonia is 1.8×10^{-5}. The smaller the value of K_b, the weaker is the base.

The words *concentrated* and *dilute* tell how much of an acid or base is dissolved in solution. These terms refer to the number of moles of the acid or base in a given volume. The words *strong* or *weak* refer to the extent of ionization of an acid or base. They indicate how many of the molecules dissociate into ions. Hydrochloric acid, HCl, is a strong acid. Gastric juice in the stomach is a dilute solution of hydrochloric acid. A relatively small number of HCl molecules are present in a given volume of gastric juice, but they are all dissociated into ions. A sample of hydrochloric acid added to a large volume of water becomes more dilute, but it is still a strong acid. Vinegar is a dilute solution of a weak acid, ethanoic acid. Pure ethanoic acid (glacial acetic acid) is still a weak acid. Any solution of ammonia, whether concentrated or dilute, will be a weak base because the amount of dissociation will be small. Solutions of ammonia can be concentrated or dilute depending on the amount of ammonia dissolved in a given volume of water.

Table 19.7 Concentrations of Some Common Laboratory Acids and Bases

Acid or base	Concentration: Moles/liter (molarity)	Concentration: Grams/liter
Concentrated hydrochloric acid	12	438
Dilute hydrochloric acid	6	219
Concentrated sulfuric acid	18	1764
Dilute sulfuric acid	6	588
Concentrated phosphoric acid	15	1470
Concentrated nitric acid	16	1008
Dilute nitric acid	6	378
Ethanoic acid, glacial	17	1020
Ethanoic acid, dilute	6	360
Dilute sodium hydroxide	6	240
Concentrated aqueous ammonia	15	255
Dilute aqueous ammonia	6	102

Concept Practice

23. Based on the first ionization constant, which acid in Table 19.6 is the strongest? Which is weakest?

24. An acid, HX, has a very small value of K_a. How do the relative amounts of H^+ and HX compare at equilibrium?

19.B Consumer Chemistry

Shampoos

Shampoos are designed for optimum compatibility with the chemical makeup of your hair. Your hair is made of keratin, a large protein molecule. Keratin is lifeless, like your nails and the outermost layer of your skin. As you can see in Figure 19.16, hair grows from a hair root embedded in a follicle buried beneath the surface of the skin. Sebaceous glands in the skin near the follicle coat the emerging hair shaft with oily sebum. Sebum makes your hair lie flat, gives your hair gloss, and prevents your hair from drying out. Shampoos are designed to remove dirt and sebum while not removing all of the oils.

The pH of a shampoo greatly affects the luster and resilience of your hair. Strands of hair are strongest and have a nice luster at slightly acid conditions of pH 5 or 6. At slightly basic pH values the cuticle swells and becomes ruffled, which causes your hair to look dull. Shampoos are usually formulated to have a pH between 5 and 8. Some manufacturers say their shampoo is "pH balanced" because it has a pH within this range.

Before the 1940s, the cleansing agent in shampoos was soap. Soap-based shampoos worked well in soft water but left a dulling film on the hair in hard water. People often removed the film by rinsing the hair with water containing lemon juice or vinegar. Today, shampoos contain a synthetic detergent, such as sodium dodecyl sulfate, which has moderate detergent action.

In addition to detergents, today's shampoos may contain several other ingredients. Many shampoos contain conditioners that replace some of the lubricant that is lost in washing. Protein shampoos can give your hair more body. Because hair is a protein, the protein in a shampoo coats the hair, making it thicker, and also "glues" split ends together. Other shampoo ingredients make the shampoo thick, control the pH, and add color and fragrance.

Some shampoos contain ingredients to control the flaking of the scalp called seborrhea, or common dandruff. These preparations usually contain pyrithione zinc, selenium sulfide, or coal tar as the active ingredient. The best results are often obtained from dandruff shampoos by switching between types at regular intervals.

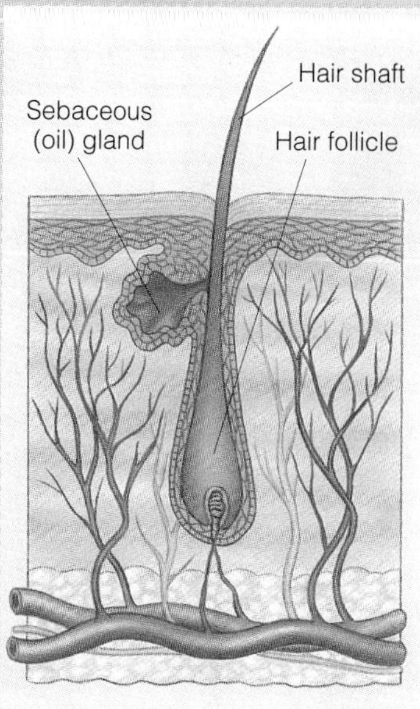

Figure 19.16 Cross section of a typical hair follicle.

Think About It

25. Interpret What is the meaning of the phrase "pH balanced" on a shampoo container?

26. Categorize Read the labels on several brands of shampoo. List the ingredients. Identify the function of each ingredient.

Objective

Calculate an acid dissociation constant, K_a, from concentration and pH measurements.

19.11 Calculating Dissociation Constants

You can calculate the acid dissociation constant, K_a, of a weak acid from experimental data. To do this, you would need to measure the equilibrium concentrations of all the substances present at equilibrium. For a weak acid you can determine these concentrations experimentally if you know two conditions. First, you must know the initial molar concentration of the acid. Second, you must know the pH (or $[H^+]$) of the solution at equilibrium.

Example 8 Calculating a Dissociation Constant

A 0.1000*M* solution of ethanoic acid is only partially ionized. From measurements of the pH of the solution, you conclude the $[H^+]$ is $1.34 \times 10^{-3}M$. What is the acid dissociation constant of ethanoic acid?

Solution

$$CH_3COOH(aq) \rightleftharpoons H^+(aq) + CH_3COO^-(aq)$$

Each molecule of CH_3COOH that ionizes gives an H^+ and a CH_3COO^- ion. Therefore at equilibrium the $[H^+] = [CH_3COO^-] = 1.34 \times 10^{-3}M$. The equilibrium concentration of CH_3COOH is the initial concentration minus the concentration of the ionized acid, $(0.1000 - 0.00134)M = 0.0987M$. These data are summarized in the following table.

Concentrations	$[CH_3COOH]$	$[H^+]$	$[CH_3COO^-]$
Initial	0.100	0	0
Change	-1.34×10^{-3}	$+1.34 \times 10^{-3}$	$+1.34 \times 10^{-3}$
Equilibrium	0.0987	1.34×10^{-3}	1.34×10^{-3}

(All concentrations are in mol/L.)

Substitute the equilibrium values into the expression for K_a

$$K_a = \frac{[H^+] \times [CH_3COO^-]}{[CH_3COOH]}$$

$$= \frac{(1.34 \times 10^{-3}) \times (1.34 \times 10^{-3})}{0.0987}$$

$$= 1.82 \times 10^{-5}$$

Practice Problems

27. A 0.200*M* solution of a weak acid has a [H^+] of $9.86 \times 10^{-5}M$.

a. What is the pH of this solution?

b. What is the value of K_a for this acid?

28. The [H^+] of a 0.100*M* methanoic acid solution is 4.2×10^{-3} mol/L. Calculate the K_a of methanoic acid.

Activity 19
Indicators from Natural Sources

Purpose

To measure the pH of various household materials by using a natural indicator to make an indicator chart.

Materials

red cabbage leaves

white vinegar (CH_3COOH)

household ammonia

baking soda ($NaHCO_3$)

1-cup measure

10 clear plastic cups

jar

tape

knife

pencil

teaspoon

ruler

clean white cloth

hot water

4 sheets of plain white paper

Procedure

1. Put 1/2 cup of finely chopped red cabbage leaves in a jar and add 1/2 cup hot water. Stir and crush the leaves with a spoon. Continue the extraction until the water is distinctly colored.

2. Strain the extract through a piece of cloth into a clean jar. This is your natural indicator.

3. Tape several sheets of paper end to end, draw a line along the center, and label it, at 2″ intervals, with the numbers 1 to 14. This is your pH scale.

4. Pour your indicator to about 1 cm depth into each of three plastic cups. To one cup add several drops of vinegar, to the second add a pinch of sodium hydrogen carbonate, and to the third add several drops of ammonia. The resulting colors indicate pH values of about 3, 9, and 11, respectively. Place these colored solutions at the appropriate positions on the pH scale.

5. Repeat the procedure given in (4) for household items such as table salt, borax, bleach, milk, lemon juice, laundry detergent, dishwashing liquid, milk of magnesia, mouthwash, toothpaste, shampoo, carbonated beverages.

Analysis and Conclusions

1. What was the initial color of the natural indicator and what was its color at acidic, neutral, and basic conditions?

2. What chemical changes were responsible for the color change?

3. Label the materials you tested as acidic, basic, or neutral.

4. In which group were the items used for personal hygiene?

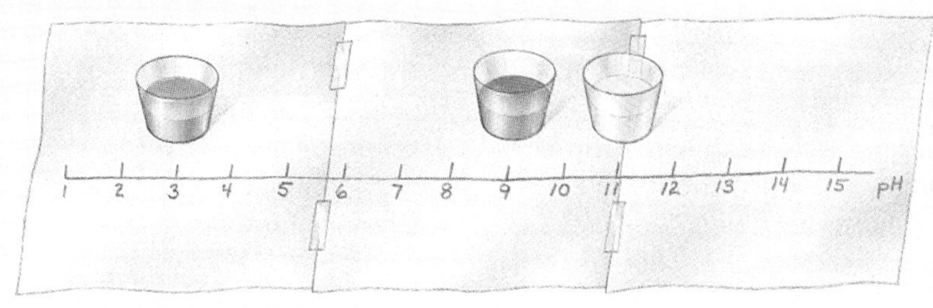

Cermets

Ceramics + Metals

A relatively new class of composite materials is attracting interest from many diverse industries. This new class of composite, called a cermet, is composed of a *cer*amic and a *met*al. The earliest cermet, tungsten carbide, replaced cobalt in high-speed tool steels nearly a half-century ago. Until recently, however, no other cermets had been developed. One of the new cermets combines equal amounts of boron carbide with aluminum to produce aluminum boron carbide. The resulting cermet is stronger than steel yet lighter than aluminum. Aluminum boron carbide can withstand major stresses without cracking or shattering and is very hard and wear-resistant. This lightweight cermet may replace steel alloys and titanium in many applications.

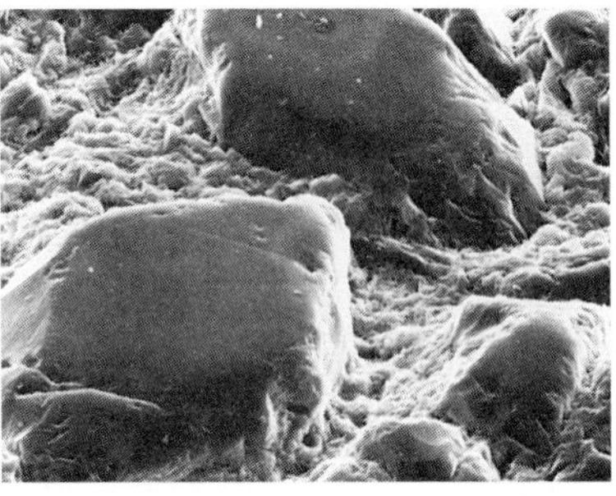

The light micrograph above shows the structure of an aluminum carbide cermet. The cermet at the right is being heated to about 800° C in a sintering furnace.

Aluminum boron carbide is also attracting commercial attention. The cermet has potential uses in helmets, bulletproof vests, and other forms of armor. Ceramics companies and manufacturers of racing bicycles have shown an interest in the composite.

Recent work has focused on the development of a commercially practical method of producing the new material. To make the cermet, boron carbide powder is first chemically washed to remove oil films and surface oxides. The powder is then packed into a mold of the intended shape and an equal amount of aluminum is placed on top of the powder. This assembly is heated to 1200°C. As the aluminum melts, it soaks into the porous boron carbide. The temperature is then lowered to 800°C and the aluminum reacts with the boron carbide, forming aluminum boron carbide.

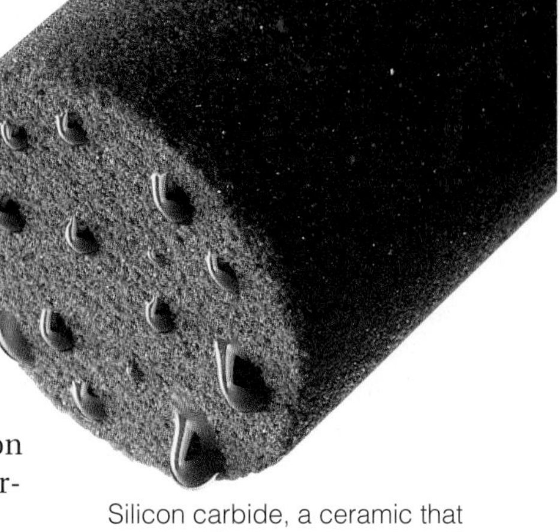

Silicon carbide, a ceramic that absorbs fluids, is used in bits for oil drilling. Analysis of its contents can determine the nature of fluids in rocks.

The specific properties of this cermet are determined by the length of the heat treatment. To attain hardness, heat treatment may be as long as 16 hours. To impart ductility and high tensile strength to the cermet three hours of heat treatment are needed. Changing the particle size of boron carbide can vary the properties of the cermet as well.

Research is currently under way to make cermets out of other metals such as nickel, magnesium, and titanium.

Think About It

29. List Write down some properties of the aluminum boron carbide cermet.

30. Apply Name some possible advantages in using the aluminum boron carbide cermet in a racing bicycle frame.

Chapter 19 Review
Acids and Bases

Key Terms

acid *19.2*
acid dissociation constant (K_a) *19.10*
acidic solution *19.3*
alkaline solution *19.3*
amphoteric *19.7*
base *19.2*
base dissociation constant (K_b) *19.10*
basic solution *19.3*
conjugate acid *19.7*
conjugate acid-base pair *19.7*
conjugate base *19.7*
diprotic acid *19.6*
hydrogen-ion acceptor *19.7*
hydrogen-ion donor *19.7*
hydronium ion (H_3O^+) *19.3*
hydroxide ion (OH^-) *19.3*
ion-product constant for water (K_w) *19.3*
Lewis acid *19.9*
Lewis base *19.9*
monoprotic acid *19.6*
neutral solution *19.3*
pH *19.4*
self-ionization *19.3*
strong acid *19.10*
strong base *19.10*
triprotic acid *19.6*
weak acid *19.10*
weak base *19.10*

Chapter Summary

Water molecules dissociate into hydrogen ions (H^+) and hydroxide ions (OH^-). The concentrations of these ions in pure water at 25°C are both equal to 1×10^{-7}mol/L.

The pH scale, which has a range from 0 to 14, is used to denote the hydrogen-ion concentration of a solution. On this scale 0 is strongly acidic, 14 is strongly basic, and 7 is neutral. Water at 25°C has a pH of 7. The pH of a solution is measured with acid-base indicators or a pH meter.

Compounds can be classified as acids or bases according to three different theories. An Arrhenius acid gives hydrogen ions in aqueous solution. An Arrhenius base gives hydroxide ions in aqueous solution. A Brønsted-Lowry acid is a proton donor. A Brønsted-Lowry base is a proton acceptor. In the Lewis theory an acid is an electron-pair acceptor. A Lewis base is an electron-pair donor.

The strength of an acid or base is determined by the degree of ionization of the substance in solution. The acid dissociation constant, K_a, is a quantitative measure of acid strength. A strong acid has a much larger K_a than a weak acid. The K_a of an acid is determined from measured pH values.

Practice Questions and Problems

31. List at least three characteristic properties each of acids and bases. *19.1*

32. Name each of these acids. *19.2*
a. HF **b.** $HClO_3$ **c.** H_2CO_3

33. Write formulas for these compounds. *19.2*
a. nitrous acid
b. aluminum hydroxide
c. hydroselenic acid
d. strontium hydroxide
e. phosphoric acid
f. ethanoic acid

34. Write an equation showing the ionization of water. *19.3*

35. What are the concentrations of H^+ and OH^- in pure water at 25°C? *19.3*

36. How is the pH of a solution calculated? *19.4*

37. Why is the pH of pure water at 25°C equal to 7.0? *19.4*

38. Calculate the pH for the following solutions and indicate whether the solution is acidic or basic. *19.4*
a. $[H^+] = 1 \times 10^{-2}$ mol/L
b. $[OH^-] = 1 \times 10^{-2}$ mol/L
c. $[OH^-] = 1 \times 10^{-8}$ mol/L
d. $[H^+] = 1 \times 10^{-6}$ mol/L

39. What are the hydroxide-ion concentrations for solutions that have the following pH values? *19.4*
a. 4.0 **b.** 8.0 **c.** 12.0

40. Calculate the pH or $[H^+]$ for each solution. *19.4*
a. $[H^+] = 2.4 \times 10^{-6}$ **c.** pH = 13.2
b. $[H^+] = 9.1 \times 10^{-9}$ **d.** pH = 6.7

41. How did Arrhenius describe acids and bases? *19.6*

42. Classify each of these as an Arrhenius acid or an Arrhenius base. *19.6*

a. $Ca(OH)_2$ **c.** KOH **e.** HBr

b. HNO_3 **d.** C_2H_5COOH **f.** H_2SO_4

43. Identify each of the acids in Problem 32 as monoprotic, diprotic, or triprotic. *19.6*

44. Write balanced equations for the reaction of each of these metals with water. *19.6*

a. lithium **b.** barium

45. Identify each of the reactants in the following equations as a hydrogen-ion donor (acid) or a hydrogen-ion acceptor (base). *19.7*

a. $HNO_3 + H_2O \rightleftharpoons H_3O^+ + NO_3^-$

b. $CH_3COOH + H_2O \rightleftharpoons H_3O^+ + CH_3COO^-$

c. $NH_3 + H_2O \rightleftharpoons NH_4^+ + OH^-$

d. $H_2O + CH_3COO^- \rightleftharpoons CH_3COOH + OH^-$

46. Label the conjugate acid-base pairs in each equation in Problem 45. *19.7*

47. What makes a substance amphoteric? *19.7*

48. Using Figure 19.13 and the visual evidence in the photo below, estimate the pH of **a.** the vinegar and **b.** the ammonia cleaner. *19.8*

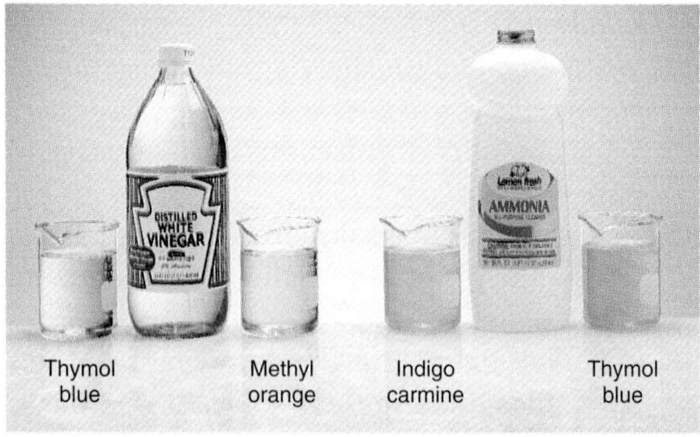

49. What are a Lewis acid and a Lewis base? What advantage does this theory have over the Arrhenius and Brønsted-Lowry theories? *19.9*

50. Write the equations for the ionization of the following acids and bases in water. *19.10*

a. nitric acid **c.** ammonia

b. ethanoic acid **d.** magnesium hydroxide

51. Define strong and weak acids and bases. *19.10*

52. Identify each of the following compounds as a strong or weak acid or base. *19.10*

a. NaOH **b.** HCl **c.** NH_3 **d.** H_2SO_4

53. Would a strong acid have a large or a small K_a? Explain. *19.11*

54. Why are $Mg(OH)_2$ and $Ca(OH)_2$ called strong bases even though their saturated solutions are only mildly basic? *19.11*

55. Write the expression for K_a for each of these acids. Assume that only one hydrogen is ionized. *19.11*

a. HI **b.** H_2CO_3

56. A 0.025*M* solution of $KHCrO_4$ has a pH of 3.50. Calculate the K_a for the equilibrium between $HCrO_4^-$ and CrO_4^{2-}. *19.11*

Mastery Questions and Problems

57. Construct a concept map using the key terms in this chapter with *acid* as the central concept.

58. Is it possible to have a concentrated weak acid? Explain.

59. Write equations that show that the hydrogen phosphate ion, HPO_4^{2-}, is amphoteric.

60. The pH of a 0.50*M* HNO_2 solution is 1.83. What is the K_a of this acid?

61. What methods might be used to reduce the amount of acid-producing substances reaching the environment?

62. Write the formula and name of the conjugate base of each Brønsted-Lowry acid.

a. HCO_3^- **b.** HI **c.** NH_4^+ **d.** H_2SO_3

63. Write the formula and name of the conjugate acid of each Brønsted-Lowry base.

a. ClO_2^- **b.** $H_2PO_4^-$ **c.** H_2O **d.** NH_3

64. It is determined that 1.40% of a 0.080*M* solution of a weak acid is ionized. Calculate the K_a for this acid.

65. Calculate the $[OH^-]$ or the pH of each solution.

a. pH = 4.6 **c.** $[OH^-] = 1.8 \times 10^{-2}$

b. pH = 9.3 **d.** $[OH^-] = 7.3 \times 10^{-9}$

66. Why does an alkaline shampoo make your hair look dull?

67. Write the three equations for the stepwise dissociation of phosphoric acid.

68. Use the Brønsted-Lowry and Lewis definitions of acids and bases to identify each reactant as an acid or a base.

a. $KOH + HBr \longrightarrow KBr + H_2O$

b. $HCl + H_2O \longrightarrow Cl^- + H_3O^+$

Critical Thinking Questions

69. Choose the term that best completes the second relationship.

a. sky:blue   acid: ____
(1) metallic   (3) sour
(2) basic   (4) bitter

b. plants:oxygen   base: ____
(1) electrons   (3) hydronium ions
(2) hydroxide ions   (4) protons

c. thermometer:degrees   indicator: ____
(1) pH   (3) H^+
(2) acid   (4) base

70. Arrhenius, Brønsted-Lowry, and Lewis all developed theories to explain acids and bases.

a. Which theory is easiest for you to understand?

b. Which theory seems the best?

c. How can three different theories all be accepted by chemists?

71. Prove the relationship pH + pOH = 14. (*Hint:* Use the expression for K_w.)

Cumulative Review

72. How would you prepare 400.0 mL of a 0.680*M* KOH solution?

73. How would each change affect the position of equilibrium of this reaction?

$$2H_2(g) + O_2(g) \rightleftharpoons 2H_2O(g) + \text{heat}$$

a. increasing the pressure

b. adding a catalyst

c. increasing the concentration of $H_2(g)$

d. cooling the reaction mixture

e. removing water vapor from the container

Challenge Questions and Problems

74. Calculate the pH of a 0.010*M* solution of sodium cyanide, NaCN. The K_b of CN^- is 2.1×10^{-5}.

75. Show that for any conjugate acid-base pair $K_aK_b = K_w$.

76. The K_w of water varies with temperature.

a. Find the pH of water for each temperature in the table. Use these data to prepare a plot of pH versus temperature.

b. What is the pH of water at 5°C?

c. At what temperature is the pH of water approximately 6.85?

Temperature (°C)	K_w	pH
0	1.137×10^{-15}	____
10	2.917×10^{-15}	____
20	6.807×10^{-15}	____
30	1.469×10^{-14}	____
40	2.917×10^{-14}	____
50	5.470×10^{-14}	____

Connections Questions

77. Why may acidic foods such as tomatoes and some fruits be safely home-canned?

78. Why was Arrhenius's explanation of the behavior of acids not originally accepted?

79. Explain the role of acids in causing tooth decay.

Write About Chemistry

80. Imagine that you are a TV reporter preparing to interview the curator of a museum that has an outdoor collection of marble statues. Prepare a list of questions related to acid rain that you would cover in the interview.

81. Some shampoos are advertised as having a low pH. What do you think "low pH" means in this instance? Research and write a short paper on the advantages and disadvantages of low-pH shampoo.

Readings and References

Gay, Kathlyn. *Acid Rain.* New York: Watts, 1983.

Visich, Marian, Jr. "Acid from the Sky." *Science Year* (1984), pp. 40–53.

20 Neutralization

Goals

- Explain how acid–base titration is used to analyze the concentration of an acid or a base.
- Explain the concept of equivalence in neutralization reactions.
- Demonstrate with equations how buffers resist changes in pH and predict whether aqueous solutions of salts will be acidic or basic.
- Give examples of the effect of a common ion on the solubilities of slightly soluble salts and determine their solubility product constants.

The effervescing tablet shown here has basic properties that can be used to neutralize acid.

Concept Overview

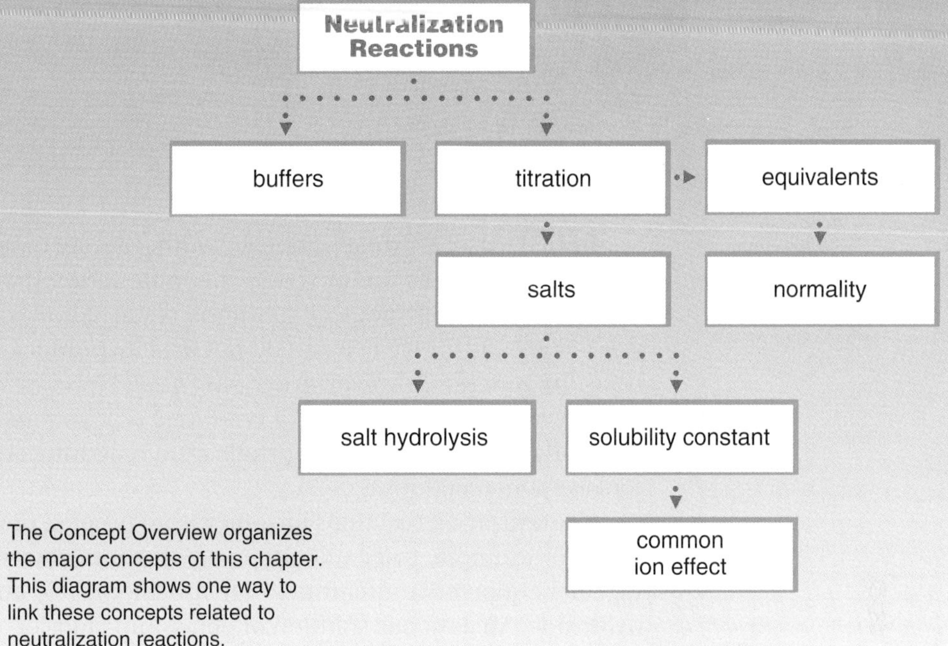

The Concept Overview organizes the major concepts of this chapter. This diagram shows one way to link these concepts related to neutralization reactions.

The properties of acids, bases, and salts help explain many diverse phenomena. For example, the usefulness of antacids depends on the process of acid-base neutralization. Farmers use a similar process to control the pH of their soil. The formation of caves and of stalactites in caves is caused by changes in the solubilities of salts. The formation of kidney stones from salts within the body is also related to solubility. Neutralization reactions and the solubilities of salts are the topics of this chapter.

20.1 Neutralization Reactions

Objective

Demonstrate your knowledge of acid-base reactions by completing and balancing a neutralization reaction.

If you mix a solution of strong acid containing hydrogen ions with a solution of strong base that has an equal amount of hydroxide ions, a neutral solution results. The final solution has properties that are characteristic of neither an acidic nor a basic solution. Consider these examples.

$$HCl(aq) + NaOH(aq) \longrightarrow NaCl(aq) + H_2O(l)$$

$$H_2SO_4(aq) + 2KOH(aq) \longrightarrow K_2SO_4(aq) + 2H_2O(l)$$

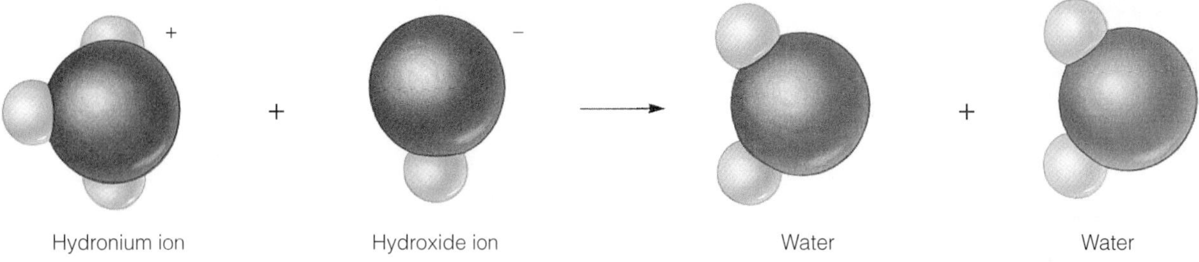

Figure 20.1 In a neutralization reaction, hydrogen ions (as hydronium ions) combine with hydroxide ions to form neutral water.

In each case, a strong acid reacts with a strong base. If solutions of these substances are mixed in the mole ratios specified by the balanced equation, neutral solutions result. Similar reactions of weak acids and/or weak bases do not usually produce neutral solutions. In general, however, *reactions in which an acid and a base react in an aqueous solution to produce a salt and water are called* **neutralization reactions**. Neutralization reactions are all double-replacement reactions.

Neutralization reactions are one way to prepare pure samples of salts. For example, you could prepare potassium chloride by mixing together equal molar quantities of hydrochloric acid and potassium hydroxide. An aqueous solution of potassium chloride would result. You could heat the solution in order to evaporate the water. This would leave potassium chloride salt. Table 20.1 lists some common salts and their applications.

Table 20.1 Some Salts and Their Applications

Name	Formula	Applications
Ammonium sulfate	$(NH_4)_2SO_4$	Fertilizer
Barium sulfate	$BaSO_4$	Gastrointestinal studies; white pigment
Calcium chloride	$CaCl_2$	Deicing roadways and sidewalks
Calcium sulfate dihydrate (gypsum)	$CaSO_4 \cdot 2H_2O$	Plasterboard
Copper sulfate pentahydrate (blue vitriol)	$CuSO_4 \cdot 5H_2O$	Dyeing, fungicide
Calcium sulfate sesquihydrate	$CaSO_4 \cdot \frac{1}{2}H_2O$	Plaster casts
Potassium chloride	KCl	Sodium-free salt substitute
Potassium permanganate	$KMnO_4$	Disinfectant and fungicide
Silver nitrate	$AgNO_3$	Cauterizing agent
Silver bromide	$AgBr$	Photographic emulsions
Sodium hydrogen carbonate (baking soda)	$NaHCO_3$	Antacid
Sodium carbonate decahydrate (washing soda)	$Na_2CO_3 \cdot 10H_2O$	Glass manufacture; water softener
Sodium chloride (table salt)	$NaCl$	Body electrolyte; chlorine manufacture
Sodium thiosulfate (hypo)	$Na_2S_2O_3$	Fixing agent in photographic process

Concept Practice

1. Write a general word equation for a neutralization reaction.

Practice Problem

2. Identify the products and write balanced equations for the following neutralization reactions.

a. $HNO_3(aq) + KOH(aq) \longrightarrow$

b. $HCl(aq) + Ca(OH)_2(aq) \longrightarrow$

c. $H_2SO_4(aq) + NH_3(aq) \longrightarrow$

Activity 20
The Neutralizing Power of Antacids

Purpose

To measure the effectiveness of antacids at neutralizing excess stomach acid.

Materials

white vinegar
sodium hydrogen carbonate
several commercial antacids
clear plastic cups
mortar and pestle
dropper
water
indicator
measuring teaspoon
paper towels

Procedure

1. Use the mortar and pestle to grind the antacid tablets into powder. Place each antacid on a paper towel. Label each paper towel with the identity of the antacid. Be careful not to mix the antacid powders.

2. Put 2 teaspoons of white vinegar (5% ethanoic acid) in a plastic cup. This will represent the excess stomach acid.

3. Add 5 drops of indicator to the vinegar. Note the color.

4. Add small amounts of sodium hydrogen carbonate to the vinegar until the system is neutral; the indicator will be blue.

5. Note the approximate amount of sodium hydrogen carbonate required to neutralize the acid. This will be your reference standard.

6. Repeat steps (2), (3), and (4) but substitute various antacid preparations for the sodium hydrogen carbonate.

7. Compare the approximate amounts of antacid required to neutralize the vinegar with your reference, sodium hydrogen carbonate.

Analysis and Conclusions

1. Make a list of the antacids tested and indicate their effectiveness with respect to the reference (sodium hydrogen carbonate).

2. List some of the ingredients in antacids and indicate which ingredients will neutralize stomach acid.

3. What is the purpose of the "nonneutralizing" components?

4. Write the equation for the neutralization of ethanoic acid by sodium hydrogen carbonate.

5. As described, this activity will give you only qualitative results. Explain what this statement means and redesign (rewrite) the activity so that the results will be quantitative.

20.A Consumer Chemistry

Antacids

Figure 20.2 Millions of people relieve their symptoms of hyperacidity by using antacids, which neutralize excess stomach acid.

Heartburn! Acid indigestion! These discomforts are caused by excessive stomach acid. The lining of your stomach secretes hydrochloric acid to aid the digestion of food. Sometimes, due to stress or overeating, your stomach produces too much acid, a condition called *hyperacidity.*

The discomfort due to hyperacidity can be relieved by taking antacids. There are many brands of antacids, which function using a variety of compounds. For example, sodium hydrogen carbonate, calcium carbonate, and magnesium hydroxide are all effective at neutralizing stomach acid. However, if the antacid neutralizes too much acid, the stomach will respond by secreting more acid and causing another bout of hyperacidity. This undesirable effect is called "acid rebound."

Sodium hydrogen carbonate ($NaHCO_3$), common baking soda, is a safe, inexpensive, and effective antacid for occasional use. However, because $NaHCO_3$ contains sodium ions, this antacid is not recommended for those who have hypertension, a condition aggravated by sodium ions. One popular antacid contains sodium hydrogen carbonate and citric acid. This antacid fizzes when placed in water because the hydrogen carbonate reacts with the acid to produce carbon dioxide gas.

Another common ingredient in antacids is calcium carbonate ($CaCO_3$). It acts quickly and is safe when taken in small amounts. Calcium carbonate has the added advantage of being a good source of the nutrient calcium. However, calcium carbonate can cause constipation and tends to produce acid rebound.

Magnesium carbonate ($MgCO_3$) and magnesium hydroxide ($Mg(OH)_2$) are also ingredients in some antacids. Milk of magnesia is a suspension of magnesium hydroxide in water. In small doses it acts as an antacid; in large doses it is a laxative.

In general, antacids are safe for occasional use and in small amounts. However, if you have severe or repeated attacks of hyperacidity you should consult a physician.

Think About It

3. List Name and write the formulas of four common antacid compounds. What ion in these compounds acts to neutralize the acid?

4. Explain Why can magnesium hydroxide be taken internally as an antacid while sodium hydroxide taken internally would cause severe injury?

20.2 Titration

It should be clear from Section 20.1 that acids and bases sometimes, but not always, react in a 1:1 mole ratio.

$$\underset{1\ \text{mol}}{HCl(aq)} + \underset{1\ \text{mol}}{NaOH(aq)} \longrightarrow \underset{1\ \text{mol}}{NaCl(aq)} + \underset{1\ \text{mol}}{H_2O(l)}$$

When sulfuric acid reacts with sodium hydroxide, however, the ratio is 1:2. Two moles of the base sodium hydroxide are required to neutralize one mole of H_2SO_4.

$$\underset{1\ \text{mol}}{H_2SO_4(aq)} + \underset{2\ \text{mol}}{2NaOH(aq)} \longrightarrow \underset{1\ \text{mol}}{Na_2SO_4(aq)} + \underset{2\ \text{mol}}{2H_2O(l)}$$

Similarly, calcium hydroxide and hydrochloric acid react in a 1:2 ratio.

$$\underset{1\ \text{mol}}{Ca(OH)_2(aq)} + \underset{2\ \text{mol}}{2HCl(aq)} \longrightarrow \underset{1\ \text{mol}}{CaCl_2(aq)} + \underset{2\ \text{mol}}{2H_2O(l)}$$

Objective

Explain the steps of a titration.

Safety

Strong bases like NaOH and KOH cause severe progressive burns. If they are spilled on you they should be flushed from the eye or skin with running water for 10 to 15 minutes.

Example 1 Finding the Moles of an Acid in Neutralization

How many moles of sulfuric acid would you require to neutralize 0.50 mol of sodium hydroxide?

Solution

Write a balanced equation for the reaction to find the acid–base mole ratio.

$$\underset{1\ \text{mol}}{H_2SO_4(aq)} + \underset{2\ \text{mol}}{2NaOH(aq)} \longrightarrow \underset{1\ \text{mol}}{Na_2SO_4(aq)} + \underset{2\ \text{mol}}{2H_2O(l)}$$

The ratio of H_2SO_4 to NaOH is 1:2. The necessary number of moles of H_2SO_4 is calculated using this ratio.

$$0.50\ \cancel{\text{mol NaOH}} \times \frac{1\ \text{mol}\ H_2SO_4}{2\ \cancel{\text{mol NaOH}}} = 0.25\ \text{mol}\ H_2SO_4$$

Practice Problems

5. How many moles of sodium hydroxide are required to neutralize 0.20 mol of nitric acid?

6. How many moles of potassium hydroxide are needed to neutralize 1.56 mol of phosphoric acid?

Figure 20.3 The juice of a red cabbage can be used as an acid–base indicator. When a solution is highly acidic, the juice turns red. As the acidity of the solution decreases (the solution becomes more basic), the color changes from red to violet to yellow.

The amount of acid (or base) in a solution can be determined by carrying out a neutralization reaction. An appropriate acid–base indicator is used to show when neutralization has occurred. Phenolphthalein is often the indicator for acid–base neutralization reactions. Solutions that contain this indicator turn from colorless to deep pink as the pH of the solution is changed from acidic to basic. Neutral solutions are very faintly pink. The steps in the neutralization, which is called *titration*, are as follows. (1) A measured volume of an acid of unknown concentration is added to a flask. (2) The indicator is added to the solution. (3) Measured volumes of a base of known concentration are mixed into the acid until the indicator barely changes color. *The solution of known concentration is called the* **standard solution**. The addition of the standard solution is carried out using a buret. This process is continued until the indicator shows that neutralization has occurred. *The point at which the indicator changes color is the* **end point** *of the titration.* The process just described is a **titration**, *the addition of a known amount of solution of known concentration to determine the concentration of another solution.* A similar procedure could be used to find the concentration of a base using a standard acid.

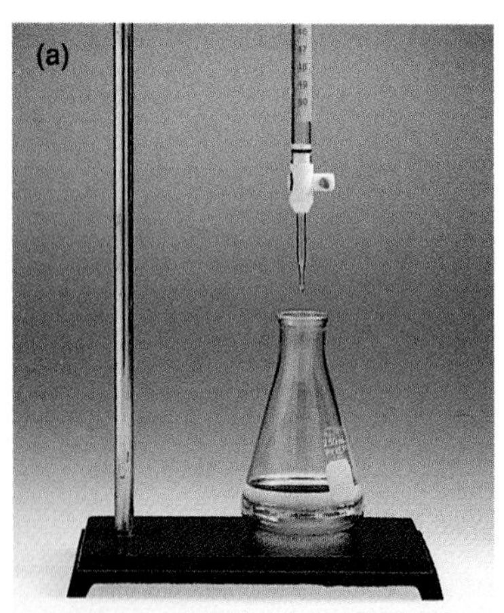
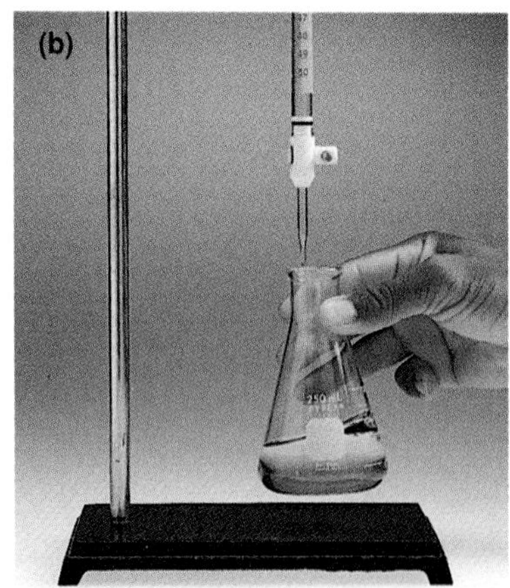
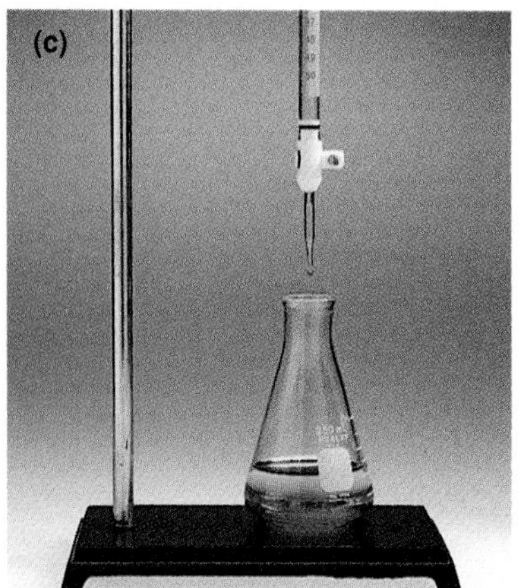

Figure 20.4 Titration of an acid with a base. **(a)** A known volume of acid in a flask is placed beneath a buret filled with a base of known concentration. **(b)** Base is slowly added from the buret to the acid. **(c)** A change in the color of the indicator signals that neutralization has occurred.

Figure 20.5 shows how the pH of a solution changes during the titration of a strong acid with a strong base. The pH of the initial acid solution is low. As the base is added, the pH increases as some of the acid is neutralized. As the titration approaches the point of neutralization, at a pH of 7, the pH increases dramatically as hydronium ions are used up. Once past the point of neutralization, additional base gives a further increase of pH.

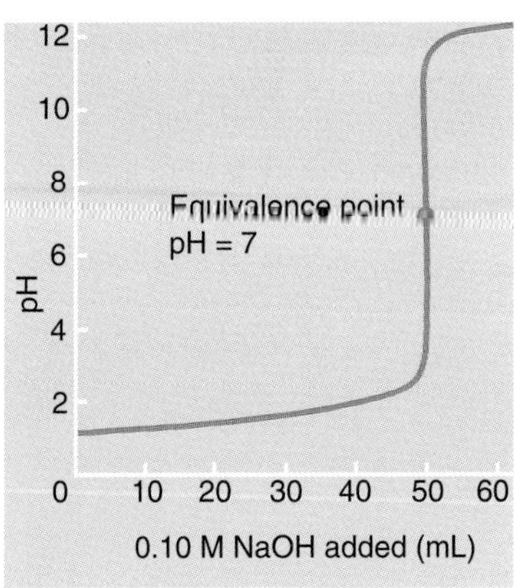

Figure 20.5 The pH curve for the titration of 50.0 mL of 0.1*M* HCl with 0.1*M* NaOH. The equivalence point occurs at 50.0 mL of NaOH added. At this point the solution contains equal amounts of OH^- ions and H^+ ions and is neutral.

Example 2 Determining the Concentration of an Acid by Titration

A 25-mL solution of H_2SO_4 is neutralized by 18 mL of 1.0*M* NaOH using phenolphthalein as an indicator. What is the concentration of the H_2SO_4 solution?

Solution

Write an equation for the neutralization.

$$H_2SO_4(aq) + 2NaOH(aq) \longrightarrow Na_2SO_4(aq) + 2H_2O(l)$$

The H_2SO_4 has two ionizable hydrogens. Thus it will take twice as many moles of NaOH for neutralization to occur. First calculate the moles of NaOH needed for neutralization. Convert mL of NaOH to L for use in this calculation.

$$0.018\,\cancel{\text{L NaOH}} \times \frac{1.0\text{ mol NaOH}}{1\,\cancel{\text{L NaOH}}} = 0.018\text{ mol NaOH}$$

Next use the equation to find the moles of H_2SO_4 neutralized.

$$0.018\,\cancel{\text{mol NaOH}} \times \frac{1\text{ mol }H_2SO_4}{2\,\cancel{\text{mol NaOH}}} = 0.0090\text{ mol }H_2SO_4$$

Then calculate the concentration of the acid.

$$\text{Molarity} = \frac{\text{moles}}{\text{liters}} = \frac{0.0090\text{ mol}}{0.025\text{ L}} = 0.36M$$

The $[H_2SO_4]$ is 0.36*M*.

Problem-Solving Tip

Converting the unit of a measurement is conveniently done by dimensional analysis.

Practice Problems

7. How many milliliters of 0.45*M* hydrochloric acid must be added to 25.0 mL of 1.00*M* potassium hydroxide to make a neutral solution?

8. What is the molarity of phosphoric acid if 15.0 mL of the solution is neutralized by 38.5 mL of 0.15*M* NaOH?

Objective

Calculate the gram equivalent mass of an acid or base.

20.3 Equivalents

In any neutralization reaction, one mole of hydrogen ions reacts with one mole of hydroxide ions. This does not mean that one mole of any acid will neutralize one mole of any base. For some acids, one mole of the acid can give one mole of hydrogen ions. HCl and HNO_3 are such acids. For other acids, one mole of the acid can give two or more moles of hydrogen ions. For example, one mole of H_2SO_4 gives two moles of hydrogen ions.

$$H_2SO_4 \longrightarrow 2H^+ + SO_4^{2-}$$

One mole of H_3PO_4 gives three moles of hydrogen ions.

$$H_3PO_4 \longrightarrow 3H^+ + PO_4^{3-}$$

A similar idea is true of bases such as $Ca(OH)_2$ and $Al(OH)_3$.

$$Ca(OH)_2 \longrightarrow Ca^{2+} + 2OH^- \qquad Al(OH)_3 \longrightarrow Al^{3+} + 3OH^-$$

They give two and three moles of hydroxide ions, respectively, for each mole of base.

Calculating the amount of acid needed to neutralize a given amount of a base would be simpler if there were a unit for the amount of an acid (or base) that will give one mole of hydrogen (or hydroxide) ions. Such a unit exists and is called an equivalent of the acid (or base). *One* **equivalent** *is the amount of an acid (or base) that will give one mole of hydrogen (or hydroxide) ions.*

Roots of Words

aequi-: (Latin) equal
valere: (Latin) to be strong
equivalence the point at which the hydrogen-ion and hydroxide-ion concentrations are equal in a solution

The concentrations of hydrogen ion and hydroxide ion are equal ($1 \times 10^{-7} M$) at the equivalence point in aqueous solutions.

One mole of HCl is one equivalent of HCl. One mole of H_2SO_4 is two equivalents of H_2SO_4. One mole of NaOH is one equivalent of NaOH. One mole of $Ca(OH)_2$ is two equivalents of $Ca(OH)_2$. One mole of HCl will neutralize one mole of NaOH. This is because one mole of each compound is also one equivalent.

$$HCl(aq) + NaOH(aq) \longrightarrow NaCl(aq) + H_2O(l)$$

One mole of HCl will not neutralize one mole of $Ca(OH)_2$.

$$2HCl(aq) + Ca(OH)_2(aq) \longrightarrow CaCl_2(aq) + 2H_2O(l)$$

In this example, two moles of acid are required to neutralize one mole of base. Two moles of HCl contains two equivalents of acid. One mole of $Ca(OH)_2$ contains two equivalents of base. In any neutralization reaction, the equivalents of acid must equal the equivalents of base.

The mass of one equivalent of a substance is called its **gram equivalent mass**. One mole of HCl is one equivalent of HCl. Its gram equivalent mass is equal to its gram molecular mass, 36.5 grams. One mole of H_2SO_4 is two equivalents of H_2SO_4. Its gram equivalent mass is only half of its gram molecular mass, or 49.0 grams.

Example 3 Calculating the Gram Equivalent Mass of a Base

What is the mass of 1 equiv of calcium hydroxide?

Solution

The gram formula mass of $Ca(OH)_2$ is 74 g. One formula unit of $Ca(OH)_2$ has two hydroxide ions.

$$Ca(OH)_2 \longrightarrow Ca^{2+} + 2OH^-$$

$$\text{Gram equivalent mass of } Ca(OH)_2 = \frac{74\ \text{g}/\cancel{\text{mol}}}{2\ \text{equiv}/\cancel{\text{mol}}} = 37\ \text{g/equiv}$$

Calcium hydroxide is 2 equiv per mol and 1 equiv of $Ca(OH)_2$ is 37 g.

Problem-Solving Tip

Check that the answer has an appropriate unit after canceling and before doing the numerical calculation.

Example 4 Finding the Equivalents in a Given Mass of an Acid

How many equivalents is 4.8 g of sulfuric acid?

Solution

The gram formula mass of H_2SO_4 is 98 g. Therefore, 4.8 g of H_2SO_4 is less than 1 mol.

$$4.8\ \cancel{\text{g}\ H_2SO_4} \times \frac{1\ \text{mol}\ H_2SO_4}{98\ \cancel{\text{g}\ H_2SO_4}} = 0.050\ \text{mol}\ H_2SO_4$$

The acid H_2SO_4 is 2 equiv per mol. Thus 0.050 mol H_2SO_4 is 0.10 equiv of H_2SO_4 and 4.8 g of H_2SO_4 is 0.10 equiv of H_2SO_4.

Problem-Solving Tip

The unit in the denominator of the conversion factor must equal the unit of the given measurement.

Concept Practice

9. What is the equivalent mass of an acid?

Practice Problems

10. Determine the gram equivalent mass and the equivalents per mole for each compound.

a. KOH **b.** HCl **c.** H_2SO_4

11. How many equivalents is each of the following?

a. 3.7 g $Ca(OH)_2$ **b.** 189 g H_2SO_4 **c.** 9.8 g H_3PO_4

Objective

Describe the procedure for preparing a dilute solution of known concentration from a more concentrated solution.

20.4 Normality

The concentrations of acids and bases can be stated in molarity. As you have seen, however, it may be more useful to know how many equivalents of acid or base a solution contains. An older unit sometimes used to express the equivalents of acids and bases is *normality.* A solution containing 1.0 equiv of an acid or base per liter has a normality of 1.0. That is, the solution is 1.0 normal (1.0*N*). *The* **normality** *of a solution is the concentration expressed as the number of equivalents of solute in 1 L of solution.*

$$\text{Normality } (N) = \text{equiv/L}$$

The numerical values of normality and molarity are equal for acids and bases that give 1 equiv of H^+ or OH^- per mole. For example, a solution containing 1 mol of NaOH per liter is 1*M* and also 1*N*. A solution containing 1 mol of H_2SO_4 per liter is 1*M* but is 2*N*. This is because H_2SO_4 contains 2 equiv per mole.

Practice Problems

12. What is the normality of the following solutions?

a. 2*M* HCl
b. 0.1*M* CH_3COOH
c. 0.3*M* H_3PO_4
d. 0.25*M* H_2SO_4
e. 0.1*M* NaOH
f. 1.0*M* $Ca(OH)_2$

13. What is the normality of the following solutions?

a. 20.0 g NaOH in 1.0 L of solution
b. 4.9 g H_2SO_4 in 500 mL of solution
c. 15.0 g HCl in 0.400 L of solution
d. 88.0 g H_3PO_4 in 1.50 L of solution
e. 80.0 g NaOH in 1.00 L of solution
f. 196 g H_3PO_4 in 2.00 L of solution

The number of equivalents of an acid or base in a known volume of a solution of known normality can be calculated.

$$\text{Number of equivalents of solution} = \text{volume (liters) of solution} \times \text{normality}$$

$$\text{Equiv} = V(\text{L}) \times N$$

Example 5 Calculating the Equivalents in a Solution

How many equivalents are in 2.5 L of 0.60*N* H_2SO_4?

Solution

Number of equivalents = *V*(L) × *N*

$$= 2.5\,\cancel{L} \times \frac{0.60\text{ equiv}}{\cancel{L}} = 1.5\text{ equiv}$$

Practice Problem

14. How many equivalents are in the following?

a. 0.55 L of 1.8*N* NaOH

b. 1.6 L of 0.50*N* H_3PO_4

c. 250 mL of 0.28*N* H_2SO_4

Solutions of known normality can be made less concentrated by diluting them with water as shown in Figure 20.6. You can calculate the changes in concentration using this relationship.

$$N_1 \times V_1 = N_2 \times V_2$$

Here N_1 and V_1 are the initial solution's normality and volume. N_2 and V_2 are the final solution's normality and volume.

Figure 20.6 When diluting an acid, *always* pour the acid slowly into water using a stirring rod as shown to avoid splashing. *Never* pour water into a concentrated acid.

Integrating Art

Bronze Patinas

Have you ever seen a statue with a greenish weathered look? This look, called a patina, gradually develops when the copper in bronze reacts with carbon dioxide in air to form copper(II) carbonate. Artists often desire patinas because they enhance the appearance of the artwork. Methods have been developed by which sculptors can quickly imitate an authentic patina. Applying an acidic solution of copper(II) sulfate and ammonium chloride to the bronze in the studio produces the patina. Chemical methods have also been developed to produce bluish-green, brown, and black patinas.

Example 6 Preparing a Dilute Solution from a Stock Solution

You need to make 250 mL of 0.10*N* sodium hydroxide from a stock solution that is 2.0*N* sodium hydroxide. How many milliliters of the stock solution must you dilute to 250 mL to get the required solution?

Solution

Use $N_1 \times V_1 = N_2 \times V_2$. You know that $N_1 = 2.0N$, $N_2 = 0.10N$, and $V_2 = 250$ mL. To find V_1, rearrange the equation and then substitute the values of N_1, N_2, and V_2.

$$V_1 = \frac{N_2 \times V_2}{N_1} = \frac{0.10\cancel{N} \times 250 \text{ mL}}{2.0\cancel{N}} = 12.5 \text{ mL} = 13 \text{ mL}$$

(to two significant figures)

Dilute 13 mL of 2.0*N* NaOH to 250 mL to make 0.1*N* NaOH.

Practice Problems

15. How would you prepare 500 mL of 0.20*N* sulfuric acid from a stock solution of 4.0*N* sulfuric acid?

16. How many milliliters of 3.0*N* KOH are needed to prepare 870 mL of 0.20*N* KOH?

Titration calculations can be done in terms of normality instead of molarity. The reason is that normality takes into account the number of ionizable hydrogens in an acid whereas molarity does not. *In a titration, the point of neutralization is called the* **equivalence point**. At the equivalence point, the numbers of equivalents of acid and base are equal. It is thus possible to calculate the number of equivalents of acid or base in an unknown sample. Let N_A and N_B be the normalities of the acid and base solutions. Let V_A and V_B be the volumes of these solutions required to give a neutral solution.

$$\text{Equivalents of acid} = N_A \times V_A$$

$$\text{Equivalents of base} = N_B \times V_B$$

The numbers of equivalents of acid and base are equal at the equivalence point.

$$N_A \times V_A = N_B \times V_B$$

The volumes V_A and V_B may be expressed in liters or milliliters, provided the same unit is used for both.

Example 7 Finding Normality by Neutralization

If it takes 35.0 mL of 0.20N HCl to neutralize 25.0 mL of an unknown base, what is the normality of the base?

Solution

$$N_B = \frac{V_A \times N_A}{V_B} = \frac{35.0 \text{ mL} \times 0.20N}{25.0 \text{ mL}} = 0.28N$$

Example 8 Calculating the Volume of an Acid Needed for Neutralization

How many milliliters of 0.500N sulfuric acid would you need to neutralize 50.0 mL of 0.200N potassium hydroxide?

Solution

$$V_A = \frac{V_B \times N_B}{N_A}$$

$$= \frac{50.0 \text{ mL} \times 0.200N}{0.500N} = 20.0 \text{ mL}$$

Practice Problems

17. How many milliliters of 0.20N NaOH must be added to 75 mL of 0.050N HCl to make a neutral solution?

18. What is the normality of a solution of a base if 25 mL is neutralized by 75 mL of 0.40N acid?

20.5 Salt Hydrolysis

Objective

Explain why aqueous solutions of some salts are acidic or basic, using the concept of hydrolysis.

Solutions of many salts are neutral, but some are acidic and others are basic. Solutions of sodium chloride and potassium sulfate are neutral. A solution of ammonium chloride is acidic. A solution of sodium ethanoate is basic. This happens because some salts promote hydrolysis. *In* **salt hydrolysis**, *the cations or anions of the dissociated salt accept hydrogen ions from water or donate hydrogen ions to water.* Depending on the direction of the hydrogen-ion

Chemistry in Careers

Museum Scientist

Museum scientists work to restore and preserve artifacts. A museum scientist might chemically treat a sculpture to halt its corrosion or examine a medieval plaque for evidence of deteriorating enamel. Recently, the National Aeronautics and Space Administration, NASA, discovered that its collection of space suits from the 1960s was rapidly deteriorating. Museum scientists from the Smithsonian Institution advised NASA on storage methods to slow the rate of decay. Many museum scientists earn an undergraduate degree in chemistry and then obtain a master's degree in the conservation and restoration of works of art.

transfer, solutions containing hydrolyzing salts may be either acidic or basic. Hydrolyzing salts are usually derived from a strong acid and a weak base or from a weak acid and a strong base.

Sodium ethanoate (CH_3COONa) is the salt of a weak acid (ethanoic acid, CH_3COOH) and a strong base (sodium hydroxide, NaOH). In solution the salt is completely ionized.

$$\underset{\text{Sodium ethanoate}}{CH_3COONa(aq)} \longrightarrow \underset{\text{Ethanoate ion}}{CH_3COO^-(aq)} + \underset{\text{Sodium ion}}{Na^+(aq)}$$

The ethanoate ion is a Brønsted-Lowry base. It establishes an equilibrium with water, forming electrically neutral ethanoic acid and hydroxide ions.

$$\underset{\substack{\text{(hydrogen-ion}\\\text{acceptor,}\\\text{Brønsted-Lowry}\\\text{base)}}}{CH_3COO^-(aq)} + \underset{\substack{\text{(hydrogen-ion}\\\text{donor,}\\\text{Brønsted-Lowry}\\\text{acid)}}}{H_2O(l)} \rightleftharpoons HC_2H_3O_2(aq) + \underset{\substack{\text{(makes the}\\\text{solution basic)}}}{OH^-(aq)}$$

This process is called hydrolysis because it splits a hydrogen ion off a water molecule. The resulting solution contains a hydroxide-ion concentration greater than the hydrogen-ion concentration. Thus the solution is basic.

Ammonium chloride (NH_4Cl) is the salt of a strong acid (hydrochloric acid, HCl) and a weak base (ammonia, NH_3). It is completely ionized in solution.

$$NH_4Cl(aq) \longrightarrow NH_4^+(aq) + Cl^-(aq)$$

The ammonium ion (NH_4^+) is a strong enough acid to donate a hydrogen ion to a water molecule, although the equilibrium is strongly to the left.

$$\underset{\substack{\text{(hydrogen-ion}\\\text{donor,}\\\text{Brønsted-Lowry}\\\text{acid)}}}{NH_4^+(aq)} + \underset{\substack{\text{(hydrogen-ion}\\\text{acceptor,}\\\text{Brønsted-Lowry}\\\text{base)}}}{H_2O(l)} \rightleftharpoons NH_3(aq) + \underset{\substack{\text{(makes the}\\\text{solution}\\\text{acidic)}}}{H_3O^+(aq)}$$

This process is also called hydrolysis. It results in the formation of unionized ammonia and hydronium ions. The $[H_3O^+]$ is greater than the $[OH^-]$. Thus a solution of ammonium chloride is acidic.

Concept Practice

19. What kinds of salts hydrolyze water?

20. Write an equation to show why an aqueous solution of sodium hydrogen carbonate is basic.

20.6 Buffers

The addition of 10 mL of 0.10M sodium hydroxide to 1 L of pure water increases the pH by 4.0 pH units (from 7.0 to 11.0). A solution containing 0.20 mol/L of both ethanoic acid and sodium ethanoate has a pH of 4.76. However, when moderate amounts of either acid or base are added to this solution, the pH changes little. For example, the addition of 10 mL of 0.10M sodium hydroxide to 1 L of this solution increases the pH by only 0.01 pH unit, from 4.76 to 4.77!

The solution of ethanoic acid and sodium ethanoate is a typical example of a *buffer*. **Buffers** *are solutions in which the pH remains relatively constant when small amounts of acid or base are added.* A buffer is a solution of a weak acid and one of its salts. It could also be a solution of a weak base and one of its salts.

A buffer solution is better able to resist drastic changes in pH than pure water. Ethanoic acid (CH_3COOH) and its anion (CH_3COO^-) act as reservoirs of neutralizing power. They react with any hydrogen ions or hydroxide ions that are added to the solution. For example, the sodium ethanoate (CH_3COONa) in the buffer solution is completely ionized.

$$\underset{\text{Sodium ethanoate}}{CH_3COONa(aq)} \longrightarrow \underset{\text{Ethanoate ion}}{CH_3COO^-(aq)} + \underset{\text{Sodium ion}}{Na^+(aq)}$$

When an acid is added to the solution, the ethanoate ions (CH_3COO^-) act as a "hydrogen-ion sponge." This creates ethanoic acid, which does not dissociate extensively in water. Thus the pH does not change appreciably.

$$\underset{\text{Ethanoate ion}}{CH_3COO^-(aq)} + \underset{\text{Hydrogen ion}}{H^+(aq)} \longrightarrow \underset{\text{Ethanoic acid}}{CH_3COOH(aq)}$$

A base is a source of hydroxide ions. When a base is added to the solution, the ethanoic acid and the hydroxide ions react to produce water and ethanoate ion.

$$\underset{\text{Ethanoic acid}}{CH_3COOH(aq)} + \underset{\text{Hydroxide ion}}{OH^-(aq)} \longrightarrow \underset{\text{Ethanoate ion}}{CH_3COO^-(aq)} + \underset{\text{Water}}{H_2O(l)}$$

The ethanoate ion is not a strong enough base to accept hydrogen ions from water extensively. Again, the pH does not change very much at all.

An ethanoate buffer cannot control the pH when too much acid is added. Then no more ethanoate ions are present to accept hydrogen ions. The buffer also becomes ineffective when too much base is added. Then no more ethanoic acid molecules are present to donate hydrogen ions. *The* **buffer capacity** *is the amount of acid or base that may be added to a buffer solution before a significant*

Objective

Define a buffer and, using equations, show how a buffer system works.

Roots of Words

buff: (Old English) firmly, sturdily

buffer a solution that resists changes in pH when small amounts of acid or base are added

Buffers consist of a solution of a weak acid and the salt of the weak acid (or a weak base and the salt of the weak base).

Table 20.2 Important Buffer Systems

Buffer name	Buffer species	Buffer pH (components 0.1 *M*)
Ethanoic acid–ethanoate ion	CH_3COOH/CH_3COO^-	4.76
Dihydrogen phosphate ion–hydrogen phosphate ion	$H_2PO_4^-/HPO_4^{2-}$	7.20
Carbonic acid–hydrogen carbonate (solution saturated with CO_2)	H_2CO_3/HCO_3^-	6.46
Ammonium ion–ammonia	NH_4^+/NH_3	9.25

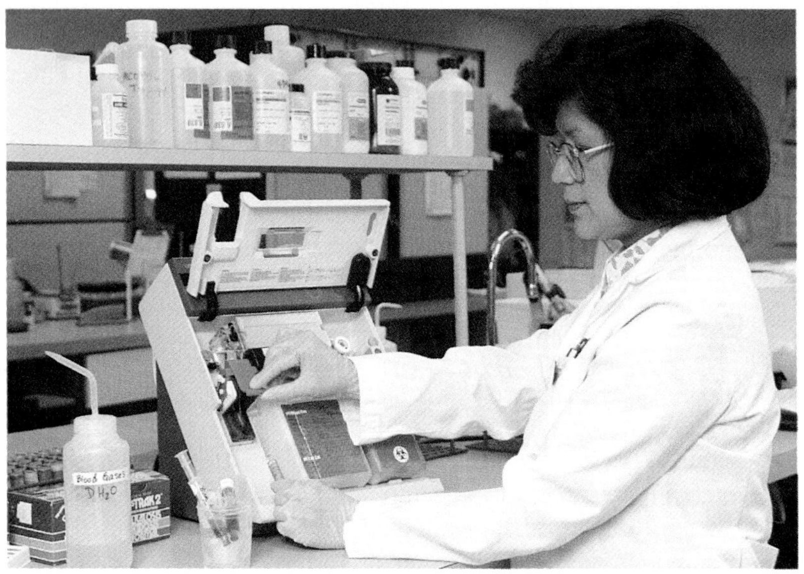

Figure 20.7 This device measures the pH of human blood.

change in pH occurs. When too much acid or base is added, the buffer capacity of a solution is exceeded. Two buffer systems are crucial in controlling pH in the human body. One is the carbonic acid–hydrogen carbonate buffer. The carbonic acid–hydrogen carbonate buffer system is responsible for maintaining blood pH within a very narrow range. The other is the monohydrogen phosphate–dihydrogen phosphate buffer. Table 20.2 lists several different buffer systems.

Example 9 Illustrating the Action of a Buffer with Equations

Using two chemical equations, show how the carbonic acid–hydrogen carbonate buffer can "mop up" hydrogen ions and hydroxide ions.

Solution

The carbonic acid–hydrogen carbonate buffer is a solution of carbonic acid (H_2CO_3) and hydrogen carbonate ions (HCO_3^-). When a base is added to this buffer, it reacts with H_2CO_3 to produce neutral water. The pH changes very little.

$$\underset{\text{Carbonic acid}}{H_2CO_3(aq)} + \underset{\text{Hydroxide ion}}{OH^-(aq)} \longrightarrow \underset{\text{Hydrogen carbonate ion}}{HCO_3^-(aq)} + \underset{\text{Water}}{H_2O(l)}$$

When an acid is added to the buffer, it reacts with HCO_3^- to produce undissociated carbonic acid. Again the pH changes very little.

$$\underset{\text{Hydrogen carbonate ion}}{HCO_3^-(aq)} + \underset{\text{Hydrogen ion}}{H^+(aq)} \longrightarrow \underset{\text{Carbonic acid}}{H_2CO_3(aq)}$$

Concept Practice

21. A buffered solution cannot absorb an indefinite amount of acid or base. Explain.

Practice Problems

22. Write reactions to show what happens when the following events occur.

a. Acid is added to a solution of HPO_4^{2-}.

b. Base is added to a solution of $H_2PO_4^-$.

23. Write equations that show what happens when acid is added to the following buffers.

a. ethanoic acid–ethanoate buffer

b. ammonium ion–ammonia buffer

Integrating Biology

Blood Buffers

Your body functions properly only when the pH of your blood lies between 6.8 and 7.8; a blood pH outside these limits is life-threatening. Your blood contains buffer systems to keep the pH between 7.35 and 7.45. The most important blood buffer consists of carbonic acid and hydrogen carbonate ions. Hydrogen ions produced by chemical reactions in your body are the main threat to your blood's pH. The buffer maintains the blood pH by removing the hydrogen ions through the following reaction.

$$\underset{\text{hydrogen carbonate ion}}{HCO_3^-(aq)} + \underset{\text{hydrogen ion}}{H^+(aq)} \rightarrow \underset{\text{carbonic acid}}{H_2CO_3(aq)}$$

20.7 The Solubility Product Constant

Objective

Calculate ion concentrations of slightly soluble salts.

Salts differ in their solubilities. In general, compounds of the alkali metals are soluble in water. For example, over 35 g of sodium chloride will dissolve in 100 mL of water. Many classes of ionic compounds, however, are insoluble. For example, many compounds that contain phosphate, sulfide, sulfite, or carbonate ions are insoluble. Exceptions are compounds in which these ions are combined with ammonium ions or alkali metal ions. Table 20.3 summarizes the solubilities of many ionic compounds in water.

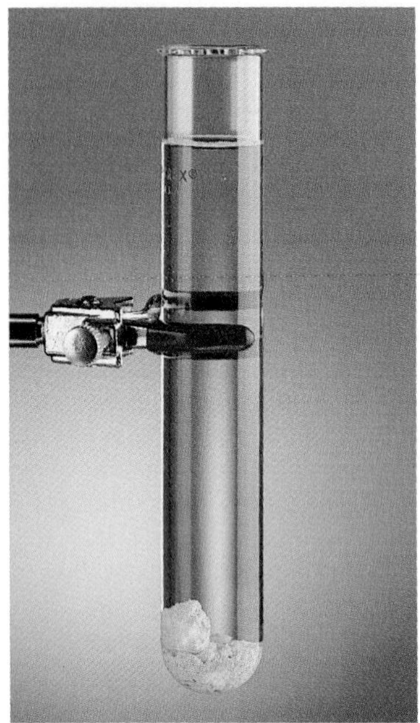

Figure 20.8 Silver chloride is slightly soluble in water.

Most "insoluble" salts dissolve to some extent in water. These salts are said to be slightly or sparingly soluble in water. For example, when the "insoluble" salt silver chloride is mixed with water, a very small amount of it dissolves as shown in Figure 20.8.

$$AgCl(s) \rightleftharpoons Ag^+(aq) + Cl^-(aq)$$

You can write an equilibrium expression for this process.

$$K_{eq} = \frac{[Ag^+] \times [Cl^-]}{[AgCl]}$$

As long as some undissolved (solid) AgCl is present, the concentration of the AgCl is constant. Thus, the concentration of AgCl can be combined with the equilibrium constant to form a new, different constant.

$$K_{eq} \times [AgCl] = [Ag^+] \times [Cl^-] = K_{sp}$$

This new constant, called the **solubility product constant,** *K_{sp}, is equal to the product of the concentration terms each raised to the power of the coefficient of the substance in the dissociation equation.* The coefficients for the dissociation of silver chloride are each 1. The value of K_{sp} for silver chloride at 25°C is 1.8×10^{-10}.

$$K_{sp} = [Ag^+] \times [Cl^-] = 1.8 \times 10^{-10}$$

Table 20.3 Solubilities of Ionic Compounds in Water

Compounds	Solubility	Exceptions
Salts of Group 1A metals and ammonia	Soluble	Some lithium compounds
Ethanoates, nitrates, chlorates, and perchlorates	Soluble	Few exceptions
Sulfates	Soluble	Compounds of Pb, Ag, Hg, Ba, Sr, and Ca
Chlorides, bromides, and iodides	Soluble	Compounds of Ag and some compounds of Hg and Pb
Sulfides and hydroxides	Most are insoluble	Alkali metal sulfides and hydroxides are soluble. Compounds of Ba, Sr, and Ca are slightly soluble.
Carbonates, phosphates, and sulfites	Insoluble	Compounds of the alkali metals and of ammonium ions

Table 20.4 Solubility Product Constants, K_{sp}, at 25°C

Salt	K_{sp}	Salt	K_{sp}	Salt	K_{sp}
Halides		Sulfates		Hydroxides	
AgCl	1.8×10^{-10}	$PbSO_4$	6.3×10^{-7}	$Al(OH)_3$	3.0×10^{-34}
AgBr	5.0×10^{-13}	$BaSO_4$	1.1×10^{-10}	$Zn(OH)_2$	3.0×10^{-16}
AgI	8.3×10^{-17}	$CaSO_4$	2.4×10^{-5}	$Ca(OH)_2$	6.5×10^{-6}
$PbCl_2$	1.7×10^{-5}	Sulfides		$Mg(OH)_2$	7.1×10^{-12}
$PbBr_2$	2.1×10^{-6}	NiS	4.0×10^{-20}	$Fe(OH)_2$	7.9×10^{-16}
PbI_2	7.9×10^{-9}	CuS	8.0×10^{-37}	Carbonates	
PbF_2	3.6×10^{-8}	Ag_2S	8.0×10^{-51}	$CaCO_3$	4.5×10^{-9}
CaF_2	3.9×10^{-11}	ZnS	3.0×10^{-23}	$SrCO_3$	9.3×10^{-10}
Chromates		FeS	8.0×10^{-19}	$ZnCO_3$	1.0×10^{-10}
$PbCrO_4$	1.8×10^{-14}	CdS	1.0×10^{-27}	Ag_2CO_3	8.1×10^{-12}
Ag_2CrO_4	1.2×10^{-12}	SnS	1.3×10^{-26}	$BaCO_3$	5.0×10^{-9}
		PbS	3.0×10^{-28}		

Example 10 Finding Ion Concentrations in a Saturated Solution

What is the concentration of silver and chloride ions in a saturated silver chloride solution at 25°C?

$$K_{sp} = 1.8 \times 10^{-10}$$

Solution

The equation shows that for each Ag^+ ion formed, one Cl^- ion is formed.

$$AgCl(s) \rightleftharpoons Ag^+(aq) + Cl^-(aq)$$

Therefore at equilibrium $[Ag^+] = [Cl^-]$.
Write the expression for K_{sp}.

$$K_{sp} = [Ag^+] \times [Cl^-] = 1.8 \times 10^{-10}$$

Substitute $[Ag^+]$ for the $[Cl^-]$ in the expression for K_{sp} and then solve for the $[Ag^+]$.

$$[Ag^+] \times [Ag^+] = 1.8 \times 10^{-10}$$

$$[Ag^+]^2 = 1.8 \times 10^{-10}$$

$$[Ag^+] = 1.3 \times 10^{-5} M$$

The equilibrium concentration of Cl^- is also $1.3 \times 10^{-5} M$.

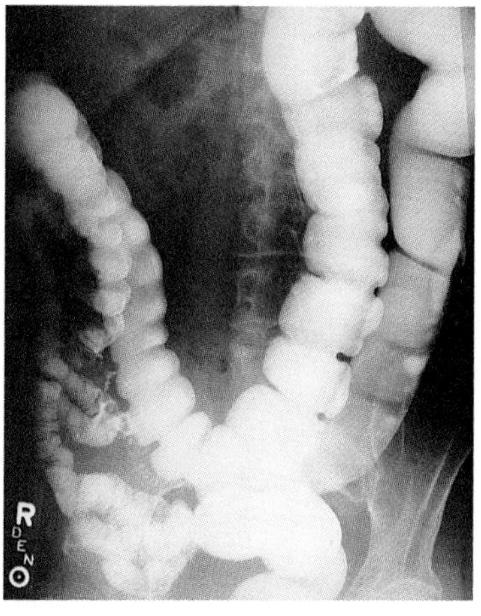

Figure 20.9 Barium sulfate is used for making X-ray images of the digestive tract. X-rays are absorbed by the salt, thereby producing light areas on the film. Barium sulfate can be used for this procedure because it is very insoluble and is not absorbed by the body. Soluble barium salts are highly toxic.

Example 11 Using K_{sp} to Calculate Ion Concentrations at Equilibrium

Calcium fluoride has a K_{sp} of 3.9×10^{-11} at 25°C. What is the fluoride ion concentration at equilibrium?

Solution

Write the equation: $CaF_2(s) \rightleftharpoons Ca^{2+}(aq) + 2F^-(aq)$.
Write the K_{sp} expression: $K_{sp} = [Ca^{2+}] \times [F^-]^2 = 3.9 \times 10^{-11}$
When the $[Ca^{2+}]$ is x, the $[F^-]$ is $2x$. (Twice as many F^- ions as Ca^{2+} ions are formed when CaF_2 dissociates.) Now substitute into the K_{sp} expression and solve for x.

$$K_{sp} = (x)(2x)^2 = 3.9 \times 10^{-11}$$

$$4x^3 = 3.9 \times 10^{-11}$$

$$x^3 = 9.8 \times 10^{-12}$$

$$x = 2.1 \times 10^{-4}$$

The $[Ca^{2+}] = 2.1 \times 10^{-4} M$. The $[F^-]$ is twice the $[Ca^{2+}]$. Thus $[F^-] = 4.2 \times 10^{-4} M$.

Concept Practice

24. Write the solubility product expression for each salt.
a. NiS **b.** $BaCO_3$ **c.** $PbCl_2$ **d.** Ag_2CrO_4

Practice Problems

25. Lead(II) sulfide, PbS, has a K_{sp} of 3×10^{-28}. What is the concentration of lead(II) ion in a saturated solution of PbS?

26. The K_{sp} of silver sulfide, Ag_2S, is 8×10^{-51}. What is the silver-ion concentration of a saturated solution of silver sulfide?

Objective

Explain the common ion effect using Le Châtelier's principle.

20.8 The Common Ion Effect

In a saturated solution of silver chloride an equilibrium is established between the solid silver chloride and its ions.

$$AgCl(s) \rightleftharpoons Ag^+(aq) + Cl^-(aq) \quad K_{sp} = 1.8 \times 10^{-10}$$

What would happen if you added some silver nitrate to this solution? Immediately after the addition, the product of the $[Ag^+]$ and the $[Cl^-]$ would be greater than K_{sp}. Applying Le Châtelier's principle, the "stress" of the additional Ag^+ can be relieved if the reaction shifts to the left. As shown in Figure 20.10 the silver ions will combine with chloride ions to form additional solid AgCl. In fact, AgCl will precipitate until the product of $[Ag^+]$ and $[Cl^-]$ once again equals 1.8×10^{-10}.

In this example, the silver ion is called a *common ion. A* **common ion** *is an ion that is common to both salts.* Adding silver nitrate to a saturated solution of AgCl causes the solubility of AgCl to be decreased. The solubility of AgCl is less in the presence of a solution of $AgNO_3$ than it is in pure water. *The lowering of the solubility of a substance by the addition of a common ion is called the* **common ion effect**.

Adding sodium chloride would also give the common ion effect in this example. The additional chloride ion, a different common ion, would cause the reaction to shift to the left. More AgCl would be formed and the solubility of AgCl would again decrease until the K_{sp} equaled 1.8×10^{-10}.

Figure 20.10 When silver nitrate is added to a saturated solution of silver chloride, additional silver chloride forms due to the common ion effect.

Example 12 Finding Equilibrium Ion Concentrations in the Presence of a Common Ion

The K_{sp} of silver iodide is 8.3×10^{-17}. What is the iodide ion concentration of a 1.00-L saturated solution of AgI to which 0.020 mol of $AgNO_3$ is added?

Solution

You first write the equation for the equilibrium.

$$AgI(s) \rightleftharpoons Ag^+(aq) + I^-(aq)$$

Then you write the expression for the solubility product.

$$K_{sp} = [Ag^+] \times [I^-] = 8.3 \times 10^{-17}$$

If the equilibrium concentration of iodide ion from the dissociation is x, then the equilibrium concentration of silver ion is $x + 0.020$. Because of the small value of K_{sp}, x will be small compared with 0.020. Therefore, the $[Ag^+]$ at equilibrium equals $x + 0.020 \approx 0.020$. Substitute these values into the K_{sp} expression.

$$K_{sp} = [Ag^+] \times [I^-] = 8.3 \times 10^{-17}$$

$$(0.020)(x) = 8.3 \times 10^{-17}$$

$$x = 4.2 \times 10^{-15}$$

The equilibrium concentration of iodide ion is $4.2 \times 10^{-15} M$.

Safety

The silver halides are used in photographic emulsions and are quite poisonous. Poisonous chemicals should not be flushed down the drain. Dispose of all chemicals properly.

Practice Problems

27. The K_{sp} of $SrSO_4$ is 3.2×10^{-7}. What is the equilibrium concentration of sulfate ion in a 1.0-L solution of strontium sulfate to which 0.10 mol of $Sr(CH_3COO)_2$ has been added?

28. What is the concentration of sulfide ion in a 1.0-L solution of iron(II) sulfide to which 0.04 mol of iron(II) nitrate has been added? The K_{sp} of FeS is 8×10^{-19}.

The solubility product, K_{sp}, can be used to predict whether a precipitate will form when solutions are mixed together. If the ion product concentration of two ions in the mixture is greater than the K_{sp} of the compound formed from the ions, a precipitate will form. If the ion product equals K_{sp}, the solution is saturated, and no precipitate will form. If the ion product is less than K_{sp}, no precipitate will form, and the solution will be unsaturated.

Example 13 Predicting Precipitation on Solution Mixing

Problem-Solving Tip

Rephrase the question: "Does the ion product exceed K_{sp}?"

Predict whether barium sulfate will precipitate when 0.50 L of 0.002*M* $Ba(NO_3)_2$ is mixed with 0.50 L of 0.008*M* Na_2SO_4 to form 1.00 L of solution. The K_{sp} of $BaSO_4$ is 1.1×10^{-10}.

Solution

The concentration of each ion is halved because the volume is doubled when the original solutions are mixed. In the final solution $[Ba^{2+}] = 0.001M$ and $[SO_4^{2-}] = 0.004M$.

$$[Ba^{2+}] \times [SO_4^{2-}] = (0.001M) \times (0.004M) = 4 \times 10^{-6}$$

Since the ion product exceeds K_{sp}, $BaSO_4$ will precipitate.

Practice Problems

29. A student prepares a solution by combining 0.025 mol $CaCl_2$ and 0.015 mol $Pb(NO_3)_2$ and adding water to make 1.0 L of solution. Will a precipitate of $PbCl_2$ form in this solution?

30. Predict whether calcium carbonate will precipitate when 0.5 L of 0.001*M* $Ca(NO_3)_2$ is mixed with 0.5 L of 0.0008*M* Na_2CO_3 to form 1.0 L of solution. The K_{sp} of $CaCO_3$ is 4.5×10^{-9}.

20.B Science, Technology, and Society

Swimming Pool Chemistry

Millions of people would face a major health risk if the swimming pools they used were not properly maintained. The major concern in swimming pool maintenance is preventing the growth of bacteria and algae. Bacteria can cause illness. Algae foul the water and can clog filters.

Chlorine compounds are usually used to disinfect the water in pools. "Liquid chlorine" sold for use in pools is a solution containing sodium hypochlorite, NaOCl. "Dry chlorine" is solid calcium hypochlorite, $Ca(OCl)_2$. When these ionic compounds are added to water, the hypochlorite ion hydrolyzes water and forms weak hypochlorous acid, HOCl.

$$OCl^-(aq) + H_2O(l) \rightleftharpoons HOCl(aq) + OH^-(aq)$$

To prevent the growth of bacteria and algae, a sufficient concentration of hypochlorous acid must be maintained. The amount of undissociated hypochlorous acid in the water depends on the water's pH. Following Le Châtelier's principle, if the pH is too high, the hydrolysis reaction shown in the first reaction equation will be shifted toward the reactants. This will result in a reduced concentration of HOCl. If the pH is too low, however, the acid content of the water can cause eye irritation. Too much acid can also damage the plaster and corrode the metal piping and filters in the pool.

If the pool pH is too high, it can be lowered by adding an acid to neutralize the excess hydroxide ions. A dilute solution of hydrochloric acid or solid sodium hydrogen sulfate can be used.

$$HCl(aq) + OH^-(aq) \longrightarrow H_2O(aq) + Cl^-(aq)$$

$$NaHSO_4(aq) + OH^-(aq) \longrightarrow Na^+(aq) + SO_4^{2-}(aq) + H_2O(l)$$

If the pool pH is too low, it can be raised by neutralizing some of the acid. Sodium carbonate (soda ash) or sodium hydrogen carbonate (baking soda) can be used.

$$Na_2CO_3(aq) + 2H^+(aq) \longrightarrow 2Na^+(aq) + H_2O(l) + CO_2(aq)$$

$$NaHCO_3(aq) + H^+(aq) \longrightarrow Na^+(aq) + H_2O(l) + CO_2(aq)$$

Figure 20.11 Proper water pH is important in maintaining swimming pool safety and comfort.

Think About It

31. Identify Which compound's concentration must be maintained to prevent bacterial growth in a swimming pool?

32. Explain Why must the pH of a swimming pool be controlled?

Chapter 20 Review

Neutralization and Salts

Key Terms

buffer *20.6*
buffer capacity *20.6*
common ion *20.8*
common ion effect *20.8*
end point *20.2*
equivalence point *20.4*
equivalent (equiv) *20.3*
gram equivalent mass *20.3*
neutralization reaction *20.1*
normality (*N*) *20.4*
salt hydrolysis *20.5*
solubility product constant (K_{sp}) *20.7*
standard solution *20.2*
titration *20.2*

Chapter Summary

In the reaction of an acid with a base, hydrogen ions and hydroxide ions react to produce water. This reaction, called neutralization, is usually carried out by titration. The end point in a titration is the point at which the indicator changes color. An indicator is chosen so that the solution reaches the end point very near the point of neutralization. At the equivalence point of a titration the number of equivalents of acid equals the number of equivalents of base.

An equivalent of an acid is the mass of the acid that provides 1 mol of hydrogen ions in solution. A solution that contains one equivalent of an acid or a base in a single liter of solution is a one normal (1*N*) solution.

A salt forms when an acid is neutralized by a base. Salts consist of an anion from the acid and a cation from the base. Salts of strong acid–strong base reactions produce neutral solutions with water. Salts formed from weak acids or weak bases hydrolyze water. They produce solutions that are acidic or basic.

Solutions that resist changes in pH are called buffer solutions. The pH of body fluids is kept within its normal range with buffers.

The solubility product constant, K_{sp}, is the equilibrium constant for the equilibrium between an ionic solid and its ions in solution. The solubility of a salt is decreased by the addition of a common ion.

Practice Questions and Problems

33. Write complete balanced equations for these acid-base reactions. Give the names of the salts produced. *20.1*

a. $H_2SO_4(aq) + KOH(aq) \longrightarrow$
b. $HCl(aq) + NH_3(aq) \longrightarrow$
c. $H_3PO_4(aq) + Ca(OH)_2(aq) \longrightarrow$
d. $HNO_3(aq) + Mg(OH)_2(aq) \longrightarrow$

34. What could happen if the antacid you take neutralizes too much stomach acid? *20.A*

35. How many moles of hydrochloric acid are required to neutralize these bases? *20.2*

a. 0.2 mol NaOH
b. 2 mol NH_4OH
c. 0.1 mol $Ca(OH)_2$

36. What is true at the end point of a titration? *20.2*

37. What is the molarity of sodium hydroxide if 20.0 mL of the solution is neutralized by the following 1.00*M* solutions? *20.2*

a. 28.0 mL of HCl
b. 17.4 mL of H_3PO_4

38. What is the equivalent mass of a base? *20.3*

39. Determine the gram equivalent mass of each compound. *20.3*

a. H_3PO_4 **c.** $Mg(OH)_2$
b. NaOH **d.** CH_3COOH

40. Determine the number of equivalents in each of the following. *20.3*

a. 20 g NaOH **c.** 9.8 g H_3PO_4
b. 7.4 g $Ca(OH)_2$ **d.** 19.6 g H_2SO_4

41. How is the normality of a solution calculated? *20.4*

42. What is the normality of each of the following solutions? *20.4*

a. 1*M* NaOH **c.** 0.2*M* KOH
b. 2*M* HNO_3 **d.** 0.1*M* H_2SO_4

43. Determine the normality of each solution. *20.4*
   a. 250 mL of solution containing 10 g of NaOH
   b. 750 mL of solution containing 4.9 g of H_2SO_4
   c. 270 mL of solution containing 0.74 g of HCl
   d. 2.80 L of solution containing 18.6 g of HNO_3
   e. 7.3 g HCl in 250 mL of solution
   f. 18.4 g HNO_3 in 1250 mL of solution
44. A student titrated several solutions of unknown concentration with various standard solutions to the point of neutralization. The volume of each unknown solution and the volume and normality of the standard solution used are given below. Calculate the normality for each unknown. *20.4*
   a. 25.0 mL H_2SO_4 required 15.0 mL of 0.100*N* NaOH
   b. 10.0 mL NaOH required 20.0 mL of 0.200*N* HCl
   c. 17.5 mL NaOH required 25.0 mL of 0.120*N* HNO_3
   d. 50.0 mL CH_3COOH required 39.6 mL of 0.0950*N* KOH
   e. 29.2 mL $Ca(OH)_2$ required 50.0 mL of 0.152*N* HNO_3
45. Explain why solutions of salts that hydrolyze water are not pH 7. *20.5*
46. Predict whether an aqueous solution of each salt will be acidic, basic, or neutral. *20.5*
   a. $NaHCO_3$
   b. NH_4NO_3
   c. KCl
   d. Na_2CO_3
   e. Na_2SO_4
   f. NH_4Cl
47. What is a buffer? *20.6*
48. Would a solution of HCl and NaCl be a good buffer? Explain. *20.6*
49. What does the solubility product constant, K_{sp}, signify? *20.7*
50. Use Table 20.4 to rank these salts from most soluble to least soluble. *20.7*
   a. CuS
   b. $BaSO_4$
   c. $SrCO_3$
   d. AgI
51. What compounds are used to chlorinate swimming pools? *20.B*
52. How does the addition of a common ion affect the solubility of another substance? *20.8*

Mastery Questions and Problems

53. Construct a concept map using the key terms with *titration* as the central concept.
54. What must be true about the concentration of two ions if precipitation occurs when solutions of the two ions are mixed?
55. How many equivalents are in the following solutions?
   a. 5.8 L of 0.55*N* HCl
   b. 330 mL of 1.4*N* H_3PO_4
   c. 0.14 L of 0.22*N* KOH
56. Acidic conditions help maintain the proper concentration of HOCl in a swimming pool. What are some negative consequences if the pool is too acidic?
57. Use the phosphate buffer ($H_2PO_4^-/HPO_4^{2-}$) to illustrate how a buffer system works. Show by means of equations how the pH of a solution can be kept almost constant when small amounts of acid or base are added.
58. Find the normality of each solution.
   a. 86.3 g $Mg(OH)_2$ in 2.5 L of solution
   b. 5.6 g HBr in 450 mL of solution
   c. 49.4 g H_2SO_3 in 1.5 L of solution
59. Write an equation for the reaction of each of these antacids with hydrochloric acid.
   a. magnesium hydroxide
   b. calcium carbonate
   c. aluminum hydroxide
60. How many milliliters of 2.00*N* NaOH would you need to dilute with water to make 250 mL of 0.100*N* NaOH?
61. What is the concentration of hydroxide ions in a saturated solution of each salt?
   a. $Zn(OH)_2$
   b. $Ca(OH)_2$
   c. $Al(OH)_3$
62. Give the reactions for the addition of base to these buffers.
   a. ammonium ion–ammonia buffer
   b. dihydrogen phosphate ion–monohydrogen phosphate ion buffer
63. What is the equilibrium concentration of barium ion in a 1.0-L saturated solution of barium carbonate to which 0.25 mol of K_2CO_3 has been added?

64. The data below were collected in a titration of 50.00 mL of ethanoic acid, CH_3COOH, of unknown concentration with 0.100*N* NaOH. Plot these data (pH on the *y* axis) to obtain a titration curve.

Volume of NaOH (mL)	pH
0	
10.00	4.15
25.00	4.76
40.00	5.36
49.00	6.45
49.99	8.55
50.00	8.73
50.01	8.89
51.00	11.00
60.00	11.96
75.00	12.30
100.00	12.52

a. What is the pH at the end point of this titration?

b. Using Figure 19.12, identify one or more indicators that could be used to determine the end point in this titration.

65. Write an equation to show that an aqueous solution of sodium ethanoate will be basic.

66. Arrange these solutions in order of decreasing acidity.

a. 0.1*N* NaOH

b. 0.1*N* HCl

c. 0.1*M* ammonium chloride

d. 0.1*M* sodium ethanoate

67. Would precipitation occur when 500 mL of a 0.02*M* solution of $AgNO_3$ is mixed with 500 mL of a 0.001*M* solution of NaCl?

Critical Thinking Questions

68. Choose the term that best completes the second relationship.

a. animal: dog   indicator: ____
(1) pH   (2) phenolphthalein
(3) titration   (4) end point

b. mole:atoms   equivalent: ____
(1) molecules   (2) acids
(3) bases   (4) ions

c. molarity:moles   normality: ____
(1) normals   (2) concentration
(3) equivalents   (4) ions

69. It is important for the pH of the blood to be maintained in the range 7.35 to 7.45. The hydrogen carbonate ion–carbonic acid buffer system is the most important of three buffer systems in the blood that help maintain this pH range. This system is represented by the following equation.

$$\underset{\text{lungs}}{H_2O(l) + CO_2(g)} \rightleftharpoons \underset{\text{blood}}{H_2CO_3(aq)} \rightleftharpoons H^+(aq) + HCO_3^-(aq)$$

Given this equation, can you explain how abnormal breathing patterns can lead to the acid–base imbalances in the blood that are called respiratory acidosis (abnormally low pH) and respiratory alkalosis (abnormally high pH)? Too-rapid and too-deep breathing, a condition called hyperventilation, leads to respiratory alkalosis. Why? Conversely, hypoventilation, the result of too-shallow breathing, can cause respiratory acidosis. Explain.

70. The following equilibria are involved in the solubility of carbon dioxide in water.

$$CO_2(g) \rightleftharpoons CO_2(aq)$$

$$CO_2(aq) + H_2O(l) \rightleftharpoons H_2CO_3(aq)$$

$$H_2CO_3(aq) \rightleftharpoons H^+(aq) + HCO_3^-(aq)$$

$$HCO_3^-(aq) \rightleftharpoons H^+(aq) + CO_3^{2-}(aq)$$

If seawater is slightly alkaline, would you expect the concentration of dissolved CO_2 to be higher or lower than in pure water? Explain.

Cumulative Review

71. Calculate the pH of solutions with the following hydrogen-ion concentrations.

a. $4.6 \times 10^{-6} M$ **c.** $3.0 \times 10^{-1} M$

b. $5.0 \times 10^{-12} M$ **d.** $9.8 \times 10^{-10} M$

72. How many grams of potassium chloride are in 45.0 mL of a 5.0% (by mass) solution?

73. Write the formula for the conjugate base of each acid.
   a. H_2SO_4 **b.** HCN **c.** H_2O **d.** NH_4^+

74. Beakers A and B below both contain the same solution. Bromcresol green has been added to beaker A, and phenolphthalein has been added to beaker B.
   a. What is the pH of the solution?
   b. How could you determine the pH more accurately?

(a) (b)

75. Which of each pair has the higher entropy?
   a. NaCl(*s*) *or* NaCl(*aq*)
   b. $CO_2(s)$ *or* $CO_2(g)$
   c. H_2O at 60°C *or* H_2O at 25°C

76. What is the molarity of the salt in the solution that results from mixing 200 mL of 1.00*M* NaOH and 200 mL of 1.00*M* HCl?

Challenge Questions and Problems

77. What is the normality of an H_2SO_4 solution if 80.0 mL of the solution reacts completely with 0.424 g of Na_2CO_3?

$$H_2SO_4(aq) + Na_2CO_3(aq) \longrightarrow H_2O(l) + CO_2(aq) + Na_2SO_4(aq)$$

78. An impure sample of $AgNO_3$ weighing 0.340 g was dissolved in water. After the addition of 10.0 mL of 0.200*N* HCl, 0.213 g of AgCl was recovered. Calculate the percentage of $AgNO_3$ in the sample.

79. Use the cyanate buffer $HOCN/OCN^-$ to illustrate how a buffer system works. Show by means of equations how the pH of a solution can be kept almost constant when small amounts of acid or base are added.

Connections Questions

80. What are the color and chemical formula of a naturally formed bronze patina?

81. Why would training in the field of chemistry be helpful to a museum scientist?

82. What is the function of the hydrogen carbonate–carbonic acid buffer system in your blood?

Write About Chemistry

83. Prepare a written summary of an interview with a farmer or gardener to discover how they measure and control the pH of the soil.

84. Report on a survey of your home for household products that are salts or contain salts.

Readings and References

Dombrink, Kathleen, and David O. Tanis. "Swimming Pool Chemistry." *ChemMatters* (April 1983), pp. 4–5.

Tanis, David. "Underground Sculpture." *ChemMatters* (February 1984), pp. 10–11.

21 Oxidation–Reduction Reactions

Goals

- Identify the oxidized and the reduced species in oxidation–reduction reactions.
- Compute oxidation numbers for atoms in compounds.
- Analyze a reaction to determine if it is an oxidation–reduction reaction.
- Apply the oxidation number change method or the half-reaction method to balance oxidation–reduction equations.

Rust is the result of the oxidation of iron metal.

Concept Overview

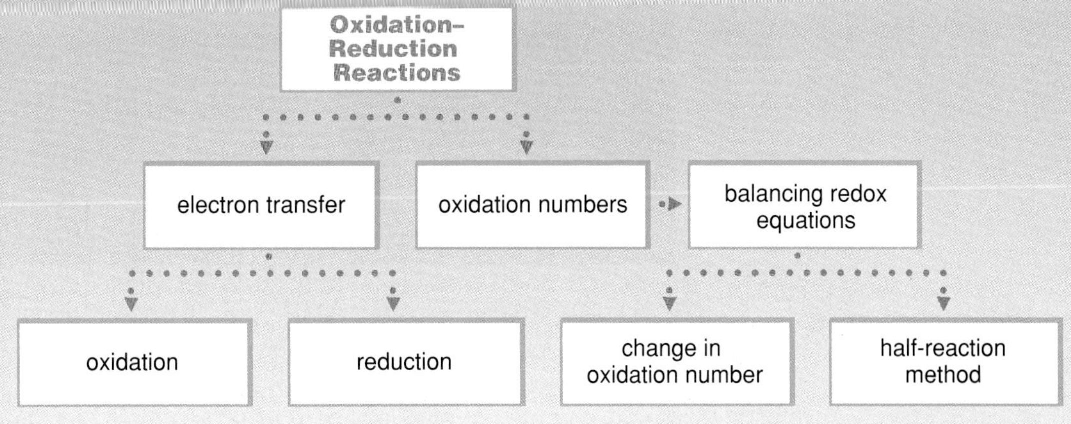

The Concept Overview organizes the major concepts of this chapter. This diagram shows one way to link these concepts related to oxidation–reduction reactions.

The combustion of gasoline in an automobile engine and the burning of wood in a fireplace are oxidation reactions. So is the "burning" of food by our bodies. Oxidation reactions are the principal source of energy on earth. All oxidation reactions are accompanied by reduction reactions. *The chemical changes that occur when electrons are transferred between reactants are known as* **oxidation–reduction reactions**. *Oxidation–reduction reactions are also called* **redox reactions**.

21.1 Oxygen in Redox Reactions

Objective

Define oxidation and reduction in terms of the loss or gain of oxygen or hydrogen.

Oxidation *originally meant the combination of an element with oxygen to give oxides.* When iron slowly turns to rust, it oxidizes to iron(III) oxide (Fe_2O_3). When carbon burns in air, it oxidizes to carbon dioxide.

$$4Fe(s) + 3O_2(g) \longrightarrow 2Fe_2O_3(s)$$

$$C(s) + O_2(g) \longrightarrow CO_2(g)$$

Compounds can also be oxidized. Methane gas (CH_4) burns in oxygen. It oxidizes to form oxides of carbon and hydrogen.

$$CH_4(g) + 2O_2(g) \longrightarrow CO_2(g) + 2H_2O(l)$$

Figure 21.1 Oxygen combines with iron to form iron(III) oxide, rust.

Over the years, **reduction** *has meant the loss of oxygen from a compound.* The reduction of iron ore to metallic iron causes the removal of oxygen from iron(III) oxide. It is done by heating the ore with charcoal.

$$\underset{\text{Iron(III) oxide}}{2Fe_2O_3(s)} + \underset{\text{Carbon}}{3C(s)} \longrightarrow \underset{\text{Iron}}{4Fe(s)} + \underset{\text{Carbon dioxide}}{3CO_2(g)}$$

As iron oxide loses oxygen, it is reduced to metallic iron. The term *reduction* refers to the fact that when a metal oxide is reduced to the metal, there is a considerable decrease in volume. In other words, the amount of solid material has been reduced.

Oxidation and reduction occur simultaneously. As iron oxide is reduced to iron by losing oxygen, carbon is oxidized to carbon dioxide by gaining oxygen. No oxidation occurs without reduction and no reduction occurs without oxidation. This is true of all redox reactions.

Integrating Photography

Redox in Photography

When black-and-white film is exposed, light activates very fine crystals of silver bromide in the film. The film is developed by placing it in a reducing solution (developer). The developer reduces the activated silver bromide crystals to black metallic silver. Unactivated silver bromide is removed from the film using a solvent solution (fixer). The areas of the film exposed to the most light appear darkest, as they have the highest concentration of metallic silver. This "reversed" image is called a negative and is used to produce a positive print of the image.

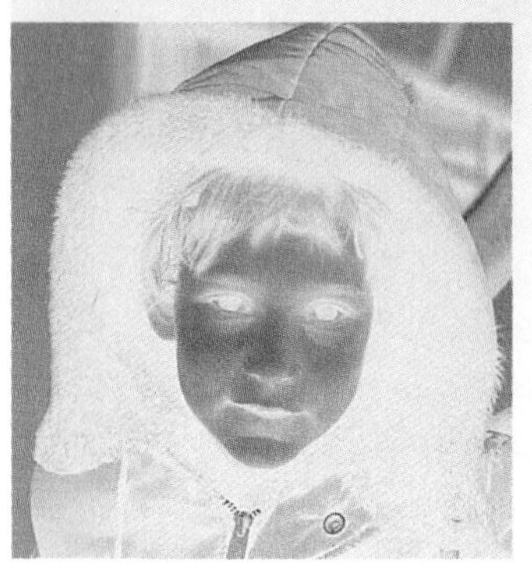

Concept Practice

1. What chemical process must always accompany a reduction reaction?

Practice Problem

2. Classify each reaction as oxidation or reduction based on the loss or gain of oxygen by a reactant. Also balance each equation.

a. $Ba(s) + O_2(g) \longrightarrow BaO(s)$

b. $CaO(s) + Al(s) \longrightarrow Al_2O_3(s) + Ca(s)$

c. $C_2H_5OH(l) + O_2(g) \longrightarrow CO_2(g) + H_2O(l)$

21.2 Electron Transfer in Redox Reactions

Objective

Identify the oxidizing and reducing agents in a redox reaction and give the characteristics of a redox reaction.

Today, chemists have extended the concepts of oxidation and reduction to include all transfers or shifts of electrons. The advantage of the new definition is that it has much wider application than the old. Hence *oxidation is complete or partial loss of electrons or gain of oxygen. Reduction is complete or partial gain of electrons or loss of oxygen.*

Oxidation	**Reduction**
Loss of electrons or gain of oxygen	Gain of electrons or loss of oxygen

It may be helpful to remember, "*LEO* the lion goes *GER*":

LEO = Losing Electrons is Oxidation

and

GER = Gaining Electrons is Reduction

Some examples will show what this means. In the reactions between a metal and nonmetal, electrons are transferred from atoms of the metal to atoms of the nonmetal. An ionic compound such as magnesium sulfide is produced.

$$\odot\text{Mg}\odot + \cdot\ddot{\text{S}}: \longrightarrow \text{Mg}^{2+} + :\ddot{\text{S}}:^{2-}$$

Magnesium atom — Sulfur atom — Magnesium ion — Sulfide ion

The net result of this reaction is a transfer of two electrons from a magnesium atom to a sulfur atom. The magnesium atom loses two electrons and is oxidized to a magnesium ion. Simultaneously the sulfur atom gains two electrons and is reduced to a sulfide ion.

Oxidation: $\cdot\text{Mg}\cdot \longrightarrow \text{Mg}^{2+} + 2e^-$ (loss of electrons)

Reduction: $\cdot\ddot{\text{S}}: + 2e^- \longrightarrow :\ddot{\text{S}}:^{2-}$ (gain of electrons)

The substance in a redox reaction that donates electrons is a **reducing agent**. By *losing electrons,* magnesium reduces sulfur. Magnesium is a reducing agent. *The substance in a redox reaction that accepts electrons is an* **oxidizing agent**. By *accepting electrons,* sulfur oxidizes magnesium. Sulfur is an oxidizing agent.

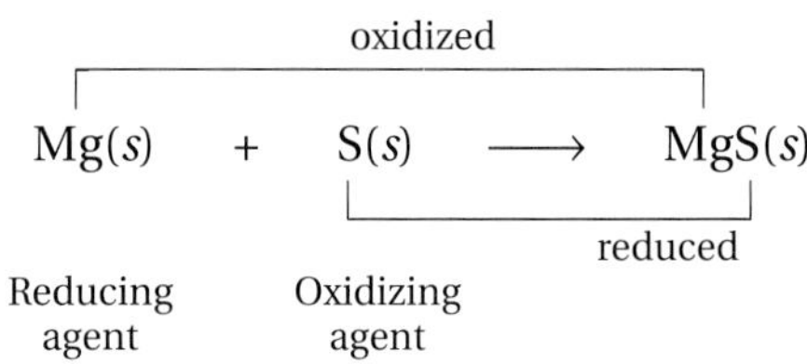

Safety

Oxidizing agents should be stored separately from other elements.

Example 1 Identifying the Reactant Oxidized and the Reactant Reduced

What is oxidized and what is reduced in this single-replacement reaction?

$$2AgNO_3(aq) + Cu(s) \longrightarrow Cu(NO_3)_2(aq) + 2Ag(s)$$

Solution

Begin by rewriting the equation and showing the ions.

$$2Ag^+ + 2NO_3^- + Cu \longrightarrow Cu^{2+} + 2NO_3^- + 2Ag$$

What has happened in this reaction? Two electrons have been transferred from a copper atom (Cu) to two silver ions (Ag^+).

$$\text{Oxidation: } Cu \longrightarrow Cu^{2+} + 2e^- \text{ (loss of electrons)}$$

$$\text{Reduction: } 2Ag^+ + 2e^- \longrightarrow 2Ag \text{ (gain of electrons)}$$

The Ag^+ gains electrons and is reduced; Cu loses electrons and is oxidized. Hence Ag^+ is the oxidizing agent and Cu is the reducing agent.

Figure 21.2 An oxyhydrogen torch can be used to weld metals like aluminum and iron. When hydrogen burns in oxygen, the redox reaction generates temperatures of about 2600°C.

You can easily see complete transfers of electrons in ionic reactions such as those just examined. What about reactions that produce covalent compounds? Consider the reaction of hydrogen and oxygen.

$$2H_2(g) + O_2(g) \longrightarrow 2H_2O(l)$$

The old definition of oxidation says that hydrogen is oxidized to water when it combines with oxygen. Electron transfer can also explain this process. Consider what happens to the bonding electrons in the reactants and in the products. The bonding electrons in the hydrogen molecule are shared equally between the hydrogens. In water, however, the bonding electrons are not shared equally between hydrogen and oxygen. (Recall that oxygen is much more electronegative than hydrogen.) The net result is a shift of bonding electrons away from hydrogen.

H—H electrons shared equally

H—O (with H below) shift of bonding electrons away from hydrogen

Hydrogen is oxidized because it experiences a partial loss of electrons. Thus, the old definition predicted correctly for the water molecule even though the electrons in this case are shared rather than transferred.

What about oxygen, the other reactant? The bonding electrons are shared equally between oxygens in the oxygen molecule, but they shift closer to oxygen in water.

O—O electrons shared equally

H—O—H: shift of bonding electrons toward oxygen

Oxygen is therefore reduced because there is a partial gain of electrons. This completes the picture of electron sharing in water.

Every redox reaction has an oxidizing agent and a reducing agent. In the reaction of hydrogen and oxygen to produce water, hydrogen is the reducing agent and oxygen is the oxidizing agent.

To summarize, oxidation–reduction reactions can be described on the basis of the addition or removal of oxygen. They can also be described on the basis of electron transfer. With compounds of carbon, the addition of oxygen or the removal of hydrogen is always oxidation. Table 21.1 lists processes that constitute oxidation and reduction. The last entry in the table mentions oxidation numbers, another way that oxidation and reduction can be described.

Table 21.1 Processes Leading to Oxidation and Reduction

Oxidation	Reduction
Complete loss of electrons (ionic reactions)	Complete gain of electrons (ionic reactions)
Shift of electrons away from an atom in a covalent bond	Shift of electrons toward an atom in a covalent bond
Gain of oxygen	Loss of oxygen
Loss of hydrogen by a covalent compound	Gain of hydrogen by a covalent compound
An increase in oxidation number	A decrease in oxidation number

Practice Problem

3. In each of the following reactions, decide which reactant is oxidized and which reactant is reduced. Also determine which reactant is the reducing agent and which is the oxidizing agent. (Use the electronegativity values in Table 13.2, page 366.)

a. $H_2(g) + Cl_2(g) \longrightarrow 2HCl(g)$

b. $N_2(g) + 3H_2(g) \longrightarrow 2NH_3(g)$

c. $S(s) + Cl_2(g) \longrightarrow SCl_2(g)$

d. $N_2(g) + 2O_2(g) \longrightarrow 2NO_2(g)$

e. $2Li(s) + F_2(g) \longrightarrow 2LiF(s)$

f. $H_2(g) + S(s) \longrightarrow H_2S(g)$

21.A Environmental Awareness

Incineration

Until a few years ago, most hazardous wastes were disposed of by dumping into landfills. Dumping created a huge problem because hazardous wastes in landfills pose a danger to public health and the environment. Government regulations now require that all hazardous waste be treated to make it nonhazardous. These regulations have effectively banned nearly all landfilling of hazardous wastes. The Environmental Protection Agency (EPA) now recommends incineration, or burning, as the method of choice for treating many of these hazardous wastes. By law, incinerators must destroy 99.99% of hazardous substances burned in them.

At first glance the incineration of hazardous wastes appears to be a very good idea. During incineration, a large mass of material is reduced to a much smaller mass of presumably harmless ash, which would take up little space in a landfill. The gases produced by incineration of organic compounds would mainly be carbon dioxide, which could be vented to the atmosphere.

The case for incineration is not as simple as just described, however. Opponents of hazardous waste incineration claim that all incinerators release toxic, persistent chemicals into the environment regardless of the operating standards. They also charge that incomplete combustion in incinerators creates new compounds that are more toxic and last longer in the environment than the original waste. Also, the large amounts of carbon dioxide released into the atmosphere from the incineration of organic compounds contribute to global warming.

The current controversy over hazardous waste incineration defies easy resolution. Nevertheless, in spite of the troubles swirling around it, the incinerator is one of the best choices for waste disposal presently available. To decrease the need for incinerators, waste elimination and minimization by recovery and recycling must become a priority. And when incinerators are used, stringent atmospheric emission standards must be enforced. Finally, attention must be given to the disposal hazards of the residual ash.

Figure 21.3 Even though by law incinerators must destroy 99.99% of the substances they burn, people are concerned these standards are not actually met during operation. Public concern over toxic emissions is a major hindrance limiting the use of incineration facilities.

Think About It

4. List What problems could result from the incineration of hazardous wastes?

5. Compare Make a comparison between the environmental problems posed by landfilling and incinerating hazardous wastes. Which method do you prefer, and why?

21.3 Assigning Oxidation Numbers

Oxidation numbers are a bookkeeping concept devised by chemists. *An* **oxidation number** *is a positive or negative number assigned to an atom according to a set of arbitrary rules.* As the next section will show, complex redox equations can be balanced by using oxidation number changes. As a general rule, an oxidation number is the charge that an atom would have if the electrons in each bond were assigned to the atom of the more electronegative element. In binary ionic compounds such as NaCl and $CaCl_2$, the oxidation numbers of the atoms are equal to their ionic charges. The compound sodium chloride is composed of sodium ions, Na^{1+}, and chloride ions, Cl^{1-}. Thus, the oxidation number of sodium is +1, and that of chlorine is −1. Notice that when writing oxidation numbers, the sign is put before the number. Sodium has an ionic charge of 1+ and an oxidation number of +1. In calcium fluoride, CaF_2, the oxidation number of calcium is +2 and that of fluorine, −1.

Because water is a molecular compound, no ionic charges are associated with its atoms. As was shown in the last section, however, oxygen is considered to be reduced in the formation of water. Oxygen is the more electronegative element. In water, the shared electrons in the bond are shifted closer to oxygen and away from hydrogen. Imagine that the two electrons contributed by the hydrogen atoms were completely transferred to the oxygen. The charges that would result from this transfer are the oxidation numbers of the elements. The oxidation number of oxygen is −2. The oxidation number of each hydrogen is +1.

Objective

Compute the oxidation number of an atom of any element in a pure substance.

Rules for Assigning Oxidation Numbers

1. The oxidation number of a monatomic ion is equal in magnitude and sign to its ionic charge. For example, the oxidation number of the bromide ion, Br^{1-}, is −1; that of the Fe^{3+} ion is +3.

2. The oxidation number of hydrogen in a compound is always +1 except in metal hydrides—for example, NaH—where it is −1.

Figure 21.4 Oxidation–reduction reactions cause corrosion. The copper on this roof reacted with carbon dioxide and water vapor in the air to form a pale green film of hydrated copper carbonate.

Biographical Note

Michael Faraday
(1791–1867)

Michael Faraday took an interest in science at an early age. At the age of thirteen, while working for a bookseller, he began building a foundation of scientific understanding by reading encyclopedias and science books. Faraday's later contributions to science are astonishing. If there had been Nobel Prizes in Faraday's day, he probably would have won six! He produced the first known chlorinated carbon compounds in 1820 and discovered benzene in 1825. He is most famous for his work with electricity. In honor of this great chemist, the amount of charge carried by one mole of electrons is called a faraday.

3. The oxidation number of oxygen in a compound is always –2 except in peroxides—for example, H_2O_2—where it is –1.

4. The oxidation number of an uncombined element is zero. For example, the oxidation number of the potassium atoms in potassium metal, K, and of the nitrogen atoms in nitrogen gas, N_2, is zero.

5. For any neutral compound, the sum of the oxidation numbers of the atoms in the compound must equal zero.

6. For a polyatomic ion, the sum of the oxidation numbers must equal the ionic charge of the ion.

Example 2 Assigning Oxidation Numbers

What is the oxidation number of each element in the following?

a. SO_2 **b.** CO_3^{2-} **c.** K_2SO_4

Solution

a. The oxidation number of oxygen is –2. There are two oxygens, and the sum of the oxidation numbers must be zero. Thus the oxidation number of sulfur is +4.

$$\overset{+4}{S}\overset{-2}{O_2}$$

b. The oxidation number of oxygen is –2.

$$\overset{?}{C}\overset{-2}{O_3^{2-}}$$

The sum of the oxidation numbers of the carbon and oxygen atoms must equal the ionic charge, 2–. The oxidation number of carbon must be +4.

$$\overset{+4}{C}\overset{-2}{O_3^{2-}}$$

c. The oxidation number of the potassium ion is +1, the same as its ionic charge. The oxidation number of oxygen is –2.

$$\overset{+1}{K_2}\overset{?}{S}\overset{-2}{O_4}$$

For the sum of the oxidation numbers in the compound to be zero, the oxidation number of sulfur must be +6.

$$\overset{+1}{K_2}\overset{+6}{S}\overset{-2}{O_4}$$

Concept Practice

6. How do you use the charge in assigning oxidation numbers to the elements in a polyatomic ion?

Practice Problem

7. Find the oxidation number of each element in these formulas.

a. P_2O_5 **b.** NH_4^+ **c.** $Na_2Cr_2O_7$ **d.** $Ca(OH)_2$

21.4 Oxidation Number Changes

Objective

Define oxidation and reduction in terms of a change in oxidation number and identify atoms being oxidized or reduced in redox reactions.

An *increase* in the oxidation number of an atom signifies *oxidation*. A *decrease* in the oxidation number of an atom signifies *reduction*. Look again at the equation in Example 1 to identify what is being oxidized and reduced on the basis of oxidation number changes. Oxidation numbers have been added to this equation.

$$\overset{+1+5-2}{2AgNO_3(aq)} + \overset{0}{Cu(s)} \longrightarrow \overset{+2\ +5-2}{Cu(NO_3)_2(aq)} + \overset{0}{2Ag(s)}$$

In this reaction, the oxidation number of silver decreases from +1 to 0. This is reduction. Silver is reduced from Ag^{+1} to Ag^0. On the other hand, copper is oxidized in this reaction. Its oxidation number increases from 0 to +2. Copper is oxidized from Cu^0 to Cu^{2+}. These results agree with those obtained by analyzing the reaction by using electron transfer.

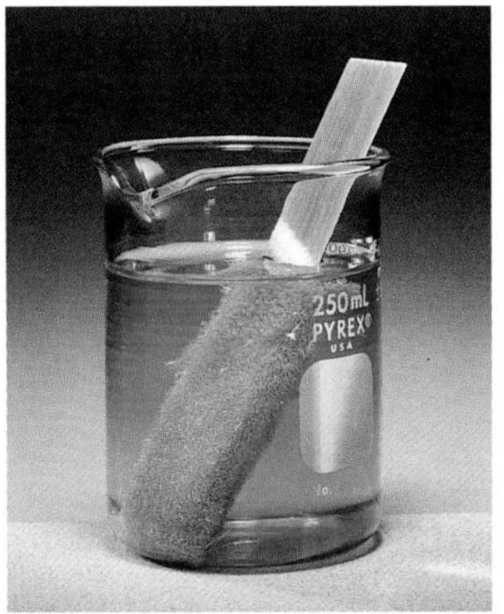

Figure 21.5 When a copper strip is placed in a colorless silver nitrate solution (left), crystals of silver coat the strip (right). The solution slowly turns blue, as a result of copper(II) nitrate formation. What change occurs in the oxidation number of the silver? How does the oxidation number of the copper change?

Safety

Many substances that are harmless in their reduced form may be toxic or corrosive in their oxidized form, or vice versa. Do not assume that all forms of a chemical are harmless just because one form is harmless.

Example 3 Identifying Elements Oxidized and Reduced

Use the changes in oxidation number to identify which elements are oxidized and reduced in each of these reactions.

a. $Cl_2(g) + 2HBr(aq) \longrightarrow 2HCl(aq) + Br_2(l)$

b. $C(s) + O_2(g) \longrightarrow CO_2(g)$

c. $Zn(s) + 2MnO_2(s) + 2NH_4Cl(aq) \longrightarrow$
$ZnCl_2(aq) + Mn_2O_3(s) + 2NH_3(g) + H_2O(l)$

Solution

A decrease in oxidation number indicates reduction. An increase in oxidation number indicates oxidation.

a. $\overset{0}{Cl_2}(g) + 2\overset{+1\,-1}{HBr}(aq) \longrightarrow 2\overset{+1\,-1}{HCl}(aq) + \overset{0}{Br_2}(l)$

The element chlorine is reduced ($0 \rightarrow -1$). The element bromine is oxidized ($-1 \rightarrow 0$).

b. $\overset{0}{C}(s) + \overset{0}{O_2}(g) \longrightarrow \overset{+4\,-2}{CO_2}(g)$

The element carbon is oxidized ($0 \longrightarrow +4$). The element oxygen is reduced ($0 \longrightarrow -2$).

c. $\overset{0}{Zn}(s) + 2\overset{+4\;-2}{MnO_2}(s) + 2\overset{-3\,+1\;-1}{NH_4Cl}(aq) \longrightarrow$
$\overset{+2\;-1}{ZnCl_2}(aq) + \overset{+3\;-2}{Mn_2O_3}(s) + 2\overset{-3\,+1}{NH_3}(g) + \overset{+1\,-2}{H_2O}(l)$

The element zinc is oxidized ($0 \rightarrow +2$). The element manganese is reduced ($+4 \rightarrow +3$).

Example 4 Identifying Oxidizing Agents and Reducing Agents

Identify the oxidizing agent and reducing agent in each of the equations in Example 3.

Solution

a. Since chlorine is reduced, Cl_2 is the oxidizing agent. Since bromine (in HBr) is oxidized, Br^{1-} is the reducing agent.

b. Carbon is the reducing agent. Oxygen is the oxidizing agent.

c. Zinc is the reducing agent. Manganese (in MnO_2) is the oxidizing agent.

Problem-Solving Tip

An oxidizing agent causes another substance to be oxidized.

Practice Problem

8. In each of the following reactions, identify the element oxidized, the element reduced, the oxidizing agent, and the reducing agent.

a. $3H_2S(aq) + 2HNO_3(aq) \longrightarrow 3S(s) + 2NO(g) + 4H_2O(l)$

b. $2PbSO_4(s) + 2H_2O(l) \longrightarrow Pb(s) + PbO_2(s) + 2H_2SO_4(aq)$

21.5 Balancing Redox Equations

Objective

Apply the oxidation number change method to balance redox equations.

Many oxidation–reduction reactions are too complex to be balanced by trial and error. Fortunately, two systematic methods are available. These are the oxidation number change method, described in this section, and the half-reaction method, Section 21.7. These methods are based on the fact that *the total number of electrons gained in reduction must equal the total number of electrons lost in oxidation.*

With the **oxidation number change method**, *a redox equation is balanced by comparing the increases and decreases in oxidation numbers.* To use this method, start with a skeleton equation.

$$Fe_2O_3(s) + CO(g) \longrightarrow Fe(s) + CO_2(g)$$

Step 1. Assign oxidation numbers to all the atoms in the equation. Write the number *above* the appropriate atoms.

$$\overset{+3}{Fe_2}\overset{-2}{O_3}(s) + \overset{+2}{C}\overset{-2}{O}(g) \longrightarrow \overset{0}{Fe}(s) + \overset{+4}{C}\overset{-2}{O_2}(g)$$

Note that the oxidation number is stated as the charge *per atom.* In Fe_2O_3, the total positive charge is +6, but the oxidation number of Fe is +3.

Step 2. Identify which atoms are oxidized and which are reduced. In this reaction, iron decreases in oxidation number from +3 to 0, a change of –3. Therefore, iron is reduced. Carbon increases in oxidation number from +2 to +4, a change of +2. Thus carbon is oxidized. Oxygen does not change in oxidation number.

Step 3. Use a line to connect the atoms that undergo oxidation and those that undergo reduction. Write the oxidation number change at the midpoint of each line.

$$\overset{+3}{Fe_2}\overset{-2}{O_3}(s) + \overset{+2}{C}\overset{-2}{O}(g) \longrightarrow \overset{0}{Fe}(s) + \overset{+4}{C}\overset{-2}{O_2}(g)$$

(C to C line: +2; Fe to Fe line: –3)

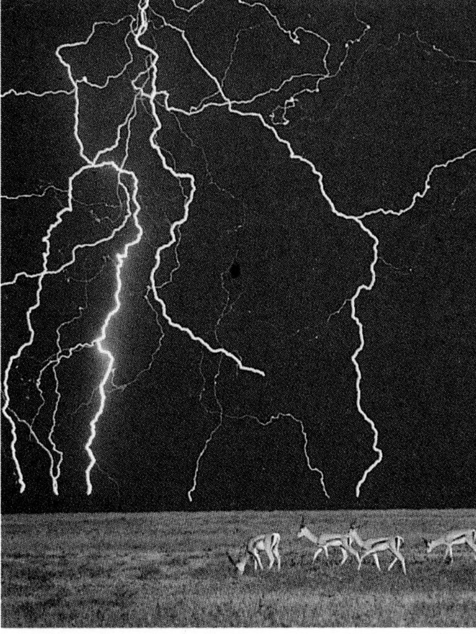

Figure 21.6 Energy from lightning produces an oxidation-reduction reaction in which nitrogen in the air reacts with oxygen in the air to form nitrogen(II) oxide, NO. Lightning plays a role in the nitrogen cycle, a cycle necessary to maintain life on Earth.

Figure 21.7 Potassium dichromate is an orange crystalline substance. It reacts with water and sulfur to form chromium(III) oxide, the green compound shown here. What are the other products?

Step 4. Make the total increase in oxidation number equal to the total decrease in oxidation number by using appropriate coefficients. In this example, the oxidation number increase should be multiplied by 3 and the oxidation number decrease should be multiplied by 2. This gives an increase of +6 and a decrease of –6. This can be done in the equation by placing the coefficient 2 in front of Fe and the coefficient 3 in front of both CO and CO_2. The formula Fe_2O_3 does not need a coefficient because the formula indicates 2Fe.

$$\overbrace{}^{3 \times (+2) = +6}$$

$$Fe_2O_3(s) + 3CO(g) \longrightarrow 2Fe(s) + 3CO_2(g)$$

$$\underbrace{}_{2 \times (-3) = -6}$$

Step 5. Finally, check to be sure that the equation is balanced for both atoms and charge. If necessary, the remainder of the equation is balanced by inspection.

$$Fe_2O_3(s) + 3CO(g) \longrightarrow 2Fe(s) + 3CO_2(g)$$

Example 5 Balancing Redox Equations by Oxidation Number Change

Balance this redox equation by using the oxidation number change method.

$$K_2Cr_2O_7(aq) + H_2O(l) + S(s) \longrightarrow KOH(aq) + Cr_2O_3(aq) + SO_2(g)$$

Solution

Step 1. Assign oxidation numbers.

$$\overset{+1\ +6\ -2}{K_2Cr_2O_7}(aq) + \overset{+1\ -2}{H_2O}(l) + \overset{0}{S}(s) \longrightarrow \overset{+1-2+1}{KOH}(aq) + \overset{+3\ -2}{Cr_2O_3}(aq) + \overset{+4-2}{SO_2}(g)$$

Steps 2 and 3. Connect the atoms that change in oxidation number. Indicate the sign and magnitude of the change.

$$\overbrace{}^{-3}$$

$$\overset{+6}{K_2Cr_2O_7}(aq) + H_2O(l) + \overset{0}{S}(s) \longrightarrow KOH(aq) + \overset{+3}{Cr_2O_3}(aq) + \overset{+4}{SO_2}(g)$$

$$\underbrace{}_{+4}$$

Step 4. Balance the increase and decrease in oxidation numbers. Four chromium atoms must be reduced [4 × (–3) = –12 decrease] for each three sulfur atoms that are oxidized [3 × (+4) = +12 increase].

Problem-Solving Tip

Break complex problems down into simpler steps.

Put the coefficient 3 in front of S and SO_2 and the coefficient 2 in front of $K_2Cr_2O_7$ and Cr_2O_3.

$$\overset{+6}{2K_2Cr_2O_7(aq)} + H_2O(l) + \overset{0}{3S(s)} \longrightarrow KOH(aq) + \overset{+3}{2Cr_2O_3(aq)} + \overset{+4}{3SO_2(g)}$$

(4)(−3) = −12 (Cr); (3)(+4) = +12 (S)

Step 5. Now finish balancing by inspection. The coefficient 4 in front of KOH balances potassium. The coefficient 2 in front of H_2O balances the hydrogen and oxygen.

$$2K_2Cr_2O_7(aq) + 2H_2O(l) + 3S(s) \longrightarrow$$

$$4KOH(aq) + 2Cr_2O_3(aq) + 3SO_2(g)$$

Concept Practice

9. How does each of these compare in every redox reaction?
a. electrons lost and electrons gained
b. increase in oxidation number of one element and decrease in oxidation of second element

Practice Problem

10. Balance each of these redox equations.
a. $Al(s) + Cl_2(g) \longrightarrow AlCl_3(s)$
b. $KClO_3(s) \longrightarrow KCl(aq) + O_2(g)$
c. $PH_3(g) + I_2(s) + H_2O(l) \longrightarrow H_3PO_2(aq) + HI(aq)$
d. $Cl_2(g) + KOH(aq) \longrightarrow KClO_3(aq) + KCl(aq) + H_2O(l)$
e. $HNO_3(aq) + H_2S(g) \longrightarrow S(s) + NO(g) + H_2O(l)$
f. $KIO_4(aq) + KI(aq) + HCl(aq) \longrightarrow KCl(aq) + I_2(s) + H_2O(l)$

21.6 Identifying Redox Reactions

Objective

Distinguish between redox and nonredox reactions.

In general, all chemical reactions can be assigned to one of two classes. In oxidation–reduction reactions, electrons are transferred from one reacting species to another. In all other reactions, electrons are not transferred. Double-replacement reactions and acid–base reactions are not redox reactions. Many single-replacement reactions, combination reactions, decomposition reactions, and combustion reactions are redox reactions.

Figure 21.8 Potassium reacts violently with water. Is this a redox reaction?

How can you determine if a reaction is a redox reaction? Use oxidation numbers. If the oxidation number of an element in a reacting species changes, then that element has undergone either oxidation or reduction. The reaction is part of a redox reaction.

Example 6 Identifying Redox Reactions

Use the change in oxidation number to identify which of these reactions are redox reactions. If a reaction is a redox reaction, name the element reduced, the element oxidized, the reducing agent, and the oxidizing agent.

a. $N_2O_4(g) \longrightarrow 2NO_2(g)$
b. $Cl_2(g) + 2NaBr(aq) \longrightarrow 2NaCl(aq) + Br_2(g)$
c. $PbCl_2(s) + K_2SO_4(aq) \longrightarrow 2KCl(aq) + PbSO_4(s)$
d. $2NaOH(aq) + H_2SO_4(aq) \longrightarrow Na_2SO_4(aq) + 2H_2O(l)$

Solution

Assign oxidation numbers to each element. A decrease in oxidation number indicates reduction. An increase indicates oxidation.

$$\overset{+4\ -2}{N_2O_4}(g) \longrightarrow 2\overset{+4\ -2}{NO_2}(g)$$

a. This is a decomposition reaction. Neither oxygen nor nitrogen changes in oxidation number. Therefore this reaction is not a redox reaction.

$$\overset{0}{Cl_2}(g) + 2\overset{+1\ -1}{NaBr}(aq) \longrightarrow 2\overset{+1\ -1}{NaCl}(aq) + \overset{0}{Br_2}(g)$$

b. This is a single-displacement reaction. The element chlorine is reduced ($0 \rightarrow -1$). The element bromine is oxidized ($-1 \rightarrow 0$). This is a redox reaction. Chlorine is the oxidizing agent; bromine is the reducing agent.

$$\overset{+2\ -1}{PbCl_2}(s) + \overset{+1\ +6\ -2}{K_2SO_4}(aq) \longrightarrow 2\overset{+1\ -1}{KCl}(aq) + \overset{+2\ +6\ -2}{PbSO_4}(s)$$

c. This is a double-replacement reaction. None of the elements change in oxidation number. This is not a redox reaction.

$$2\overset{+1\ -2\ +1}{NaOH}(aq) + \overset{+1\ +6\ -2}{H_2SO_4}(aq) \longrightarrow \overset{+1\ +6\ -2}{Na_2SO_4}(aq) + 2\overset{+1\ -2}{H_2O}(l)$$

d. This is an acid–base reaction. None of the elements change in oxidation number. This is not a redox reaction.

Concept Practice

11. Name some general types of reactions that are typically redox reactions.

Practice Problem

12. Identify which of these are oxidation–reduction reactions. If a reaction is a redox reaction, name the element oxidized and the element reduced.

a. $BaCl_2(aq) + 2KIO_3(aq) \longrightarrow Ba(IO_3)_2(s) + 2KCl(aq)$
b. $H_2CO_3(aq) \longrightarrow H_2O(l) + CO_2(g)$
c. $Mg(s) + Br_2(l) \longrightarrow MgBr_2(s)$
d. $NH_4NO_2(s) \longrightarrow N_2(g) + 2H_2O(l)$
e. $2KClO_3(s) \longrightarrow 2KCl(s) + 3O_2(g)$
f. $CaCO_3(s) + 2HCl(aq) \longrightarrow CaCl_2(aq) + H_2O(l) + CO_2(g)$
g. $CuO(s) + H_2(g) \longrightarrow Cu(s) + H_2O(l)$

21.7 Using Half-Reactions to Balance Redox Equations

Objective

Apply the half-reaction method to balance redox equations.

Another method can be used to balance redox equations. *The* **half-reaction method** *is used to balance redox equations by balancing the oxidation and reduction half-reactions.* The procedure is different but the outcome is the same as with the oxidation number change method. The first step in the half-reaction method is to divide the overall reaction into two parts. *A* **half-reaction** *is an equation showing either the reduction or the oxidation of a species in an oxidation–reduction reaction.* Next, you balance each half-reaction. The number of electrons gained by the reduction half-reaction must be equal to the number of electrons lost by the oxidation half-reaction. Finally, you add the two half-reactions to give a balanced equation. The half-reaction method is particularly useful for balancing equations for ionic reactions.

The oxidation of sulfur with nitric acid in aqueous solution is our example.

$$S(s) + HNO_3(aq) \longrightarrow SO_2(g) + NO(g) + H_2O(l)$$

Step 1. Write the equation in ionic form. (*Hint:* Only HNO_3 is ionized. The products are covalent compounds.)

$$S(s) + H^+(aq) + NO_3^-(aq) \longrightarrow SO_2(g) + NO(g) + H_2O(l)$$

Figure 21.9 An oxidation–reduction reaction allows fireflies to produce light. The light is used to attract mates.

Table 21.2 Oxidation Numbers of Sulfur in Different Compounds	
Compound	**Oxidation Number**
H_2SO_4	+6
SO_3	+6
H_2SO_3	+4
SO_2	+4
$Na_2S_2O_3$	+2
SCl_2	+2
S_2Cl_2	+1
S	0
H_2S	−1

Step 2. Write separate half-reactions for the oxidation and reduction processes. (*Hint:* Sulfur is oxidized because its oxidation number increases from 0 to 4. Nitrogen is reduced because its oxidation number decreases from +5 to +2.)

$$\text{Oxidation: } S(s) \rightarrow SO_2(g) \qquad \text{Reduction: } NO_3^-(aq) \rightarrow NO(g)$$

Step 3. Balance the atoms in the half-reactions.

a. *Balance the oxidation half-reaction.* Since this reaction takes place in acid solution, you can use H_2O and H^+ to balance oxygen and hydrogen as needed. Sulfur is already balanced. You can add two molecules of H_2O to balance the oxygen.

$$2H_2O(l) + S(s) \longrightarrow SO_2(g)$$

Oxygen is now balanced, but you must add four hydrogens to the right to balance those on the left.

$$2H_2O(l) + S(s) \longrightarrow SO_2(g) + 4H^+(aq)$$

This half-reaction is now balanced in terms of atoms.

b. *Balance the reduction half-reaction.* Nitrogen is already balanced. Add two molecules of H_2O to balance the oxygen.

$$NO_3^-(aq) \longrightarrow NO(g) + 2H_2O(l)$$

Oxygen is balanced, but you must add four hydrogens ($4H^+$) to the left to balance hydrogen.

$$4H^+(aq) + NO_3^-(aq) \longrightarrow NO(g) + 2H_2O(l)$$

This half-reaction is now balanced in terms of atoms.

Step 4. Add sufficient electrons to one side of each half-reaction to balance the charges. Four electrons are needed on the right side in the oxidation half-reaction. Three electrons are needed on the left side in the reduction half-reaction.

$$\text{Oxidation: } 2H_2O(l) + S(s) \longrightarrow SO_2(g) + 4H^+(aq) + 4e^-$$

$$\text{Reduction: } 4H^+(aq) + NO_3^-(aq) + 3e^- \longrightarrow NO(g) + 2H_2O(l)$$

Each half-reaction is balanced with respect to atoms and charge.

Step 5. Multiply each half-reaction by an appropriate number to make the electron changes equal. In any redox reaction, the electrons lost in oxidation must be equal to the electrons gained in reduction. If the oxidation half-reaction is multiplied by 3 and the reduction half-reaction by 4, the number of electrons lost in oxidation and the number of electrons gained in reduction both equal 12.

$$\text{Oxidation: } 6H_2O(l) + 3S(s) \longrightarrow 3SO_2(g) + 12H^+(aq) + 12e^-$$

$$\text{Reduction: } 16H^+(aq) + 4NO_3^-(aq) + 12e^- \longrightarrow 4NO(g) + 8H_2O(l)$$

Step 6. Add the half-reactions and subtract terms that appear on both sides of the equation.

$$\overset{4}{\cancel{16}}H^+(aq) + \cancel{6H_2O(l)} + 4NO_3^-(aq) + 3S(s) + \cancel{12e^-} \longrightarrow$$

$$3SO_2(g) + 4NO(g) + \cancel{12H^+(aq)} + \cancel{12e^-} + \overset{2}{\cancel{8}}H_2O(l)$$

Now you can write the balanced equation.

$$4H^+(aq) + 4NO_3^-(aq) + 3S(s) \longrightarrow 3SO_2(g) + 4NO(g) + 2H_2O(l)$$

or

$$4HNO_3(aq) + 3S(s) \longrightarrow 3SO_2(g) + 4NO(g) + 2H_2O(l)$$

Example 7 Balancing Redox Equations by the Half-Reaction Method

Balance the reaction that occurs between permanganate ions, MnO_4^-, and chloride ions, Cl^-, in acid solution. The products are manganese(II) ions, Mn^{2+}, and chlorine gas, Cl_2.

Solution

Step 1. Write the unbalanced reaction in ionic form.

$$MnO_4^-(aq) + Cl^-(g) \longrightarrow Mn^{2+}(aq) + Cl_2(g)$$

Step 2. Write the half-reactions for oxidation and reduction.

Oxidation: $Cl^- \longrightarrow Cl_2$

Reduction: $MnO_4^- \longrightarrow Mn^{2+}$

Step 3. Balance the atoms. Because the solution is acidic, you can use H_2O and H^+ to balance the hydrogen and oxygen if necessary.

Oxidation: $2Cl^- \longrightarrow Cl_2$ (atoms balanced)

Reduction: $MnO_4^- + 8H^+ \longrightarrow Mn^{2+} + 4H_2O$ (atoms balanced)

Step 4. Balance the charges. Add electrons as needed.

Oxidation: $2Cl^- \longrightarrow Cl_2 + 2e^-$ (charges balanced)

Reduction: $MnO_4^- + 8H^+ + 5e^- \longrightarrow Mn^{2+} + 4H_2O$ (charges balanced)

Step 5. Make the electron charges equal. Multiply the oxidation half-reaction by 5 and the reduction half-reaction by 2. Ten electrons are lost in oxidation, and ten electrons are gained in reduction.

Integrating Food Science

Antioxidants

Have you ever smelled the unpleasant odor of rancid butter or meat? Rancidity is partly the result of oxidation of the natural fats contained in foods. To slow the oxidation process, fatty foods contain natural substances called antioxidants. The most common natural antioxidant is a fatty molecule called α-tocopherol—more commonly known as vitamin E. Manufacturers of packaged foods often supplement natural antioxidants with synthetic additives in order to extend the shelf life of their products. The two most common antioxidants added to foods are butylated hydroxytoluene (BHT) and butylated hydroxyanisole (BHA). BHA and BHT can extend the shelf life of products for months and are generally considered safe for human consumption.

Oxidation: $10Cl^- \longrightarrow 5Cl_2 + 10e^-$

Reduction: $2MnO_4^- + 16H^+ + 10e^- \longrightarrow 2Mn^{2+} + 8H_2O$

Step 6. Add the half-reactions and subtract terms that appear on both sides of the equation.

$$2MnO_4^- + 16H^+ + 10Cl^- + \cancel{10e^-} \longrightarrow 2Mn^{2+} + 5Cl_2 + 8H_2O + \cancel{10e^-}$$

The balanced ionic equation is the net equation,

$$2MnO_4^- + 16H^+ + 10Cl^- \longrightarrow 2Mn^{2+} + 5Cl_2 + 8H_2O$$

In this example, the permanganate ions come from potassium permanganate, $KMnO_4$. The chloride ions were from HCl. As an additional step, the spectator ions should be added to the equation.

Step 7. Add the spectator ions and balance. (Spectator ions *are those that do not change oxidation number or composition during a reaction.*) The K^+ and Cl^- ions can now be added.

$$2K^+ + 2MnO_4^- + 16H^+ + 16Cl^- \longrightarrow$$

$$2Mn^{2+} + 4Cl^- + 5Cl_2 + 8H_2O + 2K^+ + 2Cl^-$$

$$\text{or} \quad 2KMnO_4(aq) + 16HCl(aq) \longrightarrow$$

$$2MnCl_2(aq) + 5Cl_2(g) + 8H_2O(l) + 2KCl(aq)$$

As a quick review, here is a summary of the steps for balancing redox equations by the ion-electron method.

Step 1. Write the equation in ionic form.

Step 2. Write separate half-reactions for oxidation and reduction.

Step 3. Balance the atoms in the half-reactions. Use H_2O and H^+ to balance oxygen and hydrogen in an acid solution. Use H_2O and OH^- for reactions in a basic solution.

Step 4. Add electrons to one side of each half-reaction to balance the charges.

Step 5. Multiply each half-reaction by an appropriate number to make the electron charges equal.

Step 6. Add the half-reactions and subtract terms that appear on both sides of the equation.

Step 7. Check the final equation to be sure that atoms are conserved, charge is conserved, and all electrons have canceled. If spectator ions are known, add them to balance the equation.

Concept Practice

13. Why is it sometimes necessary to add H_2O and H^+ and H_2O and OH^- to redox half-reactions?

Practice Problem

14. Balance each of these equations by the ion-electron method.

a. $ClO_3^-(aq) + I^-(aq) \longrightarrow Cl^-(aq) + I_2(aq)$ [acid solution]

b. $MnO_2(s) + H^+(aq) + NO_2^-(aq) \longrightarrow$
$NO_3^-(aq) + Mn^{2+}(aq) + H_2O(l)$ [acid solution]

c. $Cl_2(g) \longrightarrow ClO_3^-(aq) + Cl^-(aq)$ [base solution]

Activity 21
Rusting

Purpose

To observe the influence of various conditions on the rusting of iron.

Materials

seven iron finishing nails (approximately 6 cm long)

pliers

scissors

copper wire

zinc strip

fine sandpaper

plastic wrap

saucer

water

petroleum jelly

paper towels

Procedure

1. Polish seven nails with sandpaper and wipe them clean with a paper towel.

2. Place two paper towels on the saucer. Trim the towels to fit and wet them with water.

3. Treat each of the seven nails as follows. Nail 1: Using pliers, bend into a "U" shape. Nail 2: Wrap one end with copper wire. Nail 3: Wrap one end with a strip of zinc. Nail 4: Smear entire nail with a thin coat of petroleum jelly. Nail 5: Cover with salt after completing step 4 below. Nail 6: Untreated. Nail 7: Untreated.

4. Place nails 1 through 6 on the wet paper towel. Make sure the nails do not touch, and cover them with a piece of plastic wrap. Place nail 7 (control) on top of the wrap.

5. Construct a table and for 24 hours periodically record your observations of the changes in each nail.

Analysis and Conclusions

1. Which nails showed evidence of rusting? Describe the conditions that promote formation of rust.

2. Which nails did not appear to rust? Explain the conditions that inhibit rust.

3. Why do auto manufacturers put a great deal of effort into "rust-proofing" new cars?

21.B Science, Technology, and Society

Biomass

Figure 21.10 Biomass-based products promise performance superior to that of traditional materials. A wood fiber–plastic composite is being used in the construction of this home.

The total mass of all of Earth's living plants and animals is called its biomass. Because biomass is renewable and virtually unlimited, it is a very attractive source of material for new products. New products could be made from biomass materials instead of materials now made from petrochemicals, thereby helping to conserve the world's nonrenewable petroleum reserves. Although biomass materials such as wood have long been used as building materials and fuel, exciting new materials are beginning to emerge from recent biomass research.

The goal of current research is to develop new biomass materials that are comparable to metals and plastics. So far, biomass research has mainly emphasized the development of wood composites as building materials. Wood composites have properties superior to those of wood. To make a wood composite, cellulose fibers are embedded in an adhesive and the mixture is molded into the desired shape. High-performance adhesives yield durable wood composites with uniform properties. Wood fiber–plastic composites are currently being developed as building materials for doors, windows, and flooring.

Unfortunately, biomass use has been very limited. This is partly due to the fact that solid materials such as wood are difficult to collect, transport, and process, whereas gases and liquids, such as petroleum and natural gas, are much easier to handle. Biomass has also been hampered because the United States does not have a national policy regarding its use. To ensure success of emerging biomass-related technologies, a greater national commitment to support research and development of biomass materials is necessary.

A greater emphasis on biomass use would also help relieve solid waste disposal problems. About 100 million tons of the municipal solid waste collected annually is cellulosic and could be burned as fuel or used to make new biomass materials. For example, used diapers are a source of high-quality cellulose fiber. These diapers, which usually end up in landfills, could be recycled into new biomass materials, saving resources and energy.

Think About It

15. Describe What are some advantages of wood fiber–plastic composite building materials?

16. Support Make an argument for the use of biomass resources instead of petroleum as raw materials for industrial manufacturing.

Superconductors

Hard to Resist

A magnetic levitation (Mag-Lev) train operating on magnetic tracks.

Trains that float in air? Miniature supercomputers? These inventions may soon become common if superconductor technology continues to advance. Superconductors are materials that conduct electricity without resistance. When an electric current flows through an ordinary conductor, such as copper wire, it encounters resistance. The resistance slows the electrons and causes the conductor to heat up. The glowing red wires in your toaster at home are a familiar example of electrical resistance generating heat. In electronic devices such as computers, getting rid of the heat is a big problem. Resistance also reduces the speed at which calculations can be performed. Building computers out of superconductors would make them faster, smaller, and cooler-running.

An important feature of a superconductor is its critical temperature, or T_c. At or below the T_c, the superconducting material conducts electricity with zero resistance. Above the T_c, the material loses its superconducting ability. Unfortunately, the T_c of all known superconductors is extremely low.

New superconductors have been developed with higher critical temperatures. For example, $Tl_2Ca_2Ba_2Cu_3O_{10}$ (thallium-calcium-barium-copper-oxide) has a T_c of 125 K. Liquid nitrogen can be used to cool the new superconductors. Liquid nitrogen boils at 77 K.

A magnet placed over a superconductor remains suspended above it in midair!

Although the newer superconductors represent a big advance in technology, their uses are still very limited. With a T_c of 125 K, superconductors are still not practical for everyday use. Also, the new higher-T_c superconductors are too brittle to be useful. Brittleness prevents these new materials from being drawn into wires or shaped into circuit boards. The search is on now for a superconductor with a T_c near room temperature.

Besides conducting electricity without resistance, superconductors are diamagnetic. A diamagnet is a material that repels magnetic fields with a force exactly equal to the force exerted on the diamagnet. Diamagnetism results in the phenomenon called levitation. A magnet placed over a superconductor remains suspended above it in midair. Trains are currently being developed that use diamagnetism to levitate over magnetic tracks. Such trains could travel almost frictionlessly because there would be no contact between the train and its magnetic tracks.

Think About It

17. Define What is the critical temperature of a superconducting material?

18. Describe What are some of the problems that limit the practical use of superconductors?

Chapter 21 Review

Oxidation–Reduction Reactions

Key Terms

half-reaction *21.7*
half-reaction method *21.7*
oxidation *21.1*
oxidation number *21.3*
oxidation number change method *21.5*
oxidation–reduction reaction *21.0*
oxidizing agent *21.2*
redox reaction *21.0*
reducing agent *21.2*
reduction *21.1*
spectator ion *21.7*

Chapter Summary

Oxidation–reduction, or redox, reactions are an important category of chemical reactions. The original meaning of oxidation was the chemical combination of a substance with oxygen. Reduction was originally the loss of oxygen. These definitions have long since been expanded. Oxidation is now considered to be any shift of electrons away from an atom. Reduction now includes any shift of electrons toward an atom. An oxidation reaction is always accompanied by a reduction reaction. The substance that does the oxidizing is called an oxidizing agent. It is reduced. The substance that does the reducing is called a reducing agent. It is oxidized.

An oxidation number can be assigned to an element in a substance according to a set of rules. The oxidation number of an element in an uncombined state is zero. The oxidation number of a monatomic ion is the same in magnitude and sign as its ionic charge. The sum of the oxidation numbers of the elements in a neutral compound is zero. In a polyatomic ion, however, the sum is equal to the charge of the ion. Oxidation numbers help you keep track of electrons in redox reactions. An oxidation number increase is oxidation. A decrease is reduction.

One method for balancing redox equations involves determining the change in oxidation number of the substances that are oxidized and reduced. Coefficients are then used to make the increase in oxidation number equal to the decrease.

The half-reaction method is another way to write a balanced equation for a redox reaction. In this method, the net ionic equation is first divided into two half-reactions. One is for the oxidation and the other is for the reduction. Each half-reaction is balanced independently for mass. H^+, OH^-, and H_2O are added as needed. The net charge on both sides is balanced by adding electrons. The half-reactions are then multiplied by factors to make the number of electrons the same in each. Finally, the half-reactions are added.

Practice Questions and Problems

19. Balance each equation. Then classify each reaction as oxidation or reduction based on the loss or gain of oxygen. *21.1*
a. $C_2H_4(g) + O_2(g) \longrightarrow CO_2(g) + H_2O(l)$
b. $KClO_3(s) \longrightarrow KCl(s) + O_2(g)$
c. $CuO(s) + H_2(g) \longrightarrow Cu(s) + H_2O(l)$
d. $H_2(g) + O_2(g) \longrightarrow H_2O(l)$

20. Define oxidation and reduction in these terms. *21.2*
a. gain or loss of electrons
b. gain or loss of hydrogen by a covalent bond
c. gain or loss of oxygen
d. shift of electrons in a covalent bond

21. Use electron transfer or electron shift to identify what is oxidized and what is reduced in each of these reactions. Use electronegativity values for molecular compounds. *21.2*
a. $2Na(s) + Br_2(l) \longrightarrow 2NaBr(s)$
b. $N_2(g) + 3H_2(g) \longrightarrow 2NH_3(g)$
c. $S(s) + O_2(g) \longrightarrow SO_2(g)$
d. $Mg(s) + Cu(NO_3)_2(aq) \longrightarrow Mg(NO_3)_2(aq) + Cu(s)$

22. Identify these reactions as either oxidation or reduction. *21.2*

a. $Li \longrightarrow Li^+ + e^-$ **c.** $Zn^{2+} + 2e^- \longrightarrow Zn$

b. $2I^- \longrightarrow I_2 + 2e^-$ **d.** $Br_2 + 2e^- \longrightarrow 2Br^-$

23. Identify the oxidizing agent and the reducing agent in each reaction in Problem 21. *21.2*

24. How are oxidation numbers determined and used? *21.3*

25. Determine the oxidation number of each element in these substances. *21.3*

a. S_2O_3 **b.** O_2 **c.** $Al_2(SO_4)_3$ **d.** Na_2O_2

26. Use the oxidation number to identify which elements are oxidized and which are reduced in each of these reactions. *21.4*

a. $2H_2(g) + O_2(g) \longrightarrow 2H_2O(l)$

b. $2KNO_3(s) \longrightarrow 2KNO_2(s) + O_2(g)$

c. $NH_4NO_2(s) \longrightarrow N_2(g) + 2H_2O(g)$

d. $PbO_2(aq) + 4HI(aq) \longrightarrow I_2(aq) + PbI_2(aq) + 2H_2O(l)$

27. Identify the oxidizing agent and reducing agent in each equation in Problem 26. *21.4*

28. Balance each of these redox equations using the oxidation number change method. *21.5*

a. $KClO_3(s) \longrightarrow KCl(s) + O_2(g)$

b. $HNO_2(aq) + HI(aq) \longrightarrow NO(g) + I_2(s) + H_2O(l)$

c. $As_2O_3(s) + Cl_2(g) + H_2O(l) \longrightarrow H_3AsO_4(aq) + HCl(aq)$

d. $Bi_2S_3(s) + HNO_3(aq) \longrightarrow Bi(NO_3)_3(aq) + NO(g) + S(s) + H_2O(l)$

e. $MnO_2(s) + H_2SO_4(aq) + H_2C_2O_4(aq) \longrightarrow MnSO_4(aq) + CO_2(g) + H_2O(l)$

f. $SbCl_5(aq) + KI(aq) \longrightarrow SbCl_3(aq) + KCl(aq) + I_2(s)$

29. Identify the oxidizing agent and the reducing agent in each reaction in Problem 28. *21.5*

30. Identify which of these equations represent redox reactions. *21.6*

a. $Li(s) + H_2O(l) \longrightarrow LiOH(aq) + H_2(g)$

b. $K_2Cr_2O_7(aq) + HCl(aq) \longrightarrow KCl(aq) + CrCl_3(aq) + H_2O(l) + Cl_2(g)$

c. $Al(s) + HCl(aq) \longrightarrow AlCl_3(aq) + H_2(g)$

d. $P_4(s) + S_8(s) \longrightarrow P_2S_5(s)$

e. $MnO(s) + PbO_2(s) \longrightarrow MnO_4^-(aq) + Pb^{2+}(aq)$ [acidic]

f. $Cl_2(g) + H_2O(l) \longrightarrow HCl(aq) + HClO(aq)$

g. $I_2O_5(s) + CO(g) \longrightarrow I_2(s) + CO_2(g)$

h. $H_2O(l) + SO_3(g) \longrightarrow H_2SO_4(aq)$

31. For each redox equation in Problem 30, identify the oxidizing agent and reducing agent. *21.6*

32. Write balanced ionic equations for the following reactions that occur in acid solution. Use the half-reaction method. *21.7*

a. $Sn^{2+}(aq) + Cr_2O_7^{2-}(aq) \longrightarrow Sn^{4+}(aq) + Cr^{3+}(aq)$

b. $CuS(s) + NO_3^-(aq) \longrightarrow Cu(NO_3)_2(aq) + NO_2(g) + SO_2(g)$

c. $I^-(aq) + NO_3^-(aq) \longrightarrow I_2(s) + NO(g)$

33. The following reactions take place in basic solution. Use the half-reaction method to write a balanced ionic equation for each. *21.7*

a. $MnO_4^-(aq) + I^-(aq) \longrightarrow MnO_2(s) + I_2(aq)$

b. $NiO_2(s) + S_2O_3^{2-}(aq) \longrightarrow Ni(OH)_2(aq) + SO_3^{2-}(aq)$

c. $Zn(s) + NO_3^-(aq) \longrightarrow NH_3(aq) + Zn(OH)_4^{2-}(aq)$

Mastery Questions and Problems

34. Construct a concept map using the key terms with *redox reaction* as the central concept.

35. Balance the equations in Problem 30 by the most appropriate method.

36. Determine the oxidation number of phosphorus in each substance.

a. P_4O_8 **d.** P_4O_6

b. PO_4^{3-} **e.** $H_2PO_4^-$

c. P_2O_5 **f.** PO_3^{3-}

37. Sodium chlorite is a powerful bleaching agent that is used in the paper and textile industries. It is prepared by this reaction.

$$4NaOH(aq) + Ca(OH)_2(aq) + C(s) + 4ClO_2(g) \longrightarrow 4NaClO_2(aq) + CaCO_3(s) + 3H_2O(l)$$

a. Identify the element oxidized in this reaction.

b. What is the oxidizing agent?

38. The following oxidation–reduction reactions take place in basic solution. Use the half-reaction method to write a balanced ionic equation for each reaction.

a. $MnO_4^-(aq) + ClO_2^-(aq) \longrightarrow MnO_2(s) + ClO_4^-(aq)$

b. $Cr^{3+}(aq) + ClO^-(aq) \longrightarrow CrO_4^{2-}(aq) + Cl^-(aq)$

c. $Mn^{3+}(aq) + I^-(aq) \longrightarrow Mn^{2+}(aq) + IO_3^-(aq)$

39. Identify the element oxidized, the element reduced, the oxidizing agent, and the reducing agent in each of these redox reactions.
a. $MnO_2(s) + HCl(aq) \longrightarrow$
$MnCl_2(aq) + Cl_2(g) + H_2O(l)$
b. $Cu(s) + HNO_3(aq) \longrightarrow$
$Cu(NO_3)_2(aq) + NO_2(g) + H_2O(l)$
c. $P(s) + HNO_3(aq) + H_2O(l) \longrightarrow$
$NO(g) + H_3PO_4(aq)$
d. $Bi(OH)_3(s) + Na_2SnO_2(aq) \longrightarrow$
$Bi(s) + Na_2SnO_3(aq) + H_2O(l)$
e. $NaCrO_2(aq) + NaClO(aq) + NaOH(aq) \longrightarrow$
$Na_2CrO_4(aq) + NaCl(aq) + H_2O(l)$
f. $V_2O_5(s) + KI(aq) + HCl(aq) \longrightarrow$
$V_2O_4(s) + KCl(aq) + I_2(s) + H_2O(l)$

40. Imagine that you live in a community that is close to an incinerator construction site. What would be your reaction?

41. Balance each of the redox equations shown in Problem 39 by using the oxidation number change method.

42. What kinds of materials make up the biomass? What energy source makes biomass a renewable resource?

Critical Thinking Questions

43. Choose the term that best completes the second relationship.
a. Oxidation:reduction fill up: ____
(1) empty (3) dry out
(2) overflow (4) splash
b. plants:oxygen reducing agent: ____
(1) reduction (3) electrons
(2) rust (4) oxygen

44. Many decomposition, single-replacement, combination, and combustion reactions are also redox reactions. Why is a double-replacement reaction never a redox reaction?

45. Many redox equations can be balanced using the techniques you learned in Chapter 7. What advantages over these techniques do the oxidation number change method and the half-reaction method offer when balancing redox equations?

Cumulative Review

46. Calculate the pH of solutions with the following hydrogen-ion or hydroxide-ion concentrations.
a. $[H^+] = 0.00001M$ **c.** $[OH^-] = 1 \times 10^{-1}M$
b. $[OH^-] = 1 \times 10^{-4}M$ **d.** $[H^+] = 3 \times 10^{-7}M$

47. Classify each of the solutions in Problem 46 as acidic, basic, or neutral.

48. How many milliliters of a 4.00M KOH solution are needed to neutralize 45.0 mL of a 2.5M H_2SO_4 solution?

49. What is the hydrogen-ion concentration of solutions with the following pH?
a. 2.0 **b.** 11.0 **c.** 8.8

50. What is the normality of the solution prepared by dissolving 46.4 g of H_3PO_4 in enough water to make 1.25 L of solution?

51. The K_{sp} of lead(II) bromide at 25°C is 2.1×10^{-6}. What is the solubility of $PbBr_2$ in moles per liter at this temperature?

52. How would you make 440 mL of 1.5M HCl solution from a stock solution of 6.0M HCl?

53. Bottles containing 0.1M solutions of Na_2SO_4, $BaCl_2$, and NaCl have had their labels accidentally switched. To discover which bottle contains the NaCl, you set up the following test. You place a clear saturated solution of $BaSO_4$ ($K_{sp} = 1.1 \times 10^{-10}$) into each of three test tubes. Then you add a few drops of each mislabeled solution to a different test tube. The results are shown below. To which tube was NaCl added? Explain your reasoning.

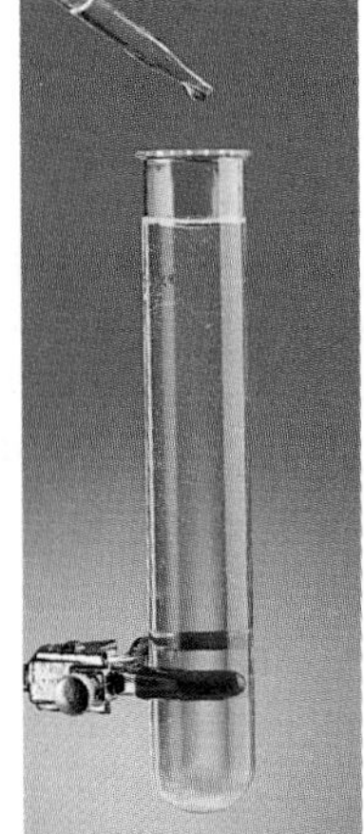
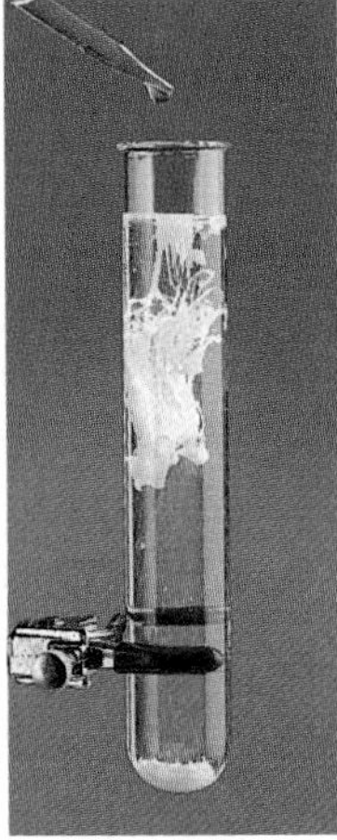

54. Identify the conjugate acid–base pairs in each of these equations.

a. $NH_4^+(aq) + H_2O(l) \rightleftharpoons NH_3(aq) + H_3O^+(aq)$

b. $H_2SO_3(aq) + NH_2^-(aq) \rightleftharpoons HSO_3^-(aq) + NH_3(aq)$

c. $HNO_3(aq) + I^-(aq) \rightleftharpoons HI(aq) + NO_3^-(aq)$

d. $H_2O(l) + ClO_4^-(aq) \rightleftharpoons HClO_4(aq) + OH^-(aq)$

55. Complete combustion of hydrocarbons involves the oxidation of both carbon and hydrogen atoms. The carbon combines with oxygen to form carbon dioxide, and the hydrogen combines with oxygen to form water. The following table lists the moles of O_2 used and the moles of CO_2 and moles of H_2O produced when a series of hydrocarbons called alkanes are burned.

a. Complete the table.

b. Based on the data, write a balanced generalized equation for the complete combustion of any alkane. Use the following form, in which the coefficients are written in terms of *x* and *y*:

$$C_xH_y + \_\_\_ O_2 \longrightarrow \_\_\_ CO_2 + \_\_\_ H_2O$$

Alkane burned	O_2 used (mol)	CO_2 produced (mol)	H_2O produced (mol)
CH_4	2	1	2
C_2H_6	3.5	2	3
C_3H_8	5	3	4
C_4H_{10}	___	___	___
C_5H_{12}	___	___	___
C_6H_{14}	___	___	___

Challenge Questions and Problems

56. How many milliliters of a 0.280*M* $K_2Cr_2O_7(aq)$ solution are needed to reduce 1.40 g of sulfur? First balance the equation.

$$K_2Cr_2O_7(aq) + H_2O(l) + S(s) \longrightarrow SO_2(g) + KOH(aq) + Cr_2O_3(aq)$$

57. How many grams of copper are needed to reduce completely the silver in 85.0 mL of a 0.150*M* $AgNO_3(aq)$ solution?

58. Carbon monoxide can be removed from the air by passing it over solid diiodine pentoxide.

$$CO(g) + I_2O_5(s) \longrightarrow I_2(s) + CO_2(g)$$

a. Balance the equation.

b. Identify the element being oxidized and the element being reduced.

c. How many grams of carbon monoxide can be removed from the air by 0.55 g of I_2O_5?

Connections Questions

59. How do the developer and the fixer function chemically in black-and-white photography?

60. Name some areas of chemistry in which Faraday worked.

61. What causes rancidity? How can this process be slowed?

Write About Chemistry

62. Every oxidation reaction must occur simultaneously with a reduction reaction. Write a paragraph describing other situations in which one event is always linked to another event.

63. Explosives and rocket fuels do their work through redox reactions. Research and write a short report on the development of either of these classes of substances.

Readings and References

Newsday. *Rush to Burn: Solving America's Garbage Crisis?* Washington, DC: Island Press, 1989.

Robson, David P. "Sunken Treasure." *ChemMatters* (April 1987), pp. 4–9.

22 Electrochemistry

Goals

- Describe how redox reactions allow the interconversion of electrical energy and chemical energy.
- Write the oxidation and reduction half-reactions for a voltaic cell.
- Compute the standard cell potential and write the overall cell reaction.
- Explain how electrolytic cells use electrical energy to cause a chemical change.

Batteries can transform chemical energy into electrical energy, using various substances. The world's largest battery, a lead acid battery at an electrical substation in Chino, California, has a capacity of 40 megawatt hours.

Concept Overview

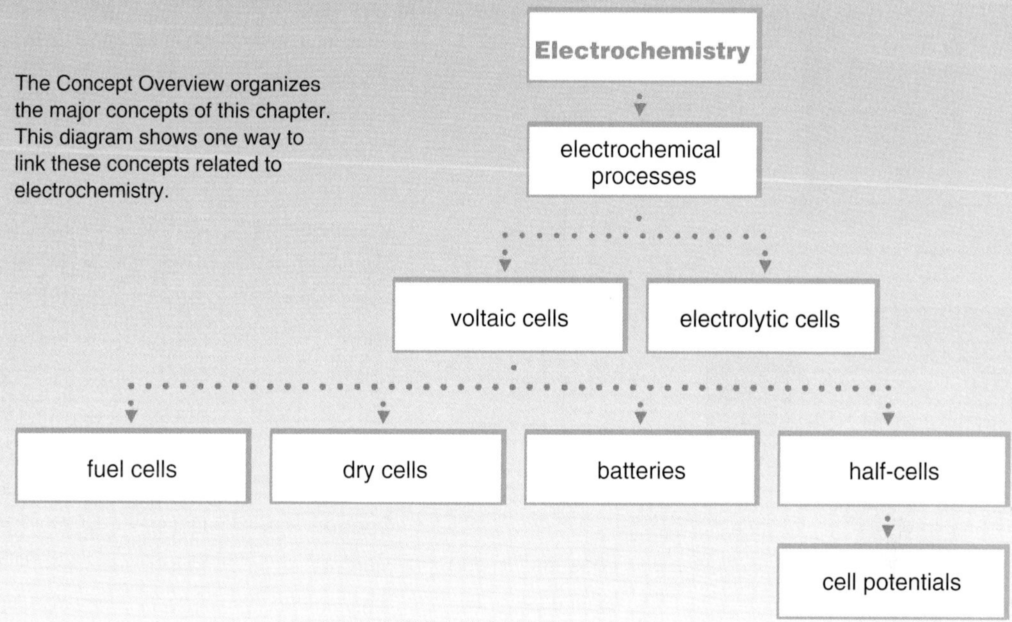

Electrochemistry has many applications in the home as well as in industry. Flashlight and automobile batteries are familiar examples. Others are the manufacture of sodium and aluminum metals and the silver plating of tableware. Biological systems also use electrochemistry to carry out nerve-impulse conduction. This chapter starts with a discussion of the relationship between redox reactions and electrochemistry.

22.1 Electrochemical Processes

Objective

Describe the nature of electrochemical processes.

When a strip of zinc metal is dipped into an aqueous solution of copper sulfate, the zinc becomes copper-plated. The net ionic equation involves only zinc and copper.

$$Zn(s) + Cu^{2+}(aq) \longrightarrow Zn^{2+}(aq) + Cu(s)$$

Electrons are transferred from zinc atoms to copper ions. This is a *redox reaction* and it occurs *spontaneously*. As the reaction proceeds, zinc atoms lose electrons as they are oxidized to zinc ions. The zinc metal slowly dissolves. At the same time, copper ions in

Figure 22.1 A spontaneous redox reaction occurs when a zinc strip is immersed in a solution of copper(II) sulfate (top). If the zinc remains in solution for a long time, the blue color of the solution fades and the zinc strip is badly corroded (bottom).

Table 22.1 Activity Series of Metals, with Half-Reactions for Oxidation Processes

	Element	Oxidation half-reactions
Most active and most easily oxidized	Lithium	$Li(s) \longrightarrow Li^{+}(aq) + e^{-}$
↓	Potassium	$K(s) \longrightarrow K^{+}(aq) + e^{-}$
	Barium	$Ba(s) \longrightarrow Ba^{2+}(aq) + 2e^{-}$
	Calcium	$Ca(s) \longrightarrow Ca^{2+}(aq) + 2e^{-}$
	Sodium	$Na(s) \longrightarrow Na^{+}(aq) + e^{-}$
	Magnesium	$Mg(s) \longrightarrow Mg^{2+}(aq) + 2e^{-}$
	Aluminum	$Al(s) \longrightarrow Al^{3+}(aq) + 3e^{-}$
	Zinc	$Zn(s) \longrightarrow Zn^{2+}(aq) + 2e^{-}$
	Iron	$Fe(s) \longrightarrow Fe^{2+}(aq) + 2e^{-}$
	Nickel	$Ni(s) \longrightarrow Ni^{2+}(aq) + 2e^{-}$
	Tin	$Sn(s) \longrightarrow Sn^{2+}(aq) + 2e^{-}$
	Lead	$Pb(s) \longrightarrow Pb^{2+}(aq) + 2e^{-}$
	Hydrogen*	$H_2(g) \longrightarrow 2H^{+}(aq) + 2e^{-}$
	Copper	$Cu(s) \longrightarrow Cu^{2+}(aq) + 2e^{-}$
Least active and least easily oxidized	Mercury	$Hg(s) \longrightarrow Hg^{2+}(aq) + 2e^{-}$
	Silver	$Ag(s) \longrightarrow Ag^{+}(aq) + e^{-}$
	Gold	$Au(s) \longrightarrow Au^{3+}(aq) + 3e^{-}$

* Hydrogen is included for reference purposes.

solution gain electrons. They are reduced to copper atoms and deposit as metallic copper. As the copper ions are gradually replaced by zinc ions, the blue color of the solution fades. Balanced half-reactions for this redox reaction can be written as follows.

$$\text{Oxidation: } Zn(s) \longrightarrow Zn^{2+}(aq) + 2e^{-}$$

$$\text{Reduction: } Cu^{2+}(aq) + 2e^{-} \longrightarrow Cu(s)$$

If you look at the activity series of metals in Table 22.1, you will see that zinc is above copper. For any two metals in the table, the metal that is the higher of the two is the more readily oxidized. As Figure 22.1 shows, when zinc is dipped in a copper sulfate solution, the zinc becomes copper-plated. By contrast, when a copper rod is dipped into a solution of zinc sulfate, the copper does not become zinc-plated. This is because copper metal is not oxidized by zinc ions. Zinc is above copper in the activity series. Zinc plating on copper is a nonspontaneous process.

The conversion of chemical energy into electrical energy and the conversion of electrical energy into chemical energy are **electrochemical processes**. All electrochemical processes involve redox reactions. The zinc–copper is an example of the conversion of chemical energy into electrical energy.

When a zinc rod is dipped into a copper sulfate solution, electrons are transferred from zinc metal to copper ions. Remember that an electric current is a flow of electrons. If a redox reaction is to be used as a source of electrical energy, however, the two half-reactions must be physically separated. That is, the electrons released by zinc must pass through an external circuit to reach the copper ions. Thus, electrical energy is produced in an electrochemical cell. Alternatively, an electric current can also be used to produce a chemical change. *An* **electrochemical cell** *is any device that converts chemical energy into electrical energy or electrical energy into chemical energy.* Redox reactions occur in electrochemical cells.

Concept Practice

1. What is meant by the term *half-reaction*? Write the half-reactions that occur when a strip of aluminum metal is dipped into a solution of copper(II) sulfate. Use the half-reactions to explain that a redox reaction takes place.

2. What would you expect to happen when a strip of lead is placed in an aqueous solution of magnesium nitrate?

22.2 Voltaic Cells

Objective

Explain a voltaic cell using a sketch, labeling the cathode, the anode, and the direction of electron flow.

The first electrochemical cell was invented by the Italian physicist Alessandro Volta (1745–1827). Volta designed a cell that can be used to generate a direct electric current (DC current). **Voltaic cells** *are electrochemical cells that are used to convert chemical energy into electrical energy.* The energy is produced by *spontaneous* redox reactions within the cell.

A **half-cell** *is one part of a voltaic cell in which either oxidation or reduction occurs.* A half-cell consists of a metal rod or strip immersed in a solution of its ions. In a typical voltaic cell, one half-cell is a zinc rod immersed in a solution of zinc sulfate. The other half-cell is a copper rod immersed in a solution of copper sulfate. The two half-cells are separated by a porous partition. *A* **salt bridge,** *which is a tube containing a conducting solution, may also be used.* These dividers allow the passage of ions from one compartment to the other but prevent the solutions from mixing completely. A wire carries the electrons in the external circuit from zinc to copper. A voltmeter or light bulb can be connected in the circuit. The driving force of such a voltaic cell is the spontaneous redox reaction between zinc metal and copper(II) ions in solution.

The zinc and copper rods in a voltaic cell are the electrodes. *An* **electrode** *is a conductor in a circuit that carries electrons to or from a substance other than a metal.* The type of electrode reaction determines whether an electrode is labeled as a cathode or an anode. Note that the name of the electrode is *not* determined by its charge. *The electrode at which oxidation occurs is the* **anode**. Electrons are produced here. Thus the anode is labeled the *negative* electrode. *The electrode at which reduction occurs is the* **cathode**. Electrons are consumed at the cathode. As a result, it is labeled the *positive* electrode. Neither electrode is really charged. All parts of the voltaic cell remain balanced in terms of charge at all times. The moving electrons balance any charge that might build up as oxidation and reduction occur.

The electrochemical process that occurs in a zinc–copper voltaic cell can best be described in a number of steps. These steps all occur at the same time.

Even a low-voltage source can have a dangerously high current if the resistance is very low. Treat all sources of electricity with care.

1. Electrons are produced at the zinc rod according to the *oxidation* half-reaction.

$$Zn(s) \longrightarrow Zn^{2+}(aq) + 2e^-$$

Because it is oxidized, the zinc rod is the anode, or the negative electrode.

2. The electrons leave the zinc anode and pass through the external circuit to the copper rod. (If a bulb is the circuit, it will light. If a voltmeter is present, it will indicate a voltage.)

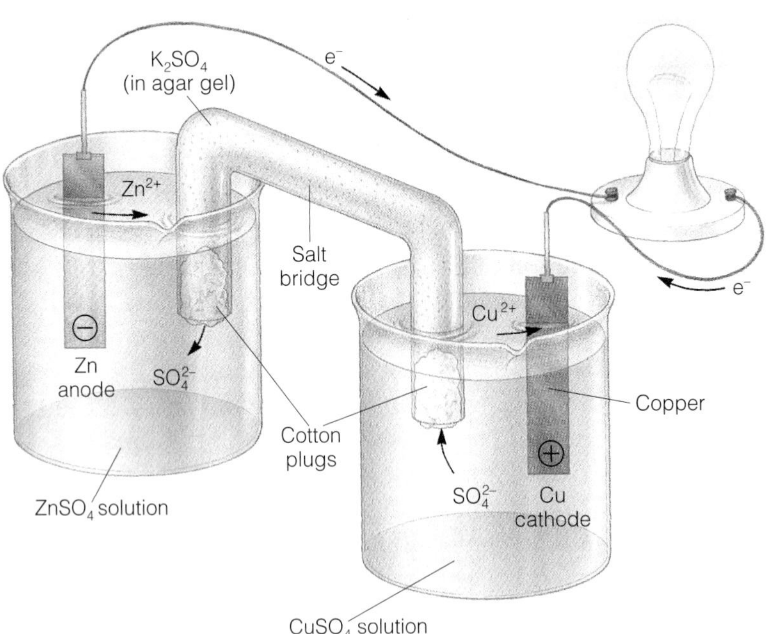

Figure 22.2 In all electrochemical cells, oxidation occurs at the anode and reduction occurs at the cathode.

3. Electrons enter the copper rod and pass to copper ions in solution. There the following *reduction* half-reaction occurs.

$$Cu^{2+}(aq) + 2e^- \longrightarrow Cu(s)$$

4. At the copper rod, copper ions are reduced. The copper rod is the cathode, or positive electrode. To complete the circuit, ions (both positive and negative) move through the aqueous solutions via the salt bridge. The two half-reactions can be summed to get the overall cell reaction. The electrons must cancel.

$$Cu^{2+}(aq) + \cancel{2e^-} \longrightarrow Cu(s)$$

$$Zn(s) \longrightarrow Zn^{2+}(aq) + \cancel{2e^-}$$

$$Zn(s) + Cu^{2+}(aq) \longrightarrow Zn^{2+}(aq) + Cu(s)$$

You can use a shorthand method to represent an electrochemical cell. For example, you can represent the zinc–copper voltaic cell as follows.

$$Zn(s) \mid ZnSO_4(aq) \parallel CuSO_4(aq) \mid Cu(s)$$

The half-cell which undergoes oxidation (the anode) is written first at the left. The double vertical lines represent the salt bridge or porous partition that separates the anode compartment from the cathode compartment. The single vertical lines indicate boundaries of phases that are in contact. For example, the zinc rod, $Zn(s)$, and the zinc sulfate solution, $ZnSO_4(aq)$, are separate phases in physical contact. When the solutions in the voltaic cells are both 1.0*M*, the cell generates an electrical potential of 1.10 volts (1.10 V). If different metals are used for the electrodes in the cell, the voltage will change. Different solution concentrations will affect the voltage as well.

The zinc-copper voltaic cell is of great historical importance, but it is no longer used commercially. Nevertheless, this cell is a convenient model to use when describing the production of electrical energy from a chemical change. Today, the more practical and compact "dry" cell is usually chosen when a portable electrical energy source is required.

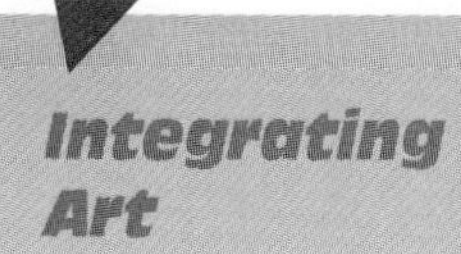

Integrating Art

Jewelry

Jewelry-making artists use the chemistry of metal plating to deposit thin layers of precious metals on much less expensive base materials. The base material that receives the precious metal plating is often an inexpensive metal such as copper. However, nonmetallic objects and even natural objects like leaves, acorns, or seashells can be used as base materials if their surface is first coated with conductive graphite. The thin plating lets most of the detail of the original object show through. The resulting jewelry combines the natural beauty of the object with the richness of precious metal and the creativity of the artist.

Concept Practice

3. In a voltaic cell, at which electrode does reduction always occur?

4. What is the source of the electrical energy produced in a voltaic cell?

22.A Environmental Awareness

Solar Cells

What would life on Earth be like without energy from the sun? The answer is simple: there would be no life. The sun provides warmth and light. Now, thanks to solar cells, energy from the sun can be used to power everything from calculators to cars. There are different types of solar cells. Photovoltaic cells convert sunlight directly into electricity. Other types of solar cells heat water to produce steam which then turns a turbine to generate electricity.

Photovoltaic cells were invented in the mid-1950s, but received little attention. During the 1950s, fossil fuels, such as gasoline and oil, were cheap and abundant. Photovoltaic cells, on the other hand, were expensive, cumbersome, and very inefficient. However, an energy crisis in the 1970s created great interest in solar energy. By 1986, a gigantic, non-photovoltaic power station had been completed in the Mohave Desert of California. In 1987, an American-built photovoltaic-powered car won a 3138 km (1950 mile) race across Australia, at a record-breaking speed of 67 km/hr (41.6 mph).

Using solar energy to generate electricity has many compelling benefits. Solar energy is unlimited, pollution-free, silent, and odorless. It does not contribute to global warming, ozone destruction, or acid rain. Solar power does not have to be mined or imported, and it is most abundant in the summer, when electricity demand is often at its peak. Unfortunately, solar energy also has a big problem, namely the inefficient conversion of sunlight into electricity. At an average efficiency of 25%, it takes a lot of photovoltaic cells to generate a small amount of electricity. Recent advances in technology, however, may help overcome this problem. Researchers have found that the efficiency of photovoltaic cells can be increased by replacing the silicon used in the cell with gallium arsenide, a synthetic material. Because electrons flow through gallium arsenide more easily than through silicon, photovoltaic cells made of this new material are more efficient. With further advances in solar technology and continued public concern over the problems created by burning fossil fuels, the future of solar energy looks bright.

Figure 22.3 Solar arrays have been effective at generating electricity on Earth as well as in space.

Think About It

5. Explain Even though sunlight is unlimited and you cannot be charged for using it, why isn't solar energy really "free"?

6. Give Examples What benefits are there to using the sun's energy to produce electricity rather than burning fossil fuels?

22.3 Dry Cells

Objective

Identify the substance oxidized and the substance reduced in a dry cell.

A type of voltaic cell that is very familiar to you is the common flashlight battery. A flashlight battery is an example of a **dry cell**, *a voltaic cell in which the electrolyte is a paste.* A zinc container is filled with a thick moist paste of manganese(IV) oxide (MnO_2), zinc chloride ($ZnCl_2$), ammonium chloride (NH_4Cl), and water. A graphite rod is embedded in the paste. The zinc container is the anode and the graphite rod is the cathode. The thick paste, surrounded by a paper liner, prevents the contents of the cell from freely mixing, so a salt bridge is not needed. The half-reactions for this cell are as follows.

Oxidation: $Zn(s) \longrightarrow Zn^{2+}(aq) + 2e^-$ (anode reaction)

Reduction: $2MnO_2(s) + 2NH_4^+(aq) + 2e^- \longrightarrow$
$Mn_2O_3(s) + 2NH_3(aq) + H_2O(l)$ (cathode reaction)

In this cell, the graphite rod serves only as a conductor and does not undergo reduction, even though it is the cathode. The manganese in MnO_2 is the species that is reduced. The electrical potential of this cell usually begins at 1.5 V but falls steadily during use to about 0.8 V. Dry cells of this construction are not rechargeable.

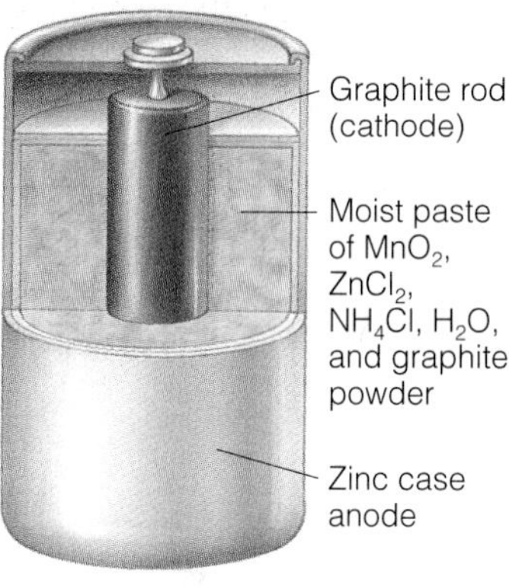

Figure 22.4 A dry cell battery is a single electrochemical cell that produces about 1.5 V. What is oxidized in this cell and what is reduced?

Concept Practice

7. Represent the electrochemical reaction of the flashlight battery by the shorthand method.

22.4 Lead Storage Batteries

Objective

Describe the reaction that occurs when a car battery discharges.

You depend on a lead storage battery to start your car. A 12-V car battery consists of six rechargeable voltaic cells connected together. *A* **battery** *is a group of cells that are connected together.* Each cell in a car battery produces about 2 V and contains two lead electrodes or grids. One of the grids, the anode, is packed with spongy lead. The other grid, the cathode, is packed with lead(IV) oxide, PbO_2. The grids are immersed in strong sulfuric acid and are separated by a perforated plate. The half-reactions for the lead storage battery are as follows.

Oxidation: $Pb(s) + SO_4^{2-}(aq) \longrightarrow PbSO_4(s) + 2e^-$

Reduction: $PbO_2(s) + 4H^+(aq) + SO_4^{2-}(aq) + 2e^- \longrightarrow$
$PbSO_4(s) + 2H_2O(l)$

Figure 22.5 A 12-V lead storage battery consists of six 2-V cells in series. The cells do not need to be in separate compartments, but this improves performance.

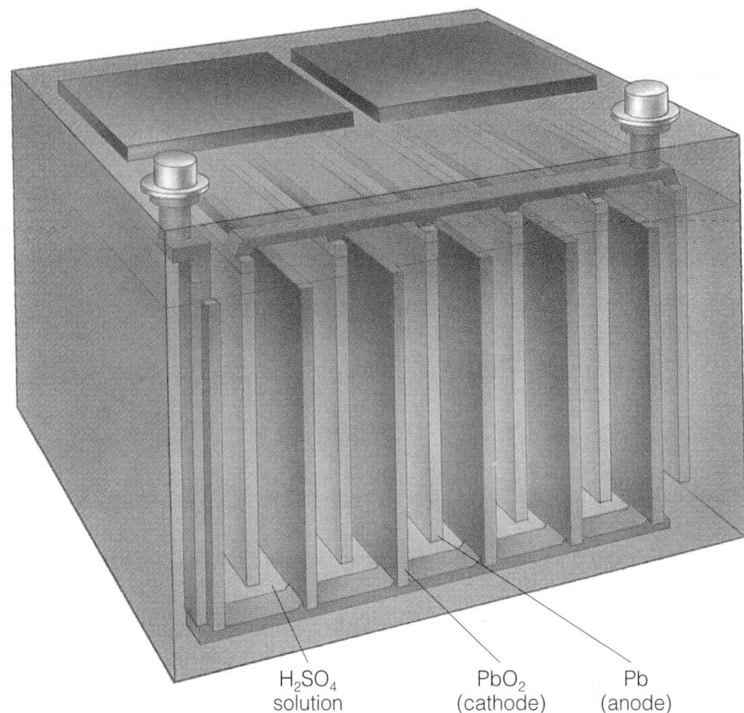

The sulfuric acid in a lead storage battery is 5*M* and is very corrosive. Handle with care.

When a lead storage battery discharges, it produces the electric power to start the car. The overall spontaneous redox reaction is the sum of the oxidation and reduction half-reactions.

$$Pb(s) + PbO_2(s) + 2H_2SO_4(aq) \longrightarrow 2PbSO_4(s) + 2H_2O(l)$$

This reaction shows that during discharge, lead sulfate slowly builds up on the plates, and the concentration of sulfuric acid decreases. The condition of a lead storage battery can be checked by measuring the specific gravity of the electrolyte, sulfuric acid. If the specific gravity is much below 1.25, the battery should be recharged.

The reverse reaction occurs when a storage battery is recharged. This reaction occurs whenever the engine in a car is running.

$$2PbSO_4(s) + 2H_2O(l) \longrightarrow Pb(s) + PbO_2(s) + 2H_2SO_4(aq)$$

This reaction is *nonspontaneous.* To make it go, a direct current must be passed through the cell in the reverse direction. In theory, a lead storage battery can be recharged indefinitely, but in practice its life span is limited. This is because small amounts of lead sulfate continually fall from the electrodes and collect on the bottom of the cell. Eventually the electrodes lose so much lead sulfate that the recharging process is ineffective or the cell is shorted out. To help overcome this problem, fuel cells with renewable electrodes have been developed in recent years.

Concept Practice

8. Explain why the specific gravity of the electrolyte in a lead storage battery decreases during the discharge process.

9. Use the shorthand method to represent the electrochemical reaction in a car battery.

22.5 Fuel Cells

Objective

Explain how a fuel cell produces electrical energy.

Fuel cells *are voltaic cells in which a fuel substance undergoes oxidation and from which electrical energy is obtained continuously.* Fuel cells do not have to be recharged. They can be designed to emit no air pollutants and to operate more quietly and more cheaply than a conventional electrical generator.

Perhaps the simplest fuel cell to visualize is the hydrogen–oxygen fuel cell. As shown in Figure 22.6 there are three compartments separated from one another by two electrodes made of porous carbon. Oxygen (the oxidizer) is fed into the cathode compartment. Hydrogen (the fuel) is fed into the anode compartment. The gases diffuse slowly through the electrodes. The electrolyte in the central

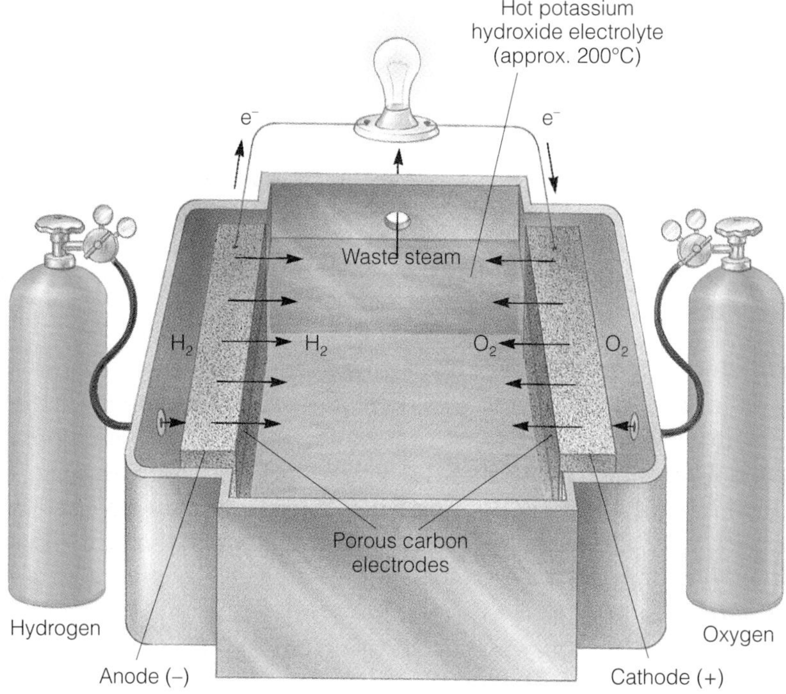

Figure 22.6 The hydrogen–oxygen fuel cell is a clean source of power. What "waste" products are produced?

compartment is a hot concentrated solution of potassium hydroxide. Electrons from the oxidation reaction at the anode pass through an external circuit to enter the reduction reaction at the cathode.

$$\text{Oxidation: } 2H_2(g) + 4OH^-(aq) \longrightarrow 4H_2O(l) + 4e^- \text{ (anode)}$$

$$\text{Reduction: } O_2(g) + 2H_2O(l) + 4e^- \longrightarrow 4OH^-(aq) \text{ (cathode)}$$

The equation for the overall reaction is the oxidation of hydrogen to form water.

$$2H_2(g) + O_2(g) \longrightarrow 2H_2O(l)$$

Other fuels, such as methane, CH_4, and ammonia, NH_3, can be used in place of hydrogen. Other oxidizers, such as chlorine, Cl_2, and ozone, O_3, can be used in place of oxygen. Fuel cells are currently being built as auxiliary power sources for submarines and other military vehicles. At present, however, they are too expensive for general use. Hydrogen–oxygen fuel cells, with a mass of approximately 100 kg each, were used in the Apollo spacecraft missions. Instead of producing toxic wastes like an internal combustion engine, these cells produce drinkable water.

Concept Practice

10. Fuel cells can be designed to generate electrical energy continuously and emit no air pollutants, yet they are not widely used. Explain.

11. Based on the half-reactions for the hydrogen–oxygen fuel cell, would KOH be consumed in this cell? Explain.

Objective

Define cell potential and describe how it is determined.

22.6 Half-Cells

The **electrical potential** *of a voltaic cell is the ability of the cell to produce an electric current.* Electrical potential is usually measured in volts (V). The potential of an isolated half-cell cannot be measured. For example, you cannot measure the electrical potential of a zinc half-cell or of a copper half-cell separately. When these two half-cells are connected to form a voltaic cell, however, the difference in potential can be measured. The electrical potential of a 1.0*M* zinc–copper cell is +1.10 V.

The electrical potential of a cell results from a competition between the two half-cells for electrons. The half-cell with the greater tendency to acquire electrons will do so and will undergo reduction. The other half-cell loses electrons and is oxidized. The half-cell in which reduction occurs has a greater reduction potential than the half-cell in which oxidation occurs. *The* **reduction potential** *of a half-cell is a measure of the tendency of a given half-reaction to occur as a reduction. The difference between the reduction potentials of the two half-cells is called the* **cell potential**.

$$\text{Cell potential} = \begin{pmatrix}\text{reduction potential}\\ \text{of half-cell in which}\\ \text{reduction occurs}\end{pmatrix} - \begin{pmatrix}\text{reduction potential}\\ \text{of half-cell in which}\\ \text{oxidation occurs}\end{pmatrix}$$

or $E^0_{cell} = E^0_{red} - E^0_{oxid}$

The **standard cell potential** (E^0_{cell}) *is the measured cell potential when the ion concentrations in the half-cells are 1.00M, gases are at a pressure of 101 kPa, and the temperature is 25°C.* The symbols E^0_{red} and E^0_{oxid} are the standard reduction potentials for the reduction and oxidation half-cells, respectively. Because half-cell potentials cannot be measured, scientists have chosen an arbitrary reference electrode. *The* **standard hydrogen electrode** *is used with other electrodes so that the reduction potentials of those cells can be measured.* The standard reduction potential of the hydrogen electrode has been assigned a value of 0.00 V.

The standard hydrogen electrode consists of a platinum electrode immersed in a solution with a hydrogen ion concentration of 1.00*M*. The solution is at 25°C. The platinum electrode is a small square of platinum foil coated with finely divided platinum (known as *platinum black*). Hydrogen gas, at a pressure of 101 kPa, is bubbled around the platinum electrode. The half-cell reaction that occurs at the platinum black surface is as follows.

$$2H^+(aq, 1M) + 2e^- \rightleftharpoons H_2(g, 101\text{ kPa}) \qquad E^0_{H^+} = 0.00\text{ V}$$

The symbol $E^0_{H^+}$ represents the standard reduction potential of H^+. The double arrows mean that the reaction is reversible. Whether this half-cell reaction occurs as a reduction or as an oxidation is determined by the reduction potential of the half-cell to which it is connected.

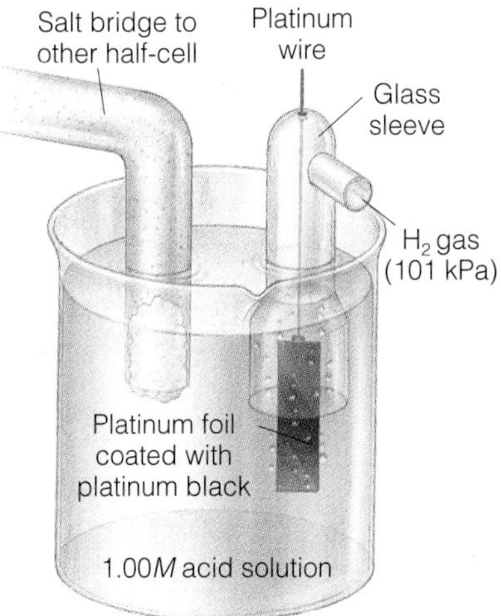

Figure 22.7 The standard hydrogen electrode is arbitrarily assigned a standard reduction potential of 0.00 V at 25°C.

Concept Practice

12. What is the difference between a *cell potential* and a *standard cell potential*?

13. How was the standard reduction potential of the hydrogen electrode determined?

22.B Science, Technology, and Society

Corrosion

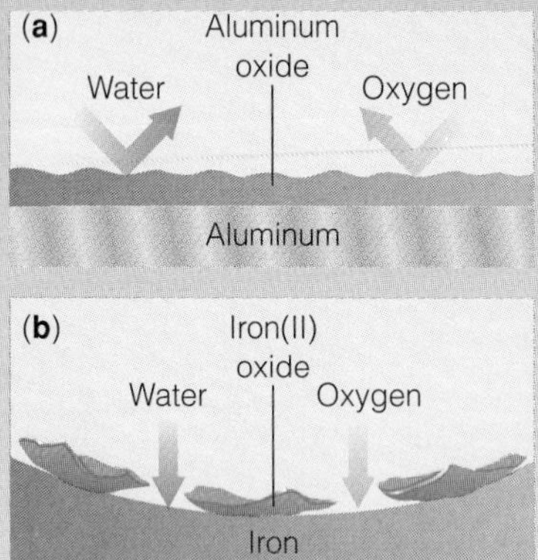

Figure 22.8 Oxidation causes the corrosion of some metals but not others. How does aluminum oxide differ from iron(III) oxide?

Billions of dollars are spent yearly to prevent and repair damage caused by the corrosion of metals. Iron and steel, common construction metals, corrode by being oxidized to metallic ions. Oxygen is the oxidant, reducing to the metal oxide or to the hydroxide ion in the corrosion reaction. Corrosion reactions occur more easily in the presence of salts and acids, which produce conductive solutions that make electron transfer easier.

Not all metals corrode easily. Gold and platinum are very resistant to losing their electrons by corrosion. Aluminum oxidizes quickly in air to form a coating that protects the aluminum object from further corrosion. However, when iron corrodes, the coating of iron oxide is not tightly packed. Water and air can penetrate it and attack more of the iron metal below the coating. The corrosion continues until the iron object is only a pile of rust.

Surface protection is one of the two primary methods used to control corrosion. In surface protection the metal surface is coated with oil, paint, or plastic. These coatings exclude air and water and thus prevent corrosion. If the coating is scratched or worn away, however, the bare metal will corrode.

Figure 22.9 Cathodic protection of a ship's hull. Zinc blocks, attached to the ship's hull, act as the anode of an electrolysis cell. The zinc oxidizes (corrodes) and releases electrons. The steel hull becomes the cathode and consumes the electrons supplied by the zinc.

Electrochemical protection is the other primary method of corrosion control. In electrochemical protection one metal is used as a sacrificial anode to save another metal. For example, to protect an iron object, a piece of magnesium is placed in electrical contact with the iron. When oxygen and water attack the iron object, the iron atoms lose electrons (the iron is oxidized). However, because magnesium is a better reducing agent than iron (it is more easily oxidized) the magnesium immediately transfers electrons to the iron ions, reducing them back to neutral iron atoms.

Sacrificial zinc and aluminum anodes are attached to piers and ship hulls to prevent corrosion damage in areas submerged in water. Underground pipelines and storage tanks are connected to magnesium anodes for protection. Obviously, it is easier and cheaper to replace a block or plate of magnesium than to replace a bridge or pipeline.

Think About It

14. Explain Why would a metal corrode more quickly in salt water than distilled water?

15. Identify What characteristic must a metal used in electrochemical protection possess?

22.7 Standard Reduction Potentials

Objective

Define the standard electrode potential of an electrode.

A voltaic cell can be made by connecting a standard hydrogen half-cell to a standard zinc half-cell. A voltaic cell is shown in Figure 22.10. To determine the overall reaction for this cell, first identify the half-cell in which reduction takes place. Reduction takes place at the cathode and oxidation takes place at the anode in all electrochemical cells. A voltmeter gives a reading of +0.76 V when the zinc electrode is connected to the negative terminal and the hydrogen electrode is connected to the positive terminal. Thus, the zinc electrode must be the anode. Zinc is oxidized. The hydrogen electrode must be the cathode. Hydrogen ions are reduced. You can now write the half-reactions and cell reaction.

$$\text{Oxidation: } Zn(s) \longrightarrow Zn^{2+}(aq) + 2e^-$$

$$\text{Reduction: } 2H^+(aq) + 2e^- \longrightarrow H_2(g)$$

$$\text{Cell reaction: } Zn(s) + 2H^+(aq) \longrightarrow Zn^{2+}(aq) + H_2(g)$$

Safety

When running an electrochemical cell, always consider whether any of the products is a flammable or toxic gas.

Use of a standard hydrogen electrode allows you to calculate the standard reduction potential for the zinc half-cell.

$$E^0_{cell} = E^0_{red} - E^0_{oxid}$$

$$= E^0_{H^+} - E^0_{Zn^{2+}}$$

The cell potential was measured as $E^0_{cell} = 0.76$ V. The reduction potential of the hydrogen half-cell is a defined standard: $E^0_{H^+} = 0.00$ V.

$$+0.76\text{ V} = 0.00\text{ V} - E^0_{Zn^{2+}}$$

$$E^0_{Zn^{2+}} = -0.76\text{ V}$$

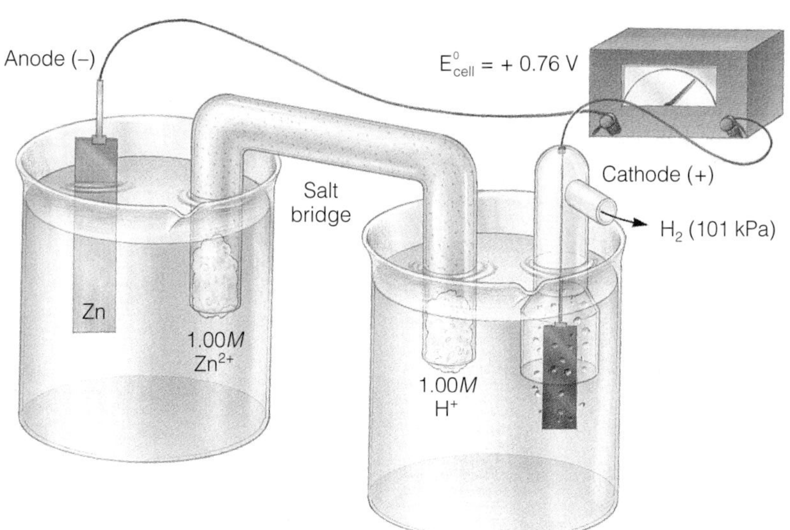

Figure 22.10 This voltaic cell consists of zinc and hydrogen half-cells. What is the measured cell potential?

Table 22.2 Reduction Potentials at 25°C with 1*M* Concentrations of Aqueous Species

Electrode	Half-reaction	E^0 (V)
Li^+/Li	$Li^+ + e^- \longrightarrow Li$	–3.05
K^+/K	$K^+ + e^- \longrightarrow K$	–2.93
Ba^{2+}/Ba	$Ba^{2+} + 2e^- \longrightarrow Ba$	–2.90
Ca^{2+}/Ca	$Ca^{2+} + 2e^- \longrightarrow Ca$	–2.87
Na^+/Na	$Na^+ + e^- \longrightarrow Na$	–2.71
Mg^{2+}/Mg	$Mg^{2+} + 2e^- \longrightarrow Mg$	–2.37
Al^{3+}/Al	$Al^{3+} + 3e^- \longrightarrow Al$	–1.66
H_2O/H_2	$2H_2O + 2e^- \longrightarrow H_2 + 2OH^-$	–0.83
Zn^{2+}/Zn	$Zn^{2+} + 2e^- \longrightarrow Zn$	–0.76
Cr^{3+}/Cr	$Cr^{3+} + 3e^- \longrightarrow Cr$	–0.74
Fe^{2+}/Fe	$Fe^{2+} + 2e^- \longrightarrow Fe$	–0.44
H_2O/H_2 (pH 7)	$2H_2O + 2e^- \longrightarrow H_2 + 2OH^-$	–0.42
Cd^{2+}/Cd	$Cd^{2+} + 2e^- \longrightarrow Cd$	–0.40
$PbSO_4/Pb$	$PbSO_4 + 2e^- \longrightarrow Pb + SO_4^{2-}$	–0.36
Co^{2+}/Co	$Co^{2+} + 2e^- \longrightarrow Co$	–0.28
Ni^{2+}/Ni	$Ni^{2+} + 2e^- \longrightarrow Ni$	–0.25
Sn^{2+}/Sn	$Sn^{2+} + 2e^- \longrightarrow Sn$	–0.14
Pb^{2+}/Pb	$Pb^{2+} + 2e^- \longrightarrow Pb$	–0.13
Fe^{3+}/Fe	$Fe^{3+} + 3e^- \longrightarrow Fe$	–0.036
H^+/H_2	$2H^+ + 2e^- \longrightarrow H_2$	0.000
$AgCl/Ag$	$AgCl + e^- \longrightarrow Ag + Cl^-$	+0.22
Hg_2Cl_2/Hg	$Hg_2Cl_2 + 2e^- \longrightarrow 2Hg + 2Cl^-$	+0.27
Cu^{2+}/Cu	$Cu^{2+} + 2e^- \longrightarrow Cu$	+0.34
O_2/OH^-	$O_2 + 2H_2O + 4e^- \longrightarrow 4OH^-$	+0.40
Cu^+/Cu	$Cu^+ + e^- \longrightarrow Cu$	+0.52
I_2/I^-	$I_2 + 2e^- \longrightarrow 2I^-$	+0.54
Fe^{3+}/Fe^{2+}	$Fe^{3+} + e^- \longrightarrow Fe^{2+}$	+0.77
Hg_2^{2+}/Hg	$Hg_2^{2+} + 2e^- \longrightarrow 2Hg$	+0.79
Ag^+/Ag	$Ag^+ + e^- \longrightarrow Ag$	+0.80
O_2/H_2O (pH 7)	$O_2 + 4H^+ + 4e^- \longrightarrow 2H_2O$	+0.82
Hg^{2+}/Hg	$Hg^{2+} + 2e^- \longrightarrow Hg$	+0.85
Br_2/Br^-	$Br_2 + 2e^- \longrightarrow 2Br^-$	+1.07
O_2/H_2O	$O_2 + 4H^+ + 4e^- \longrightarrow 2H_2O$	+1.23
MnO_2/Mn^{2+}	$MnO_2 + 4H^+ + 2e^- \longrightarrow Mn^{2+} + 2H_2O$	+1.28
$Cr_2O_7^{2-}/Cr^{3+}$	$Cr_2O_7^{2-} + 14H^+ + 6e^- \longrightarrow 2Cr^{3+} + 7H_2O$	+1.33
Cl_2/Cl^-	$Cl_2 + 2e^- \longrightarrow 2Cl^-$	+1.36
PbO_2/Pb^{2+}	$PbO_2 + 4H^+ + 2e^- \longrightarrow Pb^{2+} + 2H_2O$	+1.46
MnO_4^-/Mn^{2+}	$MnO_4^- + 8H^+ + 5e^- \longrightarrow Mn^{2+} + 4H_2O$	+1.51
$PbO_2/PbSO_4$	$PbO_2 + 4H^+ + SO_4^{2-} + 2e^- \longrightarrow PbSO_4 + 2H_2O$	+1.69
F_2/F^-	$F_2 + 2e^- \longrightarrow 2F^-$	+2.87

The standard reduction potential for the zinc half-cell is –0.76. The value is negative because the tendency for zinc ions to be reduced in this cell is less than that of hydrogen ions (H^+). Consequently, zinc metal is oxidized.

Many different half-cells can be paired with the hydrogen half-cell in a similar manner. The standard reduction potential for each half-cell can be obtained. With a standard copper half-cell, for example, the measured standard cell potential is +0.34 V. Copper is the cathode (the positive electrode) and Cu^{2+} is reduced to Cu when the cell operates. The hydrogen half-cell is the anode (the negative electrode) and H_2 is oxidized to H^+. You calculate the standard reduction potential for copper as follows.

$$\begin{aligned} E^0_{cell} &= E^0_{red} - E^0_{oxid} \\ &= E^0_{Cu^{2+}} - E^0_{H^+} \\ +0.34\text{ V} &= E^0_{Cu^{2+}} - 0.00 \\ E^0_{Cu^{2+}} &= +0.34\text{ V} \end{aligned}$$

These calculations show that the standard reduction potential of copper is +0.34 V. The value is positive because the tendency for copper ions to be reduced in this cell is greater than that of hydrogen ions.

Table 22.2 lists some standard reduction potentials at 25°C. These are arranged in increasing order. The half-reactions at the top of the table have the least tendency to occur as reductions. The half-reactions at the bottom of the table have the greatest tendency to occur as reductions.

Concept Practice

16. How does the order of the metals in Table 22.1 compare to the order in Table 22.2? Why?

22.8 Calculating Cell Potentials

Objective

Compute the standard cell potential using standard electrode potentials.

In order to function, a cell must be constructed of two half-cells. The half-cell reaction having the *more positive* reduction potential occurs as a reduction in the cell. With this in mind, it is possible to calculate cell potentials and write cell reactions for cells before they have been assembled. You can use standard reduction potentials for the various half-cells to predict in which of the half-cells reduction and oxidation will occur.

Integrating Metallurgy

Anodizing

Anodizing is an electrolytic process for applying a corrosion-resistant oxide coating to aluminum and certain other metals. When a current flows through an electrolytic cell containing an aluminum anode, a thin coat of aluminum oxide forms on the surface of the aluminum. Immersion of the object in pure boiling water permanently seals the anodized coating against corrosion. Anodization of aluminum alloys can produce metallic red, metallic blue, and a host of other metallic colors on the metal surface. Also, the high porosity of the oxide coating permits it to absorb dyes, pigments, and lubricants.

Example 1 Calculating the Standard Cell Potential

Calculate the standard cell potential of a cell composed of the half-cells Zn | Zn^{2+} and Cu | Cu^{2+}. Write the half-cell reactions for the anode and cathode processes and the cell reaction.

Solution

Table 22.2 gives the following standard reaction potentials.

$$Zn^{2+}(aq) + 2e^- \longrightarrow Zn(s) \qquad E^0_{Zn^{2+}} = -0.76\,V$$

$$Cu^{2+}(aq) + 2e^- \longrightarrow Cu(s) \qquad E^0_{Cu^{2+}} = +0.34\,V$$

Because Cu^{2+} has the more positive reduction potential, it occurs as a reduction in the cell. The zinc is oxidized.
The standard cell potential is the reduction potential of the reduction half-cell minus the reduction potential of the oxidation half-cell.

$$\begin{aligned} E^0_{cell} &= E^0_{red} - E^0_{oxid} \\ &= E^0_{Cu^{2+}} - E^0_{Zn^{2+}} \\ &= +0.34\,V - (-0.76\,V) \\ &= +1.10\,V \end{aligned}$$

In this cell, Zn is oxidized at the anode and Cu^{2+} is reduced at the cathode. The standard cell potential is 1.10 V. The half-reactions are as follows.

$$\text{Oxidation: } Zn(s) \longrightarrow Zn^{2+}(aq) + 2e^- \text{ (anode)}$$

$$\text{Reduction: } Cu^{2+}(aq) + 2e^- \longrightarrow Cu(s) \text{ (cathode)}$$

The cell reaction is the sum of the half-reactions.

$$Cu^{2+}(aq) + Zn(s) \longrightarrow Cu(s) + Zn^{2+}(aq)$$

Example 2 Finding the Cell Reaction and Standard Cell Potential

What are the cell reaction and the standard cell potential for a voltaic cell composed of the following half-cells?

$$Fe^{3+}(aq) + e^- \longrightarrow Fe^{2+}(aq) \qquad E^0_{Fe^{3+}} = +0.77\,V$$

$$Ni^{2+}(aq) + 2e^- \longrightarrow Ni(s) \qquad E^0_{Ni^{2+}} = -0.25\,V$$

Which half-cell is the cathode?

Solution

The reaction in the half-cell with the more positive reduction potential occurs as a reduction. In this cell Fe^{3+} is reduced to Fe^{2+}. Ni is oxidized to Ni^{2+}. Because reduction takes place in the Fe^{3+} half-cell, this half-cell contains the cathode. Because the oxidation takes place in the Ni half-cell, this half-cell contains the anode. The half-cell reactions are as follows.

$$\text{Oxidation:}\quad Ni(s) \longrightarrow Ni^{2+}(aq) + 2e^- \text{ (anode)}$$

$$\text{Reduction:}\quad Fe^{3+}(aq) + e^- \longrightarrow Fe^{2+}(aq) \text{ (cathode)}$$

Before you add the half-reactions, you must take care that the electrons cancel.

$$Ni(s) \longrightarrow Ni^{2+}(aq) + 2e^-$$

$$2[Fe^{3+}(aq) + e^- \longrightarrow Fe^{2+}(aq)]$$

$$\overline{Ni(s) + 2Fe^{3+}(aq) \longrightarrow Ni^{2+}(aq) + 2Fe^{2+}(aq)}$$

You can now calculate the standard cell potential.

$$\begin{aligned} E^0_{cell} &= E^0_{red} - E^0_{oxid} \\ &= E^0_{Fe^{3+}} - E^0_{Ni^{2+}} \\ &= +0.77\text{ V} - (-0.25) \\ &= +1.02\text{ V} \end{aligned}$$

Note that the E^0 of a half-cell is not multiplied by any number even if one of the equations was multiplied by a coefficient to make the electrons cancel.

Practice Problems

17. A voltaic cell is constructed using electrodes with the following half-reactions.

$$Cu^{2+}(aq) + 2e^- \longrightarrow Cu(s) \qquad E^0_{Cu^{2+}} = +0.34\text{ V}$$

$$Al^{3+}(aq) + 3e^- \longrightarrow Al(s) \qquad E^0_{Al^{3+}} = -1.66\text{ V}$$

Write the cell reaction. Calculate the standard cell potential.

18. A voltaic cell is constructed using electrodes with the following half-reactions.

$$Ag^{+}(aq) + e^- \longrightarrow Ag(s) \qquad E^0_{Ag^{+}} = +0.80\text{ V}$$

$$Cu^{2+}(aq) + 2e^- \longrightarrow Cu(s) \qquad E^0_{Cu^{2+}} = +0.34\text{ V}$$

Determine the cell reaction and the standard cell potential.

The use of standard reduction potentials makes it possible to predict whether or not a redox reaction will take place. The reactants do not need to be paired in a voltaic cell. The half-reaction with the more positive reduction potential always undergoes reduction. Therefore, the other half-reaction has to undergo oxidation.

If the cell potential for the redox reaction, as written, is positive, then the reaction is spontaneous. If the cell potential is negative, then the reaction is nonspontaneous. It will be spontaneous in the reverse direction and the cell potential will be equally positive.

Example 3 Determining Reaction Spontaneity

Problem-Solving Tip

Rephrase the question, "Is the standard cell potential a positive value?"

Is the following redox reaction spontaneous as written?

$$Ni(s) + Fe^{2+}(aq) \longrightarrow Ni^{2+}(aq) + Fe(s)$$

Solution

The half-reactions are as follows.

$$\text{Oxidation: } Ni(s) \longrightarrow Ni^{2+}(aq) + 2e^-$$

$$\text{Reduction: } Fe^{2+}(aq) + 2e^- \longrightarrow Fe(s)$$

The standard reduction potentials are found in Table 22.2.

$$Ni^{2+}(aq) + 2e^- \longrightarrow Ni(s) \qquad E^0_{Ni^{2+}} = -0.25\text{ V}$$

$$Fe^{2+}(aq) + 2e^- \longrightarrow Fe(s) \qquad E^0_{Fe^{2+}} = -0.44\text{ V}$$

The standard cell potential is the difference of the potentials of the iron half-cell and nickel half-cell.

$$\begin{aligned} E^0_{cell} &= E^0_{red} - E^0_{oxid} \\ &= E^0_{Fe^{2+}} - E^0_{Ni^{2+}} \\ &= -0.44\text{ V} - (-0.25\text{ V}) \\ &= -0.19\text{ V} \end{aligned}$$

Since the standard cell potential is a negative number, the redox equation is nonspontaneous as written. Energy would have to be applied to make this reaction occur.

Practice Problems

19. Calculate the cell potential for this spontaneous redox reaction.

$$Co^{2+}(aq) + Fe(s) \longrightarrow Fe^{2+}(aq) + Co(s)$$

20. Determine which of these redox reactions will occur spontaneously and calculate the standard cell potential in each case.

a. $Cu(s) + 2H^+(aq) \longrightarrow Cu^{2+}(aq) + H_2(g)$

b. $2Ag(s) + Fe^{2+}(aq) \longrightarrow 2Ag^+(aq) + Fe(s)$

c. $3Zn^{2+}(aq) + 2Cr(s) \longrightarrow 3Zn(s) + 2Cr^{3+}(aq)$

22.9 Electrolytic Cells

Objective

Distinguish between electrolytic and voltaic cells and list some applications of each.

The section on voltaic cells described how a spontaneous chemical reaction can be used to generate a flow of electrons (an electric current). This section will show how an electric current can be used to make a nonspontaneous redox reaction go. *The process in which electrical energy is used to bring about a chemical change is called* **electrolysis**. The apparatus in which electrolysis is carried out is an electrolytic cell.

Electrolytic cells *are electrochemical cells used to cause a chemical change through the application of electrical energy.* An electrolytic cell is any cell that uses electrical energy (DC current) to make a nonspontaneous redox reaction go to products.

In both voltaic and electrolytic cells, electrons flow from the anode to the cathode in the external circuit. In both types of cells, the electrode at which the reduction reaction occurs is the cathode. The electrode at which oxidation occurs is the anode. In an electrolytic cell, however, the flow of electrons is being "pushed" by an outside source such as a battery. The cathode is called the negative

Figure 22.11 Electrolytic cells for chlorine-caustic soda production.

Figure 22.12 Comparison of **(a)** a voltaic cell and **(b)** an electrolytic cell. The name of the electrode is determined by the process that occurs there, and not by the electrode's charge. The redox process in the voltaic cell is spontaneous. The redox process in the electrolytic cell is nonspontaneous.

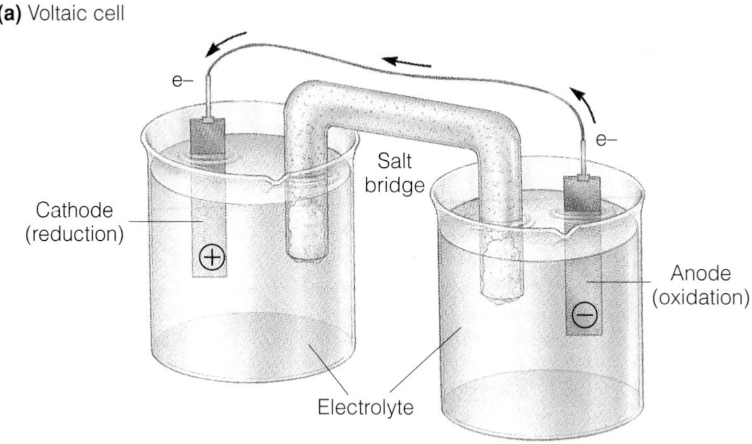

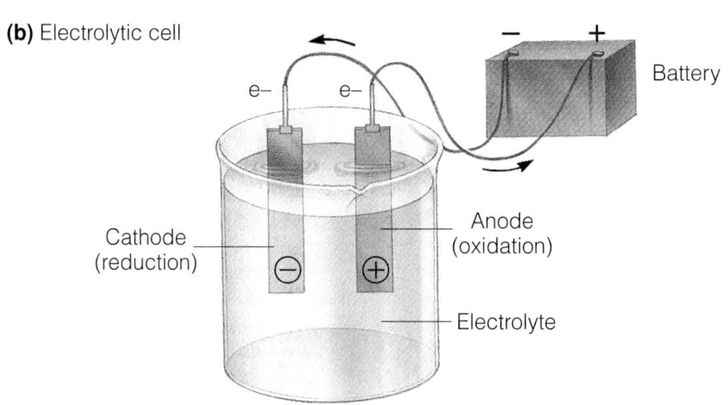

electrode of the electrolytic cell. This is because it is connected to the negative electrode of the battery, the anode. (Remember that in a voltaic cell, the anode is the *negative* electrode and the cathode is the *positive* electrode.) The anode in the electrolytic cell is called the positive electrode. This is because it is connected to the positive electrode of the battery (the battery's cathode). It is important to remember these conventions.

Electrolysis of Water When a current is applied via two electrodes in pure water, nothing happens. There is no current flow and no electrolysis. When an electrolyte is added, such as H_2SO_4 or KNO_3 in low concentration, the solution conducts and electrolysis takes place as shown in Figure 22.13. The products of the electrolysis of water are hydrogen and oxygen. Water is reduced to hydrogen at the cathode.

$$2H_2O(l) + 2e^- \longrightarrow H_2(g) + 2OH^-(aq)$$

Water is oxidized at the anode.

$$2H_2O(l) \longrightarrow O_2(g) + 4H^+(aq) + 4e^-$$

The region around the cathode turns basic due to an increase in OH^- ions. The region around the anode turns acidic due to an increase in H^+ ions. The overall cell reaction is obtained by adding the half-reactions.

$$2[2H_2O(l) + 2e^- \longrightarrow H_2(g) + 2OH^-(aq)]$$
$$2H_2O(l) \longrightarrow O_2(g) + 4H^+(aq) + 4e^-$$
$$\overline{6H_2O(l) \longrightarrow 2H_2(g) + O_2(g) + 4H^+(aq) + 4OH^-(aq)}$$

Some of the ions produced re-form into reactants.

$$4H^+(aq) + 4OH^-(aq) \longrightarrow 4H_2O(l)$$

These are not included in the net reaction.

$$2H_2O(l) \xrightarrow{\text{electrolysis}} 2H_2(g) + O_2(g)$$

Figure 22.13 When an electric current is passed through water, the water decomposes into oxygen and hydrogen.

In some cases, the electrolyte is more easily oxidized or reduced than water. Then the products of electrolysis are substances other than hydrogen and oxygen. An example is the electrolysis of brine.

Electrolysis of Brine Chlorine gas, hydrogen gas, and sodium hydroxide are three important industrial chemicals. They are produced simultaneously by electrolysis of a concentrated aqueous sodium chloride solution (brine). The electrolytic cell for this process is shown in Figure 22.14. During electrolysis, chloride ions are oxidized to produce chlorine gas at the anode. Water is reduced to produce hydrogen gas at the cathode. Sodium ions are not reduced to sodium metal in the process because water molecules

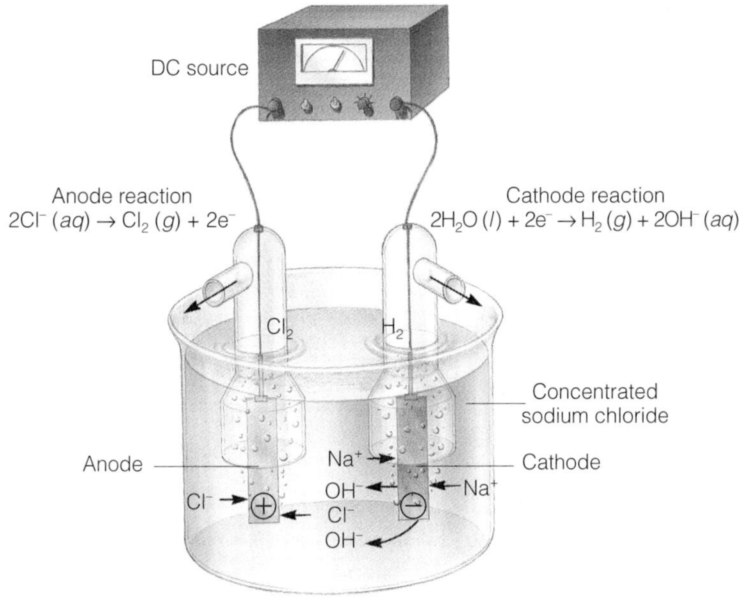

Figure 22.14 The electrolysis of a concentrated solution of sodium chloride produces which two gases?

are more easily reduced than sodium ions. The reduction of water produces hydroxide ions as well as hydrogen gas. Thus the electrolyte in solution becomes sodium hydroxide.

$$\text{Oxidation (anode):}\quad 2Cl^-(aq) \longrightarrow Cl_2(g) + 2e^-$$

$$\text{Reduction (cathode):}\quad 2H_2O(l) + 2e^- \longrightarrow H_2(g) + 2OH^-(aq)$$

The overall ionic equation is the sum of the two half-reactions.

$$2Cl^-(aq) + 2H_2O(l) \longrightarrow Cl_2(g) + H_2(g) + 2OH^-(aq)$$

The spectator ion, Na^+, can be included in the equation to show the formation of sodium hydroxide.

$$2NaCl(aq) + 2H_2O(l) \longrightarrow Cl_2(g) + H_2(g) + 2NaOH(aq)$$

Chloride ions are eliminated from solution and hydroxide ions are formed. The electrolyte gradually changes from sodium chloride to sodium hydroxide. When the sodium hydroxide solution is about 10%, it is removed from the cell and processed further.

Electrolysis of Molten Sodium Chloride Sodium and chlorine are both of commercial importance. Sodium is used in sodium vapor lamps and as the coolant in some nuclear power reactors. Chlorine, a toxic greenish-yellow gas, is used to sterilize drinking water and is important in the manufacture of polyvinyl chloride and various pesticides. These two elements are produced when molten

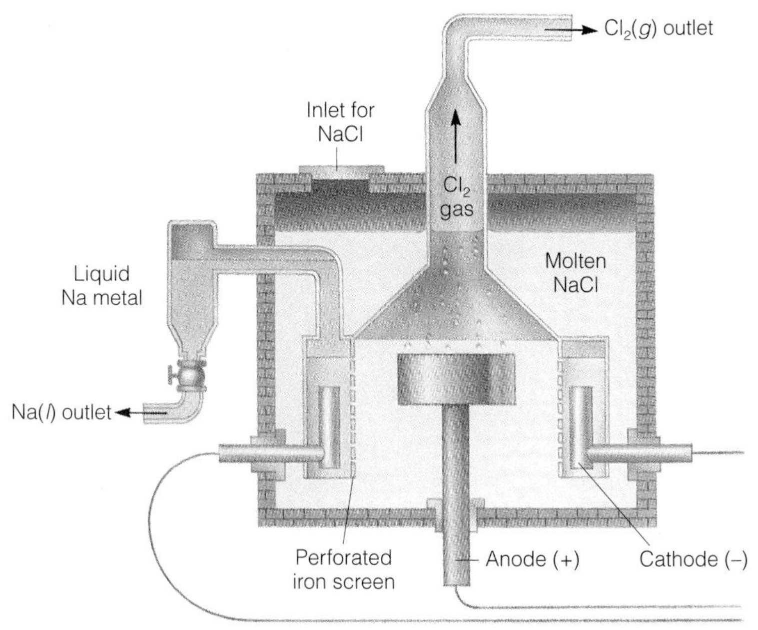

Figure 22.15 The Downs cell is used for the electrolysis of molten NaCl. The circular cathode is separated from the anode by a perforated iron screen. The cell operates at 600°C to maintain the salt in a molten state. The liquid metal, having a low density, floats to the top in the molten NaCl, where it is drawn off. The chlorine gas bubbles up and out of the molten NaCl and is collected.

sodium chloride is electrolyzed. Chlorine gas comes off at the anode and molten sodium collects at the cathode. The electrolytic cell in which the process is carried out commercially is called the Downs cell. Its design allows fresh sodium chloride to be added as required. The design also keeps the products apart so that they will not react to re-form sodium chloride. The half-reactions and overall cell reaction are as follows.

Oxidation (anode): $2Cl^-(l) \longrightarrow Cl_2(g) + 2e^-$

Reduction (cathode): $2Na^+(l) + 2e^- \longrightarrow 2Na(l)$

Cell reaction: $2NaCl(l) \longrightarrow 2Na(l) + Cl_2(g)$

Electroplating and Related Processes Electroplating is the deposition of a thin layer of a metal on an object in an electrolytic cell. It has many important applications. An object may be electroplated to protect the surface of the base metal from corrosion or to make it more attractive. The layer of the deposited metal is very thin, usually from 5×10^{-5} cm to 1×10^{-3} cm thick. Metals commonly used for electroplating include gold, silver, copper, nickel, and chromium. For example, an object that is to be silver-plated is made the cathode in a cell, while metallic silver is made the anode. A silver cyanide solution is the electrolyte. When a DC current passes through the electrolyte, silver ions move to the object to be plated. The ions pick up electrons and are deposited as silver atoms.

$$\text{Cathode reaction: } Ag^+(aq) + e^- \xrightarrow{\text{electrolysis}} Ag(s)$$

The net result is that silver is transferred from the silver electrode to the object being plated. Controlling this reaction is a fine art. Many factors contribute to the quality of the metal coating that is formed. In the plating solution, the concentration of the cations to be reduced is carefully controlled. The solution must contain compounds to control the acidity, and to increase the conductivity. Some solutions contain compounds that form complex ions with the cation to be reduced. Other compounds make the metal coating brighter or smoother. In many plating cells, the anode must be shaped like the object at the cathode in order to plate all parts of the cathode evenly.

Several techniques involve the deposition of metal at the cathode of a cell. In *electroforming,* an object is reproduced by making a metal "mold" of it at the cathode. A phonograph record, for example, can be coated with metal so that it will conduct electricity. It is then electroplated to get a thick coating. This coating can be stripped off and used as a mold to produce copies of the record.

Chemistry in Careers

Electroplating Technician

Many high-technology applications require electroplating thin layers of gold, silver, copper, nickel, or chromium onto a base metal. Electroplating technicians play a key role in these manufacturing applications. Although electroplating generally follows documented procedures, an electroplating technician must understand how to manipulate many variables in order to achieve consistently good results. Small differences in variables such as electric current or chemical purity can cause big differences in the quality of the plating. A solid understanding of the chemistry involved allows the technician to adjust these variables properly.

Impure metals can be purified in electrolytic cells. In *electrowinning*, the cations of molten salts or aqueous solutions are reduced at the cathode to give very pure metals. Electrowinning from molten salt is the only method for obtaining pure sodium and other very reactive metals. In *electrorefining*, a piece of impure metal is made the anode of the cell. It is oxidized to the cation and then reduced to the pure metal at the cathode. This technique is used to obtain ultrapure silver, lead, and copper.

Other electrolytic processes are centered on the anode rather than the cathode. In *electropolishing*, an object at the anode is dissolved selectively to give it a high polish. In *electromachining*, a piece of metal at the anode dissolves to give an exact copy of the object that is the cathode.

Concept Practice

21. How does the purpose of an electrolytic cell differ from that of a voltaic cell?

22. What are the products of the electrolysis of the following?
a. brine **b.** molten sodium chloride **c.** water

Activity 22
A Lemon Battery

Purpose

To make a functioning model of a simple voltaic cell.

Materials

lemon
copper strip (1 cm x 3 cm)
zinc strip (1 cm x 3 cm)
fine sandpaper
voltmeter (optional)

Procedure

1. Polish the copper and zinc strips with sandpaper.

2. Push the zinc strip into the lemon. Leave about 1.5 cm of the zinc strip sticking out.

3. Push the copper strip into the lemon about 1 cm away from the zinc strip. Leave about 1.5 cm of the copper strip sticking out.

4. Touch both metal strips at the same time with your tongue and observe what happens.

5. If you have a voltmeter, measure the voltage of your lemon battery.

Analysis and Conclusions

1. Describe the sensation you get on your tongue.

2. Which is the more active metal in the "lemon" battery? Explain.

3. Which metal is the anode; which metal is the cathode?

4. Write the equation for the anode and cathode reactions.

5. What would you expect to happen if in place of the lemon you were to use an orange?

6. If you connected 12 lemon batteries together in series you would get about 12 V. Could you use this assembly to start your car? Explain your answer.

Chapter 22 Review
Electrochemistry

Key Terms

anode *22.2*
battery *22.4*
cathode *22.2*
cell potential *22.6*
dry cell *22.3*
electrical potential *22.6*
electrochemical cell *22.1*
electrochemical process *22.1*
electrode *22.2*
electrolysis *22.9*
electrolytic cell *22.9*
fuel cell *22.5*
half-cell *22.2*
reduction potential *22.6*
salt bridge *22.2*
standard cell potential *22.6*
standard hydrogen electrode *22.6*
voltaic cell *22.2*

Chapter Summary

Spontaneous redox equations can be used to generate electrical energy in voltaic cells. Conversely, electrical energy can be used to make nonspontaneous reactions go in electrolytic cells. In either type of electrochemical cell, the electrode at which oxidation occurs is the anode and the electrode at which reduction occurs is the cathode.

In a voltaic cell, the half-reactions take place in half-cells. The half-cells are separated by a porous plate or salt bridge. This barrier prevents the contents of the two half-cells from mixing but permits the passage of ions between the half-cells. Reduction occurs at the cathode (the positively charged electrode) and oxidation occurs at the anode (the negatively charged electrode). Electrons are transferred in the external circuit from the anode to the cathode. The half-cell with the higher reduction potential undergoes reduction; the other half-cell undergoes oxidation. The cell potential is the difference between the reduction potentials of the half-cells.

The reduction potential of an isolated half-cell cannot be measured. Values can be assigned, however, by comparing them to a reference electrode. The reference used is the standard hydrogen electrode, which is given a reduction potential of 0.00 volts. Half-cells more easily reduced than the reference electrode have positive reduction potentials. Half-cells less easily reduced have negative reduction potentials.

Using your knowledge of electrochemistry, you can design cells and batteries to provide electrical energy for specific purposes. The dry cell, the battery commonly used in flashlights, is not rechargeable. The lead storage battery, as used in automobiles, is rechargeable. Fuel cells do not have to be recharged. The fuels that they consume are fed into the cell continuously.

In electrolysis, a flow of electrons causes reduction at the cathode (the negatively charged electrode) and oxidation at the anode (the positively charged electrode). In an electrolytic cell electrical energy is used to bring about desirable redox reactions. Electrolytic cells are used in electroplating, in refining metals, and in the production of such important chemicals as sodium hydroxide, aluminum and sodium metals, and chlorine gas.

Practice Questions and Problems

23. Predict the result when a strip of copper is dipped into a solution of iron(II) sulfate. *22.1*

24. For each of the pairs of metals listed below, decide which metal is the more readily oxidized. *22.1*

a. Hg and Cu **c.** Ni and Mg **e.** Pb and Zn
b. Ca and Al **d.** Sn and Ag **f.** Cu and Al

25. Explain the function of the salt bridge in a voltaic cell. *22.2*

26. What material is (a) the anode and (b) the cathode made of in a flashlight battery? *22.3*

27. Describe the composition of the anode, cathode, and electrolyte in a fully charged lead storage battery. *22.4*

28. List the advantages of a fuel cell over a lead storage battery. *22.5*

29. What is the purpose of using the standard hydrogen electrode as a reference electrode? *22.6*

30. What is the electrical potential of a cell? *22.6*

31. The standard reduction potential for the cadmium half-cell is –0.40 V. What does this mean? *22.7*

32. Explain how you would determine the standard reduction potential for the aluminum half-cell. *22.7*

33. Use the information in Table 22.2 to calculate standard cell potentials for these voltaic cells. *22.8*

    a. $Ni \mid Ni^{2+} \parallel Cl_2 \mid Cl^-$ **b.** $Sn \mid Sn^{2+} \parallel Ag^+ \mid Ag$

34. What processes occur at the anode and cathode in an electrolytic cell? *22.9*

35. Why is a *direct current* and not an *alternating current* used in electroplating metals? *22.9*

36. Describe briefly how you would electroplate a teaspoon with silver. *22.9*

Mastery Questions and Problems

37. Construct a concept map using the key terms and using *electrochemical cell* as the central concept.

38. Distinguish between a voltaic cell and an electrolytic cell.

39. Why is it not possible to measure the potential of an isolated half-cell?

40. Describe the composition of the anode, cathode, and electrolyte of a fully discharged lead storage battery.

41. Predict what will happen, if anything, when an iron nail is dipped into a solution of copper sulfate. Write the oxidation and reduction half-reactions for this process and the balanced equation for the overall reaction.

42. Calculate E^0_{cell} and write the overall cell reaction for these cells:

    a. $Sn \mid Sn^{2+} \parallel Pb^{2+} \mid Pb$

    b. $H_2 \mid H^+ \parallel Br_2 \mid Br^-$

43. Even though the cost of solar energy currently is greater than that of many other forms of energy, other benefits are derived by using solar energy. Explain.

44. What property of lead(II) sulfate and lead(IV) oxide makes it unnecessary to have salt bridges in a lead storage battery?

45. Complete this table of data for the electrolysis of water.

H_2O used	H_2 formed	O_2 formed
a. 2.0 mol	____ mol	____ mol
b.____ mol	____ g	16.0 g
c.____ mL	10.0 g	____ g
d. 44.4 g	____ g	____ g
e.____ g	8.8 L(STP)	____ L (STP)
f. 66.0 mL	____ g	____ L (STP)

46. What type of corrosion protection would be best for an underground fuel storage tank?

Critical Thinking Questions

47. Choose the term that best completes the second relationship.

    a. battery:cells herd: ____
    (1) birds (3) trees
    (2) sheep (4) fuel cells

    b. river:water electrode: ____
    (1) electrons (3) salt bridge
    (2) anode (4) ions

    c. anode:electrons fire hydrant: ____
    (1) fire (3) dogs
    (2) firefighter (4) water

48. For any voltaic cell, chemists consider the electrode that produces electrons to be negative, the anode. Most dictionaries define the anode as the positively charged electrode. How can you account for this disagreement?

Cumulative Review

49. A sample of oxygen gas has a volume of 500 mL at 30°C. What is the new volume of the gas if the temperature is raised to 60°C while the pressure is kept constant?

50. Balance these equations.

a. $H_2S(g) + HNO_3(aq) \longrightarrow S(s) + NO(g) + H_2O(l)$

b. $AgNO_3(aq) + Pb(s) \longrightarrow Pb(NO_3)_2(aq) + Ag(s)$

c. $Cl_2(g) + NaOH(aq) \longrightarrow NaCl(aq) + NaClO_3(aq) + H_2O(l)$

d. $CuO(s) + NH_3(aq) \longrightarrow N_2(g) + Cu(s) + H_2O(l)$

e. $Mg(OH)_2(s) + HBr(aq) \longrightarrow MgBr_2(aq) + H_2O(l)$

f. $Al_2O_3(s) + H_2SO_4(aq) \longrightarrow Al_2(SO_4)_3(aq) + H_2O(l)$

51. Concentrated nitric acid is 16*M*. How would you prepare 500 mL of 1.0*M* HNO_3?

52. What is the oxidation number of the italicized element in each of these formulas?

a. $K_2\mathit{Cr}_2O_7$ **c.** $\mathit{Mn}O_4^-$

b. $K\mathit{I}O_3$ **d.** $\mathit{Fe}Cl_3$

Challenge Questions and Problems

53. This spontaneous redox reaction occurs in the voltaic cell illustrated below.

$$Ni^{2+}(aq) + Fe(s) \longrightarrow Ni(s) + Fe^{2+}(aq)$$

a. Identify the anode and the cathode.

b. Assign charges to the electrodes.

c. Write the half-reactions.

d. Calculate the standard cell potential when the half-cells are at standard conditions.

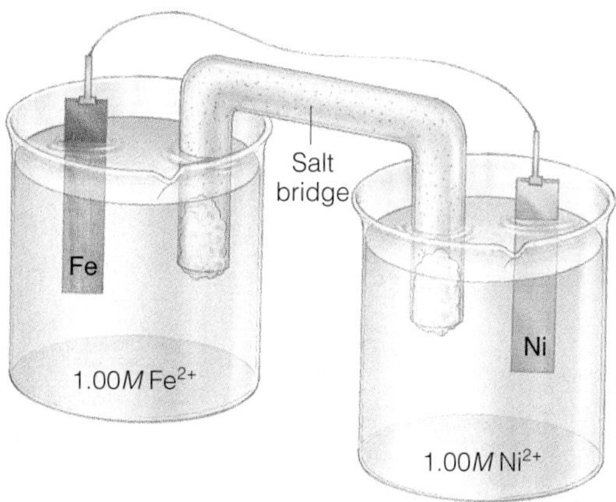

54. Write the overall cell reactions and calculate E^0_{cell} for voltaic cells composed of the following sets of half-reactions.

a. $AgCl(s) + e^- \rightleftharpoons Ag(s) + Cl^-(aq)$

$Ni^{2+}(aq) + 2e^- \rightleftharpoons Ni(s)$

b. $Al^{3+}(aq) + 3e^- \rightleftharpoons Al(s)$

$Cl_2(g) + 2e^- \rightleftharpoons 2Cl^-(aq)$

55. Impure copper is purified in an electrolytic cell. Design an electrolytic cell that will allow you to carry out this process. Give the oxidation and reduction half-reactions and a balanced equation for the overall reaction.

Connections Questions

56. How must a nonconducting material be prepared before it can be plated with metal?

57. What makes the process of anodizing unique among all electroplating techniques?

58. How has the shift from heavy industry to the electronics era affected the work of an electroplating technician?

Write About Chemistry

59. Interview a local recycler of automobile lead acid batteries and write a report summarizing what you learned.

60. Imagine that you are an outer shell electron in an atom of a metal anode of a voltaic cell. Write a short description of the cell, tracing your movement and indicating where oxidation and reduction are taking place.

Readings and References

Wilt, Rachel. "Leaf Jewelry." *ChemMatters* (December 1987), pp. 14–15.

23 Metals and Nonmetals

Goals

- Describe the properties and uses of the representative metals and nonmetals.
- Explain methods for obtaining specific metals and nonmetals from their compounds and ores.
- Explain the unique nature of hydrogen and the noble gases.
- Describe the properties of specific transition metals.

The United States produces about 8.2×10^{10} kg of raw steel in a given year. In general, steels are alloys containing metals, mostly iron, and nonmetals, always including carbon.

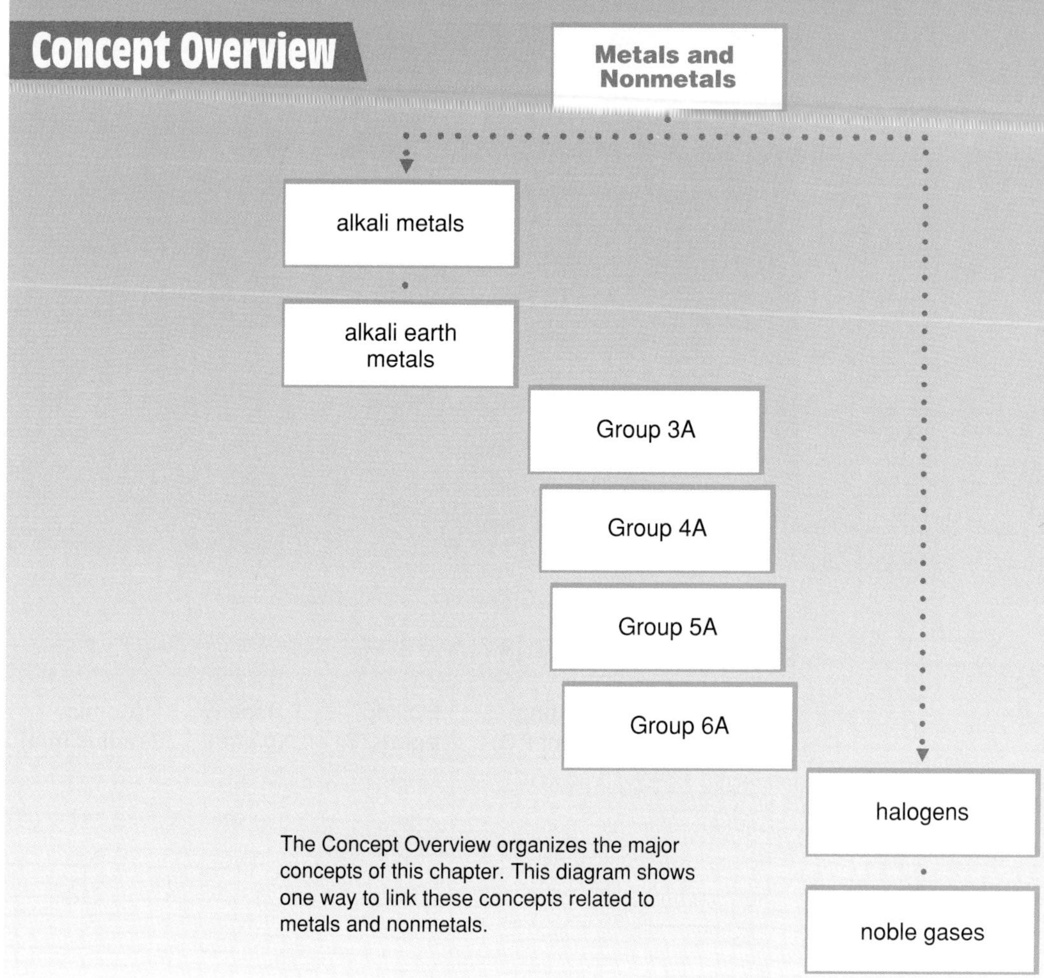

The Concept Overview organizes the major concepts of this chapter. This diagram shows one way to link these concepts related to metals and nonmetals.

Only about one-third of the more than one hundred known elements are nonmetals. These elements exhibit a wide range of properties. They have common physical and chemical characteristics, however, that distinguish them from metals. The nonmetallic elements are found in the upper right corner of the periodic table. This chapter describes some of the distinctive properties of nonmetals as well as metals and their practical applications.

23.1 The Alkali Metals

Objective

Describe the sources, properties, and uses of the Group 1A alkali metals.

The alkali metals are the Group 1A elements. Rich deposits of alkali metal salts are found all over the world. The Bonneville Salt Flats in Utah and deposits at Searles Lake, California, contain huge quantities of sodium chloride and other alkali salts. The evaporation of ancient seas left large deposits that are now underground near the

Figure 23.1 Large amounts of sodium chloride are produced by the evaporation of seawater.

Table 23.1 Some Physical Properties of the Alkali Metals

Element	Melting point (°C)	Boiling point (°C)	Density (g/cm^3)	Atomic radius (nm)
Lithium	179	1336	0.53	0.123
Sodium	98	883	0.97	0.157
Potassium	64	758	0.86	0.203
Rubidium	39	700	1.53	0.216
Cesium	28	670	1.90	0.235

Roots of Words

al aqali: (Arabic) the ashes
alkali a chemical base

Wood ashes, which are rich in alkali metal oxides, produce basic solutions when steeped in water.

Gulf Coast shores of Texas and Louisiana. Alkali metal salts are very soluble in water. Rainwater leaches them out of the soil, and rivers carry them to the sea. Seawater is about 3%, by mass, alkali metal salts. Figure 23.1 shows that seawater is a source of table salt.

The Group 1A elements are the most reactive metals known. Alkali metals are not found free in nature but are combined with nonmetals as alkali salts. Within the group, cesium and rubidium are the most reactive. Each of the alkali metals reacts violently with cold water, producing hydrogen gas and a solution of the metal hydroxide (an alkali or base). Sodium, for example, reacts with cold water, forming sodium hydroxide and releasing hydrogen gas.

$$2Na(s) + 2H_2O(l) \longrightarrow 2NaOH(aq) + H_2(g)$$

The reaction of alkali metals with water is so rapid and exothermic that the hydrogen often burns as it is produced. They will also react vigorously with the moisture in your skin and should never be handled with bare hands. The alkali metals are usually stored under oil or kerosene to keep the metal from reacting with oxygen and moisture in the air.

The alkali metals have low densities, low melting points, and good electrical conductivity. Some of the physical properties of the alkali metals are listed in Table 23.1. These metals have the consistency of stiff modeling clay and are soft enough to be cut with a knife, as in Figure 23.2. The freshly cut surface is shiny, with the typical silvery luster of a metal. The surface quickly dulls on exposure to air due to a rapid reaction with oxygen and moisture.

Figure 23.2 Freshly cut sodium is shiny, but it quickly reacts with oxygen in the air to become dull.

Sodium is the only alkali metal manufactured on a large scale. To produce the free metal, sodium ions must be reduced. Metallic sodium is usually produced by the electrolysis of molten sodium chloride. Chlorine gas is a valuable by-product of this process.

Sodium is used in sodium vapor lamps and in the production of many chemicals. Liquid sodium is an excellent conductor of heat. It is often used in nuclear reactors to remove heat from the reactor core.

Concept Practice

1. Why are alkali metals stored under kerosene or mineral oil? Why must they be kept dry?

2. Would you expect to find pure samples of alkali metals in the earth's crust? Explain.

23.2 The Alkaline Earth Metals

Objective

Describe the sources, properties, and uses of the alkaline earth metals in Group 2A.

The alkaline earth metals are the elements in Group 2A. Alkaline earth metal salts are less soluble in water than the corresponding alkali metal salts. Nevertheless, the sea is a rich source of the ions of two of the alkaline earth metals—magnesium and calcium ions. Calcium ions in seawater are used by shellfish in building their calcium carbonate shells.

Some of the alkaline earth carbonates and sulfates are insoluble enough to resist weathering and the leaching action of rainwater. The most common mineral form of calcium carbonate is limestone. It is often made up of compressed layers of seashells. The White Cliffs of Dover on the southern coast of England are another form of calcium carbonate. Shells of microscopic marine animals have been pressed into a natural chalk.

The alkaline earth metals react with water to produce alkaline solutions. They are extracted from the mineral ores that since early times have been called "earths." While they are not found

Figure 23.3 Calcium carbonate occurs naturally in several forms.

Figure 23.4 Alkaline earth metals are less reactive than the alkali metals. Here, calcium reacts with water. What are the products of the reaction?

Table 23.2 Some Physical Properties of the Alkaline Earth Metals

Element	Melting point (°C)	Boiling point (°C)	Density (g/cm^3)	Atomic radius (nm)
Beryllium	1280	1500	1.86	0.089
Magnesium	651	1107	1.75	0.136
Calcium	851	1487	1.55	0.174
Strontium	800	1366	2.60	0.191
Barium	850	1537	3.59	0.198

uncombined in nature, the alkaline earth metals are less chemically reactive than the Group 1A metals. They need not be stored under oil. Barium is the most reactive element in the group. Look at Figure 23.4. Calcium, strontium, and barium react with cold water to produce hydrogen, but more slowly than Group 1A metals do. Beryllium and magnesium react only with hot water or steam.

The alkaline earth metals are harder than the alkali metals. They have a gray-white luster but tarnish quickly in air to form a tough, thin oxide coating. The coating protects the metal, particularly beryllium and magnesium, from further oxidation. This allows alloys of these metals to be used as low-density structural materials. Some physical properties of the alkaline earth metals are listed in Table 23.2.

Calcium and magnesium are the most important alkaline earth metals. Calcium is produced by the electrolysis of molten calcium chloride in a reaction similar to that used to produce sodium. By contrast, magnesium is prepared from seawater as illustrated in the flowchart in Figure 23.5. Magnesium is an important structural material and is the chief component in a number of high-tensile-strength, low-density alloys. These properties make these alloys valuable in aircraft and spacecraft construction. Magnesium is present in asbestos, which was used as an insulating material. Notice the fibers of asbestos in Figure 23.6. Asbestos use has been largely discontinued because its fibers are known to cause lung cancer.

Calcium oxide, commonly called **lime**, *or quicklime, is an important industrial chemical.* Calcium oxide is made by the high-temperature decomposition of limestone in a lime kiln.

$$\underset{\text{Limestone}}{CaCO_3(s)} \xrightarrow{900°C} \underset{\text{Lime}}{CaO(s)} + CO_2(g)$$

The reaction of quicklime with water is called slaking. The process is exothermic and the product is **slaked lime**, *calcium hydroxide.*

$$\underset{\text{Lime}}{CaO(s)} + H_2O(l) \longrightarrow \underset{\text{Slaked lime}}{Ca(OH)_2(aq)} + \text{heat}$$

Slaked lime is used to make plaster and mortar and to neutralize acid soils.

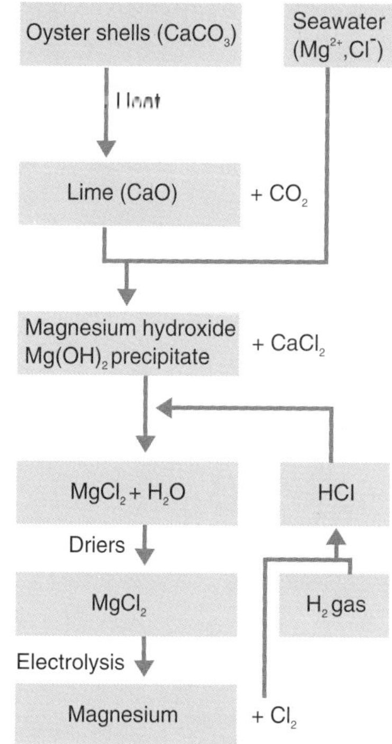

Figure 23.5 Seawater is the main source of magnesium compounds. Most commercial magnesium is prepared electrolytically from magnesium chloride. Each ton of seawater yields about 3 kg of magnesium.

Concept Practice

3. How does the reactivity of the Group 2A metals compare to that of the Group 1A metals?

4. Which alkaline earth metals react with cold water and which do not? Write a typical equation that shows such a reaction.

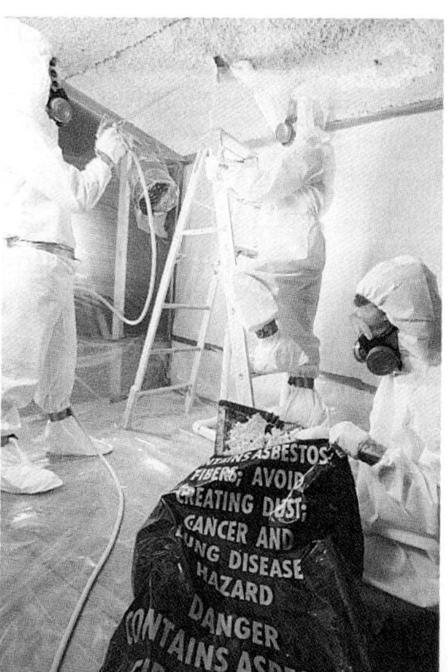

Figure 23.6 Magnesium is present in asbestos, which is a fibrous form of the mineral serpentine. Asbestos was used as an insulation material until it was discovered that inhalation of its fibers causes lung cancer.

Objective

Describe the sources, properties, and uses of aluminum and the other Group 3A elements.

23.3 Aluminum and the Group 3A Elements

Boron is the first element in Group 3A. Boron occurs naturally in borate minerals. Borate minerals are rare. However, large deposits of the mineral borax are found in the arid regions of the United States, particularly the Mohave Desert and Death Valley, California. Borax was once hauled from Death Valley by twenty-mule teams.

Purified borax or sodium tetraborate decahydrate ($Na_2B_4O_7 \cdot 10H_2O$) is a soft, colorless crystalline substance. Borax has many uses: for pottery glazes in the ceramics industry; as a component of glass; as a flux in soldering and welding; and as a water softener, disinfectant, and fertilizer additive.

Pure boron is a black, lustrous nonmetal. Boron is also a semiconductor. Boron can be prepared by the reaction of its oxide with magnesium metal.

$$B_2O_3(s) + 3Mg(s) \longrightarrow 2B(s) + 3MgO(s)$$

Figure 23.7 Rubies are aluminum oxide in which a few of the aluminum ions are replaced by chromium ions.

The elements that follow boron in Group 3A are the metals aluminum, gallium, indium, and thallium.

Aluminum is the most abundant metal in the earth's crust. Aluminum does not exist in the uncombined state in nature but is a major component of many rocks and minerals. Aluminum is commonly found as the very hard corundum (impure aluminum oxide). Cut forms of corundum are the commonly known gemstones ruby and sapphire. Corundum, in its less desirable form, is used as the abrasive in emery powder and grinding wheels. As a pure metal, aluminum has strength and ductility as well as a low density, good electrical conductivity, and corrosion resistance. These properties make it a valuable structural and manufacturing metal. When aluminum is exposed to air, a tough film of oxide quickly forms, protecting it from further corrosion by oxygen and water.

Until the end of the last century, aluminum sold for the same price as silver. At that time only the rich could afford aluminum items. Aluminum was expensive because there was no practical way to produce it. The first commercial process for the production of aluminum was invented almost simultaneously by Paul Heroult, a Frenchman, and Charles Hall, an American. Hall's chemistry professor challenged his class to find a cheap way to produce aluminum. Hall set up a laboratory in a woodshed. He found that cryolite, Na_3AlF_6, would dissolve aluminum oxide. A low-melting solution formed, from which aluminum could be obtained by electrolysis. This process is essentially the method used for aluminum production today. Aluminum is used widely in lightweight structural materials for aircraft production and in the manufacture of cookware.

Figure 23.8 Aluminum is particularly useful in the construction of aircraft because it is lightweight and very strong. It also reacts with oxygen to form a protective coating of aluminum oxide that will not react with water.

Gallium, indium, and thallium are quite rare. One interesting use of gallium is in thermometers because of its extraordinarily wide liquid temperature range. Gallium has a melting point of 30°C and a boiling point of 1980°C. Gallium is a semiconductor and is used in the manufacture of some semiconductor components.

Concept Practice

5. Describe the physical properties of aluminum that make it a commercially valuable metal.

23.4 Carbon and the Group 4A Elements

Objective

Describe the sources, properties, and uses of carbon and the other elements in Group 4A.

Two of the most important elements on earth are in Group 4A. Carbon is the fundamental element in the molecules of all living things, while silicon is the basic element of the geologic world.

Diamond and graphite are the two familiar allotropes of carbon. Diamond, the hardest material known, behaves like a typical nonmetal. It is transparent and an insulator. Graphite, however, is soft, black, and opaque and is a good conductor of electricity. Graphite is used for electrodes and is the "lead" in pencils. In the late 1980s a third allotrope of carbon, buckminsterfullerene, was isolated from

Figure 23.9 Diamond, graphite, and soot (which contains buckminsterfullerene) are three allotropes of carbon.

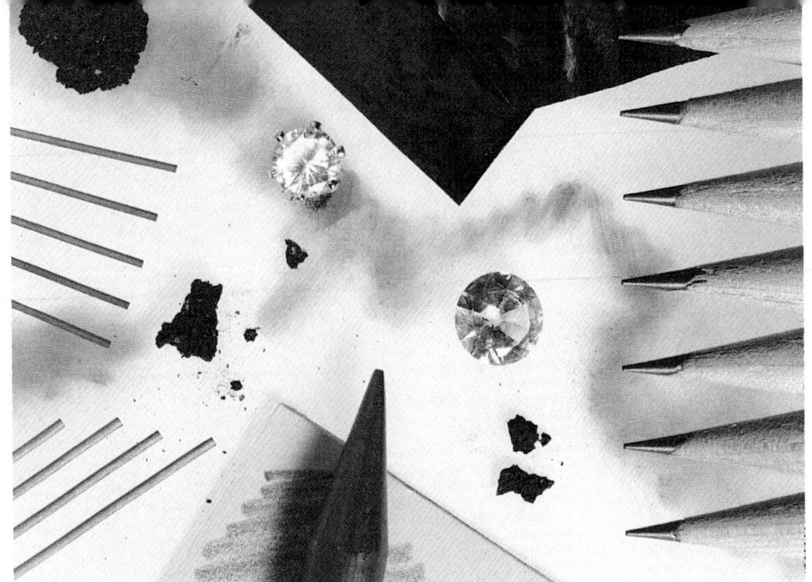

soot. You can compare the three allotropes of carbon in Figure 23.9. The unique properties of this newly discovered molecular form of carbon are described in Chapter 9. In general, carbon-containing compounds, of which there are about 4 million, are called organic compounds. Organic compounds are the basis of all living things.

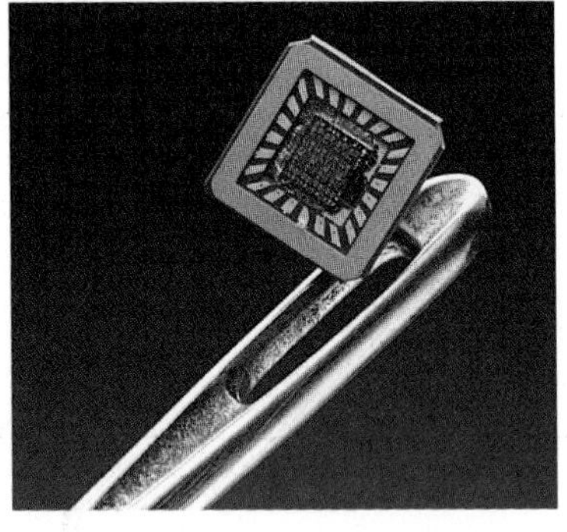

Figure 23.10 Semiconductors made of silicon are used in calculators and computers. Each chip may contain over a million transistors.

Silicon is the second most abundant element in the earth's crust. Silicon occurs in nature in the combined state as silicon dioxide (SiO_2), an essential component of sand, and as silicates in rocks, soils, and clays. Silicon and germanium, the third element in Group 4A, are semiconductors. Both substances are insulators at low temperatures. At high temperatures, however, they conduct electricity. These two elements, when highly purified, form the foundation of transistor technology. A silicon computer chip is shown in Figure 23.10. They are also used in photocells for solar power units.

Tin and lead are the remaining elements in Group 4A. Tin and lead are both typical metals. Because they are not very reactive, tin and lead have many uses as free metals. Tin is a soft, silvery metal that can be rolled into thin sheets to make tinfoil. Tin is applied as a thin coating to iron or steel to make tin cans. The tin protects the iron against corrosion by acidic foods. Tin has been used for centuries in various alloys such as bronze and solder. Bronze is an alloy of tin and copper. Plumber's solder is an alloy of tin and lead. The tin compound stannous fluoride (SnF_2) is an important ingredient in some toothpastes.

Lead melts at a low temperature, 327°C, and is easily obtained from its sulfide ore galena, PbS. Lead was known to the Egyptians as early as 3000 B.C. and since Roman times has been used in plumbing. The toxicity of lead is a major health concern, and the use of lead in certain products is now regulated.

Concept Practice

6. The properties of the three allotropes of carbon vary dramatically, yet each is composed of carbon atoms. Explain.

7. Which of the Group 4A elements are used in electronic equipment?

23.5 Nitrogen and the Group 5A Elements

Objective

Describe the sources, properties, and uses of nitrogen and the other Group 5A elements.

Another periodic trend, a change in physical state, is introduced with Group 5A. The first element, nitrogen, is a gas at room temperature. In descending order the next elements are phosphorus (a solid nonmetal) and arsenic and antimony, which are metalloids. The last element, bismuth, is a metal.

Nitrogen is essential to living organisms. Although about 80% of the air you breathe in is nitrogen, you cannot use it in this form. Fortunately, bacteria in the soil and in the root nodules of peas, beans, and other legumes "fix" atmospheric nitrogen into a usable form. Plants use the "fixed" nitrogen compounds to synthesize proteins and other biologically important nitrogen-containing compounds.

Nitrogen is isolated commercially from air by two processes. In one method, nitrogen is fractionally distilled from liquefied air. Because liquid nitrogen boils at a lower temperature than liquid oxygen, nitrogen distills off first. You can see liquid nitrogen in Figure 23.11. In the second method, nitrogen is isolated by moving air over red-hot coke, which is almost pure carbon. The carbon combines with oxygen to form carbon dioxide, while the nitrogen remains unchanged.

Nitrogen is a colorless, odorless, tasteless gas, composed of diatomic molecules, N_2. It is slightly soluble in water. Its melting point is –210°C and its boiling point is –196°C.

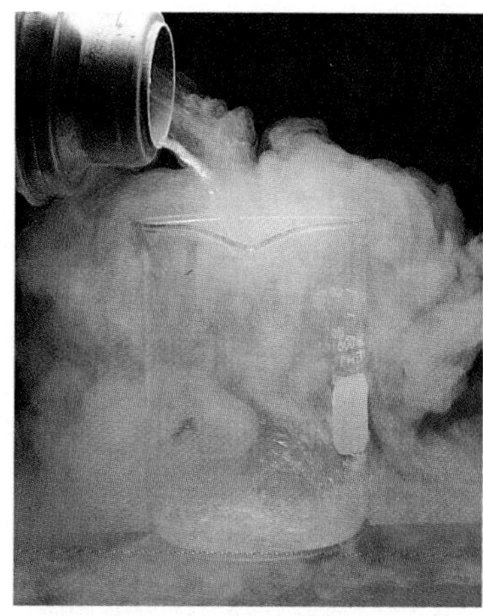

Figure 23.11 Liquid nitrogen boils away quickly when poured from an insulated flask into a beaker at room temperature. The smokelike effect in the beaker is caused by the condensation of water vapor from the air.

Figure 23.12 The seeds of legumes are an excellent source of protein. Legumes do not depend on nitrogen in the soil.

Figure 23.13 In the Haber-Bosch process, nitrogen and hydrogen combine to form ammonia. The hydrogen is derived from the reaction of steam with methane. What is the source of the nitrogen?

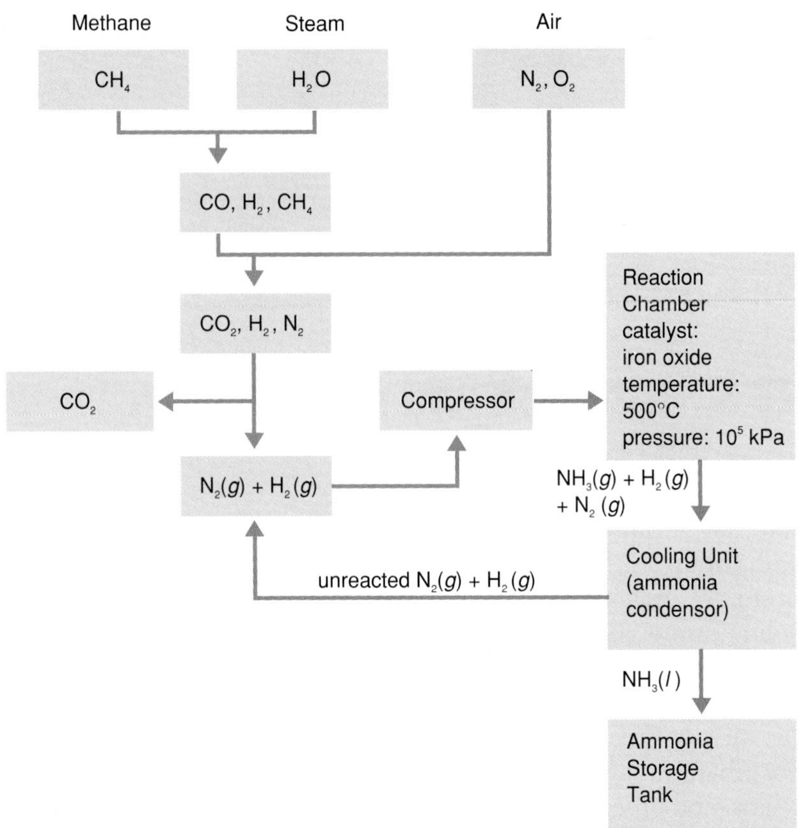

Figure 23.14 Pure, liquid ammonia is called anhydrous ammonia and is used extensively as a fertilizer.

The most important industrial uses of atmospheric nitrogen are in the manufacture of ammonia by the Haber-Bosch process and nitric acid by the Ostwald method. In the Haber-Bosch process, shown in the flowchart in Figure 23.13, nitrogen and hydrogen gases are heated to 500°C at up to 100 MPa in the presence of an iron catalyst. The equation follows.

$$N_2(g) + 3H_2(g) \xrightleftharpoons{Fe} 2NH_3(g)$$

The ammonia gas that is produced is separated from the reactant gases by liquefaction.

Ammonia is a colorless gas with a strong, irritating odor. The gas is very soluble in water. Aqueous ammonia is weakly basic and is a component of many cleaning products. Liquid ammonia, aqueous ammonia, and several ammonium salts are used as fertilizers. Liquid ammonia is also called anhydrous ammonia. It is sometimes applied under pressure directly to the soil, as shown in Figure 23.14. Liquid ammonia is also used as a refrigerant, particularly in the frozen food industry. Another ammonia-containing compound, ammonium sulfate, is the most important solid fertilizer in the world today.

Figure 23.15 White (or yellow) phosphorus is very reactive and must be stored in water. Red phosphorus is much more stable.

About one-quarter of all the ammonia produced is made into nitric acid. This acid is used in etching processes and in the production of fertilizers and dyes. Nitric acid is also an important raw material in the manufacture of explosives. Nitric acid is made commercially from ammonia by a process that was invented by a German chemist, Wilhelm Ostwald (1854–1932).

Like nitrogen, phosphorus is also essential to living organisms. Phosphorus is present in the double strands of DNA, bones, and teeth. Phosphorus is also part of ATP (adenosine triphosphate), which is the principal energy-storage molecule in living systems. Phosphorus occurs mainly in the form of phosphate rock. Look at Figure 23.15. Pure phosphorus is prepared in a white (or yellow) form and a red form. The white form is very reactive. White phosphorus is usually stored under water to prevent a reaction with oxygen from the air. Red phosphorus is a less active form used in the manufacture of matches.

Arsenic, antimony, and bismuth occur in nature in the form of sulfide ores. They are not essential to organisms. Alloys containing antimony and bismuth are used in making metal type for printing because they expand as they solidify. Characters of type must be identical. Thus, during manufacture it is important to use metals that expand to fill the type molds completely.

Integrating Home Economics

Beating Egg Whites

Cooks are often disappointed to see that egg whites beaten in glass or ceramic bowls wilt after a few hours. However, professional chefs have known for more than 200 years that the secret of firm, stable beaten egg whites is to use a copper bowl. These chefs' success appears to hinge on the reaction of trace amounts of copper from the bowl with an egg-white protein molecule called conalbumin. The conalbumin reacts with copper to form a yellowish copper-conalbumin complex. This complex interacts with other protein molecules in the egg white, forming a sturdy molecular network. The network is quite stable and holds the structure of the beaten egg white firmly in place.

Concept Practice

8. In what two major forms is nitrogen present on earth?

9. Give four physical properties of ammonia.

10. What are three uses of nitric acid?

Objective

Describe the sources, properties, and uses of the Group 6A elements oxygen and sulfur and their compounds.

23.6 Oxygen and the Group 6A Elements

The Group 6A elements are oxygen, sulfur, selenium, tellurium, and polonium. Oxygen, a gas, continues the periodic trend started by nitrogen in Group 5A. Sulfur is a nonmetal that occurs free in nature as a brittle yellow solid. Selenium and tellurium are both solids. They are metalloids—borderline between metals and nonmetals. Polonium, the last element in the group, is a radioactive metal that occurs only in trace quantities in radium-containing ores.

Oxygen is the earth's most abundant element. It accounts for 60% by mass of the human body, 50% by mass of the earth's crust, and 20% by volume of the air we breathe. Most oxygen is combined in the silicate rocks of the earth's crust.

Figure 23.16 The paramagnetism of oxygen becomes apparent when liquid oxygen is poured between two magnets.

The primary source of commercial oxygen, O_2, is air. Relatively pure oxygen is obtained by liquefying air and then fractionally distilling the liquid. Oxygen distills off at –183°C. When cooled, oxygen condenses to a clear blue liquid that freezes at –218°C. Look at the liquid oxygen in Figure 23.16. In liquid form, oxygen is attracted to a magnet. This property, called paramagnetism, is caused by the presence of unpaired electrons in the oxygen molecule. The major commercial use of oxygen is in the basic oxygen process for the manufacture of steel.

Oxygen tanks are carried in airplanes for use at high altitudes. Medical emergency teams administer oxygen to victims of smoke inhalation, electrical shock, or drowning. For certain medical conditions, such as emphysema or gas poisoning, a patient may need to breathe air enriched with oxygen for long periods of time.

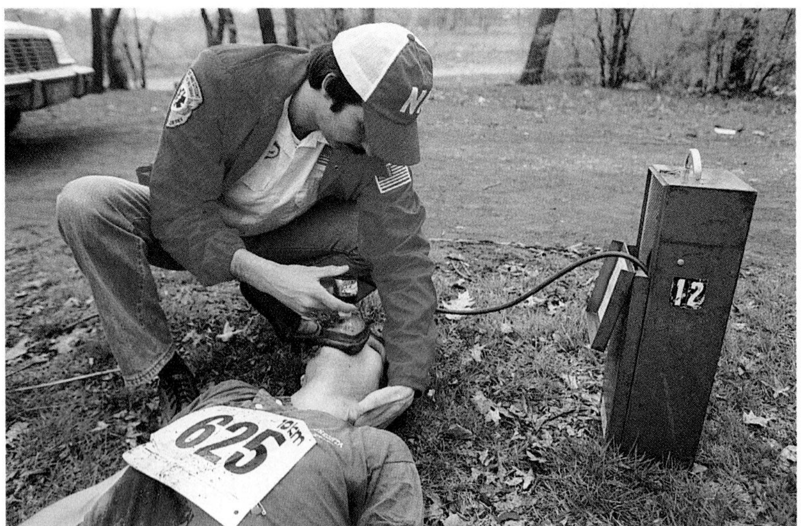

Figure 23.17 Oxygen is often administered to emergency medical patients who have difficulty breathing.

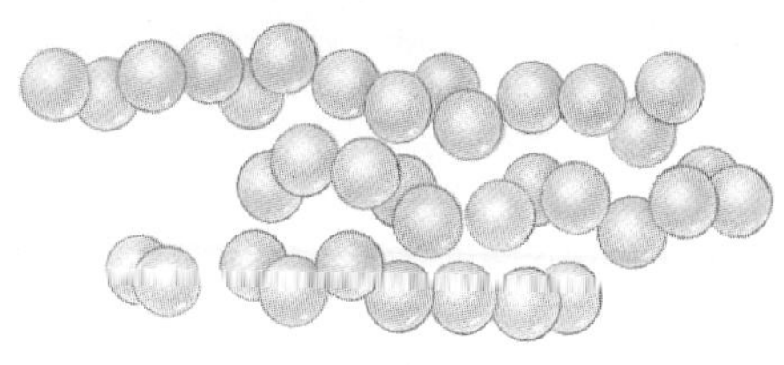

(a) Molten sulfur

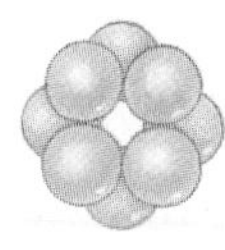

(b) Crystalline sulfur

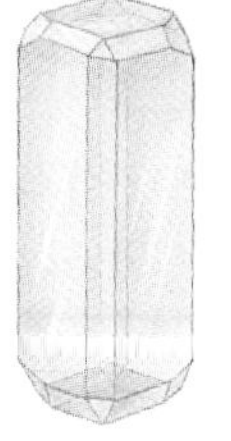

(c) Monoclinic crystals

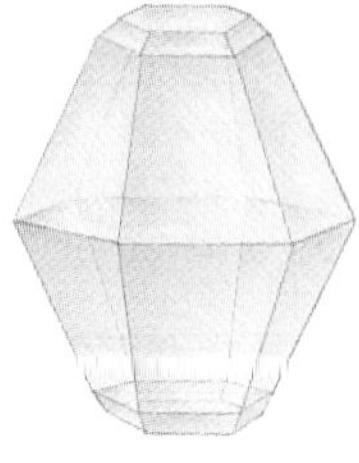

(d) Rhombic crystals

Figure 23.18 **(a)** Near the boiling point, sulfur chains break into smaller groups and individual atoms. **(b)** Crystalline sulfur exists as S_8 molecules. As sulfur cools, the needlelike monoclinic crystals **(c)** gradually change to the rhombic form **(d)**.

Ozone, which has the molecular formula O_3, is an allotrope of oxygen. Ozone is produced near high-voltage generators, during electrical storms, and in the earth's upper atmosphere, in the ozone layer. The ozone layer protects living things from excess ultraviolet light. In the 1970s, it was discovered that chlorofluorocarbons or CFCs used on earth had begun to destroy the ozone layer. The nations of the world have agreed to reduce production of CFCs and hope for 100% elimination by the year 2000.

Ozone is a pale blue gas with a characteristic odor. When cooled to –112°C, ozone condenses to a deep blue, explosive liquid. Ozone is a strong oxidizing agent. It is used commercially as a bleach and to sterilize water.

When substances combine chemically with oxygen, the process is called oxidation. The product of an oxidation reaction is an oxide. Oxides of all the elements, except the noble gases and a few inactive metals, can be prepared simply by heating the element with oxygen. In general, oxides of metals are solids and many react with water to form bases. Oxides of nonmetals may be solid, liquid, or gas and many react with water to form acids.

Sulfur has been known since ancient times to be a pale yellow, tasteless, odorless, water-insoluble, brittle solid. Sulfur occurs in the elemental state in large underground deposits. Sulfur is an extremely important raw material in the chemical industry. Sulfur is used in the preparation of paints, plastics, drugs, and dyes but its major uses are in the manufacture of sulfuric acid and the vulcanization of rubber. Sulfuric acid is the most widely used industrial chemical.

Figure 23.19 This sulfur is the amorphous form. What are its properties?

Sulfur occurs in several allotropic forms. When molten sulfur cools below 119°C, it forms eight-membered rings of covalently bonded sulfur atoms (S_8) arranged in monoclinic crystals. Below 95.5°C, the sulfur changes to rhombic sulfur. The crystal forms of sulfur are shown in Figure 23.18. A third form of sulfur is the dark brown rubberlike allotrope known as amorphous sulfur or "plastic sulfur." This can be produced by pouring molten sulfur, near its boiling point, into cold water, as shown in Figure 23.19. Amorphous solids do not have a distinct crystal form. Within hours, the amorphous sulfur loses its elasticity as it is converted to rhombic crystals.

Figure 23.20 Selenium has more electrical conductivity in the light than in the dark. Thus, one of its applications is in light meters for cameras.

Biographical Note

Jacqueline K. Barton
(1952–)

Jacqueline Barton is an innovator in the use of complexes of platinum and other simple inorganic molecules to probe the structure and chemistry of biological molecules. Her research work has revealed much information about changes in structure that occur along the giant DNA molecule. Barton's pioneering work in applications of inorganic chemistry to biology has been recognized with many scientific prizes. Although she never took high school chemistry, Barton earned her bachelor's and Ph.D. degrees in chemistry. She is currently a professor of chemistry at the California Institute of Technology.

Sulfur can be purified by boiling it and condensing the vapor. Tiny rhombic crystals form in flowerlike patterns on the walls of the condensation chamber. This powder is called "flowers of sulfur."

Sulfur is a reactive element. When heated, it burns readily in air or oxygen, producing an irritating, toxic gas, sulfur dioxide. Sulfur dioxide will combine with more oxygen in the presence of a catalyst to form sulfur trioxide.

$$2SO_2(g) + O_2(g) \xrightarrow{\text{catalyst}} 2SO_3(g)$$

This reaction of sulfur dioxide with oxygen is the basis for the manufacture of sulfuric acid by the contact process.

When heated with metals (except gold and platinum), sulfur forms compounds called sulfides. Hydrogen sulfide, a poisonous gas that smells like rotten eggs, is prepared by the action of an acid on a sulfide.

$$FeS(s) + 2HCl(aq) \longrightarrow FeCl_2(aq) + H_2S(g)$$

Selenium is a semiconductor. It is a poor conductor of electricity in the dark, but its conductivity increases greatly in the light. Because of this property, selenium is used in photoelectric cells, in exposure meters for cameras, and in light-sensitive switches. The xerographic process of photocopying also depends on the photoconductivity of selenium.

Tellurium is a very rare element. Its compounds are toxic, and the element itself plays no known role in living organisms.

Concept Practice

11. Name at least one industrial use of oxygen, sulfur, and selenium.

12. Give three physical properties of each substance.
a. oxygen **b.** ozone **c.** sulfur

23.A Science, Technology, and Society

Sulfur and Sulfuric Acid

The annual production of sulfuric acid in North America is more than fifty million metric tons! Practically every industry uses some sulfuric acid. Almost half the world's production goes into the manufacture of fertilizers such as ammonium sulfate and superphosphate. Large amounts of sulfuric acid are used in the metal industry for pickling iron and steel. Pickling involves putting a metal in a chemical bath to remove oxides on the metal surface. Sulfuric acid is also essential in petroleum refining. The raw material for the manufacture of sulfuric acid is sulfur.

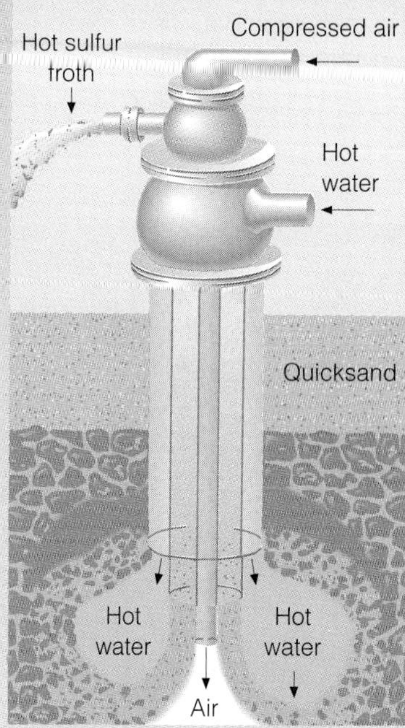

Figure 23.21 Sulfur deposits deep within the earth are mined by the Frasch process. The sulfur, melted by hot water and whipped into a froth by compressed air, rises to the surface.

Some of the world's richest deposits of elemental sulfur are on the Gulf Coast in Louisiana and Texas. These deposits are not easily mined because they are buried under several hundred feet of quicksand. A German-American engineer, Herman Frasch (1851–1914), devised an ingenious method for getting this sulfur out of the ground. The method takes advantage of sulfur's low melting point (119°C). Eighty percent of the world's sulfur output is produced by the Frasch process.

In the Frasch process, wells are drilled into the sulfur bed. Then an arrangement of three concentric tubes (with 2.5 cm, 7.5 cm, and 15 cm diameters) is installed, as in Figure 23.21. Superheated water (180°C) under pressure is pumped down the outside tube to melt the sulfur. Compressed air is pumped down the center tube. A frothy mixture of air, water, and molten sulfur rises up the third tube. The molten sulfur, 99.5% pure, is pumped into large storage vats, where it cools and solidifies into huge blocks. For shipping, the sulfur is loosened by dynamite blasting and loaded into freight cars.

The principal use of sulfur is in the manufacture of sulfuric acid. Sulfuric acid is the most widely used compound in the chemical industry. Today, sulfuric acid is produced mainly by the contact process. First, sulfur is burned in air to produce sulfur dioxide. Then the sulfur dioxide is oxidized to sulfur trioxide in the presence of a vanadium oxide catalyst. The entire process is called the contact process because the key reaction takes place when the reactants are in contact with the surface of the solid catalyst.

Think About It

13. Interpret In your own words, explain the Frasch process.

14. Deduce A country's annual increase in sulfuric acid consumption is one indicator of its industrial and agricultural growth. Explain.

Safety

Never add water to concentrated sulfuric acid. The heat generated may cause the water to boil, spattering the acid.

Objective

Describe the sources, properties, and uses of the halogens and the compounds of these Group 7A elements.

23.7 The Halogens

The halogens, Group 7A, do not exist in nature in the uncombined state, but their compounds are fairly abundant. The salts sodium chloride, sodium bromide, and sodium iodide are found in seawater and salt beds. Calcium fluoride is the mineral fluorspar.

The halogens are fluorine, chlorine, bromine, iodine, and astatine. They form a homogeneous family of nonmetals. The first two elements, fluorine and chlorine, are yellowish-green gases at room temperature and atmospheric pressure. They continue the periodic trend shown by nitrogen and oxygen. Bromine is a dark red liquid. Iodine is a purple-black crystalline solid with a metallic sheen. The last element, astatine, is a rare radioactive solid that has not been well investigated.

Figure 23.22 A heated piece of steel wool reacts vigorously in chlorine gas. The "smoke" is actually fine particles of the iron(III) chloride that form.

The free halogens are very reactive and must be handled with extreme caution. Nevertheless, compounds of fluorine, chlorine, and iodine are essential to your well-being and must be included in your diet. Fluorine, as fluoride ion, is beneficial in the formation and maintenance of healthy teeth. Chlorine, as chloride ion, is an important component of the blood and other body fluids. Iodine, as the iodide ion, is necessary to prevent goiter, an enlargement of the thyroid gland.

The halogens have many other uses. A dilute solution of chlorine is used as a bleaching and disinfecting agent. Silver chloride and silver bromide are light-sensitive and are used to make photographic film. Fluorine is used in the manufacture of nonstick (polytetrafluoroethylene) coatings that are applied to frying pans and other cookware.

Most of the compounds of halogens are soluble in water. Thus halide ions are abundant in seawater and salt beds formed by the evaporation of salt water. The concentration of halide ions in seawater is given in Table 23.3.

Table 23.3 Concentration of Halide Ions in Seawater

Ion	g/L
F^-	1.3×10^{-3}
Cl^-	1.9×10^{1}
Br^-	6.5×10^{-2}
I^-	5.0×10^{-5}

Fluorine was known in compounds long before it was isolated as an element. In 1886 French chemist Henri Moissan made fluorine. He did it by electrolyzing an ice-cold solution of potassium fluoride in hydrogen fluoride. Fluorine is still made this way today.

Chlorine gas is made commercially by the electrolysis of a sodium chloride solution. In a separate process, the hydrogen also produced is burned in the chlorine to make hydrogen chloride gas. This is an important source of hydrochloric acid.

Bromine is obtained commercially from seawater and salt-well brines. Sodium chloride in the water is allowed to crystallize, leaving a solution that contains the more soluble bromides. Chlorine gas, more electronegative than bromine, is then used to displace bromide ions from the solution.

$$2NaBr(aq) + Cl_2(g) \longrightarrow 2Na(aq) + Br_2(l)$$

At one time, iodine was extracted from the ashes of certain seaweeds that concentrate iodine from seawater. Now it is produced commercially from sodium iodate, which occurs as an impurity in the deposits of sodium nitrite.

$$2NaIO_3(aq) + 5NaHSO_3(aq) \longrightarrow$$
$$2Na_2SO_4(aq) + 3NaHSO_4(aq) + H_2O(l) + I_2(s)$$

Fluorine is the most electronegative and chemically reactive of all the nonmetals. It is also the strongest elemental oxidizing agent known. Fluorine forms compounds with all elements except helium, neon, and argon. The reactivity of the halogens decreases as their size and mass increase. Thus, iodine is the least reactive of the common halogens.

With the exception of hydrogen fluoride, the hydrogen halides are highly ionized in water, forming strong acids. Hydrofluoric acid is a weak acid because it is weakly ionized in water. The large electronegativity difference between hydrogen and fluorine (4.0 – 2.1 = 1.9) explains why. Hydrogen fluoride molecules are very polar and strongly hydrogen-bonded to one another. The other hydrogen halides exhibit this effect to a much lesser degree.

Hydrogen fluoride is used to etch designs in glass and to frost light bulbs. For many years, it had to be stored in wax containers. Today, plastic bottles are used instead.

The enrichment of uranium is another important use of fluorine. In the process for separating the isotopes of uranium, the metal is converted to uranium hexafluoride (UF_6), a gas. The diffusion of this gas allows the separation of U-235, the fissionable isotope, from the nonfissionable isotope, U-238,

Large amounts of chlorine are used in the purification of city water supplies, swimming pools, and sewage. Because chlorine in solution is a powerful oxidizing agent, it kills disease-causing bacteria. Chlorine is also used in the synthesis of vinyl chloride, $CH_2{=}CHCl$, which reacts to form polyvinyl chloride (PVC). PVC, a plastic, is used for floor coverings, phonograph records, and other vinyl products.

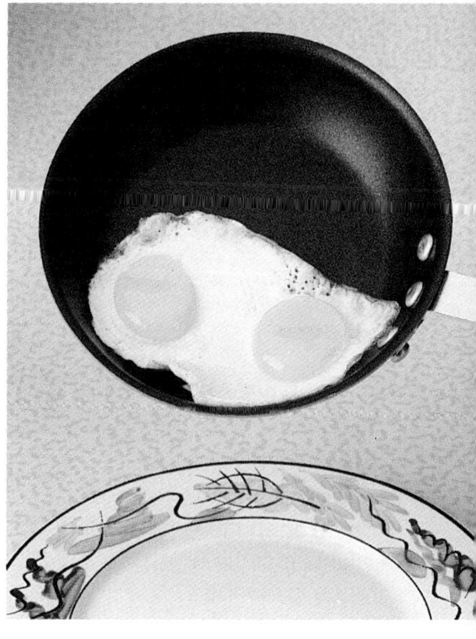

Figure 23.23 One common nonstick coating is a heat-resistant plastic composed of fluorine and carbon.

Concept Practice

15. Give the names and molecular formulas of the halogens.

16. Why is chlorine added to drinking water and swimming pool water?

17. How is chlorine gas prepared for commercial use?

Objective

Describe the sources, properties, and uses of hydrogen as a unique element.

23.8 Hydrogen

Hydrogen is the most abundant element in the universe. Free, or elemental, hydrogen is very rare on earth, but compounds of hydrogen are common. They account for about 1% of the earth's crust. Water is the most abundant hydrogen-containing compound. Combined with carbon and oxygen, hydrogen is present in all sugars, starches, fats, and proteins. These complex compounds are abundant in living tissues. Coal, natural gas, and petroleum products such as gasoline also contain hydrogen, as shown in Figure 23.24.

Naturally occurring hydrogen is composed of three isotopes. The most abundant isotope is protium. It is commonly called hydrogen. Protium (hydrogen-1) and deuterium (hydrogen-2) account for approximately 99.98% and 0.02% of a sample, respectively. Tritium, an unstable form of hydrogen, is present in extremely small amounts.

Hydrogen usually appears at the top of Group 1A in the periodic table. Hydrogen is not a metal, nor is it a good conductor of heat or electricity. Like the alkali metals, however, hydrogen does react with the halogens. In some periodic tables hydrogen also appears at the top of Group 7A. This position has some validity because, like the halogens, hydrogen has one electron less than helium, the noble gas it precedes. Like the halogens, hydrogen reacts with the alkali metals. Thus hydrogen is unique.

Hydrogen combines directly with a number of metallic and nonmetallic elements. With chlorine, it forms hydrogen chloride (HCl); with calcium, calcium hydride (CaH_2); with nitrogen (at 100 mPa and 500°C), ammonia (NH_3). Because it loses its single electron easily, hydrogen is a good reducing agent.

Roots of Words

hydor: (Greek) water
genes: (Greek) born
hydrogen the simplest and lightest of the elements, atomic number 1

Hydrogen is so called because water is generated, or born, by the combustion of hydrogen.

Figure 23.24 Hydrogen is seldom found free in nature but is present in a large number of compounds. All of these items contain compounds of hydrogen.

Figure 23.25 Mixtures of hydrogen and oxygen explode violently when ignited by a spark. The Hindenburg was only one of 73 hydrogen-filled dirigibles that burned. The nonflammable gas helium is now used to inflate balloons and blimps.

The major use of hydrogen is in the manufacture of ammonia. Large volumes of hydrogen, however, are used in the conversion of vegetable oils such as peanut and coconut oil into solid fats. This process, called hydrogenation, involves treating an oil with hydrogen at high temperature and pressure in the presence of a catalyst. Solid shortenings and margarine are produced in this way.

Hydrogen can be prepared commercially from water by the Bosch process. In this method, steam is passed over red-hot iron filings. The iron combines with the oxygen in steam and hydrogen gas is liberated.

$$3Fe(s) + 4H_2O(g) \longrightarrow Fe_3O_4(s) + 4H_2(g)$$

More than half of the hydrogen produced in North America is produced by the reaction between steam and natural gas, called steam reforming. Methane reacts with steam over a finely divided nickel catalyst at 700°C to 1000°C.

$$CH_4(g) + H_2O(g) \xrightarrow{\text{catalyst}} CO(g) + 3H_2(g)$$

Safety

Do not ignite any quantity of hydrogen larger than the volume of a small test tube. If oxygen has mixed with the hydrogen, the explosion could shatter the container, particularly if it is scratched or weakened from use.

Concept Practice

18. What are the names, atomic symbols, and mass numbers of the isotopes of hydrogen?

Objective

Describe the sources, properties, and uses of the Group 0 noble gases.

23.9 The Noble Gases

When compared with all other elements, Group 0 elements (helium, neon, argon, krypton, xenon, and radon) are extremely unreactive. For this reason the elements are now called *noble gases*. This name emphasizes the tendency of these elements to exist as separate atoms rather than in combination with other atoms.

The name *rare gases* was originally used to describe the Group 0 elements because they occur in the atmosphere in very small amounts. Early chemists also called these elements *inert gases* because they rarely combine with other elements. In 1962, however, a Canadian chemist named Neil Bartlett prepared xenon tetrafluoride (XeF_4). Since that time, compounds of krypton and radon have also been prepared.

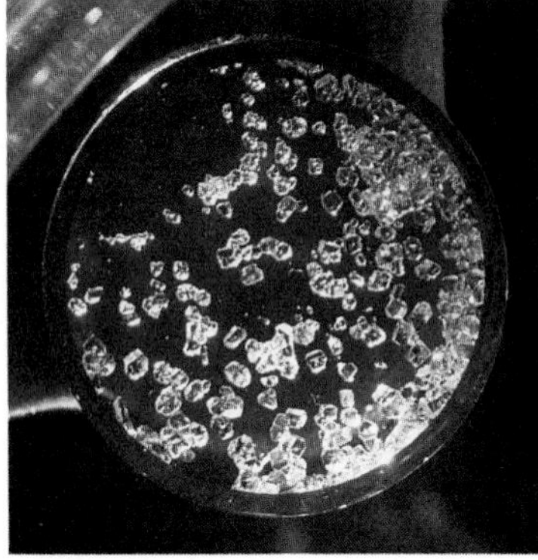

Figure 23.26 Xenon tetrafluoride is one of the few compounds that can be formed from a noble gas.

Despite their low reactivity, the noble gases have many uses. Helium is used to fill weather balloons. Both helium and neon are mixed with oxygen for use in artificial atmospheres such as those required in deep-sea diving. Argon, krypton, and xenon are used to produce the inert atmospheres needed for photographic flashbulbs and aluminum welding. They are also used to fill gas discharge tubes for advertising.

Figure 23.27 Underwater living quarters, such as the one shown, commonly have an artificial atmosphere consisting primarily of oxygen and a noble gas.

Concept Practice

19. The elements in Group 0 have been called *rare, inert,* and *noble.* Explain the origin of each of these terms.

Activity 23
Preparation and Properties of Oxygen

Purpose

To prepare oxygen gas and to observe some of its properties.

Materials

hydrogen peroxide
(3% solution from drugstore)

fresh raw red meat

toothpicks

candle

matches

test tubes
(or small plastic cups)

corks to fit test tubes
(or plastic film wrap)

stirring rod

water

dropper

tongs or tweezers

Procedure

1. Put a small piece of the raw meat, sufficient to cover a dime, into a test tube. Add about 10 mL of water and stir and grind the meat with the stirring rod until the water is deep red.

2. Fill another test tube about one-third full with the hydrogen peroxide solution.

3. Add three or four drops of the meat extract to the hydrogen peroxide solution.

4. When the bubbling and foaming have stopped, cork or cover the test tube.

5. Hold a toothpick with tongs and light it from a candle flame. When it is burning well, blow it out, uncover the test tube, and put the glowing end of the toothpick into the test tube.

Analysis and Conclusions

1. What is the gas that is released from the hydrogen peroxide solution? Write an equation for this decomposition reaction.

2. What happened to the glowing toothpick?

3. What would you expect to observe if you were to cook the meat before you ground it with water to make the extract? Explain.

23.10 The Transition Metals

Objective

Describe the sources, properties, and uses of some of the transition metals.

Most metals come from mineral deposits in the earth. *Minerals that are used for the commercial production of metals are called* **ores.** **Metallurgy** *involves the various procedures used to separate metals from their ores.* Many of these techniques were developed over the centuries by trial and error. Three basic steps are involved: concentrating the ore, chemically reducing the ore to the metal, refining and purifying the metal.

You can see from the periodic table that the transition metals are divided into ten groups. Starting with Group 3B on the left, they continue through Group 7B on the right. Group 7B is followed by three groups that together make up Group 8B. The last two groups are Groups 1B and 2B. Among the transition metals, with increase in atomic number, there is an increase in the number of electrons in the next-to-highest energy level. The transition metals exhibit typical metallic properties. In general, they are ductile, malleable, and good conductors of heat and electricity. With the exception of copper and gold, they have a silvery luster.

Some important uses of the transition metals are shown in Table 23.4. Tungsten, a hard brittle solid with a melting point of 3400°C, is used in light-bulb filaments. At the other end of the scale is mercury, with a melting point of –38°C; it is used in making thermometers. The excellent reflective qualities of silver (the high luster) make it the ideal coating for mirrors, as shown in Figure 23.29. The production of copper wire in enormous quantities attests

Figure 23.28 Most metals are refined from ores. Those shown here (clockwise from the top) are vanadinite (vanadium), hematite (iron), wulfenite (lead/molybdenum), sphalerite (zinc), galena (lead), and malachite with azurite (copper) in the center.

Table 23.4 Common Transition Metals and Their Uses

Metal	Uses
Cadmium (Cd)	Batteries; control rods for nuclear reactors
Chromium (Cr)	Plating; making stainless steel
Cobalt (Co)	Alloys; treatment of cancer (Co-60 only)
Copper (Cu)	Electrical wiring; plumbing; coinage
Gold (Au)	Jewelry; ornaments; standard of wealth
Iron (Fe)	Steel; magnets
Manganese (Mn)	Steel; nonferrous alloys
Mercury (Hg)	Lamps; switches; thermometers; barometers
Nickel (Ni)	Hardens steel; plating; catalyst
Platinum (Pt)	Catalyst; electronics; lab-ware; jewelry
Silver (Ag)	Mirrors; jewelry; photography; coins
Tantalum (Ta)	Surgery; corrosion-resistant equipment
Titanium (Ti)	Combustion chambers for rockets and jets
Tungsten (W)	Filaments for light bulbs; alloys
Vanadium (V)	Shock-resistant steel alloys; catalyst
Zinc (Zn)	Galvanized iron; brass; dry cells

Figure 23.29 Because of its high luster, metallic silver is used to plate mirrors.

to the high electrical conductivity of copper. Alloy steels with widely different characteristics are made by adding small amounts of cobalt, copper, chromium, nickel, or vanadium to iron. Your body also needs transition metals to function normally. Iron is required in the production of hemoglobin. Cobalt is part of vitamin B_{12} molecules. Both zinc and copper are necessary components of many biological enzymes.

The transition metals vary greatly in their chemical reactivity. The elements scandium, yttrium, and lanthanum are similar to the Group 1A and 2A metals. They are easily oxidized on exposure to air and react with water to liberate hydrogen. In contrast, platinum and gold are extremely unreactive and resist oxidation. Most compounds of the transition metals are colored and show multiple-formula combinations with other elements.

Making up about 5% of the earth's crust, iron is the second most abundant metal. (Aluminum is the most abundant.) Iron is the cheapest metal and, in the form of steel, the most useful. Common iron minerals are Fe_2O_3 (the red oxide, hematite) and Fe_3O_4 (magnetite). Millions of tons of iron are produced annually in the United States by the reaction of Fe_2O_3 with coke. This reaction is carried out in a blast furnace, shown in Figure 23.30. A modern blast furnace produces about 5000 tons of iron daily.

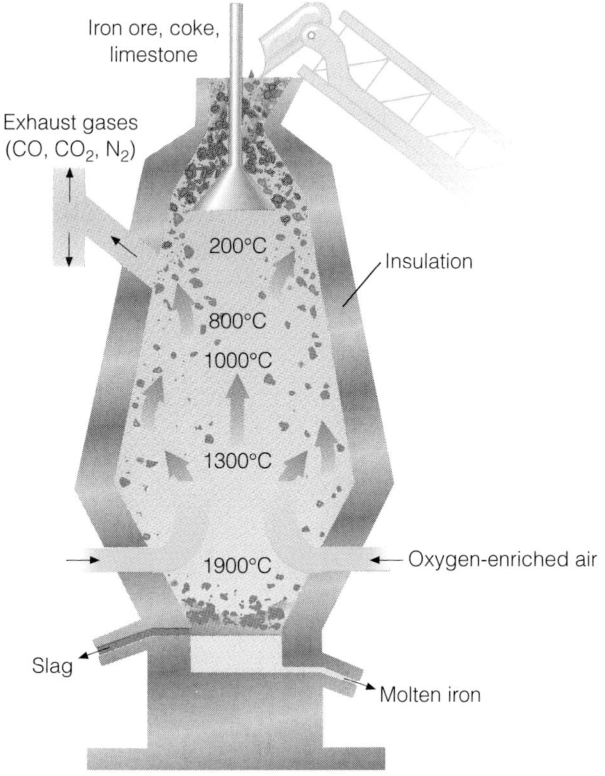

Figure 23.30 A blast furnace is about 30 m high and 10 m in diameter. Iron ore, limestone, and coke (a form of carbon) are added at the top. During the process, carbon, the reducing agent, is oxidized to CO_2. The limestone converts sand in the ore to silicate slag.

Integrating Oceanography

Deep-Sea Minerals

Minerals have been found in the undersea ridges of the Pacific Ocean near Hawaii. Mineral-laden water coming from vents along the faults and fissures of the underwater mountains and craters produces rich deposits of chromium, cobalt, copper, gold, iron, manganese, nickel, and zinc. Where the tectonic plates of the earth's crust are separating, seawater comes into contact with liquid magma of the underlying volcanic rocks. Superheated water then extracts minerals from crust material as it moves upward from the magma and escapes through vents on the ocean floor. These minerals are deposited in immense underwater fields on the ocean floor.

Figure 23.31 Gold was often used to adorn the dead. Here, an Egyptian funerary mask is shown.

Unlike iron, nickel and cobalt are resistant to atmospheric corrosion. Nickel is often used to electroplate iron and steel objects before they are plated with chromium. **Monel metal**, *a strong, corrosion-resistant alloy of nickel and copper,* is used for the propeller shafts of seagoing vessels.

Copper, silver, and gold have low chemical reactivity and often occur naturally in the free state. They are called "coinage metals" and were the first metals collected and worked by humans. In the Middle East, copper and gold artifacts dating back to about 7000 B.C. have been found.

Copper is the most widely used metal for electrical wiring. Only silver is a better conductor of electricity. Copper is also widely used in plumbing for pipes that carry hot or cold water.

Figure 23.32 Copper is commonly used in many forms.

Figure 23.33 Gold is often used for the contacts on computer chips.

Silver occurs as the free metal and as the sulfide ore argentite, Ag_2S. Most commercial silver is produced as a by-product in the processing of copper, lead, and zinc ores. Silver is recovered from the muddy layers that collect on the bottom of electrolysis tanks in copper refining. Because of its high luster, silver reflects light extremely well and has long been used to coat the backs of mirrors. The light-sensitive silver halides are also utilized in photographic processes.

Gold occurs chiefly as small particles of the free metal in veins of quartz. About 5 g of gold is produced from a metric ton of gold-bearing rock. Gold is also recovered as a by-product of copper refining. Gold is the most malleable and ductile of all metals and can be pounded into sheets so thin that they transmit light. Gold leaf, as it is called, is used in decorative lettering and other forms of ornamentation. Corrosion resistance coupled with high electrical and thermal conductivity makes gold valuable in high-technology industries. Gold is used to plate the contacts in microcircuits, as shown in Figure 23.33, and to cover the external surfaces of satellite components.

Concept Practice

20. What is an ore?

21. What are hematite and magnetite?

23.B Environmental Awareness

Toxic Metals

Safety

Many toxic substances can be absorbed through the skin. Avoid skin contact with chemicals whenever possible. Wash your hands thoroughly after handling chemicals, and never eat or drink in the laboratory.

Metals are among the industrial waste products that contaminate the environment. Some metals are essential for human nutrition in trace amounts. Still, higher concentrations are toxic. Others belong to a group of heavy metals that have no known biological function in humans. For example, low concentrations of lead, cadmium, and mercury produce toxic effects. In the body, heavy-metal ions eventually cause irreversible damage to the central nervous system.

For example, mercury is highly toxic and is a serious environmental pollutant. Scientists have only recently discovered that bacteria convert insoluble forms of mercury, once thought harmless, into highly toxic dimethyl mercury, $(CH_3)_2Hg$. This volatile liquid can enter the body through the skin or via the lungs.

For decades mercury and mercury salts have been used in industrial processes. As a result, large quantities of these substances have been discarded into the environment. Much of this mercury has collected in lake and stream sediments. Here, dimethyl mercury accumulates in the tissues of aquatic plants and small animals. Like other heavy metals, mercury is eliminated from living tissues very slowly. Thus, mercury moves up the food chain, becoming more concentrated with each step. This sequence makes some fish unfit for human consumption and creates a long-term environmental hazard.

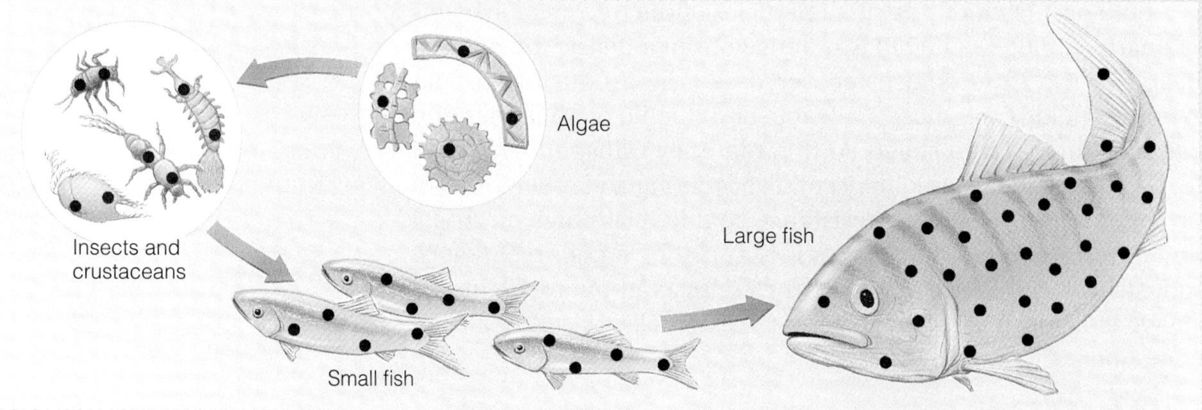

Figure 23.34 Heavy-metal atoms and compounds containing these atoms are represented by the black dots in this illustration.

Think About It

22. Explain How does mercury get in the food chain?

23. Support Justify the presence of some toxic metals in the body.

MATERIALS SCIENCE

Ceramics

From Bathtubs to Boom Boxes

From the ancient vases of prehistoric people to the space shuttle, the history of human civilization can be traced through the science of ceramics. People have been using ceramics for more than 10,000 years.

What are the unique properties of ceramics that make them so valuable and versatile? Ceramics have very high melting temperatures and are good thermal insulators. For example, the ceramic tiles on the space shuttle protect it from the intense heat of reentering the earth's atmosphere. Ceramics are also good electrical insulators, making them valuable in the electronics industry. Ceramics are very hard and able to withstand compression. These properties have made ceramic tile a popular material for the construction of floors and walkways. Ceramics are chemically unreactive and resistant to corrosion. Therefore, many ceramic vases and mosaics unearthed by archaeologists are as beautiful today as they were thousands of years ago.

The properties of a given ceramic result from its complex crystalline structure. Ceramics may have differences in appearance and usage, but they share some common components. All ceramics are made of inorganic powders, such as sand or dry clay. At some point in the production process the powders are subjected to high temperatures and undergo chemical and physical changes. At high temperatures the particles in clay, for example, become permanently rigid due to the formation of silicate chains. As a consequence, fired clay will not disperse in water. Some ceramics, such as porcelain and brick, are molded and dried in a drying oven before being fired in a kiln. The drying process removes water uniformly from the object and prevents cracking and warping during the high-temperature firing. A new type of ceramic called glass ceramic is made from glass that is cooled slowly to produce a crystalline structure. These glass ceramics are very shatter-resistant.

Ceramic engineers can control the structure, and therefore the properties, of a ceramic by varying the powder components and heat treatment used to manufacture it. Most ceramics contain oxides, such as silicon dioxide (SiO_2). Oxides cannot react with oxygen, and therefore they resist corrosion. Silicon nitride (Si_3N_4) is a ceramic that does not contain oxides, yet it is still resistant to corrosion. In the future, Si_3N_4 may be used to build automobile engines. Ceramic engines could run hotter and more efficiently than the metal engines of today. Without a doubt, ceramic engineers will find many more innovative applications for ceramics in the future.

Think About It

24. Identify Name some ceramics that you come into contact with in a typical day.

25. List What are some important properties of ceramics?

Chapter 23 Review
Metals and Nonmetals

Key Terms

lime *23.2*
metallurgy *23.10*
Monel metal *23.10*
ore *23.10*
slaked lime *23.2*

Chapter Summary

The alkali metals have low ionization energies and high reactivities. Because they ionize so readily, the alkali metals do not occur naturally as free metals.

The alkaline earth metals are also not found free in nature. They are less reactive, however, than the alkali metals. Calcium and magnesium are the two most important alkaline earth metals. Alkaline earth oxides such as calcium oxide (lime) and calcium hydroxide (slaked lime) have many industrial uses.

Aluminum, in Group 3A, is the most abundant metal in the earth's crust. It is not found as a free metal. Its value in industry derives from its corrosion resistance and electrical conductivity.

Carbon and silicon, in Group 4A, are the basic elements of life and minerals, respectively. Tin and lead are the metals of Group 4A. They have numerous uses both as the free metal and in alloys such as bronze and solder.

Nitrogen is found in the free state as N_2. It comprises 80% of the air by volume. Two important nitrogen compounds are ammonia and nitric acid. Ammonia is used to make cleaning products and fertilizers. Nitric acid is used to make fertilizers and explosives.

Oxygen is the most abundant element in the earth's crust. It exists freely in the atmosphere as O_2. Most of the earth's oxygen, however, is found in numerous compounds. Ozone, O_3, is an allotrope of oxygen formed in the upper atmosphere. Oxygen's primary industrial use is in the production of steel. Sulfur readily forms compounds with most metals and nonmetals. Some uses of sulfur are the manufacture of sulfuric acid and rubber.

The halogens do not occur in the free state. They exist in nature as halide ions found in seawater and salt beds. Fluorine is used for the inhibition of tooth decay. Chlorine, a powerful oxidizing agent, is used in disinfectants and in the manufacture of vinyl products.

Free hydrogen is rare on Earth. However, hydrogen-containing compounds such as water are abundant. The three isotopes of hydrogen are protium, deuterium, and tritium. Hydrogen is used as a reducing agent, in ammonia production, and in the hydrogenation of vegetable oils.

The noble gases are so named because of their low reactivity. These Group 0 elements have many uses. While Group 0 elements are very unreactive, a few compounds of some of these elements have been prepared.

Many transition metals, such as cobalt, chromium, and nickel, are used to make alloys. Monel metal is a corrosion-resistant alloy of copper and nickel. Copper, silver, and gold are excellent conductors.

Practice Questions and Problems

26. When sodium is exposed to oxygen, it forms sodium peroxide, Na_2O_2. When this compound is added to water, it gives a solution of sodium hydroxide. The same solution can be obtained by adding sodium to water. Write balanced equations for these reactions. *23.1*

27. What are the group names for the elements in Group 1A and Group 2A? *23.2*

28. What is lime? How is lime made from calcium carbonate, $CaCO_3$? *23.2*

29. Name an aluminum ore rich in Al_2O_3. *23.3*

30. Name the three allotropes of carbon. *23.4*

31. What are two forms of elemental phosphorus? How do they differ in reactivity with oxygen? *23.5*

32. Why is atmospheric nitrogen not directly useful to plants? How can atmospheric nitrogen be utilized by plants? *23.5*
33. List major uses of ammonia in industry. *23.5*
34. In what three major forms is oxygen present on Earth? *23.6*
35. What is the volume percentage of oxygen in the earth's atmosphere? What are the other components of air? *23.6*
36. Explain the term *paramagnetism.* Use liquid oxygen as your example. *23.6*
37. What is the largest industrial use of oxygen? *23.6*
38. Where is ozone produced naturally? *23.6*
39. Complete and balance these equations. *23.6*
    a. $Mg(s) + O_2(g) \longrightarrow$ **c.** $S(s) + O_2(g) \longrightarrow$
    b. $H_2(g) + O_2(g) \longrightarrow$
40. Describe the common allotrope of sulfur that is stable at room temperature. *23.6*
41. What are some uses of sulfur? *23.A*
42. Describe how iodine is obtained commercially. *23.7*
43. By what process is fluorine made? *23.7*
44. Give colors and physical states at STP of chlorine, bromine, and iodine. *23.7*
45. What is the largest industrial use of hydrogen? *23.8*
46. Name three practical uses of various noble gases. *23.9*
47. Suggest reasons why copper, silver, and gold are valued for the manufacture of electronic devices. Why is copper preferred to silver and gold for home wiring? *23.10*
48. Write formulas for the oxides of iron. *23.10*
49. Nickel is an important metal. Why? What is Monel metal? *23.10*
50. Copper, silver, and gold are among the few metals that have been used for thousands of years. Explain why. *23.10*

Mastery Questions and Problems

51. Use the periodic table as the basis of a concept map of the major topics of this chapter.
52. Name the two allotropic forms of oxygen. Describe one method of preparation for each.
53. The data table below shows the quantities of iron ore (Fe_2O_3) and coke (C) that react in a blast furnace to produce pig iron.
    a. Complete the table.
    b. Plot moles of iron ore (*y* axis) versus moles of carbon (*x* axis).
    c. From the slope of the line, determine the mole ratio by which iron reacts with carbon in a blast furnace.

Mass of Fe_2O_3 (kg)	Amount of Fe_2O_3 (mol)	Mass of C (kg)	Amount of C (mol)
8.65×10^4	____	1.95×10^4	____
1.26×10^5	____	2.84×10^4	____
2.01×10^5	____	4.54×10^4	____
6.56×10^5	____	1.48×10^5	____
9.61×10^5	____	2.17×10^5	____

54. At which electrode is the free metal produced in the electrolysis of a metal compound? Explain your answer.
55. Calculate the percentage of cobalt in cobaltite containing 72.6% CoAsS by mass. How many kilograms of cobalt would be contained in 1000 kg of the ore?
56. Explain why superheated water and compressed air are used in sulfur recovery by the Frasch process. What conditions do not allow sulfur to be mined, like coal, for example?
57. Large volumes of hydrogen are used in the hydrogenation of vegetable oils. Describe the process and comment on its commercial value.
58. Distinguish between oxygen and ozone.
59. Write a balanced equation for the reaction of hydrogen with these elements.
    a. nitrogen **b.** chlorine **c.** calcium
60. List all of the halogens in order of increasing electronegativity.
61. List some of the major uses of sulfuric acid in industry.
62. Explain why ammonia exhibits many water-like properties.

63. The data table below lists the melting and boiling points of the halogens.

a. Describe the trends you observe.

b. Explain these trends. Are they likely to occur with other groups in the periodic table?

Element	Melting point (°C)	Boiling point (°C)
F	−219	−188
Cl	−107	−34
Br	−7	58
I	113	184

Critical Thinking Questions

64. Choose the term that best completes the second relationship.

a. oxygen gas: ozone monoclinic sulfur: _____
(1) molten sulfur (3) sulfur dioxide
(2) rhombic sulfur (4) flowers of sulfur

b. sister:brother beryllium: _____
(1) cesium (3) barium
(2) lead (4) sodium

c. protium:deuterium nitrogen-14: _____
(1) isotope (3) carbon-14
(2) tritium (4) nitrogen-15

65. Hydrogen and helium are by far the most abundant elements in the universe. Why are the free, or elemental, forms of hydrogen and helium very rare on Earth?

66. The period of human history called the Bronze Age began about 3000 B.C. and was followed by the Iron Age. Why was bronze widely used before iron?

Cumulative Review

67. Write the formula of each compound.

a. calcium oxide **d.** aluminum oxide
b. mercury(II) oxide **e.** sulfur dioxide
c. carbon monoxide

68. Calculate the mass percent of metal in each of the following mineral compounds.

a. Fe_3O_4 **b.** Fe_2O_3 **c.** CoAsS

69. Write complete electron configurations for the following.

a. Fe **c.** Ag **e.** Cu **g.** Zn
b. V **d.** Fe^{3+} **f.** Ni^{2+} **h.** Ag^{+}

70. A sample of spring water contains 46.0 mg of magnesium ions per liter.

a. What is the molarity of Mg^{2+} in the sample?

b. How much water contains 1.00 mol Mg^{2+}?

71. What ions are produced when the following substances are dissolved in water?

a. LiBr **b.** $Ca(OH)_2$ **c.** KI **d.** $CdBr_2$

72. Classify each of the following compounds as a nonelectrolyte, a weak electrolyte, or a strong electrolyte.

a. CH_3COCH_3 (acetone) **d.** KNO_3
b. C_2H_5OH (ethyl alcohol) **e.** Na_2SO_3
c. CH_3COOH (acetic acid) **f.** $CaCl_2$

73. Balance the following equation.

$$IO_3^-(aq) + Cr(OH)_4^-(aq) \longrightarrow I^-(aq) + CrO_4^{-2}(aq) \text{ (basic)}$$

74. Determine the oxidation number of nitrogen in each of the following.

a. N_2 **c.** NO_2 **e.** NO_2^-
b. NO_3^- **d.** N_2O

75. Identify the oxidizing agent and the reducing agent in the following reaction.

$$I_2O_5(s) + 5CO(g) \longrightarrow 5CO_2(g) + I_2(s)$$

76. Calcium carbonate is used as an antacid to neutralize HCl in the stomach. Write the equation for the neutralization reaction.

Challenge Questions and Problems

77. Calculate the mass in kilograms of sulfur dioxide produced in the roasting of 1000 kilograms of chalcocite ore containing Cu_2S 7.2%, Ag_2S 0.6%, and no other sulfur compounds.

78. A 0.50-g sample of metallic sodium is converted to NaCl by reaction with chlorine gas. What volume of Cl_2 at 20°C and 740 mm Hg will be required to react completely with the sodium?

79. How many kilograms of Br^- are there in a cubic kilometer of seawater?

80. Azurite, a dark blue copper mineral shown above, has the following composition: Cu 55.3%, C 6.97%, O 37.1%, H 0.585%. Find the simplest formula of this mineral.

81. How many grams of sulfur dioxide are produced when 200 g of sulfur is burned in oxygen? What volume would the sulfur dioxide occupy at STP?

82. Coal contains sulfur. When coal is burned the sulfur is oxidized to sulfur dioxide, SO_2. In the graph below, the SO_2 emissions of coal-burning electric plants in a recent year are shown to vary according to generating capacity and plant age. In this year all coal-burning electric plants emitted approximately 13 million tons of SO_2.

a. What are the three types of plants with the largest SO_2 emissions?

b. Approximately what percentages of the year's emissions were due to the three types of plants identified in part a?

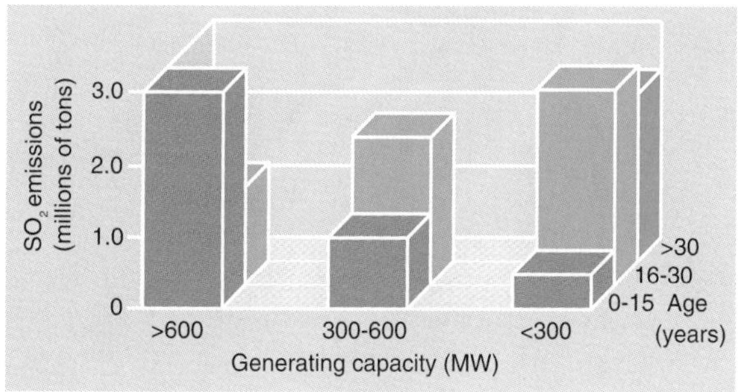

83. Hydrogen peroxide decomposes according to the equation

$$2H_2O_2 \longrightarrow 2H_2O + O_2$$

A solution is 3.00% H_2O_2 by volume. The density of H_2O_2 is 1.44 g/cm^3. How many liters of oxygen gas, measured at STP, are produced when 1 L of 3.00% H_2O_2 is decomposed?

Connections Questions

84. Discuss the origin of mineral-rich nodules found on the ocean floor.

85. How do trace amounts of copper contribute to a better meringue?

86. What is unique about Jacqueline Barton's approach to the study of biological molecules?

Write About Chemistry

87. Imagine that you discovered the first of the noble gas elements. What problems might you have convincing the rest of the scientific community of your discovery?

88. There are tons of the precious metals silver and gold in the oceans of the world. Discuss the pros and cons of trying to recover these metals.

Readings and References

Cotterill, Rodney. *The Cambridge Guide to the Material World.* Cambridge University Press, 1989.

Heiserman, David L. *Exploring Chemical Elements and Their Compounds.* Blue Ridge Summit, PA: TAB, 1992.

Smith, Jillyn. "The New Gold Rush." *ChemMatters* (October 1989), pp. 4–8.

VanOrden, Naola. "Asbestos." *ChemMatters* (February 1992), pp. 4–7.

24 Hydrocarbon Compounds

Goals

- Identify and draw structures of simple alkanes, alkenes, and alkynes.
- Give examples of *cis-trans* geometric isomerism in substituted alkenes.
- Deduce the origins of stereoisomerism in organic chemistry.
- Describe the refining of petroleum.
- Describe some of the important products produced by the destructive distillation of coal.

Hydrocarbon compounds are components of various fuels. The most common hydrocarbon fuel is gasoline. Across the United States, the average miles per gallon of gasoline is only 16.3. That's 6.95 km/L.

Concept Overview

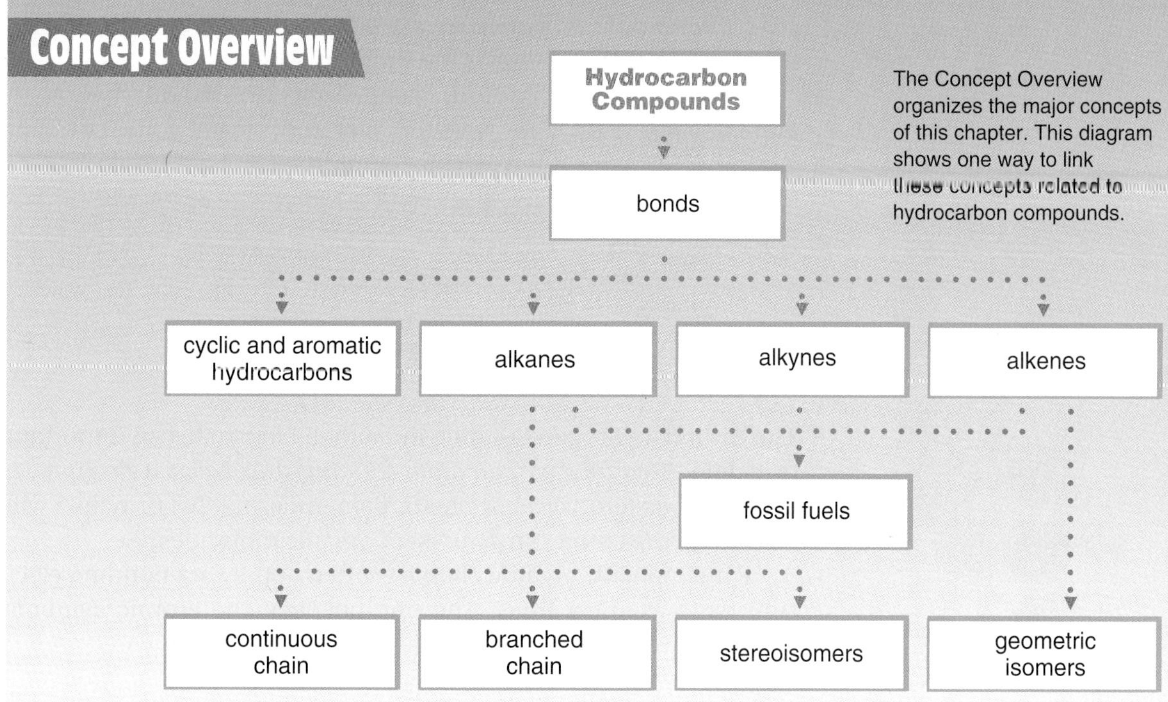

Scientists of 165 years ago believed the ability to produce carbon compounds rested exclusively with living things. The creation of carbon compounds was thought to be directed by a mysterious "vital force." Vitalism was rudely shattered in 1828 by a German chemist named Friedrich Wöhler (1800–1882). Wöhler discovered one way to make a carbon-containing compound in the absence of any living agent.

Since Wöhler's day, the definition of organic chemistry has been extended to include the study of all carbon compounds, regardless of their origin. Organic chemists have discovered how carbon compounds can be synthesized, or built, from simpler materials by ordinary chemical reactions. *Organic compounds that contain only carbon and hydrogen are called* **hydrocarbons**.

24.1 Hydrocarbon Bonds

Objective

Construct the electron dot structures of simple alkanes.

Methane is the major component of natural gas. Methane is sometimes called "marsh gas" because it is formed by the action of bacteria on decaying vegetation in swamps and other marshy areas. The methane molecule, which contains four hydrogens and one carbon, is a good example of carbon–hydrogen bonding. The simplest organic molecules are the **alkanes**, *which are hydrocarbons* *that contain only single covalent bonds.* Methane, a gas at standard temperature and pressure, is the simplest alkane.

A carbon atom has four valence electrons. Four hydrogen atoms, each with one valence electron, form four covalent carbon–hydrogen bonds. This combination is a molecule of methane.

$$\cdot\dot{\underset{\cdot}{C}}\cdot \;+\; 4H\cdot \;\longrightarrow\; \begin{matrix} & H & \\ H & \!:\!\underset{\cdot\cdot}{\overset{\cdot\cdot}{C}}\!:\! & H \\ & H & \end{matrix}$$

Carbon atom | Hydrogen atoms | Methane molecule

Figure 24.1 This three-dimensional model shows the tetrahedral shape of the methane molecule.

The carbon–hydrogen bonding in methane illustrates an important principle. *Because a carbon atom contains four valence electrons, it always forms four covalent bonds.* Remembering this principle will help you write correct structures for organic molecules.

For simplicity, organic chemists often abbreviate bonding electron pairs as short lines. The line between the atomic symbols represents two bonding electrons.

$$\begin{matrix} & H & \\ & | & \\ H- & C & -H \\ & | & \\ & H & \end{matrix}$$

Line represents shared electron pair

Methane molecule

Structural formulas are convenient to write on a page. Keep in mind, though, that they are only two-dimensional representations of three-dimensional molecules. Molecular models represent the shapes of molecules more accurately. These shapes are predicted by VSEPR theory and hybrid orbital theory. For example, methane has the tetrahedral shape shown in Figure 24.1.

Carbon has the unique ability to make stable carbon–carbon bonds and to form chains. This is the major reason for the vast number of organic molecules. Silicon also forms short chains, but they are unstable in an oxygen environment.

Alkanes are highly flammable. Mixtures of air and hydrocarbons can be explosive.

Ethane, C_2H_6, is the simplest alkane containing a carbon–carbon bond. Like methane, ethane is a gas at standard temperature and pressure. When ethane is formed from carbon and hydrogen, two carbon atoms share a pair of electrons. A carbon–carbon covalent bond is formed. The remaining six valence-shell electrons form bonding electron pairs with the electrons from six hydrogen atoms.

$$2\cdot\dot{\underset{\cdot}{C}}\cdot + 6H\cdot \longrightarrow \cdot\dot{\underset{\cdot}{C}}-\dot{\underset{\cdot}{C}}\cdot + 6H\cdot \longrightarrow \begin{matrix} & H & & H & \\ & | & & | & \\ H- & C & - & C & -H \\ & | & & | & \\ & H & & H & \end{matrix}$$

Ethane

Concept Practice

1. Draw the electron dot structure for the three-carbon propane molecule, C_3H_8.

2. How many single bonds are in a propane molecule? How many single bonds does each carbon have?

24.2 Continuous-Chain Alkanes

Objective

Write structural, condensed, and molecular formulas of the continuous-chain hydrocarbons.

Carbon–carbon bonds may repeat in organic molecules. **Continuous-chain alkanes** *contain any number of carbon atoms bonded in a straight chain.* To draw a structural formula for an alkane, just write the symbol for carbon as many times as necessary to get the proper chain length. Then fill in with hydrogens and lines representing covalent bonds. Remember that carbon has four covalent bonds. Table 24.1 shows the continuous-chain alkanes containing up to ten carbons. Note that the names of alkanes always end with *–ane.*

The continuous-chain alkanes are an example of a homologous series. *A group of compounds forms a* **homologous series** *if there is a constant increment of change in molecular structure from one compound in the series to the next.* The increment of change in the continuous-chain alkanes is the $-CH_2-$ group. For example, propane and butane are *homologs* of each other. Note that as the number of carbons in this series increases, so does the boiling point. This is also true of the melting point.

Table 24.1 Structural Formulas of the First Ten Continuous-Chain Alkanes

Name	Molecular formula	Structural formula	Boiling point (°C)
Methane	CH_4	CH_4	–161.0
Ethane	C_2H_6	CH_3CH_3	–88.5
Propane	C_3H_8	$CH_3CH_2CH_3$	–42.0
Butane	C_4H_{10}	$CH_3CH_2CH_2CH_3$	0.5
Pentane	C_5H_{12}	$CH_3CH_2CH_2CH_2CH_3$	36.0
Hexane	C_6H_{14}	$CH_3CH_2CH_2CH_2CH_2CH_3$	68.7
Heptane	C_7H_{16}	$CH_3CH_2CH_2CH_2CH_2CH_2CH_3$	98.5
Octane	C_8H_{18}	$CH_3CH_2CH_2CH_2CH_2CH_2CH_2CH_3$	125.6
Nonane	C_9H_{20}	$CH_3CH_2CH_2CH_2CH_2CH_2CH_2CH_2CH_3$	150.7
Decane	$C_{10}H_{22}$	$CH_3CH_2CH_2CH_2CH_2CH_2CH_2CH_2CH_2CH_3$	174.1

Complete structural formulas show all the atoms and bonds in a molecule. Sometimes, however, shorthand or condensed structural formulas work just as well. **Condensed structural formulas** *leave out some bonds and/or atoms from the structural formula.* You must understand that these bonds and atoms are there. The following listing shows several ways to draw condensed structural formulas for butane.

C_4H_{10} — Molecular formula.

$$\begin{array}{ccccccccc}
 & H & & H & & H & & H & \\
 & | & & | & & | & & | & \\
H- & C & - & C & - & C & - & C & -H \\
 & | & & | & & | & & | & \\
 & H & & H & & H & & H &
\end{array}$$

Complete structural formula.

$CH_3-CH_2-CH_2-CH_3$ — Condensed structural formula; C—H bonds understood.

$CH_3CH_2CH_2CH_3$ — Condensed structural formula; C—H and C—C bonds understood.

$CH_3(CH_2)_2CH_3$ (Methylene units; Subscript) — Condensed structural formula: all bonds understood; parentheses indicate CH_2 units are linked together in a continuous chain (the $-CH_2-$ unit is called a methylene group); subscript 2 to the right of parenthesis indicates there are two methylene units linked together.

C—C—C—C — Carbon skeleton; all hydrogens and C—H bonds understood.

The names listed in Table 24.1 are recommended by the International Union of Pure and Applied Chemistry (IUPAC). You may wish to memorize these names. They are the basis of *a precise, internationally accepted system of naming organic compounds called the* **IUPAC system**. Note, however, that organic chemists still rely on a mixture of systematic, semisystematic, and common names in spite of the precision of the IUPAC system.

Figure 24.2 Pressurized tanks of propane and butane are used by campers as heating, lighting, and cooking fuels. They are also used in rural areas where gas pipelines are not available.

Example 1 Drawing Structural Formulas for Alkanes

Draw complete structural formulas for the continuous-chain alkanes that have three and four carbons.

Solution

$$\begin{array}{ccccccccc} & & H & & H & & H & & \\ & & | & & | & & | & & \\ H & - & C & - & C & - & C & - & H \\ & & | & & | & & | & & \\ & & H & & H & & H & & \end{array} \qquad \begin{array}{ccccccccccc} & & H & & H & & H & & H & & \\ & & | & & | & & | & & | & & \\ H & - & C & - & C & - & C & - & C & - & H \\ & & | & & | & & | & & | & & \\ & & H & & H & & H & & H & & \end{array}$$

Practice Problem

3. Draw complete structural formulas for the continuous-chain alkanes with five and six carbons.

Concept Practice

4. Name the following alkanes.

a. $$\begin{array}{ccccccccc} & & H & & H & & H & & \\ & & | & & | & & | & & \\ H & - & C & - & C & - & C & - & H \\ & & | & & | & & | & & \\ & & H & & H & & H & & \end{array}$$

b. $$\begin{array}{ccccccccccccc} & & H & & H & & H & & H & & H & & \\ & & | & & | & & | & & | & & | & & \\ H & - & C & - & C & - & C & - & C & - & C & - & H \\ & & | & & | & & | & & | & & | & & \\ & & H & & H & & H & & H & & H & & \end{array}$$

c. $$\begin{array}{ccccccccccccccc} & & H & & H & & H & & H & & H & & H & & \\ & & | & & | & & | & & | & & | & & | & & \\ H & - & C & - & C & - & C & - & C & - & C & - & C & - & H \\ & & | & & | & & | & & | & & | & & | & & \\ & & H & & H & & H & & H & & H & & H & & \end{array}$$

Many organic compounds are best known by their common names. These names bear no relation to the IUPAC name or to the molecular structure of the compounds. Nevertheless, these names have been used for a long time. Many organic compounds isolated from nature have common names that reflect their origin. For example, penicillin is named from the mold *Penicillium notatum.* In most instances, common names are simpler than IUPAC names, which can become long and cumbersome. Scientists also use semisystematic names, which are mixtures of IUPAC and common names. This is similar to the way that immigrants lapse into their native tongue when they have an important idea to express. Like any living language, the language of science is constantly changing. IUPAC, semisystematic, and common names are used in this book.

Integrating Ecology

Oil Spills

Spilled oil from oil tankers can destroy fragile marine ecosystems. Because cleaning up oil spills is difficult and expensive, researchers are developing new cleanup technologies and safer transportation methods. Most current cleanup methods involve containing the oil and either pumping it away or soaking it up with absorbent materials. Some of the new developments include the genetic engineering of bacteria to "eat" up the oil spill and the design of double-hulled tankers which are less likely to spill their oil in a collision.

24.A Environmental Awareness

Recycling Plastics

You walk across a carpet made of old plastic bottles. You put on a jacket made from old plastic bottles. You stroll to the park and sit on a bench made from more old plastic bottles! What's going on? The answer is plastics recycling.

Plastics are among the most important materials to recycle. Made from polymers of organic molecules, some plastics can easily be reprocessed. Yet currently, only about 5% of the plastics used in the United States are recycled.

Plastics recycling is important for several reasons. Plastics are made from crude oil, a nonrenewable resource that is too precious to waste. Also, the incineration of plastics can release toxic gases into the air. Finally, since plastics do not degrade quickly, they can remain unchanged in dumps and landfills for decades.

The various types of plastics are not compatible with one another and must be sorted before they can be recycled. Mixed plastics produce a low-grade recycled product sold as "plastic lumber." Plastic lumber can be used as a wood substitute for decks and park benches. Careful sorting yields a higher-quality recycled product useful for carpet yarn, toys, and fiberfill insulation in clothing. To assist sorting, the plastics industry has devised a number code to identify certain commonly used plastics. The code usually appears inside a triangle on the bottom of the item. For example, the number 1 refers to polyethylene terephthalate, which is used for soft-drink bottles.

Besides recycling, the other possible solution to the problem of plastic garbage is to produce plastics that degrade naturally. Researchers have developed plastics that contain up to 60% starch. Microbes consume the starch, leaving behind a degraded plastic polymer. Because the polymer itself remains, these plastics are not truly biodegradable. Plastics containing starch are commonly used to make supermarket sacks. Although the development of truly degradable plastics may offer a solution to the plastics problem, recycling remains a sound, sustainable method of garbage and resource management. Now, will that be paper or plastic?

Table 24.2 Plastic Container Code System

Code		Material
♳ 1	PETE	Polyethylene terephthalate (PET)*
♴ 2	HDPE	High-density polyethylene
♵ 3	V	Vinyl/polyvinyl chloride (PVC)*
♶ 4	LDPE	Low-density polyethylene
♷ 5	PP	Polypropylene
♸ 6	PS	Polystyrene
♹ 7	Other	All other resins and layered multimaterial

* Trademarks

Think About It

5. Suppose If the Earth's supply of petroleum and coal is exhausted, where will the raw material for plastics come from?

6. Describe What problems arise when plastics are disposed of **(a)** by incineration and **(b)** in a landfill? Which of these methods do you think is least damaging to the environment? Explain.

24.3 Branched-Chain Alkanes

Objective

Write the structural formula of an alkane given its IUPAC name, and vice versa.

Hydrogens are not the only atoms that can bond to the carbons in a hydrocarbon. The halogens and groups of atoms including carbon, hydrogen, oxygen, nitrogen, sulfur, or phosphorus may commonly take the place of a hydrogen atom. *Such an atom or group of atoms is called a* **substituent**.

```
      ↙ Substituent            ↙  ↙  ↙ —Substituents
    C                         C   C   C
    |                         |   |   |
  →C—C—C                  →C— C   C —C—C—C
 Parent alkane (propane)   Parent alkane (hexane)
```

Three common substituent groups are the methyl group (CH_3—), the ethyl group (CH_3CH_2—), and the propyl group ($CH_3CH_2CH_2$—). *A hydrocarbon substituent is called an* **alkyl group**. It can be one or several carbons long. An alkyl group consists of an alkane with one terminal hydrogen removed. Alkyl groups are named by removing the *-ane* ending from the parent hydrocarbon name and adding *-yl.*

When substituent alkyl groups are added to a straight-chain hydrocarbon, "branches" are formed. *An alkane with one or more alkyl groups is a* **branched-chain alkane**. The IUPAC rules for naming branched-chain alkanes are quite straightforward. The following compound can be used as an example.

```
 7     6     5     4    3    2    1
CH3—CH2—CH2—CH—CH—CH—CH3
             |    |    |
            CH2  CH3  CH3
             |
            CH3
```

1. *Find the longest continuous chain of carbons in the molecule.* This chain is used as the parent structure. In the example, the longest continuous chain contains seven carbons. Therefore the parent hydrocarbon structure is heptane.

2. *Number the carbons in the main chain in sequence.* In doing this, start at the end that will give the groups attached to the chain the *smallest numbers.* This has already been done in the preceding example. In this instance the numbers go from right to left, which places the substituent groups at carbon atoms 2, 3, and 4. If the chain were numbered from left to right, the groups would be at positions 4, 5, and 6. These are higher numbers and therefore violate the rule.

3. *Add numbers to the names of the substituent groups to identify their positions on the chain.* These numbers become prefixes to the name of the parent alkane. In this example the substituents and positions are 2-methyl, 3-methyl, and 4-ethyl.

Figure 24.3 This is a ball-and-stick model of 4-ethyl-2,3-dimethylheptane.

4. *Use prefixes to indicate the appearance of a group more than once in the structure.* Common prefixes are *di* (twice), *tri* (three times), *tetra* (four), and *penta* (five). This example has two methyl substituents. Thus the word *dimethyl* will be part of the complete compound name.

5. *List the names of alkyl substituents in alphabetical order.* For purposes of alphabetizing, you ignore the prefixes *di, tri,* and so on. In this example, the 4-ethyl group is listed before the 2-methyl and 3-methyl groups (which are combined as 2,3-dimethyl in the name). Thus, no matter how many you have, ethyl, methyl, and propyl groups would always be named in that order.

6. *Use proper punctuation.* This is very important in writing the names of organic compounds in the IUPAC system. Commas are used to separate numbers. Hyphens are used to separate numbers and words. *The name of the alkane is written as one word.* The demonstration compound, then, would be written as dimethylheptane, *not* dimethyl heptane.

According to the IUPAC rules, the name of this compound is 4-ethyl-2,3-dimethylheptane. A ball-and-stick model of this compound appears in Figure 24.3.

Example 2 Naming Alkanes

Name these compounds using the IUPAC system. (*Note:* The longest continuous chain is *not* written in a straight line in molecule **a**.)

a.

$$\begin{array}{c} \qquad\qquad\quad CH_3 \\ \qquad\qquad\quad | \\ CH_3-CH_2-C-CH_3 \\ \qquad\qquad\quad | \\ \qquad\qquad\quad CH_2 \\ \qquad\qquad\quad | \\ \qquad\qquad\quad CH_2 \\ \qquad\qquad\quad | \\ \qquad\qquad\quad CH_3 \end{array}$$

c.

$$\begin{array}{ccccccccc} & & CH_3 & & & & CH_3 & & \\ & & | & & & & | & & \\ CH_3 & - & C & - & CH_2 & - & C & - & CH_3 \\ & & | & & & & | & & \\ & & CH_3 & & & & CH_3 & & \end{array}$$

b.

$$\begin{array}{ccccccccccc} & & & & CH_3 & & & & CH_3 & & \\ & & & & | & & & & | & & \\ CH_3 & - & CH_2 & - & CH & - & CH_2 & - & CH & - & CH_3 \end{array}$$

Solution

a. 3,3-dimethylhexane
b. 2,4-dimethylhexane
c. 2,2,4,4-tetramethylpentane

Problem-Solving Tip

The longest chain may not always be written in a straight line.

Problem-Solving Tip

There must be a sufficient number of hydrogens on each carbon such that every carbon atom has four bonds.

With an alkane name and knowledge of the IUPAC rules, it is easy to reconstruct the structural formula.

1. *Find the root word* (ending in *-ane*) *in the hydrocarbon name.* Then write the longest carbon chain to create the parent structure.

2. *Number the carbons on this parent carbon chain.*

3. *Identify the substituent groups.* Attach the substituents to the numbered parent chain at the proper positions.

4. *Add hydrogens as needed.*

Example 3 Drawing Structural Formulas of Alkanes

Draw complete structural formulas for the following compounds.

a. 3-ethylhexane **b.** 2,2,4-trimethylpentane

Solution

a.

$$\begin{array}{cccccc} & & CH_3 & & & \\ & & | & & & \\ & & CH_2 & & & \\ & & | & & & \\ CH_3- & CH_2- & CH- & CH_2- & CH_2- & CH_3 \\ 1 & 2 & 3 & 4 & 5 & 6 \end{array}$$

b.

$$\begin{array}{ccccc} & CH_3 & & CH_3 & \\ & | & & | & \\ CH_3- & C- & CH_2- & CH- & CH_3 \\ & | & & & \\ 1 & 2\ CH_3 & 3 & 4 & 5 \end{array}$$

Concept Practice

7. Name the following compounds according to the IUPAC system.

a.

$$\begin{array}{cccc} CH_3- & CH_2- & CH- & CH_3 \\ & & | & \\ & & CH_3 & \end{array}$$

b.

$$\begin{array}{ccccc} CH_2- & CH_2- & CH- & CH_2- & CH_3 \\ | & & | & & \\ CH_3 & & CH_2 & & \\ & & | & & \\ & & CH_3 & & \end{array}$$

Practice Problem

8. Draw a structural formula for each of the following compounds.

a. 2,3-dimethylhexane **b.** 3-ethyl-2,4-dimethyloctane

Objective

Construct all possible structural isomers for simple alkane molecules.

24.4 Properties of Alkanes

You know that oil and water do not mix. Organic molecules, such as hydrocarbons, are not attracted to water. The reason is that hydrocarbon molecules are not polar. Their nonpolarity arises from the almost equal sharing of electrons in the carbon–carbon and carbon–hydrogen bonds. The attractions that hold nonpolar molecules together are the very weak van der Waals forces. Thus hydrocarbons of low formula mass tend to be gases or low-boiling-point liquids. Weak intermolecular forces cannot hold these molecules in the solid state.

If oil doesn't dissolve in water, what does it dissolve in? A good rule of thumb is that "like dissolves like." That is, two nonpolar compounds will form a solution, as will two polar compounds. By contrast, a nonpolar compound and a polar compound will not form a solution.

You can sometimes draw the structures of two or more alkanes that have the same molecular formula but different molecular structures. *Compounds that have the same molecular formula but different molecular structures are called* **structural isomers**. For example, two different molecules have the formula C_4H_{10}: butane and 2-methylpropane. They are isomers of each other.

$$CH_3-CH_2-CH_2-CH_3$$

Butane (C_4H_{10})
(bp 0°C)

$$\begin{array}{c} \quad CH_3 \\ \quad | \\ CH_3-CH-CH_3 \end{array}$$

2-Methylpropane (C_4H_{10})
(bp −10.2°C)

Structural isomers differ in their physical properties, such as boiling points and melting points. They also have different chemical reactivities. In general, the more highly branched the hydrocarbon structure, the lower its boiling point compared with the boiling points of its other structural isomers. For example, 2-methylpropane has a lower boiling point than butane.

Concept Practice

9. Why are alkane molecules nonpolar?

Practice Problem

10. Draw all the structural isomers with the molecular formula C_6H_{14}. Name each one. (For convenience, you may want to draw only the carbon skeleton for each structure.)

24.5 Alkenes and Alkynes

Objective

Write the structural formula of an alkene given its IUPAC name, and vice versa.

The carbon–carbon bonds in alkanes are examples of single bonds. Multiple bonds between carbons also exist. *Organic compounds containing carbon–carbon double bonds are called* **alkenes**. This is the carbon–carbon double bond found in alkenes.

$$\rangle C{=}C \langle$$

Organic compounds that contain double and triple carbon–carbon bonds are called **unsaturated compounds**. This is because they contain fewer than the maximum number of hydrogens in their structure. *The alkanes (which contain the maximum number of hydrogens) are called* **saturated compounds**.

To name an alkene by the IUPAC system, find the longest continuous chain in the molecule that contains the double bond. This chain is the parent alkene. It gets the root name of the alkane with the same number of carbons plus the ending *-ene.* The chain is numbered so that the carbon atoms of the double bond get the lowest possible numbers. Substituents on the chain are named and numbered the same way as for the alkanes. Ethene and propene are the simplest alkenes. They are often called by the common names ethylene and propylene. Here are some examples of the structures and IUPAC names of simple alkenes.

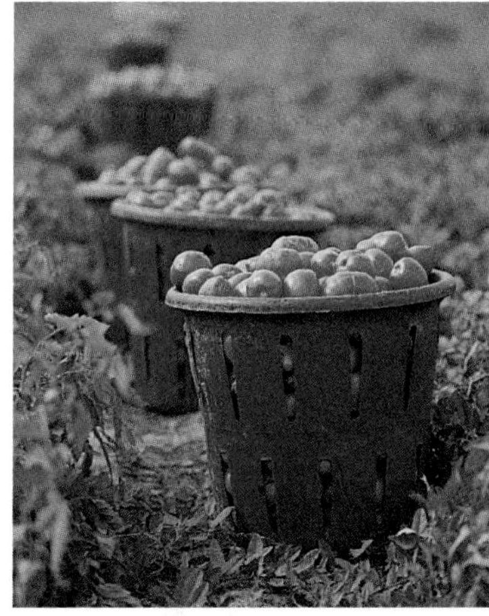

Figure 24.4 Ethene plays a vital role in the development of plants. Ethene-treated tomatoes ripen at the same time so that they can be harvested more efficiently.

$H_2C{=}CH_2$ (each C bearing two H)
Ethene
(ethylene, the simplest alkene)

$CH_3{-}CH{=}CH{-}H$
Propene
(propylene)

$H_2C{=}CH{-}CH_2{-}CH_3$
1-Butene

$CH_3{-}CH{=}CH{-}CH_3$
2-Butene
(1-butene and 2-butene are structural isomers of C_4H_8)

$CH_3{-}CH(CH_3){-}CH{=}CH{-}CH_3$
4-Methyl-2-pentene

No rotation occurs about a carbon–carbon double bond. The four hydrogens that project from the double-bonded carbons in ethene lie in a plane and are 120° apart. This is the maximum separation of atoms that can be attained without breaking bonds.

Figure 24.5 The six atoms of ethene lie in one plane. Rotation does not occur about the double bond.

Organic compounds containing carbon–carbon triple bonds are called **alkynes**. Like alkenes, alkynes are unsaturated compounds. This is the carbon–carbon triple bond found in alkynes.

$$-C{\equiv}C-$$

Alkynes are not plentiful in nature. The simplest alkyne is the gas ethyne, C_2H_2. The single bonds that extend from the carbons involved in the carbon–carbon triple bond of ethyne are separated by the maximum angle of 180°. Thus ethyne is a linear molecule.

The major attractions among these molecules, whether alkanes, alkenes, or alkynes, are weak van der Waals forces. As a result, the introduction of a double or triple bond into a hydrocarbon does not have a dramatic effect on typical physical properties such as the boiling point.

Figure 24.6 This is a ball-and-stick model of ethyne, the simplest alkyne. Rotation about the triple bond does not occur.

Safety

Alkenes and alkynes are very reactive because of the presence of double and triple bonds.

Table 24.3 Boiling Points of Homologous Alkanes, Alkenes, and Alkynes

Name	Molecular structure	Boiling point (°C)
C_2		
Ethane	$CH_3{-}CH_3$	–88.5
Ethene	$CH_2{=}CH_2$	–103.9
Ethyne	$CH{\equiv}CH$	–81.8
C_3		
Propane	$CH_3CH_2CH_3$	–42.0
Propene	$CH_3CH{=}CH_2$	–47.0
Propyne	$CH_3C{\equiv}CH$	–23.3
C_4		
Butane	$CH_3CH_2CH_2CH_3$	–0.5
1-Butene	$CH_3CH_2CH{=}CH_2$	–6.3
1-Butyne	$CH_3CH_2C{\equiv}CH$	8.6
C_5		
Pentane	$CH_3CH_2CH_2CH_2CH_3$	36.0
1-Pentene	$CH_3CH_2CH_2CH{=}CH_2$	30.0
1-Pentyne	$CH_3CH_2CH_2C{\equiv}CH$	40.0

Concept Practice

11. You can't draw a structural formula for *methene*. Explain.

Practice Problem

12. Draw all the alkenes with the molecular formula C_4H_8. Name each compound.

24.B Consumer Chemistry

Textiles and Fabrics

When you shop for clothing, you are often interested in the material the clothing is made from, as well as its style and color. Silk, wool, and cotton have been woven and spun into fabric for clothing for hundreds of years. These fibrous natural materials have great tensile strength and are well suited for weaving and spinning. However, in the past 50 years natural fibers have been largely replaced by synthetic polymers. "Synthetics" have properties similar or superior to those of natural fibers.

Synthetic fibers can be divided into two groups depending on the starting material: cellulosic and noncellulosic. Cellulosic fibers have cellulose derived from wood pulp or cotton as the starting material. Rayon and acetate are cellulosic fibers. Noncellulosic fibers are manufactured from petrochemicals and include nylon, polyesters, and acrylics. About 80% of the synthetic fibers used are derived from petroleum.

Unlike many natural fibers, synthetics resist shrinking and stretching, and they do not wrinkle from wear or washing. Furthermore, synthetics are not subject to moth attacks, which can destroy natural fiber garments.

Polyester fibers are often combined with cotton or other natural fibers to make very practical wash-and-wear clothing. These blended fabrics combine the comfortable feel of natural fibers with the wrinkle and shrink resistance of synthetics. Polyester–cotton blends are widely used for shirts, sportswear, and bed sheets.

Although synthetics may not wrinkle or shrink, many people prefer to wear clothing made of only natural fibers. For these consumers, the feel and breathability of the natural fibers are more important than wrinkle resistance. Others prefer to wear natural-fiber clothing because they want to avoid products made from nonrenewable resources such as petroleum.

For the protection of the consumer, all apparel sold in the United States must be identified as to fiber content, country of origin, and care requirements. The fiber-content label must list all fibers that make up at least 5% of the fabric.

Figure 24.7 The properties of synthetic fibers make them ideal for use in extreme conditions.

Think About It

13. Infer What might be some disadvantages of the increasing usage of synthetic fibers?

14. Create Suggest a unique combination of properties that you would like to see in a synthetic fiber.

Objective

Distinguish between structural isomers and geometric isomers.

24.6 Geometric Isomers

The lack of rotation around carbon–carbon double bonds has an important structural implication. Look at the structure of 2-butene in Figure 24.8. Two arrangements are possible for the methyl groups with respect to the rigid double bond. *In the* ***trans*** **configuration** *the substituted groups are on opposite sides of the double bond. In the* ***cis*** **configuration** *the substituted groups are on the same side of the double bond. Trans*-2-butene and *cis*-2-butene are geometric isomers. **Geometric isomers** *differ only in the geometric relationship of their substituted groups.* Like other structural isomers, isomeric 2-butenes are distinguishable by their different physical and chemical properties. The substituent groups attached to the carbons of the double bond do not need to be the same. Geometric isomerism is possible whenever each carbon of the double bond has at least one substituent.

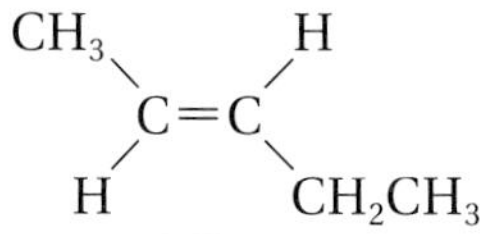

CH_3 (top left), H (top right), C=C, H (bottom left), CH_2CH_3 (bottom right)
trans-2-Pentene

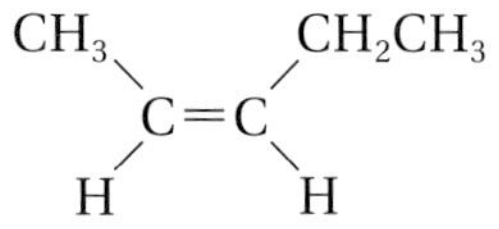

CH_3 (top left), CH_2CH_3 (top right), C=C, H (bottom left), H (bottom right)
cis-2-Pentene

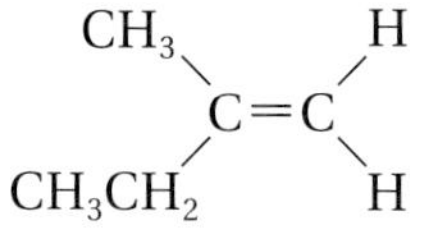

CH_3 (top left), H (top right), C=C, CH_3CH_2 (bottom left), H (bottom right)
2-Methyl-1-butene
(no *cis, trans* isomers)

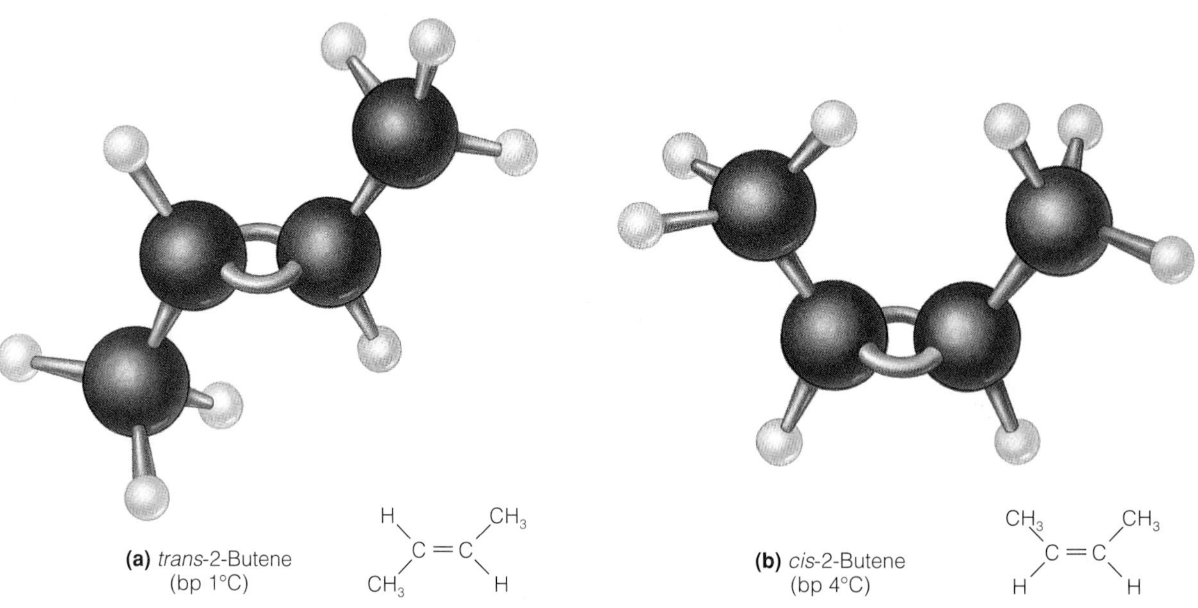

Figure 24.8 These are the two geometric isomers of 2-butene. How does the *trans* configuration differ from the *cis* configuration?

(a) *trans*-2-Butene (bp 1°C)

(b) *cis*-2-Butene (bp 4°C)

Concept Practice

15. How do geometric isomers differ from structural isomers?

16. Are these two structures geometric isomers? Explain.

$$\begin{matrix} CH_3 & & CH_3 \\ & C=C & \\ H & & H \end{matrix} \qquad \begin{matrix} H & & H \\ & C=C & \\ CH_3 & & CH_3 \end{matrix}$$

24.7 Stereoisomers

Objective

Identify the asymmetric carbon in a stereoisomer.

Placing an object in front of a mirror can give two different results. If the object is symmetrical, like a ball, then its mirror image is superimposable. That is, the appearance of the ball and its reflection are indistinguishable. By contrast, a pair of hands are distinguishable even though they consist of identical parts. The right hand reflects as a left hand and the left hand reflects as a right hand. Your hands are examples of nonsuperimposable mirror images. They are mirror images that cannot be placed on top of each other to obtain a match. Many pairs of ordinary objects like ears, feet, shoes, and bird wings are similarly related.

Recall that four groups attached to a carbon by single covalent bonds form a tetrahedron with the carbon at the center. In Figure 24.9 the carbon has four *different* groups attached: —F, —H, —Cl, and —Br. *A carbon with four different groups attached is called an*

Figure 24.9 Stereoisomers are mirror-image molecules that cannot be superimposed on each other. Notice that the reflection cannot be superimposed onto the original molecule.

Biographical Note

W. Lincoln Hawkins
(1911–1992)

The reliability of telephone systems is in part due to the work of W. Lincoln Hawkins. His discovery made it possible to produce long-lasting polyethylene-clad telephone cable. During his long career as an industrial chemist, Hawkins produced 19 U.S. patents, 129 foreign patents, three books, and numerous articles. Also, his intense interest in science education helped expand scientific career opportunities for African Americans. Hawkins earned his undergraduate degree at Rensselaer Polytechnic Institute in New York and his doctorate from McGill University in Montreal, Canada. He was honored in 1992 with the National Medal of Technology.

asymmetric carbon. Compounds whose molecules contain an asymmetric carbon have handedness. For these compounds, two kinds of molecules exist that are related to one another in much the same way as a pair of hands. Figure 24.9 shows the mirror images of CHFClBr. Like hands, these mirror images are nonsuperimposable. Unless bonds are broken, these molecules cannot be superimposed. The four atoms attached to the carbon will not all match at once. **Stereoisomers** *are molecules of the same molecular structure that differ only in the arrangement of the atoms in space.* The mirror images of CHFClBr are stereoisomers.

Example 4 Identifying Asymmetric Carbon Atoms

Which of the following compounds have an asymmetric carbon?

a. CH_3CHCH_3 (with OH on the central carbon)

b. $CH_3CHCH_2CH_3$ (with OH on the second carbon)

c. CH_3CHCHO (with OH on the second carbon)

d. CH_3CHOH (with OH on the second carbon)

Solution

An asymmetric carbon has four different groups attached. It may help you to draw the structures in a more complete form.

a. The central carbon has one H, one OH, and two CH_3 groups attached. It is not asymmetric because two of the four groups attached are the same.

$$CH_3-\overset{\displaystyle H}{\underset{\displaystyle OH}{C}}-CH_3$$

b. The central carbon has one H, one OH, one CH_3, and one CH_2CH_3 group attached. Because these four groups are different from one another, the central carbon is asymmetric. The asymmetric carbon can be marked with an asterisk. Neither of the other carbons in this molecule is asymmetric (check to be sure).

$$CH_3-\overset{\displaystyle H}{\underset{\displaystyle OH}{\overset{*}{C}}}-CH_2CH_3$$

c. This molecule also has an asymmetric carbon. It is marked with an asterisk.

$$\begin{array}{c} \text{H} \\ | \\ \text{CH}_3-\overset{*}{\text{C}}-\text{CHO} \\ | \\ \text{OH} \end{array}$$

d. This molecule does not have an asymmetric carbon.

$$\begin{array}{c} \text{H} \\ | \\ \text{CH}_3-\text{C}-\text{OH} \\ | \\ \text{OH} \end{array}$$

Concept Practice

17. Do all molecules have stereoisomers? Explain.

18. Which of the following objects would have a nonsuperimposable mirror image? (Ignore designs or other markings.)

a. clam shell **c.** wood screw **e.** baseball bat
b. car **d.** fingerprint

Activity 24 Stereoisomers

Purpose

To observe the three-dimensional shapes of molecules.

Materials

4 balloons, 1 each of four different colors

string

mirror

Procedure

1. Inflate all four of the balloons to approximately the same size and tie a knot in each of their necks.

2. Take the four balloons and tie their necks closely together with string.

Analysis and Conclusions

1. Describe the general shape adopted by the balloons.

2. Hold the arrangement of balloons in front of a mirror. Is its image the same as the original arrangement?

3. Carefully slide two of the balloons in the arrangement past one another so that they change positions. Comment on the arrangement of the colors compared with the former arrangement.

4. If the arrangement had two balloons of the same color, would its mirror image be the same as or different from the object?

5. Explain what a stereoisomer is in terms of your balloon models.

6. How are your feet like your balloon models?

Objective

List and construct the structures of simple cyclic and aromatic compounds.

24.8 Cyclic and Aromatic Hydrocarbons

In some hydrocarbon compounds, the two ends of a carbon chain are attached to form a ring. *Compounds that contain a hydrocarbon ring are* **cyclic hydrocarbons**. The structures of some cyclic hydrocarbons are shown in Figure 24.10. Rings containing from 3 to 20 carbons are found in nature. Five- and six-membered rings are the most abundant. *All hydrocarbon compounds which do not contain rings are known as* **aliphatic compounds**. They include compounds with both short and long carbon chains.

A special group of unsaturated cyclic hydrocarbons are known as **arenes**. These compounds contain single rings or groups of rings. The arenes were originally called aromatic compounds because many of them have pleasant odors. Benzene, C_6H_6, is the simplest arene. *Today the term* **aromatic compound** *is applied to any substance in which the bonding is like that of benzene.*

The benzene molecule has a six-membered carbon ring with a hydrogen attached to each carbon. This leaves one electron from each carbon free to participate in a double bond. Two different structures with double bonds can be written for benzene.

H H H H H H ← Single bond   H H H H H H ← Double bond

These structural formulas show only the extremes in electron sharing between any two adjacent carbons in benzene. One extreme is a normal single bond. The other extreme is a normal double bond. *Resonance occurs when two or more equally valid structures can be drawn for a molecule.* The benzene molecule exhibits resonance. Benzene and other molecules that exhibit resonance are more stable than similar molecules that do not exhibit resonance. Thus benzene is not as reactive as six-carbon alkenes.

Because of resonance, the bonding in benzene and related arenes is unique. The benzene molecule is perfectly flat. Bending or twisting would disrupt the electron sharing and the molecule's stability. You can use a circle to show the presence of resonance in a benzene ring (shown below at left and center). The traditional structure (shown on the right) is used in this text.

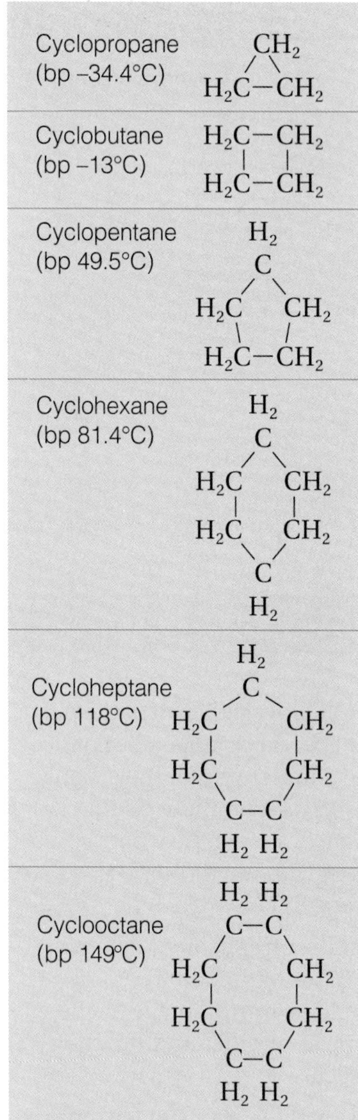

Figure 24.10 Cycloalkanes are named after the parent alkane. Cycloalkenes are similar but are not shown here.

The inscribed circle is a good way to represent the nature of resonance bonding. However, it does not show the number of electrons involved.

Compounds containing substituents attached to the benzene ring are named as derivatives of benzene. Sometimes the benzene ring is named as a substituent on an alkane. In such instances the C_6H_5- group is called a phenyl group.

CH_3 (on benzene ring)
Methylbenzene (toluene)

$CH_3-CH_2-CH-CH_2-CH_2-CH_3$ (phenyl on C-3)
3-Phenylhexane

CH_2-CH_3 (on benzene ring)
Ethylbenzene

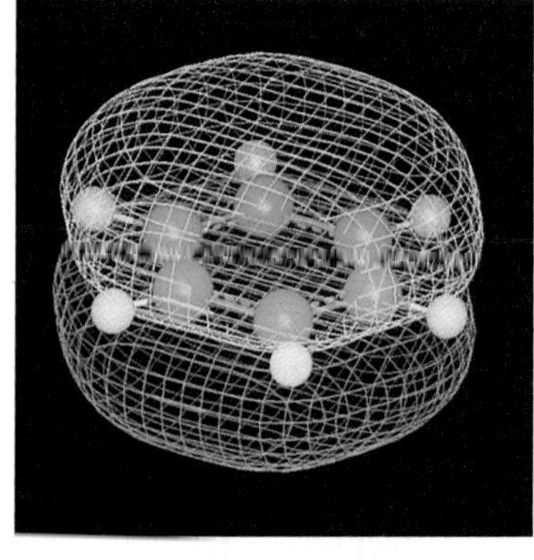

Figure 24.11 Benzene is a planar symmetrical molecule. Shown here is a computer-generated ball-and-stick model of benzene inside a model of its molecular surface.

Concept Practice

19. Both cyclohexane and benzene have six carbons bonded in a ring. What are some differences between these two compounds?

20. Name the following compounds.

a. (benzene ring)$-CH_2CH_2CH_3$

b. $CH_3-CH-CH_3$ (benzene ring on central carbon)

Safety

Benzene is a known carcinogen and is not recommended for use in schools. Several of its derivatives are also suspected carcinogens or are highly toxic.

Some derivatives of benzene have two substituents. Such derivatives are called *disubstituted benzenes.* Three different structural isomers occur for the liquid aromatic compound dimethylbenzene, $C_6H_4(CH_3)_2$. Once again, the physical properties of structural isomers are different, as indicated by their boiling points.

CH_3, CH_3
1,2-Dimethylbenzene (*o*-dimethylbenzene, *o*-xylene) (bp 144°C)

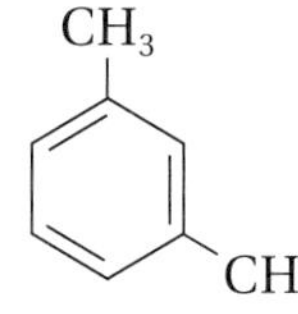

CH_3, CH_3
1,3-Dimethylbenzene (*m*-dimethylbenzene, *m*-xylene) (bp 139°C)

CH_3, CH_3
1,4-Dimethylbenzene (*p*-dimethylbenzene, *p*-xylene) (bp 138°C)

In the IUPAC naming system, the possible positions of two substituents in disubstituted benzene are designated as 1,2; 1,3; or 1,4. In common names for disubstituted benzenes the terms *ortho*, *meta*, and *para* (abbreviated *o*, *m*, and *p*) are used in place of numbers. The dimethylbenzenes are also called xylenes.

Objective

Describe the origins of coal and the various products it yields.

24.9 Coal

Geologists believe that coal had its origin some 300 million years ago. At that time, huge tree ferns and mosses grew abundantly in swampy tropical regions. When the plants died, they formed thick layers of decaying vegetation. They were eventually covered by layer after layer of soil and rock, which caused a build-up of intense pressure. This pressure, together with the heat from the interior of the earth, slowly turned these plant remains into coal.

The first stage in the formation of coal is an intermediate material known as *peat*. Peat is a soft, brown, spongy, fibrous material rather like decayed and compressed garden refuse. It has a very high water content when first dug out of a "peat bog." After it has been allowed to dry, it produces a low-cost but smoky fuel. If peat is left in the ground, it continues to change. After a long period of time it loses most of its fibrous texture and becomes *lignite*, or brown coal. Lignite is much harder than peat and has a higher carbon content (about 50%). The water content, however, is still high. Continued pressure and heat slowly change lignite to *bituminous*, or soft coal. Bituminous coal has a lower water content and higher carbon content (70–80%) than lignite. In some regions of the earth's crust, even greater pressures have been exerted. In those places, such as in eastern Pennsylvania, coal has been changed into *anthracite*, or hard coal. Anthracite has a carbon content that exceeds 80%, making it an excellent fuel source.

Coal is obtained from both underground and surface mines. It is usually found in seams from 1 to 3 meters thick. In North America, coal mines are usually less than 100 meters underground. Much of the coal is so close to the surface that it is strip-mined. By contrast, many coal mines in Europe and other parts of the world go down 1000 to 1500 meters.

Coal consists largely of condensed ring compounds of very high molecular mass. These compounds have a very high proportion of carbon compared with hydrogen. Due to the high proportion of these aromatic compounds, coal leaves more soot upon burning than do the more aliphatic fuels obtained from petroleum. The majority of the coal burned in North America contains about 7% sulfur. Sulfur burns to form SO_2 and SO_3, which are major air pollutants.

Figure 24.12 Underground coal seams may be thin and wandering, making mining difficult and hazardous. Modern machinery is reducing the number of miners who have to work underground.

Coal may be distilled to obtain a variety of products: coal gas, coal tar, ammonia, and coke. Coal gas consists mainly of hydrogen, methane, and carbon monoxide. All of these are flammable. Coal tar can be distilled further into benzene, toluene, naphthalene, phenol, and pitch. Coke is used as a fuel in many industrial processes. Because it is almost pure carbon, coke produces intense heat and little or no smoke when it burns. The ammonia from distilled coal is converted to ammonium sulfate for use as a fertilizer.

Concept Practice

21. Rank these materials in order of increasing hardness: bituminous coal, peat, lignite, and anthracite coal.

22. Discuss the chemical structure of coal.

24.10 Natural Gas and Petroleum

Objective

Describe the formation of petroleum and natural gas deposits.

Much of the world's need for energy is supplied by burning fossil fuels. These fuels are organic in nature because they are derived from the decay of organisms in geologic history. Natural gas and petroleum are two important fossil fuels. They contain mostly aliphatic, or open-chain hydrocarbons.

Petroleum, or crude oil, was first discovered seeping out of rocks. Petroleum and natural gas had their origin in marine life buried in the sediments of the oceans millions of years ago. Heat, pressure, and the action of bacteria changed this residue into petroleum and natural gas. The natural gas is often found overlying the oil deposits or in separate pockets in rock.

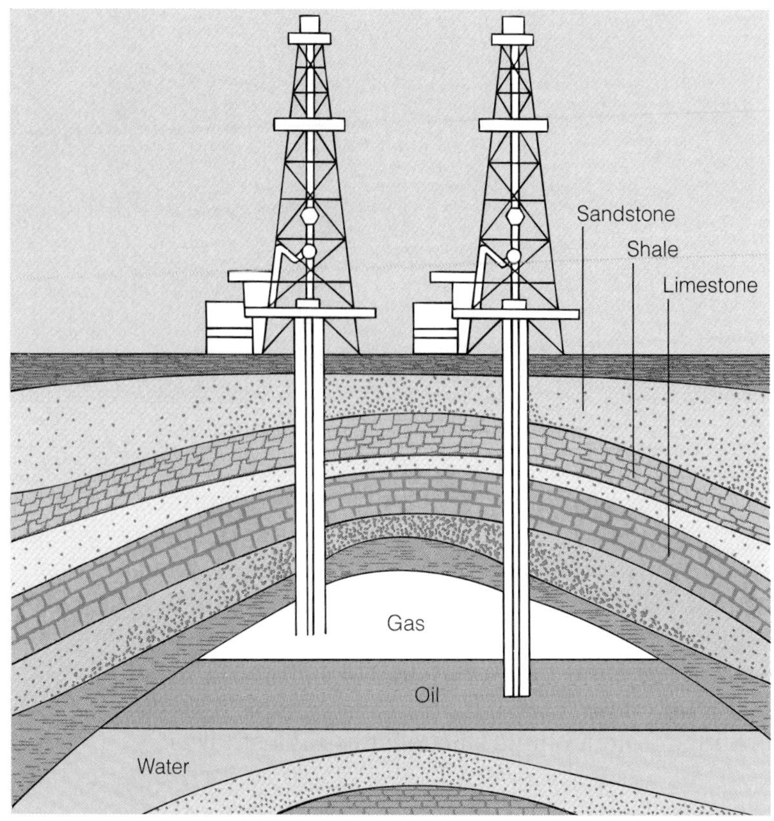

Figure 24.13 Natural gas and oil are typically found in dome-shaped geological formations. Sometimes the gas is under pressure and will force the oil up the well pipe, but pumping is usually required.

Integrating Geology

Petrochemical Exploration

Searching for and finding petroleum deposits is a lucrative and financially risky business. Petroleum prospectors use many technologies to examine the geology of the Earth's surface searching for likely areas for deposits. Infrared photographs taken from space clearly show rock fractures indicative of oil deposits. Underground contour maps obtained through seismographic studies are also analyzed for likely deposits. Prospectors also use a gravity meter to search for areas of reduced gravity on the surface, as such areas are likely to be over oil deposits.

Natural gas is an important source of alkanes of low molecular mass. Typically, natural gas is composed of about 80% methane, 10% ethane, 4% propane, and 2% butane. The remaining 4% consists of nitrogen and higher-molecular-mass hydrocarbons. Natural gas also contains a small amount of the noble gas helium and is one of its major sources. Methane is the major constituent of natural gas. It is especially prized for combustion because it burns with a hot, clean flame.

$$CH_4(g) + 2O_2(g) \longrightarrow CO_2(g) + 2H_2O(l) + \text{heat}$$

Propane and butane are also good heating fuels. They are separated from the other gases by liquefaction. They are sold in liquid form in pressurized tanks as liquid petroleum gas (LPG).

A sufficient supply of oxygen is necessary to oxidize a hydrocarbon fuel completely and to obtain the greatest amount of heat. Complete combustion of a hydrocarbon gives a blue flame. Incomplete combustion gives a yellow flame. This is due to the formation of small, glowing carbon particles that are deposited as soot when they cool. Carbon monoxide, a toxic gas, is also formed along with carbon dioxide and water during incomplete combustion.

$$6CH_4(g) + 9O_2(g) \longrightarrow 2C(s) + 2CO(g) + 2CO_2(g) + 12H_2O(l)$$

Table 24.4 Fractions Obtained from Crude Oils

Fraction	Composition of carbon chains	Boiling range (°C)	Percent of crude oil
Natural gas	C_1 to C_4	Below 20	10%
Petroleum ether (solvent)	C_5 to C_6	30 to 60	
Naphtha (solvent)	C_7 to C_8	60 to 90	
Gasoline	C_6 to C_{12}	75 to 200	40%
Kerosene	C_{12} to C_{15}	200 to 300	10%
Fuel oils, mineral oil	C_{15} to C_{18}	300 to 400	30%
Lubricating oil, petroleum jelly, greases, paraffin wax, asphalt	C_{16} to C_{24}	Over 400	10%

The organic compounds found in petroleum are more complex than those in natural gas. Most of its hydrocarbons are continuous-chain and branched-chain alkanes. Petroleum also contains small amounts of aromatic compounds and small amounts of sulfur-, oxygen-, and nitrogen-containing organic compounds.

Vast deposits of petroleum were discovered in the United States in 1859 and in the Middle East in 1908. Petroleum has since been found in other parts of the world as well. Crude oil must be refined before it is commercially useful. Petroleum refining consists of distilling crude oil to divide it into fractions according to boiling point. Each fraction contains several different hydrocarbons. The fractions, which have a variety of uses, are shown in Table 24.4.

The fractions containing compounds of higher molecular mass can be "cracked" to produce the more useful short-chain components of gasoline and kerosene. **Cracking** *is a controlled process by which hydrocarbons are broken down or rearranged into smaller, more useful molecules.* Hydrocarbons are cracked with the aid of a catalyst or with heat. By this process, petroleum is the principal source of raw materials for the organic chemicals industry. For example, the low-molecular-mass alkanes are starting materials for the manufacture of paints and plastics.

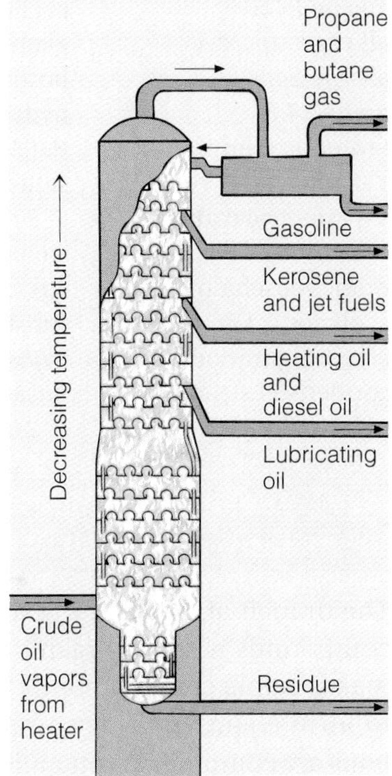

Figure 24.14 Petroleum is refined by fractional distillation. First the crude oil is heated so that it vaporizes and rises through the column. Compounds with the highest boiling points condense first near the bottom. Compounds with the lowest boiling points condense last near the top.

Concept Practice

23. Define *petroleum refining* and *cracking.*

Practice Problem

24. Write an equation for the complete combustion of octane.

Chapter 24 Review
Hydrocarbon Compounds

Key Terms

aliphatic compound *24.8*
alkane *24.1*
alkene *24.5*
alkyl group *24.3*
alkyne *24.5*
arene *24.8*
aromatic compound *24.8*
asymmetric carbon *24.7*
branched-chain alkane *24.3*
cis configuration *24.6*
condensed structural formula *24.2*
continuous-chain alkane *24.2*
cracking *24.9*
cyclic hydrocarbon *24.8*
geometric isomer *24.6*
homologous series *24.2*
hydrocarbon *24.0*
IUPAC system *24.2*
saturated compound *24.5*
stereoisomer *24.7*
structural isomer *24.4*
substituent *24.3*
trans configuration *24.6*
unsaturated compound *24.5*

Chapter Summary

The branch of chemistry that deals with carbon compounds is called organic chemistry. Carbon makes stable covalent bonds with other carbons to form chain and ring compounds. Hydrocarbons are compounds containing only carbon and hydrogen. Many hydrocarbons have structural isomerism. That is, molecules with a common formula have different structures.

Alkanes contain only carbon–carbon single bonds. The groups attached to single bonds in continuous-chain alkanes rotate freely about the bonds at room temperature. Alkenes are unsaturated hydrocarbons. That is, they contain one or more carbon–carbon double bonds. Alkenes may exhibit geometric isomerism. Geometric isomers are *cis* or *trans* according to whether substituent groups are on the same side or on opposite sides of the double bond. Alkynes are also unsaturated compounds. They contain one or more carbon–carbon triple bonds. Rotation about the multiple bonds of alkenes and alkynes does not occur under ordinary conditions. Some organic molecules exhibit stereoisomerism. Stereoisomers are related in much the same way as the right hand is related to the left. Stereoisomerism can occur if four different groups are attached to carbon.

Aromatic hydrocarbons or arenes are related to the hydrocarbon benzene. Benzene is rather unusual among hydrocarbons. As a result of resonance, the interior bonds of the benzene ring are somewhere between ordinary single bonds and double bonds. Benzene is less reactive than ordinary alkenes because of this unusual bonding.

Aliphatic, or open-chain, hydrocarbons come mainly from petroleum. Aromatic hydrocarbons come mainly from coal. Many hydrocarbons are obtained directly from crude petroleum by distillation. The molecular structures of the hydrocarbons present in natural petroleum can be reorganized into other useful products by the cracking process.

Practice Questions and Problems

25. What is the number of covalent bonds formed by carbon? *24.1*

26. Name the alkanes that have the following formulas. *24.2*

a. $CH_3CH_2CH_3$

b. $CH_3(CH_2)_6CH_3$

c.

```
     H  H  H  H  H
     |  |  |  |  |
  H—C—C—C—C—C—H
     |  |  |  |  |
     H  H  H  H  H
```

27. Draw structural formulas for these compounds. *24.3*

a. pentane
b. 3-ethylpentane
c. 4-ethyl-2,3,4-trimethylnonane
d. 3,5-diethyl-2,3-dimethyl-5-propyldecane

28. Write structures for the alkyl groups derived from methane, ethane, and propane. *24.3*

29. Why are the following names incorrect? What are the correct names? *24.3*

a. 2-dimethylpentane

b. 1,3-dimethylpropane

c. 3-methylbutane

d. 3,4-dimethylbutane

30. Give the IUPAC name for each compound. *24.3*

a.
$$\begin{array}{l} CH_3{-}\underset{\displaystyle CH_3}{\underset{|}{CH}}{-}\underset{\displaystyle CH_3}{\underset{|}{CH_2}} \end{array}$$

b.
$$CH_3{-}\underset{\displaystyle CH_3}{\underset{|}{CH}}{-}\underset{\displaystyle CH_3}{\underset{|}{CH}}{-}CH_3$$

c.
$$CH_3{-}\underset{\underset{\displaystyle CH_3}{\underset{|}{CH_2}}}{\underset{|}{CH}}{-}CH_2{-}\underset{\displaystyle CH_3}{\underset{|}{CH_2}}$$

31. Draw one structural isomer of each of the following compounds. *24.4*

a.
$$CH_3{-}\overset{\displaystyle CH_3}{\overset{|}{\underset{\displaystyle CH_3}{\underset{|}{C}}}}{-}CH_3$$

b.
$$CH_3{-}\overset{\displaystyle CH_3}{\overset{|}{CH}}{-}\underset{\underset{\displaystyle CH_3}{\underset{|}{CH_2}}}{\underset{|}{CH}}{-}CH_3$$

c.
$$CH_3{-}\overset{\displaystyle CH_3}{\overset{|}{CH}}{-}CH_2{-}\underset{\underset{\displaystyle CH_3}{\underset{|}{CH_2}}}{\underset{|}{CH}}{-}\overset{\displaystyle CH_3}{\overset{|}{\underset{\underset{\displaystyle CH_3}{\underset{|}{CH_2}}}{\underset{|}{CH}}}}$$

32. Explain the difference between saturated and unsaturated hydrocarbons. *24.5*

33. Draw a structural formula for each alkene with the molecular formula C_5H_{10}. Name each of these compounds. *24.5*

34. Give a systematic name for these alkenes. *24.5*

a. $CH_3CH{=}CH_2$

b.
$$\begin{array}{ccc} CH_3 & & H \\ & C{=}C & \\ H & & CH_2CH_3 \end{array}$$

c.
$$CH_3\underset{\displaystyle CH_3}{\underset{|}{C}}HCH_2CH{=}CH_2$$

d.
$$\begin{array}{ccc} CH_3 & & CH_2CH_3 \\ & C{-}C & \\ CH_3 & & CH_2CH_3 \end{array}$$

e.
$$CH_2{=}CHCH_2\underset{\displaystyle CH_2CH_3}{\underset{|}{CH_2}}$$

35. Show how lack of rotation about a carbon–carbon double bond leads to geometric isomerism. Use the isomers of 2-pentene to illustrate your answer. *24.6*

36. Draw a structural formula or carbon skeleton for each of the following alkenes. Include both *cis* and *trans* forms if the compound has geometric isomers. *24.6*

a. 2-pentene

b. 2-methyl-2-pentene

c. 3-methyl-2-pentene

37. For which of the following molecular formulas can mirror image molecules be drawn? Why? *24.7*

a. CH_2Cl_2

b.
$$HS{-}\overset{\displaystyle F}{\overset{|}{\underset{\displaystyle F}{\underset{|}{C}}}}{-}OH$$

c. $CH_3CF_2CH_3$

d.
$$CH_3CH_2{-}\overset{\displaystyle CH_3}{\overset{|}{\underset{\displaystyle F}{\underset{|}{C}}}}{-}Br$$

38. Draw a structure for each compound. *24.8*

a. *p*-diethylbenzene

b. 2-methyl-3-phenylpentane

c. *p*-xylene

d. toluene

39. Explain why both of these structures represent 1,2-diethylbenzene. *24.8*

CH_2CH_3 CH_2CH_3 CH_2CH_3 CH_2CH_3

40. The seven organic chemicals produced in the largest amounts in the United States in a recent year are listed in the following table. Answer these questions based on the data given for the amount of each compound produced. *24.8*

a. How many billion kilograms of aromatic compounds on the list were produced?

b. Of the total mass of all seven compounds produced, what percent by mass was made up of aliphatic compounds?

c. The molecules of many of the compounds on this list have double bonds. Propose an explanation for this fact.

Chemical	Amount produced (kg × 10^9)
Ethylene	15.9
Propylene	8.4
Urea	6.8
Ethylene dichloride	6.3
Benzene	5.3
Ethyl benzene	4.3
Vinyl chloride	3.7

41. How does the amount of sulfur in coal affect its potential use? *24.10*

42. Does crude oil contain mostly aliphatic or aromatic hydrocarbons? *24.9*

43. Write a balanced equation for the complete combustion of pentane. *24.9*

Mastery Questions and Problems

44. Write structural formulas for each of the following compounds.

a. propyne

b. cyclohexane

c. 2-phenylpropane

d. 2,2,4-trimethylpentane

e. 2,3-dimethylpentane

f. 1,1-diphenylhexane

45. Construct a concept map using the key terms in the chapter with *hydrocarbon* as the central concept.

46. For each hydrocarbon pictured below, identify the type of bonding and name the compound.

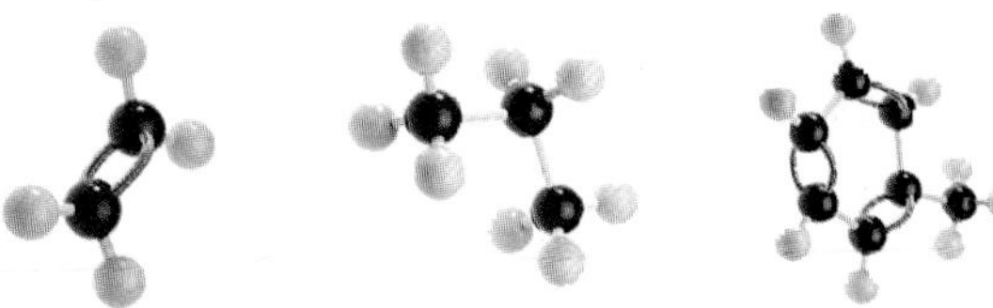

47. Name the next three higher homologs of ethane.

48. Draw electron dot structures for these compounds.

a. ethene

b. propane

c. ethyne

d. cyclobutane

49. Compare these three molecular structures. Which would you expect to be most stable? Why?

Critical Thinking Questions

50. Choose the term that best completes the second relationship.

a. tree:branch — hydrocarbon chain:_____
(1) alkyl group (2) methane
(3) isomer (4) double bond

b. cyclic:aliphatic — circle:_____
(1) oval (2) parallelogram
(3) square (4) line

c. propane:three — hexene:_____
(1) seven (2) six
(3) five (4) four

51. Why do most cyclic hydrocarbons have higher boiling points than alkanes with the same number of carbons?

52. Do you think that the use of plastics should be unregulated, regulated, or banned? Explain the reason for your choice.

53. How could the composition of gasoline be altered to increase the ease of starting a car in cold weather?

54. Discuss what problems might occur if the world returned to using only natural fibers. What advantages would there be?

Cumulative Review

55. What are the pH values for aqueous solutions containing each of the following hydroxide ion concentrations?

a. $1.00 \times 10^{-4}M$ **b.** $3.92 \times 10^{-7}M$ **c.** $0.01M$ **d.** $0.005M$

56. Give the oxidation number of each element in the following compounds.

a. $CaCO_3$ **b.** Cl_2 **c.** $LiIO_3$ **d.** Na_2SO_3

57. Draw electron dot structures and predict the shapes of the following molecules.

a. PH_3 **b.** CO **c.** CS_2 **d.** CF_4

58. Write equilibrium constant expressions for the following reactions.

a. $Cl_2(g) + I_2(g) \rightleftharpoons 2ICl(g)$

b. $2HBr(g) \rightleftharpoons H_2(g) + Br_2(g)$

c. $2S_2Cl_2(g) + 2H_2O(g) \rightleftharpoons 4HCl(g) + 3S(g) + SO_2(g)$

d. $N_2(g) + 3H_2(g) \rightleftharpoons 2NH_3(g)$

59. Identify any incorrect formulas among the following compounds.

a. H_2O_2 **b.** $NaIO_4$ **c.** SrO **d.** CaS_2 **e.** $CaHPO_4$ **f.** $BaOH$

60. A colorless solution of unknown pH turns blue when tested with the acid-base indicator bromthymol blue. It remains colorless when tested with phenolphthalein.

a. What is the approximate pH of the solution?

b. How could you determine the pH more accurately?

Challenge Questions and Problems

61. The knocking properties of fuels for gasoline engines are based on standards of heptane, which causes severe engine knocking, and 2,2,4-trimethylpentane ("isooctane"), which is better than most other fuels. The *octane number* of gasoline is the percentage of 2,2,4-trimethylpentane in heptane that is required to match the knocking properties of the fuel. What are the octane numbers of gasolines available in your neighborhood? To what percentages of 2,2,4-trimethylpentane in heptane do they correspond? How might it be possible to achieve octane numbers greater than 100? On the basis of the behavior of 2,2,4-trimethylpentane and heptane, would you expect pentane or 2,2-dimethylpropane to give the best performance as a fuel in a gasoline engine?

Connections Questions

62. What are some techniques used in cleaning up an oil tanker spill?

63. Name some methods used in oil prospecting.

64. What industry has benefited from the work of W. Lincoln Hawkins?

Write About Chemistry

65. Fossil fuels are the raw materials for many consumer products. Do you think it is wise to continue to use the limited supplies of fossil fuels as an energy source? Explain.

66. Fruits are sometimes picked while green and transported long distances, after which they are exposed to ethene gas, which speeds the ripening process. Research and write a short paper detailing the advantages and disadvantages of using ethene to speed the ripening of fruits.

Readings and References

Dean, John A. *Handbook of Organic Chemistry.* New York: McGraw-Hill, 1987.

Nagel, Miriam C. "The Fruits of Ethylene." *ChemMatters* (April 1989), pp. 11–13.

Smith, Trevor. "Camping Stoves." *ChemMatters* (April 1992), pp. 7–11.

25 Functional Groups and Organic Reactions

Goals

- Identify simple substituted organic compounds.
- Identify the molecular and structural formulas of organic compounds.
- Categorize organic compounds according to their functional groups.
- Describe the physical and chemical properties of organic compounds based on their functional groups.
- List the products of oxidation–reduction reactions in organic chemistry.

Shown here is a computer-enhanced version of the DNA molecule. DNA is a nucleic acid, a huge chain-linked polymer found primarily in cell nuclei. The molar masses of different DNA molecules are in the millions or maybe billions of grams.

Concept Overview

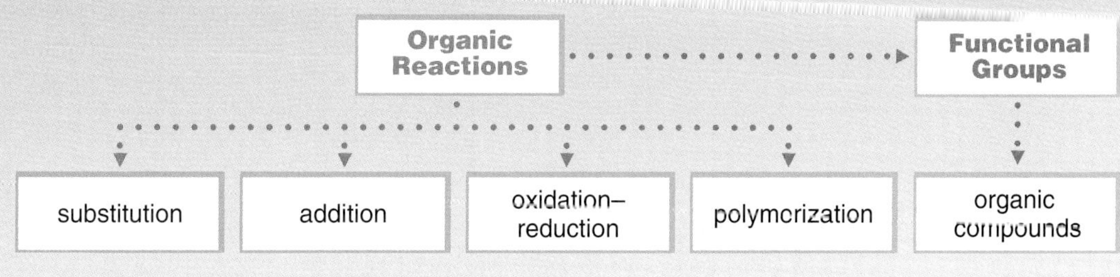

The Concept Overview organizes the major concepts of this chapter. This diagram shows one way to link these concepts related to functional groups and organic reactions.

The previous chapter introduced hydrocarbon chains and rings. These are essential components of every organic compound. Yet in most chemical reactions involving organic molecules, the hydrocarbon skeletons of the molecules are chemically inert. Thus the chemistry of the alkanes is very limited. Most organic chemistry involves substituents attached to hydrocarbon chains. This chapter discusses some of these substituents and their chemical reactions.

25.1 Functional Groups

Objective

Identify a molecule's functional group.

The substituents of organic molecules often contain oxygen, nitrogen, sulfur, or phosphorus. They are called functional groups because they are the chemically functional parts of the molecules. *A* **functional group** *is a specific arrangement of atoms in an organic compound that is capable of characteristic chemical reactions.* Most organic chemistry is functional group chemistry. You can classify organic compounds into categories according to their functional groups. The symbol R is used to represent any carbon chains or rings attached to the functional group. The double and triple bonds of alkenes and alkynes are chemically reactive and are considered functional groups. On the next page, Table 25.1 lists the other functional groups covered in this book. You can refer to this table when you encounter an unfamiliar group.

Table 25.1 Organic Compounds Classified by Functional Group

Compound type	Compound structure	Functional group
Halocarbon	R—X (X = F, Cl, Br, I)	Halogen
Alcohol	R—OH	Hydroxyl
Ether	R—O—R	Ether
Aldehyde	$R-\overset{O}{\overset{\|\|}{C}}-H$	Carbonyl
Ketone	$R-\overset{O}{\overset{\|\|}{C}}-R$	Carbonyl
Carboxylic acid	$R-\overset{O}{\overset{\|\|}{C}}-OH$	Carboxyl
Ester	$R-\overset{O}{\overset{\|\|}{C}}-O-R$	Ester
Amine	$R-NH_2$	Amino

Concept Practice

1. Identify the functional group in each of the following structures.

a. CH_3-OH

b. $CH_3-CH_2-NH_2$

c. 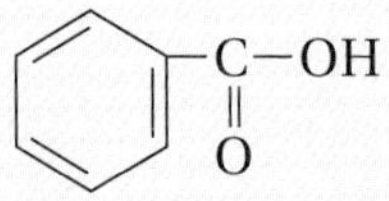 $C_6H_5-\underset{O}{\underset{\|\|}{C}}-OH$ (benzene ring attached to C—OH with C=O)

d. $CH_3-CH_2-CH_2-Br$

e. $CH_3-CH_2-O-CH_2-CH_2-CH_3$

2. What does *R* in the formula R—CHO represent?

Objective

Explain physical property differences in a class of organic compounds based on their molecular structure.

25.2 Halocarbons

Halocarbons *are a class of organic compounds containing covalently bonded fluorine, chlorine, bromine, or iodine.* Very few halocarbons are found in nature. Nevertheless, they are readily prepared and used for many purposes. For example, halocarbons are widely used as anesthetics and insecticides.

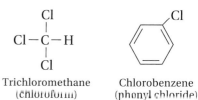

CH_3-Cl	$CH_3-C(CH_3)(Br)-CH_3$	$H(H)C=C(Cl)(H)$	$Cl-C(Cl)(Cl)-H$	C_6H_5Cl
Chloromethane (methyl chloride)	2-Bromo-2-methylpropane (*tert*-butyl bromide)	Chloroethene (vinyl chloride)	Trichloromethane (chloroform)	Chlorobenzene (phenyl chloride)

The IUPAC rules for naming halocarbons are based on the name of the parent hydrocarbon. The halogen groups are simply added as substituents. Above are some examples of IUPAC names for simple halocarbons. (Common names are in parentheses.)

Common names of halocarbons consist of two parts. The first part names the hydrocarbon part of the molecule as an alkyl group, such as methyl or ethyl. The second part gives the halogen an *-ide* ending. Methyl chloride, CH_3Cl, is an example. Remember, however, that the bonding in a halocarbon is covalent, not ionic.

On the basis of their common names, *halocarbons in which a halogen is attached to a carbon of an aliphatic chain are called* **alkyl halides**. Table 25.2 gives names for alkyl groups besides those of methyl, ethyl, and propyl. *Halocarbons in which a halogen is attached to a carbon of an arene ring are called* **aryl halides**.

Safety

Many halogenated hydrocarbons are extremely toxic, carcinogenic, flammable, or all three.

Table 25.2 Names of Some Common Alkyl Groups

Name	Alkyl group	Remarks
Isopropyl	$CH_3-CH(CH_3)-$	The prefix *iso* - is used when there is a methyl group on the carbon second from the unsubstituted end of the longest chain.
Isobutyl	$CH_3-CH(CH_3)-CH_2-$ (primary carbon)	The carbon joining this alkyl group to another group is bonded to one other carbon; it is a *primary carbon*.
Secondary butyl (*sec*-butyl)	$CH_3-CH_2-CH(-)-CH_3$ (secondary carbon)	The carbon joining this alkyl group to another group is bonded to two other carbons; it is a *secondary carbon*.
Tertiary butyl (*tert*-butyl)	$CH_3-C(CH_3)(CH_3)-$ (tertiary carbon)	The carbon joining this alkyl group to another group is bonded to three carbons; it is a *tertiary carbon*.
Vinyl	$H_2C=CH-$	When used as an alkyl group in giving compounds common names, this group is called *vinyl*.
Phenyl	C_6H_5-	Phenyl is derived from benzene.

Table 25.3 Some Halocarbons and Their Uses

Halocarbon	Use
$CH_3—CH_2—Cl$ Chloroethane (ethyl chloride)	A local anesthetic. Its rapid evaporation on the skin (bp 13°C) cools nerve endings and cuts down transmission of pain.
CCl_2F_2 Dichlorodifluoromethane (freon 12) and CCl_3F Trichlorofluoromethane (freon 11)	Freon is the Du Pont trade name for fluorinated compounds of this type. They are used as refrigerants. Freons are nontoxic, odorless, and nonflammable. Some are also used in specialized fire extinguishers.
Cl–C_6H_4–Cl *p*-Dichlorobenzene	Used as a moth repellent.
$(ClC_6H_4)_2CH–CCl_3$ Dichlorodiphenyltrichloroethane (DDT)	A persistent pesticide. DDT was widely used as an insecticide from about 1950 to 1970. Its use is now limited because of its persistence in the environment. It is nonbiodegradable.

Table 25.4 Molecular Masses and Boiling Points of the Chloromethanes

Molecular structure	Name	Formula mass	Boiling point(°C)
CH_4^*	Methane	16	–161
CH_3Cl	Chloromethane (methyl chloride)	50.5	–24
CH_2Cl_2	Dichloromethane (methylene chloride)	85.0	40
$CHCl_3$	Trichloromethane (chloroform)	129.5	61
CCl_4	Tetrachloromethane (carbon tetrachloride)	154	74

* Included for purposes of comparison.

Table 25.3 gives the structures and uses of some halocarbons. The attractions between halocarbon molecules are primarily the result of the weak van der Waals interactions called dispersion forces. These attractions increase with the degree of halogen substitution. More highly halogenated organic compounds therefore have higher boiling points, as shown for the chloromethanes in Table 25.4.

Concept Practice

3. Write IUPAC names for each of these halocarbons.

a. (benzene ring with Br substituent) **b.** CH_3CH_2Cl **c.** $CH_3CHCH{=}CH_2$ with Cl on the second carbon

4. Give the structural formula for each of the following compounds.

a. isopropyl chloride

b. 1-iodo-2,2-dimethylpentane

c. *p*-bromotoluene

25.3 Substitution Reactions

Objective

Describe the characteristics of a substitution reaction.

Organic reactions often proceed more slowly than the reactions of inorganic molecules and ions. This is because reactions of organic molecules commonly involve the breaking of relatively strong covalent bonds. Chemists are therefore constantly seeking new catalysts and improved procedures for conducting organic reactions. Many organic reactions are complex. They often produce a mixture of products. The desired product must then be separated by distillation, crystallization, or other means. A common type of organic reaction is **substitution**, *the replacement of an atom or group of atoms by another atom or group of atoms.*

A halogen can replace the hydrogen on an alkane to produce a halocarbon. The symbol X stands for a halogen in this generalized equation.

$$\underset{\text{Alkane}}{R{-}H} + \underset{\text{Halogen}}{X_2} \longrightarrow \underset{\text{Halocarbon}}{R{-}X} + \underset{\text{Hydrogen halide}}{HX}$$

Figure 25.1 Some halocarbons are used as pesticides. Short-lived pesticides break down within about a week. They are preferred to pesticides that break down slowly.

Integrating Medicine

Salicylates

Early practitioners of folk medicine knew that willow bark extract was an effective fever reducer. In 1860 chemists isolated salicylic acid as the effective chemical in the extract. Salicylic acid is a good pain reliever (analgesic) and fever reducer (antipyretic), but it has a sour taste and can irritate the stomach. Acetylsalicylic acid, commonly known as aspirin, was introduced in 1899 and is now widely used as an antipyretic and analgesic. Another salicylic acid derivative, methyl salicylate or oil of wintergreen, is a popular flavoring agent.

Sunlight or another source of ultraviolet radiation is usually a sufficient catalyst for this reaction. From the generalized equation, you can write a specific one.

$$\underset{\text{Methane}}{CH_4} + \underset{\text{Chlorine}}{Cl_2} \longrightarrow \underset{\text{Chloromethane}}{CH_3Cl} + \underset{\text{Hydrogen chloride}}{HCl}$$

Even under controlled conditions, this halogenation reaction forms a mixture of mono-, di-, tri-, and tetrachloromethanes.

If benzene is treated with a halogen in the presence of a catalyst, substitution of a ring hydrogen occurs. Iron compounds are often used as catalysts for aromatic substitution reactions. A rusty nail dropped in the reaction flask works fine.

$$\underset{\text{Benzene}}{C_6H_5\text{—}H} + \underset{\text{Bromine}}{Br_2} \xrightarrow{\text{catalyst}} \underset{\text{Bromobenzene (phenyl bromide)}}{C_6H_5\text{—}Br} + \underset{\text{Hydrogen bromide}}{H\text{—}Br}$$

Halogens on carbon chains are readily displaced by hydroxide ions to produce an alcohol and a salt. The general reaction follows.

$$\underset{\text{Halocarbon}}{R\text{—}X} + \underset{\text{Hydroxide ion}}{OH^-} \xrightarrow[100°C]{H_2O} \underset{\text{Alcohol}}{R\text{—}OH} + \underset{\text{Halide ion}}{X^-}$$

Chemists usually use aqueous solutions of sodium or potassium hydroxide as the source of hydroxide ions. Fluoro groups are not easily displaced. Hence fluorocarbons are seldom, if ever, used to make alcohols. Here are two specific examples.

$$\underset{\text{Iodomethane (methyl iodide)}}{CH_3\text{—}I(l)} + \underset{\text{Potassium hydroxide}}{KOH(s)} \xrightarrow[100°C]{H_2O} \underset{\text{Methanol}}{CH_3\text{—}OH(l)} + \underset{\text{Potassium iodide}}{KI(aq)}$$

$$\underset{\text{Bromoethane (ethyl bromide)}}{CH_3CH_2Br(l)} + \underset{\text{Sodium hydroxide}}{NaOH(s)} \xrightarrow[100°C]{H_2O} \underset{\text{Ethanol}}{CH_3CH_2OH(l)} + \underset{\text{Sodium bromide}}{NaBr(aq)}$$

Concept Practice

5. Write an equation for the synthesis of 2–propanol from potassium hydroxide and 2–bromopropane.

6. Write the names of all possible dichloropropanes that could be formed from the chlorination of propane.

25.A Environmental Awareness

Transporting Chemicals

A truck overturns on the highway, spilling a mysterious white substance onto the road. Within minutes, the road is closed. Dressed in protective gear, an emergency response team arrives to begin the cleanup. Rush-hour traffic backs up in both directions, while a sample of the substance is rushed to a laboratory for identification. Hours later, the substance is found to be ordinary sodium chloride and the road is reopened. The residents of the area were lucky this time. But without information about the contents of the truck, the delay was a necessary precaution. Next time, the chemical danger might be real.

Trucks carry approximately 900 million tons of hazardous materials along the highways of the United States each year. More than 99.99% of these hazardous cargoes reach their destinations safely. Nevertheless, the few accidents that do result in chemical spills present a serious threat. In a recent survey of environmental policies, state legislators placed transportation of hazardous materials at the top of their list of concerns.

In the United States, the Federal Department of Transportation encourages the use of the United Nations classification system. In this system, shipped materials are assigned an internationally recognized name and number. Placards, like those shown in Figure 25.2, displaying the identification number and any potential hazard are placed on the sides and ends of tank trucks. In the event of an accident or spill, an emergency response crew can call the *Chem*ical *T*ransportation *E*mergency *C*enter (CHEMTREC). CHEMTREC will use the number to identify the material and inform the cleanup crew of the proper emergency procedures to follow. The resources available at CHEMTREC can provide information about health hazards, risk of fire or explosion, and cleanup procedures. With this information readily available, spills can be handled swiftly and efficiently, minimizing the risks to people and the environment.

Of course, the identification of hazardous materials cannot prevent accidents. But the United Nations classification system can help to reduce the consequences of the few accidents involving hazardous chemical spills that do occur.

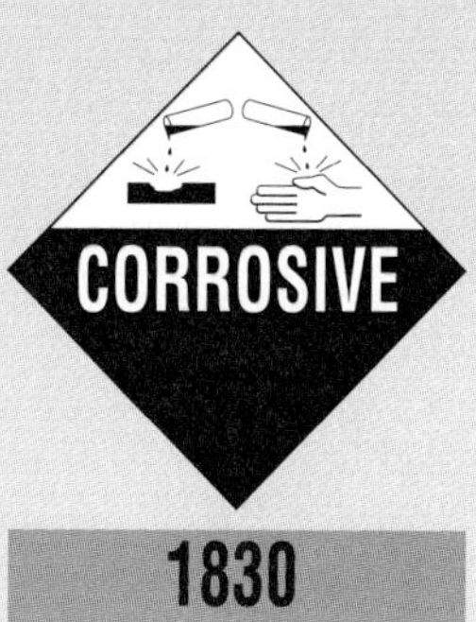

Figure 25.2 Placards displaying the identification number and potential hazards associated with acetone (1090) and sulfuric acid (1830).

Think About It

7. **Describe** What is the function of CHEMTREC?

8. **Describe** How would you respond if you witnessed an accident in which liquid began leaking out of a tank truck?

Objective

Identify an alcohol as primary, secondary, or tertiary.

25.4 Alcohols

Alcohols *are organic compounds with an —OH group.*

$$\begin{array}{c} \ddot{\text{O}} \\ \text{R}\diagup\;\;\diagdown\text{H} \end{array}$$

Alcohol molecule

The —OH functional group in alcohols is called a **hydroxyl group** *or hydroxy function.* It is not a hydroxide ion because the oxygen is covalently bonded to carbon. Aliphatic alcohols can be arranged in structural categories according to the number of R groups attached to the carbon with the hydroxyl group.

Primary alcohol	$R-CH_2-OH$	Only one R group is attached to C—OH of a primary (abbreviated 1°) alcohol.
Secondary alcohol	$\begin{array}{c} \text{R} \\ \vert \\ \text{R}-\text{CH}-\text{OH} \end{array}$	Two R groups are attached to C—OH of a secondary (2°) alcohol.
Tertiary alcohol	$\begin{array}{c} \text{R} \\ \vert \\ \text{R}-\text{C}-\text{OH} \\ \vert \\ \text{R} \end{array}$	Three R groups are attached to C—OH of a tertiary (3°) alcohol.

Both IUPAC and common names are used for alcohols. To name continuous-chain and substituted alcohols by the IUPAC system, drop the *-e* ending of the parent alkane name and add the ending *-ol.*

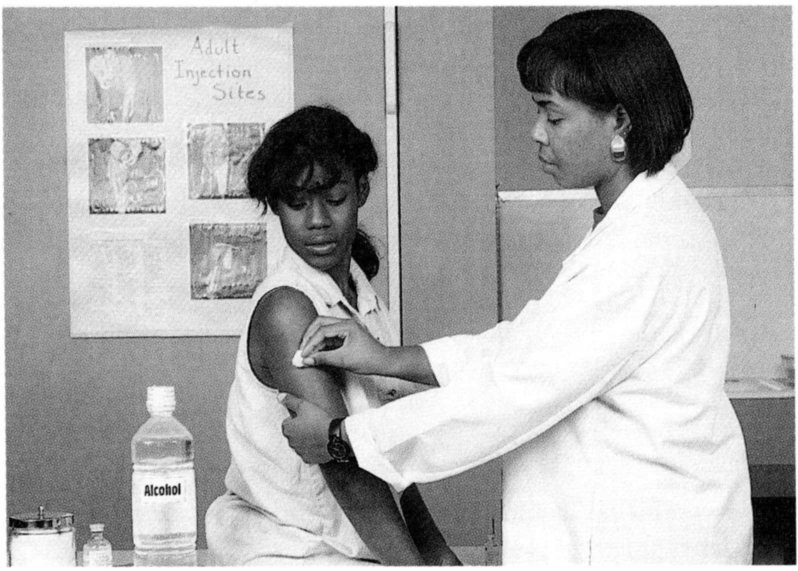

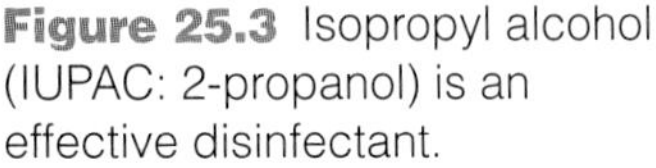

Figure 25.3 Isopropyl alcohol (IUPAC: 2-propanol) is an effective disinfectant.

The parent alkane is the longest continuous chain of carbons that includes the carbon attached to the hydroxyl group. In numbering the longest continuous chain, the position of the hydroxyl group is given the lowest possible number. Alcohols containing two, three, and four —OH substituents are named diols, triols, and tetrols.

Common names of aliphatic alcohols are written in the same way as those of the halocarbons. The alkyl group methyl, for example, is named and followed by the word alcohol, as in methyl alcohol. Compounds with more than one —OH substituent are commonly called glycols. Here are some simple aliphatic alcohols along with their IUPAC and common names.

$CH_3{-}OH$
Methanol
(methyl alcohol)

$CH_3{-}CH_2{-}OH$
Ethanol
(ethyl alcohol)

$CH_3{-}CH_2{-}CH_2{-}OH$
1-Propanol
(propyl alcohol)

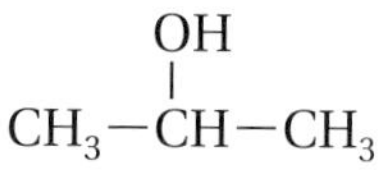

$CH_3{-}CH(OH){-}CH_3$
2-Propanol
(isopropyl alcohol)

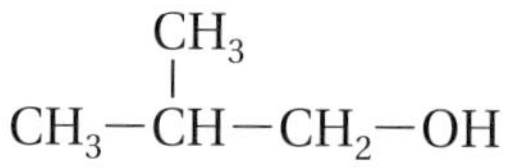

$CH_3{-}CH(CH_3){-}CH_2{-}OH$
2-Methyl-1-propanol
(isobutyl alcohol)

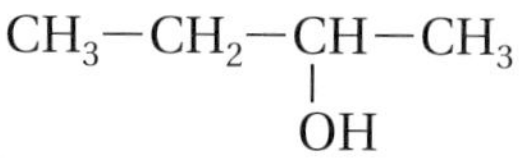

$CH_3{-}CH_2{-}CH(OH){-}CH_3$
2-Butanol
(*sec*-butyl alcohol)

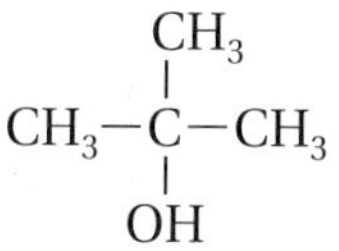

$CH_3{-}C(CH_3)(OH){-}CH_3$
2-Methyl-2-propanol
(*tert*-butyl alcohol)

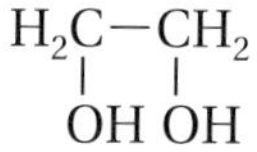

$H_2C(OH){-}CH_2(OH)$
1,2-Ethanediol
(ethylene glycol)

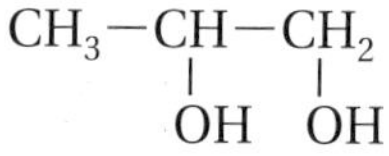

$CH_3{-}CH(OH){-}CH_2(OH)$
1,2-Propanediol
(propylene glycol)

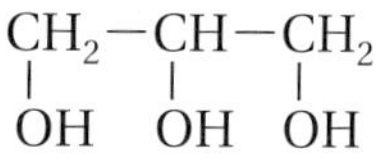

$CH_2(OH){-}CH(OH){-}CH_2(OH)$
1,2,3-Propanetriol
(glycerol)

Phenols are compounds in which a hydroxyl group is attached directly to an aromatic ring. Phenol is the parent compound. Cresol is the common name for the *o*, *m*, and *p* structural isomers of methylphenol.

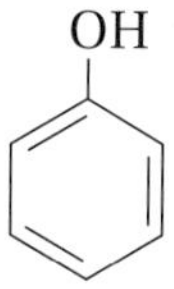

OH
Phenol

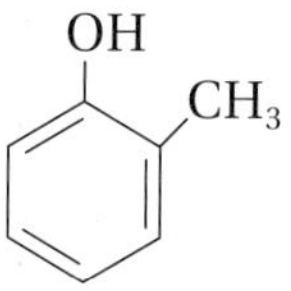

OH, CH_3
2-Methylphenol
(*o*-cresol)

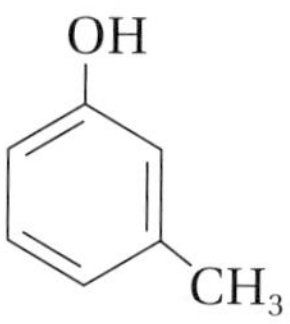

OH, CH_3
3-Methylphenol
(*m*-cresol)

OH, CH_3
4-Methylphenol
(*p*-cresol)

Concept Practice

9. Give the following alcohols IUPAC names.

a. $CH_3CH_2CH_2CH_2OH$

b.
$$\begin{array}{l} \quad\;\; CH_3 \\ \quad\quad\; | \\ CH_3CHOH \end{array}$$

c.
$$\begin{array}{l} \quad\quad\quad\quad\; CH_3 \\ \quad\quad\quad\quad\quad | \\ CH_3CH_2CHCH_2OH \end{array}$$

10. Classify each of the alcohols in Problem 9 as primary, secondary, or tertiary.

Objective

List some important uses of aliphatic alcohols.

25.5 Properties of Alcohols

Like water, alcohols exhibit intermolecular hydrogen bonding. Thus, alcohols boil at a higher temperature than alkanes and halocarbons containing comparable numbers of atoms.

Since alcohols are derivatives of water, you might expect them to be soluble in water. To a point that is correct. Alcohols of up to four carbons are soluble in water in all proportions. The solubility of alcohols with four or more carbons in the chain is usually much less. The reason is that alcohols consist of two parts: the carbon chain and the hydroxyl group. These parts are in opposition to each other. The carbon chain is nonpolar and is not attracted to water. The polar hydroxyl group, however, strongly interacts with water through hydrogen bonding.

Figure 25.4 The main ingredient in many antifreezes/coolants is 1,2-ethanediol (common name, ethylene glycol). It has a higher boiling point and lower freezing point than water. Most overheating problems occur because of mechanical failures in a car's cooling system.

Figure 25.5 Ethanol is prepared commercially by the hydration of ethene or by the fermentation of sugars.

Many aliphatic alcohols are used in laboratories, clinics, and industry. Isopropyl alcohol (IUPAC: 2-propanol), a colorless, nearly odorless liquid (bp 82°C), is also called rubbing alcohol. It is used for massages and as a base for perfumes, creams, lotions, and other cosmetics. Look at Figure 25.4. Ethylene glycol (IUPAC: 1,2-ethanediol) is the principal ingredient of certain antifreezes and has a boiling point of 197°C. Its advantages over other high-boiling liquids are its solubility in water and a freezing point of −17.4°C. If water is added to ethylene glycol, the mixture freezes at an even lower temperature. A 50% (v/v) aqueous solution of ethylene glycol freezes at −36°C. Glycerol (IUPAC: 1,2,3-propanetriol) is a viscous, water-soluble liquid. Glycerol is used as a moistening agent in cosmetics, foods, and drugs and is a component of fats and oils.

Ethyl alcohol (IUPAC: ethanol), which has a boiling point of 78.5°C, is also called grain alcohol. It is an important industrial chemical. Some ethanol is still produced by yeast fermentation of sugar. **Fermentation** *is the production of ethanol from sugars by the action of yeast or bacteria.* The enzymes of the yeast or bacteria serve as catalysts for the transformation. The breakdown of the sugar glucose, $C_6H_{12}O_6$, is an important fermentation reaction.

$$\underset{\text{Glucose}}{C_6H_{12}O_6(aq)} \longrightarrow \underset{\text{Ethanol}}{2CH_3CH_2OH(aq)} + \underset{\substack{\text{Carbon}\\ \text{dioxide}}}{2CO_2(g)}$$

Ethanol is the intoxicating substance in alcoholic beverages. Ethanol is a depressant. Taken in large enough doses at once, it can be fatal. Over time, consistent abuse of alcoholic beverages can damage the liver, which can lead to death.

The ethanol used in industrial applications is denatured. **Denatured alcohol** *is ethanol with an added substance to make it immediately toxic.* Methyl alcohol (IUPAC: methanol) is often the denaturant. It is sometimes called wood alcohol because before 1925 it was prepared by the distillation of wood. Wood alcohol is extremely toxic. As little as 10 mL has been reported to cause permanent blindness and as little as 30 mL, death.

Concept Practice

11. Show how hydrogen bonds form between molecules of these pairs of compounds.
  a. water–water
  b. water–methanol
  c. methanol–methanol

Objective

List the structures that are products of an addition reaction.

25.6 Addition Reactions

Carbon–carbon single bonds are not easy to break. One of the bonds in an alkene double bond is somewhat weaker, however, than a carbon–carbon single bond. Thus, it is sometimes possible for a compound of general structure X—Y to add to a double bond. *In an* **addition reaction** *a substance is added at the double or triple bond of an alkene or alkyne.* Addition reactions are an important method of introducing new functional groups into organic molecules. In this general reaction, X and Y stand for the two parts of the compound which are added.

$$\mathrm{>C{=}C<} + \mathrm{X{-}Y} \longrightarrow \mathrm{-\underset{|}{\overset{X}{\overset{|}{C}}}-\underset{|}{\overset{Y}{\overset{|}{C}}}-}$$

The addition of water to an alkene is a **hydration reaction**. Hydration reactions usually occur when the alkene and water are heated to about 100°C in the presence of a trace of strong acid. The acid serves as a catalyst for the reaction. Hydrochloric or sulfuric acid is generally used. The addition of water to ethene is a typical hydration reaction.

$$\underset{\text{Ethene}}{\mathrm{H_2C{=}CH_2}} + \underset{\text{Water}}{\mathrm{H{-}OH}} \xrightarrow{H^+} \underset{\text{Ethanol}}{\mathrm{H{-}\underset{H}{\overset{H}{C}}{-}\underset{H}{\overset{OH}{C}}{-}H}}$$

When the reagent X—Y is a halogen molecule like chlorine or bromine, the product of the reaction is a disubstituted halocarbon.

$$\underset{\text{Ethene (colorless)}}{\mathrm{H_2C{=}CH_2}} + \underset{\text{Bromine (brownish orange)}}{\mathrm{Br{-}Br}} \longrightarrow \underset{\text{1,2-Dibromoethane (colorless)}}{\mathrm{H{-}\underset{H}{\overset{Br}{C}}{-}\underset{H}{\overset{Br}{C}}{-}H}}$$

The addition of bromine to carbon–carbon multiple bonds is often used as a chemical test for unsaturation in an organic molecule. Bromine has a brownish-orange color, but most organic compounds of bromine are colorless. The test for unsaturation is done by adding a few drops of a 1% solution of bromine in carbon tetrachloride (CCl_4) to the suspected alkene. As seen in Figure 25.6, the loss of the orange color is a positive test for unsaturation.

Figure 25.6 When a few drops of bromine solution (beaker on left) are added to an unsaturated organic compound, the bromine becomes colorless (right). This forms the basis of a test for unsaturated compounds.

Hydrogen halides such as HBr or HCl can also add to a double bond. The product contains only one substituent. It is called a monosubstituted halocarbon.

$$H_2C{=}CH_2 + H{-}Cl \longrightarrow H{-}CH_2{-}CHCl{-}H$$

Ethene (ethylene) + Hydrogen chloride ⟶ Chloroethane (ethyl chloride)

In a **hydrogenation reaction**, *hydrogen is added to a carbon–carbon double bond to give an alkane.* A hydrogenation reaction usually requires a catalyst. Finely divided platinum (Pt) or palladium (Pd) is often used. Such a process is used to hydrogenate unsaturated oils to make margarine.

$$H_2C{=}CH_2 + H{-}H \xrightarrow{Pt} H{-}CH_2{-}CH_2{-}H$$

Ethene + Hydrogen ⟶ Ethane

$$C_6H_{10} + H{-}H \xrightarrow{Pt} C_6H_{12}$$

Cyclohexene + Hydrogen ⟶ Cyclohexane

The hydrogenation of a double bond is a reduction reaction. Ethene is reduced to ethane, for example, and cyclohexene is reduced to cyclohexane.

Benzene resists hydrogenation. It also resists the addition of a halogen or a hydrogen halide. At high temperatures and high pressures of hydrogen, however, three molecules of hydrogen reduce one molecule of benzene to cyclohexane.

$$C_6H_6 + 3H{-}H \xrightarrow{Pt} C_6H_{12}$$

Benzene + Hydrogen ⟶ Cyclohexane

Concept Practice

12. Write the structure for the expected product of each of these reactions.

a. $CH_2{=}CHCH_2CH_3 + Br_2 \longrightarrow$

b. $CH_3CH{=}CHCH_3 + I_2 \longrightarrow$

c. $CH_3CH{=}CHCH_3 + H_2 \xrightarrow{Pt}$

d. 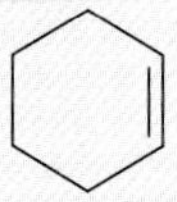 (cyclohexene) $+ Cl_2 \longrightarrow$

13. Give the structure for the expected organic product from each of these reactions.

a. 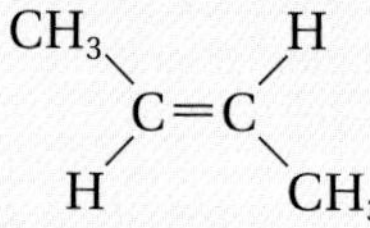 $CH_3(H)C{=}C(H)CH_3 + HBr \longrightarrow$

b. 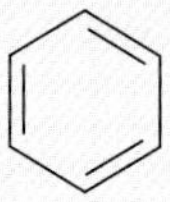 (benzene) $+ Cl_2 \xrightarrow{catalyst}$

c. 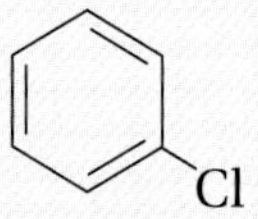 (chlorobenzene, Cl) $+ 3H_2 \xrightarrow[pressure]{catalyst}$

25.7 Ethers

Objective

Identify and draw structural formulas for simple ethers.

Ethers *are compounds in which oxygen is bonded to two carbon groups: R—O—R.* Ethers are easy to name. The alkyl groups attached to the ether linkage are named in alphabetical order and are followed by the word *ether.*

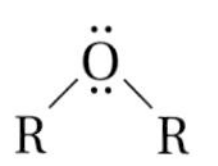

$$R{-}\ddot{\underset{\cdot\cdot}{O}}{-}R \qquad CH_3CH_2{-}O{-}CH_3$$

Ether molecule — Ethylmethyl ether

Ethylmethyl ether and methylphenyl ether are nonsymmetric. The R groups attached to the ether oxygen are different. When the R groups are the same, the ether is symmetric. Symmetric ethers are named by using the prefix *di-*. Sometimes, however, the prefix *di-* is dropped and a compound such as diethyl ether is simply called ethyl ether.

$$CH_3CH_2{-}O{-}CH_2CH_3 \qquad CH_3{-}O{-}C_6H_5 \qquad C_6H_5{-}O{-}C_6H_5$$

Diethyl ether (ethyl ether) — Methylphenyl ether (anisole) — Diphenyl ether (phenyl ether)

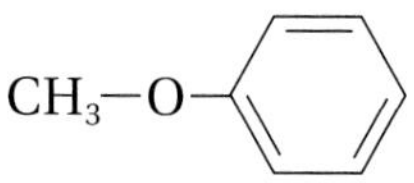

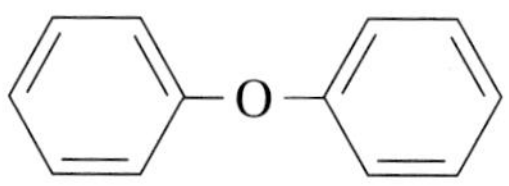

Safety

Diethyl ether is highly flammable, and when old it may contain explosive peroxides. It is not recommended for use in schools.

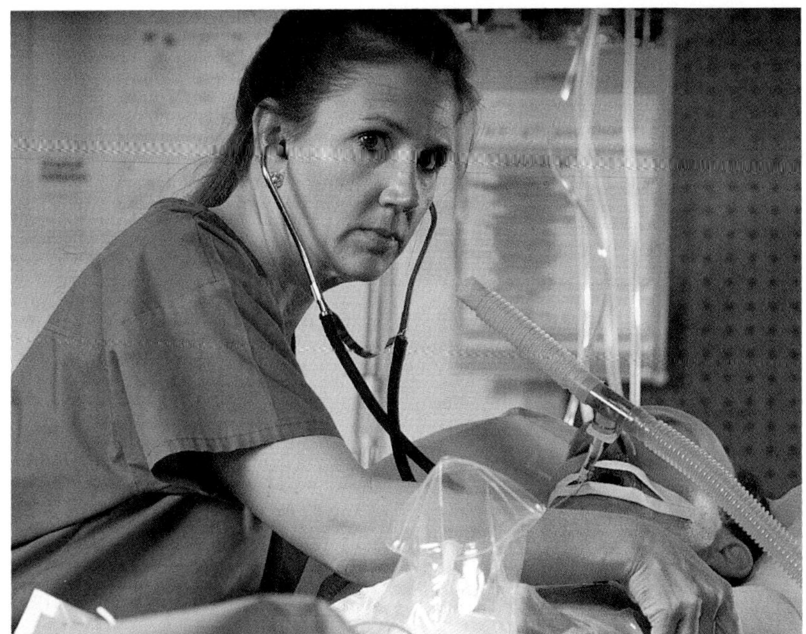

Figure 25.7 Halocarbons such as halothane, enflurane, and isoflurane are now used as general anesthetics. What was the first reliable general anesthetic?

Diethyl ether, a volatile liquid (bp 35°C), was the first reliable general anesthetic. Originally reported in 1842 by Crawford W. Long, an American physician, diethyl ether was used by doctors for over a century. It has been replaced by other anesthetics because it is highly flammable and often causes nausea.

Ethers are usually lower-boiling than alcohols of comparable formula mass. They are higher-boiling than comparable hydrocarbons and halocarbons. Ethers are more soluble than hydrocarbons and halocarbons but less soluble than alcohols. The reason is that the oxygens in ethers are hydrogen acceptors, but ethers have no hydroxyl hydrogens to donate in hydrogen bonding.

Concept Practice

14. Name the following ethers.

a. $CH_3OCH_2CH_3$

b. (benzene ring)$-O-CH_2CH_3$

c. $CH_2{=}CHOCH{=}CH_2$

d. $\underset{\displaystyle CH_3}{CH_3CH}O\underset{\displaystyle CH_3}{CH}CH_3$

15. Explain why diethyl ether is more soluble in water than is dihexyl ether. Would you expect propane to be more soluble than diethyl ether in water? Why?

Objective

Explain some physical properties of aldehydes and ketones based on their molecular structure.

Safety

Formaldehyde is known to cause cancer and mutations in animals.

25.8 Aldehydes and Ketones

A **carbonyl group** *consists of a carbon atom and an oxygen atom joined by a double bond.* It is found in two groups of compounds called aldehydes and ketones.

Aldehydes *are organic compounds in which the carbon of the carbonyl group is always joined to at least one hydrogen.* The general formula for an aldehyde is RCHO.

Ketones *are organic compounds in which the carbon of the carbonyl group is joined to two other carbons.* The abbreviated form for a ketone is RCOR.

$$\underset{\text{Ketone}}{R-\overset{\overset{\displaystyle O}{\|}}{C}-R}\ \longleftarrow \text{Carbonyl group} \qquad \underset{\text{Aldehyde}}{R-\overset{\overset{\displaystyle O}{\|}}{C}-H}\ \longleftarrow \text{Carbonyl group}$$

The IUPAC system may be used for naming aldehydes and ketones. For either class, you must first identify the longest hydrocarbon chain that contains the carbonyl group. The *-e* ending of the hydrocarbon is replaced by *-al* to designate an aldehyde. In the IUPAC system, the continuous-chain aldehydes are named methanal, ethanal, propanal, butanal, and so forth.

Ketones are named by changing the ending of the longest continuous carbon chain that contains the carbonyl group from *-e* to *-one.* Table 25.5 demonstrates this. If the carbonyl group could occur at several places on the chain, then its position is designated by the lowest possible number.

Aldehydes and ketones can form weak hydrogen bonds between the carbonyl oxygen and the hydrogens of water. The lower members of the series, methanal (formaldehyde), ethanal (acetaldehyde), and propanone (acetone), are soluble in water in all proportions. As the length of the hydrocarbon chain increases, water solubility decreases. When the carbon chain exceeds five or six carbons, solubility of both aldehydes and ketones is very low. As might be expected, all aldehydes and ketones are soluble in nonpolar solvents.

Aldehydes and ketones cannot form intermolecular hydrogen bonds because they lack hydroxyl (—OH) groups. Consequently, they have boiling points lower than those of the corresponding alcohols. The aldehydes and ketones can attract one another, however, through polar-polar interactions of their carbonyl groups. Consequently, their boiling points are higher than those of the corresponding alkanes. These attractive forces account for the fact that nearly all aldehydes and ketones are either liquids or solids at room temperature. The exception is methanal, which is an irritating pungent gas. Table 25.6 compares the boiling points of alkanes, aldehydes, and alcohols of similar formula mass.

Table 25.5 Some Common Aldehydes and Ketones

Condensed formula	Structural formula	IUPAC name	Common name
Aldehydes			
HCHO	$H-\overset{\overset{\displaystyle O}{\|}}{C}-H$	Methanal	Formaldehyde
CH_3CHO	$CH_3-\overset{\overset{\displaystyle O}{\|}}{C}-H$	Ethanal	Acetaldehyde
C_6H_5CHO	$C_6H_5-\overset{\overset{\displaystyle O}{\|}}{C}-H$	Benzaldehyde	Benzaldehyde
$C_6H_5CH{=}CHCHO$	$C_6H_5-CH{=}CH-\overset{\overset{\displaystyle O}{\|}}{C}-H$	3-Phenyl-2-propenal	Cinnamaldehyde
$CH_3O(OH)C_6H_3CHO$	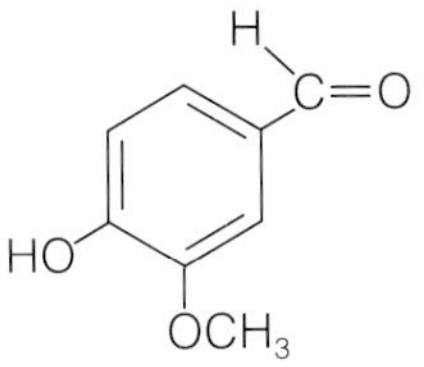 H–C=O, HO, OCH_3 on benzene ring	4-Hydroxy-3-methoxybenzaldehyde	Vanillin
Ketones			
CH_3COCH_3	$CH_3-\overset{\overset{\displaystyle O}{\|}}{C}-CH3$	Propanone	Acetone (dimethyl ketone)
$C_6H_5COC_6H_5$	$C_6H_5-\overset{\overset{\displaystyle O}{\|}}{C}-C_6H_5$	Diphenylmethanone	Benzophenone (diphenyl ketone)

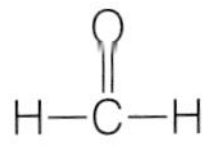

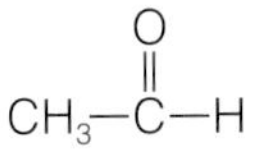

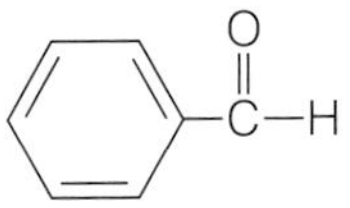

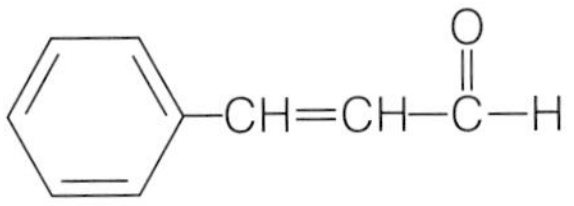

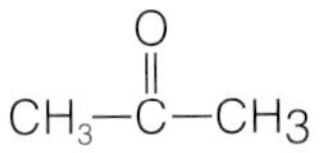

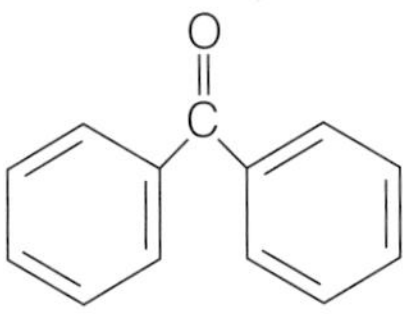

Table 25.6 Boiling Points of Some Compounds with One and Two Carbons

Compound	Formula	Formula mass	Boiling point (°C)	Comments
One Carbon				
Methane	CH_4	16	−161	No hydrogen-bonding or polar–polar interactions
Methanal	HCHO	26	−21	Polar–polar interactions
Methanol	CH_3OH	32	65	Hydrogen bonding
Two carbons				
Ethane	C_2H_6	30	−89	No hydrogen-bonding or polar–polar interactions
Ethanal	CH_3CHO	44	20	Polar–polar interactions
Ethanol	CH_3CH_2OH	46	78	Hydrogen bonding

Figure 25.8 The seeds from this orchid are the source of natural vanilla flavor for ice cream and many other foods. Vanillin is also produced synthetically.

A wide variety of aldehydes and ketones have been isolated from plants and animals. Many of them, particularly those with high formula masses, have fragrant or penetrating odors. They are usually known by their common names, which indicate their natural sources or perhaps a characteristic property. Aromatic aldehydes are often used as flavoring agents. Benzaldehyde is the simplest aromatic aldehyde. Also known as "oil of bitter almond," benzaldehyde is a constituent of the almond. It is a colorless liquid with a pleasant almond odor. Cinnamaldehyde imparts the characteristic odor of oil of cinnamon. Vanillin, which is responsible for the popular vanilla flavor, was at one time obtainable only from the podlike capsules of certain climbing orchids like the one shown in Figure 25.8. Today much vanillin is synthetically produced.

The simplest aldehyde, methanal, is very important industrially but inconvenient to handle in the gaseous state. Methanal is usually available as a 40% aqueous solution, known as formalin. Formalin is used to preserve biological specimens. The methanal in solution combines with protein in tissues to make them hard and insoluble in water. This process prevents the specimen from decaying. The greatest use of methanal is in the manufacture of synthetic resins.

The most important industrial ketone is propanone. It is a colorless volatile liquid that boils at 56°C. Propanone is used as a solvent for resins, plastics, and varnishes and is often found in nail polish removers. Moreover, propanone is miscible with water in all proportions.

Safety

Propanone is highly flammable. Do not use flammable liquids near open flames.

Concept Practice

16. Give the IUPAC name for each of the following aldehydes and ketones.

a. CH_3CH_2CHO

b. $CH_3CH_2CH_2\overset{O}{\overset{\|}{C}}CH_2CH_3$

c. $CH_3CH_2\overset{CH_3}{\overset{|}{C}}HCH_2CHO$

d. $CH_3\overset{O}{\overset{\|}{C}}CH_2CH_3$

17. How would you expect the boiling points of propane, propanol, and propanal to compare?

25.9 Carboxylic Acids

Objective

Identify and write the structural formulas for common carboxylic acids.

A **carboxyl group** *consists of a carbonyl group attached to a hydroxyl group, as shown here.*

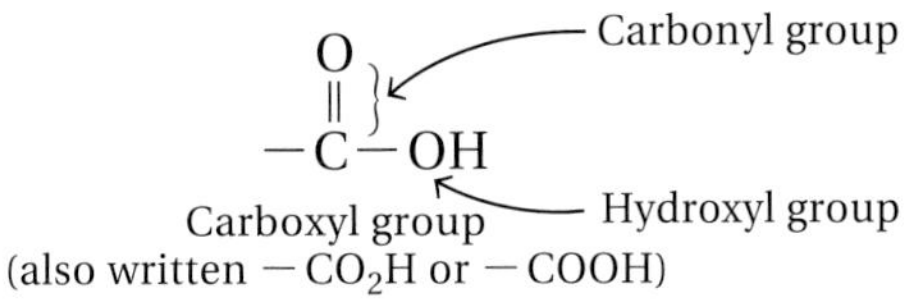

$$-\overset{O}{\overset{\|}{C}}-OH$$

Carbonyl group

Hydroxyl group

Carboxyl group
(also written $-CO_2H$ or $-COOH$)

Carboxylic acids *are compounds with a carboxyl group.* The general formula of a carboxylic acid is RCOOH. Carboxylic acids are weak acids because they ionize slightly in solution to give a carboxylate ion and a proton.

$$R-\overset{O}{\overset{\|}{C}}-OH \rightleftharpoons R-\overset{O}{\overset{\|}{C}}-O^- + H^+$$

Carboxylate ion   Proton

In the IUPAC system for naming carboxylic acids, the *-e* ending of the parent alkane is replaced by the ending *-oic acid.* The parent alkane is the hydrocarbon with the longest continuous carbon chain containing the carboxyl group.

Carboxylic acids are abundant and widely distributed in nature. Many have common names derived from a Greek or Latin word describing their natural sources. For example, the common name for ethanoic acid is acetic acid. Acetic acid is produced when wine turns sour and becomes vinegar. The pungent aroma of vinegar comes from its acetic acid. *Many continuous-chain carboxylic acids were first isolated from fats and are called* **fatty acids**. Propionic acid, the three-carbon acid, literally means "first fatty acid."

Roots of Words

acetum: (Latin) vinegar
acetic acid is an organic acid of molecular formula CH_3COOH

Common vinegar contains about 5% (v/v) acetic acid.

Table 25.7 Saturated Aliphatic Carboxylic Acids

Formula	Carbon atoms	IUPAC name	Common name	Melting point (°C)
$HCOOH$	1	Methanoic acid	Formic acid	8
CH_3COOH	2	Ethanoic acid	Acetic acid	17
CH_3CH_2COOH	3	Propanoic acid	Propionic acid	–22
$CH_3(CH_2)_2COOH$	4	Butanoic acid	Butyric acid	–6
$CH_3(CH_2)_4COOH$	6	Hexanoic acid	Caproic acid	–3
$CH_3(CH_2)_6COOH$	8	Octanoic acid	Caprylic acid	16
$CH_3(CH_2)_8COOH$	10	Decanoic acid	Capric acid	31
$CH_3(CH_2)_{10}COOH$	12	Dodecanoic acid	Lauric acid	44
$CH_3(CH_2)_{12}COOH$	14	Tetradecanoic acid	Myristic acid	58
$CH_3(CH_2)_{14}COOH$	16	Hexadecanoic acid	Palmitic acid	63
$CH_3(CH_2)_{16}COOH$	18	Octadecanoic acid	Stearic acid	70

Figure 25.9 Candles being manufactured in a candlemaking factory. Standard commercial candles are a mixture of 60% paraffin, 35% stearic acid, and 5% beeswax.

Common names are used more often than IUPAC names for carboxylic acids. Table 25.7 lists the names and formulas of some common aliphatic carboxylic acids.

The low-formula-mass members of the aliphatic carboxylic acid series are colorless, volatile liquids. They have sharp, unpleasant odors. The smells of rancid butter and dirty feet are due in part to butyric acid. The higher members of the series are nonvolatile, low-melting, waxy solids. Stearic acid (C_{18}) is obtained from beef fat and is used to make inexpensive wax candles as shown in Figure 25.9. Stearic acid and other long-chain fatty acids have very little odor.

Like alcohols, carboxylic acids can form intermolecular hydrogen bonds. Because of this, carboxylic acids are higher boiling and higher melting than other compounds of similar formula mass. All aromatic carboxylic acids are crystalline solids when they are at room temperature.

The carboxyl group in carboxylic acids is polar, and it readily forms hydrogen bonds with water molecules. Methanoic, ethanoic, propanoic, and butanoic acids are completely miscible with water. The solubility of carboxylic acids of higher formula mass drops off sharply. Most carboxylic acids dissolve in organic solvents like ethanol or propanone.

Concept Practice

18. How would you expect the water solubility of ethanoic and decanoic acids to compare?

19. What are the products of each of the following reactions?

a. $HCOOH + KOH \longrightarrow$

b. $CH_3CH_2COOH + NaOH \longrightarrow$

c. $CH_3COOH + NaOH \longrightarrow$

25.10 Oxidation–Reduction Reactions

Objective

Show how alcohols, aldehydes and ketones, and acids are related by oxidation and reduction reactions.

Remember that oxidation is the gain of oxygen, loss of hydrogen, or loss of electrons. Reduction is just the reverse: loss of oxygen, gain of hydrogen, or gain of electrons. Oxidation and reduction reactions are coupled. One does not occur without the other.

In organic chemistry, the number of oxygens and hydrogens attached to carbon indicates the degree of oxidation of a compound. The fewer hydrogens on a carbon–carbon bond, the more oxidized the bond. For example, ethane (an alkane) can be oxidized to ethene (an alkene) and then to ethyne (an alkyne). *The loss of hydrogen is a* **dehydrogenation reaction**. Strong heating and a catalyst are usually necessary to make dehydrogenation reactions occur. The loss of each molecule of hydrogen involves the loss of two electrons from hydrogen. The remaining carbon electrons pair to make a second or third bond, as shown below.

$$\underset{\text{(most reduced)}}{\text{Least oxidized}}\ H_3C{-}CH_3 \xrightarrow[\text{oxidation}]{\text{loss of hydrogen (dehydrogenation)}} H_2C{=}CH_2 \xrightarrow[\text{oxidation}]{\text{loss of hydrogen (dehydrogenation)}} H{-}C{\equiv}C{-}H\ \underset{\text{(least reduced)}}{\text{Most oxidized}}$$

These reactions can be reversed. Alkynes can be reduced to alkenes, and alkenes can be reduced to alkanes by the addition of hydrogen to a double bond.

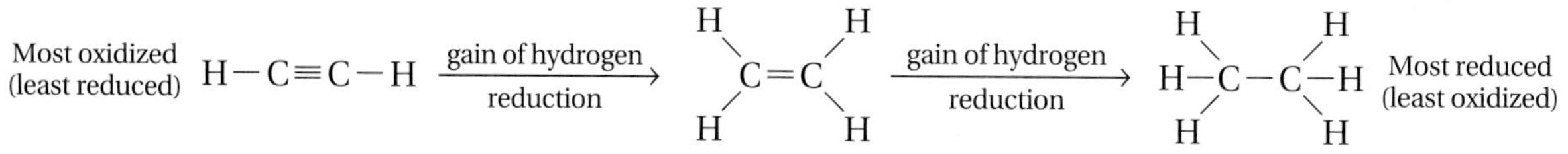

$$\underset{\text{(least reduced)}}{\text{Most oxidized}}\ \ H-C\equiv C-H \xrightarrow[\text{reduction}]{\text{gain of hydrogen}} H_2C=CH_2 \xrightarrow[\text{reduction}]{\text{gain of hydrogen}} H_3C-CH_3\ \ \underset{\text{(least oxidized)}}{\text{Most reduced}}$$

Oxidation in organic chemistry also involves the number and degree of oxidation of the oxygens attached to carbon. For example, methane may be oxidized to carbon dioxide (methane gains oxygens and loses hydrogens). Methane is oxidized to methanol, to methanal, to methanoic acid, and finally to carbon dioxide. This sequence of oxidations occurs for other alkanes. Each series consists of an alkane, alcohol, aldehyde (or ketone), carboxylic acid, and carbon dioxide. The carbon dioxide is most oxidized or least reduced, and the alkane is least oxidized or most reduced.

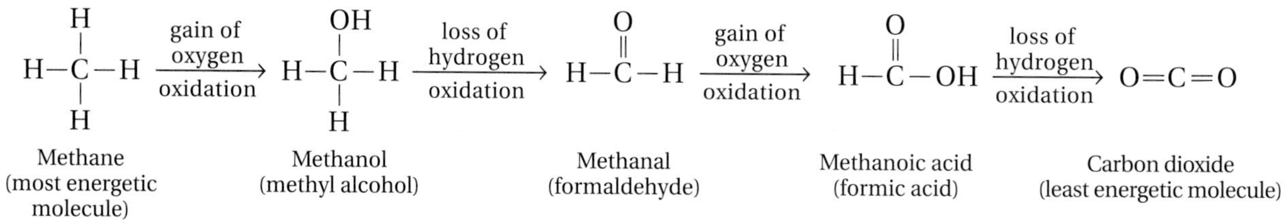

$$CH_4 \xrightarrow[\text{oxidation}]{\text{gain of oxygen}} CH_3OH \xrightarrow[\text{oxidation}]{\text{loss of hydrogen}} HCHO \xrightarrow[\text{oxidation}]{\text{gain of oxygen}} HCOOH \xrightarrow[\text{oxidation}]{\text{loss of hydrogen}} O=C=O$$

Methane (most energetic molecule) — Methanol (methyl alcohol) — Methanal (formaldehyde) — Methanoic acid (formic acid) — Carbon dioxide (least energetic molecule)

Oxidation reactions are energy-releasing. *The more reduced a carbon compound, the more energy it can release upon its complete oxidation to carbon dioxide.* The energy-releasing properties of oxidation reactions are extremely important for energy production in living systems. This is also why the combustion of hydrocarbons such as methane is a good source of energy.

Primary alcohols can be oxidized to aldehydes and secondary alcohols can be oxidized to ketones.

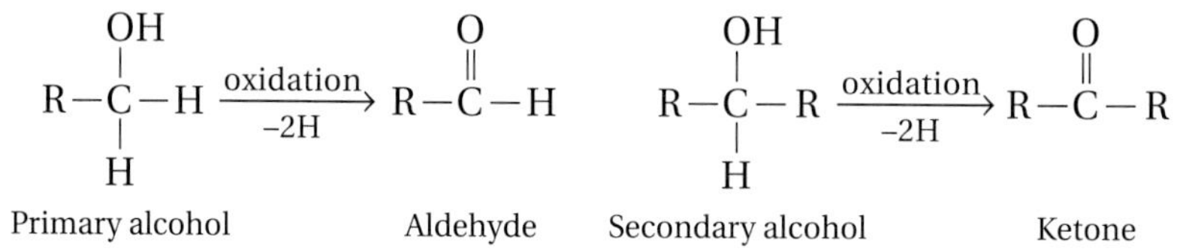

$$\underset{\text{Primary alcohol}}{R-CH(OH)-H} \xrightarrow[-2H]{\text{oxidation}} \underset{\text{Aldehyde}}{R-C(=O)-H} \qquad \underset{\text{Secondary alcohol}}{R-CH(OH)-R} \xrightarrow[-2H]{\text{oxidation}} \underset{\text{Ketone}}{R-C(=O)-R}$$

Tertiary alcohols cannot be oxidized because no hydrogen is present on the carbon bearing the hydroxyl group. Compare the structures below.

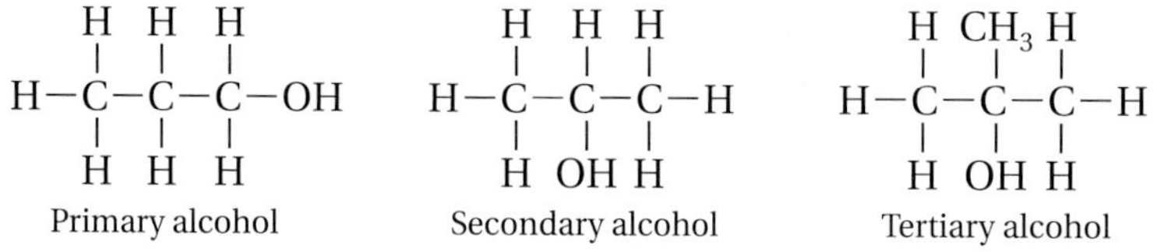

$$\underset{\text{Primary alcohol}}{CH_3-CH_2-CH_2-OH} \qquad \underset{\text{Secondary alcohol}}{CH_3-CH(OH)-CH_3} \qquad \underset{\text{Tertiary alcohol}}{CH_3-C(CH_3)(OH)-CH_3}$$

The primary alcohols methanol and ethanol can be oxidized to aldehydes by warming them at about 50°C with acidified potassium dichromate ($K_2Cr_2O_7$). In these reactions, methanol produces formaldehyde and ethanol produces acetaldehyde.

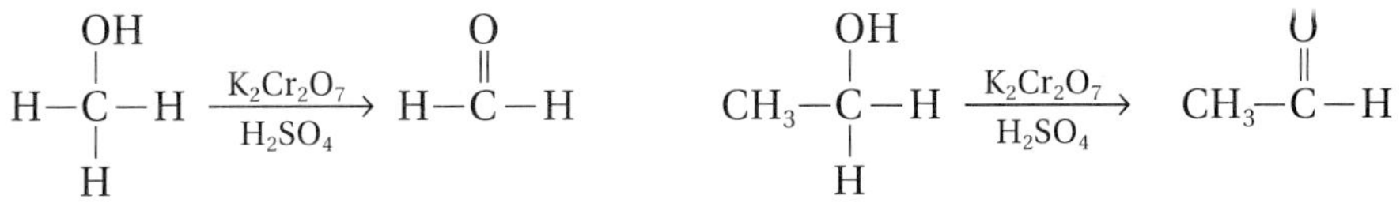

$$\underset{\substack{\text{Methanol}\\\text{(methyl alcohol)}\\\text{(bp 65°C)}}}{H-\overset{\overset{\displaystyle OH}{|}}{\underset{\underset{\displaystyle H}{|}}{C}}-H} \xrightarrow[H_2SO_4]{K_2Cr_2O_7} \underset{\substack{\text{Methanal}\\\text{(formaldehyde)}\\\text{(bp −21°C)}}}{H-\overset{\overset{\displaystyle O}{\|}}{C}-H} \qquad \underset{\substack{\text{Ethanol}\\\text{(ethyl alcohol)}\\\text{(bp 78°C)}}}{CH_3-\overset{\overset{\displaystyle OH}{|}}{\underset{\underset{\displaystyle H}{|}}{C}}-H} \xrightarrow[H_2SO_4]{K_2Cr_2O_7} \underset{\substack{\text{Ethanal}\\\text{(acetaldehyde)}\\\text{(bp 21°C)}}}{CH_3-\overset{\overset{\displaystyle O}{\|}}{C}-H}$$

Preparing an aldehyde by this method is often a problem because aldehydes are easily oxidized to carboxylic acids.

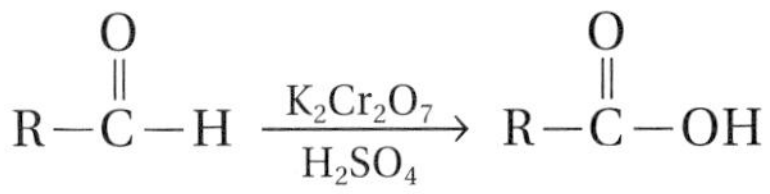

$$\underset{\text{Aldehyde}}{R-\overset{\overset{\displaystyle O}{\|}}{C}-H} \xrightarrow[H_2SO_4]{K_2Cr_2O_7} \underset{\text{Carboxylic acid}}{R-\overset{\overset{\displaystyle O}{\|}}{C}-OH}$$

Further oxidation is not a problem, however, with aldehydes that have low boiling points, such as acetaldehyde. The reason is that the product can be distilled from the reaction mixture as it is formed.

Oxidation of the secondary alcohol 2-propanol by warming it with acidified potassium dichromate produces acetone.

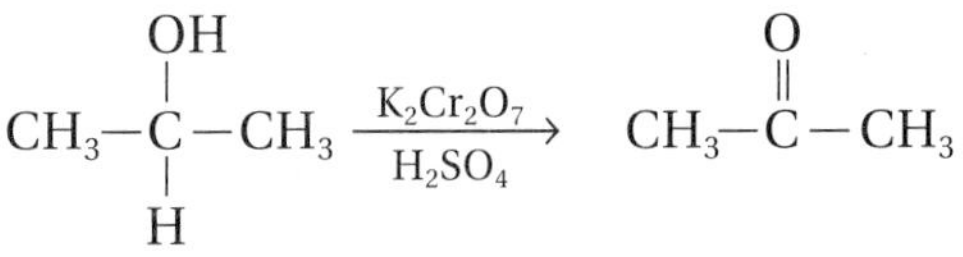

$$\underset{\substack{\text{2-Propanol}\\\text{(isopropyl alcohol)}}}{CH_3-\overset{\overset{\displaystyle OH}{|}}{\underset{\underset{\displaystyle H}{|}}{C}}-CH_3} \xrightarrow[H_2SO_4]{K_2Cr_2O_7} \underset{\substack{\text{Propanone}\\\text{(acetone)}}}{CH_3-\overset{\overset{\displaystyle O}{\|}}{C}-CH_3}$$

Ketones are resistant to further oxidation. Thus, there is no need to remove them from the reaction mixture during the course of the reaction.

Concept Practice

20. Give the name and structure of the alcohol that must be oxidized to make the following compounds.

a. CH_3CH_2CHO **b.** $CH_3CH_2\overset{\overset{\displaystyle O}{\|}}{C}CH_3$

c. $CH_3CH_2\overset{\overset{\displaystyle CH_3}{|}}{C}HCHO$

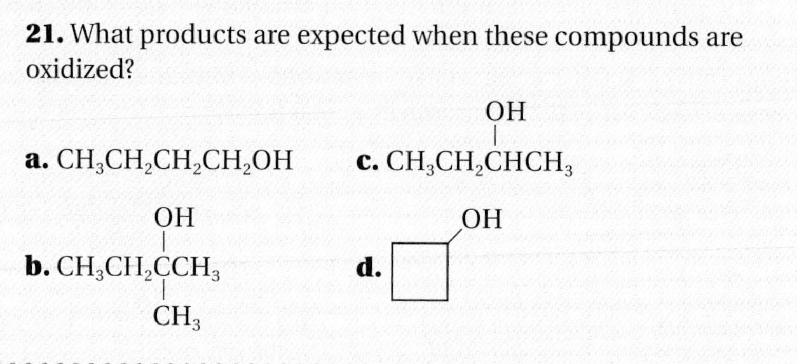

21. What products are expected when these compounds are oxidized?

a. $CH_3CH_2CH_2CH_2OH$

b. $CH_3CH_2C(OH)(CH_3)CH_3$

c. $CH_3CH_2CH(OH)CH_3$

d. cyclobutanol (square ring with OH)

Chemists have taken advantage of the ease with which an aldehyde can be oxidized to develop several tests for their detection. **Benedict's** *and* **Fehling's tests** *are commonly used for aldehyde detection.* Benedict's and Fehling's reagents are deep blue alkaline solutions of copper(II) sulfate of slightly differing composition. As you can see in Figure 25.10, when an aldehyde is oxidized with Benedict's or Fehling's reagent, a bright red precipitate of copper(I) oxide (Cu_2O) is obtained.

$$\underset{\text{Ethanal}}{CH_3{-}\overset{\overset{\displaystyle O}{\|}}{C}{-}H(aq)} + \underset{\substack{\text{Copper(II) ion}\\ \text{complex}\\ \text{(blue solution)}}}{2Cu^{2+}(aq)} + 5OH^-(aq) \longrightarrow \underset{\substack{\text{Ethanoic acid}\\ \text{(as ethanoate}\\ \text{ion)}}}{CH_3{-}\overset{\overset{\displaystyle O}{\|}}{C}{-}O^-(aq)} + \underset{\substack{\text{Copper(I)}\\ \text{oxide (red}\\ \text{precipitate)}}}{Cu_2O(s)} + 3H_2O(l)$$

The aldehyde is oxidized to ethanoic acid. Copper(II) ions (Cu^{2+}) are reduced to copper(I) ions (Cu^+).

Figure 25.10 When an aldehyde is mixed with Fehling's reagent (left) and heated, a brick-red precipitate forms (right). The blue copper(II) ions in Fehling's reagent are reduced to copper(I) ions in the red precipitate of copper(I) oxide, Cu_2O.

25.B Historical Notebook

Artificial Sweeteners

A wide range of sweet-tasting compounds have been discovered that are unrelated to sucrose (cane sugar). Some of these compounds were discovered because of the previously accepted practice of tasting new compounds. However, you should never taste *any* chemical!

Saccharin, discovered in 1878, is currently the most commonly used artificial sweetener. It is about 300 times sweeter than sugar, but it has a bitter aftertaste. Because it passes through your digestive system unchanged, saccharin has no food value. High doses of saccharin have been shown to produce cancer in mice. In 1978 saccharin was banned from use by the U.S. Congress. However, the ban has been suspended until the results of some studies are released.

In 1883, a sweet-tasting synthetic organic compound was produced from urea. Called dulcin, it was introduced as a sugar substitute in the 1890s. Dulcin did not leave a bitter aftertaste. But in 1951, when a toxicity study by the Food and Drug Administration found dulcin to be unsafe, it was withdrawn from the U.S. market.

Cyclamate, an odorless white crystalline powder with a sweetening power about 30 times that of sugar, was discovered in 1937. It was used as a nonnutritive sweetener in dietetic foods and was the most popular artificial sweetener in the 1960s. Unlike saccharin, cyclamate survives cooking without decomposition. Cyclamate was banned from use in the United States and the United Kingdom in 1970 when tests showed it to be potentially harmful.

In 1983 aspartame, a methyl ester of the dipeptide aspartylphenylalanine, appeared on the market. Aspartame was actually discovered in 1965 and approved for use in the United States in 1974. However, it was banned from 1975 until 1981. Aspartame is more than 200 times sweeter than sucrose. Now approved for use in more than 30 countries, aspartame has been widely accepted in the food industry as a substitute for saccharin. The main advantage of aspartame over saccharin is its taste, which is very similar to that of cane sugar. Products that contain aspartame must carry a warning label for people who suffer from the hereditary disease phenylketonuria (PKU). People who have PKU are unable to break down phenylalanine and must therefore limit its intake.

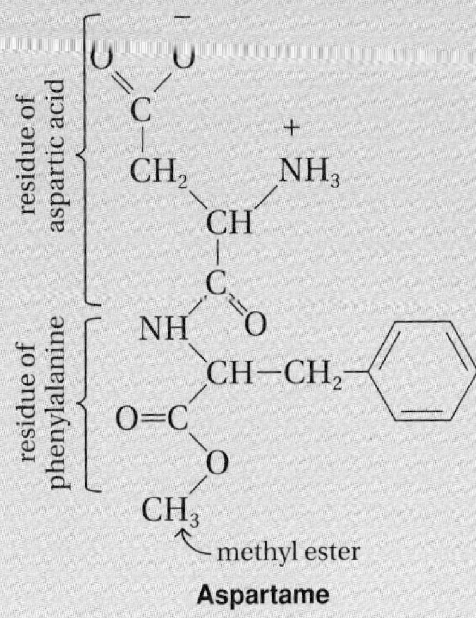

Aspartame

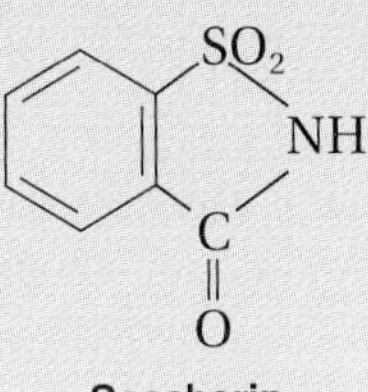

Saccharin

Figure 25.11 Aspartame and saccharin are the two most common artificial sweeteners. Currently saccharin is sold with a warning that says it may be hazardous to your health.

Think About It

22. Identify Name four functional groups found in aspartame.

23. Explain What is the health risk that aspartame poses for individuals with PKU?

Objective

List the products of the hydrolysis of an ester.

25.11 Esters

Esters *are derivatives of carboxylic acids in which the —OH of the carboxyl group has been replaced by an —OR from an alcohol.* They contain a carbonyl group and an ether link to the carbonyl carbon. Many esters have pleasant, fruity odors. Naturally occurring esters are responsible for the characteristic odors of such fruits as blueberries, pineapples, apples, pears, bananas, and many others.

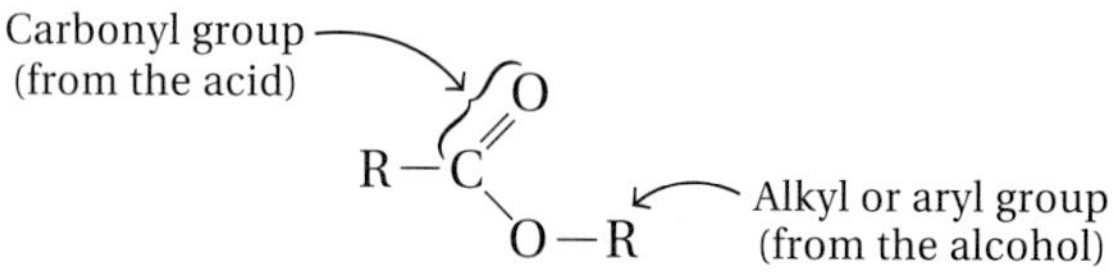

Carbonyl group (from the acid) → $R-C(=O)-O-R$ ← Alkyl or aryl group (from the alcohol)

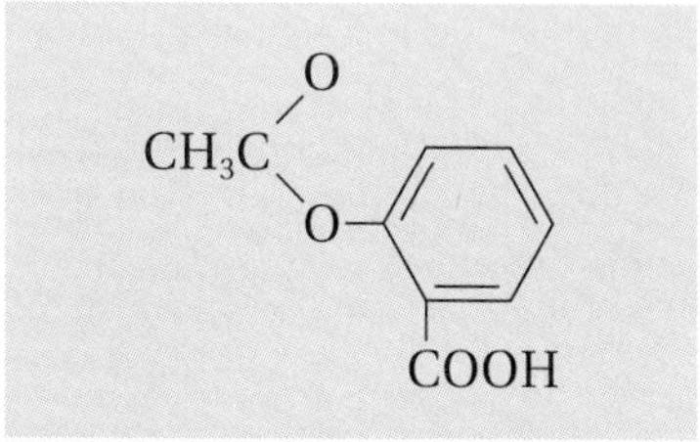

$CH_3C(=O)-O-C_6H_4-COOH$

Figure 25.12 An ester of great commercial importance is acetylsalicylic acid, commonly called aspirin. The R groups in its structure are a methyl group and a benzoic acid group.

The abbreviated formula for a carboxylate ester is RCOOR. The R group can be short chains or long chains, aliphatic (alkyl) or aromatic (aryl), saturated or unsaturated.

Simple esters are neutral substances. The molecules are polar but cannot form hydrogen bonds with one another. The reason is that they contain no hydrogen attached to oxygen or another electronegative atom. As a result, only weak attractions hold ester molecules to each other. Esters are much lower boiling than the strongly hydrogen-bonded carboxylic acids from which they are derived. The low-formula-mass esters are somewhat soluble in water. Esters containing more than four or five carbons have very limited solubility.

If an ester is heated with water for several hours, usually very little happens. In strong acid or base solutions, however, the ester breaks down. An ester is hydrolyzed by the addition of water to produce a carboxylic acid and an alcohol. The reaction is rapid in acidic solution because it is catalyzed by hydrogen ions.

$$\underset{\text{Ethyl ethanoate}}{CH_3-\overset{O}{\overset{\|}{C}}-OCH_2CH_3} + H-OH \overset{H^+}{\rightleftharpoons} \underset{\text{Ethanoic acid}}{CH_3-\overset{O}{\overset{\|}{C}}-OH} + \underset{\text{Ethanol}}{HOCH_2CH_3}$$

Figure 25.13 Esters give fruits their characteristic flavors and odors.

Hydroxide ions also catalyze this reaction. The usual agent for ester hydrolysis is an aqueous solution of sodium hydroxide or potassium hydroxide. Because many esters do not dissolve in water, a solvent like ethanol is added to make the solution homogeneous. The reaction mixture is usually heated. All the ester is converted to products. The carboxylic acid product is in solution as its sodium or potassium salt.

$$\underset{\text{Ethyl ethanoate}}{CH_3-\overset{O}{\overset{\|}{C}}-OCH_2CH_3} + H_2O \xrightarrow{NaOH} \underset{\text{Sodium ethanoate}}{CH_3-\overset{O}{\overset{\|}{C}}-O^-Na^+} + \underset{\text{Ethanol}}{HOCH_2CH_3}$$

If the reaction mixture is acidified, the carboxylic acid is formed.

$$\underset{\text{Sodium ethanoate}}{CH_3-\overset{\overset{O}{\|}}{C}-O^-Na^+} + HCl \longrightarrow \underset{\text{Ethanoic acid}}{CH_3-\overset{\overset{O}{\|}}{C}-OH} + NaCl$$

Esters may be prepared from an acid and an alcohol. Esterification is the formation of an ester from a carboxylic acid and a primary or secondary alcohol. The reactants are heated with a trace of mineral acid as a catalyst. The reaction is reversible.

$$\underset{\text{Carboxylic acid}}{R-C(=O)-OH} + \underset{\text{Alcohol}}{RO-H} \overset{H^+}{\rightleftharpoons} \underset{\text{Carboxylate ester}}{R-C(=O)-OR} + \underset{\text{Water}}{H-OH}$$

For example, ethanoic acid and ethanol react to form ethyl ethanoate, an ester.

$$\underset{\text{Ethanoic acid}}{CH_3-C(=O)-OH} + \underset{\text{Ethanol}}{CH_3CH_2O-H} \overset{H^+}{\rightleftharpoons} \underset{\text{Ethyl ethanoate}}{CH_3-C(=O)-OCH_2CH_3} + \underset{\text{Water}}{H_2O}$$

Chapter 18 showed how the equilibrium in a reversible reaction can be disturbed to improve the product yield. Esterification reactions can be pushed to completion in two different ways. An excess of one of the reactants (acid or alcohol) can be used. As an alternative, the water from the reaction mixture can be removed as it is produced.

Concept Practice

24. Write the structures of the expected products for these reactions.

a. $CH_3CH_2COOCH_2CH_3 \xrightarrow{NaOH}$

b. $CH_3COO-C_6H_5 \xrightarrow{KOH}$ (phenyl ester; benzene ring)

c. $CH_3CH_2COOCH_2\underset{\underset{CH_3}{|}}{CH}CH_3 \xrightarrow{HCl}$

25. What reactants are needed to make the ester propyl ethanoate?

Integrating Health

Saturated Versus Unsaturated Fats

The amount and type of fat in your diet are important to your health. Many Americans are overweight because they eat too much fatty food. Also, a high saturated fat intake, along with high cholesterol levels, has been linked to hardening of the arteries (atherosclerosis). Nutritionists recommend that your fat intake should not exceed 30% of your total daily calorie intake and that only a third of this fat should be saturated. The main sources of fat in your diet are dairy products, vegetable oils and shortenings, margarine, meat products, seeds, and nuts.

REDUCED CALORIES AND REDUCED FAT
60% LESS FAT
-&-
50% LESS CALORIES
THAN REGULAR SOUR CREAM

Objective

Describe the characteristics of the formation of a polymer.

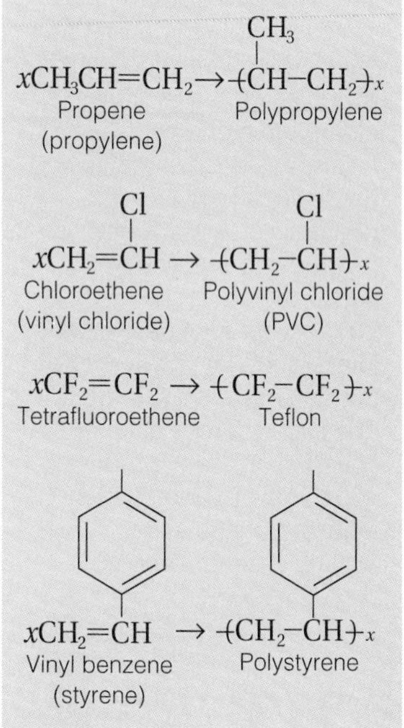

25.12 Polymerization

Most of the reactions that have been examined so far have involved reactants and products of low molecular mass. Some of the most important organic compounds made by chemists, however, are giant molecules called polymers. *A* **polymer** *is a large molecule formed by the covalent bonding of repeating smaller molecules.* Most polymerization reactions require a catalyst.

Monomers *are molecules that combine to form the repeating unit of a polymer.* Some polymers contain only one type of monomer. Others contain two or more types of monomers. The two most common ways to join monomers are addition polymerization and condensation polymerization.

Addition polymerization occurs when unsaturated monomers react to form a polymer. Addition polymerization is a specific type of addition reaction. Ethene undergoes addition polymerization. The molecules bond to one another to form the long-chain polymer polyethylene.

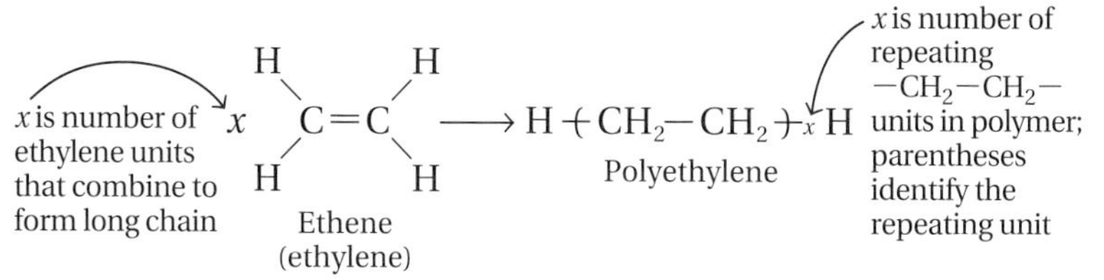

$$x\,\mathrm{H_2C{=}CH_2} \longrightarrow \mathrm{H{-}\!\!\left(CH_2{-}CH_2\right)_{\!x}\!{-}H}$$

Ethene (ethylene) → Polyethylene

x is number of ethylene units that combine to form long chain

x is number of repeating $-CH_2-CH_2-$ units in polymer; parentheses identify the repeating unit

$$x\mathrm{CH_3CH{=}CH_2} \rightarrow \mathrm{\left(CH(CH_3){-}CH_2\right)_{\it x}}$$
Propene (propylene) → Polypropylene

$$x\mathrm{CH_2{=}CHCl} \rightarrow \mathrm{\left(CH_2{-}CHCl\right)_{\it x}}$$
Chloroethene (vinyl chloride) → Polyvinyl chloride (PVC)

$$x\mathrm{CF_2{=}CF_2} \rightarrow \mathrm{\left(CF_2{-}CF_2\right)_{\it x}}$$
Tetrafluoroethene → Teflon

$$x\mathrm{CH_2{=}CH(C_6H_5)} \rightarrow \mathrm{\left(CH_2{-}CH(C_6H_5)\right)_{\it x}}$$
Vinyl benzene (styrene) → Polystyrene

Figure 25.14 The structures of some important addition polymers of alkenes.

Polyethylene is an important industrial product because it is chemically unreactive and easy to clean. It is used to make refrigerator dishes, plastic milk bottles, laboratory wash bottles, and many other familiar items found in homes and laboratories. By shortening or lengthening the carbon chains, chemists can control the

Figure 25.15 Polymers such as polyvinyl chloride (PVC), polypropylene, and polyethylene are used to make all of the items shown here and many more.

physical properties of polyethylene. Polyethylene containing relatively short chains ($x = 100$) has the consistency of paraffin wax. Polyethylene with long chains ($x = 1000$) is harder and more rigid. Polymers of substituted ethenes can also be prepared. As you can see in Figure 25.15, the properties of polymers make them useful for many products.

Condensation polymers are formed by the head-to-tail joining of monomer units. This is usually accompanied by the loss of a small molecule, such as water. The formation of polyesters is an example of condensation. Polyesters are high-formula-mass polymers consisting of many repeating units of dicarboxylic acids and dihydroxy alcohols joined by ester bonds. The formation of a polyester is represented by a block diagram. Note that condensation polymerization always requires that there be *two* functional groups on each molecule.

$$x\text{HO}-\overset{\overset{\displaystyle O}{\|}}{C}-\square-\overset{\overset{\displaystyle O}{\|}}{C}-\text{OH} + x\text{HO}-\bigcirc-\text{OH} \longrightarrow \left[\overset{\overset{\displaystyle O}{\|}}{C}-\square-\overset{\overset{\displaystyle O}{\|}}{C}-\text{O}-\bigcirc-\text{O}\right]_x + 2x\text{H}_2\text{O}$$

Dicarboxylic acid | Dihydroxy alcohol | Representative polymer unit of a polyester

Concept Practice

26. Different samples of a polymer such as polyethylene can have different properties. Explain.

25.13 Carbohydrates

Objective

Distinguish among common mono-, di-, and polysaccharides.

Carbohydrates abound in nature. Among the many forms are starch, table sugar, cotton, and wood. **Carbohydrates** *are monomers and polymers of aldehydes and ketones that have numerous hydroxy groups attached.* The name carbohydrate comes from the early observation that many of these compounds have the general formula $C_n(H_2O)_n$. As a result they appear to be "hydrates of carbon." An examination of the molecular structures will show that this is erroneous. Nevertheless, the name has stuck.

The simplest carbohydrate molecules are simple sugars called **monosaccharides**. These names are used interchangeably. Glucose and fructose are examples of simple sugars. They are structural isomers because they both have the molecular formula $C_6H_{12}O_6$. Glucose has an aldehyde functional group. Fructose has a ketone functional group. They undergo many of the same reactions as ordinary aldehydes and ketones.

Glucose and its cyclic form

Fructose and its cyclic form

In aqueous solution, sugars such as glucose and fructose exist in dynamic equilibrium in both the cyclic and straight-chain forms. The cyclic form predominates. Glucose is abundant in plants and animals. Depending on the source, it has been called corn sugar, grape sugar, and blood sugar. Fructose occurs in a large number of fruits and in honey.

The cyclic forms of two simple sugars can be linked together with the loss of water. The linkage of glucose and fructose by means of a condensation reaction gives sucrose, common table sugar. *Sugars which are formed from two monosaccharides are known as* **disaccharides**. Sucrose is a disaccharide.

Glucose + Fructose $\xrightarrow{-H_2O}$ Sucrose

Figure 25.16 Carbohydrates are the most abundant and least expensive sources of energy in food. The foods in the top photo all contain natural sugars. The foods in the bottom photo are good sources of starch.

Sucrose is obtained mainly from the juice of sugar cane and sugar beets. The world's production from these sources exceeds 7 x 10^9 metric tons per year.

The formation of a disaccharide is sometimes the first step in a condensation polymerization. *The linkage of many monosaccharide monomers produces* **polysaccharides**. Starches, the major storage form of glucose in plants, are polymers consisting of glucose monomers. As shown in Figure 25.17, a typical linear starch molecule contains hundreds of the glucose monomers. Some starches are branched molecules, with each branch containing about a dozen glucose units. Glycogen is the animal form of starch. It is more highly branched than plant starches.

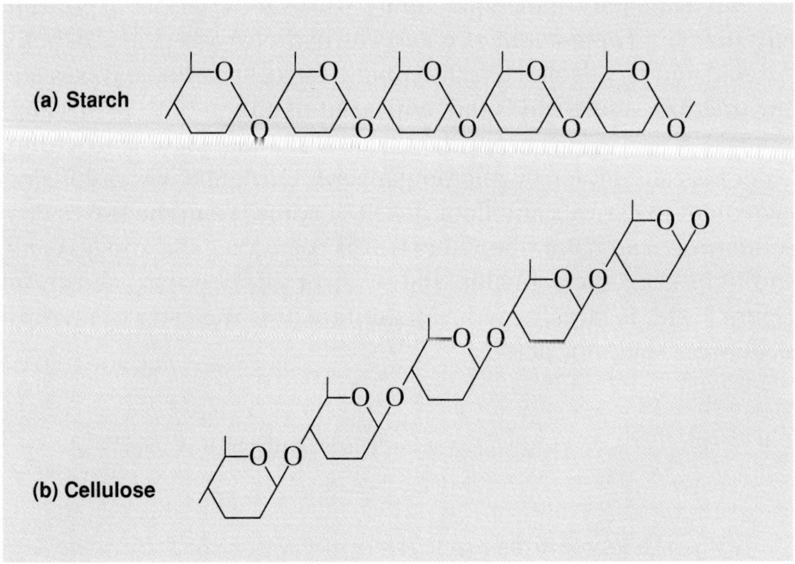

(a) Starch

(b) Cellulose

Figure 25.17 Starch and cellulose are similar polymers made up of hundreds of glucose monomers. They differ in the orientation of the bond between the glucose units. This causes starch to be readily digestible and cellulose to be undigestible by most organisms.

Cellulose is probably the most abundant biological molecule. Figure 25.17 shows that cellulose is also a polymer of glucose. The orientation of the bond linking the glucose monomers is different from the orientation in starch. Starch is edible and partially soluble in water. Cellulose can be digested by only a few microorganisms such as those that live in the digestive tract of cattle and termites. It is insoluble in water and forms rigid structures with other cellulose molecules. Cellulose is therefore an important structural polysaccharide. Plant cell walls, as in wood, are made of cellulose. Cotton is about 80% pure cellulose.

Concept Practice

27. Glycogen and cellulose have different properties but both are composed of glucose units. Explain.

28. Distinguish between sucrose, glucose, and fructose.

25.14 Lipids

Objective

Describe the physical properties of lipids.

Lipids *are a large class of relatively water-insoluble compounds that includes fats, oils, and waxes.* As a group, lipids tend to dissolve in organic solvents like ether and chloroform. This property sets them apart from carbohydrates, proteins, and nucleic acids, the other great classes of biological molecules.

Figure 25.18 Bees construct their honeycomb from beeswax, myricyl palmitate. Waxes are esters of a long-chain fatty acid and a long-chain alcohol.

Waxes are part of the lipid family. **Waxes** *are esters of long-chain fatty acids and long-chain alcohols.* The hydrocarbon chains of both the acid and the alcohol usually contain 10 to 30 carbons. Waxes are low-melting, stable solids that appear in nature in both plants and animals. A wax coat protects the surfaces of many plant leaves from water loss and attack by microorganisms. Carnauba wax is a major ingredient in car wax and floor polish. It comes from the leaves of a South American palm tree. Other waxes coat skin, hair, and feathers and help keep them pliable and waterproof. Beeswax, shown in Figure 25.18, is largely myricyl palmitate. It is the ester of myricyl alcohol and palmitic acid.

$$CH_3(CH_2)_{14}-\overset{\overset{\displaystyle O}{\|}}{C}-O-(CH_2)_{29}CH_3$$

Myricyl palmitate

Natural **triglycerides** *are triesters of long-chain fatty acids* (C_{12} *through* C_{24}*) and glycerol.* They are the major components of animal fats and oils. Triglycerides are simple lipids. They are important as the storage form of fat in the human body. The following equation shows the general reaction for the formation of triglycerides.

$$\begin{matrix} CH_2OH & HO-\overset{\overset{O}{\|}}{C}-R & & CH_2-O-\overset{\overset{O}{\|}}{C}-R & \\ | & & & | & \\ CHOH & + \; HO-\overset{\overset{O}{\|}}{C}-R & \longrightarrow & CH-O-\overset{\overset{O}{\|}}{C}-R & + \; 3H_2O \\ | & & & | & \\ CH_2OH & HO-\overset{\overset{O}{\|}}{C}-R & & CH_2-O-\overset{\overset{O}{\|}}{C}-R & \end{matrix}$$

Glycerol — 3 Fatty acid molecules — Triglyceride (triester of glycerol) — Water

From the organic chemist's point of view, fats and oils are simply esters. Like other esters, fats and oils are easily hydrolyzed in the presence of acids and bases. *The hydrolysis of oils or fats by boiling them with aqueous sodium hydroxide is called* **saponification**. This process is used to make soap.

$$\begin{matrix} CH_2-O-\overset{\overset{O}{\|}}{C}-(CH_2)_{16}CH_3 & & & CH_2-OH & \\ | & & & | & \\ CH-O-\overset{\overset{O}{\|}}{C}-(CH_2)_{16}CH_3 & + \; 3NaOH & \longrightarrow & CH-OH & + \; 3CH_3(CH_2)_{16}\overset{\overset{O}{\|}}{C}-O^-Na^+ \\ | & & & | & \\ CH_2-O-\overset{\overset{O}{\|}}{C}-(CH_2)_{16}CH_3 & & & CH_2-OH & \end{matrix}$$

Tristearin (a triester) — Glycerol — Sodium stearate (soap)

Soaps are the alkali metal (Na, K, or Li) salts of fatty acids. Soap is made by heating beef tallow or coconut oil in large kettles with an excess of sodium hydroxide. When sodium chloride is added to the saponified mixture, the sodium salts of the fatty acids separate as a thick curd of crude soap. Glycerol is an important by-product of the reaction. It is recovered by evaporating the water layer. The crude soap is then purified. Coloring agents and perfumes are added according to market demands.

Concept Practice

29. Write the complete structure for glyceryl tristearate, a simple triglyceride.

30. What is a soap? Give the name and formula of a typical soap molecule.

25.15 Amino Acids, Peptides, Proteins, and Enzymes

Objective

Describe the bonding in a protein molecule.

An **amino acid** *is a compound that contains amino* ($-NH_2$) *and carboxylic acid* ($-COOH$) *groups in the same molecule.* To most chemists and biochemists, however, the term is usually reserved for amino acids that are formed and used in living organisms. All 20 amino acids common in nature have a skeleton consisting of a carboxylic acid group and an amino group covalently bonded to a central atom. The remaining two groups on the central carbon are hydrogen and an R group that constitutes the amino acid side chain.

$$\begin{array}{c} R \leftarrow \text{Side chain} \\ | \\ H_2N-C-COOH \\ | \\ H \end{array}$$

Amino group → H_2N; Carboxylic acid group → $COOH$

The chemical natures of the side-chain groups account for differences in amino acid properties. Some side chains are aliphatic or aromatic hydrocarbons. Others are acidic or basic. Still others are neutral but polar.

Table 25.8 on the next page gives the names of the amino acids with their three-letter abbreviations. Actually, the structures of the

Table 25.8 Abbreviations for Amino Acids

Amino acid	Abbreviation
alanine	Ala
arginine	Arg
asparagine	Asn
aspartic acid	Asp
cysteine	Cys
glutamine	Gln
glutamic acid	Glu
glycine	Gly
histidine	His
isoleucine	Ile
leucine	Leu
lysine	Lys
methionine	Met
phenylalanine	Phe
proline	Pro
serine	Ser
threonine	Thr
tryptophan	Try
tyrosine	Tyr
valine	Val

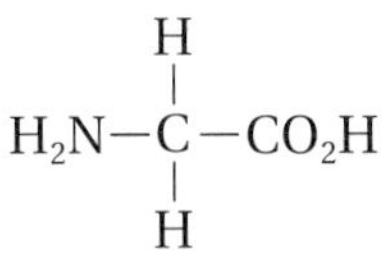

H
$H_2N-C-CO_2H$
H
Glycine

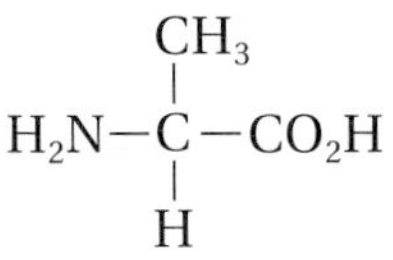

CH_3
$H_2N-C-CO_2H$
H
Alanine

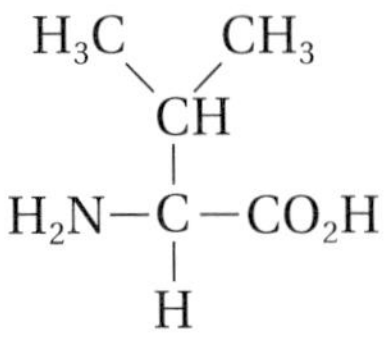

H_3C CH_3
CH
$H_2N-C-CO_2H$
H
Valine

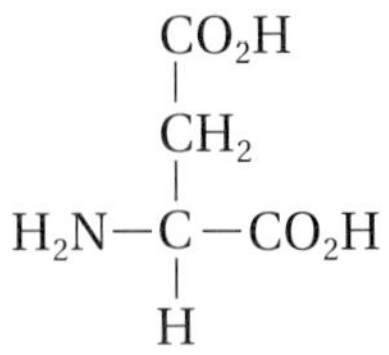

CO_2H
CH_2
$H_2N-C-CO_2H$
H
Aspartic acid

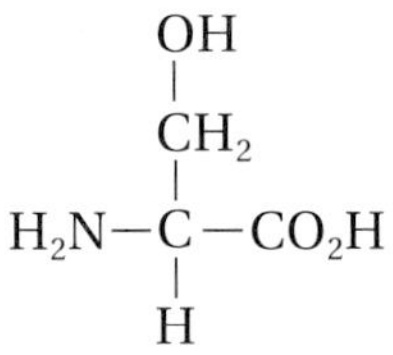

OH
CH_2
$H_2N-C-CO_2H$
H
Serine

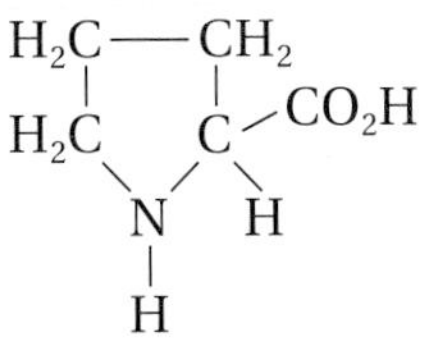

H_2C-CH_2
H_2C $C-CO_2H$
N H
H
Proline

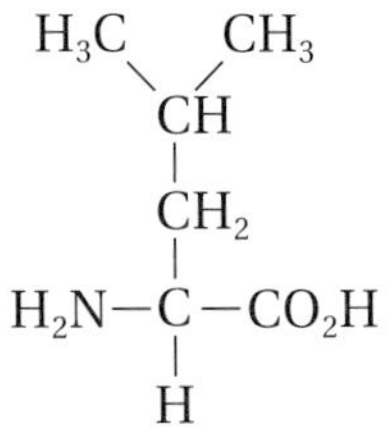

H_3C CH_3
CH
CH_2
$H_2N-C-CO_2H$
H
Leucine

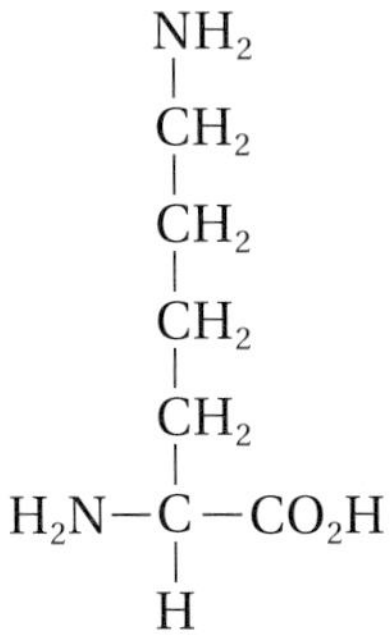

NH_2
CH_2
CH_2
CH_2
CH_2
$H_2N-C-CO_2H$
H
Lysine

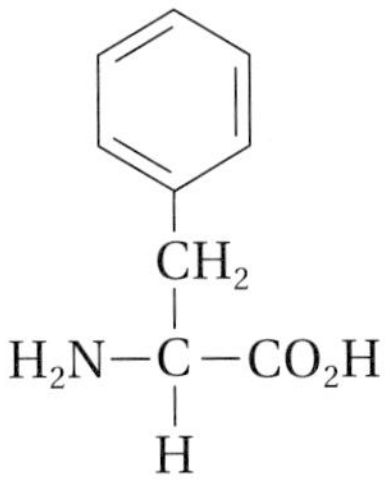

CH_2
$H_2N-C-CO_2H$
H
Phenylalanine

amino acids shown above are not correct. The acid–base properties of carboxylic acids and amino groups alter these structures. The weakly acidic proton of the carboxylic acid group easily transfers to the amino group to form an internal salt. Thus amino acids are really ionic compounds. As previously discussed, ionic compounds generally have much higher melting points than molecular compounds. *The internal salts of amino acids are called* **zwitterions**. In the pure solid state and in aqueous solution near neutral pH, the amino acids exist almost completely as zwitterions.

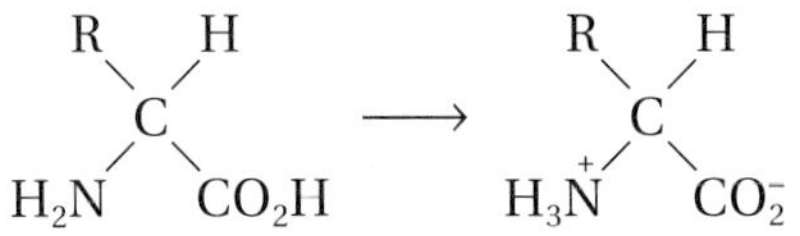

$$\underset{\text{Amino acid}}{(R)(H)C(H_2N)(CO_2H)} \longrightarrow \underset{\text{Zwitterion}}{(R)(H)C(H_3\overset{+}{N})(CO_2^-)}$$

A **peptide** *is any combination of amino acids in which the amino group of one amino acid is united with the carboxylic acid group of another amino acid.* The bonds between the amino acids always involve the central amino group and the central carboxylic acid group. The side chains are not involved in this bonding.

$$\mathrm{H_2N-\underset{\underset{H}{|}}{\overset{\overset{R}{|}}{C}}-\overset{\overset{O}{\|}}{C}-OH} + \mathrm{H-\underset{\underset{H}{|}}{N}-\underset{\underset{H}{|}}{\overset{\overset{R}{|}}{C}}-\overset{\overset{O}{\|}}{C}-OH} \longrightarrow \mathrm{H_2N-\underset{\underset{H}{|}}{\overset{\overset{R}{|}}{C}}-\overset{\overset{O}{\|}}{C}-\underset{\underset{H}{|}}{N}-\underset{\underset{H}{|}}{\overset{\overset{R}{|}}{C}}-\overset{\overset{O}{\|}}{C}-OH} + H_2O$$

Amino acid Amino acid Peptide

More amino acids may be added in the same fashion to form long chains. This is another example of condensation polymerization. *The bond between the carbonyl group of one amino acid and the nitrogen of the next amino acid in the peptide chain is called a* **peptide bond**. It is also called a peptide link.

As more amino acids are added, a backbone common to all peptide molecules is formed. *Any peptide with more than ten amino acid residues is called a* **polypeptide**. In theory, the process of adding amino acids to a peptide chain may be continued indefinitely. *A peptide with more than about 100 amino acids is called a* **protein**. On the average, a molecule of 100 amino acids has a molecular mass of 10 000 amu.

The order in which the amino acids of a peptide or protein molecule are linked is the amino acid sequence of that molecule. Differences in the chemical and physiological properties of peptides and proteins result from differences in the amino acid sequence. The number of ways in which 20 amino acids can be linked in a protein molecule is very large. For example, as many as 20^{100} amino acid sequences are possible for a protein of 100 amino acids containing all 20 amino acids.

The long peptide chains of proteins are folded into relatively stable shapes. Sections of chain may coil into a regular spiral known as a helix. Peptide chains may also be arranged side by side to form a wavy sheet. Much irregular folding of the chains also occurs. Protein shape is maintained by hydrogen bonds between adjacent parts of the folded chains. Covalent bonds also form between sulfur atoms in cysteine amino acids that are folded near each other. Thus, separate polypeptide chains may be joined into a single protein.

Enzymes *are proteins that act as biological catalysts.* They increase the rates of chemical reactions in living things. In 1926, the American chemist James B. Sumner reported the first isolation and crystallization of an enzyme. The enzyme he isolated was urease. It is able to hydrolyze urea, a constituent of urine, into ammonia and carbon dioxide. (The strong smell of dirty diapers allowed to stand for a time is the result of the action of bacteria that contain this enzyme.)

$$\mathrm{NH_2-\overset{\overset{O}{\|}}{C}-NH_2}(aq) + H_2O(l) \xrightarrow{\text{urease}} 2NH_3(g) + CO_2(g)$$

Urea Water Ammonia Carbon dioxide

Biographical Note

Joanne Stubbe

(1947–)

Joanne Stubbe has worked in several biochemically related areas during her career. Her achievements include studies of how enzymes catalyze the reactions of nucleotide metabolism. She has also probed the steps involved in the cleavage of deoxyribonucleic acid by antitumor antibiotics. Her work is so well thought of that she has received several prizes for excellence in chemistry. Stubbe received her bachelor's degree in chemistry from the University of Pennsylvania and her doctorate in organic chemistry from the University of California, Berkeley. She is currently a professor in the Chemistry and Biochemistry Departments at the Massachusetts Institute of Technology.

Sumner demonstrated that urease is a protein. The idea that a protein could be a catalyst was disputed initially. Since then, hundreds of enzymes have been isolated and structurally characterized as proteins.

Besides being able to promote reactions, enzymes have two other properties of true catalysts. First, they are unchanged by the reaction they catalyze. Second, enzymes do not change the normal position of a chemical equilibrium. The same amount of product is eventually formed whether or not an enzyme is present. Few reactions in cells ever reach equilibrium, however. The products are rapidly converted to another substance in a further enzyme-catalyzed reaction. According to Le Châtelier's principle, the removal of a reaction product pulls the reaction toward completion.

Most of the chemical changes that occur in the cell are catalyzed by enzymes. *Substrates* are the molecules on which an enzyme acts. As Figure 25.19 shows, substrates are transformed into products by bond-making and bond-breaking processes. In an enzymatic reaction, the substrate interacts with side chains of the amino acids on the enzyme. These interactions cause the making and breaking of bonds.

To get some idea of the tremendous efficiency of enzymes, consider carbonic anhydrase. This enzyme catalyzes only one reversible reaction. It breaks down carbonic acid to water and carbon dioxide.

$$H_2CO_3(aq) \xrightleftharpoons{\text{carbonic anhydrase}} CO_2(g) + H_2O(l)$$

A single molecule of carbonic anhydrase can catalyze the breakdown of about 36 million molecules of carbonic acid in one minute!

A substrate molecule must make contact with an enzyme molecule before it can be transformed into product. Once the substrate has made contact, it must bind to the enzyme. The *active site* is the place on an enzyme where processes that convert substrates to

Figure 25.19 An enzyme speeds up a chemical reaction. Each enzyme has a distinctively shaped active site. Only molecules with complementary shapes can attach to the enzyme. Some enzymes catalyze decomposition reactions. Others catalyze combination reactions.

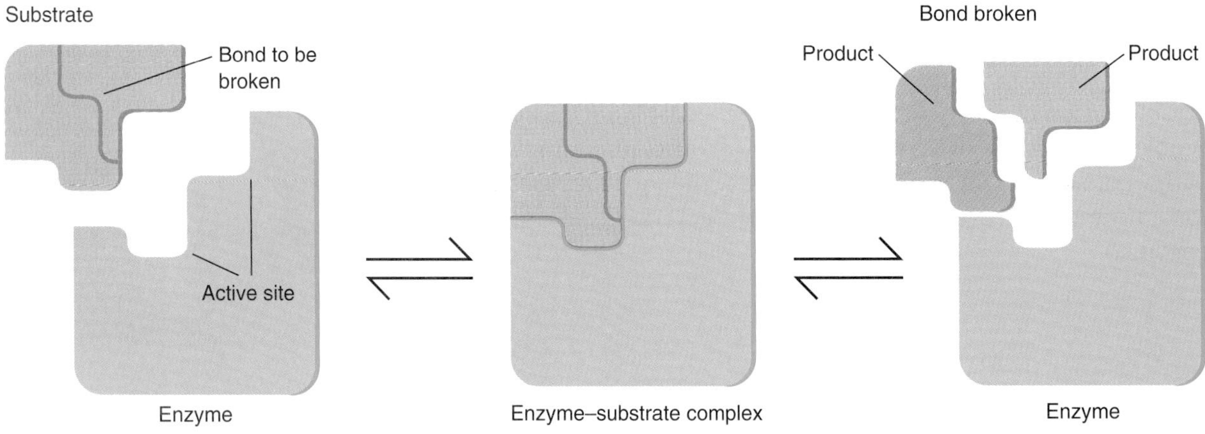

products can take effect. The active site is usually a pocket or crevice formed by folds in the peptide chains of the protein. The active site of each enzyme has a distinctive shape. Only the substrate molecule for that enzyme will fit into it, much as only one key will fit into a certain lock. Thus each enzyme catalyzes only one chemical reaction with only one substrate. An *enzyme-substrate complex* is formed when an enzyme molecule and a substrate molecule are joined.

Some enzymes can catalyze the transformation of biological substrates without assistance. Other enzymes need nonprotein coenzymes, also called cofactors, to assist the transformation. *Coenzymes* are metal ions or small organic molecules that must be present for an enzyme-catalyzed reaction to occur. The metal ion is usually magnesium, potassium, iron, or zinc.

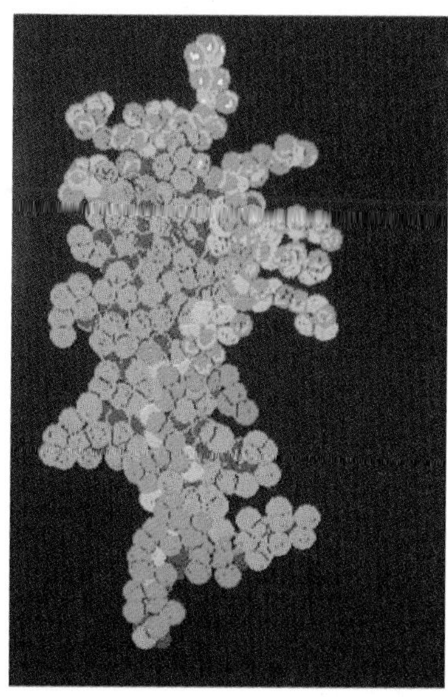

Figure 25.20 This is a space-filling model of the enzyme ribonuclease. The distinctive shape of the enzyme is important for its function as a biological catalyst.

Concept Practice

31. Draw the amino acid glycine as a zwitterion.

32. List the properties of enzymes that make them biological catalysts.

25.16 Nucleic Acids

Objective

Describe the chemical structure of DNA.

Nucleic acids *are polymers found primarily in cell nuclei.* They are indispensable components of every living thing. The kinds of nucleic acids found in cells are *d*eoxyribo*n*ucleic *a*cid (DNA) and *r*ibo*n*ucleic *a*cid (RNA). DNA stores the information needed to make proteins and governs the reproduction and growth of cells and new organisms. RNA has a key role in the transmission of the information stored in DNA.

The monomers that make up DNA and RNA are called **nucleotides**. Nucleic acids are therefore polynucleotides. Each nucleotide consists of a phosphate group, a five-carbon sugar, and a nitrogen-containing compound called a nitrogen base.

$$\text{Phosphate} + \text{Sugar} + \text{Base} \rightarrow \underbrace{\text{Phosphate} - \text{Sugar} - \text{Base}}_{\text{Nucleotide}}$$

The sugar units in the nucleotides of DNA are the five-carbon monosaccharide deoxyribose. The base may be one of four compounds. Adenine and guanine are each composed of a double ring.

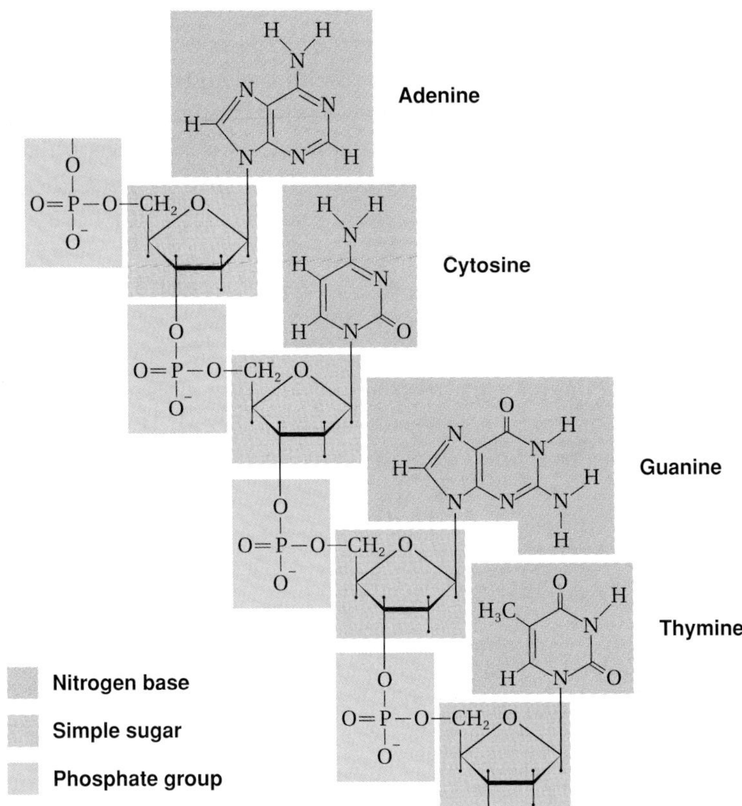

Figure 25.21 The nucleotide monomers of DNA are linked together through their phosphate groups.

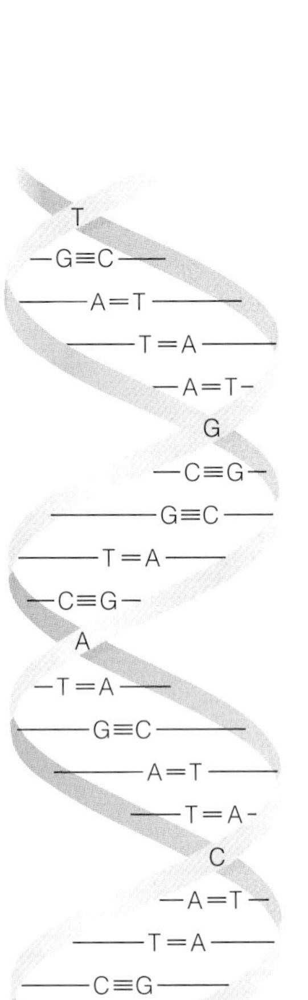

Figure 25.22 The DNA molecule is often referred to as a double helix. The nitrogen bases form hydrogen bonds to hold the two polynucleotide strands together.

Thymine and cytosine are each composed of a single ring. These bases are abbreviated as A, G, T, and C and are shown in the DNA molecule in Figure 25.21. Ribose, which has one more oxygen than deoxyribose, is the sugar in the nucleotide monomers of RNA. The base thymine is never found in RNA. Instead, it is replaced by a fifth base, uracil, abbreviated U.

Chemists studying nucleic acids have discovered that the amount of A in DNA is always equal to the amount of T (A = T). Similarly, the amount of G is always equal to the amount of C (G = C). The significance of this fact was not apparent until 1953. At that time, James Watson and Francis Crick proposed that DNA molecules consist of two polynucleotide chains wrapped into a spiral shape. This is the famous double helix of DNA, and it can be seen in Figure 25.22. For bases to fit neatly into the double helix, every double-ringed base must be matched with a single-ringed base on the opposing strand. The pairing of A with T and G with C provides the best possible fit. It also gives the maximum number of hydrogen bonds between the opposing bases. Thus, A—T and G—C make the most stable arrangement in the double helix.

The molecular masses of DNA molecules reach into the millions and possibly billions. Even with only four bases, the number of possible sequences of nucleotides in a DNA chain is enormous. The order of the nitrogen bases A, T, G, and C in the DNA of an organism constitutes the genetic plan for that organism. Differences in the number and order of the bases in DNA are ultimately responsible for the diversity of living creatures.

Concept Practice

33. Differentiate between a nucleotide and a nucleic acid.

34. What is the structural difference between the sugar unit in RNA and the sugar unit in DNA?

Activity 25
A DNA Model

Purpose

To model a segment of a DNA molecule.

Materials

cardboard tube insert from a paper-towel roll

two different-colored markers

wooden toothpicks

thumbtack

Procedure

1. Outline the spiral seam on the insert with a marker. Using a different colored marker, draw a second spiral midway between the lines of the first.

2. Hold the insert vertically. Label the upper end of one spiral line 3' and its lower end 5'; label the upper end of the other spiral line 5' and its lower end 3'.

3. Starting at the upper end, mark each spiral line at 5-cm intervals. Label each of these intervals with an "S" to represent the *deoxyribose sugar* unit of the DNA backbone; label the midpoint between each "S" on the spiral with a "P" to represent the *phosphate* unit.

4. Take about a dozen toothpicks and color each along half its length with a marker. Each toothpick represents a hydrogen-bonded *complementary base pair*—one end is a purine and the other end is a pyrimidine.

5. Use a thumbtack to make a hole at the center of each "S". Begin at the upper end and push a toothpick through the hole in an "S" and guide it so that it emerges through the hole in the "S" on the opposite side of the insert. Continue for other holes.

6. Your model of the DNA double helix is now complete.

Analysis and Conclusions

1. DNA is described as a polynucleotide. What is the composition of a *nucleotide*?

2. Where are the hydrogen bonds that hold the complementary base pairs together located?

3. What is the location of the sugar-phosphate backbones of the DNA double helix?

4. The spiral lines on the insert depict the two antiparallel strands of the DNA double helix. What does this mean and what is the significance of the 3' and 5' labels? Consult a biology reference if necessary.

Chitin

A Versatile Polymer Comes Out of Its Shell

What is a plentiful natural resource currently regarded as trash? It is chitin, (pronounced *KITE en*), a major component of the shells of arthropods and the cell walls of fungi.

CH_2OH, O, H, H, OH, H, H, –O–, H, NH, O=C, CH_3, n

Chitin

One of the most plentiful organic substances on Earth, chitin can be extracted from shellfish waste that would otherwise be thrown away. For example, in North Carolina alone there are 42 crab packing companies, each of which generates up to about 8000 pounds of shell wastes per week. The goal of current research is to use this waste to produce fibers and films that can be used in the manufacture of new products.

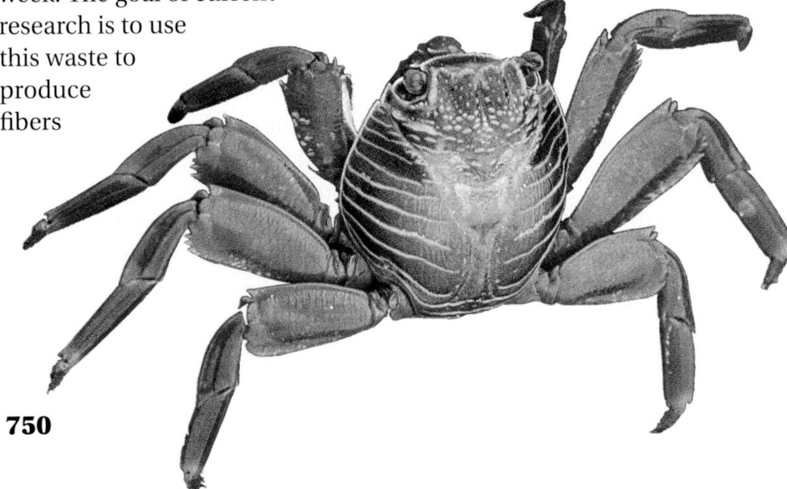

The structure of the chitin molecule can be changed to form chitosan by heating chitin with sodium hydroxide. Chitosan can then be made into useful fibers and films. The polymers chitin and chitosan have proven medical applications and are completely biodegradable and compatible with body tissues. The polymers also bind with metal ions, a quality which makes them excellent water purifiers. To date, chitin and chitosan have had limited use in applications such as wastewater treatment, recovery of food-processing by-products, and as cosmetic ingredients. But experts predict that these two polymers will have important uses in a vast number of areas.

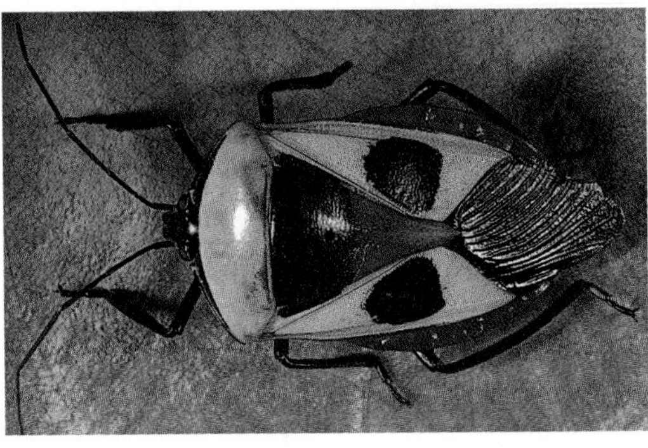

Researchers are looking at ways to modify the molecules so that the chitosan fibers and films do not lose their strength in water. This is a major disadvantage of fiber- and film-forming materials based on natural polysaccharides. Chitosan is a long, chainlike molecule. The molecules are laid out in an extended, linear fashion to form fibers. The molecules in the fibers absorb water readily because of their chemical structure. The water acts as a lubricant between the fiber structures, making them plastic and pliable and very weak. Perhaps by chemical crosslinking—adding a substance that holds the long, chainlike molecules together with covalent bonds—the chitosan structure can be made stable when wet.

The U.S. Army is interested in chitosan films as a possible biodegradable packaging material for meals-ready-to-eat (MREs). The North Carolina Textile Foundation is also interested in the results of the research. They wish to establish a state policy that promotes the use of chitin and simultaneously benefits the environment.

Think About It

35. Describe How is chitosan made?

36. Explain What are an advantage and a disadvantage of using chitosan as a packaging material?

Chapter 25 Review

Functional Groups and Organic Reactions

Key Terms

addition reaction *25.6*
alcohol *25.4*
aldehyde *25.8*
alkyl halide *25.2*
amino acid *25.15*
aryl halide *25.2*
Benedict's test *25.10*
carbohydrate *25.13*
carbonyl group *25.8*
carboxyl group *25.9*
carboxylic acid *25.9*
dehydrogenation reaction *25.10*
denatured alcohol *25.5*
disaccharide *25.13*
enzyme *25.15*
ester *25.11*
ether *25.7*
fatty acid *25.9*
Fehling's test *25.10*
fermentation *25.5*
functional group *25.1*
halocarbon *25.2*
hydration reaction *25.6*
hydrogenation reaction *25.6*
hydroxyl group *25.4*
ketone *25.8*
lipid *25.14*
monomer *25.12*
monosaccharide *25.13*
nucleic acid *25.16*
nucleotide *25.16*
peptide *25.15*
peptide bond *25.15*
polymer *25.12*
polypeptide *25.15*
polysaccharide *25.13*
protein *25.15*
saponification *25.14*
substitution *25.3*
triglyceride *25.14*
wax *25.14*
zwitterion *25.15*

Chapter Summary

The chemical reactions of most organic compounds involve functional groups. A common functional group is the carbon–carbon double bond of an alkene. It undergoes the addition of water to form an alcohol. It can add a hydrogen halide or halogen to form a halocarbon, and it can add hydrogen to form an alkane. Alkenes also undergo additional polymerization to form useful materials such as polyethylene. The benzene ring usually undergoes substitution rather than addition.

Common functional groups containing oxygen include ethers, aldehydes, ketones, carboxylic acids, and esters. The latter four types of functional groups contain the carbon–oxygen double bond or carbonyl group. Alcohols may be oxidized to aldehydes or ketones. Aldehydes may be oxidized to carboxylic acids. Fehling's and Benedict's solutions can be used to detect the presence of aldehydes. Esters result from the combination of carboxylic acids and alcohols. Hydrolysis of an ester produces these components. Condensation polymerization of monomer units containing hydroxyl and carboxyl groups in the same molecule gives polyesters.

Carbohydrates, lipids, proteins, and nucleic acids are the major types of biological molecules. The carbohydrates are often found in nature as simple molecules containing one or a few sugar units. Condensation polymers containing hundreds or thousands of sugar units, as in starch and glycogen, are also found. Lipids are a class of compounds that include fats, oils, and waxes. The simplest lipids are triglycerides, esters of long-chain fatty acids and glycerol. Soaps are the alkali metal salts of fatty acids. Peptides and proteins are condensation polymers of amino acids. Likewise, the nucleic acids are condensation polymers of monomer units called nucleotides. Nucleic acids are essential to all life functions.

Practice Questions and Problems

37. Write a general structure for each of these types of compounds *25.1*
a. halocarbon **b.** ketone **c.** ester **d.** amide

38. Write a structural formula for each of the following compounds. *25.2*
a. 1,2,2-trichlorobutane
b. 1,3,5-tribromobenzene
c. 1,2-dichlorocyclohexane

39. Name the following halocarbons. *25.2*
a. $CH_2{=}CHCH_2Cl$
b. $CH_3CH(CH_3)CH_2CH(Cl)CH_2Cl$ (drawn with CH_3 above the second carbon and Cl above the fourth carbon)
c. benzene ring with Br at positions 1 and 3

40. Write structural formulas and give IUPAC names for all the isomers of these compounds. *25.2*
a. $C_3H_6Cl_2$ **b.** C_4H_9Br

41. What organic products are formed in the following reactions? *25.3*

a. 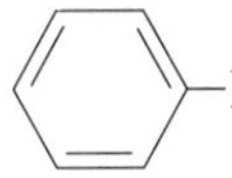 C_6H_5–Br + NaOH $\xrightarrow{\text{heat}}$ ____ + NaBr

b. 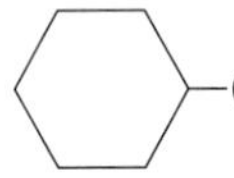 C_6H_{11}–Cl + NaOH $\longrightarrow$ ____ + NaCl

c. CH_3CHCl + NaOH $\longrightarrow$ ____ + NaCl
 (with CH_3 on the second carbon)

d.  C_6H_6 + Br_2 $\xrightarrow{\text{catalyst}}$ ____ + HBr

42. Explain how the United Nations chemical classification system works. *25.A*

43. Write the name (IUPAC, common, or both) for each of the following alcohols. *25.4*
a. $CH_3CH_2CHCH_3$ (OH on third carbon)
b. CH_3CHCH_2OH (CH_3 on second carbon)
c. $CH_3CHCH_2CH_2OH$ (CH_3 on second carbon)
d. $CH_3CH_2CCH_2CH_3$ (CH_3 and OH on third carbon)

44. Identify each of the alcohols in Problem 43 as primary, secondary, or tertiary. *25.5*

45. Write structures and names of the products obtained upon addition of each of the following reagents to ethene. *25.6*
a. HBr **b.** Cl_2 **c.** H_2O **d.** H_2 **e.** HCl

46. Explain why 1-butanol has a higher boiling point than diethyl ether. Which compound would you expect to be more soluble in water? Why? *25.7*

47. What is a carbonyl group? Explain why a carbon–carbon double bond is nonpolar but a carbon–oxygen double bond is very polar. *25.8*

48. Propane ($CH_3CH_2CH_3$) and acetaldehyde (CH_3CHO) have the same molecular mass, but propane boils at –42°C and acetaldehyde boils at 20°C. Account for this difference. *25.8*

49. Name these aldehydes and ketones. *25.8*
a. $CH_3\overset{O}{\overset{\|}{C}}CH_3$
b. CH_3CHCH_2CHO (CH_3 on second carbon)
c. 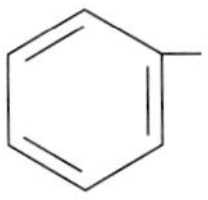 C_6H_5–CH_2CHO
d. 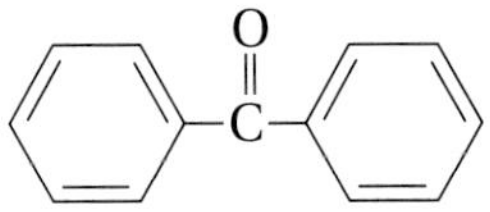 C_6H_5–$\overset{O}{\overset{\|}{C}}$–$C_6H_5$
e. CH_3CHO
f. $CH_3CH_2\overset{O}{\overset{\|}{C}}CH_2CH_2CH_3$

50. Give common names for each of the following carboxylic acids. *25.9*
a. HCOOH **c.** CH_3CH_2COOH
b. CH_3COOH **d.** $CH_3(CH_2)_{16}COOH$

51. Complete the reactions by writing the structure of the expected products. *25.10*
a. $CH_3CH_2OH \xrightarrow{K_2Cr_2O_7}$
b. $CH_3CH_2CHO \xrightarrow{K_2Cr_2O_7}$
c. $CH_3CH_2CHOH \xrightarrow{K_2Cr_2O_7}$ (CH_3 on third carbon)
d. 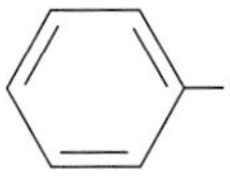 C_6H_5–$CH_2CHO \xrightarrow{K_2Cr_2O_7}$
e. $CH_3CH_2\overset{O}{\overset{\|}{C}}CH_3 \xrightarrow{K_2Cr_2O_7}$

52. Write the name and structure of the alcohol that must be oxidized to make each of the following carbonyl compounds. *25.10*
a. HCHO
b. $CH_3\overset{O}{\overset{\|}{C}}CH_3$
c. CH_3CHCHO (CH_3 on second carbon)
d. 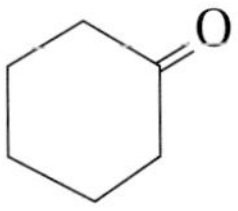 cyclohexanone (ring with =O)

53. Why is the practice of describing the taste of a newly discovered compound no longer used? *25.B*

54. Complete the following reactions by writing the structures of the expected products and by naming each of the reactants and products. *25.11*

a. $CH_3COOCH_3 + H_2O \xrightarrow{HCl}$

b. $CH_3CH_2CH_2COOCH_2CH_2CH_3 + H_2O \xrightarrow{NaOH}$

c. $HCOOCH_2CH_3 + H_2O \xrightarrow{KOH}$

55. Write the structure and name of the ester that could be produced from each of the following reactions. *25.11*

a. formic acid + methanol $\longrightarrow$

b. butyric acid + ethanol $\longrightarrow$

c. acetic acid + propanol $\longrightarrow$

56. What is the structure of the repeating units in a polymer in which the monomer is each compound? *25.12*

a. 1-butene

b. 1,2-dichloroethene

57. Give a source and use for each. *25.13*

a. starch **b.** cellulose **c.** glycogen

58. A solution of glucose is treated with Benedict's solution. What should happen? Why? *25.13*

59. Name the two classes of organic compounds that are produced when waxes are hydrolyzed. *25.14*

60. The following compound is hydrolyzed by boiling with sodium hydroxide. What are the saponification products? *25.14*

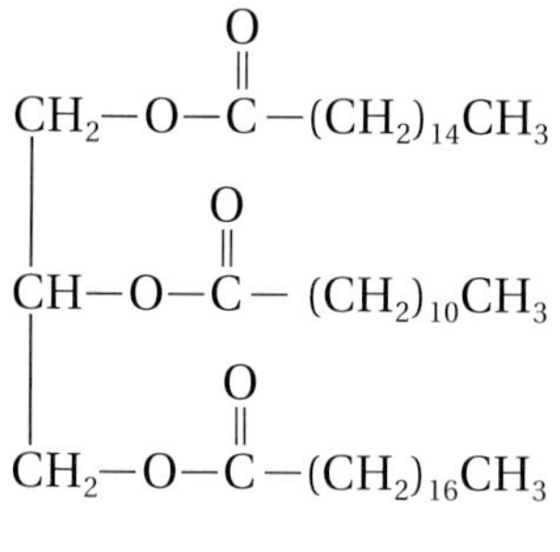

$$\begin{array}{l} CH_2{-}O{-}\overset{O}{\overset{\|}{C}}{-}(CH_2)_{14}CH_3 \\ | \\ CH{-}O{-}\overset{O}{\overset{\|}{C}}{-}(CH_2)_{10}CH_3 \\ | \\ CH_2{-}O{-}\overset{O}{\overset{\|}{C}}{-}(CH_2)_{16}CH_3 \end{array}$$

61. Write the structure and identify the R group for these amino acids. *25.15*

a. alanine **b.** serine **c.** phenylalanine

62. What is the name given to the amide bond connecting two amino acids in a peptide chain? *25.15*

63. Consider the tripeptide seryl-glycyl-phenylalanine. How many peptide bonds does this molecule have? *25.15*

64. What is meant by the amino acid sequence of a protein? *25.15*

65. Cells contain two types of nucleic acids. What are they called? *25.16*

66. What are the parts of a nucleotide? *25.16*

67. What type of bonding holds a DNA double helix together? *25.16*

68. Which of the following base pairs are found in a DNA molecule? *25.16*

a. A—A **b.** A—T **c.** C—G **d.** G—C **e.** G—A

Mastery Questions and Problems

69. Construct a concept map using the key terms to summarize oxidation–reduction reactions of organic compounds. Begin with the compound ethanol. Write the name, the class, and the formula for each product.

70. Predict which of the following compounds has the highest boiling point. Formula masses are given in parentheses.

a. CH_3CHO (44)

b. CH_3CH_2OH (46)

c. $CH_3CH_2CH_3$ (44)

71. Classify each of these compounds as an alcohol, a phenol, or an ether.

a. (naphthalene ring)—OH

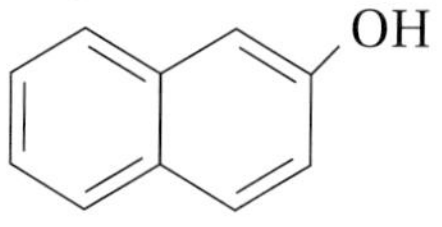

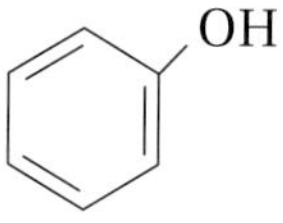

b. (benzene ring)—O—(benzene ring)

c. (benzene ring)—CH_2OH

d. (benzene ring)—OH

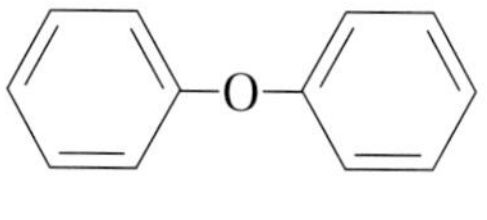

e. $CH_3CH_2\underset{\underset{CH_3}{|}}{C}HOH$

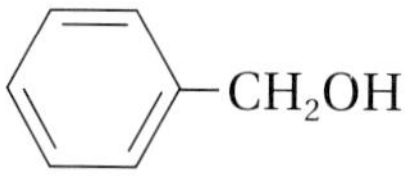

72. Write the structural formulas for the products of these reactions.

a. $CH_3CH_2CH{=}CH_2 + Cl_2 \longrightarrow$

b. $CH_3CH_2CH{=}CH_2 + Br_2 \longrightarrow$

c. 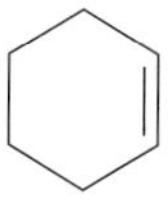 (cyclohexene) + HBr $\longrightarrow$

73. For each compound pictured in a model below, identify the functional group and name the compound. The red atoms represent oxygen.

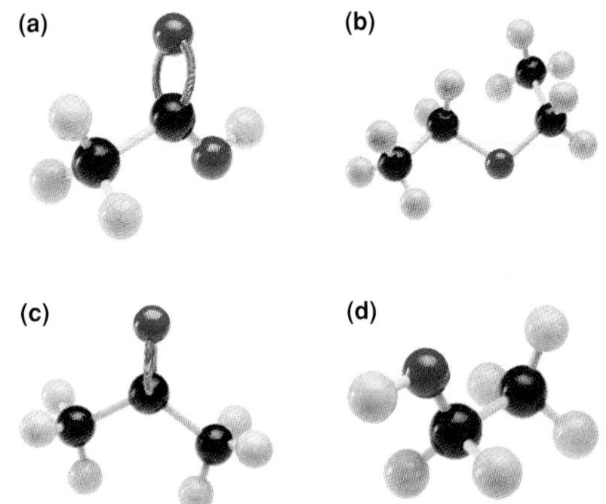

74. Write the structures and names of the expected products for each of the following reactions.

a. $CH_3COOH + CH_3OH \xrightarrow{H^+}$

b. $CH_3CH_2CH_2COOCH_2CH_3 + H_2O \xrightarrow{NaOH}$

c. $CH_3CH_2OH \xrightarrow{K_2Cr_2O_7}$

d. $CH_3CH_2CH_2COOH + NaOH \longrightarrow$

Critical Thinking Questions

75. Choose the term that best completes the second relationship.

a. animals:carbon dioxide yeast: ____
(1) oxygen (2) methanol
(3) ethanol (4) sugar

b. polymer:monomer protein: ____
(1) monosaccharide (2) fatty acid
(3) nucleic acid (4) amino acid

c. cow:horse aldehyde: ____
(1) ketone (2) alcohol
(3) ester (4) ether

76. Benzene is poisonous and a proven carcinogen. Yet many compounds containing benzene rings, such as benzaldehyde, are common in foods we eat. Why are some organic compounds with phenyl groups entirely safe to eat?

77. The outside layer of an animal cell, called the cell membrane, is composed mainly of a double layer of lipid molecules. What properties important to cells does such a membrane possess?

Cumulative Review

78. A solution is made by diluting 250 mL of 0.210*M* $Ca(NO_3)_2$ solution with water to a final volume of 450 mL. Calculate the molarity of $Ca(NO_3)_2$ in the diluted solution.

79. In a saturated solution containing undissolved solute, the solute is continually dissolving but the solution concentration remains constant. Explain.

80. What is the maximum number of orbitals in the *p* sublevel of an atom?
a. 1 **b.** 3 **c.** 5 **d.** 9

81. Using electron dot structures, illustrate the formation of F^- from a fluorine atom and of a hydroxide ion from atoms of hydrogen and oxygen.

82. Calculate the mass, in grams, of one liter of SO_2 at standard temperature and pressure.

83. Name the following acids and bases.
a. HNO_3 **c.** HNO_2 **e.** $HClO_4$
b. H_2SO_3 **d.** $Ca(OH)_2$ **f.** H_3PO_4

84. Give the oxidation numbers of the following atoms.
a. Mn in $(MnO_4)^-$
b. Cr in Cr_2O_3
c. C in $(C_2O_4)^{2-}$
d. P in PH_3

Challenge Questions and Problems

85. Hydrocarbons from petroleum are an important source of raw material for the chemical industry. Using reactions covered in this chapter and any required inorganic chemicals, propose a scheme for the manufacture of ethylene glycol, a major component of antifreeze, from petrochemical ethene.

86. Five continuous-chain organic compounds are listed in the table below. Although the molecular masses of these compounds are similar, their boiling points are not. Propose an explanation.

Structure of compound	Molecular mass	Boiling point (°C)
$CH_3CH_2CH_2CH_2CH_3$	72	36
$CH_3CH_2{-}O{-}CH_2CH_3$	74	35
$CH_3CH_2CH_2Cl$	79	47
$CH_3CH_2CH_2CHO$	72	76
$CH_3CH_2CH_2CH_2OH$	74	118

87. Cholesterol is a compound that is in our diet and is also synthesized in the liver. Sometimes it is deposited on the inner walls of blood vessels, causing hardening of the arteries. Describe the structural features and functional groups of this important molecule.

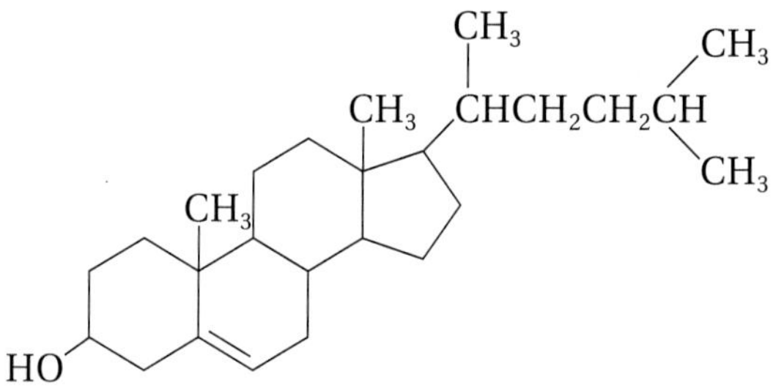

Connections Questions

88. What is a natural source of salicylic acid? What useful properties do salicylic acid and acetylsalicylic acid share?

89. What are some of the areas of chemistry that Joanne Stubbe has contributed to?

90. What health risks are related to a high-fat diet?

Write About Chemistry

91. Should genetically engineered plants or bacteria be introduced into the environment? Write a paragraph and present a well-reasoned argument for one side of this issue.

92. Write a poem praising the virtues of a particular class of organic compound. For example, you might dwell on the wondrous aroma of the esters or the sweetness of some of the carbohydrates.

Readings and References

Emsley, John. "Artificial Sweeteners." *ChemMatters* (February 1988), pp. 4–8.

Freidel, Robert. "The Plastics Man." *Science 84* (November 1984), pp. 49–51.

Twigg, John. *Looking at Plastics and Other Big Molecules.* North Pomfret, Vermont: B. T. Batsford, 1986.

26 Nuclear Chemistry

Goals

- Explain the processes of radioactivity and radioactive decay.
- Distinguish between isotopes and radioisotopes.
- Describe the characteristics of alpha, beta, and gamma radiation and list their origins.
- Define the terms *nuclear stability, half-life,* and *transmutation.*
- Explain the operation of the Geiger counter.

The largest number of dominoes that has ever been toppled in a row is 281,581. It took 31 days to set them up but only about 13 minutes for them to fall. Nuclear fission can be likened to the chain reaction of dominoes falling one on another.

Concept Overview

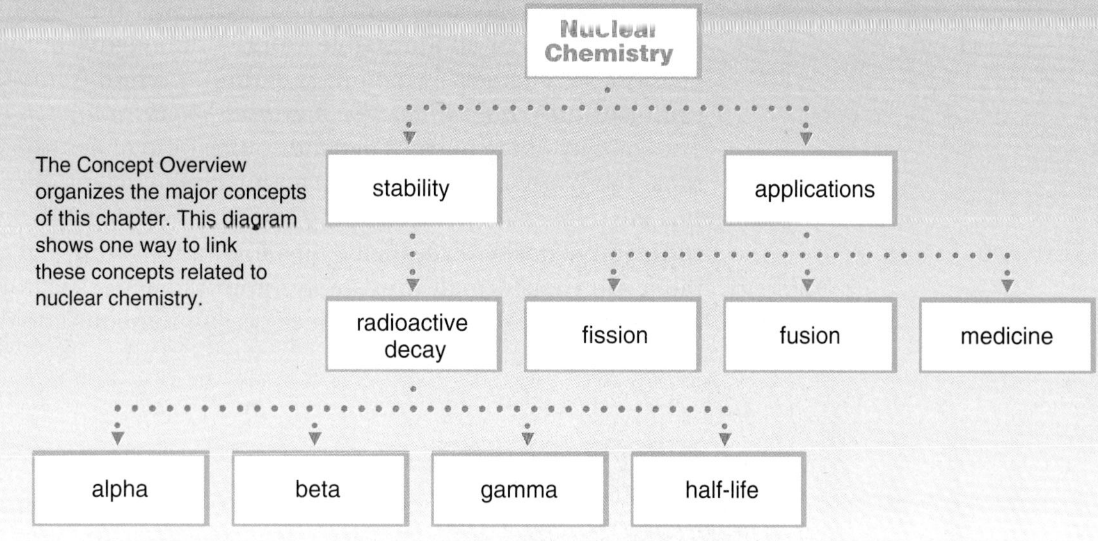

The preceding chapters have focused on chemical reactions. In such reactions atoms gain stability by attaining stable electron configurations. This chapter deals with nuclear reactions. In nuclear reactions certain unstable isotopes called radioisotopes gain stability by making changes within their nuclei. These changes are accompanied by the emission of large amounts of radiation energy. Unlike a chemical reaction, a nuclear reaction is not affected by changes in temperature or pressure or the presence of a catalyst. A nuclear reaction is unaffected by the compound an element is in. A nuclear reaction cannot be slowed down, speeded up, or turned off.

26.1 Radioactivity

Objective

Define radioisotope, radioactive decay, and transmutation.

In 1896 the French chemist Antoine Henri Becquerel (1852–1908) accidentally discovered that uranium emits invisible rays. He had stored some uranium salts next to some wrapped photographic film plates. When the plates were developed they were black, as if they had been exposed to light. At that time two of Becquerel's graduate students were Marie Curie (1867–1934) and Pierre Curie (1859–1906). The Curies were able to show that the fogging of the plates was caused by rays emitted by the uranium in the ore. Marie named *the process by which uranium gives off rays* **radioactivity**. *The penetrating rays emitted by a radioactive source are one type of* **radiation**. Pierre assisted Marie in isolating several radioactive elements. Together with Becquerel in 1903, the Curies won the Nobel Prize in Physics for this work.

Becquerel's discovery of radioactivity was the deathblow to Dalton's theory of an indivisible atom. A radioactive atom undergoes drastic changes as it emits radiation. *Certain isotopes, called* **radioisotopes**, *are radioactive because they have unstable nuclei.* The stability of the nucleus depends on its ratio of neutrons to protons. Too many neutrons lead to an unstable nucleus. *An unstable nucleus loses energy by emitting radiation during the process of* **radioactive decay**. Eventually, unstable radioisotopes of one element are transformed into stable (nonradioactive) isotopes of a different element. Radioactive decay is spontaneous and does not require any input of energy.

Concept Practice

1. Radioisotopes are a subset of isotopes. Explain.

2. What part of an atom changes during radioactive decay ?

Objective

Describe the composition and penetrating power of alpha, beta, and gamma radiation.

26.2 Types of Radiation

Several types of radiation can be emitted during radioactive decay. They include alpha radiation (Greek α), beta radiation (Greek β), and gamma radiation (Greek γ). Table 26.1 summarizes the properties of different types of radiation. The radiation from a radioactive source can be separated into different types by an electric or magnetic field as shown in Figure 26.1.

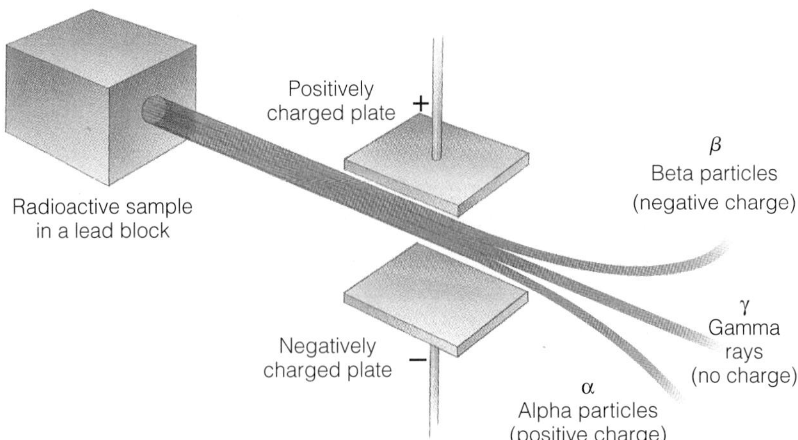

Figure 26.1 An electric field has different effects on the three types of radiation. Alpha particles and beta particles are deflected in opposite directions. Gamma rays are undeflected.

Table 26.1 Characteristics of Some Ionizing Radiations			
Property	**Alpha radiation**	**Beta radiation**	**Gamma radiation**
Composition	Alpha particle (helium nucleus)	Beta particle (electron)	High-energy electromagnetic radiation
Symbol	α, ${}^{4}_{2}He$	β, ${}^{0}_{-1}e$	γ
Charge	2+	1–	0
Mass (amu)	4	1/1837	0
Common source	Radium-226	Carbon-14	Cobalt-60
Approximate energy	5 MeV*	0.05 to 1 MeV	1 MeV
Penetrating power	Low (0.05 mm body tissue)	Moderate (4 mm body tissue)	Very high (penetrates body easily)
Shielding	Paper, clothing	Metal foil	Lead, concrete (incompletely shields)

*(1 MeV = 1.60×10^{-13} J)

Alpha radiation *consists of helium nuclei that have been emitted from a radioactive source.* **Alpha particles** *contain two protons and two neutrons and have a double positive charge.* In writing nuclear reactions, an alpha particle is written as ${}^{4}_{2}He$ or α. The charge is omitted.

The radioisotope uranium-238 releases alpha radiation. Figure 26.2 shows how uranium-238 is transformed into another radioisotope, thorium-234.

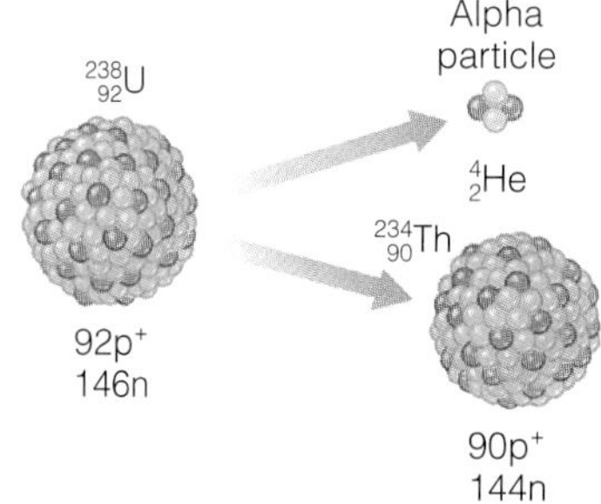

Figure 26.2 What particle is emitted when uranium-238 decays to thorium-234?

$$\underset{\text{Uranium-238}}{{}^{238}_{92}U} \xrightarrow{\text{radioactive decay}} \underset{\text{Thorium-234}}{{}^{234}_{90}Th} + \underset{\text{Alpha particle}}{{}^{4}_{2}He} \quad (\alpha \text{ emission})$$

When an atom loses an alpha particle, the atomic number of the product atom is lower by two and its mass number is lower by four. Because of their large mass and charge, alpha particles do not travel very far and are not very penetrating. Alpha particles are easily stopped by a sheet of paper or even by the dead cells on the surface of the skin. However, radioisotopes that emit alpha particles are dangerous when ingested. The particles do not have to travel far to penetrate the soft tissue inside the body and cause damage. Be careful in handling radioisotopes.

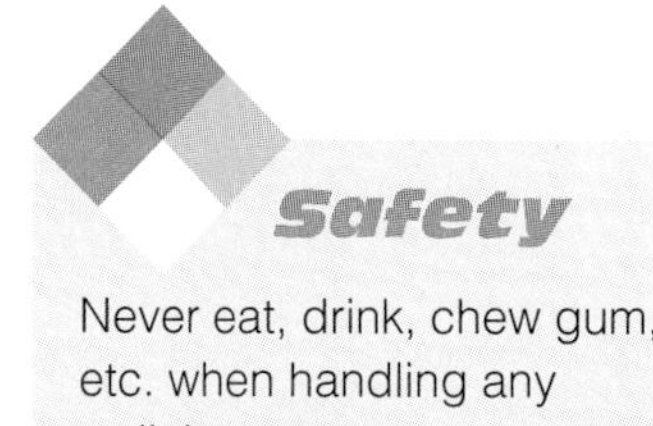

Safety

Never eat, drink, chew gum, etc. when handling any radioisotopes.

Beta radiation *consists of fast-moving electrons formed by the decomposition of a neutron of an atom.* The neutron breaks into a proton and an electron. *The resultant fast-moving electrons are called* **beta particles**.

$$\underset{\text{Neutron}}{{}^{1}_{0}n} \longrightarrow \underset{\text{Proton}}{{}^{1}_{1}H} + \underset{\text{Electron (beta particle)}}{{}^{0}_{-1}e}$$

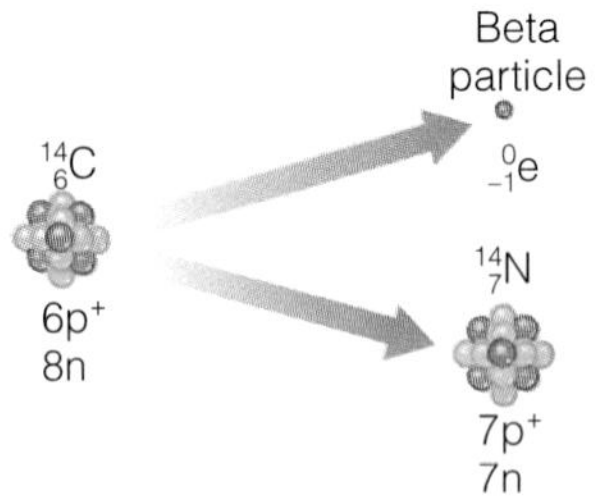

Figure 26.3 What particle is emitted when carbon-14 decays to nitrogen-14?

The proton stays in the nucleus and the energetic electron is ejected from the atom. Figure 26.3 shows that carbon-14 emits a beta particle as it undergoes radioactive decay to form nitrogen-14.

$$\underset{\text{Carbon-14 (radioactive)}}{^{14}_{6}\text{C}} \longrightarrow \underset{\text{Nitrogen-14 (stable)}}{^{14}_{7}\text{N}} + \underset{\text{Beta particle}}{^{0}_{-1}\text{e}} \qquad (\beta \text{ emission})$$

The mass number of the nitrogen-14 atom is the same as that of carbon-14. The atomic number has increased by 1. However, the nucleus contains one more proton and one less neutron.

Beta particles have half the charge of and are much lighter than alpha particles. Consequently, they are much more penetrating. Beta particles are stopped by aluminum foil or thin pieces of wood.

Gamma radiation *is electromagnetic radiation.* Visible light (the light people see) is also electromagnetic radiation, but of much lower energy. Gamma rays are often emitted by the nuclei of disintegrating radioactive atoms along with alpha or beta radiation.

$$\underset{\text{Thorium-230}}{^{230}_{90}\text{Th}} \longrightarrow \underset{\text{Radon-226}}{^{226}_{88}\text{Ra}} + \underset{\text{Alpha particle}}{^{4}_{2}\text{He}} + \underset{\text{Gamma ray}}{\gamma}$$

$$\underset{\text{Thorium-234}}{^{234}_{90}\text{Th}} \longrightarrow \underset{\text{Protactinium-234}}{^{234}_{91}\text{Pa}} + \underset{\text{Beta particle}}{^{0}_{-1}\text{e}} + \underset{\text{Gamma ray}}{\gamma}$$

Safety

It is easier to prevent spills than to decontaminate a spill area. Keep radioisotope containers in secondary containers to prevent spills. Work in trays rather than directly on the lab bench.

Gamma rays have no mass and no electrical charge. Thus the emission of gamma radiation does not alter the atomic number or mass number of an atom.

X-radiation is not emitted during radioactive decay. It is produced as excited electrons in certain metals lose their energy. Except for their origins, gamma rays and X-rays are essentially the same. Both gamma rays and X-rays pass easily through paper, wood, and the human body. They can be stopped, although not completely, by several meters of concrete or several centimeters of lead.

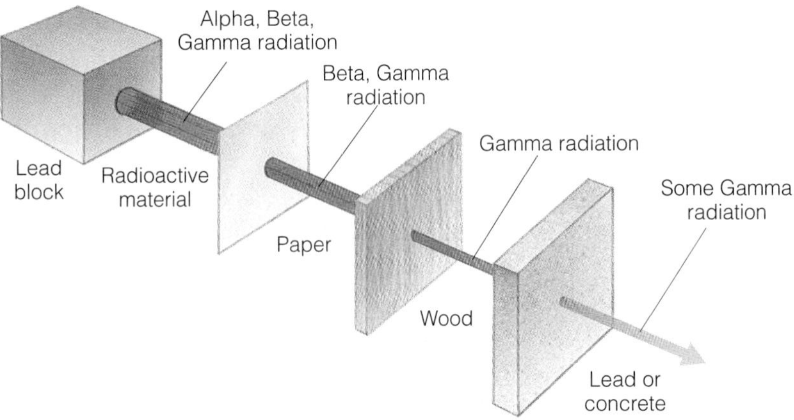

Figure 26.4 Alpha particles, because of their large mass and charge, have the least penetrating power. Gamma rays have no mass or charge and are very penetrating.

Concept Practice

3. Tell how alpha, beta, and gamma radiation are distinguished on the basis of the following.
a. mass **b.** charge **c.** penetrating power

Practice Problem

4. The disintegration of the radioisotope radium-226 produces an isotope of the element radon and alpha radiation. The atomic number of radium (Ra) is 88; the atomic number of radon (Rn) is 86. Write a balanced equation for this decay.

Activity 26
Measuring Inverse Square Relationships

Purpose

To make a graph that shows that radiation intensity decreases with the inverse square of the distance from the source.

Materials

flashlight

duct tape

scissors

posterboard, white
(50 cm × 50 cm)

meter stick or tape measure

graph paper

Procedure

Note: Measure and record all distances in this activity in centimeters.

1. Stick strips of duct tape over the end of a flashlight, leaving a 1-centimeter-square hole at its center for light to pass through.

2. Measure the distance from the bulb filament to the front surface of the flashlight. Record this measurement as distance *A*.

3. Place the flashlight on a flat, horizontal surface.

4. Mount a large piece of white posterboard in front of the flashlight, perpendicular to the horizontal surface.

5. Switch the flashlight on.

6. Measure the distance from the front surface of the flashlight to the vertical board. Record this measurement as distance *B*. Measure the length of one side of the projected square image on the vertical board and record this as measurement *L*.

7. Move the flashlight backward (at least 10 cm) from the vertical board. Measure and record the distances *B* and *L*. Repeat this step several times.

8. Graph L vs. $A + B$ (graph 1) and L^2 vs. $A + B$ (graph 2).

Analysis and Conclusions

1. Compare graph 1 to graph 2.

2. As the flashlight is moved away from the vertical board, what do you notice about the intensity of the light in the illuminated square?

3. When the distance of the flashlight from the board is doubled, what can you say about the area of the illuminated square? When the distance is tripled?

4. Comment on the appropriate distance a desk lamp should be for optimal lighting.

26.A Consumer Chemistry

Irradiated Foods

Figure 26.5 The FDA requires this symbol to appear on irradiated retail foods.

Radiation! The word alone scares most people. Yet, subjecting food to radiation, a process called irradiation, may help provide healthful, nutritious food to a hungry world.

Irradiation dramatically increases the shelf life of food in two ways. First, the harmful effect of ionizing radiation destroys most food-spoiling organisms. Mold, bacteria, and insects are controlled by irradiation. Second, irradiated vegetables such as potatoes and onions do not sprout during storage.

During irradiation, food is exposed to ionizing gamma radiation produced by cobalt-60 decay. The radiation penetrates the food, killing microbes and insects. The food itself does not retain any radiation and it does not become radioactive.

Food-related illnesses cost Americans billions of dollars each year in medical bills and lost wages. In developing countries, pests and spoilage can claim up to 30% of the harvest. Chemical preservatives and pesticides can reduce food losses, but these solutions may involve potential health risks as well. In an effort to reduce the cost of food spoilage, the United Nations, the World Health Organization, and over 30 nations including the United States have approved the use of food irradiation.

Although irradiation was approved in the United States in the 1980s, the food industry has not made widespread use of the technique. Critics of food irradiation have many reasons for their disapproval. Irradiation alters the food somewhat, especially at high doses. Substances produced during irradiation, called radiolytic products, can give food a bad taste or smell. While radiolytic products appear to be harmless, they occur in such small quantities that they are difficult to study. Vitamins can also be destroyed, and the texture of protein can be affected. Because there is no reliable test to determine whether food has been irradiated, regulation is difficult. Opponents fear that illegal, repeated irradiation may be used as a substitute for proper food handling. The use and disposal of radioactive cobalt-60 could also create a problem.

People also initially mistrusted the canning, freezing, and microwaving of food. Perhaps someday food irradiation will be as common as other processing techniques.

Think About It

5. List What are two positive results of irradiating food ?

6. Support Would you eat irradiated foods ? Why or why not ?

26.3 Nuclear Stability

About 1500 different nuclei are known. Of these only 264 are stable. Stable nuclei do not decay or change with time. The stability of a nucleus depends on its neutron-to-proton ratio. For elements of low atomic number, below about 20, this ratio is 1. This means that the nuclei have equal numbers of neutrons and protons. For example, the isotopes $^{12}_{6}C$, $^{14}_{7}N$, and $^{16}_{8}O$ are stable. Above atomic number 20 the stable nuclei have more neutrons than protons. The neutron-to-proton ratio reaches about 1.5 with heavy elements. The lead isotope $^{206}_{82}Pb$ is stable. Its ratio is $\frac{124}{82} \approx 1.5$.

A plot of the number of neutrons versus the number of protons for the known stable nuclei is given in Figure 26.6. *The stable nuclei on a neutron-vs.-proton plot are located in a* **band of stability.** The nuclei that fall outside the band of stability undergo spontaneous radioactive decay. The type of decay that occurs depends on the position of the nucleus with respect to the band of stability.

Nuclei in *region A,* to the left of the band of stability, have too many neutrons. They turn a neutron into a proton by emitting a beta particle (an electron) from the nucleus.

$$^{1}_{0}n \longrightarrow {}^{1}_{1}H + {}^{0}_{-1}e$$

Objective

Write balanced nuclear equations for alpha and beta decay processes.

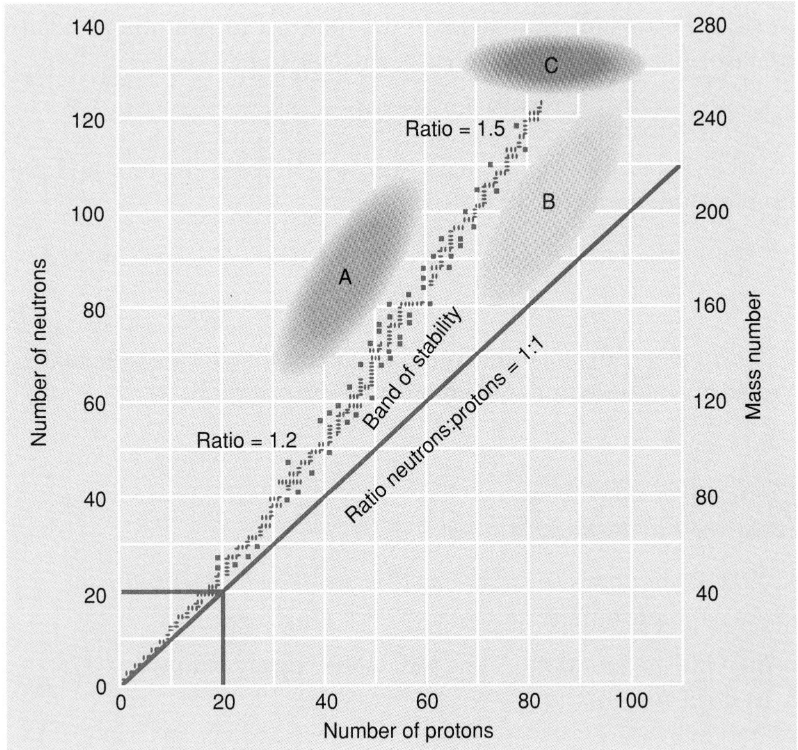

Figure 26.6 On a number of neutron versus number of proton plot, stable nuclei form a pattern known as the band of stability. For isotopes of small atomic number, the stable ratio is 1:1; for heavier isotopes it increases to about 1.5:1. In region A, unstable nuclei undergo beta decay. In region B they convert a proton to a neutron. In region C they undergo alpha particle emission. (The solid line is a reference line for a neutron-to-proton ratio of 1:1.)

Integrating Physics

Particle Accelerators

Since the 1930s, physicists have used particle accelerators to probe the mysteries of the atom. In a particle accelerator a beam of subatomic particles traveling near the speed of light collides with a nucleus, smashing it into fragments. New particles are created during these collisions as the relativity effect turns energy into matter. These particles leave a trail of bubbles in a detection device called a bubble chamber. Researchers have discovered that protons and neutrons consist of even smaller particles called quarks. Quarks are thought to be held together by other particles called gluons.

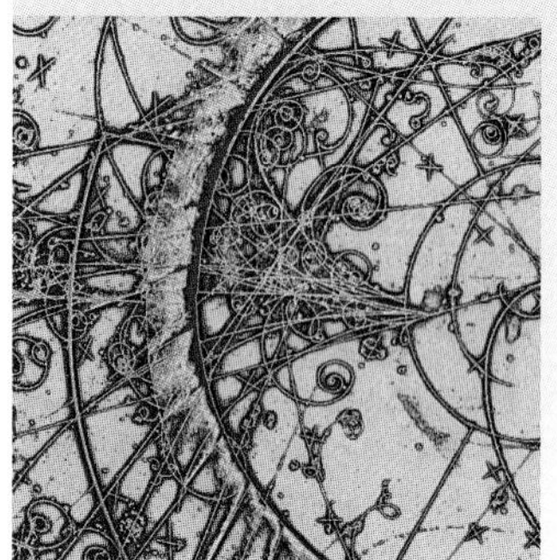

This process is known as *beta decay* or *beta emission.* It produces a simultaneous increase in the number of protons and decrease in the number of neutrons.

$$^{66}_{29}\text{Cu} \longrightarrow {}^{66}_{30}\text{Zn} + {}^{0}_{-1}\text{e}$$

$$^{14}_{6}\text{C} \longrightarrow {}^{14}_{7}\text{N} + {}^{0}_{-1}\text{e}$$

Nuclei in *region B,* to the right of the band of stability, have too many protons. They increase their stability by converting a proton to a neutron. An electron is captured in this process.

$$^{59}_{28}\text{Ni} + {}^{0}_{-1}\text{e} \longrightarrow {}^{59}_{27}\text{Co}$$

$$^{37}_{18}\text{Ar} + {}^{0}_{-1}\text{e} \longrightarrow {}^{37}_{17}\text{Cl}$$

A **positron** *is a particle with the mass of an electron but a positive charge,* $^{0}_{+1}\text{e}$. A positron may be emitted as a proton is converted to a neutron.

$$^{8}_{5}\text{B} \longrightarrow {}^{8}_{4}\text{Be} + {}^{0}_{+1}\text{e}$$

$$^{15}_{8}\text{O} \longrightarrow {}^{15}_{7}\text{N} + {}^{0}_{+1}\text{e}$$

When a proton is converted to a neutron the atomic number decreases by one, the number of neutrons increases by one, but the mass number remains the same.

Region C is above the upper end of the band of stability. The nuclei in this region are especially heavy. They have both too many neutrons and too many protons. They emit alpha particles. Alpha emission results in an increase in the neutron-to-proton ratio. This is a favorable change and increases nuclear stability.

$$^{204}_{82}\text{Pb} \longrightarrow {}^{200}_{80}\text{Hg} + {}^{4}_{2}\text{He}$$

In alpha emission, the mass number decreases by four and the atomic number decreases by two.

$$^{226}_{88}\text{Ra} \longrightarrow {}^{222}_{86}\text{Rn} + {}^{4}_{2}\text{He}$$

$$^{232}_{90}\text{Th} \longrightarrow {}^{228}_{88}\text{Ra} + {}^{4}_{2}\text{He}$$

All nuclei with an atomic number greater than 83 are radioactive. A majority of these undergo alpha emission.

Concept Practice

7. What happens to an atom with a nucleus that falls outside the band of stability ?

8. Write an equation for the radioactive decay of fluorine-17 by positron emission.

26.4 Half-Life

Objective

Compute the amount of radioisotope remaining at a given time using the half-life method, and explain how radioisotopes can be used to date objects.

Every radioisotope has a characteristic rate of decay measured by its half-life. *The* **half-life** *($t_{\frac{1}{2}}$) is the time required for one-half of the atoms of a radioisotope to emit radiation and to decay to products.* After one half-life, one-half of the original radioactive atoms have decayed into atoms of a new element. The other one-half remain unchanged. After a second half-life only one-quarter of the original radioactive atoms remain. If the masses of the reactants and products of a nuclear reaction were determined with a sensitive balance, it would appear that the mass was conserved. But nuclear reactions differ from chemical reactions. An infinitesimally small quantity of mass is lost. The lost mass is converted to radiation energy.

Half-lives may be as short as a fraction of a second or as long as several million years. Many artificially produced radioisotopes have very short half-lives. This feature is a great advantage in nuclear medicine. The rapidly decaying isotopes are not long-term biological radiation hazards.

One isotope, uranium-238, decays through a complex series of radioactive intermediates to the stable isotope lead-206 as shown in Figure 26.8. The age of certain rocks is determined by measuring the ratio of uranium-238 to lead-206. The half-life of uranium-238 is 4.5×10^9 years. Thus it is possible to use this method to date rocks as old as our solar system (4.6×10^9 years).

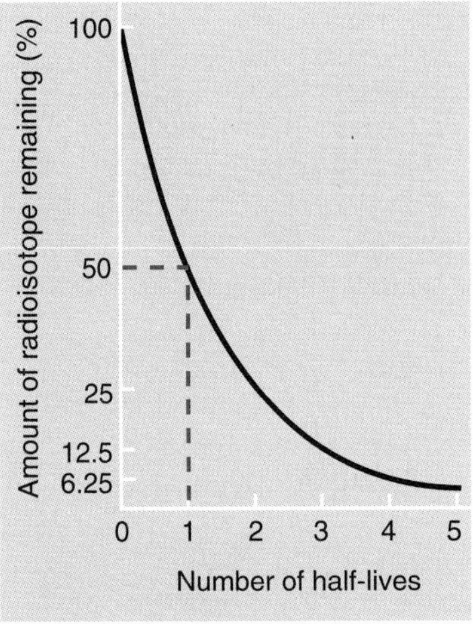

Figure 26.7 This decay curve for a radioactive element shows that after each half-life, one-half of the remaining original radioactive atoms have decayed into atoms of a new element.

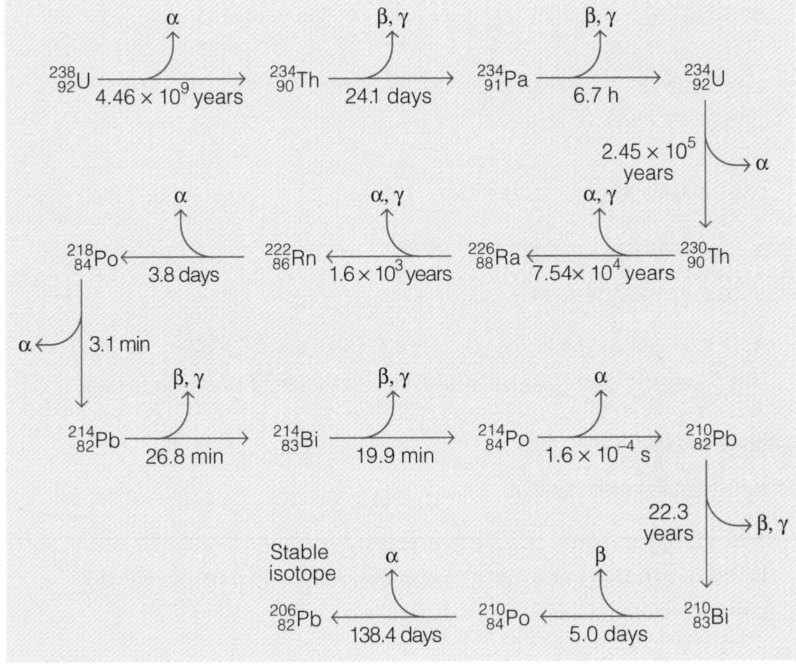

Figure 26.8 Uranium-238 decays through a complex series of radioactive intermediates, including radon (Rn) gas. What is the stable end product of this series?

Integrating Archaeology

Carbon-14 Dating

All living organisms contain carbon-12 and carbon-14 in a fixed ratio. However, after the organism dies, this ratio changes as the carbon-14 decays to nitrogen-14. Archaeologists use this fact to establish the age of fossils and ancient artifacts. For example, a fossil might have a carbon-14 concentration of one-half its original value. Knowing carbon-14 has a half life of 5730 years, it can be determined that the fossil is about 5730 years old. Carbon-14 dating is used to determine accurately the age of objects that are between 200 and 50 000 years old.

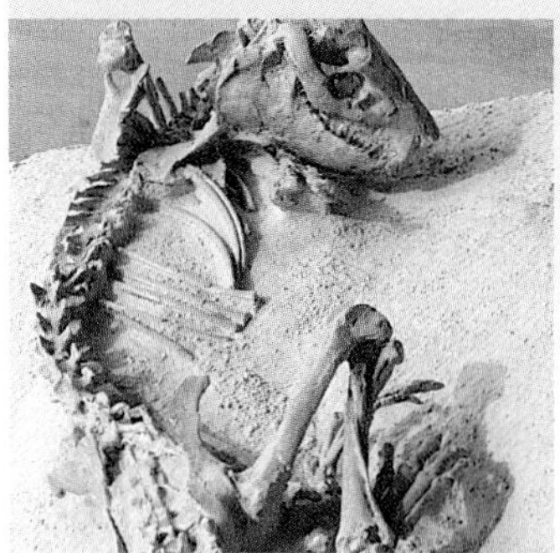

Table 26.2 Half-lives and Radiation of Some Naturally Occurring Radioisotopes

Isotope	Half-life	Radiation emitted
Carbon-14	5.73×10^3 years	β
Potassium-40	1.25×10^9 years	β, γ
Radon-222	3.8 days	α
Radium-226	1.6×10^3 years	α, γ
Thorium-230	7.54×10^4 years	α, γ
Thorium-234	24.1 days	β, γ
Uranium-235	7.0×10^8 years	α, γ
Uranium-238	4.46×10^9 years	α

Example 1 Using Half-lives in Calculations

Nitrogen-13 emits beta radiation and decays to carbon-13 with $t_{\frac{1}{2}} = 10$ min. Assume a starting mass of 2.00 g of nitrogen-13.

a. How long is four half-lives ?

b. How many grams of nitrogen-13 will still exist after three half-lives ?

Solution

a. One half-life is equal to 10 min. Four half-lives is 4×10 min., which equals 40 min.

b.

Number of half-lives	Mass of nitrogen-13
0	2.00 g
1	1.00 g
2	0.50 g
3	0.25 g

After three half-lives, 0.25 g remains.

Concept Practice

9. A sample of thorium-234 has a half-life of 25 days. Will all the thorium undergo radioactive decay in 50 days ? Explain.

Practice Problem

10. Manganese-56 is a beta emitter with a half-life of 2.6 h. What is the mass of manganese-56 in a 1-mg sample of the isotope after 10.4 h ?

26.5 Transmutation Reactions

Objective

Write equations to show how transuranium elements are synthesized by transmutation.

The conversion of an atom of one element to an atom of another element is called **transmutation.** Radioactive decay is one way in which transmutations occur. A transmutation can also occur when high-energy particles bombard the nucleus of an atom. The high-energy particles may be protons, neutrons, or alpha particles. Many transmutations occur in nature. For example, the production of carbon-14 from nitrogen-14 occurs in the upper atmosphere. Uranium-238 undergoes 14 transmutations before reaching a stable isotope. Many other transmutations are done in laboratories or in nuclear reactors. The earliest artificial transmutation was performed in 1919 by Ernest Rutherford. He bombarded nitrogen gas with alpha particles to produce an unstable isotope of fluorine as shown in Figure 26.9.

$$\underset{\text{Nitrogen-14}}{{}^{14}_{7}\text{N}} + \underset{\text{Alpha particle}}{{}^{4}_{2}\text{He}} \longrightarrow \underset{\text{Fluorine-18}}{{}^{18}_{9}\text{F}}$$

The fluorine isotope quickly decomposes to a stable isotope of oxygen and a proton. This experiment eventually led to the discovery of the proton.

$$\underset{\text{Fluorine-18}}{{}^{18}_{9}\text{F}} \longrightarrow \underset{\text{Oxygen-17}}{{}^{17}_{8}\text{O}} + \underset{\text{Proton}}{{}^{1}_{1}\text{H}}$$

James Chadwick's discovery of the neutron in 1932 also involved a transmutation experiment. The neutrons were produced in Chadwick's experiment when beryllium-9 was bombarded with alpha particles.

$$\underset{\text{Beryllium-9}}{{}^{9}_{4}\text{Be}} + \underset{\text{Alpha particle}}{{}^{4}_{2}\text{He}} \longrightarrow \underset{\text{Carbon-12}}{{}^{12}_{6}\text{C}} + \underset{\text{Neutron}}{{}^{1}_{0}\text{n}}$$

Roots of Words

transmutare: (Latin) to change
transmutation the conversion of an atom of one element into an atom of another element by the emission of radiation

The transmutation of ${}^{239}_{93}\text{Np}$ to ${}^{239}_{94}\text{Pu}$ occurs upon loss of a beta particle.

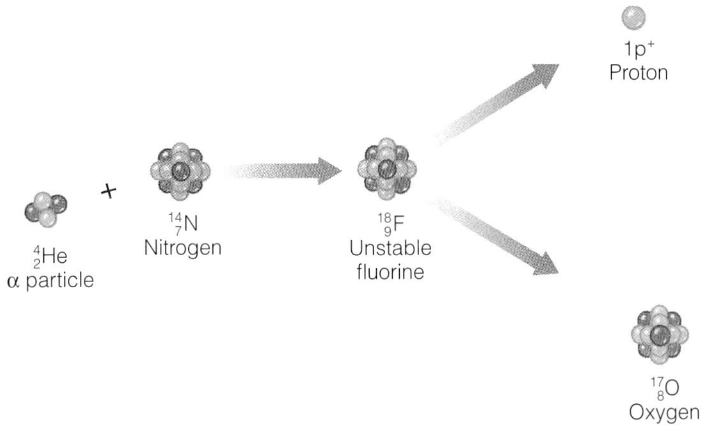

Figure 26.9 In 1919, Ernest Rutherford carried out the first artificial transmutation when he bombarded nitrogen gas with alpha particles. What particles were formed?

The elements in the periodic table with atomic numbers above 92 are called the **transuranium elements.** None of them occur in nature and all of them are radioactive. These elements have been synthesized in nuclear reactors and nuclear accelerators, which accelerate the bombarding particles to very high speeds.

When uranium-238 is bombarded with slow neutrons from a nuclear reactor, some uranium nuclei capture neutrons to produce uranium-239.

$$^{238}_{92}\text{U} + {}^{1}_{0}\text{n} \longrightarrow {}^{239}_{92}\text{U}$$

Uranium-239 is radioactive and emits a beta particle. The product isotope is the artificial radioactive element neptunium with atomic number 93.

$$^{239}_{92}\text{U} \longrightarrow {}^{239}_{93}\text{Np} + {}^{0}_{-1}\text{e}$$

Neptunium is unstable and emits a beta particle to produce a second artificial element, plutonium. Plutonium has an atomic number of 94.

$$^{239}_{93}\text{Np} \longrightarrow {}^{239}_{94}\text{Pu} + {}^{0}_{-1}\text{e}$$

Plutonium and neptunium are both transuranium elements. They do not occur in nature. Each has an atomic number greater than 92. Neptunium and plutonium, the first artificial elements ever made, were synthesized in 1940. Since that time 15 more transuranium elements, atomic numbers 95 through 109, have been synthesized.

Concept Practice

11. Which atomic particle must undergo a change in number during every transmutation reaction ?

12. What is the difference between natural and artificial radioactivity ?

Objective

Explain how a fission nuclear power plant operates.

26.6 Nuclear Fission

When the nuclei of certain isotopes are bombarded with neutrons, they undergo **fission,** *which is the splitting of a nucleus into smaller fragments.* Uranium-235 and plutonium-239 are fissionable materials. Look at Figure 26.10. A fissionable atom such as uranium-235 breaks into two fragments of roughly the same size when it is struck by a slow-moving neutron. At the same time, more neutrons are released.

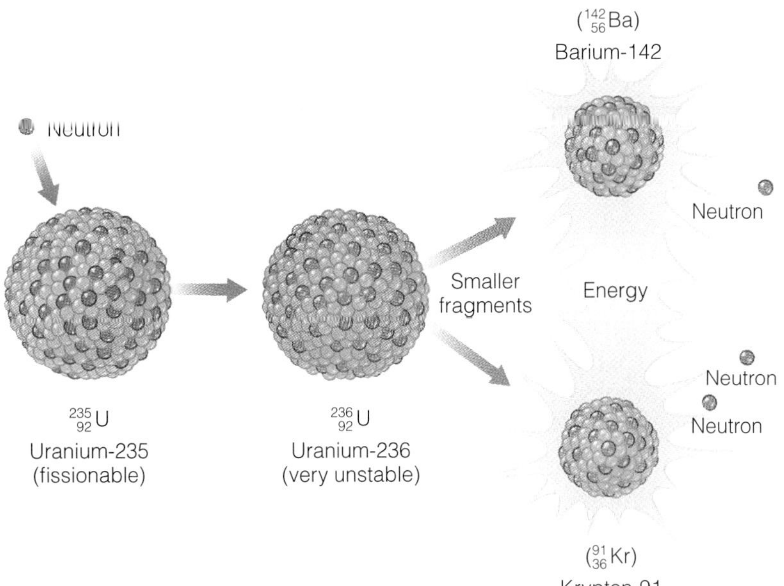

Figure 26.10 In nuclear fission, uranium-235 breaks into two fragments, releasing energy and more neutrons. The released neutrons can split other uranium-235 atoms, creating a chain reaction.

These neutrons strike the nuclei of other uranium-235 atoms, continuing fission by a chain reaction. In a chain reaction, some of the neutrons produced react with other fissionable atoms, producing more neutrons that react with still more fissionable atoms.

Fission unleashes enormous amounts of energy. The fission of 1 kg of uranium-235 releases an amount of energy equal to that generated in the explosion of 20 000 tons of dynamite. If a nuclear chain reaction is uncontrolled, the energy release is nearly instantaneous. Atomic bombs are devices that start uncontrolled nuclear chain reactions.

Fission can be controlled so that energy is released more slowly. Nuclear reactors use controlled fission to produce useful energy. In the controlled fission reaction within the nuclear reactor, much of the energy generated appears as heat. The heat is removed from the reactor core by a suitable coolant fluid (usually liquid sodium or water). The heat is used to generate steam to drive a turbine. The spinning turbine generates electricity.

The control of fission in a nuclear reactor involves two steps. The steps are neutron moderation and neutron absorption. A description of the steps follows.

1. Neutron moderation *slows down the neutrons so that they can be captured by the reactor fuel to continue the chain reaction.* The reactor fuel is usually uranium-235. Most of the neutrons produced by uranium are moving so fast that they will pass right through the nucleus without being absorbed. Water and carbon are good moderators because they slow down the neutrons so that the chain reaction can be sustained.

Roots of Words

fissus: (Latin) split
fission the splitting of a nucleus into smaller particles, accompanied by the release of neutrons and a large amount of energy

Controlled nuclear fission is used to produce energy in nuclear reactors.

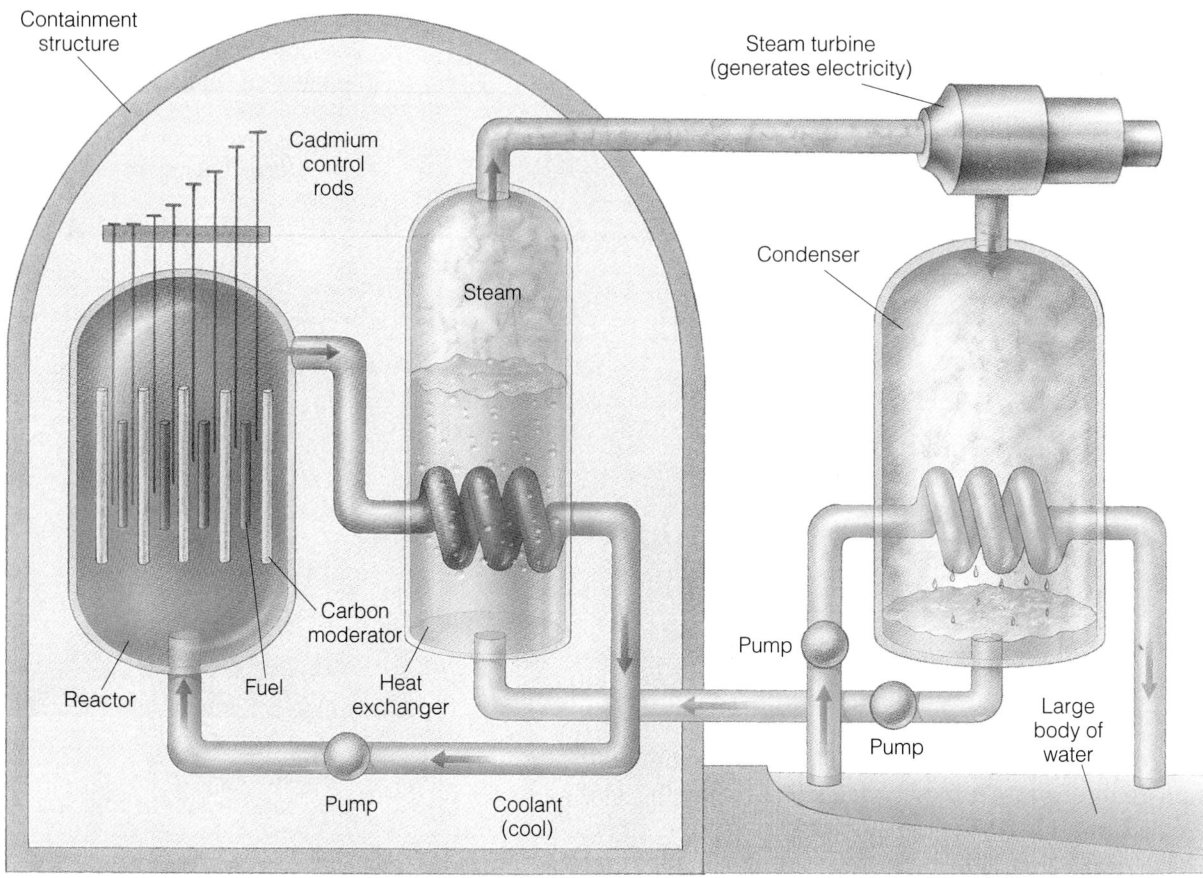

Figure 26.11 All nuclear reactors have five basic components: fuel, moderator, control rods, coolant, and shielding. Heat produced by the fission process is removed from the reactor and is used to turn water to steam. A steam-driven turbine is used to generate electricity.

2. Neutron absorption *decreases the number of slow neutrons.* To prevent the chain reaction from going too fast, some of the slowed neutrons must be trapped before they hit fissionable atoms. Neutron absorption is carried out by the use of control rods made of a material such as cadmium that absorbs neutrons. When the control rods extend almost all the way into the reactor core, they absorb many neutrons and fission occurs slowly. As the rods are pulled out, they absorb fewer neutrons and the fission process speeds up. If the chain reaction were to go too fast, heat might be produced faster than it could be removed by the coolant. In that case, the reactor core would overheat. This could lead to mechanical failures and release of radioactive materials into the atmosphere. Ultimately, a meltdown of the reactor core may occur. A nuclear reactor can never produce a nuclear explosion. The fuel elements are widely separated and cannot physically connect to produce a critical mass.

Once a nuclear reactor is started, it remains highly radioactive for many generations. Shields are used to protect the reactor structure from radiation damage. Walls of high-density concrete are designed to protect the operating personnel.

Concept Practice

13. Explain the term *nuclear chain reaction.*

14. How is the chain reaction in a nuclear reactor controlled ?

26.7 Nuclear Fusion

Objective

Describe nuclear fusion and write an equation representing solar fusion.

The sun is an extraordinary energy source. The energy released from the sun is the result of nuclear fusion, or thermonuclear reaction. **Fusion** *occurs when two nuclei combine to produce a nucleus of heavier mass.* In solar fusion, hydrogen nuclei (protons) are fused to make helium nuclei. The reaction requires two beta particles.

$$4\,{}^{1}_{1}\mathrm{H} + 2\,{}^{0}_{-1}\mathrm{e} \longrightarrow {}^{4}_{2}\mathrm{He} + \text{energy}$$

Fusion reactions release more energy than fission reactions. However, fusion reactions take place only at very high temperatures—in excess of 40 000 000°C.

Controlled nuclear fusion is appealing as an energy source on earth. The potential fuels are inexpensive and readily available, and fusion products are usually not radioactive. The problems with fusion are in achieving the high temperatures necessary to start the reaction and in containing the reaction. One reaction that scientists are studying is the combination of a deuterium nucleus and a tritium nucleus to form a helium nucleus.

$${}^{2}_{1}\mathrm{H} + {}^{3}_{1}\mathrm{H} \longrightarrow {}^{4}_{2}\mathrm{He} + {}^{1}_{0}\mathrm{n} + \text{energy}$$

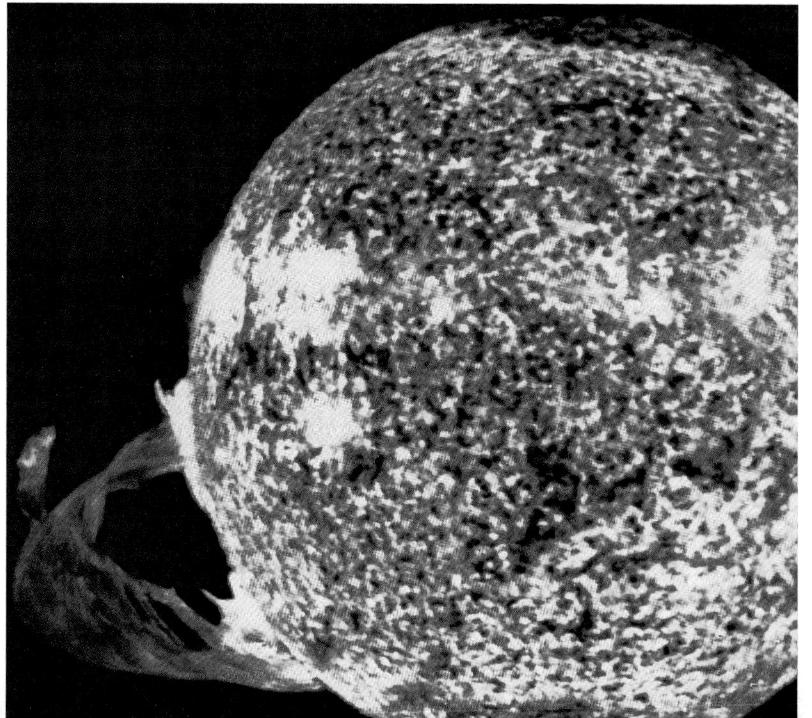

Figure 26.12 Thermonuclear fusion reactions occurring in the sun have provided the Earth with energy for billions of years.

Figure 26.13 The JET experimental tokamak is a nuclear reactor in which magnets are used to confine a hydrogen plasma within a doughnut-shaped torus. Thirty-two D-shaped coils create a magnetic field that holds the hot corrosive plasma away from the walls of the vacuum vessel. The inner and outer field coils are used to adjust the shape of the plasma.

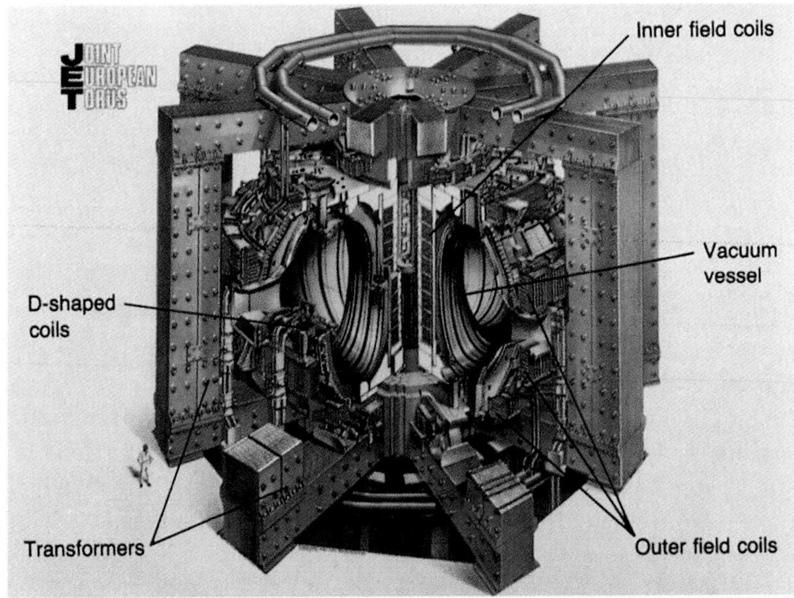

Roots of Words

fusus: (Latin) melted together
fusion the combination of two light nuclei to produce a nucleus of heavier mass, accompanied by the release of a large amount of energy

Controlled nuclear fusion reactions have tremendous potential as clean, abundant sources of energy.

The high temperatures required to initiate fusion reactions have been achieved by using an atomic bomb. It is the triggering device for setting off the hydrogen bomb, which is an uncontrolled fusion device. It is clearly of no use, however, as a controlled generator of power.

At the high temperatures involved, matter exists as a *plasma.* Containing the plasma is a formidable task. No known structural material can withstand the high temperatures and corrosive effects of plasmas. Magnetic fields are used to confine and control high-temperature dense plasmas. The most notable successes have been achieved in the Joint European Torus (JET) project, shown in Figure 26.13. This is a 14-nation collaborative venture based in the United Kingdom. JET has reached the required temperatures, densities, and degree of confinement in separate plasma experiments. JET was the first to generate a significant amount of fusion power (nearly 2.0 megawatts) for a short period. A team from Europe, the United States, Russia, and Japan are proceeding with plans to build an experimental reactor.

Concept Practice

15. Name a natural nuclear fusion reactor.

16. Assuming technical problems could be overcome, what are some advantages of producing electricity in a fusion reactor ?

26.B Environmental Awareness

Radon Gas

In the 1970s, radon provoked concern as a widespread environmental hazard. At first, radon was found in houses built on the tailings of uranium and phosphate mines. Studies have discovered radon gas in homes in nearly every part of the country.

Radon is a natural product of the decay of radioactive minerals that contain uranium-238 (^{238}U). Radon from these minerals in the earth can seep through cracks in basement floors. Because radon is denser than air, it tends to collect in the lower levels of a house. Testing homes for radon can be done easily, and it is recommended in regions of the country where the gas is known to be a potential problem. High levels of radon are reduced by improved ventilation in basements and closed areas where radon can collect. Cracks in basements can also be sealed.

Although it is probably wise to reduce radon in homes that contain high levels of the gas, the methods for its reduction are expensive, and the need for them in most cases has been questioned. Radon in homes is proving to be an excellent example of a scientific dispute among reputable scientists on both sides of the controversy. The major argument against widespread concern about household radon is the scientific evidence that links the level of radon to the incidence of lung cancer. Miners of uranium and silver get lung cancer in numbers far in excess of the general population. This could be due to high levels of radon in the mines. Critics note, however, that there is no clear understanding of the risks at low concentrations. These critics argue that, while it is true that the sample of miners studied did have high rates of lung cancer, other effects were not taken into account. For example, mines contain more dust than homes. Radioactive particles can cling to the dust, which then lodges in the lungs. This inhaled radioactive dust, the argument goes, is a much greater hazard than radon gas, which is breathed in and out of the lungs in a short time. Additional studies are being conducted to find the scientific truth. In the meantime, it is difficult for citizens to know whether radon should be of the widespread concern found in the press.

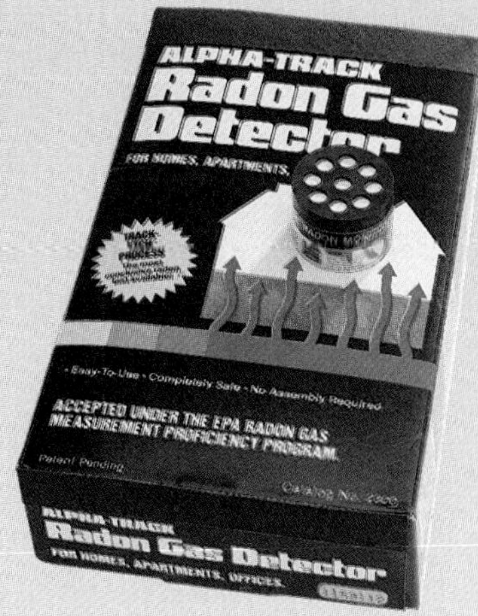

Figure 26.14 A commercially available radon test kit can be used to determine the concentration of radon gas in a building.

Think About It

17. Identify What is the origin of radon gas in the basement of a typical home ?

18. Explain Has your home been tested for radon ? Do you think all homes need to be tested ?

Objective

Describe three methods of detecting radiation, and list each method's limitations.

26.8 Detecting Radiation

The radiation emitted by radioisotopes (and X-rays) is ionizing radiation. **Ionizing radiation** *knocks electrons off some atoms of the bombarded substance to produce ions.* Ionizing radiation cannot be detected with any of our senses. Instead, various instruments and monitoring devices are used to do the job.

A **Geiger counter** *uses a gas-filled metal tube to detect radiation.* The tube is connected to a power supply and has a central wire electrode. When ionizing radiation penetrates the thin window at one end of the tube, the gas inside becomes ionized. When charged ions and free electrons are produced, the gas becomes an electrical conductor. Each time a Geiger tube is exposed to radiation, a current flows. The bursts of current drive electronic counters or cause audible clicks from a built-in speaker. Geiger counters are used primarily to detect beta radiation. A typical Geiger counter is shown in Figure 26.15. Alpha particles cannot pass through the end window. Most gamma rays and X-rays pass through the gas, causing few ionizations.

A **scintillation counter** *uses a phosphor to detect radiation.* Ionizing radiation striking the specially coated surface, or phosphor, produces bright flashes of light (scintillations). The number of flashes and their respective energies are detected electronically. They are then converted into electronic pulses that are measured and recorded. Scintillation counters have been designed to detect all types of ionizing radiation. This device is similar to a television

Figure 26.15 Radiation cannot be seen, heard, felt, or smelled (left). Thus warning signs and radiation detection instruments are used to alert people to the presence of radiation and to monitor its level. The Geiger counter (right) is widely used to detect beta radiation.

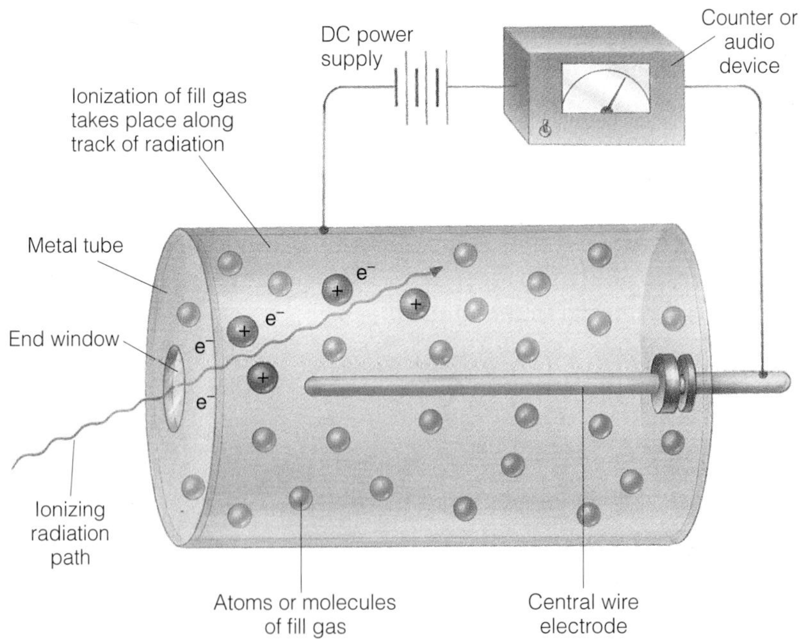

screen coated with zinc sulfide, ZnS, as the phosphor. The electrons from the TV gun striking the phosphor of the screen also produce scintillations. The pattern of scintillations is the TV picture.

Film badges are important radiation detectors for persons near radiation sources. *A* **film badge** *consists of several layers of photographic film covered with black lightproof paper encased in a plastic or metal holder.* It is worn all the time a person is at work. At frequent specific intervals, depending on the type of work involved, the film is removed and developed. The strength and type of radiation exposure are determined from any darkening of the film. Records are kept of the results. Film badges do not protect a person from radiation exposure. They merely serve as precautionary monitoring devices. Protection against radiation is achieved by keeping a safe distance away from the source and using adequate shielding.

Figure 26.16 The film badge detector is worn by people who work with radiation. The film inside the badge darkens in proportion to the amount of radiation it receives.

Concept Practice

19. What is an advantage of a scintillation counter over a Geiger counter?

20. A radioactive solution containing an alpha emitter accidentally gets on your hands. You wash them with soap and water and then check them with a Geiger counter for residual radioactive contamination. The Geiger counter does not register any radioactivity. Are your hands positively free from radioactive contamination ? Explain.

26.9 Radioisotopes in Research and Medicine

Objective

List applications of radioisotopes in research and medicine.

Although radiation can be harmful and should always be handled with care, it can be used safely and is important in many scientific procedures. Neutron activation analysis is used to detect trace amounts of elements in samples. In this technique, a sample is bombarded with neutrons from a radioactive source. This causes the atoms in the sample to become radioactive. The half-life and type of radiation emitted by the radioisotopes are detected and processed by a computer. Because this information is characteristic for each element, scientists can tell what radioisotopes are produced and what elements were originally present in the sample. This is one of the most sensitive techniques for detecting trace amounts of elements. It is capable of measuring 10^{-9} g of an element

Biographical Note

Rosalyn Yalow
(1921–)

The radioimmunoassay (RIA) is one of the most sensitive methods used to detect minute traces of substances in the body. The RIA was developed through the pioneering work of Rosalyn Yalow. Thanks to Yalow, today there are RIAs for hundreds of hormones, drugs, enzymes, and viruses. RIAs are used to diagnose diseases such as diabetes, growth disorders, and hypertension. Blood banks use RIAs to screen out hepatitis-infected blood. Yalow received her doctoral degree in physics from the University of Illinois at the age of 23. In 1977 she was awarded the Nobel Prize in Medicine for her development of RIAs.

in a sample. Neutron activation analysis is used by museums to detect art forgeries and by crime laboratories to analyze gunpowder.

Radioisotopes called tracers are used to study chemical reactions and molecular structures. One of the reactants, labeled with a radioisotope, is added to the reaction mixture. After the reaction is over, the radiation of the product is measured to determine the uptake of the tracer. By comparing this amount with the amount originally added, much can be learned about the reaction mechanism. Reactions with many steps can be studied using this method.

Radioisotopes are also used in agricultural research to test the effects of herbicides, pesticides, and fertilizers. The tracer is introduced into the substance being tested to make it radioactive. Next, the plants are treated with the radioactively labeled substance. Then, the radioactivity of the plants is measured to determine the location of the substance. Often the tracer is also monitored in animals that consume the plants, in water, and in soil. These studies help scientists determine the effects of the substance.

Radioisotopes are used to diagnose some diseases. Iodine-131 is used to detect thyroid problems. The thyroid gland extracts iodide ions from the blood stream and uses them to make thyroxine. To diagnose thyroid disease, the patient is given a drink containing a small amount of iodine-131. After about two hours, the amount of iodide uptake is measured by scanning the patient's throat with a radiation detector. Figure 26.17 shows an image of a scanned thyroid gland. In a similar way, technetium-99m is used to detect brain tumors and phosphorus-32 is used to detect skin cancer.

Radiation is valuable for the treatment of some cancers. This group of diseases is characterized by rapidly dividing abnormal cells. These cells are usually more sensitive to radiation than are

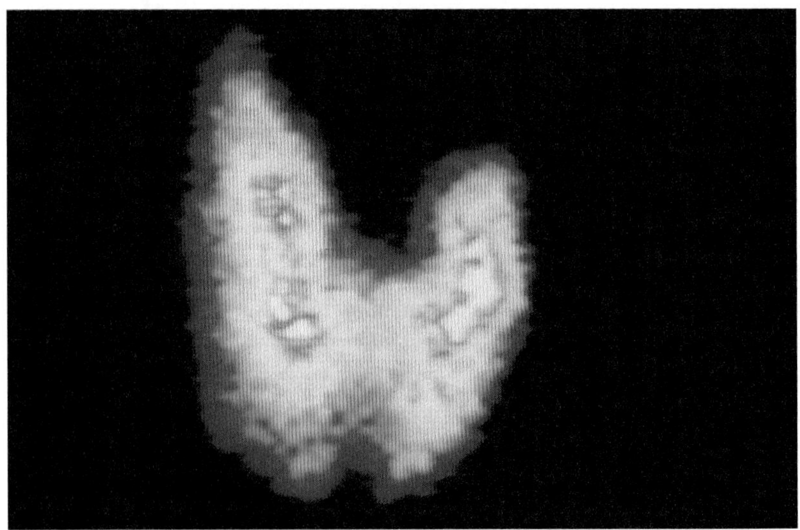

Figure 26.17 This scanned image of a thyroid gland shows where radioactive iodine-131 has been absorbed. Doctors use these images to identify thyroid disorders.

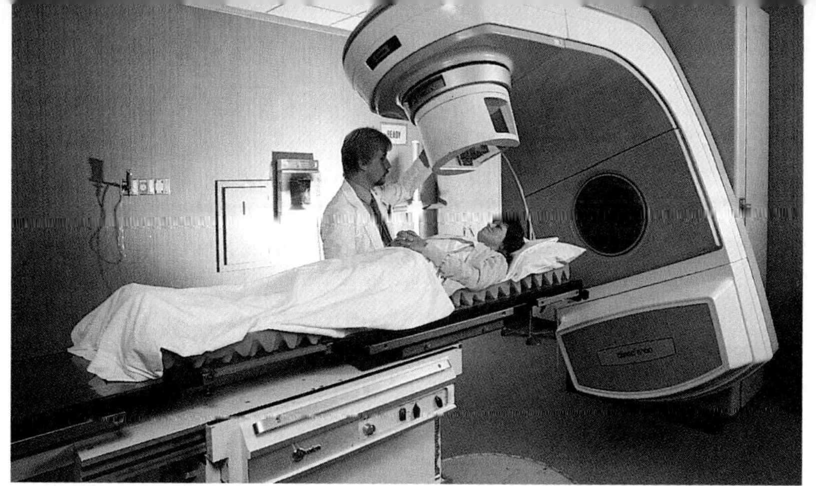

Figure 26.18 Radiation therapy is a commonly used method for treating cancer. This unit emits a narrow, intense beam of radiation that destroys the ability of cells to reproduce. Cancer cells are more sensitive to radiation than normal cells because they divide more rapidly. Cells are most vulnerable when they are dividing.

normal cells. The cancerous area can be treated with radiation to kill the cancer cells. Some normal cells are also killed, however, and cancer cells at the center of the tumor may be radiation resistant. Therefore, the benefits of killing the cancer cells and the risks to the patient must be evaluated before radiation treatment is carried out.

In teletherapy, a narrow beam of high-intensity gamma radiation is directed at the cancerous tissue. Cobalt-60 and cesium-137 are commonly used as radiation sources. To minimize damage to healthy tissue, the patient is positioned so that only the cancerous region is within the radiation beam at all times. The unit rotates so that the radiation dose to the skin and surrounding normal tissue is minimized and distributed in a belt all the way around the patient.

Salts of radioisotopes are sealed in gold tubes and directly implanted in tumors. These "seeds" emit beta and gamma rays, which kill the surrounding cancer cells. Because the radioisotope is in a sealed container, the excretions of patients undergoing this therapy are not radioactive.

Pharmaceuticals containing radioisotopes of gold, iodine, or phosphorus are sometimes given in radiation therapy. A dose of iodine-131, larger than that used to detect thyroid diseases, can be given to treat the disease. The radioactive iodine collects in the thyroid and emits beta and gamma rays to provide therapy. Because the radioisotope is not sealed, the patient's excretions are radioactive and must be specially handled.

Concept Practice

21. What are some uses of radioactive tracers?

22. What is an advantage of using a radioactive "seed" to treat a cancerous tumor?

Chapter 26 Review

Nuclear Chemistry

Key Terms

alpha particle *26.2*
alpha radiation *26.2*
band of stability *26.3*
beta particles *26.2*
beta radiation *26.2*
film badge *26.8*
fission *26.6*
fusion *26.7*
gamma radiation *26.2*
Geiger counter *26.8*
half-life ($t_{\frac{1}{2}}$) *26.4*
ionizing radiation *26.8*
neutron absorption *26.6*
neutron moderation *26.6*
positron *26.3*
radiation *26.1*
radioactive decay *26.1*
radioactivity *26.1*
radioisotope *26.1*
scintillation counter *26.8*
transmutation *26.5*
transuranium element *26.5*

Chapter Summary

Isotopes with unstable nuclei are radioactive and are called radioisotopes. The nuclei of radioisotopes emit radiation as they decay to stable nuclei. The radiation may be alpha, beta, or gamma. Alpha radiation consists of alpha particles (positively charged helium nuclei) that are easily stopped by a sheet of paper. Beta radiation is composed of fast-moving beta particles, which are electrons. Beta radiation is more penetrating than alpha radiation; it is stopped by aluminum foil. Gamma radiation is electromagnetic radiation similar to visible light, but much more energetic. Gamma radiation has no mass or charge. It is extremely penetrating. Lead bricks and concrete reduce the intensity of gamma radiation but do not completely stop it. Specially built instruments produce X-radiation, which is essentially the same as gamma radiation.

Every radioisotope decays at a characteristic rate. The half-life is the time required for one-half of the nuclei in a radioisotope to decay. The product nuclei may or may not be radioactive. Half-lives vary from fractions of a second to millions of years.

The decay of radioisotopes is represented by nuclear equations. When a radioactive nucleus emits an alpha particle, its atomic number decreases by 2 and its mass number decreases by 4. When a beta particle is emitted, the atomic number increases by 1 and the mass number stays the same. When a gamma ray is emitted, the atomic number and the mass number stay the same.

Nuclear fission occurs when fissionable isotopes are bombarded with neutrons. The isotopes split into two fragments of about the same size, and in the process they release more neutrons. Some of these neutrons strike other fissionable nuclei, releasing more neutrons, which split more nuclei. This is called a chain reaction. Fission releases enormous amounts of energy. Controlled fission is the energy source in every nuclear power plant. In nuclear fusion small nuclei fuse to make heavier nuclei. The sun's energy is released when hydrogen nuclei fuse to make helium nuclei. Fusion releases even more energy than fission.

Radiation may be detected with a Geiger counter or a scintillation counter. The film badge is an important personnel radiation detector. The radiation its wearer receives is detected by darkening of the encased film.

Practice Questions and Problems

23. Explain the difference between the terms *isotope* and *radioisotope. 26.1*

24. Write the symbol and state the charge for each. *26.2*

a. an alpha particle
b. a beta particle
c. a gamma ray

25. Alpha radiation is emitted during the disintegration of the following isotopes. Write balanced nuclear equations for their decay processes. Name the element produced in each case. *26.2*

a. uranium-238 ($^{238}_{92}U$)
b. thorium-230 ($^{230}_{90}Th$)
c. uranium-235 ($^{235}_{92}U$)
d. radon-222 ($^{222}_{86}Rn$)

26. The following radioisotopes are beta emitters. Write balanced nuclear equations for their decay processes. *26.2*

a. carbon-14 ($^{14}_{6}C$) **c.** potassium-40 ($^{40}_{19}K$)
b. strontium-90 ($^{90}_{38}Sr$) **d.** nitrogen-13 ($^{13}_{7}N$)

27. How are the atomic number and mass of a nucleus affected by loss of the following? *26.2*

a. a beta particle
b. an alpha particle
c. a gamma ray

28. The following radioactive nuclei decay by emitting alpha particles. Write the product of the decay process for each. *26.2*

a. $^{238}_{94}Pu$ **c.** $^{210}_{84}Po$
b. $^{210}_{83}Bi$ **d.** $^{230}_{90}Th$

29. How do you know if you are buying food that has been irradiated? *26.A*

30. Identify the more stable isotope in each of the following pairs. *26.3*

a. $^{14}_{6}C$, $^{13}_{6}C$ **c.** $^{16}_{8}O$, $^{18}_{8}O$
b. $^{3}_{1}H$, $^{1}_{1}H$ **d.** $^{14}_{7}N$, $^{15}_{7}N$

31. Name the elements represented by the following symbols and indicate which of them would have *no* stable isotopes. *26.3*

a. Pt **c.** Fr **e.** Xe **g.** V
b. Th **d.** Tc **f.** Cf **h.** Pd

32. Explain the term *half-life*. *26.4*

33. The mass of cobalt-60 in a sample is found to have decreased from 0.8 g to 0.2 g in a period of 10.5 years. From this information, calculate the half-life of cobalt-60. *26.4*

34. A patient is administered 20 mg of iodine-131. How much of this isotope will remain in the body after 40 days if the half-life of iodine-131 is 8 days? *26.4*

35. Explain the process of transmutation. Write at least three nuclear equations to illustrate your answer. *26.5*

36. What are the transuranium elements? Why are they unusual? *26.5*

37. Complete and balance the equations for the following nuclear reactions. *26.5*

a. $^{27}_{13}Al + ^{4}_{2}He \longrightarrow ^{30}_{14}Si +$
b. $^{214}_{83}Bi \longrightarrow ^{4}_{2}He +$
c. $^{27}_{14}Si \longrightarrow ^{0}_{-1}e +$
d. $^{66}_{29}Cu \longrightarrow ^{66}_{30}Zn +$

38. Describe the process of nuclear fission. *26.6*

39. Name one fissionable material that occurs in nature and one that is artificial. *26.6*

40. Fusion reactions produce enormous amounts of energy. Why don't we see power stations operating fusion devices? *26.7*

41. Why are X-rays and the radiation emitted by radioisotopes called *ionizing radiation*? *26.8*

42. What is the purpose of wearing a film badge when working with radiation sources? *26.8*

43. Why is it unclear whether radon gas should be considered a serious health risk? *26.B*

44. Explain how iodine-131 is used in both the diagnosis and treatment of thyroid cancer. *26.9*

Mastery Questions and Problems

45. Write nuclear equations for these conversions.

a. $^{30}_{15}P$ to $^{30}_{14}Si$
b. $^{13}_{6}C$ to $^{14}_{6}C$

46. Complete these nuclear reactions.

a. $^{32}_{15}P \longrightarrow \_\_\_\_ + ^{0}_{-1}e$
b. $\_\_\_\_ \longrightarrow ^{14}_{7}N + ^{0}_{-1}e$
c. $^{238}_{92}U \longrightarrow ^{234}_{90}Th + \_\_\_\_$
d. $^{141}_{56}Ba \longrightarrow \_\_\_\_ + ^{0}_{-1}e$

47. Write nuclear equations for the beta decay of the following isotopes.

a. $^{90}_{38}Sr$ **b.** $^{14}_{6}C$
c. $^{137}_{55}Cs$ **d.** $^{239}_{93}Np$

48. Write a nuclear reaction for each of these word equations.

a. Radon-222 emits an alpha particle to form polonium-218.
b. Radium-230 is produced when thorium-234 emits an alpha particle.
c. When polonium-210 emits an alpha particle the product is lead-206.

49. Describe the various contributions the following people made to the fields of nuclear and radiation chemistry.

a. Marie Curie
b. Antoine Becquerel
c. James Chadwick
d. Ernest Rutherford

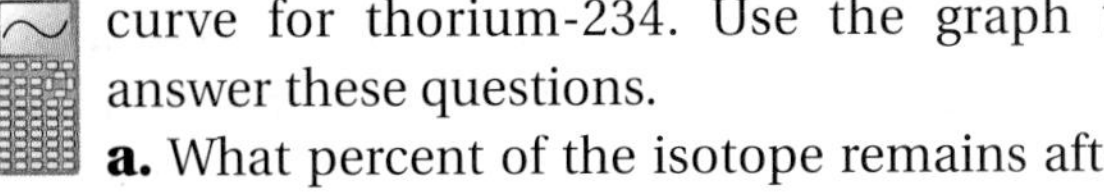

50. The graph below shows the radioactive decay curve for thorium-234. Use the graph to answer these questions.

a. What percent of the isotope remains after 60 days ?

b. How many grams of a 250-g sample of thorium-234 would remain after 40 days ?

c. How many days would pass while 44 g of thorium-234 decayed to 4.4 g of thorium-234 ?

d. What is the half-life of thorium-234 ?

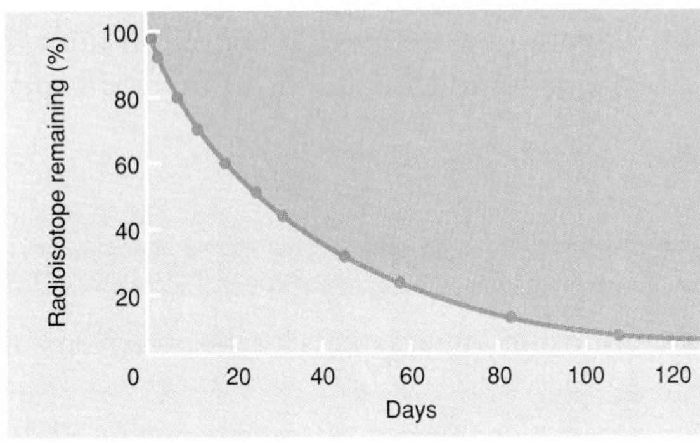

51. Construct a concept map using the key terms with *radioisotopes* as the central concept.

52. What is the difference between the nuclear reactions taking place in the sun and the nuclear reactions taking place in a nuclear reactor ?

Critical Thinking Questions

53. Choose the term that best completes the second relationship.

a. decomposition:combination fission:____

(1) energy (3) radioactivity
(2) nuclei (4) fusion

b. female:male electron: ____

(1) positron (3) beta particle
(2) neutron (4) alpha particle

c. umbrella:rain wood: ____

(1) radioactive decay (3) beta radiation
(2) gamma radiation (4) X-radiation

54. How is the half-life of an element similar to a single elimination sports tournament? How is it different?

55. Why do the large mass and size of an alpha particle limit its penetrating power?

56. Why are radioisotopes of C, N, and O especially harmful to living creatures ?

Cumulative Review

57. What is the Pauli exclusion principle ? What is Hund's rule ?

58. Balance the following equations.

a. $Ca(OH)_2 + HCl \longrightarrow CaCl_2 + H_2O$

b. $Fe_2O_3 + H_2 \longrightarrow Fe + H_2O$

c. $NaHCO_3 + H_2SO_4 \longrightarrow Na_2SO_4 + CO_2 + H_2O$

59. You have a 0.30*M* solution of sodium sulfate. What volume in milliliters must be measured to give 0.0020 mol of sodium sulfate ?

60. How many protons, neutrons, and electrons are in an atom of each isotope ?

a. iron-59 **c.** chromium-52

b. uranium-235

61. Identify the bonds between the following pairs of atoms as ionic or covalent.

a. carbon and silicon

b. calcium and fluorine

c. sulfur and nitrogen

62. How many cm^3 of hydrogen gas, at STP, will be produced when 10.00 g of magnesium metal reacts with an excess of sulfuric acid ? How many moles is this ?

Challenge Questions and Problems

63. The radioisotope cesium-137 has a half-life of 30 years. A sample decays at the rate of 544 counts/min (544 cpm) in 1985. In what year will the decay rate be 17 cpm ?

64. Bismuth-211 is a radioisotope. It decays by alpha emission to yield another radioisotope which emits beta radiation as it decays to a stable isotope. Write equations for the nuclear reactions and name the decay products.

65. What isotope remains after three beta particles and five alpha particles are lost from the thorium-234 isotope. (Refer to the uranium-238 decay series to check your answer.)

Connections Questions

66. What happens in particle accelerators ?

67. What assumption must be made about the historical ratio of carbon-14 to carbon-12 if carbon-14 dating is to be accurate ?

68. What is the importance of the RIA techniques developed by Rosalyn Yalow ?

Write About Chemistry

69. Write a paragraph analyzing the logic of these three sentences.
(1) Radiation kills fast-growing cells.
(2) Cancer cells are fast growing.
(3) Therefore, radiation kills only cancer cells.

70. Nuclear wastes from power plants pose a significant environmental problem. Write a list of questions that should be discussed in any debate about constructing more nuclear power plants.

Readings and References

Atwood, Charles H. "Nuclear Diagnosis." *ChemMatters* (December 1985), pp. 4–7.

Wolfson, Richard. *Nuclear Choices: A Citizens Guide to Nuclear Technology.* Cambridge, MA: MIT Press, 1991.

Table A.1 Some Properties of the Elements

Element	Symbol	Atomic number	Atomic mass	Melting point (°C)	Boiling point (°C)	Density (g/cm^3) (gases at STP)	Major oxidation states
Actinium	Ac	89	(227.042)	1050	3200	10.07	+3
Aluminum	Al	13	26.98154	660.37	2467	2.6989	+3
Americium	Am	95	243	994	2607	13.67	+3, +4, +5, +6
Antimony	Sb	51	121.75	630.74	1950	6.691	–3, +3, +5
Argon	Ar	18	39.948	–189.2	–185.7	0.0017837	
Arsenic	As	33	74.9216	817	613	5.73	–3, +3, +5
Astatine	At	85	(210)	302	337	—	
Barium	Ba	56	137.33	725	1640	3.5	+2
Berkelium	Bk	97	(247)	986	—	14.78	
Beryllium	Be	4	9.01218	1278	2970	1.848	+2
Bismuth	Bi	83	208.9804	271.3	1560	9.747	+3, +5
Boron	B	5	10.81	2079	3675	2.34	+3
Bromine	Br	35	79.904	–7.2	58.78	3.12	–1, +1, +5
Cadmium	Cd	48	112.41	320.9	765	8.65	+2
Calcium	Ca	20	40.08	839	1484	1.55	+2
Californium	Cf	98	(251)	900	—	14	
Carbon	C	6	12.011	3550	4827	2.267	–4, +2, +4
Cerium	Ce	58	140.12	799	3426	6.657	+3, +4
Cesium	Cs	55	132.9054	28.40	669.3	1.873	+1
Chlorine	Cl	17	35.453	–100.98	–34.6	0.003214	–1, +1, +5, +7
Chromium	Cr	24	51.996	1857	2672	7.18	+2, +3, +6
Cobalt	Co	27	58.9332	1495	2870	8.9	+2, +3
Copper	Cu	29	63.546	1083.4	2567	8.96	+1, +2
Curium	Cm	96	(247)	1340	—	13.51	+3
Dysprosium	Dy	66	162.50	1412	2562	8.550	+3
Einsteinium	Es	99	(252)	—	—	—	
Erbium	Er	68	167.26	159	2863	9.066	+3
Europium	Eu	63	151.96	822	1597	5.243	+2, +3
Fermium	Fm	100	(257)	—	—	—	
Fluorine	F	9	18.998403	–219.62	–188.54	0.001696	–1
Francium	Fr	87	(223)	27	677	—	+1
Gadolinium	Gd	64	157.25	1313	3266	7.9004	+3
Gallium	Ga	31	69.72	29.78	2403	5.904	+3
Germanium	Ge	32	72.59	937.4	2830	5.323	+2, +4
Gold	Au	79	196.9665	1064.43	3080	19.3	+1, +3
Hafnium	Hf	72	178.49	2227	4602	13.31	+4
Helium	He	2	4.00260	–272.2	–268.934	0.001785	
Holmium	Ho	67	164.9304	1474	2695	8.795	+3
Hydrogen	H	1	1.00794	–259.14	–252.87	0.00008988	+1
Indium	In	49	114.82	156.61	2080	7.31	+1, +3
Iodine	I	53	126.9045	113.5	184.35	4.93	–1, +1, +5, +7
Iridium	Ir	77	192.22	2410	4130	22.42	+3, +4
Iron	Fe	26	55.847	1535	2750	7.874	+2, +3
Krypton	Kr	36	83.80	–156.6	–152.30	0.003733	
Lanthanum	La	57	138.9055	921	3457	6.145	+3
Lawrencium	Lr	103	(260)	—	—	—	+3
Lead	Pb	82	207.2	327.502	1740	11.35	+2, +4
Lithium	Li	3	6.941	180.54	1342	0.534	+1
Lutetium	Lu	71	174.967	1663	3395	9.840	+3
Magnesium	Mg	12	24.305	648.8	1090	1.738	+2
Manganese	Mn	25	54.9380	1244	1962	7.32	+2, +3, +4, +7
Mendelevium	Md	101	257	—	—	—	+2, +3

Table A.1 Some Properties of the Elements (cont.)

Element	Symbol	Atomic number	Atomic mass	Melting point (°C)	Boiling point (°C)	Density (g/cm³) (gases at STP)	Major oxidation states
Mercury	Hg	80	200.59	−38.842	356.58	13.546	+1, +2
Molybdenum	Mo	42	95.94	2617	4612	10.22	+6
Neodymium	Nd	60	144.24	1021	3068	6.90	+3
Neon	Ne	10	20.179	−248.67	−246.048	.0008999	
Neptunium	Np	93	237.0482	640	3902	20.25	+3, +4, +5, +6
Nickel	Ni	28	58.69	1453	2732	8.902	+2, +3
Niobium	Nb	41	92.9064	2468	4742	8.57	+3, +5
Nitrogen	N	7	14.0067	209.86	195.8	.0012500	−3, +3, +5
Nobelium	No	102	(259)	—	—	—	+2, +3
Osmium	Os	76	190.2	3045	5027	22.57	+3, +4
Oxygen	O	8	15.9994	−218.4	−182.962	.001429	−2
Palladium	Pd	46	106.42	1554	2970	12.02	+2, +4
Phosphorus	P	15	30.97376	44.1	280	1.82	−3, +3, +5
Platinum	Pt	78	195.08	1772	3827	21.45	+2, +4
Plutonium	Pu	94	(244)	641	3232	19.84	+3, +4, +5, +6
Polonium	Po	84	(209)	254	962	9.32	+2, +4
Potassium	K	19	39.0982	63.25	760	.862	+1
Praseodymium	Pr	59	140.9077	931	3512	6.64	+3
Promethium	Pm	61	(145)	1168	2460	7.22	+3
Protactinium	Pa	91	231.0359	1560	4027	15.37	+4, +5
Radium	Ra	88	226.0254	700	1140	5.5	+2
Radon	Rn	86	(222)	−71	−61.8	.00973	
Rhenium	Re	75	186.207	3180	5627	21.02	+4, +6, +7
Rhodium	Rh	45	102.9055	1966	3727	12.41	+3
Rubidium	Rb	37	85.4678	38.89	686	1.532	+1
Ruthenium	Ru	44	101.07	2310	3900	12.41	+3
Samarium	Sm	62	150.36	1077	1791	7.520	+2, +3
Scandium	Sc	21	44.9559	1541	2831	2.989	+3
Selenium	Se	34	78.96	217	684.9	4.79	−2, +4, +6
Silicon	Si	14	28.0855	1410	2355	2.33	−4, +2, +4
Silver	Ag	47	107.8682	961.93	2212	10.50	+1
Sodium	Na	11	22.98977	97.81	882.9	0.971	+1
Strontium	Sr	38	87.62	769	1384	2.54	+2
Sulfur	S	16	32.06	112.8	444.7	2.07	−2, +4, +6
Tantalum	Ta	73	180.9479	2996	5425	16.654	+5
Technetium	Tc	43	(98)	2172	4877	11.50	+4, +6, +7
Tellurium	Te	52	127.60	449.5	989.8	6.24	−2, +4, +6
Terbium	Tb	65	158.9254	1356	3123	8.229	+3
Thallium	Tl	81	204.383	303.5	1457	11.85	+1, +3
Thorium	Th	90	232.0381	1750	4790	11.72	+4
Thulium	Tm	69	168.9342	1545	1947	9.321	+3
Tin	Sn	50	118.69	231.968	2270	7.31	+2, +4
Titanium	Ti	22	47.88	1660	3287	4.54	+2, +3, +4
Tungsten	W	74	183.85	3410	5660	19.3	+6
Uranium	U	92	238.0289	1132.3	3818	18.95	+3, +4, +5, +6
Vanadium	V	23	50.9415	1890	3380	6.11	+2, +3, +4, +5
Xenon	Xe	54	131.29	−111.9	−107.1	.005887	
Ytterbium	Yb	70	173.04	819	1194	6.965	+2, +3
Yttrium	Y	39	88.9059	1522	3338	4.469	+3
Zinc	Zn	30	65.38	419.58	907	7.133	+2
Zirconium	Zr	40	91.22	1852	4377	6.506	+4
Element 104	(Rf)	104					
Element 105	(Ha)	105					
Element 106		106					
Element 107		107					
Element 109		109					

Table A.2 Electron Configurations of the Elements

	Elements	Sublevels																		
		1*s*	2*s*	2*p*	3*s*	3*p*	3*d*	4*s*	4*p*	4*d*	4*f*	5*s*	5*p*	5*d*	5*f*	6*s*	6*p*	6*d*	6*f*	7*s*
1	hydrogen	1																		
2	helium	2																		
3	lithium	2	1																	
4	beryllium	2	2																	
5	boron	2	2	1																
6	carbon	2	2	2																
7	nitrogen	2	2	3																
8	oxygen	2	2	4																
9	fluorine	2	2	5																
10	neon	2	2	6																
11	sodium	2	2	6	1															
12	magnesium	2	2	6	2															
13	aluminum	2	2	6	2	1														
14	silicon	2	2	6	2	2														
15	phosphorus	2	2	6	2	3														
16	sulfur	2	2	6	2	4														
17	chlorine	2	2	6	2	5														
18	argon	2	2	6	2	6														
19	potassium	2	2	6	2	6		1												
20	calcium	2	2	6	2	6		2												
21	scandium	2	2	6	2	6	1	2												
22	titanium	2	2	6	2	6	2	2												
23	vanadium	2	2	6	2	6	3	2												
24	chromium	2	2	6	2	6	5	1												
25	manganese	2	2	6	2	6	5	2												
26	iron	2	2	6	2	6	6	2												
27	cobalt	2	2	6	2	6	7	2												
28	nickel	2	2	6	2	6	8	2												
29	copper	2	2	6	2	6	10	1												
30	zinc	2	2	6	2	6	10	2												
31	gallium	2	2	6	2	6	10	2	1											
32	germanium	2	2	6	2	6	10	2	2											
33	arsenic	2	2	6	2	6	10	2	3											
34	selenium	2	2	6	2	6	10	2	4											
35	bromine	2	2	6	2	6	10	2	5											
36	krypton	2	2	6	2	6	10	2	6											
37	rubidium	2	2	6	2	6	10	2	6			1								
38	strontium	2	2	6	2	6	10	2	6			2								
39	yttrium	2	2	6	2	6	10	2	6	1		2								
40	zirconium	2	2	6	2	6	10	2	6	2		2								
41	niobium	2	2	6	2	6	10	2	6	4		1								
42	molybdenum	2	2	6	2	6	10	2	6	5		1								
43	technetium	2	2	6	2	6	10	2	6	5		2								
44	ruthenium	2	2	6	2	6	10	2	6	7		1								
45	rhodium	2	2	6	2	6	10	2	6	8		1								
46	palladium	2	2	6	2	6	10	2	6	10										
47	silver	2	2	6	2	6	10	2	6	10		1								
48	cadmium	2	2	6	2	6	10	2	6	10		2								
49	indium	2	2	6	2	6	10	2	6	10		2	1							
50	tin	2	2	6	2	6	10	2	6	10		2	2							
51	antimony	2	2	6	2	6	10	2	6	10		2	3							
52	tellurium	2	2	6	2	6	10	2	6	10		2	4							
53	iodine	2	2	6	2	6	10	2	6	10		2	5							
54	xenon	2	2	6	2	6	10	2	6	10		2	6							

Table A.2 Electron Configurations of the Elements (cont.)

Elements	Sublevels																		
	1s	2s	2p	3s	3p	3d	4s	4p	4d	4f	5s	5p	5d	5f	6s	6p	6d	6f	7s
55 cesium	2	2	6	2	6	10	2	6	10		2	6			1				
56 barium	2	2	6	2	6	10	2	6	10		2	6			2				
57 lanthanum	2	2	6	2	6	10	2	6	10		2	6	1		2				
58 cerium	2	2	6	2	6	10	2	6	10	2	2	6			2				
59 praseodymium	2	2	6	2	6	10	2	6	10	3	2	6			2				
60 neodymium	2	2	6	2	6	10	2	6	10	4	2	6			2				
61 promethium	2	2	6	2	6	10	2	6	10	5	2	6			2				
62 samarium	2	2	6	2	6	10	2	6	10	6	2	6			2				
63 europium	2	2	6	2	6	10	2	6	10	7	2	6			2				
64 gadolinium	2	2	6	2	6	10	2	6	10	7	2	6	1		2				
65 terbium	2	2	6	2	6	10	2	6	10	9	2	6			2				
66 dysprosium	2	2	6	2	6	10	2	6	10	10	2	6			2				
67 holmium	2	2	6	2	6	10	2	6	10	11	2	6			2				
68 erbium	2	2	6	2	6	10	2	6	10	12	2	6			2				
69 thulium	2	2	6	2	6	10	2	6	10	13	2	6			2				
70 ytterbium	2	2	6	2	6	10	2	6	10	14	2	6			2				
71 lutetium	2	2	6	2	6	10	2	6	10	14	2	6	1		2				
72 hafnium	2	2	6	2	6	10	2	6	10	14	2	6	2		2				
73 tantalum	2	2	6	2	6	10	2	6	10	14	2	6	3		2				
74 tungsten	2	2	6	2	6	10	2	6	10	14	2	6	4		2				
75 rhenium	2	2	6	2	6	10	2	6	10	14	2	6	5		2				
76 osmium	2	2	6	2	6	10	2	6	10	14	2	6	6		2				
77 iridium	2	2	6	2	6	10	2	6	10	14	2	6	7		2				
78 platinum	2	2	6	2	6	10	2	6	10	14	2	6	9		1				
79 gold	2	2	6	2	6	10	2	6	10	14	2	6	10		1				
80 mercury	2	2	6	2	6	10	2	6	10	14	2	6	10		2				
81 thallium	2	2	6	2	6	10	2	6	10	14	2	6	10		2	1			
82 lead	2	2	6	2	6	10	2	6	10	14	2	6	10		2	2			
83 bismuth	2	2	6	2	6	10	2	6	10	14	2	6	10		2	3			
84 polonium	2	2	6	2	6	10	2	6	10	14	2	6	10		2	4			
85 astatine	2	2	6	2	6	10	2	6	10	14	2	6	10		2	5			
86 radon	2	2	6	2	6	10	2	6	10	14	2	6	10		2	6			
87 francium	2	2	6	2	6	10	2	6	10	14	2	6	10		2	6			1
88 radium	2	2	6	2	6	10	2	6	10	14	2	6	10		2	6			2
89 actinium	2	2	6	2	6	10	2	6	10	14	2	6	10		2	6	1		2
90 thorium	2	2	6	2	6	10	2	6	10	14	2	6	10		2	6	2		2
91 protactinium	2	2	6	2	6	10	2	6	10	14	2	6	10	2	2	6	1		2
92 uranium	2	2	6	2	6	10	2	6	10	14	2	6	10	3	2	6	1		2
93 neptunium	2	2	6	2	6	10	2	6	10	14	2	6	10	4	2	6	1		2
94 plutonium	2	2	6	2	6	10	2	6	10	14	2	6	10	6	2	6			2
95 americium	2	2	6	2	6	10	2	6	10	14	2	6	10	7	2	6			2
96 curium	2	2	6	2	6	10	2	6	10	14	2	6	10	7	2	6	1		2
97 berkelium	2	2	6	2	6	10	2	6	10	14	2	6	10	9	2	6			2
98 californium	2	2	6	2	6	10	2	6	10	14	2	6	10	10	2	6			2
99 einsteinium	2	2	6	2	6	10	2	6	10	14	2	6	10	11	2	6			2
100 fermium	2	2	6	2	6	10	2	6	10	14	2	6	10	12	2	6			2
101 mendelevium	2	2	6	2	6	10	2	6	10	14	2	6	10	13	2	6			2
102 nobelium	2	2	6	2	6	10	2	6	10	14	2	6	10	14	2	6			2
103 lawrencium	2	2	6	2	6	10	2	6	10	14	2	6	10	14	2	6	1		2
104 unnilquadium	2	2	6	2	6	10	2	6	10	14	2	6	10	14	2	6	2		2?
105 unnilpentium	2	2	6	2	6	10	2	6	10	14	2	6	10	14	2	6	3		2?
106 unnilhexium	2	2	6	2	6	10	2	6	10	14	2	6	10	14	2	6	4		2?
107 unnilseptium	2	2	6	2	6	10	2	6	10	14	2	6	10	14	2	6	5		2?
108 unniloctium	2	2	6	2	6	10	2	6	10	14	2	6	10	14	2	6	6		2?
109 unnilennium	2	2	6	2	6	10	2	6	10	14	2	6	10	14	2	6	7		2?

Table A.3 Symbols of Common Elements

Ag	silver	Cu	copper	O	oxygen
Al	aluminum	F	fluorine	P	phosphorus
As	arsenic	Fe	iron	Pb	lead
Au	gold	H	hydrogen	Pt	platinum
Ba	barium	Hg	mercury	S	sulfur
Bi	bismuth	I	iodine	Sb	antimony
Br	bromine	K	potassium	Sn	tin
C	carbon	Mg	magnesium	Sr	strontium
Ca	calcium	Mn	manganese	Ti	titanium
Cl	chlorine	N	nitrogen	U	uranium
Co	cobalt	Na	sodium	W	tungsten
Cr	chromium	Ni	nickel	Zn	zinc

Table A.4 Symbols of Common Polyatomic Ions

$C_2H_3O_2^-$	acetate	$Cr_2O_7^{2-}$	dichromate	NH_4^+	ammonium
ClO^-	hypochlorite	HCO_3^-	hydrogen carbonate	NO_3^-	nitrate
ClO_2^-	chlorite		(bicarbonate)	NO_2^-	nitrite
ClO_3^-	chlorate	H_3O^+	hydronium	O_2^{2-}	peroxide
ClO_4^-	perchlorate	HPO_4^{2-}	hydrogen phosphate	OH^-	hydroxide
CN^-	cyanide	HSO_3^-	hydrogen sulfite	PO_4^{3-}	phosphate
CO_3^{2-}	carbonate	HSO_4^-	hydrogen sulfate	SO_3^{2-}	sulfite
CrO_4^{2-}	chromate	MnO_4^-	permanganate	SO_4^{2-}	sulfate

Table A.5 Other Symbols and Abbreviations

α	alpha rays	gmm	gram molecular mass	m	mass
β	beta rays	H	enthalpy	m	molality
γ	gamma rays	H_f	heat of formation	mL	milliliter (*volume*)
Δ	change in	h	hour	mm	millimeter (*length*)
δ^-, δ^+	partial ionic charge	h	Planck's constant	mol	mole (*amount*)
λ	wavelength	Hz	hertz (*frequency*)	mp	melting point
π	pi bond	J	joule (*energy*)	N	normality
σ	sigma bond	K	kelvin (*temperature*)	n^0	neutron
ν	frequency	K_a	acid dissociation constant	n	number of moles
amu	atomic mass unit	K_b	base dissociation constant	n	principal quantum number
(*aq*)	aqueous solution	K_b	molal boiling point	P	pressure
atm	atmosphere (*pressure*)		elevation constant	p^+	proton
bp	boiling point	K_{eq}	equilibrium constant	Pa	pascal (*pressure*)
°C	degree Celsius (*temperature*)	K_f	molal freezing point	R	ideal gas constant
c	speed of light in a vacuum		depression constant	S	entropy
cm	centimeter (*length*)	K_w	ion product constant	s	second
D	density		for water	(*s*)	solid
E	energy	K_{sp}	solubility product constant	SI	International System
e^-	electron	kcal	kilocalorie (*energy*)		of Units
fp	freezing point	kg	kilogram (*mass*)	STP	standard temperature
G	Gibb's free energy	kPa	kilopascal (*pressure*)		and pressure
g	gram (*mass*)	L	liter (*volume*)	T	temperature
(*g*)	gas	(*l*)	liquid	$t_{1/2}$	half-life
gam	gram atomic mass	M	molarity	V	volume
gfm	gram formula mass	m	meter (*length*)	v	velocity, speed

Table A.6 Standard Heats of Formation (ΔH_f^0) at 25°C and 101.3 kPa

Substance	ΔH_f^0 (kJ/mol)
$Al_2O_3(s)$	−1676.0
$Br_2(g)$	30.91
$Br_2(l)$	0.0
C(*s*, diamond)	1.9
C(*s*, graphite)	0.0
$CH_4(g)$	−74.86
$CO(g)$	−110.5
$CO_2(g)$	−393.5
$CaCO_3(s)$	−1207.0
$CaO(s)$	−635.1
$Cl_2(g)$	0.0
$F_2(g)$	0.0
$Fe(s)$	0.0
$Fe_2O_3(s)$	−822.1
$H_2(g)$	0.0
$H_2O(g)$	−241.8
$H_2O(l)$	−285.8
$H_2O_2(l)$	−187.8
$HCl(g)$	−92.31
$H_2S(g)$	−20.1
$I_2(g)$	62.4
$I_2(s)$	0.0
$N_2(g)$	0.0
$NH_3(g)$	−46.19
$NO(g)$	90.37
$NO_2(g)$	33.85
$Na_2CO_3(s)$	−1131.1
$NaCl(s)$	−411.2
$O_2(g)$	0.0
$O_3(g)$	142.0
P(*s*, white)	0.0
P(*s*, red)	−18.4
S(*s*, rhombic)	0.0
S(*s*, monoclinic)	0.30
$SO_2(g)$	−296.8
$SO_3(g)$	−395.7

Table A.7 Physical Constants

Atomic mass unit	$1 \text{ amu} = 1.6605 \times 10^{-24}$ g
Avogadro's number	$N = 6.0221 \times 10^{23} \frac{\text{particles}}{\text{mole}}$
Gas constant	$R = 8.31 \frac{\text{L} \times \text{kPa}}{\text{K} \times \text{mol}}$
Ideal gas molar volume	$V_m = 22.414 \frac{\text{L}}{\text{mol}}$
Masses of fundamental particles	
Electron (e^-)	$m_e = 0.0005486$ amu $= 9.1096 \times 10^{-28}$ g
Proton (p^+)	$m_p = 1.007277$ amu $= 1.67261 \times 10^{-24}$ g
Neutron (n^0)	$m_n = 1.008665$ amu $= 1.67492 \times 10^{-24}$ g
Speed of light (in vacuum)	$c = 2.997925 \times 10^{8} \frac{\text{m}}{\text{s}}$

Table A.8 Solubilities of Compounds at 25°C and 101.3 kPa

	acetate	bromide	carbonate	chlorate	chloride	hydroxide	iodide	nitrate	oxide	perchlorate	phosphate	sufate	sulfide
aluminum	S	S	—	S	S	I	S	S	I	S	I	S	d
ammonium	S	S	S	S	S	S	S	S	—	S	S	S	S
barium	S	S	I	S	S	S	S	S	sS	S	I	I	d
calcium	S	S	I	S	S	S	S	S	sS	S	I	sS	I
copper(II)	S	S	—	S	S	I	S	S	I	S	I	S	I
iron(II)	S	S	I	S	S	I	S	S	I	S	I	S	I
iron(III)	S	S	—	S	S	I	S	S	I	S	I	sS	d
lithium	S	S	sS	S	S	S	S	S	S	S	sS	S	S
magnesium	S	S	I	S	S	I	S	S	I	S	I	S	d
potassium	S	S	S	S	S	S	S	S	S	S	S	S	S
silver	sS	I	I	S	I	—	I	S	I	S	I	sS	I
sodium	S	S	S	S	S	S	S	S	S	S	S	S	S
strontium	S	S	I	S	S	S	S	S	S	S	I	I	I
zinc	S	S	I	S	S	I	S	S	I	S	I	S	I

Key:
S = soluble
sS = slightly soluble
I = insoluble
d = decomposes in water
— = no such compound

B.1 Exponential (Scientific) Notation

Addition and Subtraction Before numbers in exponential form are added or subtracted, the exponents must be the same. For example, what is the sum of 5.4×10^3 and 6.0×10^2? Rewrite the second number so that the exponent is a three, $6.0 \times 10^2 = 0.60 \times 10^3$. Now add the numbers.

$$\begin{aligned}(5.4 \times 10^3) + (0.60 \times 10^3) &= (5.4 + 0.60) \times 10^3 \\ &= 6.0 \times 10^3\end{aligned}$$

Similarly,

$$\begin{aligned}(3.42 \times 10^{-5}) - (2.5 \times 10^{-6}) &= (3.42 \times 10^{-5}) - (0.25 \times 10^{-5}) \\ &= (3.42 - 0.25) \times 10^{-5} \\ &= 3.17 \times 10^{-5}\end{aligned}$$

Practice Problem

1. Do each problem and express the answer in scientific notation.

a. $5.2 \times 10^4 + 2.7 \times 10^4$
b. $9.4 \times 10^{-2} - 2.1 \times 10^{-2}$
c. $6.6 \times 10^{-8} - 4.0 \times 10^{-9}$
d. $6.7 \times 10^{-2} - 3.0 \times 10^{-3}$
e. $23.4 \times 10^5 + 9.5 \times 10^4$
f. $568 \times 10^3 + 2 \times 10^5$
g. $3.75 \times 10^5 + 653 \times 10^3$
h. $0.0073 \times 10^5 - 61000 \times 10^{-2}$

Multiplication and Division To multiply numbers written in exponential form, multiply the coefficients and add the exponents.

$$\begin{aligned}(3 \times 10^4) \times (2 \times 10^2) &= (3 \times 2) \times 10^{4+2} \\ &= 6 \times 10^6 \\ (2.1 \times 10^3) \times (4.0 \times 10^{-7}) &= (2.1 \times 4.0) \times 10^{3+(-7)} \\ &= 8.4 \times 10^{-4} \\ (8.0 \times 10^{-2}) \times (7.0 \times 10^{-5}) &= (8.0 \times 7.0) \times 10^{-2+(-5)} \\ &= 56 \times 10^{-7} \\ &= 5.6 \times 10^{-6}\end{aligned}$$

Practice Problem

2. Answer each problem in scientific notation.

a. $(2 \times 10^9) \times (4 \times 10^3)$

b. $(6.2 \times 10^{-3}) \times (1.5 \times 10^1)$

c. $10^{-4} \times 10^8 \times 10^{-2}$

d. $(3.4 \times 10^{-3}) \times (2.5 \times 10^{-5})$

e. $(0.10 \times 10^5) \times (4.9 \times 10^{-2})$

f. $(88 \times 10^2) \times (0.15 \times 10^4)$

To divide numbers written in exponential form, divide the coefficients and subtract the exponent in the denominator from the exponent in the numerator.

$$\frac{3.0 \times 10^5}{6.0 \times 10^2} = \left(\frac{3.0}{6.0}\right) \times 10^{5-2} = 0.50 \times 10^3$$

$$= 5.0 \times 10^2$$

$$\frac{8.4 \times 10^{-6}}{2.1 \times 10^2} = \left(\frac{8.4}{2.1}\right) \times 10^{-6-(+2)} = 4.0 \times 10^{-8}$$

$$\frac{4.56 \times 10^5}{2.93 \times 10^{-3}} = \left(\frac{4.56}{2.93}\right) \times 10^{5-(-3)} = 1.56 \times 10^8$$

Practice Problem

3. Do each problem and express the answer in scientific notation.

a. $\frac{8.8 \times 10^6}{2.2 \times 10^1}$

b. $\frac{5.2 \times 10^2}{1.3 \times 10^{-7}}$

c. $\frac{10^8 \times 10^{-3}}{10^{-4} \times 10^5}$

d. $\frac{1 \times 10^{-7}}{1 \times 10^{-9}}$

e. $\frac{0.40 \times 10^{-4}}{5.7 \times 10^1}$

f. $\frac{6.8 \times 10^{12}}{0.22 \times 10^{-4}}$

g. $\frac{13.6 \times 10^{12}}{8.00 \times 10^{15}}$

h. $\frac{753 \times 10^6}{0.300 \times 10^{-8}}$

B.2 Algebraic Equations

Many relationships in chemistry can be expressed by simple algebraic equations. Often an equation is not given in the form that is most useful for a particular problem. In such a case you must first solve the equation for the unknown quantity. Solving an equation means rearranging it so that the unknown quantity is on one side of the equation and all the known quantities are on the other side. For instance, consider the following equation.

$$K = °C + 273$$

It states the relationship between the Kelvin and Celsius temperature scales (Chapter 2). Can this equation be used to find the Celsius temperature equivalent to 400 K? Yes, it can, if the equation is first solved for the unknown quantity, °C.

An equation is solved using the laws of equality. The **laws of equality** are summarized as follows. *If equals are added to, subtracted from, multiplied by, or divided by equals, the results are equal.* In other words, you can perform any of these mathematic operations on an equation and not destroy the equality, *as long as you do the same thing to both sides of the equation.* The laws of equality apply to any legitimate mathematic operation, including squaring, taking square roots, and taking the logarithm.

To solve the equation in the example for °C, subtract 273 from both sides of the equation.

$$K = °C + 273$$

$$K - 273 = °C + \cancel{273} - \cancel{273}$$

$$°C = K - 273$$

Once you have solved an equation, substitute in the known quantities and calculate the value of the unknown quantity. A temperature of 400 K is converted to °C as follows.

$$°C = K - 273 = 400 - 273 = 127°C$$

The relationship between the Fahrenheit and Celsius temperature scales is °F = 1.8 × °C + 32. Use this relationship to find the Celsius temperature equivalent to 392°F.

To solve for °C, both the 1.8 and the 32 must be moved to the other side of the equation. Since the 32 is added to the quantity (1.8 times °C), first subtract 32 from both sides of the equation.

$$°F = (1.8 \times °C) + 32$$

$$°F - 32 = (1.8 \times °C) + \cancel{32} - \cancel{32}$$

$$°F - 32 = (1.8 \times °C)$$

Now divide each side of the equation by 1.8.

$$\frac{°F - 32}{1.8} = \frac{\cancel{1.8} \times °C}{\cancel{1.8}}$$

$$°C = \frac{°F - 32}{1.8}$$

Finally, substitute the given quantity.

$$C° = \frac{392 - 32}{1.8} = \frac{360}{1.8} = 200°C$$

An equation that shows how the volume of a gas changes with a change in temperature (Chapter 11) is as follows.

$$\frac{V_1}{T_1} = \frac{V_2}{T_2}$$

What is the value of T_2 when $V_1 = 5.0$ L, $V_2 = 15$ L, and $T_1 = 200$ K? Solve for T_2.

$$T_2 = \frac{V_2 \times T_1}{V_1}$$

Substitute the given quantities into the solved equation.

$$T_2 = \frac{15\,\cancel{L} \times 200\text{ K}}{5.0\,\cancel{L}} = 600\text{ K}$$

Practice Problems

4. Solve for T: $P \times V = n \times R \times T$

5. Solve for V_1: $\frac{P_1 \times V_1}{T_1} = \frac{P_2 \times V_2}{T_2}$

6. Solve for v: $E = (m \times v^2)/2$

7. Solve for P_B: $P_T = P_A + P_B + P_C$

8. Solve each of these equations for h. Calculate a value for h if $g = 12$, $k = 0.4$, and $m = 1.5$.

a. $kh = \frac{g}{m}$

b. $\frac{g - m}{h} = k$

c. $gh - k = m$

d. $\frac{mk}{g + h} = 2$

B.3 Percents

Percent means "parts of 100" or "parts per 100 parts." In slightly different terms, a percent is a part of a whole expressed in hundredths. The idea of a percent should be very familiar to you. Many times examination grades are expressed as a percent. What does a grade of 88% mean? Since the word percent (%) means "per 100 parts," 88% = 88/100, or 88 questions correct (the part) out of a possible 100 questions (the whole).

You are generally evaluated on exams that do not have 100 questions. Your grade can still be expressed as a percent. What is your grade if you get 24 questions correct on a 30-question exam? The part over the whole, expressed as a percent, is calculated as follows.

$$\frac{\text{Part}}{\text{Whole}} = \frac{\text{number correct}}{\text{number possible}} = \frac{24 \text{ questions correct}}{30 \text{ questions possible}} = 0.80 \text{ or } \frac{80}{100} \text{ or } 80\%$$

Based on the definition of percent, 0.80, 80/100, and 80% express the same idea: eighty hundredths or 80 "per 100 parts." Mathematically, 0.80 can be shown to be equal to 80/100 because multiplying by 100/100 does not change the value of a number.

$$\frac{0.80}{1} \times \frac{100}{100} = \frac{80}{100}$$

An alternate way to calculate a percent is to multiply the ratio of the part over the whole by 100%.

$$\text{Percent} = \frac{\text{part}}{\text{whole}} \times 100\%$$

Practice Problem

9. Calculate a percent grade for each exam.
a. Eleven questions correctly answered on a 15-question exam.
b. Forty-one questions correctly answered on a 50-question exam.
c. Seventeen questions correctly answered on a 30-question exam.

A percent represents a relationship between two quantities and, as such, it can be used as a conversion factor (Chapter 3). For example, a friend tells you that she got a grade of 95% on a 40-question examination. How many questions did she answer correctly? A grade of 95% means 95 questions correct for each 100 questions possible.

$$40 \text{ questions possible} \times \frac{95 \text{ questions correct}}{100 \text{ questions possible}} = 38 \text{ questions correct}$$

As a final example of using a percent, six students are absent from class. If 80% of the students are present, what is the class enrollment? Since 80% of the class is present, the six students absent must represent 20% of the class. This absence rate of 20% means that 20 students are absent for each 100 students enrolled. Starting with the given, the number of students enrolled is calculated.

$$6\ \cancel{\text{students absent}} \times \frac{100\ \text{students enrolled}}{20\ \cancel{\text{students absent}}} = \frac{600}{20} = 30\ \text{students enrolled}$$

Practice Problems

10. The antiseptic hydrogen peroxide is often sold as a 3.0% (by mass) solution, the rest being water. How many grams of hydrogen peroxide are in 750 g of this solution?

11. A nighttime cold medicine is 22% alcohol (by volume). How many mL of alcohol are in a 250 mL bottle of this medicine?

B.4 Graphing

The relationship between two variables in an experiment is often determined by graphing the experimental data. A graph is a "picture" of the data. Once a graph is constructed, additional information can be derived about the variables.

In constructing a graph we must first label the axes. The independent variable is plotted on the *x-axis* (*abscissa*). This is the horizontal axis. The independent variable is generally controlled by the experimenter. When the independent variable is changed, a corresponding change in the dependent variable is measured. The dependent variable is plotted on the *y-axis* (*ordinate*). This is the vertical axis. The label on each axis should include the unit of the quantity being graphed.

Before data can be plotted on a graph, each axis must be scaled. The scale must take into consideration the smallest and largest values of each quantity. Each interval (square on the graph paper) on the scale must represent the same amount. To make it easy to find numbers along the scale, the interval chosen is usually a multiple of 1, 2, 5, or 10. Although each scale can start at zero, this is not always practical.

Data is plotted by putting a point at the intersection of corresponding values of each pair of measurement. This is illustrated in the next example.

Once the data have been plotted, the points are connected by a smooth curve. This is not the same as "connecting-the-dots," which is an incorrect approach to drawing a line. A smooth curve comes as close as possible to all the plotted points. It may in fact not touch any of them.

Depending on the relationship between two variables the curve may or may not be a straight line. Two common curves are shown in graphs A and B.

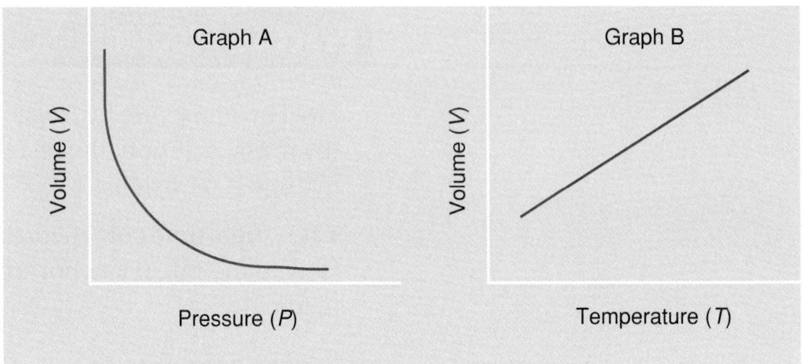

Graphs similar to these are found in Chapter 11 of the text. Graph A is typical of an inverse proportionality. As the independent variable (P) increases, the dependent variable (V) decreases. The product of the two variables at any point on the curve of an inverse proportionality is a constant. For graph A, $V \times P = \text{constant}$.

The straight line in graph B is typical of a direct proportionality. As the independent variable (T) increases, there is a corresponding increase in the dependent variable (V). A straight line is represented by this general equation.

$$y = mx + b$$

Here y and x are the variables plotted on the vertical and horizontal axes respectively; m is the slope of the line; and b is the intercept on the y-axis.

The y intercept, b, is the value of y when x is zero. The slope, m, is the ratio of the change in y (Δy) for a corresponding change in x (Δx). This relationship is often symbolized in the following way.

$$m = \frac{\Delta y}{\Delta x}$$

As an example, consider this data about a bicyclist's trip. Assume that the bicyclist rode at a constant speed.

distance from home (km)	15	25	35	50	75
time (hours)	1	2	3	4.5	7

Let's graph this data using time as the independent variable, and then use the graph to answer the following questions.

a. How far from home was the bicyclist at the start of the trip?

b. How many hours did it take the bicyclist to get 40 km from home?

c. What was the bicyclist's average speed, in kilometers per hour, on the trip?

The plotted points are shown in Figure 1. Each point was plotted by finding the value of time on the x-axis, then moving up vertically to the value of the other variable (distance). A smooth curve, which in this case happens to be a straight line, has been drawn through the points.

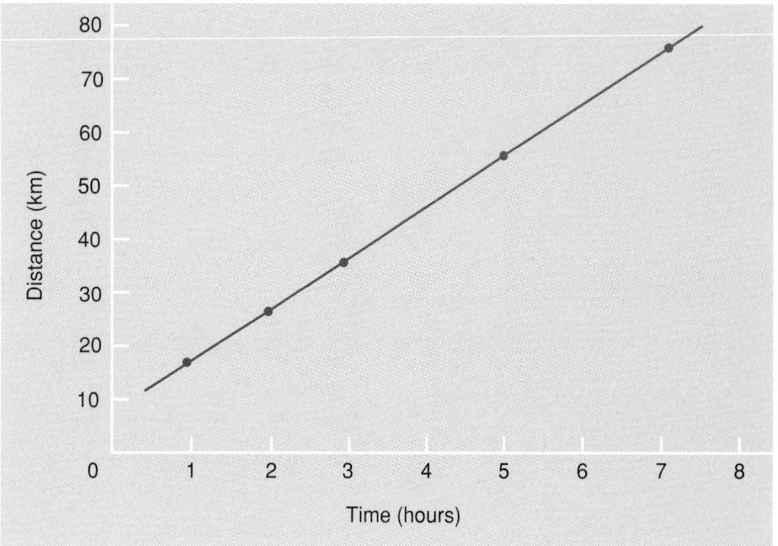

a. The graph in Figure 2 shows that the bicyclist started the trip 5 km from home. This is the value of the vertical axis (distance) when the time elapsed is zero (point a on the graph).

b. Find the given value, 40 km, on the vertical axis in Figure 2. Move to the right (horizontally) in the graph until you reach the line. Drop down vertically and read the value of time at this point (point b). It takes the bicyclist 3.5 hr to get 40 km from home. As another, similar example, how far is the bicyclist from home after riding 5 hr? Using the graph in Figure 2, start at 5 hr and go up to the line. Then move horizontally to the left. The distance, point c, is 55 km.

c. Speed is distance/time. The average speed of the bicyclist is the slope of the line. Calculate the slope using the data points from the previous part of this problem.

$$m = \frac{\Delta y}{\Delta x} = \frac{55 \text{ km} - 40 \text{ km}}{5 \text{ hr} - 3.5 \text{ hr}} = \frac{15 \text{ km}}{1.5 \text{ hr}} = 10 \text{ km/hr}$$

The equation for this line shows the relationship between time and distance traveled by the bicyclist.

$$\text{Distance} = (10 \text{ km/hr})(\text{time}) + 5 \text{ km}$$

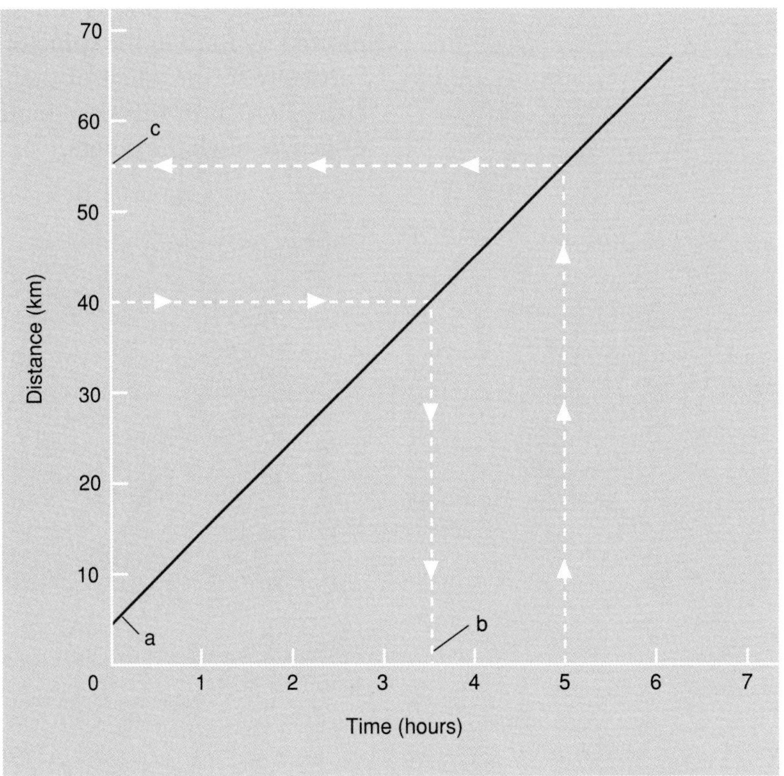

Practice Problems

12. Use the data in the following table to draw a graph that shows the relationship between the Fahrenheit and Celsius temperature scales. Make degrees Fahrenheit the dependent variable. Use the graph to derive an equation between °F and °C. Then use the graph or the equation to complete the data table.

°F	50	212	356	−4	—	70	400
°C	10	100	180	−20	70	—	—

13. A bicyclist wants to ride 100 kilometers. The data on the next page show the time required to ride 100 kilometers at different average speeds.

Time (hours)	4	5	8	10	15	20
Average speed (km/hr)	25	20	12.5	10	6.6	5

a. Graph the data, using average speed as the independent variable.
b. Is this a direct or inverse proportionality?
c. Use the graph to determine what average speed must be maintained to complete the ride in 12 hours.
d. If a bicyclist maintains an average speed of 18 km/hr, how many hours does it take to ride 100 km?

14. The pressure of a fixed volume of gas varies with the temperature. A student collected the following data.

Temperature (°C)	10	20	40	70	100
Pressure (mm Hg)	726	750	800	880	960

a. Graph the data, using pressure as the dependent variable.
b. Is this a direct or inverse proportionality?
c. At what temperature is the gas pressure 722 mm Hg?
d. What is the pressure of this gas at a temperature of 0°C?
e. How does the pressure change with a change in temperature? That is, what is the slope of the line?
f. Write an equation relating pressure and temperature for this gas.

B.5 Logarithms

A logarithm is the exponent to which a fixed number (base) must be raised in order to produce a given number. Common logarithms use 10 as the base. A logarithm to the base 10 of a number is the exponent to which 10 must be raised to obtain the number. If $x = 10^y$, then $\log x = y$. Here x is the number and y is the logarithm of x to the base 10.

Common logarithms must not be confused with natural logarithms which use base e, where $e = 2.71828$. When base 10 is used, logarithm is abbreviated $\log_{10}$, or often simply log. When the base e is used, logarithm is abbreviated ln.

The logarithm of a number has two parts, the characteristic, or whole-number part, and the mantissa, or decimal part. In the example log 421.6 = 2.6249, the characteristic is 2 and the mantissa is 0.6249.

For numbers written in standard exponential form, the characteristic corresponds to the exponent of 10.

$$\log 10^1 = 1,\ \log 10^2 = 2,\ \log 10^3 = 3,\ \log 10^{-2} = -2$$

The mantissa is the decimal part of a logarithm and can be looked up in a "log table." The number of significant figures in a logarithm is the number of figures in the mantissa.

As an example, the logarithm of 176 is found as follows.

1. Write 176 in exponential notation as 1.76×10^2.
2. Locate the number 1.7 in the column labeled N; then under the column headed 6 read the mantissa as 0.2455.
3. Because 1.76×10^2 contains only three significant figures, the mantissa is rounded off to three digits. Thus the mantissa is 0.246.
4. The characteristic is the exponent, 2.
5. The logarithm of 176 is 2.246 or log 176 = 2.246.

Logarithms can also be found using the log key of a calculator. Simply enter the number and press the key labeled "log".

Practice Problem

15. Write the logarithms of the following numbers.
a. 3.45 **b.** 0.0087 **c.** 456 **d.** 3.11×10^{-5} **e.** 1.48×10^9

The reverse process of converting a logarithm into a number is referred to as obtaining the antilogarithm. The antilogarithm of the logarithm of a number is the number itself. Here x represents any number.

$$\text{antilog}(\log x) = x$$

Antilogarithms can be obtained from a table of common logarithms. They can also be obtained with a calculator by using the "antilog" key, the "10^x" key, or the "inverse" key in conjunction with the "log" key.

For example, what is the antilog of the logarithm 4.618? Look in the body of the log table for the mantissa, 0.618. This value is found in the row with an N of 4.1 and in the column labeled 5. Thus the antilog of 0.618 is 4.15. The characteristic is 4. This corresponds to an exponential term of 10^4. The number whose log is 4.618 is 4.15×10^4.

Practice Problem

16. Use a log table or a calculator to find the numbers (antilogarithms) which have the following logarithms.
a. 2.56 **b.** 6.11 **c.** –3.55 **d.** 1.03 **e.** 0.962

There are rules based on the laws of exponents that must be followed when using logarithms for calculations. The logarithm of the product of two numbers is the sum of the number's logs.

$$\log(a \times b) = \log a + \log b$$

The log of the ratio of two numbers is the difference between the log of the denominator subtracted from the log of the numerator.

$$\log(a/b) = \log a - \log b$$

Table B.1 Common Logarithms

x	0	1	2	3	4	5	6	7	8	9
1.0	.0000	.0043	.0086	.0128	.0170	.0212	.0253	.0294	.0334	.0374
1.1	.0414	.0453	.0492	.0531	.0569	.0607	.0645	.0682	.0719	.0755
1.2	.0792	.0828	.0864	.0899	.0934	.0969	.1004	.1038	.1072	.1106
1.3	.1139	.1173	.1206	.1239	.1271	.1303	.1335	.1367	.1399	.1430
1.4	.1461	.1492	.1523	.1553	.1584	.1614	.1644	.1673	.1703	.1732
1.5	.1761	.1790	.1818	.1847	.1875	.1903	.1931	.1959	.1987	.2014
1.6	.2041	.2068	.2095	.2122	.2148	.2175	.2201	.2227	.2253	.2279
1.7	.2304	.2330	.2355	.2380	.2405	.2430	.2455	.2480	.2504	.2529
1.8	.2553	.2577	.2601	.2625	.2648	.2672	.2695	.2718	.2742	.2765
1.9	.2788	.2810	.2833	.2856	.2878	.2900	.2923	.2945	.2967	.2989
2.0	.3010	.3032	.3054	.3075	.3096	.3118	.3139	.3160	.3181	.3201
2.1	.3222	.3243	.3263	.3284	.3304	.3324	.3345	.3365	.3385	.3404
2.2	.3424	.3444	.3464	.3483	.3502	.3522	.3541	.3560	.3579	.3598
2.3	.3617	.3636	.3655	.3674	.3692	.3711	.3729	.3747	.3766	.3784
2.4	.3802	.3820	.3838	.3856	.3874	.3892	.3909	.3927	.3945	.3962
2.5	.3979	.3997	.4014	.4031	.4048	.4065	.4082	.4099	.4116	.4133
2.6	.4150	.4166	.4183	.4200	.4216	.4232	.4249	.4265	.4281	.4298
2.7	.4314	.4330	.4346	.4362	.4378	.4393	.4409	.4425	.4440	.4456
2.8	.4472	.4487	.4502	.4518	.4533	.4548	.4564	.4579	.4594	.4609
2.9	.4624	.4639	.4654	.4669	.4683	.4698	.4713	.4728	.4742	.4757
3.0	.4771	.4786	.4800	.4814	.4829	.4843	.4857	.4871	.4886	.4900
3.1	.4914	.4928	.4942	.4955	.4969	.4983	.4997	.5011	.5024	.5038
3.2	.5051	.5065	.5079	.5092	.5105	.5119	.5132	.5145	.5159	.5172
3.3	.5185	.5198	.5211	.5224	.5237	.5250	.5263	.5276	.5289	.5307
3.4	.5315	.5328	.5340	.5353	.5366	.5378	.5391	.5403	.5416	.5428
3.5	.5441	.5453	.5465	.5478	.5490	.5502	.5514	.5527	.5539	.5551
3.6	.5563	.5575	.5587	.5599	.5611	.5623	.5635	.5647	.5658	.5670
3.7	.5682	.5694	.5705	.5717	.5729	.5740	.5752	.5763	.5775	.5786
3.8	.5798	.5809	.5821	.5832	.5843	.5855	.5866	.5877	.5888	.5899
3.9	.5911	.5922	.5933	.5944	.5955	.5966	.5977	.5988	.5999	.6010
4.0	.6021	.6031	.6042	.6053	.6064	.6075	.6085	.6096	.6107	.6117
4.1	.6128	.6138	.6149	.6160	.6170	.6180	.6191	.6201	.6212	.6222
4.2	.6232	.6243	.6253	.6263	.6274	.6284	.6294	.6304	.6314	.6325
4.3	.6335	.6345	.6355	.6365	.6375	.6385	.6395	.6405	.6415	.6425
4.4	.6435	.6444	.6454	.6464	.6474	.6484	.6493	.6503	.6513	.6522
4.5	.6532	.6542	.6551	.6561	.6571	.6580	.6590	.6599	.6609	.6618
4.6	.6628	.6637	.6646	.6656	.6665	.6675	.6684	.6693	.6702	.6712
4.7	.6721	.6730	.6739	.6749	.6758	.6767	.6776	.6785	.6794	.6803
4.8	.6812	.6821	.6830	.6839	.6848	.6857	.6866	.6875	.6884	.6893
4.9	.6902	.6911	.6920	.6928	.6937	.6946	.6955	.6964	.6972	.6981
5.0	.6990	.6998	.7007	.7016	.7024	.7033	.7042	.7050	.7059	.7067
5.1	.7076	.7084	.7093	.7101	.7110	.7118	.7126	.7135	.7143	.7152
5.2	.7160	.7168	.7177	.7185	.7193	.7202	.7210	.7218	.7226	.7235
5.3	.7243	.7251	.7259	.7267	.7275	.7284	.7292	.7300	.7308	.7316
5.4	.7324	.7332	.7340	.7348	.7356	.7364	.7372	.7380	.7388	.7396

Table B.1 Common Logarithms (cont.)

x	0	1	2	3	4	5	6	7	8	9
5.5	.7404	.7412	.7419	.7427	.7435	.7443	.7451	.7459	.7466	.7474
5.6	.7482	.7490	.7497	.7505	.7513	.7520	.7528	.7536	.7543	.7551
5.7	.7559	.7566	.7574	.7582	.7589	.7597	.7604	.7612	.7619	.7627
5.8	.7634	.7642	.7649	.7657	.7664	.7672	.7679	.7686	.7694	.7701
5.9	.7709	.7716	.7723	.7731	.7738	.7745	.7752	.7760	.7767	.7774
6.0	.7782	.7789	.7796	.7803	.7810	.7818	.7825	.7832	.7839	.7846
6.1	.7853	.7860	.7868	.7875	.7882	.7889	.7896	.7903	.7910	.7917
6.2	.7924	.7931	.7938	.7945	.7952	.7959	.7966	.7973	.7980	.7987
6.3	.7993	.8000	.8007	.8014	.8021	.8028	.8035	.8041	.8048	.8055
6.4	.8062	.8069	.8075	.8082	.8089	.8096	.8102	.8109	.8116	.8122
6.5	.8129	.8136	.8142	.8149	.8156	.8162	.8169	.8176	.8182	.8189
6.6	.8195	.8202	.8209	.8215	.8222	.8228	.8235	.8241	.8248	.8254
6.7	.8261	.8267	.8274	.8280	.8287	.8293	.8299	.8306	.8312	.8319
6.8	.8325	.8331	.8338	.8344	.8351	.8357	.8363	.8370	.8376	.8382
6.9	.8388	.8395	.8401	.8407	.8414	.8420	.8426	.8432	.8439	.8445
7.0	.8451	.8457	.8463	.8470	.8476	.8482	.8488	.8494	.8500	.8506
7.1	.8513	.8519	.8525	.8531	.8537	.8543	.8549	.8555	.8561	.8567
7.2	.8573	.8579	.8585	.8591	.8597	.8603	.8609	.8615	.8621	.8627
7.3	.8633	.8639	.8645	.8651	.8657	.8663	.8669	.8675	.8681	.8686
7.4	.8692	.8698	.8704	.8710	.8716	.8722	.8727	.8733	.8739	.8745
7.5	.8751	.8756	.8762	.8768	.8774	.8779	.5785	.8791	.8797	.8802
7.6	.8808	.8814	.8820	.8825	.8831	.8837	.8842	.8848	.8854	.8859
7.7	.8865	.8871	.8876	.8882	.8887	.8893	.8899	.8904	.8910	.8915
7.8	.8921	.8927	.8932	.8938	.8943	.8949	.8954	.8960	.8965	.8971
7.9	.8976	.8982	.8987	.8993	.8998	.9004	.9009	.9015	.9020	.9025
8.0	.9031	.9036	.9042	.9047	.9053	.9058	.9063	.9069	.9074	.9079
8.1	.9085	.9090	.9096	.9101	.9106	.9112	.9117	.9122	.9128	.9133
8.2	.9138	.9143	.9149	.9154	.9159	.9165	.9170	.9175	.9180	.9186
8.3	.9191	.9196	.9201	.9206	.9212	.9217	.9222	.9227	.9232	.9238
8.4	.9243	.9248	.9253	.9258	.9263	.9269	.9274	.9279	.9284	.9289
8.5	.9294	.9299	.9304	.9309	.9315	.9320	.9325	.9330	.9335	.9340
8.6	.9345	.9350	.9355	.9360	.9365	.9370	.9375	.9380	.9385	.9390
8.7	.9395	.9400	.9405	.9410	.9415	.9420	.9425	.9430	.9435	.9440
8.8	.9445	.9450	.9455	.9460	.9465	.9469	.9474	.9479	.9484	.9489
8.9	.9494	.9499	.9504	.9509	.9513	.9518	.9523	.9528	.9533	.9538
9.0	.9542	.9547	.9552	.9557	.9562	.9566	.9571	.9576	.9581	.9586
9.1	.9590	.9595	.9600	.9605	.9609	.9614	.9619	.9624	.9628	.9633
9.2	.9638	.9643	.9647	.9652	.9657	.9661	.9666	.9671	.9675	.9680
9.3	.9685	.9689	.9694	.9699	.9703	.9708	.9713	.9717	.9722	.9727
9.4	.9731	.9736	.9741	.9745	.9750	.9754	.9759	.9763	.9768	.9773
9.5	.9777	.9782	.9786	.9791	.9795	.9800	.9805	.9809	.9814	.9818
9.6	.9823	.9827	.9832	.9836	.9841	.9845	.9850	.9854	.9859	.9863
9.7	.9868	.9872	.9877	.9881	.9886	.9890	.9894	.9899	.9903	.9908
9.8	.9912	.9917	.9921	.9926	.9930	.9934	.9939	.9943	.9948	.9952
9.9	.9956	.9961	.9965	.9969	.9974	.9978	.9983	.9987	.9991	.9996

Chapter 1

1. Pure chemistry accumulates knowledge for its own sake. Applied chemistry aims to attain specific goals.
2. **a.** analytical chemistry
   b. organic chemistry
   c. biochemistry
3. The hypothesis guides the design of the experiment.
4. A law. The statement summarizes facts; it does not give an explanation.
5. Not, perhaps, in the modern sense of the word. Eighteenth century chemistry was a quantitative science aimed at understanding the natural world. Alchemists had a narrow, specific goal guiding their work.
6. Melting point, boiling point, and density.
7. **a.** solid **b.** liquid **c.** gas
8. a vapor.
9. b., c., and d.
10. chlorine, mercury, bromine, and water.
11. one
12. **a.** heterogeneous **b.** heterogeneous **c.** homogeneous
13. **a.** element **b.** mixture **c.** mixture
    d. element **e.** mixture **f.** mixture
14. A mixture of at least one solid and one liquid. The liquid component(s) evaporate, leaving behind the solid component(s).
15. **a.** tin **b.** copper **c.** sulfur
    d. cadmium **e.** phosphorus **f.** chlorine
16. Carbon, hydrogen, oxygen, and sodium.
17. Color change, energy absorbed or evolved, gas or solid produced, odor change.
18. **a.** chemical **b.** physical **c.** chemical **d.** physical
19. It does not attempt to explain, therefore it is not a theory.
20. The iron combines with oxygen in the air.
21. 4.8 g+ 38.4 g = 43.2 g
22. Answers to the first question will vary. In general, students should suggest that they would need a chemical analysis of the piece and advice from an art historian.
23. When new materials become available, new products and processes soon follow.

Chapter 2

1. Answers will vary; use a more precise volumetric measure such as a measuring cup.
2. **a.** qualitative **b.** quantitative
   c. quantitative **d.** qualitative
3. **a.** precision **b.** accuracy **c.** precision
   d. precision **e.** accuracy **f.** accuracy
4. When using an improperly calibrated measuring device.
5. **a.** 3.27×10^{-22} grams
   b. 3.01×10^{23} hydrogen molecules
6. **a.** 9.14×10^{1} m **b.** 1.54×10^{-10} m **c.** 6.378×10^{6} m
   d. 8×10^{-6} m **e.** 1.496×10^{11} m
7. **a.** 5.730×10^{-2}, 4 **b.** 8.765×10^{3}, 4
   c. 7.3×10^{-4}, 2 **d.** 1.2×10^{1}, unlimited
   e. 1.0×10^{-2}, 2 **f.** 5.07×10^{2}, unlimited
8. **a.** 8.71×10^{1} m, 9×10^{1} m
   b. 4.36×10^{8} m, 4×10^{8} m
   c. 1.55×10^{-2} m, 2×10^{-2} m
   d. 9.01×10^{3} m, 9×10^{3} m
   e. 1.78×10^{-3} m, 2×10^{-3} m
   f. 6.30×10^{2} m, 6×10^{2} m
9. **a.** 79.2 m, 7.92×10^{1} m **b.** 7.33 m, 7.33×10^{0} m
   c. 11.53 m, 1.153×10^{1} m **d.** 17.3 m, 1.73×10^{1} m
10. **a.** 18 m^2, 1.8×10^{1} m^2
    b. 0.000052 m^2, 5.2×10^{-5} m^2
    c. 675 m, 6.75×10^{2} m
    d. 0.21 m, 2.1×10^{-1} m
    e. 0.587 min., 5.87×10^{-1} min.
11. **a.** amount of substance, mol
    b. density, kg/m^3 or g/cm^3
    c. time, s
    d. pressure, Pa
    e. length, m
    f. mass, kg
12. **a.** base **b.** derived **c.** base
    d. derived **e.** base **f.** base
13. **a.** The plans would not be useful to anyone without the same stick.
    b. With the exception of the United States, the plans would not be useful throughout most of the world.
    c. The plans would be useful throughout most of the world.
14. Answers will vary.
15. From smallest to largest: b, d, a, f, e, c.
16. **a.** 2.4 mm **b.** 16.4 cm **c.** 25.4 cm
17. Volume is a length measurement cubed.
18. $21 \text{ cm} \times 12 \text{ cm} \times 3.5 \text{ cm} = 8.8 \times 10^{2} \text{ cm}^3$
19. $V = 3.14 \times (3.0 \text{ cm})^2 \times 28 \text{ cm} = 7.9 \times 10^{2} \text{ cm}^3$
20. Your weight decreases; your mass remains constant.
21. **a.** 1 cg = 0.01 g **b.** 1 μg = 0.000 001 g
    c. 1 kg = 1000 g **d.** 1 mg = 0.001 g
22. The density does not change. Density is independent of the amount of substance.
23. $\text{Density} = \frac{\text{mass}}{\text{volume}} = \frac{612 \text{ g}}{245 \text{ cm}^3} = 2.50 \text{ g/cm}^3$

    Aluminum has a density of 2.70 g/cm^3. The metal is not aluminum.
24. $\text{Density} = \frac{\text{mass}}{\text{volume}} = \frac{15.8 \text{ g}}{19.7 \text{ cm}^3} = 0.802 \text{ g/cm}^3$

    The ball will sink because its density is greater than the density of gasoline (0.70 g/cm^3).
25. Specific gravity is a ratio of two density measurements so the density units cancel.
26. **a.** 2.70 **b.** 13.6 **c.** 0.917
27. K = 170 + 273 = 443 K
28. °C = 87 − 273 = − 186°C
29. You would need to know how accurate the measurement needs to be, and whether safety is a factor. An organic-filled thermometer is safer than a mercury-filled thermometer but less accurate.
30. Yes. It would be less expensive, and a high degree of precision is not needed for home use.
31. The absolute value of the error is used.
32. $\text{Percent error} = \frac{|208-200|}{208} \times 100 = 4\%$

Chapter 3

1. Answers will vary.
2. 48 cm. It may help for the students to make a sketch in order to solve this problem.
3. Answers will vary.
4. Step 1. You want to find the best route.
   Step 2. You know your starting location and your destination.
   Step 3. You consider the distances and road quality to map out a route.
   Step 4. You travel over the planned route.
   Step 5. You arrive at your destination and discuss your trip.
5. The density of silicon is 2.33 g/cm^3.

$$\text{Volume} = \frac{\text{mass}}{\text{density}} = \frac{62.9\ \cancel{g}}{2.33\ \cancel{g}/cm^3}$$

$$= 62.9\ \cancel{g} \times \frac{1\ cm^3}{2.33\ \cancel{g}} = 27.0\ cm^3$$

6. $4\ K - 273 = -269°C$
7. **a.** Mass = volume × density

$$= 1.35\ \cancel{cm^3} \times \frac{19.3\ g}{1\ \cancel{cm^3}} = 26.1\ g$$

b. $26.1\ \cancel{g} \times \frac{\$11}{1\ \cancel{g}} = \$287.10$

8. $37°C + 273 = 310\ K$
9. $\frac{1\ g}{100\ cg}, \frac{100\ cg}{10^3\ mg}, \frac{1\ g}{10^3\ mg}, \frac{100\ cg}{1\ g}, \frac{10^3\ mg}{100\ cg}, \frac{10^3\ mg}{1\ g}$
10. $48.0°C\ \cancel{\text{temp. inc}} \times 1\ \frac{1.8°F\ \text{temp. inc}}{1°C\ \cancel{\text{temp. inc}}} = 86.4°F$
11. There is 26.0 g of silver in 40.0 g of the amalgam.

$$25.0\ \cancel{\text{g amalgam}} \times \frac{26.0\ \text{g silver}}{40.0\ \cancel{\text{g amalgam}}} = 16.3\ \text{g silver}$$

12. $0.20\ h \times \frac{60\ min}{1\ h} \times \frac{60\ s}{1\ min} = 720\ s$
13. The unit of the conversion factor in the denominator must be identical to the unit in the given measurement.
14. Estimate an answer to see if your calculator answer makes sense and round the answer off to the correct number of significant figures.
15. **a.** $0.044\ \cancel{km} \times \frac{1000m}{1\ \cancel{km}} = 44\ m$

b. $4.6\ \cancel{mg} \times \frac{1g}{1000\cancel{mg}} = 4.6 \times 10^{-3}\ g$

c. $8.9\ \cancel{m} \times \frac{10\ dm}{1\ \cancel{m}} = 89\ dm$

d. $0.107\ \cancel{g} \times \frac{100\ cg}{1\ \cancel{g}} = 10.7\ cg$

e. $15\ \cancel{cm^3} \times \frac{1\ L}{1000\ cm^3} = 1.5 \times 10^{-2}\ L$

f. $7.38\ \cancel{g} \times \frac{1\ kg}{1000\ \cancel{g}} = 7.38 \times 10^{-3}\ kg$

g. $6.7\ \cancel{s} \times \frac{1000\ ms}{1\ \cancel{s}} = 6.7 \times 10^{+3}\ ms$

h. $94.5\ \cancel{g} \times \frac{1\ 000\ 000\ \mu g}{1\ \cancel{g}} = 9.45 \times 10^7\ \mu g$

16. **a.** $14.8\ \cancel{g} \times \frac{1\ cm^3}{2.34\ \cancel{g}} = 6.32\ cm^3\ B$

b. $2.8\ \cancel{L} \times \frac{1.78\ g}{1\ \cancel{L}} = 5.0\ g\ Ar$

c. $4.62\ \cancel{g} \times \frac{1\ cm^3}{13.5\ \cancel{g}} = 0.342\ cm^3\ Hg$

17. Same as Problem 16.
18. No. A calculator does not solve chemistry problems. A calculator is a tool for doing mathematical calculations.
19. The product is the single conversion factor that could have been used to work the problem.
20. **a.** $157\ \cancel{cs} \times \frac{1\ s}{100\ \cancel{cs}} = 1.57\ s$

b. $42.7\ \cancel{L} \times \frac{1000\ mL}{1\ \cancel{L}} = 4.27 \times 10^4\ mL$

c. $261\ \cancel{nm} \times \frac{1\ \cancel{m}}{10^9\ \cancel{nm}} \times \frac{10^3\ mm}{1\ \cancel{m}} = 2.61 \times 10^{-4}\ mm$

d. $0.065\ \cancel{km} \times \frac{1000\ \cancel{m}}{1\ \cancel{km}} \times \frac{10\ dm}{1\ \cancel{m}} = 6.5 \times 10^2\ dm$

e. $642\ \cancel{cg} \times \frac{1\ \cancel{g}}{100\ \cancel{cg}} \times \frac{1\ kg}{1000\ \cancel{g}} = 6.42 \times 10^{-3}\ kg$

f. $8.25 \times 10^2\ \cancel{cg} \times \frac{1\ \cancel{g}}{100\ \cancel{cg}} \times \frac{10^9\ ng}{1\ \cancel{g}} = 8.25 \times 10^9\ ng$

21. Density = mass/volume

$$m = dv$$

$$v = 4.5\ cm \times 6.4\ cm \times 1.6\ \cancel{dm} \times \frac{10\ cm}{1\ \cancel{dm}}$$

$$= 468\ cm^3$$

$$m = 19.3\ g/\cancel{cm^3} \times 468\ \cancel{cm^3}$$

$$= 9032.4\ g = 9.0 \times 10^3 g = 9.0\ kg$$

22. $1\ \cancel{m^3} \times \frac{(100\ cm)^3}{1\ \cancel{m^3}} = 10^6\ cm^3$

$1\ cm^3 = 1\ mL$

$10^6\ cm^3 = 10^6\ mL$

23. **a.** $\frac{0.44\ \cancel{mL}}{1\ \cancel{min}} \times \frac{1\ \cancel{min}}{60\ s} \times \frac{10^3\ \mu L}{1\ \cancel{mL}} = 7.3\ \mu L/s$

b. $\frac{7.86\ \cancel{g}}{\cancel{cm^2}} \times \frac{1\ \cancel{cm^2}}{100\ mm^2} \times \frac{1000\ mg}{1\ \cancel{g}} = 78.6\ mg/mm^2$

c. $\frac{1.54\ \cancel{kg}}{1\ \cancel{L}} \times \frac{1\ \cancel{L}}{1000\ cm^3} \times \frac{1000\ g}{1\ \cancel{kg}} = 1.54\ g/cm^3$

24. $1\ \cancel{m^3} \times \frac{(100\ cm)^3}{1\ \cancel{m^3}} = 10^6\ cm^3$

$$10^6\ \cancel{cm^3} \times \frac{19.3\ g}{\cancel{cm^3}} = 19.3 \times 10^6\ \cancel{g} \times \frac{1\ kg}{10^3\ \cancel{g}}$$

$$= 1.93 \times 10^4\ kg$$

25. $1\ \cancel{L} \times \frac{1000\ \cancel{cm^3}}{1\ \cancel{L}} \times \frac{(10\ mm)^3}{1\ \cancel{cm^3}} = 10^6\ mm^3$

$$\frac{7.0 \times 10^6\ RBC}{1\ \cancel{mm^3}} \times \frac{10^6\ \cancel{mm^3}}{1\ L} = 7.0 \times 10^{12}\ \text{RBC per liter}$$

26. No. You may never have a need for the larger quantity or it may be a product that would spoil over time.
27. Answers will vary. They could include coatings for cookware, for drill bits and other cutting tools, and for computer chips.

Chapter 4

1. Democritus approached the subject logically, yet without any experimental data. Dalton based his ideas on the analysis of data obtained by experiment.
2. All the statements agree with Dalton's theories. Statement a relates to part 1 of Dalton's theory. Statements b and c relate to part 2. Statement d relates to part 3.

3. No: the negative charges of all electrons are balanced by the positive charges in the nucleus.
4. **a.** A beam of electrons (cathode rays) is deflected by an electric field toward the positive plate.
   b. The cathode rays were always composed of electrons regardless of the metal used in the electrodes or the gas used in the cathode ray tube.
5. Rutherford thought that the electrons and protons were evenly distributed through the volume of an atom and that the alpha particles would pass right through. Instead, some of the alpha particles struck the relatively massive nucleus and bounced back.
6. All nuclei are positively charged, so they repel the alpha particle, which is also positively charged.
7. An atom is neutral because the number of protons equals the number of electrons, so positive and negative charges cancel. Neutrons have no electric charge.
8. The number of protons equals the atomic number.
9.

Element	Symbol	Atomic Number	Number of Protons
potassium	K	19	19
boron	B	5	5
sulfur	S	16	16
yttrium	Y	39	39

10.

Atomic Number	Mass Number	Number of Protons	Number of Neutrons	Number of Electrons	Symbol of Element
9	19	9	10	9	F
14	29	14	15	14	Si
22	47	22	25	22	Ti
25	55	25	30	25	Mn

11. **a.** The number 195 is the mass number (# of protons + # of neutrons)
   b. $^{195}_{78}Pt$
12. **a.** 7 neutrons **b.** 8 neutrons **c.** 138 neutrons
13. Isotopes of an element have the same number of protons and electrons, so their chemical properties are the same. Isotopes have different numbers of neutrons.
14. $^{16}_{8}O$ $^{17}_{8}O$ $^{18}_{8}O$
15. $^{64}_{30}Zn$ has 34 neutrons, 30 protons, and 30 electrons. $^{66}_{30}Zn$ has 36 neutrons, 30 protons, and 30 electrons. $^{67}_{30}Zn$ has 37 neutrons, 30 protons, and 30 electrons. $^{68}_{30}Zn$ has 38 neutrons, 30 protons, and 30 electrons. $^{70}_{30}Zn$ has 40 neutrons, 30 protons, and 30 electrons.
16. Answers will vary, but should focus on the fact that it is cheaper to prevent toxic waste pollution than to clean it up.
17. Chemical extraction, groundwater "pump and treat," or bioremediation can be used to purify contaminated water. Incineration or containment can be used for contaminated land.
18. The abundance of all the isotopic species, as well as their mass numbers, must be known.
19. Since the average atomic mass is close to that of ^{28}Si, you can conclude that it is the most abundant isotope, with the heavier isotopes contributing less than 10%.
20. The average atomic mass of Cu is given by:

$$\begin{aligned} 62.93 \text{ amu} \times 0.692 &= 43.5 \text{ amu} \\ 64.93 \text{ amu} \times 0.308 &= \underline{20.0 \text{ amu}} \\ \text{Total} &= 63.5 \text{ amu} \end{aligned}$$

21. Answers will vary.

Chapter 5

1. **a.** metal **b.** metalloid **c.** metal
   d. nonmetal **e.** metal
2. silicon, sulfur, barium
3. Ions are formed when atoms lose electrons or gain electrons.
4. **a.** Al^{3+}, aluminum ion
   b. 2 electrons gained, sulfide ion
   c. Sr, 2 electrons lost, strontium ion
   d. Br-, bromide ion
5. Ionic compounds are electrically neutral; the net positive charge on the cations is exactly balanced by the net negative charge on the anions.
6. Ionic, because of high melting point.
7. **a.** carbon 6, hydrogen 8, oxygen 6
   b. carbon 5, hydrogen 8, oxygen 4, nitrogen 1, sodium 1
   c. carbon 12, hydrogen 22, oxygen 11
   d. carbon 7, hydrogen 5, nitrogen 3, oxygen 6
   e. nitrogen 2, hydrogen 4, oxygen 3
8. **a.** ionic **b.** molecular **c.** ionic
   d. molecular **e.** ionic **f.** molecular
9. Law of definite proportions
10. Compound A $\dfrac{2.98 \text{ g Pb}}{0.461 \text{ g O}} = \dfrac{6.46 \text{ g Pb}}{1.00 \text{ g O}}$

    Compound B $\dfrac{9.89 \text{ g Pb}}{0.763 \text{ g O}} = \dfrac{13.0 \text{ g Pb}}{1.00 \text{ g O}}$

    $\dfrac{13.0 \text{ g Pb (in compound B)}}{6.46 \text{ g Pb (in compound A)}} = \dfrac{2}{1}$

    The mass ratio of the lead to oxygen in the compounds is 2:1.
11. There is a fear that many natural products with potential medicinal value will be lost forever.
12. Answers will vary.
13. **a.** O^{2-} **b.** Pb^{2+} **c.** Li^{+}
    d. N^{3-} **e.** Cu^{2+} **f.** F^{-}
14. **a.** barium ion **b.** iodide ion
    c. silver ion **d.** mercury (II) ion
    e. phosphide ion **f.** tin(IV) ion
15. possible answer: ammonium, NH_4^+
16. It would be impossible to memorize common names of millions of compounds.
17. zero
18. **a.** Na_2O **b.** SnS_2 **c.** KCl **d.** Mg_3N_2
19. Knowing the number of each ion in the formula and the ionic charge of the anion, the charge of the cation must be such that the net ionic charge is zero.
20. **a.** aluminum fluoride
    b. iron(II) sulfide or ferrous sulfide
    c. calcium oxide
    d. copper(I) selenide or cuprous selenide
21. When more than one polyatomic ion is needed to balance a formula.
22. **a.** $CaCO_3$ **b.** $Ba(HCO_3)_2$ **c.** LiClO **d.** $Sn(Cr_2O_7)_2$
23. **a.** aluminum hydroxide **b.** sodium iodide
    c. tin(II) phosphate **d.** sodium chromate
24. **a.** $Cr(NO_2)_3$ **b.** magnesium phosphate
    c. lithium fluoride **d.** $NaClO_4$
    e. lead(II) acetate **f.** $Mg(HCO_3)_2$
25. **a.** carbon disulfide **b.** dichlorine heptoxide
    c. dinitrogen pentoxide **d.** carbon tetrachloride
    e. chromium(III) chloride
26. **a.** CBr_4 **b.** N_2H_4 **c.** BCl_3 **d.** P_2O_3
27. When traffic is not heavy.
28. hydrogen

29. a. calcium carbonate
b. potassium permanganate
c. lead(II) chromate
d. calcium hydrogen phosphate
e. tin(II) dichromate
f. magnesium phosphide
g. ammonium sulfate
h. iodine monochloride
i. sodium nitrite

30. a. $Sn(OH)_2$ **b.** BaF_2 **c.** I_4O_9
d. $Fe_2(C_2O_4)_3$ **e.** CaS **f.** $Al(HCO_3)_3$
g. Na_3PO_4 **h.** $KClO_4$ **i.** S_2O_3 **j.** $Mg(NO_3)_2$

31. Answers may vary, but may include the idea that SiO_2 is an ionic compound; however, glass does not form crystals like an ionic solid. Its liquid-like behavior resembles that of a molecular compound.

Chapter 6

1. Answers will vary but may include: nuts and bolts, other fruits and vegetables, and landscaping rock or mulch.

2. $0.5 \text{ bushel} \times \frac{90 \text{ apples}}{1 \text{ bushel}} \times \frac{2.0 \text{ kg}}{12 \text{ apples}} = 7.5 \text{ kg}$

3. $15 \text{ kg} \times \frac{12 \text{ apples}}{2.0 \text{ kg}} \times \frac{8 \text{ seeds}}{1 \text{ apple}} = 720 \text{ seeds}$

4. Reduction or elimination of lead in paint; elimination of lead from gasoline; removal of lead-based paints from interiors of buildings.

5. Environmental, health, and economic factors.

6. $2.80 \times 10^{24} \text{ atoms Si} \times \frac{1 \text{ mol Si}}{6.02 \times 10^{23} \text{ atoms Si}}$

$= 4.65 \text{ mol Si}$

7. $0.360 \text{ mol Ag} \times \frac{6.02 \times 10^{23} \text{ atoms Ag}}{1 \text{ mol Ag}}$

$= 2.17 \times 10^{23} \text{ atoms Ag}$

8. a. 3 **b.** 4 **c.** 3 **d.** 9

9. $2.14 \text{ mol CO} \times \frac{6.02 \times 10^{23} \text{ molecules CO}}{1 \text{ mol CO}}$

$= 1.29 \times 10^{24} \text{ molecules CO}$

10. $4.65 \times 10^{24} \text{ molecules } NO_2$

$\times \frac{1 \text{ mol } NO_2}{6.02 \times 10^{23} \text{ molecules } NO_2} = 7.72 \text{ moles } NO_2$

11. Answers will vary.

12. Round off the gram atomic mass to tenths.
a. 23.0 g **b.** 79.0 g **c.** 207.2 g

13. a. $2 \text{ mol C} \times \frac{12.0\text{g}}{1 \text{ mol}} = 24.0 \text{ g}$

$6 \text{ mol H} \times \frac{1.0 \text{ g}}{1 \text{ mol}} = 6.0 \text{ g}$

$\text{gmm } C_2H_6 = 30.0 \text{ g}$

b. $1 \text{ mol P} \times \frac{31.0 \text{ g P}}{1 \text{ mol P}} = 31.0 \text{ g P}$

$3 \text{ mol Cl} \times \frac{35.5 \text{ g Cl}}{1 \text{ mol Cl}} = 106.5 \text{ g Cl}$

$\text{gmm } PCl_3 = 137.5 \text{ g}$

c. $3 \text{ mol C} \times \frac{12.0 \text{ g}}{1 \text{ mol}} = 36.0 \text{ g C}$

$8 \text{ mol H} \times \frac{1.0 \text{ g}}{1 \text{ mol}} = 8.0 \text{ g H}$

$1 \text{ mol O} \times \frac{16.0 \text{ g O}}{1 \text{ mol}} = 16.0 \text{ g O}$

$\text{gmm } C_3H_7OH = 60.0 \text{ g}$

d. $2 \text{ mol N} \times \frac{14.0 \text{ g N}}{1 \text{ mol N}} = 28.0 \text{ g N}$

$5 \text{ mol O} \times \frac{16.0 \text{ g O}}{1 \text{ mol O}} = 80.0 \text{ g O}$

$\text{gmm } N_2O_5 = 108.0 \text{ g}$

14. a. 139.6 g **b.** 84.0 g **c.** 294.3 g

15. Answers may vary but should include:
Step 1. Determine the moles of each atom from the formula.
Step 2. Look up the atomic mass of each element.
Step 3. Multiply the number of moles of each atom by its molar mass.
Step 4. Sum these products.

16. 71.0 g

17. N, 14.0 g
N_2, 28.0 g
H_2O, 18.0 g
Ca^{2+}, 40.1 g
CaF_2, 78.1 g
$C_{12}H_{22}O_{11}$, 342 g

18. a. $0.720 \text{ mol Be} \times \frac{9.01 \text{ g Be}}{1 \text{ mol Be}} = 6.49 \text{ g Be}$

b. $2.40 \text{ mol } N_2 \times \frac{28.0 \text{ g } N_2}{1 \text{ mol } N_2} = 67.2 \text{ g } N_2$

c. $10.0 \text{ mol Cr} \times \frac{52.0 \text{ g Cr}}{1 \text{ mol Cr}} = 520 = 5.20 \times 10^2 \text{ g Cr}$

d. $3.32 \text{ mol K} \times \frac{39.1 \text{ g K}}{1 \text{ mol K}} = 129.8 = 1.30 \times 10^2 \text{ g K}$

e. $4.52 \times 10^{-3} \text{ mol } C_{20}H_{42} \times \frac{282 \text{ g } C_{20}H_{42}}{1 \text{ mol } C_{20}H_{42}} = 1.27 \text{ g } C_{20}H_{42}$

f. $0.0112 \text{ mol } K_2CO_3 \times \frac{138.2 \text{ g } K_2CO_3}{1 \text{ mol } K_2CO_3} = 1.55 \text{ g } K_2CO_3$

g. $0.160 \text{ mol } H_2O_2 \times \frac{34.0 \text{ g } H_2O_2}{1 \text{ mol } H_2O_2} = 5.44 \text{ g } H_2O_2$

h. $5.08 \text{ mol } Ca(NO_3)_2 \times \frac{164.1 \text{ g } Ca(NO_3)_2}{1 \text{ mol } Ca(NO_3)_2}$

$= 8.34 \times 10^2 \text{ g } Ca(NO_3)_2$

19. a. 2.50 mole H_2 **b.** 2.40×10^{-6} mol Li_2HPO_4
c. 1.80 mol Ar **d.** 3.43×10^{-2} mol B
e. 0.688 mol CH_4 **f.** 8.82 mol $(NH_4)_2CO_3$
g. 6.93 mol Al **h.** 2.13 mol SnF_2

20. Same volume but different masses; equal volumes of gases have the same number of molecules at the same temperature and pressure.

21. a. $3.20 \times 10^{-2} \text{ mol } CO_2 \times \frac{22.4 \text{ L } CO_2}{1 \text{ mol } CO_2} = 0.717 \text{ L } CO_2$

b. $0.960 \text{ mol } CH_4 \times \frac{22.4 \text{ L } CH_4}{1 \text{ mol } CH_4} = 21.5 \text{ L } CH_4$

c. $3.70 \text{ mol } N_2 \times \frac{22.4 \text{ L } N_2}{1 \text{ mol } N_2} = 82.9 \text{ L } N_2$

22. a. $67.2\ \text{L SO}_2 \times \frac{1\ \text{mol SO}_2}{22.4\ \text{L SO}_2} = 3.00\ \text{mol SO}_2$

b. $0.880\ \text{L He} \times \frac{1\ \text{mol He}}{22.4\ \text{L He}} = 0.0393\ \text{mol He}$

$= 3.93 \times 10^{-2}\ \text{mol He}$

c. $1.00 \times 10^3\ \text{L C}_2\text{H}_6 \times \frac{1\ \text{mol C}_2\text{H}_6}{22.4\ \text{L C}_2\text{H}_6} = 44.6\ \text{mol C}_2\text{H}_6$

23. At STP the gfm of any gas occupies a volume of 22.4 L.

a. gas A: $22.4\ \text{L} \times \frac{1.25\ \text{g}}{1\ \text{L}} = 28.0$ (nitrogen)

b. gas B: $22.4\ \text{L} \times \frac{2.86\ \text{g}}{1\ \text{L}} = 64.1$ (sulfur dioxide)

c. gas C: $22.4\ \text{L} \times \frac{0.714\ \text{g}}{1\ \text{L}} = 16.0\ \text{g}$ (methane)

24. a. $\frac{39.9\ \text{g Ar}}{1\ \text{mol Ar}}$

b. $\frac{1\ \text{mol F}_2}{22.4\ \text{L F}_2}$

c. $\frac{1\ \text{mol NO}_2}{6.02 \times 10^{23}\ \text{molecules NO}_2}$

25. In each problem you are asked to find the number of particles in a given mass. In each solution you go through an intermediate unit: dozens of apples and moles of carbon.

26. $1\ \text{atom Hg} \times \frac{1.00\ \text{mol Hg}}{6.02 \times 10^{23}\ \text{atoms Hg}} \times \frac{200.6\ \text{g Hg}}{1.00\ \text{mol Hg}} = 3.33 \times 10^{-22}\ \text{g}$

27. $9.00\ \text{L CO}_2 \times \frac{1.00\ \text{mol CO}_2}{22.4\ \text{L CO}_2} \times \frac{6.02 \times 10^{23}\ \text{molec. CO}_2}{1\ \text{mol CO}_2}$

$= 2.42 \times 10^{23}$ molecules of CO_2 or of any gas at STP.

28. a. 9.03 g Mg + 3.48 g N = 12.51 g total

$\%\text{Mg} = \frac{9.03\ \text{g}}{12.51\ \text{g}} \times 100\% = 72.2\%\ \text{Mg}$

$\%\text{N} = \frac{3.48\ \text{g}}{12.51\ \text{g}} \times 100\% = 27.8\%\ \text{N}$

b. Total mass = 29.0 g Ag + 4.30 g S = 33.3 g

$\%\text{Ag} = \frac{29.0\ \text{g}}{33.3\ \text{g}} \times 100\% = 87.1\%\ \text{Ag}$

$\%\text{S} = \frac{4.30\ \text{g}}{3.33\ \text{g}} \times 100\% = 12.9\%\ \text{S}$

c. 222.6 g Na + 77.4 g O = 300.0 g total

$\%\text{Na} = \frac{222.6\ \text{g}}{300.0\ \text{g}} \times 100\% = 74.2\%\ \text{Na}$

$\%\text{O} = \frac{77.4\ \text{g}}{300.0\ \text{g}} \times 100\% = 25.8\%\ \text{O}$

29. a. gfm C_2H_6 = 30.0 g

$\%\text{C} = \frac{24.0\ \text{g}}{30.0\ \text{g}} \times 100\% = 80.0\%\ \text{C}$

$\%\text{H} = \frac{6.0\ \text{g}}{30.0\ \text{g}} \times 100\% = 20.0\%\ \text{H}$

b. gfm $NaHSO_4$ = 120.1 g

$\%\text{Na} = \frac{23.0\ \text{g}}{120.1\ \text{g}} \times 100\% = 19.2\%\ \text{Na}$

$\%\text{H} = \frac{1.0\ \text{g}}{120.1\ \text{g}} \times 100\% = 0.83\%\ \text{H}$

$\%\text{S} = \frac{32.1\ \text{g}}{120.1\ \text{g}} \times 100\% = 26.7\%\ \text{S}$

$\%\text{O} = \frac{64.0\ \text{g}}{120.1\ \text{g}} \times 100\% = 53.3\%\ \text{O}$

c. gfm $Ca(C_2H_3O_2)_2$ = 158.1 g

$\%\text{Ca} = \frac{40.1\ \text{g}}{158.1\ \text{g}} \times 100\% = 25.4\%\ \text{Ca}$

$\%\text{C} = \frac{48.0\ \text{g}}{158.1\ \text{g}} \times 100\% = 30.4\%\ \text{C}$

$\%\text{H} = \frac{6.0\ \text{g}}{158.1\ \text{g}} \times 100\% = 3.8\%\ \text{H}$

$\%\text{O} = \frac{64.0\ \text{g}}{158.1\ \text{g}} \times 100\% = 40.5\%\ \text{O}$

d. gfm HCN = 27.0 g

$\%\text{H} = \frac{1.0\ \text{g}}{27.0\ \text{g}} \times 100\% = 3.7\%\ \text{H}$

$\%\text{C} = \frac{12.0\ \text{g}}{27.0\ \text{g}} \times 100\% = 44.4\%\ \text{C}$

$\%\text{N} = \frac{14.0\ \text{g}}{27.0\ \text{g}} \times 100\% = 51.9\%\ \text{N}$

e. gfm H_2O = 18.0 g

$\%\text{H} = \frac{2.0\ \text{g}}{18.0\ \text{g}} \times 100\% = 11\%\ \text{H}$

$\%\text{O} = \frac{16.0\ \text{g}}{18.0\ \text{g}} \times 100\% = 89\%\ \text{O}$

30. a. Percent of H in C_2H_6 is 20%, or 20 g H per 100 g C_2H_6.

$350\ \text{g C}_2\text{H}_6 \times \frac{20\ \text{g H}}{100\ \text{g C}_2\text{H}_6} = 70\ \text{g H}$

b. $20.2\ \text{g NaHSO}_4 \times \frac{0.83\ \text{g H}}{100\ \text{g NaHSO}_4} = 0.17\ \text{g H}$

c. $124\ \text{g Ca(C}_2\text{H}_3\text{O}_2)_2 \times \frac{3.8\ \text{g H}}{100\ \text{g Ca(C}_2\text{H}_3\text{O}_2)_2} = 4.71\ \text{g H}$

d. $378\ \text{g HCN} \times \frac{3.7\ \text{g H}}{100\ \text{g HCN}} = 14\ \text{g H}$

e. $100\ \text{g H}_2\text{O} \times \frac{11\ \text{g H}}{100\ \text{g H}_2\text{O}} = 11\ \text{g H}$

31. because of its relative scarcity

32. Answers will vary, but should convey the idea that unsalted or "lightly salted" food products are advertised as being better for you.

33. a. molecular
b. molecular
c. molecular and empirical
d. molecular and empirical
e. molecular

34. a. $94.1\ \text{g O} \times \frac{1.00\ \text{mol O}}{16.0\ \text{g O}} = 5.88\ \text{mol O}$

$\frac{5.88\ \text{mol O}}{5.88} = 1\ \text{mol O}$

$5.9\ \text{g H} \times \frac{1.00\ \text{mol H}}{1.0\ \text{g H}} = 5.9\ \text{mol H}$

$\frac{5.9\ \text{mol H}}{5.88} = 1\ \text{mol H}$ Empirical formula = HO

b. Calculate the lowest whole-number ratio of moles.

$$79.9\ \cancel{g\ C} \times \frac{1.00\ mol\ C}{12.0\ \cancel{g\ C}} = 6.66\ mol\ C$$

$$\frac{6.66\ mol\ C}{6.66} = 1\ mol\ C$$

$$20.1\ \cancel{g\ H} \times \frac{1.00\ mol\ H}{1.00\ \cancel{g\ H}} = 20.1\ mol\ H$$

$$\frac{20.1\ mol\ H}{6.66} = 3\ mol\ H \qquad \text{Empirical formula} = CH_3$$

c. $$67.6\ \cancel{g\ Hg} \times \frac{1.00\ mol\ Hg}{200.6\ \cancel{g\ Hg}} = 0.337\ mol\ Hg$$

$$\frac{0.337\ mol\ Hg}{0.336} = 1\ mol\ Hg$$

$$10.8\ \cancel{g\ S} \times \frac{1.00\ mol\ S}{32.1\ \cancel{g\ S}} = 0.336\ mol\ S$$

$$\frac{0.336\ mol\ S}{0.336} = 1\ mol\ S$$

$$21.6\ \cancel{g\ O} \times \frac{1.00\ mol\ O}{16.0\ \cancel{g\ O}} = 1.35\ mol\ O$$

$$\frac{1.35\ mol\ O}{0.336} = 4\ mol\ O \qquad \text{Empirical formula } HgSO_4$$

d. $$27.59\ \cancel{g\ C} \times \frac{1.00\ mol\ C}{12.0\ \cancel{g\ C}} = 2.30\ mol\ C$$

$$\frac{2.30\ mol\ C}{1.15} = 2\ mol\ C$$

$$1.15\ \cancel{g\ H} \times \frac{1.00\ mol\ H}{1.00\ \cancel{g\ H}} = 1.15\ mol\ H$$

$$\frac{1.15\ mol\ H}{1.15} = 1\ mol\ H$$

$$16.09\ \cancel{g\ N} \times \frac{1.00\ mol\ N}{14.0\ \cancel{g\ N}} = 1.15\ mol\ N$$

$$\frac{1.15\ mol\ N}{1.15} = 1\ mol\ N$$

$$55.17\ \cancel{g\ O} \times \frac{1.00\ mol\ O}{16.0\ \cancel{g\ O}} = 3.45\ mol\ O$$

$$\frac{3.45\ mol\ O}{1.15} = 3\ mol\ O \qquad \text{Empirical formula} = C_2HNO_3$$

e. $$17.6\ \cancel{g\ Na} \times \frac{1.00\ mol\ Na}{23.0\ \cancel{g\ Na}} = 0.765\ mol\ Na$$

$$\frac{0.765\ mol\ Na}{0.763} = 1\ mol\ Na$$

$$39.7\ \cancel{g\ Cr} \times \frac{1.00\ mol\ Cr}{52.0\ \cancel{g\ Cr}} = 0.763\ mol\ Cr$$

$$\frac{0.763\ mol\ Cr}{0.763} = 1\ mol\ Cr$$

$$42.7\ \cancel{g\ O} \times \frac{1.00\ mol\ O}{16.0\ \cancel{g\ O}} = 2.67\ mol\ O$$

$$\frac{2.67\ mol\ O}{0.763} = 3.50\ mol\ O$$

The result is $Na_1Cr_1O_{3.5}$. To get the lowest whole-number ratio, multiply through by 2. The empirical formula is $Na_2Cr_2O_7$.

35. Calculate the relative number of moles from the given masses.

a. $$9.03\ \cancel{g\ Mg} \times \frac{1.00\ mol\ Mg}{24.3\ \cancel{g\ Mg}} = 0.372\ mol\ Mg$$

$$\frac{0.372\ mol\ Mg}{0.249} = 1.5\ mol\ Mg$$

$$3.48\ \cancel{g\ N} \times \frac{1.00\ mol\ N}{14.0\ \cancel{g\ N}} = 0.249\ mol\ N$$

$$\frac{0.249\ mol\ N}{0.249} = 1\ mol\ N$$

The result is $Mg_{1.5}N_1$. Multiply through by 2. Empirical formula = Mg_3N_2

b. $$29.0\ \cancel{g\ Ag} \times \frac{1.00\ mol\ Ag}{107.9\ \cancel{g\ Ag}} = 0.269\ mol\ Ag$$

$$\frac{0.269\ mol\ Ag}{0.134} = 2\ mol\ Ag$$

$$4.30\ \cancel{g\ S} \times \frac{1.00\ mol\ S}{32.1\ \cancel{g\ S}} = 0.134\ mol\ S$$

$$\frac{0.134\ mol\ S}{0.134} = 1\ mol\ S$$

Empirical formula = Ag_2S

c. $$222.6\ \cancel{g\ Na} \times \frac{1.00\ mol\ Na}{23.0\ \cancel{g\ Na}} = 9.68\ mol\ Na$$

$$\frac{9.68\ mol\ Na}{4.84} = 2\ mol\ Na$$

$$77.4\ \cancel{g\ O} \times \frac{1.00\ mol\ O}{16.0\ \cancel{g\ O}} = 4.84\ mol\ O$$

$$\frac{4.84\ mol\ O}{4.84} = 1\ mol\ O$$

Empirical formula = Na_2O

36. Calculate the empirical formula.

$$58.8\ \cancel{g\ C} \times \frac{1.00\ mol\ C}{12.0\ \cancel{g\ C}} = 4.90\ mol\ C$$

$$\frac{4.90\ mol\ C}{1.96} = 2.50\ mol\ C$$

$$9.8\ \cancel{g\ H} \times \frac{1.00\ mol\ H}{1.00\ \cancel{g\ H}} = 9.8\ mol\ H$$

$$\frac{9.80\ mol\ H}{1.96} = 5.00\ mol\ H$$

$$31.4\ \cancel{g\ O} \times \frac{1.00\ mol\ O}{16.0\ \cancel{g\ O}} = 1.96\ mol\ O$$

$$\frac{1.96\ mol\ O}{1.96} = 1\ mol\ O$$

The result is $C_{2.5}H_5O_1$. Multiply through by 2. The empirical formula is $C_5H_{10}O_2$. This is also the molecular formula since the gfm of $C_5H_{10}O_2$ is 102 g, which is the gmm of the compound.

37. Calculate the empirical formula. The mass of hydrogen is: 7.36 g − 6.93 g = 0.43 g H

$$6.93\ \cancel{g\ O} \times \frac{1.00\ mol\ O}{16.0\ \cancel{g\ O}} = 0.433\ mol\ O$$

$$\frac{0.433\ mol\ O}{0.43} = 1\ mol\ O$$

$$0.43\ \cancel{g\ H} \times \frac{1.0\ mol\ H}{1.0\ \cancel{g\ H}} = 0.43\ mol\ H$$

$$\frac{0.43 \text{ mol H}}{0.43} = 1 \text{ mol H}$$

The empirical formula is HO. The gfm of HO is 17; the gmm of the compound is 34.0. It takes 34 g/17 g, or 2 empirical formula units to make the molecular formula. The molecular formula is H_2O_2.

Chapter 7

1. The arrow separates the reactants from the products. A plus sign separates individual reactants and individual products from one another.
2. **a.** copper(II) sulfide + oxygen → copper + sulfur dioxide
   b. hydrogen + oxygen → water
   c. sodium bicarbonate → sodium carbonate + carbon dioxide + water
3. **a.** $S(s) + O_2(g) \rightarrow SO_2(g)$
   b. $KClO_3(s) \xrightarrow[MnO_2]{\Delta} + KCl(s) + O_2(g)$
   c. $HgS(s) + O_2(g) \xrightarrow{\Delta} Hg(l) + SO_2(g)$
4. **a.** Gaseous ammonia and oxygen react in the presence of platinum to produce nitrogen monoxide gas and water vapor.
   b. Aqueous solutions of sulfuric acid and barium chloride, when mixed, produce a precipitate of barium sulfate and aqueous hydrochloric acid.
   c. The gas dinitrogen trioxide reacts with water to produce an aqueous solution of nitrous acid.
5. **a.** $C + 2F + 2G \rightarrow CF_2G_2$
   b. $F + 3W + S + 2P \rightarrow FW_3SP_2$
6. A balanced equation obeys the law of conservation of mass.
7. You must never change the formula of a reactant or product to balance an equation because this would change the chemical reaction.
8. **a.** $2PbO_2 \rightarrow 2PbO + O_2$
   b. $4P + 5O_2 \rightarrow P_4O_{10}$
   c. $2Al + N_2 \rightarrow 2AlN$
   d. $2Fe(OH)_3 \rightarrow Fe_2O_3 + 3H_2O$
   e. $(NH_4)_2CO_3 \rightarrow 2NH_3 + H_2O + CO_2$
   f. $2NaCl + H_2SO_4 \rightarrow Na_2SO_4 + 2HCl$
   g. $4H_2 + Fe_3O_4 \rightarrow 3Fe + 4H_2O$
   h. $2Al + 3CuSO_4 \rightarrow Al_2(SO_4)_3 + 3Cu$
9. **a.** $2C + O_2 \rightarrow 2CO$
   b. $2KNO_3 \rightarrow 2KNO_2 + O_2$
   c. $H_2 + S \rightarrow H_2S$
   d. $2FeCl_3 + 3Ca(OH)_2 \rightarrow 2Fe(OH)_3 + 3CaCl_2$
   e. $2Na + 2H_2O \rightarrow 2NaOH + H_2$
10. Answers may vary but may include: bound books have the advantage of the ability to browse and are not tied to a microfilm reader; they have the disadvantages of deterioration over time and the space required for storage. Microfilm has the advantages of being long lasting and reduced in storage space; disadvantages include often being hard to read and they cannot be picked up to browse.
11. Answers will vary; preservation of historically and culturally important books and manuscripts.
12. Actually carry out the chemical reaction in the laboratory and identify the products formed.
13. Use ionic charges to write an electrically neutral formula.
14. No; when two nonmetals combine, they may form many different compounds depending on the reaction conditions.
15. **a.** $2Mg + O_2 \rightarrow 2MgO$
    b. $4P + 5O_2 \rightarrow P_4O_{10}$
    c. $Ca + S \rightarrow CaS$
    d. $2Fe + O_2 \rightarrow 2FeO$
    e. $N_2O_5 + H_2O \rightarrow 2HNO_3$
16. **a.** HBr **b.** NaCl
17. **a.** $2Ag_2O \xrightarrow{heat} 4Ag + O_2$
    b. $NiCO_3 \xrightarrow{heat} NiO + CO_2$
    c. $NH_4NO_3 \xrightarrow{heat} N_2O + 2H_2O$
18. **a.** sodium displaces iron
    b. tin displaces silver
    c. zinc displaces hydrogen
19. **a.** N.R.
    b. $Zn + 2AgNO_3 \rightarrow Zn(NO_3)_2 + 2Ag$
    c. $2Al + 3H_2SO_4 \rightarrow Al_2(SO_4)_3 + 3H_2$
    d. $Cl_2 + 2KI \rightarrow 2KCl + I_2$
    e. $2Li + 2H_2O \rightarrow 2LiOH + H_2$
    f. N.R.
20. **a.** $2HCl + Ca(OH)_2 \rightarrow CaCl_2 + 2H_2O$
    b. $3Ag_2SO_4 + 2AlCl_3 \rightarrow 6AgCl + Al_2(SO_4)_3$
    c. $3KOH + H_3PO_4 \rightarrow K_3PO_4 + 3H_2O$
    d. $3H_2SO_4 + 2Al(OH)_3 \rightarrow Al_2(SO_4)_3 + 6H_2O$
    e. $SrBr_2 + (NH_4)_2CO_3 \rightarrow SrCO_3 + 2NH_4Br$
21. oxygen
22. carbon dioxide and water
23. **a.** $C_4H_8 + 6O_2 \rightarrow 4CO_2 + 4H_2O$
    b. $C_6H_{12}O_6 + 6O_2 \rightarrow 6CO_2 + 6H_2O$
    c. $2C_8H_{18} + 25O_2 \rightarrow 16CO_2 + 18H_2O$
24. A fuel, oxygen, and energy to initiate the combustion.
25. A fire extinguisher that controls one type of fire may actually enhance other types of combustion reactions. For example, water is not sprayed on burning magnesium because the intense heat can decompose the water, producing flammable hydrogen and oxygen gases.
26. **a.** 2 **b.** 3 **c.** 1 **d.** 5 **e.** 4
27. **a.** $3Hf + 2N_2 \rightarrow Hf_3N_4$ combination
    b. $Mg + H_2SO_4 \rightarrow MgSO_4 + H_2$ single replacement
    c. $2C_2H_6 + 7O_2 \rightarrow 4CO_2 + 6H_2O$ combustion
    d. $Pb(NO_3)_2 + 2NaI \rightarrow PbI_2 + 2NaNO_3$ double replacement
    e. $3Fe + 2O_2 \rightarrow Fe_3O_4$ combination
    f. $2Pb(NO_3)_2 \rightarrow 2PbO + 4NO_2 + O_2$ decomposition
    g. $Hg(NO_3)_2 + 2NH_4SCN \rightarrow Hg(SCN)_2 + 2NH_4NO_3$ double replacement
    h. $(NH_4)_2SO_4 + 2NaOH \rightarrow 2NH_3 + 2H_2O + Na_2SO_4$ double replacement, then decomposition
28. A complete ionic equation includes all chemical species present as reactants and products. A net ionic equation eliminates spectator ions and shows only those chemical species involved in the reaction.
29. **a.** $Pb^{2+}(aq) + 2I^-(aq) \rightarrow PbI_2(s)$
    b. $Zn(s) + 2H^+(aq) \rightarrow Zn^{2+}(aq) + H_2(g)$
    c. $H^+(aq) + OH^-(aq) \rightarrow H_2O(l)$
30. **a.** $2Al(s) + 6H^+(aq) \rightarrow 2Al^{3+}(aq) + 3H_2(g)$
    b. $H^+(aq) + OH^-(aq) \rightarrow H_2O(l)$
31. Composites are lighter (less dense), stronger, do not rust.
32. Answers will vary but may include golf clubs, tennis racquets, and baseball bats.

Chapter 8

1. Answers will vary but should include the correct number of "parts" to make the product.

2. The balanced equation to make a tricycle (FSW_3HP_2) is:
$F + S + 3W + H + 2P \rightarrow FSW_3HP_2$
number of seats:

$$288\ \cancel{FSW_3HP_2} \times \frac{1\ S}{1\ \cancel{FSW_3HP_2}} = 288\ S$$

number of wheels:

$$288\ \cancel{FSW_3HP_2} \times \frac{3\ W}{1\ \cancel{FSW_3HP_2}} = 864\ W$$

number of pedals:

$$288\ \cancel{FSW_3HP_2} \times \frac{2\ P}{1\ \cancel{FSW_3HP_2}} = 576\ P$$

3. The coefficients give the relative number of particles and moles of reactants and products. If the reacting substances are gases, the coefficients also give the relative volumes.
4. The number of moles of reactants and products depends on the chemical reaction. For some reactions, moles of reactants and products are equal, but this is not generally the case. Balanced equations will vary.

5. a. $2H_2(g) + O_2(g) \rightarrow 2H_2O(g)$
2 molecules H_2 + 1 molecule O_2 → 2 molecules H_2O
2 mol H_2 + 1 mol O_2 → 2 mol H_2O
$(2 \times 2.0\ g) + 32.0\ g = 2 \times 18.0\ g$
36.0 g = 36.0 g (law of conservation of mass)

b. $C_2H_2(g) + 5O_2(g) \rightarrow 4CO_2(g) + 2H_2O(l)$
2 molecules C_2H_2 + 5 molecules O_2 →
4 molecules CO_2 + 2 molecules H_2O
2 mol C_2H_2 + 5 mol O_2 → 4 mol CO_2 + 2 mol H_2O
$(2 \times 26.0\ g) + (5 \times 32.0\ g) = (4 \times 44.0\ g) + (2 \times 18.0\ g)$
212.0 g = 212.0 g (law of conservation of mass)

c. $2K(s) + 2H_2O(l) \rightarrow 2KOH(aq) + H_2(g)$
2 atoms K + 2 molecules H_2O → 2 formula units KOH + 1 molecule H_2
2 mol K + 2 mol H_2O → 2 mol KOH + 1 mol H_2
$(2 \times 39.1\ g) + (2 \times 18.0\ g) = (2 \times 56.1\ g) + 2.0\ g$
114.2 g = 114.2 g (law of conservation of mass)

6. Answers will vary but should include the idea of writing a ratio using the coefficients of two substances from a balanced equation as the number of moles of each substance reacting or being formed.

7. a. $\frac{4\ mol\ Al}{3\ mol\ O_2}\ \frac{3\ mol\ O_2}{4\ mol\ Al}\ \frac{4\ mol\ Al}{2\ mol\ Al_2O_3}$

$\frac{2\ mol\ Al_2O_3}{4\ mol\ Al}\ \frac{3\ mol\ O_2}{2\ mol\ Al_2O_3}\ \frac{2\ mol\ Al_2O_3}{3\ mol\ O_2}$

b. $3.7\ \cancel{mol\ Al_2O_3} \times \frac{4\ mol\ Al}{2\ \cancel{mol\ Al_2O_3}} = 7.4\ mol\ Al$

c. $14.8\ \cancel{mol\ Al} \times \frac{3\ mol\ O_2}{4\ \cancel{mol\ Al}}\ 11.1\ mol\ O_2$

d. $0.78\ \cancel{mol\ O_2} \times \frac{2\ mol\ Al_2O_3}{3\ \cancel{mol\ O_2}} = 0.52\ mol\ Al_2O_3$

8. Answers will vary but include a number of chemistry, physics, biology, and math courses. Skills include lab techniques, analytical thinking, oral and written communication.
9. A quantitative analysis describes the exact amount of a substance, such as a drug. A qualitative analysis compares materials, such as matching paint samples.
10. The coefficients only indicate the relative number of moles (or particles) or reactants and products.

11. a. $49.0\ \cancel{g\ H_2O} \times \frac{1\ \cancel{mol\ H_2O}}{18.0\ \cancel{g\ H_2O}} \times \frac{1\ mol\ CaC_2}{2\ \cancel{mol\ H_2O}}$
$= 1.36\ mol\ CaC_2$

b. $5.00\ \cancel{g\ CaC_2} \times \frac{1\ \cancel{mol\ CaC_2}}{64.1\ \cancel{g\ CaC_2}} \times \frac{1\ \cancel{mol\ C_2H_2}}{1\ \cancel{mol\ CaC_2}}$
$\times \frac{26.0\ g\ C_2H_2}{1\ \cancel{mol\ C_2H_2}} = 2.03\ g\ C_2H_2$

c. $0.89\ \cancel{mol\ C_2H_2} \times \frac{1\ \cancel{mol\ Ca(OH)_2}}{1\ \cancel{mol\ C_2H_2}}$
$\times \frac{74.1\ g\ Ca(OH)_2}{1\ \cancel{mol\ Ca(OH)_2}} = 66\ g\ Ca(OH)_2$

d. Use the mole interpretation of the balanced equation and show that the mass of the reactants equals the mass of the products.
$64.1\ g + (2 \times 18.0\ g) = 26.0\ g + 74.1\ g$
100.1 g = 100.1 g

12. a. $52.0\ \cancel{g\ C_2H_2} \times \frac{1\ \cancel{mol\ C_2H_2}}{26.0\ \cancel{g\ C_2H_2}} \times \frac{4\ \cancel{mol\ CO_2}}{2\ \cancel{mol\ C_2H_2}}$
$\times \frac{44.0\ g\ CO_2}{1\ \cancel{mol\ CO_2}} = 176\ g\ CO_2$

$52.0\ \cancel{g\ C_2H_2} \times \frac{1\ \cancel{mol\ C_2H_2}}{26.0\ \cancel{g\ C_2H_2}} \times \frac{2\ \cancel{mol\ H_2O}}{2\ \cancel{mol\ C_2H_2}}$
$\times \frac{18.0\ g\ H_2O}{1\ \cancel{mol\ H_2O}} = 36.0\ g\ H_2O$

b. $52.0\ \cancel{g\ C_2H_2} \times \frac{1\ \cancel{mol\ C_2H_2}}{26.0\ \cancel{g\ C_2H_2}} \times \frac{5\ \cancel{mol\ O_2}}{2\ \cancel{mol\ C_2H_2}} \times \frac{32.0\ g\ O_2}{1\ \cancel{mol\ O_2}}$
$= 160\ g\ O_2 = 1.60 \times 10^2\ g\ O_2$

c. mass reactants = mass products
$52.0\ g\ C_2H_2 + 160\ g\ O_2 = 176\ g\ O_2 + 36.0\ g\ H_2O$
212 g = 212 g

13. Answers will vary but may include issues of health, safety, environmental, economic, and political.

14. a. $\frac{16.0\ g\ CH_4}{1\ mol\ CH_4}$

b. $\frac{1\ mol\ CH_4}{22.4\ L\ CH_4}$

c. $\frac{1\ mol\ CH_4}{6.02 \times 10^{23}\ molecules\ CH_4}$

15. a. $9.40\ \cancel{L\ H_2} \times \frac{2\ L\ HF}{1\ \cancel{L\ H_2}} = 18.8\ L\ HF$

b. $20.0\ \cancel{L\ HF} \times \frac{1\ \cancel{mol\ HF}}{22.4\ \cancel{L\ HF}} \times \frac{1\ \cancel{mol\ H_2}}{2\ \cancel{mol\ HF}}$
$\times \frac{6.02 \times 10^{23}\ molecules\ H_2}{1\ \cancel{mol\ H_2}}$
$= 2.69 \times 10^{23}\ molecules\ H_2$

c. $7.42 \times 10^{24}\ \cancel{molecules\ HF} \times \frac{1\ \cancel{mol\ HF}}{6.02 \times 10^{23}\ \cancel{molecules\ HF}}$
$\times \frac{1\ \cancel{mol\ SnF_2}}{2\ \cancel{mol\ HF}} \times \frac{156.7\ g\ SnF_2}{1\ \cancel{mol\ SnF_2}} = 9.66 \times 10^2\ g\ SnF_2$

16. The amount of the limiting reagent determines the maximum amount of product that can be formed. The excess reagent is only partially consumed in the reaction.
17. Answers will vary but may include various mass and volume units as well as the number of representative particles.

18. 1. Complete combustion:

a. $2.70 \text{ mol } C_2H_4 \times \frac{3 \text{ mol } O_2}{1 \text{ mol } C_2H_4} = 8.10 \text{ mol } O_2$ required:

O_2 is limiting

b. $6.30 \text{ mol } O_2 \times \frac{2 \text{ mol } H_2O}{3 \text{ mol } O_2} = 4.20 \text{ mol } H_2O$

c. Calculate the moles of C_2H_4 that react with 6.30 mol O_2.

$6.30 \text{ mol } O_2 \times \frac{1 \text{ mol } C_2H_4}{3 \text{ mol } O_2} = 2.10 \text{ mol } C_2H_4$ used;

excess $C_2H_4 = 2.70 - 2.10 = 0.60 \text{ mol } C_2H_4$

2. Incomplete combustion:

a. $2.70 \text{ mol } C_2H_4 \times \frac{2 \text{ mol } O_2}{1 \text{ mol } C_2H_4} = 5.40 \text{ mol } O_2$ required;

O_2 is excess, C_2H_2 is limiting

b. $2.70 \text{ mol } C_2H_4 \times \frac{2 \text{ mol } H_2O}{1 \text{ mol } C_2H_4} = 5.40 \text{ mol } H_2O$

c. excess $O_2 = 6.30 - 5.40 = 0.90 \text{ mol } O_2$

19. a. Find the moles of each reactant.

$6.00 \text{ g HCl} \times \frac{1 \text{ mol HCl}}{36.5 \text{ g HCl}} = 0.164 \text{ mol HCl}$

$5.00 \text{ g Mg} \times \frac{1 \text{ mol Mg}}{24.3 \text{ g Mg}} = 0.206 \text{ mol Mg}$

Since there are not twice as many moles of HCl compared to moles of Mg, HCl is limiting

$0.164 \text{ mol HCl} \times \frac{1 \text{ mol } H_2}{2 \text{ mol HCl}} \times \frac{2.00 \text{ g } H_2}{1 \text{ mol } H_2} = 0.164 \text{ g } H_2$

b. $0.164 \text{ g } H_2 \times \frac{1 \text{ mol } H_2}{2.0 \text{ g } H_2} \times \frac{22.4 \text{ L } H_2}{1 \text{ mol } H_2} = 1.84 \text{ L } H_2$

20. a. $2H_2(g) + O_2(g) \rightarrow 2H_2O(g)$

Hydrogen and oxygen react in a 2:1 volume ratio, therefore hydrogen is the limiting reagent.

$200 \text{ cm}^3 H_2 \times \frac{2 \text{ cm}^3 H_2O}{2 \text{ cm}^3 H_2} = 200 \text{ cm}^3 H_2O$

(assuming 3 significant figures)

b. There is an excess of 50 cm^3 of oxygen.

21. The actual yield is an experimentally determined value; a theoretical yield in a value calculated using the balanced chemical equation. The percent yield is a ratio of the actual yield over the theoretical yield expressed as a percent.

22. $1.87 \text{ g Al} \times \frac{1 \text{ mol Al}}{27.0 \text{ g Al}} \times \frac{3 \text{ mol Cu}}{2 \text{ mol Al}} \times \frac{63.5 \text{ g Cu}}{1 \text{ mol Cu}}$

$= 6.60 \text{ g Cu (theoretical yield)}$

$\% \text{ yield} = \frac{\text{actual yield}}{\text{theoretical yield}} \times 100\%$

$\% \text{ yield} = \frac{4.65 \text{ g Cu}}{6.60 \text{ g Cu}} \times 100\% = 70.5\%$

23. $15.0 \text{ g } Sb_2S_3 \times \frac{1 \text{ mol } Sb_2S_3}{339.9 \text{ g } Sb_2S_3} \times \frac{2 \text{ mol Sb}}{1 \text{ mol } Sb_2S_3}$

$\times \frac{121.8 \text{ g Sb}}{1 \text{ mol Sb}} = 10.8 \text{ g Sb}$

$\% \text{ yield} = \frac{9.84 \text{ g Sb}}{10.8 \text{ g Sb}} \times 100\% = 91.1\%$

Chapter 9

1. Answers will vary but should include the ideas of particles moving in rapid, random motion and undergoing elastic collisions.

2. A hunter stalks prey downwind so that the motion of the molecules of the air carries the hunter's scent molecules away from the prey.

3. The collision of gas particles with an object causes pressure.

4. pascal (Pa), millimeter of mercury (mm Hg), and atmosphere (atm) The pascal is the SI unit.

5. a. $190 \text{ mm Hg} \times \frac{1 \text{ atm}}{760 \text{ mm Hg}} \times \frac{101.3 \text{ kPa}}{1 \text{ atm}} = 25 \text{ kPa}$

b. $190 \text{ mm Hg} \times \frac{1 \text{ atm}}{760 \text{ mm Hg}} = 0.25 \text{ atm}$

6. $33.7 \text{ kPa} \times \frac{1 \text{ atm}}{101.3 \text{ kPa}} = 0.333 \text{ atm}$

The pressure on top of Mt. Everest is greater than 0.25 atm.

7. Burning sulfur produces sulfur dioxide and sulfur trioxide gases which contribute to environmental problems, such as acid rain.

8. Answers will vary but may include: asphalting roads, constructing barrier reefs to prevent erosion, and paving playgrounds.

9. The Kelvin temperature of a substance is directly proportional to the average kinetic energy of the particles of the substance.

10. There is no change in the average kinetic energy.

11. The average kinetic energy increases by a factor of three.

$\frac{900 \text{ K}}{300 \text{ K}} = 3$

12. The particles of gases and liquids are in constant motion. Unlike those of gases, the particles of liquids are attracted to one another. As a result, particles in a liquid are closer together than particles in a gas.

13. A liquid is *condensed* in the sense its volume is minimally affected by an increase in pressure.

14. In both situations, particles with sufficient kinetic energy move from the liquid to the vapor phase. A dynamic equilibrium is set up between a contained liquid and its vapor. This doesn't happen with an uncontained liquid because the vapor diffuses into the air.

15. Vapor pressure is the result of collisions of vaporized particles of a liquid with the walls of a sealed container. A dynamic equilibrium exists between the liquid and vapor in a closed container when the rate of evaporation of the liquid equals the rate of condensation of the vapor.

16. The bubbles of vapor formed within the liquid are of the same pressure as the atmospheric pressure. Thus, they can escape the liquid surface. The liquid boils.

17. Particles in solids are packed tightly together and vibrate about fixed points. In liquids, particles are packed relatively tightly together but can move relative to one another.

18. Ionic compounds have crystalline structures with relatively high melting points.

19. Liquid crystals maintain molecular order in the liquid state. In a smectic or cholesteric liquid crystal, the distance between the layer of crystals is temperature dependent and determines the color of reflected light. Light transmission is controlled in a nematic liquid crystal by varying the electrical charge.

20. The moisture in the food has sublimed and then condensed on the container's lid.

21. The vapor pressure of the substance in the solid state is so great that the vapor is formed directly from the solid.

22. A phase diagram shows you the state of a substance at a given temperature and pressure. It also shows you the conditions at which phase changes occur.

23. The triple point is the temperature and pressure at which an equilibrium exists between all three phases of a substance.

24. A plasma is composed of electrons and atomic nuclei and most can only exist at very high temperatures.

25. Buckminsterfullerene and its chemical modified forms have many potential uses ranging from semiconductors and superconductors to medicines and lubricants.

Chapter 10

1. Answers will vary, but should include the idea that energy is conserved in every physical and chemical process.

2. Heat flows from the object with the higher temperature to the object with the lower temperature.

3. The chemical composition of the substance and its mass.

4. 1 Cal = 1000 cal = 1 kcal

5. With complete combustion the bar will produce 175 000 cal of heat.

6. $175 \text{ cal} \times \frac{4186 \text{ J}}{1 \text{ cal}} = 7.33 \times 10^5 \text{ J}$

7. It takes 32.0 cal to raise 32.0 g H_2O 1°C. To increase the temperature 55.0°C (80.0°C − 25.0°C) would take:

$$\frac{32.0 \text{ cal}}{1°\text{C}} \times 55.0°\text{C} = 1.76 \times 10^3 \text{ cal}$$

$$1.76 \times 10^3 \text{ cal} \times \frac{4.186 \text{ J}}{1 \text{ cal}} = 7.37 \times 10^3 \text{ J}$$

8. Specific heat is measured in J/(g × °C) because specific heat is defined as the amount of heat it takes to raise the temperature of one gram of a substance 1°C.

9. The specific heat of both will be the same because specific heat is measured per gram.

10. $C_{Ag} = \frac{42.8 \text{ J/°C}}{181 \text{ g}} = 0.236 \frac{\text{J}}{\text{g} \times °\text{C}}$

11. $C_{\text{olive oil}} = \frac{435 \text{ J}}{3.4 \text{ g} \times (85°\text{C} - 21°\text{C})} = 2.0 \frac{\text{J}}{\text{g} \times °\text{C}}$

12. It is important to define both the system and its surroundings because you are interested in heat flow across the boundary between the two.

13. The reacting chemicals are the system; the water is the surroundings.

14. enthalpy

15.
$$\begin{aligned}\Delta H &= (100.0 \text{ mL} \times 1.00 \text{ g/mL}) \times [4.18 \text{ J/g} \times °\text{C}] \times (26.0°\text{C} - 22.5°\text{C})\\ &= 100.0 \text{ g} \times 4.18 \text{ J/(g} \times °\text{C}) \times 3.5°\text{C}\\ &= 1.5 \times 10^3 \text{ J} = 1.5 \text{ kJ}\end{aligned}$$

16. The process is carried out at a pressure of one atmosphere and all reactants and products are in their usual physical state at 25°C.

17. Heat of reaction is the heat released or absorbed in a chemical change.

18. $12.5 \text{ g } C_2H_5OH \times \frac{1 \text{ mol } C_2H_5OH}{46.0 \text{ g } C_2H_5OH} \times \frac{1235 \text{ kJ}}{1 \text{ mol } C_2H_5OH} = 336 \text{ kJ}$

19. $5.66 \text{ g } CS_2 \times \frac{1 \text{ mol } CS_2}{76.2 \text{ g } CS_2} \times \frac{89.3 \text{ kJ}}{1 \text{ mol } CS_2} = 6.63 \text{ kJ}$

20. $0.58 \text{ mol } CH_4 \times \frac{890.4 \text{ kJ}}{1 \text{ mol } CH_4} = 5.2 \times 10^2 \text{ kJ}$

21. Burning plant material generates carbon dioxide. Clearing vast expanses of vegetation decreases the amount of carbon dioxide consumed in photosynthesis.

22. $8.46 \text{ g } D_2O \times \frac{1 \text{ mol } D_2O}{20.0 \text{ g } D_2O} \times \frac{6.34 \text{ kJ}}{1 \text{ mol } D_2O} = 2.68 \text{ kJ}$

23. When steam condenses it releases a substantial amount of heat—its molar heat of fusion.

24. $0.46 \text{ g } C_2H_5Cl \times \frac{1 \text{ mol } C_2H_5Cl}{64.5 \text{ g } C_2H_5Cl} \times \frac{26.4 \text{ kJ}}{1 \text{ mol } C_2H_5Cl} = 0.19 \text{ kJ}$

25. $88.0 \text{ kJ} \times \frac{1 \text{ mol } NH_4NO_3}{25.7 \text{ kJ}} = 3.42 \text{ mol } NH_4NO_3$

26. Factors might include, among other things, illness, sports training, dieting for weight loss, dieting for weight gain.

27. Answers will vary but should include that idea that you can algebraically add together chemical equations and their enthalpies to get the enthalpy a different chemical reaction.

28. The sign of ΔH is changed. The sign is changed because exothermic reactions in reverse become endothermic and vice versa.

29.
$$\begin{array}{ll} 2Al(s) + \frac{3}{2}O_2(g) \rightarrow Al_2O_3(s) & \Delta H = -1669.8 \text{ kJ}\\ Fe_2O_3(s) \rightarrow 2Fe(s) + \frac{3}{2}O_2(g) & \Delta H = +824.2 \text{ kJ}\\ \hline 2Al(s) + Fe_2O_3(s) \rightarrow 2Fe(s) + Al_2O_3(s) & \Delta H = -845.6 \text{ kJ}\end{array}$$

30.
$$\begin{array}{ll} 2[H_2O_2(l) \rightarrow H_2(g) + O_2(g)] & \Delta H = 187.9 \text{ kJ} \times 2\\ 2H_2O_2(l) \rightarrow 2H_2(g) + 2O_2(g) & \\ 2[H_2(g) + \frac{1}{2}O_2(g) \rightarrow H_2O(l)] & \Delta H = -285.8 \text{ kJ} \times 2\\ 2H_2(g) + O_2(g) \rightarrow 2H_2O(l) & \\ \hline 2H_2O_2(l) \rightarrow 2H_2O(l) + O_2(g) & \Delta H = -195.8 \text{ kJ}\end{array}$$

31. 0 kJ

32. $\Delta H = H_f^\circ(\text{products}) = H_f^\circ(\text{reactants})$

a.
$$\begin{aligned}\Delta H &= -393.5 \text{ kJ} + (2 \text{ mol})(-285.8 \text{ kJ/mol}) - (-74.86 \text{ kJ})\\ &= -393.5 \text{ kJ} - 571.6 \text{ kJ} + 74.86 \text{ kJ}\\ &= -890.2 \text{ kJ}\end{aligned}$$

b.
$$\begin{aligned}\Delta H &= (2 \text{ mol})(-395.7 \text{ kJ/mol}) - (2 \text{ mol})(-296.8 \text{ kJ/mol})\\ &= -791.4 \text{ kJ} - (-593.6 \text{ kJ})\\ &= -197.8 \text{ kJ}\end{aligned}$$

Chapter 11

1. Add 100 times as much gas.

2. If the amount of gas is to be doubled while the volume is kept the same, the pressure in the container must be doubled.

3. Increase the volume by a factor of four.

4. $P_1 \times V_1 = P_2 \times V_2$, P = pressure; V = volume; the subscript 1 represents the starting conditions; the subscript 2, the final conditions. Temperature is not in the expression and is therefore constant.

5. $2.50 \text{ L} \times \frac{100 \text{ kPa}}{40 \text{ kPa}} = 6.3 \text{ L}$

6. The volume decreases. The molecules with less kinetic energy cause less pressure on the inside of the balloon.

7. $T_1 = 327\text{ °C} + 273 = 600 \text{ K}$
$T_2 = 275\text{ °C} + 273 = 300 \text{ K}$
The temperature decreases, therefore volume decreases.

$$V_2 = \frac{6.8 \text{ L} \times 300 \text{ K}}{600 \text{ K}} = 3.4 \text{ L}$$

8. High temperatures can increase the pressure of the gas remaining in the container sufficiently to cause it to explode.

9. The temperature decreases, therefore pressure decreases.

$$P_2 = \frac{6.58 \text{ kPa} \times 210 \text{ K}}{540 \text{ K}} = 2.56 \text{ kPa}$$

10. $\frac{P_1 \times V_1}{T_1} = \frac{P_2 \times V_2}{T_2}$

When the pressure is constant, $P_1 = P_2$, so the pressure terms cancel, leaving an equation for Charles' law.

11. $\frac{P_1 \times V_1}{T_1} = \frac{P_2 \times V_2}{T_2}$

When the volume is constant, $V_1 = V_2$, so the volume terms cancel, leaving the equation for the temperature–pressure relationship.

12. $V_2 = \frac{1.0 \text{ L} \times 150 \text{ kPa} \times 373 \text{ K}}{600 \text{ kPa} \times 298 \text{ K}} = 0.31 \text{ L}$

13. $n = \frac{(1800 \text{ kPa}) \times (680 \text{ L})}{8.31 \times \frac{\text{L} \times \text{kPa}}{\text{K} \times \text{mol}} \times 600 \text{ K}} = 2.5 \times 10^2 \text{ mol}$

14. $n = \frac{(100 \text{ kPa}) \times (2.2 \text{ L})}{8.31 \times \frac{\text{L} \times \text{kPa}}{\text{K} \times \text{mol}} \times 310 \text{ K}} = 0.085 \text{ mol air}$

$$0.085 \text{ mol air} \times \frac{29.0 \text{ g air}}{1 \text{ mol air}} = 2.5 \text{ g air}$$

15. Rapid production of gaseous products and heat.
16. The gases would have equal numbers of particles.
17. $P_T = 20.0 \text{ kPa} + 46.7 \text{ kPa} + 26.7 \text{ kP} = 93.4 \text{ kPa}$
18. $P_{CH_4} = 101.30 \text{ kPa} - 101.2 \text{ kPa} = 0.1 \text{ kPa}$
19. Answers will vary but should include the concept that equal volumes of gases contain an equal number of particles.
20. This is the volume of 1 mol of any gas at STP.
21. One mole of any gas at STP occupies a volume of 22.4 L. One mole of any substance contains 6.02×10^{23} particles.

$$11.2 \text{ L } H_2 \times \frac{1 \text{ mol } H_2}{22.4 \text{ L } H_2} = \frac{11.2}{22.4} = 0.500 \text{ mol } H_2$$

$$0.500 \text{ mol } H_2 \times \frac{6.02 \times 10^{23} \text{ molecules } H_2}{1 \text{ mol } H_2} = 3.01 \times 10^{23} \text{ molecules } H_2$$

22. $0.25 \text{ mol} \times \frac{22.4 \text{ L}}{1 \text{ mol}} = 5.6 \text{ L}$

23. $8.8 \text{ g } CO_2 \times \frac{1 \text{ mol } CO_2}{44.0 \text{ g } CO_2} \times \frac{22.4 \text{ L } CO_2}{1 \text{ mol } CO_2} = 4.5 \text{ L } CO_2$

24. Carbon monoxide and nitrogen have identical molar masses of 28.0 g.

25. $\frac{\text{Rate } H_2}{\text{Rate } Cl_2} = \frac{\text{formula mass}_{Cl_2}}{\text{formula mass}_{H_2}} = \frac{71}{2} = \frac{8.4}{1.4} = 6.0$

Hydrogen diffuses six times faster than chlorine.

26. Gas particles have a finite volume and are attracted to one another, especially at low temperatures.
27. Answers will vary.
28. At lower temperatures gas particles are attracted to one another; gas particles also have a finite volume.
29. The molar volume of an *ideal* gas is 22.41 L at STP. The molar volume of a *real* gas is less than 22.41 L. Intermolecular forces hold the gas particles together and reduce the volume. The decrease in volume depends upon the strength of the intermolecular attractive forces. Nonpolar O_2 and N_2 molecules behave like ideal gases. Their attractive forces are insignificant and their molar volumes are 22.41 L. The bonds in CH_4 are weakly polar but the molecule is nonpolar. Very weak intermolecular attractive forces reduce the molar volume to 22.38 L. The bonds in CO_2 are moderately polar. The attractive forces between CO_2 molecules decrease the molar volume to 22.26 L. Ammonia molecules are polar and also form intermolecular hydrogen bonds. The strong attractive forces between the molecules reduce the molar volume to 22.06 L.
30. The gear supplies air at a pressure equal to the external pressure at that depth.
31. The bends, ruptured lungs.
32. The most striking property of an aerogel is its very low density.
33. Answers will vary but may include use as an insulator or lightweight structural material.

Chapter 12

1. Protons and electrons.
2. The electrons have a fixed energy. They jump to other energy levels only by emitting or absorbing a quantum of energy.
3. The mathematical solution to the Schrödinger equation.
4. A region in space around the nucleus in which there is a high probability of finding an electron.
5. **a.** 3 **b.** 1 **c.** 7 **d.** 3 **e.** 5 **f.** 9
6. Tungsten-filament bulb because the heated filament gives off white light.
7. Fluorescent lights are much more energy efficient.
8. $3d$, $4s$, $3p$, $3s$, $2p$
9. **a.** Boron has an atomic number of 5, an electron configuration of $1s^22s^22p^1$, and one unpaired electron.
b. Fluorine has an atomic number of 9, an electron configuration of $1s^22s^22p^5$, and one unpaired electron.
10. Using the Aufbau diagram molybdenum and silver would each have 2 electrons in the $5s$ orbital rather than the 1 electron as shown on the periodic table. The difference is due to the stability of the half filled and filled d sublevel.
11. Violet, indigo, blue, green, yellow, orange, red. VIBGYOR.
12. Frequency is the number of wave cycles that pass a given point per unit time. Frequency units are cycles/sec or reciprocal seconds or hertz. Frequency and wavelength are inversely related.

13. $\nu = \frac{c}{\lambda} = \frac{3.00 \times 10^{10} \text{ cm s}^{-1}}{5.00 \times 10^{-6} \text{ cm}}$

$= 6.00 \times 10^{15} \text{ s}^{-1}$ (ultraviolet)

14. $\nu = \frac{c}{\lambda} = \frac{3.00 \times 10^{10} \text{ cm s}^{-1}}{6.56 \times 10^{-5} \text{ cm}}$

$= 4.57 \times 10^{14} \text{ s}^{-1}$ (visible, orange-red)

15. Various plants, animals, and minerals.
16. Classical physics views energy changes as continuous. In the quantum concept, energy changes occur in tiny discrete units called quanta.

17. $E = h \times \nu$

$= 6.62 \times 10^{-34} \text{ J s} \times 5.80 \times 10^{14} \text{ s}^{-1}$

$= 3.84 \times 10^{-19} \text{ J}$

18. Light shining on a metal surface causes electrons to leave the surface. Classical physics assumed any wavelength of light could cause the photoelectric effect. Actually, however, only light with some minimum frequency and threshold energy can cause an electron to be ejected.

19. $E = h \times \nu$

$= 6.62 \times 10^{-34} \text{ J s} \times 3.20 \times 10^{11} \text{ s}^{-1}$

$= 2.12 \times 10^{-22} \text{ J}$

20. The electron of the hydrogen atom is raised (excited) to the next highest energy level.
21. The ground state is the lowest energy level of an electron.

The excited state is an energy state higher than the ground state.

22. Since mass is in the denominator, an increase in mass will always give a shorter wavelength.

Chapter 13

1. Increasing atomic mass and similarities of properties.
2. 68 = gallium and 70 = germanium
3. Answers include beryllium, magnesium, strontium, and barium.
4. A period is a horizontal row. A group is a vertical column.
5. Answers will vary.
6. Answers will vary.
7. Phosphates tie up calcium and magnesium ions. Phosphates promote excessive algae growth in rivers and lakes.
8. Representative elements: Groups 1A-7A, Group 0. Transition elements: Groups 1B-8B. Inner transition elements: a separate section between Groups 3B and 4B
9. Na, Mg, Cl
10. a. Boron has 5 electrons. Reading the periodic table from left to right we have the first period, $1s^2$, and the second period, $2s^22p^1$. There is one electron in the $2p$ sublevel because boron is the third element in the p block.
b. Magnesium has 12 electrons. The first two periods are $1s^22s^22p^6$. Next we have $3s^2$, which completes the electron configuration.
c. Vanadium has 26 electrons. We go through the first three periods, $1s^22s^22p^63s^23p^6$, then $4s^2$ and finally $3d^3$. Vanadium is the third element in the d block, and the complete electron configuration is $1s^22s^22p^63s^23p^63d^34s^2$.
d. Strontium, with 38 electrons, is in the fifth period. To get to strontium we pass through $1s^22s^22p^63s^23p^64s^23d^{10}4p^6$, and finally $5s^2$. The electron configuration for strontium is $1s^22s^22p^63s^23p^63d^{10}4s^24p^65s^2$.
11. a. The inert gas in period three is argon: $1s^22s^22p^63s^23p^6$.
b. The element in group 4A, period 4 is germanium with 32 electrons, $1s^22s^22p^63s^23p^63d^{10}4s^24p^2$.
c. Group 2A, period 6 is barium with 56 electrons, $1s^22s^22p^63s^23p^63d^{10}4s^24p^64d^{10}5s^25p^66s^2$.
12. F has a smaller atomic radius than O because F has one more nuclear charge. F has a smaller radius than Cl because F has eight fewer electrons and one less occupied energy level.
13. Sodium, aluminum, sulfur, chlorine; periodic trend.
14. The first ionization energy is the energy needed to remove the outermost electron. The second ionization energy is the energy needed to remove the second-outermost electron.
15. a. boron
b. magnesium
c. aluminum
16. CFCs are currently used in some refrigeration units and air conditioners. The chlorine atoms from CFCs destroy ozone molecules.
17. Increased UV light at the earth's surface can cause mutations, blindness, cancer, and crop damage.
18. a. Na **b.** S^{2-} **c.** I^- **d.** Al
19. Noble gases, with rare exception, do not form compounds.
20. a. sodium
b. phosphorus
21. Silicon, germanium, gallium, arsenic, and boron
22. Answers will vary but could include automobile, boom box, microwave, wrist watch, alarm clock, portable CD player, computer, television, and calculator.

Chapter 14

1. a. 1 **b.** 4 **c.** 2 **d.** 6
2. a. $K\cdot$ **b.** $\cdot\dot{\underset{\cdot}{C}}\cdot$ **c.** $\cdot Mg\cdot$ **d.** $:\dot{\underset{\cdot}{O}}:$
3. Most metal atoms lose 1, 2, or 3 electrons to achieve a noble-gas electron configuration.
4. $Cu^+: 1s^22s^22p^63s^23p^63d^{10}$
$Au^+: 1s^22s^22p^63s^23p^63d^{10}4s^24p^64d^{10}5s^25p^65d^{10}$
$Cd^{2+}: 1s^22s^22p^63s^23p^63d^{10}4s^24p^64d^{10}$
$Hg^{2+}: 1s^22s^22p^63s^23p^63d^{10}4s^24p^64d^{10}5s^25p^65d^{10}$
5. Most nonmetals gain 1, 2, or 3 electrons to achieve a noble-gas electron configuration.
6. a. lose 2
b. gain 1
c. lose 3
d. gain 2
7. a. S^{2-} **b.** Na^+ **c.** F^- **d.** Ba^{2+}
8. Superplastic steel is much more malleable and can be directly formed into various shapes.
9. a. $K^+:\ddot{\underset{\cdot\cdot}{I}}:^-$, KI
b. $Ca^{2+}:\ddot{\underset{\cdot\cdot}{S}}:^{2-}$, CaS
c. $\begin{matrix} \dot{Al}\cdot \\ \vdots \\ Al\cdot \end{matrix} + \begin{matrix} \cdot\ddot{O}: \\ \cdot\ddot{O}: \\ \cdot\ddot{O}: \end{matrix} \rightarrow \begin{matrix} Al^{3+} \\ Al^{3+} \end{matrix} \begin{matrix} :\ddot{O}:^{2-} \\ :\ddot{O}:^{2-} \\ :\ddot{O}:^{2-} \end{matrix}$ or Al_2O_3
d. $\begin{matrix} Na^+ \\ Na^+ \\ Na^+ \end{matrix} :\ddot{\underset{\cdot\cdot}{P}}:^{3-}$, Na_3P
10. a. potassium iodide
b. calcium sulfide
c. aluminum oxide
d. sodium phosphide
11. a. K^+I^-
KI
b. $Ca^{2+}S^{2-}$
CaS
c. $Al^{3+}O^{2-}$
Al_2O_3
d. Na^+P^{3-}
Na_3P
12. Answers will vary but should include the idea of a solid containing atoms, ions, or molecules in a regular, repeating three dimensional pattern.
13. No. The packing of ions in a crystalline structure depends on a number of factors including the relative sizes of the ions. The coordination number of an element can vary from compound to compound.
14. ductile: can be drawn into wires; malleable: can be hammered into different shapes
15. a. Cr^{3+} $1s^2\,2s^2\,2p^6\,3s^2\,3p^6\,3d^3$ or [Ar] $3d^3$
b. Mn^{3+} $1s^2\,2s^2\,2p^6\,3s^2\,3p^6\,3d^4$ or [Ar] $3d^4$
c. Fe^{3+} $1s^2\,2s^2\,2p^6\,3s^2\,3p^6\,3d^5$ or [Ar] $3d^5$
16. Answers will vary.
17. Steel is an alloy. Various steels will contain different proportions of Fe, C, B, Cr, Mn, Mo, Ni, W and V.

Chapter 15

1. The structural formula identifies the elements in the compound and their respective number and arrangement of atoms in the molecule.
2. Because ionic compounds do not exist as individual molecules, a formula unit indicates the lowest whole-number

ratio of ions in the compound. The molecular formula indicates the atoms in a molecule of the compound.

3. a. :C̈l:C̈l:

b. :B̈r:B̈r:

c. :Ï:Ï:

4. 6; 6

5. Atoms form double or triple bonds in order to achieve an octet of electrons.

6. 2, 3

7. The element for which there is one atom is the central atom of the molecule.

8. a. H:S̈:H

b. H:P̈:H
  H

c. :C̈l:F̈:

9. One atom contributes both electrons to a coordinate covalent bond.

10. $[:\ddot{O}:\ddot{S}:\ddot{O}: \text{ with } :\ddot{O}: \text{ above and below}]^{2-}$ $[:\ddot{O}:C \text{ with } :\ddot{O}: \text{ above and } \ddot{O} \text{ below right}]^{2-}$

11. Each has more than one electron dot structure.

12. $[\ddot{O}::C:\ddot{O}:, :\ddot{O}: \text{ below}]^{2-} \longleftrightarrow [:\ddot{O}:C::\ddot{O}:, :\ddot{O}: \text{ below}]^{2-} \longleftrightarrow [:\ddot{O}:C:\ddot{O}:, :O: \text{ double-bonded below}]^{2-}$

13. The skin is producing more of the pigment melanin, which helps to screen out some of the damaging radiation.

14. A sunscreen absorbs specific wavelengths of UV light. Sunscreens that contain zinc oxide and titanium dioxide block out all of the sun's harmful radiation.

15. The measured mass of a paramagnetic substance will appear to be more when measured in the presence of a magnetic field than when measured in the absence of a magnetic field.

16. a. diamagnetic

b. paramagnetic

c. paramagnetic

d. diamagnetic

17. A sigma bond is formed by the overlap of two *s* orbitals, the overlap of an *s* and a *p* orbital, or the end-to-end overlap of two *p* orbitals. In the hydrogen molecule, for example, the two *s* orbitals overlap to create a sigma bond.

18. There are three sigma bonds and two pi bonds.

19. tetrahedral

20. a. In a methane molecule, the four valence electron pairs repel each other forming the corners of a tetrahedron in which the pairs are equidistant from each other. The bond angle is 109.5°.

b. In an ammonia molecule, the four valence-electron pairs repel each other, but the unshared pair repels the bonded pairs more strongly. The bond angle is 107°.

c. In a water molecule, the four valence electron pairs repel each other but the unshared pairs repel the bonded pairs more strongly. The bond angle is 105°.

21. a. trigonal planar

b. tetrahedral

c. linear

22. The 2*s* and the 2*p* orbitals form three sp^2 hybrid orbitals in the carbon atom and each oxygen atom. One sp^2 hybrid orbital from each atom forms a sigma bond between each oxygen atom and the carbon atom. Then pi bonds between each oxygen atom and the carbon atom are formed by the unhybridized 2*p* orbitals.

23. The two atoms must have different electronegativities.

24. a. covalent (moderately polar)

b. ionic

c. covalent (very polar)

d. covalent (very polar)

e. ionic

f. nonpolar covalent

25. In order of increasing polarity: e, c, d, b, a.

26. There are polar bonds in each molecule. HF is a polar molecule because the bonding electrons are "pulled" toward the fluorine end of the molecule. CCl_4 is a nonpolar molecule because the atoms are oriented symmetrically such that the bond polarities cancel.

27. a. $\overset{\delta+}{H}:\overset{\delta-}{\ddot{O}}:\overset{\delta-}{\ddot{O}}:\overset{\delta+}{H}$ **b.** $:\overset{\delta+}{\ddot{Br}}:\overset{\delta-}{\ddot{Cl}}:$ **c.** $\overset{\delta+}{H}:\overset{\delta-}{\ddot{Br}}:$ **d.** $\overset{\delta+}{H}:\overset{\delta-}{\ddot{O}}:\overset{\delta+}{H}$

28. Increasing bond dissociation energy is linked to lower chemical reactivity.

29. Bond dissociation energy for 1 mol of C-H single bonds in 393 kJ. 0.1 mol methane (CH_4) has 0.4 mol C-H single bonds. To dissociate all the C-H bonds in 0.1 mol methane requires

$$393\ \frac{\text{kJ}}{\cancel{\text{mol}}} \times 0.4\ \cancel{\text{mol}} = 157\ \text{kJ}$$

30. H₃N:····H—N̈H₂ (H—N(H)(H): ···· H—N:(H)(H))

H₂Ö:····H—N̈H₂ (H—O:(H) ···· H—N:(H)(H))

31. c, a, b

32. There are no molecules in a network solid; the atoms in a network solid are covalently bonded in a large array.

33. b, c, d

34. The curing agent reacts with the epoxy prepolymer to form the interlocking polymer.

35. The bonding in the epoxy is stronger than the bonding in wood.

36. Nanostructured materials are composed of very thin layers of metals or metal alloys. They are very strong and resistant.

37. Answers will vary but will include applications in which strength and durability of the materials are important.

Chapter 16

1. A hydrogen atom covalently bonded to oxygen, a highly electronegative atom, is electrostatically attracted to an unshared electron pair of an oxygen atom of another water molecule.

2. Surface tension is the inward pulling force which minimizes the surface area of a liquid. Surface molecules are attracted to the liquid molecules below but not to the air. Interior molecules are attracted in all directions.

3. Some water molecules have sufficient energy to leave the surface of the liquid. Vapor pressure is the pressure of the water vapor above the liquid.

4. The soap acts as a wetting agent or surfactant, allowing you to wet the car down more effectively.

5. Answers will vary. An argument for tertiary treatment is to minimize pollution of streams, lakes, and the ground water. An argument against tertiary treatment is the cost and whether the benefit justifies the cost.

6. The three quantities are mass, change in temperature, and change in heat.

7. No. Specific heat is expressed as a quantity per gram.
8. Hydrogen bonds hold water molecules together, making it harder for them to escape.
9. To vaporize 1 g water at its boiling point requires 2260 J. To vaporize 5.0 mg water requires

$$5.0 \text{ mg} \times \frac{10^{-3} \text{ g}}{1 \text{ mg}} \times 2260 \frac{\text{J}}{\text{g}} = 11.3 \text{ J} = 11 \text{ J (2 sig. fig.)}$$

10. Ice floats in liquid water. Solids generally sink in their liquids because a substance is generally more dense in the solid state.
11. To melt 1 g of ice at 0°C requires 334 J or 0.334 kJ. To melt 24 g of ice requires

$$24 \text{ g} \times 0.334 \frac{\text{kJ}}{\text{g}} = 8.016 \text{ kJ} = 8.0 \text{ kJ (2 sig. fig.)}$$

12. Solutions are homogeneous mixtures in which a solute is dissolved in a solvent. Aqueous solutions have water as the solvent.
13. $HC_2H_3O_2$ is the solute; water is the solvent.
14. The positive ions are attracted by the negatively charged end of the polar water molecule; the negative ions are attracted by the positively charged end. As the ions are pulled away from the crystal, they are surrounded by the water molecules.
15. a. HCl and c. NH_3 will dissolve because they are polar; b. NaI and d. $MgSO_4$ will dissolve because they are ionic; e. CH_4 and g. gasoline will not dissolve because they are nonpolar; and f. $CaCO_3$ will not dissolve because of strong ionic forces.
16. Electrolytes can conduct an electrical current in aqueous solution or in the molten state; nonelectrolytes cannot.
17. $CaCl_2(s) \rightarrow Ca^{2+}(aq) + 2Cl^-(aq)$
18. Answers will vary.
19. A suspension is a mixture with large particles which slowly settle on standing. A colloid is a mixture with particles of intermediate size which do not settle.
20. Emulsions are colloidal dispersions of liquids in liquids. An emulsifying agent attracts both of the liquids and holds them in suspension.
21. The particles in a solution are too small to scatter light.
22. Water in the crystal structure of a substance.
23. **a.** $Na_2SO_4 \cdot 10H_2O$
    b. $MgSO_4 \cdot 7H_2O$
    c. $Ba(OH)_2 \cdot 8H_2O$
24. **a.** sodium carbonate decahydrate
    b. $MgCO_3 \cdot 3H_2O$
    c. magnesium phosphate tetrahydrate
    d. $Ca(NO_3)_2 \cdot 3H_2O$
    e. cobalt(II) chloride dihydrate
25. First calculate the gram formula mass of the hydrate and of the attached water. Then calculate the percent of water.

$$\begin{array}{lrl} \text{Cu:} & 1 \times 63.5 = & 63.5 \\ \text{S:} & 1 \times 32.1 = & 32.1 \\ \text{O:} & 4 \times 16.0 = & 64.0 \\ H_2O\text{:} & 5 \times 18.0 = & 90.0 \\ \hline & & 249.6 \text{ g/mol} \end{array}$$

$$\text{Percent } H_2O = \frac{\text{mass of } H_2O}{\text{mass of hydrate}} = \frac{90.0 \text{ g}}{249.6 \text{ g}} = 36.1\%$$

Chapter 17

1. The *solvent* is the substance in which the *solute* is dissolved.
2. Agitation, temperature, solute particle size.
3. **a.** Add more solvent.
   b. Add solute until no more will dissolve.
4. *Miscible* liquids dissolve in each other, but *immiscible* liquids do not.
5. The solubility of NaCl is 36.2 g NaCl per 100 mL of solution at 25°C.

$$750 \text{ mL} \times \frac{36.2 \text{ g NaCl}}{100 \text{ mL solution}} = 271.5 = 272 \text{ g NaCl}$$

6. Solubility usually increases with an increase in temperature.
7. No. If there were undissolved solute the "excess" solute would come out of solution.
8. Henry's law relates the solubility of a gas to the pressure of the gas above the liquid. (Temperature is constant.)

$$\frac{S_1}{P_1} = \frac{S_2}{P_2}$$

$$P_2 = \frac{S_2 \times P_1}{S_1} = \frac{(9.5 \text{ g/L})(100 \text{ kPa})}{(3.6 \text{ g/L})}$$

$$= 264 \text{ kPa} = 2.6 \times 10^2 \text{ kPa}$$

(to 2 sig. fig.)

9. No. Good nutrition depends of the proper amounts of the basic food groups.
10. Answers will vary but could include information about the percent of saturated and unsaturated fat, the percent of calories that come from fat, and whether the protein is complete.
11. Molarity gives you the exact number of moles of solute per liter of solution. Dilute and concentrated are relative terms and are not quantitative.
12. Molarity $(M) = \dfrac{\text{number of moles of solute}}{\text{number of liters of solution}}$

Change the given volume to the unit liters:

$$250 \text{ mL} \times \frac{1 \text{ L}}{1000 \text{ mL}} = 0.25 \text{ L}$$

$$\text{Molarity} = \frac{0.70 \text{ mol}}{0.25 \text{ L}} = 2.8M$$

13. $\text{Moles glucose} = \dfrac{36.0 \text{ mol}}{180.0 \text{ g/mol}} = 0.20 \text{ mol}$

$$\text{Molarity} = \frac{0.20 \text{ mol}}{2.0 \text{ L}} = 0.10M$$

14. 2.0M $CaCl_2$ means 2.0 mol $CaCl_2$ per 1.0 L.

$$250 \text{ mL} \times \frac{1.0 \text{ L}}{1000 \text{ mL}} \times \frac{2.0 \text{ mol } CaCl_2}{1.0 \text{ L}} = 0.50 \text{ mol } CaCl_2$$

To find the mass of $CaCl_2$, you need its gram formula mass (gfm).

$$\begin{array}{lrl} \text{Ca:} & 1 \times 40.0 = & 40.1 \text{ g} \\ \text{Cl:} & 2 \times 35.5 = & 71.0 \text{ g} \\ \hline & & 111.1 \text{ g/mol} \end{array}$$

$$\text{Mass of } CaCl_2 = 0.50 \text{ mol } CaCl_2 \times \frac{111.1 \text{ g } CaCl_2}{1 \text{ mol } CaCl_2}$$

$= 55.5 = 56$ g $CaCl_2$

15. No. The 0.5M solution is already more dilute than the 1.0M solution needed.
16. For dilution problems: $M_1 \times V_1 = M_2 \times V_2$
The volume of stock solution needed is

$$V_1 = \frac{M_2 \times V_2}{M_1} = \frac{0.2 \text{ M} \times 250 \text{ mL}}{1.0 \text{ M}} = 50 \text{ mL}$$

Use a pipet to transfer 50 mL of the 1.0M solution to a 250-mL volumetric flask. Then add distilled water up to the mark.

17. The percent should be given as volume/volume or mass/volume.

18. Percent (m/v) $= \dfrac{\text{mass of solute (g)}}{\text{volume of solution (mL)}} \times 100\%$

$= \dfrac{2.7 \text{ g}}{75 \text{ mL}} \times 100\% = 3.6\% \; CuSO_4 \text{ (m/v)}$

19. Iron(II), calcium, and magnesium cations; sulfate and hydrogen carbonate anions.
20. Advantages: soaps and detergents are more effective, cleaning is easier. Disadvantages: cost of equipment, salt for regeneration, and extra water; potential health problems associated with increased sodium intake.
21. Concentrated. The concentrated solution would give more dissolved particles and the boiling point elevation is proportional to the number of dissolved particles.
22. **a.** $MgF_2(aq)$
    b. $KI(aq)$
    c. $KI(aq)$
23. A 1*M* solution has 1 mol solute dissolved in 1 L of solution. A 1 *m* solution has 1 mol solute dissolved in 1000 g of solvent.
24. Molality $= \dfrac{\text{moles of solute}}{\text{1000 g of solvent}}$

Use a conversion factor to convert 10.0 g NaCl in 600.0 g H_2O to grams of NaCl in 1000 g H_2O.

$1000 \text{ g } H_2O \times \dfrac{10.0 \text{ g NaCl}}{600.0 \text{ g } H_2O} = 16.7 \text{ g NaCl}$

Convert 16.7 g NaCl to moles.
gfm NaCl = 23.0 + 35.5 = 58.5 g

$16.7 \text{ g NaCl} \times \dfrac{1 \text{ mol NaCl}}{58.5 \text{ g NaCl}} = 0.285 \text{ mol NaCl}$

When 10.0 g NaCl is dissolved in 600.0 g H_2O, the resulting solution is 0.285 molal NaCl.

25. Convert 300.0 g C_2H_5OH to moles.
gfm C_2H_5OH = 24.0 + 5.0 + 16.0 + 1.0 = 46.0 g

$300.0 \text{ g } C_2H_5OH \times \dfrac{1 \text{ mol } C_2H_5OH}{46.0 \text{ g } C_2H_5OH} = 6.52 \text{ mol } C_2H_5OH$

Convert 500.0 g H_2O to moles.
gfm H_2O = 2.0 + 16.0 = 18.0 g

$500.0 \text{ g} \times \dfrac{1 \text{ mol } H_2O}{18.0 \text{ g } H_2O} = 27.8 \text{ mol } H_2O$

The mole fraction of ethanol, X_E, in the solution is the number of moles of ethanol divided by the total number of moles in solution.

$X_E = \dfrac{n_E}{n_E + n_{H_2O}} = \dfrac{6.52 \text{ mol}}{6.52 \text{ mol} + 27.8 \text{ mol}} = 0.190$

The mole fraction of water, X_{H_2O}, is the number of moles of water divided by the total number of moles in solution.

$X_{H_2O} = \dfrac{n_{H_2O}}{n_{H_2O} + n_E} = \dfrac{27.8 \text{ mol}}{27.8 \text{ mol} + 6.52 \text{ mol}} = 0.810$

Total = 1.000

26. **a.** Determine the molality of the solution.

$\dfrac{\text{mol } Na_2SO_4}{1000 \text{ g } H_2O} = \dfrac{1.40 \text{ mol } Na_2SO_4}{1750 \text{ g } H_2O} \times \dfrac{1000 \text{ g } H_2O}{1 \text{ kg } H_2O}$
$= 0.800 \; m$

One mol of Na_2SO_4 in water gives 3 mol of particles.
$Na_2SO_4(s) \rightarrow 2 \; Na^+(aq) + SO_4^{2-}(aq)$
The molality of total particles is:
$3 \times 0.800 \; m = 2.40 \; m$
The freezing point depression is:
$\Delta T_f = K_f m = 1.86°C/m \times 2.40 \; m = 4.46°C$
The freezing point of this solution is:
$0°C - 4.46°C = -4.46°C$

b. The molality of the solution is:

$\dfrac{\text{mol } MgSO_4}{1000 \text{ g } H_2O} = \dfrac{0.60 \text{ mol } MgSO_4}{100 \text{ g } H_2O} \times \dfrac{1000 \text{ g } H_2O}{1 \text{ kg } H_2O} = 6.0 \; m$

One mol of $MgSO_4$ gives 2 mol of particles.
$MgSO_4(s) \rightarrow Mg^{2+}(aq) + SO_4^{2-}(aq)$
Molality of total particles is:
$2 \times 6.0 \; m = 12.0 \; m$
The freezing point depression is:
$\Delta T_f = K_f m = 1.86°C/m \times 12.0 \; m = 22.3°C$
The freezing point of this solution is:
$0°C - 22.3°C = -22.3°C$

27. The boiling point elevation ($4 \times 0.52°C = 2.08°C$) and freezing point depression ($4 \times -1.86 = -7.44°C$) both show that the compound gave 4 mol of particles in solution. The formula must be $FeCl_3$.
28. The mass of the solute, mass of the solvent, boiling point of solvent, boiling point of solution.
29. The molal freezing point content for H_2O is:

$K_f = 1.86°C/m = 1.86 \dfrac{°C \text{ kg of } H_2O}{\text{mol of solute}}$

The observed freezing point depression is:
$\Delta T_f = 0.390°C$
First calculate the molarity of the solution.
$\Delta T_f = K_f \times m$

$m = \dfrac{\Delta T_f}{K_f} = \dfrac{0.390°C}{\dfrac{1.86°C \text{ kg of } H_2O}{\text{mol of solute}}} = 0.210 \dfrac{\text{mol of solute}}{\text{kg of } H_2O}$

Now calculate moles of solute in solution.

$0.210 \dfrac{\text{mol of solute}}{\text{kg of } H_2O} \times 475 \text{ g } H_2O \times \dfrac{1 \text{ kg of } H_2O}{1000 \text{ g } H_2O}$
$= 0.0998 \text{ mol solute}$

Finally, use number of moles of solute and its mass to determine the molecular mass of the solute.

$\text{Molecular mass of solute} = \dfrac{\text{mass of solute}}{\text{moles of solute}}$
$= \dfrac{3.90 \text{ g}}{0.0998 \text{ g}}$
$= 39.1 \text{ g/mol}$

30. Greater strength, corrosion resistance, hardness, and thickness; a greater variety of materials can be both coated and used as the coating.
31. Answers will vary but could include prohibitive cost and the scale of the project.

Chapter 18

1. No. The collision must have sufficient energy to break and form bonds.
2. The number of atoms, ions, or molecules that react in a given time to form products.
3. Rate = 1.0 mol Zn/5.3 months = 0.19 mol Zn/month
4. Reactions caused by bacteria in food lead to spoilage. These reactions are faster at room temperature than in the cold. Bacteria also multiply faster in a warm environment.
5. **a.** Increased temperature usually speeds up a reaction. Decreased temperature usually slows down a reaction.
   b. Increased concentration speeds up a reaction. Decreased concentration slows down a reaction.
   c. Smaller particle size speeds up a reaction. Larger particle size slows down a reaction.
   d. The use of a catalyst speeds up a reaction.

6. Double arrows show that the reaction is reversible.
7. At equilibrium the concentrations of reactants and products do not change.
8. Light.
9. Decrease unnecessary driving; carpool.
10. Only in reversible reactions that involve gaseous reactants and/or products.
11. **a.** reactants favored
    b. reactants favored
    c. products favored
    d. products favored
    e. no change
    f. products favored
12. As heat.
13. Waste heat from chemical reactions in the body maintain body temperature at 37°C. Similarly, waste heat from industrial processes and electrical generation can be used to heat water, buildings, and so on.
14. Spontaneous reactions yield the products under the stated conditions. The spontaneous reaction chosen might be an oxidation-reduction reaction or an acid-base reaction.
15. Depending on the reaction, a change in temperature or pressure.
16. Unfavorable.
17. **a.** playing cards in use
    b. a dissolved sugar cube
    c. 1 g of powdered salt
18. No; some spontaneous processes are endothermic because of their favorable entropy change.
19. The favorable exothermic change of this process offsets the unfavorable entropy change.
20. $K_{eq} = \dfrac{[NH_3]^2}{[H_2]^3 \times [N_2]}$
21. $K_{eq} = \dfrac{[0.10]}{[0.15]^3 \times [0.25]}$
    $= 12 \text{ (2 sig. fig.)}$
22. $K_{eq} = \dfrac{[H_2] \times [I_2]}{[HI]^2}$
23. **a.** products favored
    b. reactants favored
    c. products favored
    d. reactants favored
24. From problem 22:
    $K_{eq} = \dfrac{[H_2] \times [I_2]}{[HI]^2}$
    If $[H_2] = 0.50$ mol, $[I_2]$ must $= 0.50$ mol according to the balanced equation.
    $[HI]^2 = \dfrac{[0.50] \times [0.50]}{0.020}$
    $= 12.5$
    $[HI] = \sqrt{12.5} = 3.5$ (to two significant figures)
25. The standard entropy in the gaseous state is greater than in the liquid state.
26. $\Delta S^0 = S^0(\text{products}) - S^0(\text{reactants})$
    Values of S^0 for products and reactants are from Table 18.2. Units are J/K.
    a. $(39.75 + 213.6) - (88.7) = 165.0$
    b. $(2 \times 69.94) - ((2 \times 130.6) + 205.0) = -326.3$
    c. $(2 \times 186.7) - (130.6 + 223) = 19.8 = 20$
    d. $(216.6 + 188.7) - (186.2 + 205.0) = 11.1$
    e. $245.3 - 152.3 = 93.0$
27. Odorless, easier cleanup, less polluting.
28. Durability, ease of care, deepness of color, and hopefully, environmentally friendly.
29. Calculate ΔG^0 to determine if it is negative (spontaneous reaction) or positive (nonspontaneous reaction). Use the ΔG_f of Table 18.4. All units are kJ/mol.
    $\Delta G^0 = \Delta G_f(\text{products}) - \Delta G_f(\text{reactants})$
    a. $(2 \times -384.03) - (2 \times 0.00 + 0.00) = -768.06$
    b. $(2 \times -1576.4) - (4 \times 0.00 + 3 \times 0.00) = -3152.8$
    The reactions are spontaneous.
30. Recall that: $\Delta G^0 = \Delta H^0 - T\Delta S^0$
    $\Delta S^0 = (2 \times 192.5) - (3 \times 130.6 + 191.5)$
    $= -198.3 \text{ J/K}$
    $= -0.198 \text{ kJ/K}$
    $\Delta H^0 = \Delta G^0 + T\Delta S^0$
    At 298 K:
    $\Delta H^0 = 2(-16.64) + (298 \times -0.198)$
    $= -92.2 \text{ kJ/2 mol } NH_3 \text{ formed}$
    $\Delta H_f^0 = -92.2 \text{ kJ} \div 2$
    $= -46.1 \text{ kJ/mol } NH_3$
31. Since the rate of a first-order reaction is directly proportional to the concentration of one reactant, the rate will be 0.25 mol/L × s when one-half the starting material remains, and 0.125 mol/L × s when one-fourth of the starting material remains.
32. When NO_2^- is doubled with NH_4^+ held constant, the rate doubles. The reaction is first-order in NO_2^-. When NH_4^+ is doubled with NO_2^- held constant, the rate also doubles. The reaction is also first-order with respect to NH_4^+, and the overall reaction is second-order.
33. **a.** converts reactants to products in a single step
    b. a product of one reaction that immediately becomes a reactant in a second reaction
    c. the sequence of elementary reactions of a complex reaction
    d. the energy the reactants must have before they can react to form an intermediate or product

Chapter 19

1. **a.** base **b.** both
   c. both **d.** acid
   e. acid
2. **a.** hydrofluoric acid
   b. phosphoric acid
   c. potassium hydroxide
   d. sulfuric acid
   e. nitrous acid
   f. magnesium hydroxide
3. **a.** H_2CrO_4 **b.** $Fe(OH)_2$ **c.** HI
   d. LiOH **e.** $HClO_2$ **f.** $HClO_4$
4. **a.** Hydroxide ion concentration is greater.
   b. Hydrogen ion concentration is greater.
   c. The concentrations are equal.
5. **a.** basic **b.** basic
   c. acidic **d.** neutral
6. $[H^+] = \dfrac{K_w}{[OH^-]} = \dfrac{1 \times 10^{-14}}{1.0 \times 10^{-3}} \times 1 \times 10^{-11} \text{ mol/L}$
   Since $[OH^-]$ is greater than $[H^+]$, the solution is basic.
7. By definition, $pH = -\log[H^+]$,
   a. $pH = -\log(1 \times 10^{-6}) = -(0.0 - 6) = 6.0$
   b. $pH = -\log(1 \times 10^{-4}) = -(0.0 - 4) = 4.0$

If the $[OH^-]$ is given, first find the $[H^+]$ using K_w; then find the pH.

c. $[H^+] = \frac{K_w}{[OH^-]} = \frac{1 \times 10^{-14}}{1 \times 10^{-2}} = 1 \times 10^{-12}$ mol/L

$pH = -\log(1 \times 10^{-12}) = -(0.0 - 12) = 12.0$

d. $[H^+] = \frac{K_w}{[OH^-]} = \frac{1 \times 10^{-14}}{1 \times 10^{-11}} = 1 \times 10^{-3}$ mol/L

$pH = -\log(1 \times 10^{-3}) = -(0.0 - 3) = 3.0$

8. The pH of a solution with a hydrogen-ion concentration of $1 \times 10^{-x}M$ is x.

a. $pH = 4.0$, $[H^+] = 1 \times 10^{-4}M$

b. $pH = 11.0$, $[H^+] = 1 \times 10^{-11}M$

c. $pH = 8.0$, $[H^+] = 1 \times 10^{-8}M$

9. First find the $[H^+]$ as in the previous example. Then use K_w to find $[OH^-]$.

a. $pH = 6.0$, $[H^+] = 1 \times 10^{-6}$

$[OH^-] = \frac{1 \times 10^{-14}}{1 \times 10^{-6}} = 1 \times 10^{-8}M$

b. $pH = 9.0$, $[H^+] = 1 \times 10^{-9}$

$[OH^-] = \frac{1 \times 10^{-14}}{1 \times 10^{-9}} = 1 \times 10^{-5}M$

c. $pH = 12.0$, $[H^+] = 1 \times 10^{-12}$

$[OH^-] = \frac{1 \times 10^{-14}}{1 \times 10^{-12}} = 1 \times 10^{-2}M$

10. a. 4.0

b. $0.001 = 1 \times 10^{-3}$, thus, $pH = 3.0$

To calculate pH, first calculate H^+. Use the definition of

$K_w = [H^+] \times [OH^-] = 1 \times 10^{-14}$

$[H^+] = \frac{1 \times 10^{-14}}{[OH^-]} = \frac{1 \times 10^{-14}}{0.01}$

$= \frac{1 \times 10^{-14}}{1 \times 10^{-2}} = 1 \times 10^{-12}$

$pH = 12$

d. $[H^+] = \frac{1 \times 10^{-14}}{[OH^-]} = \frac{1 \times 10^{-14}}{1 \times 10^{-6}} = 1 \times 10^{-8}$

$pH = 8$

11. By the burning of oil and coal for heating and industrial uses, and the burning of gasoline and other fuels for transportation.

12. Answers will vary but should include such ideas as limiting recreational driving and reducing overall energy consumption.

13. a. $[H^+] = 5.0 \times 10^{-6}$

$pH = -\log(5.0) - \log(10^{-6})$
$= -(0.70) - (-6)$
$= 5.30$

b. $[H^+] = 8.3 \times 10^{-10}$

$pH = -\log(8.3) - \log(10^{-10})$
$= -(0.92) - (-10)$
$= 9.08$

c. $[H^+] = \frac{1 \times 10^{-14}}{2.0 \times 10^{-5}} = 5 \times 10^{-10}$

$pH = -\log(5.0) - \log(10^{-10})$
$= -(0.70) - (-10)$
$= 9.30$

d. $[H^+] = \frac{1 \times 10^{-14}}{4.5 \times 10^{-11}} = 2.2 \times 10^{-4}$

$pH = -\log(2.2) - \log(10^{-4})$
$= -(0.34) - (-4)$
$= 3.66$

14. a. $[H^+] = 1 \times 10^{-5}M$

b. $pH = 5.80$
$[H^+] = (10^{0.20})(10^{-6}) = 1.6 \times 10^{-6}M$

c. $pH = 12.20$
$[H^+] = (10^{0.80})(10^{-13}) = 6.3 \times 10^{-13}M$

d. $pH = 2.64$
$[H^+] = (10^{0.36})(10^{-3}) = 2.3 \times 10^{-3}M$

15. a. diprotic

b. triprotic

c. monoprotic

16. a. $2K + 2H_2O \rightarrow 2KOH + H_2$

b. $Ca + 2H_2O \rightarrow Ca(OH)_2 + H_2$

c. $KOH \rightarrow K^+ + OH^-$

d. $Mg(OH)_2 \rightarrow Mg^{2+} + 2OH^-$

17. In the Brønsted-Lowry theory, acids are hydrogen ion donors and bases are hydrogen ion acceptors. This explains why a compound without hydroxide ions behaves like a base.

18.

HNO_3	+	H_2O	$\rightleftharpoons$	H_3O^+	+	NO_3^-
acid (hydrogen-ion donor)		base (hydrogen-ion acceptor)		conjugate acid		conjugate base
CO_3^{2-}	+	H_2O	$\rightleftharpoons$	HCO_3^-	+	OH^-
base (hydrogen-ion acceptor)		acid (hydrogen-ion donor)		conjugate acid		conjugate base

19. a. green to yellow

b. green to blue

20. A pH meter measures hydrogen ion concentration to 0.01 pH units. Most indicators change color over a range of 2–3 pH units.

21. A Lewis base; it has a non-bonding pair of electrons that it can donate.

22. a. H^+ is the Lewis acid;
H_2O is the Lewis base.

b. $AlCl_3$ is the Lewis acid;
Cl^- is the Lewis base.

23. strongest: oxalic acid
weakest: carbonic acid

24. The [HX] is much greater than the $[H^+]$.

25. The pH has been adjusted in the range of 5 to 8.

26. Detergents include sodium lauryl sulfate and ammonium lauryl sulfate. Other answers will vary but may include fragrances, artificial colors, and preservatives.

27. a. $pH = -\log[H^+]$
$= -\log(9.86 \times 10^{-5}) = -(\log 9.86 + \log 10^{-5})$
$= -(0.994) - (-5)$
$= -0.994 + 5$
$= 4.006$

b. $K_a = \frac{[H^+][A^-]}{[HA]} = \frac{(9.86 \times 10^{-5}) \times (9.86 \times 10^{-5})}{0.200}$
$= 4.86 \times 10^{-8}$

28. $K_a = \frac{[H^+] \times [CHO_2^-]}{[HCHO_2]}$

$[H^+] = [CHO_2^-] = 4.2 \times 10^{-3}$

$[HCHO_2] = (0.100) - (4.2 \times 10^{-3})$
$= (1.00 \times 10^{-1}) - (0.042 \times 10^{-1})$
$= 0.96 \times 10^{-1}$

$K_a = \frac{(4.2 \times 10^{-3}) \times (4.2 \times 10^{-3})}{(0.96 \times 10^{-1})} = 1.8 \times 10^{-4}$

1.8×10^{-4}

29. Hard and wear resistant; very strong for its density.
30. Strength, durability, and low density.

Chapter 20

1. Acid + base → salt + water
2. **a.** $HNO_3 + KOH \rightarrow KNO_3 + H_2O$
b. $2HCl + Ca(OH)_2 \rightarrow CaCl_2 + 2H_2O$
c. $H_2SO_4 + 2NH_3 \rightarrow (NH_4)_2SO_4$
3. Sodium hydrogen carbonate ($NaHCO_3$), calcium carbonate ($CaCO_3$), magnesium carbonate ($MgCO_3$), magnesium hydroxide [$Mg(OH)_2$], aluminum hydroxide [$Al(OH)_3$], and aluminum sodium dihydroxy carbonate [$AlNa(OH)_2CO_3$]. HCO_3^-, CO_3^{2-}, or OH^- ions neutralize the acid.
4. Magnesium hydroxide has a very low solubility.
5. Write the equation for the neutralization.
$NaOH + HNO_3 \rightarrow NaNO_3 + H_2O$

$$0.20\ \cancel{\text{mol HNO}_3} \times \frac{1\ \text{mol NaOH}}{1\ \cancel{\text{mol HNO}_3}} = 0.20\ \text{mol NaOH}$$

6. Write a balanced equation for the reaction to find the acid-base mole ratio.
$H_3PO_4(aq) + 3KOH(aq) \rightarrow K_3PO_4(aq) + 3H_2O(l)$
1 mol 3 mol 1 mol 3 mol
The ratio of H_3PO_4 to KOH is 1:3. The necessary number of moles of KOH is calculated using this ratio.

$$1.56\ \cancel{\text{mol H}_3\text{PO}_4} \times \frac{3\ \text{mol KOH}}{1\ \cancel{\text{mol H}_3\text{PO}_4}} = 4.68\ \text{mol KOH}$$

7. Write the equation for the neutralization.
$HCl + KOH \rightarrow KCl + H_2O$

$$0.025\ \cancel{\text{L KOH}} \times \frac{1\ \cancel{\text{mol KOH}}}{1\ \cancel{\text{L KOH}}} \times \frac{1\ \cancel{\text{mol HCl}}}{1\ \cancel{\text{mol KOH}}} \times \frac{1\ \cancel{\text{L HCl}}}{0.45\ \cancel{\text{mol HCl}}} \times \frac{103\ \text{mL HCl}}{1\ \cancel{\text{L HCl}}} = 56\ \text{mL HCl}$$

8. Write the equation for the neutralization.
$H_3PO_4 + 3NaOH \rightarrow Na_3PO_4 + 3H_2O$

$$0.0385\ \cancel{\text{L NaOH}} \times \frac{0.15\ \cancel{\text{mol NaOH}}}{1\ \cancel{\text{L NaOH}}} \times \frac{1\ \text{mol H}_3\text{PO}_4}{3\ \cancel{\text{mol NaOH}}} = 0.00193\ \text{mol H}_3\text{PO}_4$$

$$\text{Molarity} = \frac{\text{mol}}{\text{L}} = \frac{0.00193\ \text{mol}}{0.015\ \text{L}} = 0.13M$$

9. Number of equivalents of solute in 1 L of solution.
10. Divide the gram equivalent mass by the number of equivalents per mol.

a. $1\ \text{Gram equiv mass KOH} = \dfrac{56.1\ \text{g}}{1} = 56.1\ \text{g}$

(1 equivalent per mole)

b. $1\ \text{Gram equiv mass HCl} = \dfrac{36.5\ \text{g}}{1} = 36.5\ \text{g}$

(1 equivalent per mol)

c. $1\ \text{Gram equiv mass H}_2\text{SO}_4 = \dfrac{98.0\ \text{g}}{2} = 49.0\ \text{g}$

(2 equivalents per mol)

11. $\text{Equiv} = \dfrac{\text{gram molecular mass}}{\text{gram equivalent mass}}$

a. $\text{Gram equiv mass Ca(OH)}_2 = \dfrac{74.0}{2} = 37.0\ \text{g}$

$$\text{Equiv Ca(OH)}_2 = \frac{3.7\ \text{g}}{37.0\ \text{g/equiv}} = 0.10\ \text{equiv}$$

b. $\text{Gram equiv mass H}_2\text{SO}_4 = \dfrac{98.0\ \text{g}}{2} = 49.0\ \text{g}$

$$\text{Equiv H}_2\text{SO}_4 = \frac{189\ \text{g}}{49.0\ \text{g/equiv}} = 3.86\ \text{equiv}$$

c. $\text{Gram equiv mass H}_3\text{PO}_4 = \dfrac{98.0\ \text{g}}{3} = 32.7\ \text{g}$

$$\text{Equiv H}_3\text{PO}_4 = \frac{9.0\ \text{g}}{32.7\ \text{g/equiv}} = 0.30\ \text{equiv}$$

12. Normality = molarity × number ionizable hydrogens
a. $2M\ HCl = 2N\ HCl$
b. $0.1M\ HC_2H_3O_2 = 0.1N\ HC_2H_3O_2$
c. $0.3M\ H_3PO_4 = 0.9N\ H_3PO_4$
(three ionizable hydrogens)
d. $0.25M\ H_2SO_4 = 0.50N\ H_2SO_4$
(two ionizable hydrogens)
e. $0.1M\ NaOH = 0.1N\ NaOH$
f. $1.0M\ Ca(OH)_2 = 2.0N\ Ca(OH)_2$
(two ionizable hydroxide ions)
13. Normality = equivalents/liter

a. $20\ \cancel{\text{g NaOH}} \times \dfrac{1\ \text{equiv NaOH}}{40\ \cancel{\text{g NaOH}}} = 0.50\ \text{equiv NaOH}$

$$N = \frac{0.50\ \text{equiv NaOH}}{1\ \text{L}} = 0.50N$$

b. $4.9\ \cancel{\text{g H}_2\text{SO}_4} \times \dfrac{1\ \text{equiv H}_2\text{SO}_4}{49.0\ \cancel{\text{g H}_2\text{SO}_4}} = 0.10\ \text{equiv H}_2\text{SO}_4$

$$N = \frac{0.10\ \text{equiv}}{0.50\ \text{L}} = 0.20N$$

c. $15.0\ \cancel{\text{g HCl}} \times \dfrac{1\ \text{equiv HCl}}{36.5\ \cancel{\text{g HCl}}} = 0.411\ \text{equiv HCl}$

$$N = \frac{0.411\ \text{equiv HCl}}{0.400\ \text{L}} = 1.03N$$

d. $88.0\ \cancel{\text{g H}_3\text{PO}_4} \times \dfrac{1\ \text{equiv H}_3\text{PO}_4}{32.7\ \cancel{\text{g H}_3\text{PO}_4}} = 2.69\ \text{equiv H}_3\text{PO}_4$

$$N = \frac{2.69\ \text{equiv H}_3\text{PO}_4}{1.50\ \text{L}} = 1.79N$$

e. $80.0\ \cancel{\text{g NaOH}} \times \dfrac{1\ \text{equiv NaOH}}{40.0\ \cancel{\text{g NaOH}}} = 2.00\ \text{equiv NaOH}$

$$N = \frac{2.00\ \text{equiv NaOH}}{1.00\ \text{L}} = 2.00N$$

f. $196\ \text{g H}_3\text{PO}_4 \times \dfrac{1\ \text{equiv H}_3\text{PO}_4}{32.7\ \text{g H}_3\text{PO}_4} = 5.99\ \text{equiv H}_3\text{PO}_4$

$$N = \frac{5.99\ \text{equiv H}_3\text{PO}_4}{2.00\ \text{L}} = 3.00N$$

14. Find the number of equivalents by multiplying the volume of the solution by the normality of the solution.

a. $0.55\ \cancel{\text{L}} \times \dfrac{1.8\ \text{equiv}}{1\ \cancel{\text{L}}} = 0.99\ \text{equiv}$

b. $1.6\ \cancel{\text{L}} \times \dfrac{0.50\ \text{equiv}}{1\ \text{L}} = 0.80\ \text{equiv}$

c. $0.25\ \cancel{\text{L}} \times \dfrac{0.28\ \text{equiv}}{1\ \cancel{\text{L}}} = 0.070\ \text{equiv}$

15. The number of equivalents must be equal before and after dilution.
$N_1 \times V_1 = N_2 \times V_2$

$$V_1 = \frac{N_2 \times V_2}{N_1} = \frac{500\ \text{mL} \times 0.20N}{4.0N} = 25\ \text{mL}$$

Dilute 25 mL of $4.0N\ H_2SO_4$ to 500 mL.
16. The number of equivalents must be equal before and after dilution.
$N_1 \times V_1 = N_2 \times V_2$

$$V_1 = \frac{N_2 \times V_2}{N_1} = \frac{0.20N \times 870 \text{ mL}}{3.0N} = 58 \text{ mL}$$

Dilute 58 mL of 3.0N KOH to 870 mL.

17. At the neutralization point, $N_A \times V_A = N_B \times V_B$.

$$V_B = \frac{N_A \times V_A}{N_B} = \frac{0.050N \times 75 \text{ mL}}{0.20N} = 19 \text{ mL}$$

18. At the equivalence point, the number of equivalents of acid and base are equal.

$N_A \times V_A = N_B \times V_B$

$$N_B = \frac{N_A \times V_A}{V_B} = \frac{0.40N \times 75 \text{ mL}}{25 \text{ mL}} = 1.2N \text{ base}$$

19. Salts with a cation from a weak base and an anion from a strong acid, or with a cation from a strong base and an anion from a weak acid.

20. $HCO_3^-(aq) + H_2O(l) \rightarrow H_2CO_3(aq) + OH^-(aq)$

21. Eventually the buffer capacity of the buffer is exceeded and the pH will change significantly with the addition of strong acid or base.

22. **a.** $HPO_4^{2-} + H^+ \rightarrow H_2PO_4^-$

b. $H_2PO_4^- + OH^- \rightarrow HPO_4^{2-} + H_2O$

23. **a.** $CH_3COO^- + H^+ \rightarrow CH_3COOH$

b. $NH_3 + H^+ \rightarrow NH_4^+$

24. **a.** $[Ni^{2+}][S^{2-}]$

b. $[Ba^{2+}][CO_3^{2-}]$

c. $[Pb^{2+}][Cl^-]^2$

d. $[Ag^+]^2[CrO_4^{2-}]$

25. Write the equation for the dissociation.

$PbS \rightleftharpoons Pb^{2+} + S^{2-}$

$K_{sp} = [Pb^{2+}] \times [S^{2-}] = 3 \times 10^{-28}$

At equilibrium, $[Pb^{2+}] = [S^{2-}]$.

Therefore: $[Pb^{2+}]^2 = 3 \times 10^{-28}$

$[Pb^{2+}] = 2 \times 10^{-14}M$

26. Write the equation for the dissociation.

$Ag_2S \rightleftharpoons 2Ag^+ + S^{2-}$

$K_{sp} = [Ag^+]^2 \times [S^{2-}] = 8 \times 10^{-51}$

When $[S^{2-}]$ is x, then $[Ag^+] = 2x$.

Substitute into the equation for K_{sp}.

$K_{sp} = (2x)^2(x) = 8 \times 10^{-51}$

$4x^3 = 8 \times 10^{-51}$

$x^3 = 2 \times 10^{-51}$

$x = 1 \times 10^{-17}$

$[Ag^+] = 2x = 2 \times 10^{-17}M$

27. $SrSO_4 \rightleftharpoons Sr^{2+} + SO_4^{2-}$

$K_{sp} = [Sr^{2+}] \times [SO_4^{2-}] = 3.2 \times 10^{-7}$

At equilibrium, $[SO_4^{2-}] = x$ and

$[Sr^{2+}] = x + 0.10 \approx 0.10$.

$K_{sp} = 0.10 \times x = 3.2 \times 10^{-7}$

$x = 3.2 \times 10^{-6}M$

28. $FeS \rightleftharpoons Fe^{2+} + S^{2-}$

$K_{sp} = [Fe^{2+}][S^{2-}] = 8 \times 10^{-19}$

At equilibrium, $[S^{2-}] = x$ and $[Fe^{2+}] = x + 0.04 \sim 0.04$

$K_{sp} = 0.04 \times x = 8 \times 10^{-19}$

$x = 2 \times 10^{-17}M$

29. Calculate the solubility product of $PbCl_2$.

$K_{sp} = [Pb^{2+}] \times [Cl^-]^2$

$= 0.015 \times (0.050)^2 = 3.75 \times 10^{-5}$

Since the calculated solubility product exceeds the K_{sp} for the saturated solution (K_{sp} of $PbCl_2 = 1.7 \times 10^{-5}$), precipitation will occur.

30. $K_{sp} = [Ca^{2+}][CO_3^{2-}] = 4.5 \times 10^{-9}$

In the 1 L of solution, from mixing $Ca(NO_3)_2$ and Na_2CO_3, $[Ca^{2+}] = 0.5 \times 10^{-3}M$ and $[CO_3^{2-}] = 4 \times 10^{-4}M$

The product $[Ca^{2+}][CO_3^{2-}] = (0.5 \times 10^{-3}) \times (4 \times 10^{-4}) = 2 \times 10^{-7}$

Since this calculated value exceeds K_{sp} of $CaCO_3$, calcium carbonate will precipitate.

31. Hypochlorous acid, HOCl

32. The [HOCl], which must be maintained at certain levels to control bacteria and algae, is dependent on the $[H^+]$ in the pool.

Chapter 21

1. Oxidation.

2. **a.** $2Ba(s) + O_2(g) \rightarrow 2BaO(s)$; oxidation

b. $3CaO(s) + 2Al(s) \rightarrow Al_2O_3(s) + 3Ca(s)$; reduction

c. $C_2H_5OH(l) + 3O_2(g) \rightarrow 2CO_2(g) + 3H_2O(l)$; oxidation

3. **a.** Since chlorine is more electronegative than hydrogen, the electrons in the H—Cl bond will be shifted toward Cl and away from H. Therefore H_2 is oxidized and Cl_2 is reduced; H_2 is the reducing agent and Cl_2 is the oxidizing agent.

b. Nitrogen is more electronegative than hydrogen. The electrons in the N—H bonds in NH_3 are shifted toward N and away from H. Therefore, H_2 is oxidized and N_2 is reduced; H_2 is the reducing agent and N_2 is the oxidizing agent.

c. Chlorine is more electronegative than sulfur. The electrons in the S—Cl bonds in SCl_2 are shifted toward Cl and away from S. Therefore S is oxidized and Cl_2 is reduced; S is the reducing agent and Cl_2 is the oxidizing agent.

d. Oxygen is more electronegative than nitrogen. The electrons in the N—O bonds in NO_2 are shifted toward oxygen and away from nitrogen. Therefore N_2 is oxidized and O_2 is reduced; N_2 is the reducing agent and O_2 is the oxidizing agent.

e. Fluorine is more electronegative than lithium. The electrons in LiF are completely transferred from Li to F_2 (LiF is an ionic compound). Therefore Li is oxidized and F_2 is reduced: Li is the reducing agent and F_2 is the oxidizing agent.

f. Sulfur is more electronegative than hydrogen. The electrons in the H—S bonds in H_2S are shifted toward the sulfur and away from the hydrogen. Therefore hydrogen is oxidized and sulfur is reduced. Hydrogen is the reducing agent and sulfur is the oxidizing agent.

4. Incineration releases some hazardous chemicals, including new compounds more toxic than the original waste. The large amounts of carbon dioxide released contribute to global warming.

5. Answers will vary but should cover such points as the availability of landfill space, problems caused by toxic wastes in landfills, and concerns about the combustion products of incineration. Answers about preferred disposal methods will vary.

6. The sum of the oxidation number must equal the charge on the polyatomic ion.

7. **a.** The oxidation number of oxygen is −2. Since there are five oxygen atoms and the sum of the oxidation numbers must be zero, the oxidation number of phosphorus must be +5.

$\overset{+5}{P_2}\overset{-2}{O_5}$

check: $(2)(+5) + (5)(-2) = 0$.

b. The oxidation number of hydrogen is +1. The sum of the oxidation numbers of the nitrogen and hydrogen must equal the ionic charge, 1+. The oxidation number of nitrogen is −3.

$\overset{-3}{N}\overset{+1}{H_4^+}$

check: (−3) + (4)(+1) = +1.

c. The oxidation number of sodium is +1 and the oxidation number of oxygen is −2. The oxidation number of chromium is +6.

$\overset{+1}{Na_2}\overset{+6}{Cr_2}\overset{-2}{O_7}$

check: (2)(+1) + (2)(+6) + (7)(−2) = 0.

d. The oxidation number of hydrogen is +1 and the oxidation number of oxygen is −2. The oxidation number of calcium is +2.

$\overset{+2}{Ca}(\overset{-2}{O}\overset{+1}{H})_2$

check: (+2) + (2)(−2) + (2)(+1) = 0.

8. Assign oxidation numbers to each element. An oxidation number decrease indicates reduction; an increase indicates oxidation.

a. $3\overset{+1}{H_2}\overset{-2}{S} + 2\overset{+1}{H}\overset{+5}{N}\overset{-2}{O_3} \rightarrow 3\overset{0}{S} + 2\overset{+2}{N}\overset{-2}{O} + 4\overset{+1}{H_2}\overset{-2}{O}$

Nitrogen is reduced (+5 → +2). Sulfur is oxidized (−2 → 0). Sulfur (as H_2S) is the reducing agent; nitrogen (as HNO_3) is the oxidizing agent.

b. $2\overset{+2}{Pb}\overset{+6}{S}\overset{-2}{O_4} + 2\overset{+1}{H_2}\overset{-2}{O} \rightarrow \overset{0}{Pb} + \overset{+4}{Pb}\overset{-2}{O_2} + 2\overset{+1}{H_2}\overset{+6}{S}\overset{-2}{O_4}$

Lead is oxidized (+2 → +4). Lead is reduced (+2 → 0). Lead (as $PbSO_4$) is both the reducing agent and the oxidizing agent.

9. a. Must be equal.

b. Must be equal in magnitude.

10. *Step 1:* Assign oxidation numbers to all the atoms in the equation.

Step 2: Identify which atoms are oxidized and which are reduced.

Step 3: Use a line to connect the atoms that undergo oxidation. Use a separate line to connect the atoms that undergo reduction.

Step 4: Use appropriate coefficients to make the total increase in oxidation number equal to the total decrease in oxidation number.

Step 5: Do a final check to ensure the equation is balanced for both atoms and charge.

a. increase (0 ⟶ +3)

oxidation

$\overset{0}{Al} + \overset{0}{Cl_2} \longrightarrow \overset{+3}{Al}\overset{-1}{Cl_3}$

reduction

decrease (0 ⟶ −1)

To balance the increase (+3) and the decrease (−1) in oxidation numbers, three chlorine atoms must be reduced (−3 decrease) for each aluminum atom that is oxidized (+3 increase). To get 3Cl on the left-hand side of the equation, put a coefficient of 3/2 in front of Cl_2.

(1)(+3) = +3

$Al + \frac{3}{2}Cl_2 \longrightarrow AlCl_3$

(3)(−1) = −3

The fractional coefficient can be removed by multiplying each term in the equation by 2.

$2Al(s) + 3Cl_2(g) \rightarrow 2AlCl_3(s)$

This equation can now be balanced.

b. decrease (+5 ⟶ −1)

reduction

$\overset{+1}{K}\overset{+5}{Cl}\overset{-2}{O_3} \longrightarrow \overset{+1}{K}\overset{-1}{Cl} + \overset{0}{O_2}$

oxidation

increase (−2 ⟶ 0)

To balance the increase (+2) and the decrease (−6) in oxidation number, three oxygen atoms must be oxidized (+6 increase) for each chlorine that is reduced (−6 decrease). To get 3 O on the right-hand side, put a coefficient of 3/2 in front of O_2.

(1)(−6) = −6

$KClO_3 \longrightarrow KCl + \frac{3}{2}O_2$

(3)(+2) = +6

The fractional coefficient can be removed by multiplying each term in the equation by 2.

$2KClO_3(s) \rightarrow 2KCl(s) + 3O_2(g)$

This equation is now balanced.

c. increase (−3 ⟶ +1)

oxidation

$\overset{-3}{P}\overset{+1}{H_3} + \overset{0}{I_2} + \overset{+1}{H_2}\overset{-2}{O} \longrightarrow \overset{+1}{H_3}\overset{+1}{P}\overset{-2}{O_2} + \overset{+1}{H}\overset{-1}{I}$

reduction

decrease (0 ⟶ −1)

To balance the increase (+4) and the decrease (−1) in oxidation numbers, one phosphorus atom must be oxidized (+4 increase) for every four iodine atoms that are reduced (−4 decrease). To get 4 I on the left-hand side, put a coefficient of 2 in front of I_2; then put a coefficient of 4 in front of HI.

(1)(+4) = +4

$PH_3 + 2I_2 + H_2O \longrightarrow H_3PO_2 + 4HI$

(4)(−1) = −4

To balance the oxygen and hydrogen (the spectator atoms), put a coefficient of 2 in front of H_2O.

$PH_3(g) + 2I_2(s) + 2H_2O(l) \rightarrow H_3PO_2(aq) + 4HI(aq)$

This equation is now balanced.

d. increase (0 ⟶ +5)

oxidation

$\overset{0}{Cl_2} + \overset{+1}{K}\overset{-2}{O}\overset{+1}{H} \longrightarrow \overset{+1}{K}\overset{+5}{Cl}\overset{-2}{O_3} + \overset{+1}{K}\overset{-1}{Cl} + \overset{+1}{H_2}\overset{-2}{O}$

reduction

decrease (0 ⟶ −1)

To balance the increase (+5) and the decrease (−1) in oxidation numbers, one chlorine atom must be oxidized (+5 increase) for every five chlorine atoms that are reduced (−5 decrease). To get a total of 6 Cl on the left-hand side, put a coefficient of 3 in front of Cl_2; then put a coefficient of 5 in front of KCl.

$$\overset{(1)(+5) = +5}{3Cl_2 + KOH \longrightarrow KClO_3 + 5KCl + H_2O}$$
$$(5)(-1) = -5$$

Finally, K, O, and H are balanced by inspection.
$3Cl_2(g) + 6KOH(aq) \rightarrow KClO_3(aq) + 5KCl(aq) + 3H_2O(l)$
This equation is balanced.

e. decrease $(+5 \longrightarrow +2)$ reduction

$$\overset{+1+5-2}{HNO_3} + \overset{+1-2}{H_2S} \longrightarrow \overset{0}{S} + \overset{+2-2}{NO} + \overset{+1-2}{H_2O}$$

oxidation increase $(-2 \longrightarrow 0)$

To balance the increase (+2) and the decrease (−3) in oxidation numbers, two nitrogen atoms must be reduced (−6 decrease) for every three sulfur atoms that are oxidized (+6 increase). Put coefficients of 2 in front of HNO_3 and NO to balance the nitrogen atoms. Put coefficients of 3 in front of H_2S and S.

$$(2)(-3) = -6$$
$$2HNO_3 + 3H_2S \longrightarrow 3S + 2NO + H_2O$$
$$(3)(+2) = +6$$

Finally, H and O are balanced by inspection.
$2HNO_3(aq) + 3H_2S(aq) \rightarrow 3S(s) + 2NO(g) + 4H_2O(l)$
This equation is balanced.

f. decrease $(+7 \longrightarrow 0)$ reduction

$$\overset{+1+7-2}{KIO_4} + \overset{+1-1}{KI} + \overset{+1-1}{HCl} \longrightarrow \overset{+1-1}{KCl} + \overset{0}{I_2} + \overset{+1-2}{H_2O}$$

oxidation increase $(-1 \longrightarrow 0)$

To balance the decrease (−7) and the increase (+1) in oxidation numbers, one iodine atom (in KIO_4) must be reduced (−7 decrease) for every seven iodine atoms (in KI) that are oxidized (+7 increase). Put a coefficient of 7 in front of KI and a coefficient of 4 in front of I_2.

$$(1)(-7) = -7$$
$$KIO_4 + 7KI + HCl \longrightarrow KCl + 4I_2 + H_2O$$
$$(7)(+1) = +7$$

Finally, balance K, H, O, and Cl by inspection.
$KIO_4(aq) + 7KI(aq) + 8HCl(aq) \rightarrow$
$8KCl(aq) + 4I_2(s) + 4H_2O(l)$
The equation is balanced.

11. Single replacement, combustion, combination, and decomposition.

12. a. This is a double-replacement reaction. There is no change in oxidation numbers, so this is not a redox reaction.

b. This is a decomposition reaction. There is no change in oxidation numbers.

c. $\overset{0}{Mg} + \overset{0}{Br_2} \rightarrow \overset{2+\ -1}{MgBr_2}$
This is a redox combination reaction. Magnesium is oxidized. It is the reducing agent. Bromine is reduced. Bromine is the oxidizing agent.

d. $\overset{-3+1+3-2}{NH_4NO_2} \rightarrow \overset{0}{N_2} + \overset{+1-2}{2H_2O}$
This is a redox decomposition reaction. Nitrogen (in NO_2^-) is reduced. It is the oxidizing agent. Nitrogen (in NH_4^+) is oxidized. It is the reducing agent.

e. $\overset{+1+5-2}{2KClO_3} \rightarrow \overset{+1-1}{2KCl} + \overset{0}{3O_2}$
This is a redox decomposition reaction. Chlorine is reduced. It is the oxidizing agent. Oxygen is oxidized. It is the reducing agent.

f. This is a double-replacement reaction followed by a decomposition reaction (of H_2CO_3). There is no change in oxidation numbers.

g. $\overset{+2-2}{CuO} + \overset{0}{H_2} \rightarrow \overset{0}{Cu} + \overset{+1-2}{H_2O}$
This is a redox reaction. Copper is reduced. It is the oxidizing agent. Hydrogen is oxidized. It is the reducing agent.

13. They may be needed to achieve mass and charge balance.

14. *Step 1:* Write the equation in ionic form.
Step 2: Write the oxidation and reduction half-reactions.
Step 3: Balance the half-reactions, using H_2O, H^+, or OH^- as needed.
Step 4: Add electrons to one side of each half-reaction to balance the charges.
Step 5: Multiply each half-reaction to make the electron charges equal.
Step 6: Add the half-reactions and subtract terms that are on both sides.
Step 7: Balance the spectator ions by inspection if they are included.

a. $ClO_3^- + I^- \rightarrow Cl^- + I_2$ (acid solution)
Oxidation: $I^- \rightarrow I_2$
Reduction: $ClO_3^- \rightarrow Cl^-$
Balance:
Oxidation: $2I^- \rightarrow I_2$
Reduction: $ClO_3^- + 6H^+ \rightarrow Cl^- + 3H_2O$
Add electrons.
Oxidation: $2I^- \rightarrow I_2 + 2e^-$
Reduction: $ClO_3^- + 6H^+ + 6e^- \rightarrow Cl^- + 3H_2O$
Multiply oxidation half-reaction by 3.
Oxidation: $6I^- \rightarrow 3I_2 + 6e^-$
Reduction: $ClO_3^- + 6H^+ + 6e^- \rightarrow Cl^- + 3H_2O$
Add the half-reactions and subtract terms.
$ClO_3^- + 6I^- + 6H^+ + \cancel{6e^-} \rightarrow Cl^- + 3I_2 + 3H_2O + \cancel{6e^-}$
The balanced equation is:
$ClO_3^-(aq) + 6I^-(aq) + 6H^+(aq) \rightarrow$
$Cl^-(aq) + 3I_2(s) + 3H_2O(l)$

b. $MnO_2 + H^+ + NO_2^- \rightarrow NO_3^- + Mn^{2+} + 2H_2O$
Oxidation: $NO_2^- \rightarrow NO_3^-$
Reduction: $MnO_2 \rightarrow Mn^{2+}$
Balance:
Oxidation: $NO_2^- + H_2O \rightarrow NO_3^- + 2H^+$
Reduction: $MnO_2 + 4H^+ \rightarrow Mn^{2+} + 2H_2O$
Add electrons.
Oxidation: $NO_2^- + H_2O \rightarrow NO_3^- + 2H^+ + 2e^-$
Reduction: $MnO_2 + 4H^+ + 2e^- \rightarrow Mn^{2+} + 2H_2O$
Since the electron charges are equal, add the half-reactions and cancel terms.

$$MnO_2 + \overset{2}{\cancel{4}}H^+ + NO_2^- + \cancel{H_2O} + \cancel{2e^-} \rightarrow$$
$$NO_3^- + Mn^{2+} + \cancel{2e^-} + \cancel{2H^+} + \overset{1}{\cancel{2}}H_2O$$

The balanced equation is:
$MnO_2(s) + 2H^+(aq) + NO_2^-(aq) \rightarrow$
$NO_3^-(aq) + Mn^{2+}(aq) + H_2O(l)$

c. $Cl_2 \rightarrow ClO_3^- + Cl$ (basic solution)
Oxidation: $Cl_2 \rightarrow ClO_3^-$
Reduction: $Cl_2 \rightarrow Cl^-$
Balance:
Oxidation: $Cl_2 + 12OH^- \rightarrow 2ClO_3^- + 6H_2O$
Reduction: $Cl_2 \rightarrow 2Cl^-$
Add electrons:
Oxidation: $Cl_2 + 12OH^- \rightarrow 2ClO_3^- + 6H_2O + 10e^-$
Reduction: $Cl_2 + 2e^- \rightarrow 2Cl^-$
Multiply the reduction half-reaction by 5.
Oxidation: $Cl_2 + 12OH^- \rightarrow 2ClO_3^- + 6H_2O + 10e^-$
Reduction: $5Cl_2 + 10e^- \rightarrow 10Cl^-$
Add the half-reactions and cancel terms.
$5Cl_2 + Cl_2 + 12OH^- + \cancel{10e^-} \rightarrow$
$2ClO_3^- + 10Cl^- + 6H_2O + \cancel{10e^-}$
The balanced equation is:
$6Cl_2(g) + 12OH^-(aq) \rightarrow 2ClO_3^-(aq) + 10Cl^- + 6H_2O(l)$

15. High strength, uniform density, durable, resist biological attack, minimal water absorption and resulting swelling.

16. Biomass resources are renewable; petroleum is not renewable.

17. The temperature below which a superconducting material has zero resistance.

18. The best technology still requires cooling with liquid nitrogen; materials are too brittle for practical use.

Chapter 22

1. The oxidation or reduction in a redox reaction.
Oxidation: $Al(s) \rightarrow Al^{3+}(aq) + 3e^-$
Reduction: $Cu^{2+}(aq) + 2e^- \rightarrow Cu(s)$

2. Nothing
Have students generalize about the nature of electrochemical processes.

3. The cathode.

4. Spontaneous redox reactions.

5. There is an economic cost to transform solar energy into a more useable form such as electrical energy.

6. Solar energy is unlimited, nonpolluting, and silent. It reduces dependence on foreign oil and does not contribute to global warming or acid rain.

7. $Zn(s) \mid ZnCl_2(aq) \parallel MnO_2(s) \mid Mn_2O_3(s)$

8. Water is produced by the redox reaction and sulfuric acid is used up.

9. $Pb(s) \mid PbSO_4(s) \parallel PbO_2(s) \mid PbSO_4(s)$

10. Fuel cells cannot generate electricity as economically as more conventional methods.

11. No; for every 4 mol of OH^- used up in the oxidation half-reaction, 4 mol of OH^- are produced in the reduction half-reaction.

12. The standard cell potential implies standard conditions. The cell potential does not.

13. It was arbitrarily set at zero.

14. Salt is a strong electrolyte and an aqueous salt solution facilitates electron transfer.

15. The sacrificing metal must be more easily oxidized than the metal it is protecting.

16. Both tables rank the elements according to their tendency to undergo oxidation/reduction.

17. The half-cell with the more positive reduction potential occurs as a reduction. In this cell Cu^{2+} is reduced and Al is oxidized. Because reduction takes place at the Cu^{2+} half-cell, this half-cell is the cathode.
The half-cell reactions are:
Oxidation: $Al(s) \rightarrow Al^{3+}(aq) + 3e^-$ (anode)
Reduction: $Cu^{2+}(aq) + 2e^- \rightarrow Cu(s)$ (cathode)
Before the reactions are added to give the overall cell reaction the electrons must cancel. Multiply each equation by a coefficient to give equal numbers of electrons.

$$2[Al(s) \rightarrow Al^{3+}(aq) + 3e^-]$$
$$3[Cu^{2+}(aq) + 2e^- \rightarrow Cu(s)]$$
$$\overline{2Al(s) + 3Cu^{2+}(aq) \rightarrow 2Al^{3+}(aq) + 3Cu(s)}$$

The standard cell potential can now be calculated.
$E^\circ_{cell} = E^\circ_{red} - E^\circ_{oxid}$
$= E^\circ_{Cu^{2+}} - E^\circ_{Al^{3+}}$
$= +0.34V - (-1.66V)$
$= +2.00V$

18. In this cell Ag^+ is reduced and Cu is oxidized. The Ag^+ half-cell is the cathode.
The half-cell reactions are:
Oxidation: $Cu(s) \rightarrow Cu^{2+}(aq) + 2e^-$ (anode)
Reduction: $Ag^+(aq) + e^- \rightarrow Ag(s)$ (cathode)
Before the reactions are added the electrons must cancel.

$$Cu(s) \rightarrow Cu^{2+}(aq) + 2e^-$$
$$2[Ag^+(aq) + e^- \rightarrow Ag(s)]$$
$$\overline{Cu(s) + 2Ag^+(aq) \rightarrow Cu^{2+}(aq) + 2Ag(s)}$$

The standard cell potential can now be calculated.
$E^\circ_{cell} = E^\circ_{red} - E^\circ_{oxid}$
$E^\circ_{cell} = E^\circ_{Ag^+} - E^\circ_{Cu^{2+}}$
$= +0.80V - (+0.34V)$
$= +0.46V$

19. Because the reaction is spontaneous as written Co^{2+} is reduced and Fe is oxidized.
The half-cell reactions are:
Oxidation: $Fe(s) \rightarrow Fe^{2+}(aq) + 2e^-$ (anode)
Reduction: $Co^{2+}(aq) + 2e^- \rightarrow Co(s)$ (cathode)
The standard cell potential can now be calculated.
$E^\circ_{cell} = E^\circ_{red} - E^\circ_{oxid}$
$= E^\circ_{Co^{2+}} - E^\circ_{Fe^{2+}}$
Substitute standard reduction potentials from Table 22.2.
$= -0.28V - (-0.44V)$
$= +0.16V$

20. a. The half-reactions are:
Oxidation: $Cu(s) \rightarrow Cu^{2+}(aq) + 2e^-$
Reduction: $2H^+(aq) + 2e^- \rightarrow H_2(g)$
The standard reduction potentials are found in Table 22.2.
$E^\circ_{Cu^{2+}} = +0.34V$
$E^\circ_{H^+} = 0.00V$
The standard cell potential is the difference of the potentials of the two cells.
$E^\circ_{cell} = E^\circ_{red} - E^\circ_{oxid}$
$= E^\circ_{H^+} - E^\circ_{Cu^{2+}}$
$= 0.00V - (+0.34V)$
$= -0.34V$
Since the standard cell potential is a negative number, the redox reaction is nonspontaneous as written.

b. The half-reactions are:
Oxidation: $Ag(s) \rightarrow Ag^+(aq) + e^-$
Reduction: $Fe^{2+}(aq) + 2e^- \rightarrow Fe(s)$
The standard reduction potentials are found in Table 22.2.
$E^\circ_{Ag^+} = +0.80V$
$E^\circ_{Fe^{2+}} = -0.44V$

The standard cell potential is the difference of the potentials of the two cells.

$$E^\circ_{cell} = E^\circ_{red} - E^\circ_{oxid}$$
$$= E^\circ_{Fe^{2+}} - E^\circ_{Ag^+}$$
$$= -0.44V - (+0.80V)$$
$$= -1.24V$$

Since the standard cell potential is a negative number, the redox reaction is nonspontaneous as written.

c. The half-reactions are:

Oxidation: $Cr(s) \rightarrow Cr^{3+}(aq) + 3e^-$

Reduction: $Zn^{2+}(aq) + 2e^- \rightarrow Zn(s)$

The standard reduction potentials are found in Table 22.2.

$E^\circ_{Cr^{3+}} = -0.74V$

$E^\circ_{Zn^{2+}} = -0.76V$

The standard cell potential is the difference of the potentials of the two cells.

$$E^\circ_{cell} = E^\circ_{red} - E^\circ_{oxid}$$
$$= E^\circ_{Zn^{2+}} - E^\circ_{Cr^{3+}}$$
$$= -0.76V - (-0.74V)$$
$$= -0.02V$$

Since the standard cell potential is a negative number, the redox reaction is nonspontaneous as written.

21. Voltaic cells use an electrochemical reaction to produce electrical energy. Electrolytic cells use electrical energy to bring about a chemical change.

22. a. sodium hydroxide, chlorine gas, and hydrogen gas
b. sodium metal and chlorine gas
c. hydrogen gas and oxygen gas

Chapter 23

1. To prevent reacting with oxygen in the air. They are kept dry to prevent reacting with water.

2. No; their chemical reactivity is too great; they react with oxygen and water.

3. Group 2A metals are less reactive than Group 1A metals.

4. Calcium, strontium, and barium react with cold water. Beryllium and magnesium react only with hot water or steam.
$Ca + 2H_2O \rightarrow Ca(OH)_2 + H_2$

5. Aluminum has strength and ductility, low density, good electrical conductivity, and high corrosion resistance.

6. The three allotropes have different structures; the carbon atoms are chemically bonded together in different arrangements.

7. Silicon and germanium are used in electronic equipment.

8. Nitrogen is found as a gas in air and in nitrogen compounds.

9. Colorless gas, strong odor, high boiling and melting point, high heat of vaporization, very soluble in water.

10. Nitric acid is used in the production of dyes, fertilizers, and explosives. It is also used for etching.

11. Oxygen is used for the manufacturing of steel; sulfur is used to produce sulfuric acid; selenium is used in producing light sensitive instruments.

12. a. colorless, odorless, gaseous
b. pale blue, odorous, gaseous
c. pale yellow, tasteless, odorless, brittle, solid.

13. Answers will vary but should indicate that superheated water and compressed air are sent down two tubes into the sulfur beds and a third tube brings sulfur froth to the surface.

14. Because sulfuric acid is used to manufacture many materials used in industry and agriculture, an increase in its consumption indicates an increase in demand for materials due to growth.

15. Fluorine, F_2; chlorine, Cl_2; bromine Br_2; iodine, I_2; astatine, At_2

16. Chlorine in solution is a strong oxidizing agent that kills disease-causing bacteria.

17. Chlorine gas is normally prepared by the electrolysis of an aqueous sodium chloride solution.

18. Protium (hydrogen-1), ^1H, mass number = 1. Deuterium (hydrogen-2), ^2H, mass number = 2. Tritium (hydrogen-3), ^3H, mass number = 3.

19. They are called *rare* because they are not plentiful, *inert* because they do not easily combine chemically with other elements, and *noble* because they are not chemically reactive and stand alone.

20. An ore is a mineral that is used for the commercial production of a metal.

21. Hematite and magnetite are the most common minerals of iron.

22. Mercury can react with organic material to form dimethyl mercury. Dimethyl mercury accumulates in aquatic organisms, and when they are consumed by larger organisms, the mercury is passed on up the food chain.

23. Trace amounts of some toxic metals are essential for human nutrition.

24. Answers will vary but could include stove tops, tiles, tools, mugs, dishes and bowls, and various other containers.

25. Low thermal conductivity, high melting point, durability, hardness, resistance to corrosion, not electrically conductive.

Chapter 24

1.
```
  H H H
H:C:C:C:H
  H H H
```

2. Ten single bonds. Each carbon has four single bonds.

3.

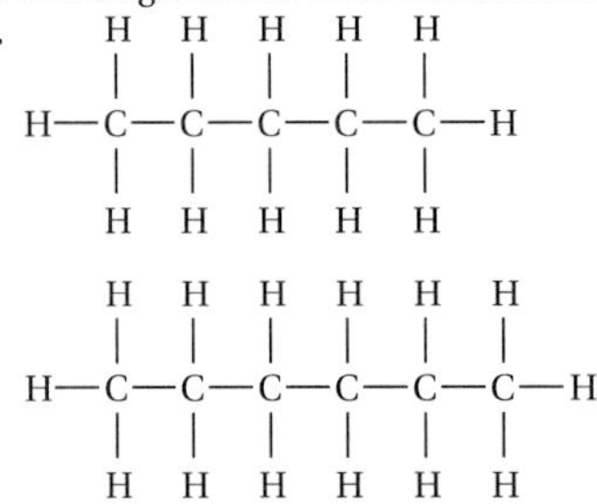

4. a. propane
b. pentane
c. hexane

5. Answers will vary but may include the biomass.

6. a. Hazardous because of the products formed during the combustion of plastic.
b. Plastics do not degrade for long periods of time. Answers will vary.

7. a. 2-methylbutane
b. 3-ethylhexane

8. a.
```
   CH3
   |
CH3CHCHCH2CH2CH3
      |
      CH3
```
2,3-dimethylhexane

b. 3-ethyl-2,4-dimethyloctane: $CH_3CH(CH_3)CH(CH_2CH_3)CH(CH_3)CH_2CH_2CH_2CH_3$

```
    CH3  CH3
    |    |
CH3CHCHCHCH2CH2CH2CH3
      |
      CH2CH3
```

3-ethyl-2,4-dimethyloctane

9. The bonds between carbons are nonpolar and the carbon-hydrogen bonds are very weakly polar; thus alkanes are nonpolar.

10. Five structural isomers of molecular formula C_6H_{14} exist.

C—C—C—C—C—C
hexane

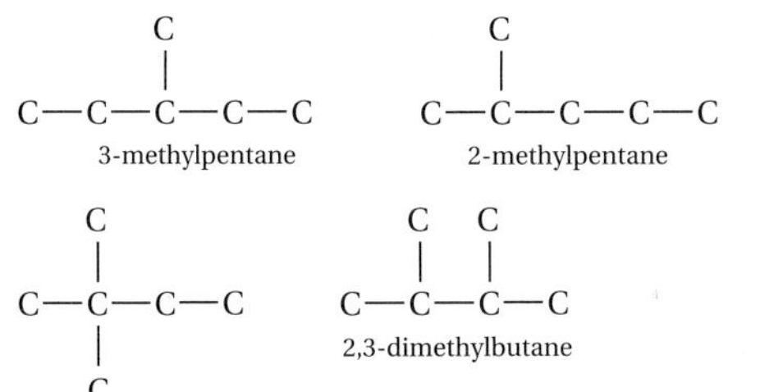

3-methylpentane

2-methylpentane

2,2-dimethylbutane

2,3-dimethylbutane

11. The name methene implies a single carbon atom; alkenes have a double bond between two carbon atoms.

12. $H_2C{=}CH{-}CH_2{-}CH_3$ 1-butene

$CH_2{=}C(CH_3){-}CH_3$ methylpropene

$CH_3{-}CH{=}CH{-}CH_3$ 2-butene

13. Most synthetic fibers are made from nonrenewable resources such as petroleum. The manufacturing processes may pollute the environment.

14. Answers will vary.

15. In structural isomers the identical atoms are bonded in different arrangements. In geometric isomers the order in which the atoms are connected are identical, only the orientation in space differs.

16. No. The structures are identical; one has just been "flipped-over."

17. No; only molecules with at least one asymmetric carbon.

18. Nonsuperimposable mirror images are given by a, b, c, d.

19. Cyclohexane has 12 hydrogen atoms; benzene has 6 hydrogen atoms. Cyclohexane has all single bonds; benzene has alternating single and double bonds for which resonance structures can be drawn.

20. a. 1-phenylpropane
b. 2-phenylpropane

21. Peat, lignite, bituminous coal, and anthracite coal

22. Coal is mostly large aromatic rings.

23. Petroleum refining: the distillation of crude oil to separate it into fractions. Cracking: the breaking down and rearranging of hydrocarbon chains into smaller molecules.

24. $2C_8H_{18} + 25O_2 \rightarrow 16CO_2 + 18H_2O$

Chapter 25

1. a. —OH, hydroxyl
b. $—NH_2$ amino
c. —COOH, carboxyl
d. —Br, halogen
e. —C—O—C, ether

2. R is any carbon chain or ring.

3. a. bromobenzene
b. chloroethane
c. 3-chloro-1-butene

4. a. $CH_3{-}CH(CH_3){-}Cl$ **b.** $ICH_2C(CH_3)_2CH_2CH_2CH_3$

c.

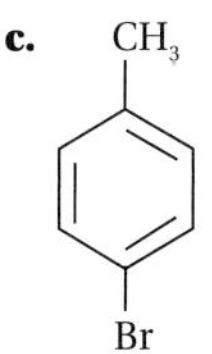

5. $CH_3CHBrCH_3 + KOH \rightarrow CH_3CHOHCH_3 + KBr$

6. 1,1-dichloropropane
1,2-dichloropropane
2,2-dichloropropane
1,3-dichloropropane

7. Quickly provides information on how to handle chemical spills and other accidents involving hazardous materials.

8. Answers will vary but may include: call 911, notify police and/or fire departments; help direct the public away from the accident site.

9. a. 1-butanol
b. 2-propanol
c. 2-methyl-1-butanol

10. a. primary
b. secondary
c. primary

11. a. H—O—H ···· O(H)—H **b.** H—O—H ···· O(H)—CH_3

c. CH_3—O—H ···· O(H)—CH_3

12. a. $CH_2BrCHBrCH_2CH_3$ **b.** $CH_3CHICHICH_3$

c. $CH_3CH_2CH_2CH_3$ **d.** 1,2-dichlorocyclohexane (Cl, Cl)

13. a. $H{-}C(CH_3)(H){-}C(CH_3)(Br){-}H$

b. **c.**

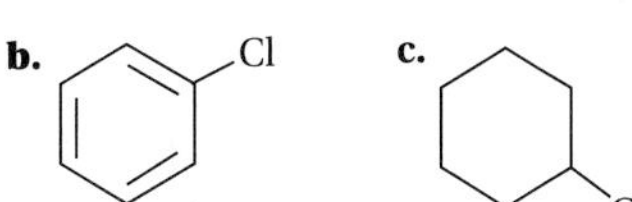

14. a. ethylmethyl ether
b. ethylphenyl ether

c. divinyl ether of vinyl ether
d. diisopropyl ethyl or isopropyl ether

15. The oxygen atom in diethyl ether polarizes the small molecule. This enables diethyl ether to dissolve in polar water. The large dihexyl ether molecule has large nonpolar parts and does not dissolve. Propane is less soluble in water than is diethyl ether because it is nonpolar.

16. a. propanal
b. 3-hexanone
c. 3-methylpentanal
d. butanone

17. In order of increasing boiling point: propane, propanal, and propanol.

18. The short chain ethanoic acid has a higher water solubility.

19. a. $HCOOH + KOH \rightarrow HCOO^-K^+ + H_2O$
b. $CH_3CH_2COOH + NaOH \rightarrow CH_3CH_2COO^-Na^+ + H_2O$
c. $CH_3COOH + NaOH \rightarrow CH_3COO^-Na^+ + H_2O$

20. a. 1-propanol, $CH_3CH_2CH_2OH$
b.
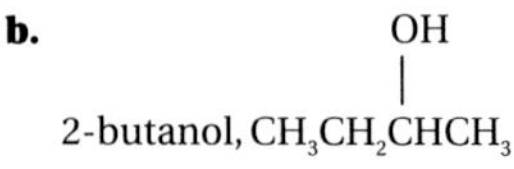

c. 2-methyl-1-butanol,
CH_3 on C-2 of $CH_3CH_2CHCH_2OH$

21. a. $CH_3CH_2CH_2COOH$
b. no reaction
c.

d. (cyclobutanone, O)

22. Amide, amine, carboxylic acid, and ester.

23. Individuals with phenylketonuria must limit their intake of aspartame.

24. a. CH_3CH_2COOH, CH_3CH_2OH
b. CH_3COOH, (benzene ring)—OH
c. CH_3CH_2COOH, CH_3CHCH_2OH (with CH_3 on the middle carbon)

25. 1-propanol and ethanoic acid

26. Properties vary with the length of chains and the amount of crosslinking.

27. The glucose units are bonded in different orientations in glycogen and cellulose.

28. Glucose and fructose both have the molecular formula $C_6H_{12}O_6$; glucose has an aldehyde group, fructose a ketone group. Sucrose, a disaccharide, and a water molecule are formed when glucose and fructose react.

29.
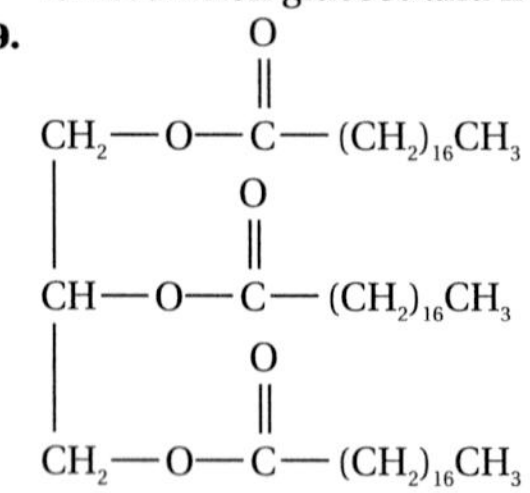

30. The alkali metal salt of a fatty acid.
Sodium stearate: $CH_3(CH_2)_{16}CO_2^-Na^+$

31.
$$H_3N^+—\underset{H}{\overset{H}{C}}—COO^-$$

32. They increase reaction rates but are unchanged by the reaction; they do not change the position of equilibrium.

33. A nucleic acid is a polymer of nucleotides.

34. The sugar unit in RNA has an additional oxygen on the —OH group attached to the second carbon.

35. Heating chitin with sodium hydroxide.

36. Advantage: it's biodegradable; disadvantage: structural instability when wet.

Chapter 26

1. Radioisotopes are those isotopes that undergo radioactive decay.

2. The nucleus undergoes change.

3.

	Alpha	Beta	Gamma
a. mass	4 amu	1/1837 amu	0
b. charge	+2	−1	0
c. penetrating power	low	moderate	high

(answers need not be in table form)

4. ${}^{226}_{88}Ra \rightarrow {}^{222}_{86}Rn + {}^{4}_{2}He$

5. Microorganism and insects are killed; some vegetables are kept from sprouting.

6. Answers will vary. Reasons for eating irradiated foods include wanting to reduce the chance of food poisoning, being able to store food longer, and not having any reasons to distrust irradiation. Reasons for not eating irradiated foods include being afraid of radiation and its misuse, not liking changes in taste and texture, and not wanting to contribute to the nuclear waste disposal problem.

7. The nucleus undergoes radioactive decay.

8. ${}^{17}_{9}F \rightarrow {}^{17}_{8}O + {}^{0}_{+1}e$

9. No. In 25 days one-half the sample will decay; in the next 25 days one-half the remaining half will decay. After 50 days one-fourth the original sample will remain.

10.

Number of half-lives	Elapsed time (hr)	Mass of ^{56}Mn
0	0	1.00 mg
1	2.6	0.50 mg
2	5.2	0.25 mg
3	7.8	0.125 mg
4	10.4	0.0625 mg

After four half-lives there is 0.0625 mg of manganese-56 left.

11. Protons.

12. Natural radioactivity is produced by radioactive elements present in nature. Artificial radioactivity is produced by elements created in nuclear reactors and accelerators.

13. A nuclear chain reaction involves the splitting of atomic nuclei that release energetic neutrons that split more nuclei.

14. The chain reaction is controlled by using neutron moderation and neutron absorption.

15. The sun and other stars are natural fusion reactors.

16. Fusion reactors use abundant, inexpensive fuels with no radioactive waste products.

17. Radon gas comes from minerals that contain uranium-238.

18. Answers will vary.

19. A Geiger counter only detects beta radiation; a scintillation counter can detect all types of ionizing radiation.
20. No. A Geiger counter cannot detect alpha radiation.
21. Tracers are used to study reaction mechanisms and to study the intake of substances in living organisms.
22. The seed can be placed at the location of the tumor and there are no radioactive waste products to be disposed of.

B.1 Exponential Notation

1. **a.** 7.9×10^4 **b.** 7.3×10^{-2} **c.** 6.2×10^{-8} **d.** 6.4×10^{-2} **e.** 2.435×10^6 **f.** 7.68×10^5 **g.** 1.028×10^6 **h.** 1.2×10^2
2. **a.** 8×10^{12} **b.** 9.3×10^{-2} **c.** 10^2 **d.** 8.5×10^{-8} **e.** 4.9×10^2 **f.** 1.32×10^7
3. **a.** 4.0×10^5 **b.** 4.0×10^9 **c.** 10^4 **d.** 1×10^2 **e.** 7.0×10^{-7} **f.** 3.1×10^{17} **g.** 1.70×10^{-3} **h.** 2.51×10^{17}

B.2 Algebraic Equations

4. $T = \dfrac{P \times V}{n \times R}$
5. $V_1 = \dfrac{P_2 \times V_2 \times T_1}{T_2 \times P_1}$
6. $V = \sqrt{\dfrac{2E}{m}}$
7. $P_B = P_T - P_A - P_C$
8. **a.** $h = 20$
   b. $h = 26.25$
   c. $h = 0.16$
   d. $h = -11.7$

B.3 Percents

9. **a.** 73% correct
   b. 82% correct
   c. 57% correct
10. 23 g hydrogen peroxide
11. 55 mL alcohol

B.4 Graphing

12.

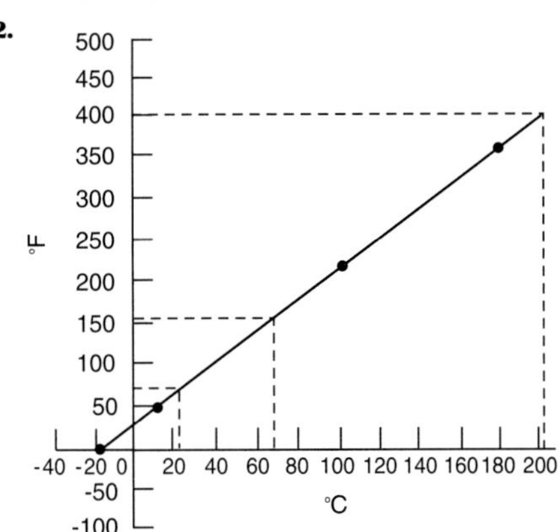

°F = (1.8 × °C) + 32
. . . 158 70 400
. . . 70 21 204

13. **a.**

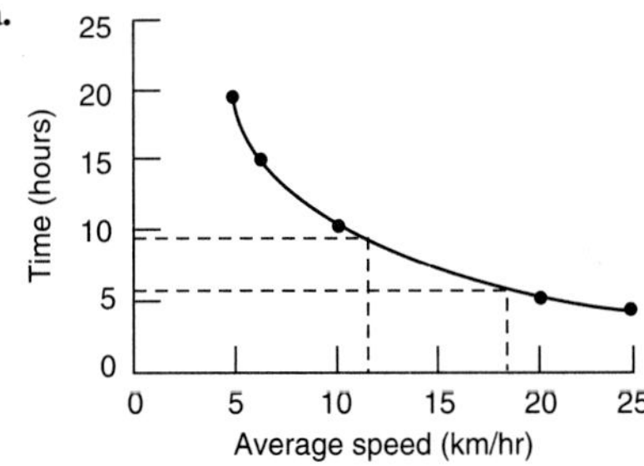

b. inverse
c. ~8.3 km/hr
d. 5.5 hours

14. **a.**

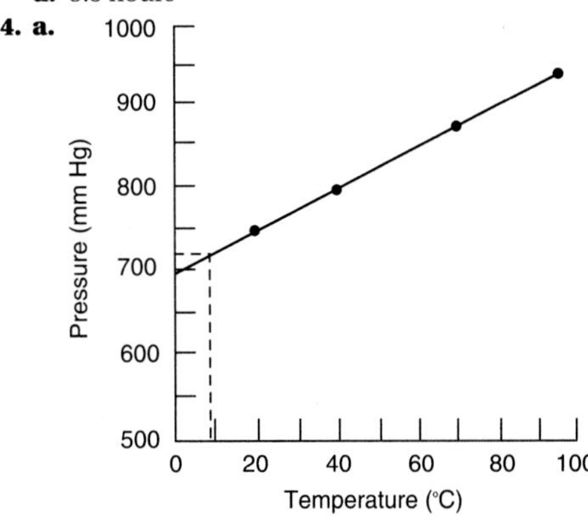

b. direct
c. ~9 °C
d. ~700 mm Hg
e. m = 2.6
f. $P = 2.6T + 700$

B.5 Logarithms

15. **a.** 0.538 **b.** −2.1 **c.** 2.66 **d.** −4.51 **e.** 9.17
16. **a.** 3.63×10^2 **b.** 1.29×10^6 **c.** 2.82×10^{-4} **d.** 1.07×10^1 **e.** 9.16

The instructions in this section are written specifically for the Texas Instruments TI-82 graphing calculator. The general operations apply to most types of graphing calculators, but the keystroking may be different.

D.1 Do This First

A. *Check for active equations* Press [Y=]. If the = sign of an equation is highlighted (shaded), then the equation is active and will appear whenever you press [GRAPH]. Deactivate an equation by using the arrow keys to place the cursor on the = sign and press [ENTER]. If you wish to delete an equation, position the cursor just to the right of the = sign and press [CLEAR].

B. *Clear the lists that you intend to use* There are several ways to clear a list. Here are the two easiest methods:

1. Press [STAT] [ENTER]. Lists 1–3 will be displayed on the screen. Use the arrow keys to place the cursor at the top of List 1, for example, so that **L1** is highlighted. Press [CLEAR] [ENTER]. List 1 is now empty. Clear any other lists in the same manner.
2. Press [STAT], then select "4" (**ClrList**) and press [ENTER]. "**ClrList**" will appear on the screen. Press [2nd] **L1**, then press [ENTER]. When List 1 has been cleared, the word "**Done**" will appear on the screen. If you wish to clear more than one list, type the names of the lists after the word "**ClrList**", separating each list name with a comma.

C. *Check for active stat plots* A stat plot is a point-by-point graph of selected lists of data.

Press [2nd] **STAT PLOT**. The **STAT PLOTS** menu will appear. If any of the three plots is active, the word "**ON**" will appear below the active plot. You can deactivate all of the plots at once by selecting "4" (**PlotsOff**) and pressing [ENTER]. The word "**Done**" will appear to indicate that all three plots have been deactivated.

To deactivate one stat plot at a time, use the down arrow to highlight the plot that you want to turn off, then press [ENTER]. The screen will change to display the parameters for the plot. Use the arrow keys to highlight the word "**Off**", then press [ENTER]. The plot has been deactivated.

D.2 Entering Data in a List and Plotting Points

A. *Entering Data in a List*

1. Clear the list or lists that you intend to use. (See section D.1, steps B1–2.)

2. Press STAT ENTER. Lists 1–3 will be displayed on the calculator screen. Use the right-hand arrow to access lists 4–6, if necessary.

3. Type a data point into the selected list and press ENTER. The value will appear as the first item in that list. Enter the remaining values in a similar manner.

4. If another list of data must be created, use the left- or right-hand arrow key to move to the desired list, then type in the data as described above.

5. If a data point is entered incorrectly, move the cursor to the value that is incorrect, type in the correct value, and press ENTER.

B. *Plotting Data*

1. Press 2nd **STAT PLOT**. The **STAT PLOTS** menu is shown on the calculator screen. Press ENTER. The **Plot1** menu will appear.

2. The cursor will be blinking over the word "**On**". Press ENTER to activate Plot 1.

3. Use the arrow keys to select the type of plot that you are preparing. The options are, in the order listed: scatter, xyLine, box plot, histogram. Use the arrow keys to place the cursor on the desired plot type, and press ENTER.

4. Identify the lists that contain the x- and y-values by placing the cursor on the appropriate list and pressing ENTER.

5. Select a mark for the plotted points by placing the cursor on the desired mark type (box, cross, or dot) and pressing ENTER. At this point, all of the parameters for your graph should be selected.

6. Press WINDOW. The **WINDOW** menu allows you to set the size of the screen for the best view of your graph. Use the down arrow key to move along the menu. Enter the appropriate maximum and minimum values for the x- and y-axes. **Xscl** and **Yscl** are the scale tick marks that you can place at regular intervals along the border of each axis. If you do not want these reference marks, type in "**0**".

7. Press GRAPH. Your data points will appear on the screen. By pressing TRACE, you can use the left- and right-hand arrows to review your data points. The x- and y-values will be displayed at the bottom of the screen.

8. (Optional) If the data points do not properly fit the screen, press [ZOOM], then select "9" (**ZoomStat**). ZoomStat reconfigures the Window menu to display all of the plotted points, making the most efficient use of the screen. The **ZoomStat** option may also be selected immediately after activating your Plot (from steps 1–5 above), if you do not wish to manually set the Window parameters.

D.3 Graphing an Equation

These directions explain the derivation of a best-fit line, or linear regression equation. Graphing other types of functions follows the same process. Other functions can be found in the **CALC** menu described below.

A. Enter the data, from which an equation will be derived, into two separate lists. If possible, place the independent variable (x) data in List 1 and the dependent variable (y) data in List 2.

B. Press [STAT], then press the right-hand arrow to open the **CALC** menu. Select option "5" (**LinReg(ax+b)**).

C. *If the* x*-values are in List 1 and the* y*-values are in List 2,* press [ENTER]. The linear regression equation will be displayed. As shown, a represents the slope of the line, b is the y-intercept, and r is the correlation coefficient.

D. *If the* x*- and* y*-values are stored in other lists,* type in the lists for each variable, with the x-variable identified first. For example, if the x-values are placed in List 3 and the y-values are in List 5, press: [2nd] **L3** [,] [2nd] **L5** after the term "**LinReg**" appears on the screen. Press [ENTER] and the linear regression equation will be displayed.

E. To prepare the linear regression equation for graphing, press [Y=]. Use the down arrow key to place the flashing cursor next to the first empty equation line. Press [VARS] and select option "5" (**Statistics...**), which opens the statistics options. Press the right-hand arrow key twice to open the **EQ** (equation) menu. Select option "7" (**RegEQ**) to access the linear regression equation derived in step C or step D above. The screen will revert to the **Y=** field, where your linear regression equation will be written and activated for graphing.

F. Press [WINDOW] to set the boundaries of the graph screen, as described in section D.2, step B6.

G. Press [GRAPH] to view a graph of the equation.

Note: The **ZoomStat** option (section D.2, step B8) works only with a plot of points, such as a scatter plot. This is the advantage of plotting the points along with an equation derived from those points.

D.4 Trace and Zoom

A. *Tracing a Scatter or xyLine Plot* Press [TRACE]. The cursor will appear as a flashing X, positioned on the first set of points placed in the lists. Use the right- and left-hand arrow keys to move from point to point. The *x*- and *y*-values will be displayed at the bottom of the screen.

B. *Estimating a Value on a Plot*

1. Press [2nd] **STAT PLOT** to open the **STAT PLOTS** menu. Use the down arrow, if necessary, to highlight the active plot. Press [ENTER] to display the **Plot** menu. Press the down arrow to reach **Type:**. Press the right-hand arrow to highlight the xyLine option. Press [ENTER], then press [GRAPH]. The graph will be data points connected by a line.

2. Press the up arrow. The cursor will appear as a cross and can be moved anywhere on the screen by using the arrow keys. The values of *x* and *y* for the cursor's position are shown at the bottom of the screen. Move the cursor to the desired spot on the xyLine and record the data.

C. *Tracing a Graphed Equation*

1. Press [TRACE]. The cursor will appear as a flashing X. Use the right- and left-hand arrow keys to move along the function. The values of *x* and *y* are shown at the bottom of the screen.

2. *Note:* The trace option can be used when an equation *and* data points are graphed simultaneously. When the trace is applied, use the up and down arrows to move to the equation or the plotted points. Occasionally, you will want to examine a very small section of a graph. The **ZBox** and **Zoom In** options on the graphing calculator work like the zoom lens on a camera, allowing you to look at your graph more closely.

The zoom options can be applied to either functions (equations) or plotted points, although they are more efficient when used with functions because the tracing is more accurate.

D. *Zooming In to Examine a Section*

1. With the graph displayed on the calculator screen, press [TRACE] and move the cursor as close as possible to the desired area. Press ZOOM, then select "2" (**Zoom In**). The graph will reappear. Press ENTER. The graph will be redrawn. Press TRACE again to examine this smaller portion of the graph. The **Zoom In** option can be applied repeatedly.

2. To return the graph to its previous dimensions, press ZOOM, select "3" (**Zoom Out**), and press ENTER.

E. *Using* **ZBox** *to Highlight and Magnify an Area of a Graph*

1. With the graph displayed, press ZOOM ENTER. The cursor appears as a very small, flashing cross. Use the arrow keys to move the cursor near the desired area, slightly above or below the plot itself. Press ENTER. The cursor will become a flashing box. Use either the right- or left-hand arrow key to drag the box across the graph, then use the up or down arrow key to open the box. The portion of the plot that you wish to analyze should be inside the box. Press ENTER and the boxed area will be displayed. If the box is improperly placed, press CLEAR and start over. **ZBox** takes a bit of practice to use effectively, but it can define a small portion of a graph more accurately than **Zoom In**.

2. **Zoom Out** *will not* revert a graph to its original dimensions after **ZBox** has been used.

D.5 Programming

Programming is a useful tool for completing redundant computations that involve multiple variables or simulating a graphic phenomenon (for example, a fractal) with a mathematical function.

The program below solves the quadratic equation and will provide you with practice in writing programs for the graphing calculator. As you know, a generic form of the quadratic equation is:

$$0 = ax^2 + bx + c$$

and the solution is:

$$\frac{x = -b \pm \sqrt{b^2 - 4ac)}}{2a}$$

A. *Creating a Program*

1. Press PRGM, then press the right-hand arrow key twice. Press ENTER to begin writing a new program. The cursor will appear as a flashing letter A, indicating that the keypad is in alpha mode.

2. Enter QUAD as the program name. If a program named QUAD already exists in your calculator, type another name in. Press

ENTER when you have completed the name. A new line will appear below the name, beginning with a colon (:).

3. Press PRGM, then press the right-hand arrow key to display the Input/Output (**I/O**) menu. Select "3" (**Disp**). This command will now appear on the first line of your program. Press 2nd **ALPHA**, which locks the keypad in alpha mode. Type in "**A?**", then press ENTER. (Quotation marks are the alpha mode of the plus sign key.) The first line of your new program is complete! A new line will appear, beginning with a colon.
4. Press PRGM, then press the right-hand arrow key to access the **I/O** menu again. Press ENTER. The word **Input** should appear on the second line of the program. Press **ALPHA A**, then press ENTER.
5. Repeat step 3, replacing **A** with **B**. The line should read: **Disp "B?"**
6. Repeat step 4, replacing **A** with **B**. The line should read: **Input B**
7. Repeat step 3, replacing **A** with **C**. The line should read: **Disp "C?"**
8. Repeat step 4, replacing **A** with **C**. The line should read: **Input C**

Now for something new, at last. The first six lines of the program allow you to type in the coefficients *a, b,* and *c* of the quadratic equation to be solved. The following lines are the two versions of the quadratic solution.

9. Enter **–**, then **ALPHA B**. Enter **+**, then 2nd **√(ALPHA B**. Enter **x**^{2} **– 4**. Enter **ALPHA A ALPHA C)**. Press **/** (the division key) **2ALPHA A**. Press STO▸ **X**, then ENTER. The line should be:

   :–B+√(B^2**–4AC)/2A→X**

10. Press PRGM, then press the right-hand arrow key. Select "3" (**Disp**), then press 2nd **ALPHA "X"** ENTER.
11. Repeat step 10, but do not type in the quotation marks. The line should be: **: Disp X**.
12. Repeat step 9, replacing the **+** (plus) sign with a **–** (minus) sign. The line should be:

    :–B–√(B^2**–4AC)/2A→X**

13. Repeat step 11. The program is now complete. Press 2nd **QUIT** to exit the programming mode.

To operate a program, press PRGM and use the down arrow key to highlight the program to be run. Press ENTER twice, and away you go.

The following is a list of each line of the QUAD program as it should appear on your calculator screen.

```
PROGRAM: QUAD
:Disp "A?"
:Input A
:Disp "B?"
:Input B
:Disp "C?"
:Input C
:-B+√(B²-4AC)/2A→X
:Disp "X"
:Disp X
:-B-√(B²-4AC)/2A→X
:Disp X
```

B. *Programming Hints* All changes to a program must be done in edit mode. Press PRGM, then press the right-hand arrow to access the edit mode. Use the down arrow to highlight the desired program and press ENTER.

1. If you need to *add a character* to a line in the program, use the arrow keys to place the cursor in the exact spot where you wish to make an addition. Press 2nd **INS**, then enter the character or characters.
2. If you need to *delete a character* in the program, place the cursor on the character to be deleted and press **DEL**.
3. If you need to *delete a line* in the program, place the cursor at the beginning of the line and press CLEAR.
4. The negative key (gray key, bottom row) and the subtract key (blue key, farthest right column) are *not* interchangeable. Make sure that you have used the proper key for the desired operation.
5. The letter **X** can be entered in two ways. You can type in **ALPHA X** or press the **X,T,θ** key. With the calculator in function or sequence mode, this key will print an **X**.

D.6 Working with Lists

A. *Using a List for a Calculation*

A mathematical operation can be performed on all data in a list. The new values are then sent to a new list for later use.

1. Press STAT ENTER. Lists 1–3 will appear on the screen. Let's say that you wish to calculate the natural logarithm of each value in List 1 and store the data in List 2. Use the arrow keys

to place the cursor at the top of List 2, highlighting **L2**. Notice that the bottom line reads **L2**.

2. If List 2 contains data, either clear the list or send the new data to an empty list. To clear List 2, with the cursor placed on **L2**, press CLEAR ENTER.
3. Press the **LN** key, then press 2nd **L1** ENTER. List 2 now contains the natural logarithm values of each number in List 1. Any other mathematical operation can be used with the lists of data following this procedure.

B. *Sorting Data*

1. To sort the data in List 1, for example, in *descending* order, press 2nd LIST. Select "2" (**SortD(**), then press 2nd **L1)** ENTER. The word "**Done**" will appear on the screen, informing you that List 1 is arranged in descending order.
2. To sort the data in List 1, for example, in *ascending* order, press 2nd **LIST**. Press ENTER, then press 2nd **L1)** ENTER. The word "**Done**" will appear on the screen.

C. *Calculating the Mean and Median Values of a List*

1. To calculate the mean of the data in List 1, for example, press 2nd LIST. Press the right-hand arrow key to acces the MATH menu, and select "3" (**mean(**). Press 2nd **L1)** ENTER. The mean value will appear on the screen.
2. To calculate the median of the data in List 1, for example, press 2nd **LIST**. Press the right-hand arrow key to access the MATH menu, and select "4" (**median(**). Press 2nd **L1)** ENTER. The median value will appear on the screen.

Note: Press 2nd **LIST** to access the common operations and calculations that can be performed on a list of data, of which mean and median are two, in a manner similar to the procedure shown above.

D.7 Using Calculation Options for Equations

An efficient way to locate specific points on the graph of an equation is to direct the graphing calculator to proceed to calculate, rather than going through the tracing process.

A. With an equation activated, press 2nd **CALC**. There are seven options in the **CALCULATE** menu. (*Note:* These options can only be used with an equation or a function.) In the following steps, we'll explore two of these options.

B. Let's say you wish to determine the value of y on a graph for a given value of x. Select "1" (**value**) and press [ENTER]. The graph will appear on the screen; at the bottom of the screen you will see: **Eval X=**. Type in the x-value and press [ENTER]. The bottom of the screen will change to display the appropriate x- and y-values.

C. Here's a second example. You are analyzing a nuclear decay graph, which is nonlinear, and wish to determine the slope of the curve at a certain point. In the **CALCULATE** menu, select "6" (**dy/dx**). The graph will appear and the cursor will be flashing. Use the left- or right-hand arrow keys to place the cursor at the desired point on the graph. Press [ENTER]. The slope (dy/dx) will be displayed at the bottom of the screen.

Note: You may use the **Zoom In** option at any time to place the cursor on the desired point more accurately. However, you must go back to the **CALCULATE** menu and select **dy/dx** again.

D.8 Example Problems

1. The table below shows the abundance of the top ten elements in the earth's crust.

Element	% by mass
oxygen	46.9
silicon	26.9
aluminum	8.08
iron	5.09
calcium	4.99
potassium	2.55
magnesium	2.33
sodium	2.13
carbon	0.52
titanium	0.50

a. Clear List 1 of your graphing calculator. Enter the percent values in List 1. What percent of the earth's crust is made up of the top ten elements?

Solution: Press [2nd] **LIST**, then press the right-hand arrow to open the **MATH** menu. Select "5" (**sum**) and press [2nd] **L1**. Press [ENTER]. The sum of List 1 is displayed, which is your answer: 99.99%.

b. What percent of the top ten elements are the alkaline earth metals?

Solution: You want to analyze calcium and magnesium from the list. Delete the sum of 99.99% from part a above from List 1. Enter **(4.99+2.33)/**. Press 2nd **LIST**, then press the right-hand arrow to open the **MATH** menu. Select "5" (**sum**) and press 2nd **L1**. Press ENTER. Multiply the calculated value by 100, or move the decimal two places to the right, to determine percent as: 7.32%.

2. An experiment was conducted to measure the effect of pressure on the volume of a gas. The results of the tests are shown in the table below.

Pressure (atm)	Volume (L)
3.0	3.00
6.0	1.50
12.0	0.750
24.0	0.375

a. Clear Lists 1 and 2 in your graphing calculator. Enter the volume data in List 1 and the pressure data in List 2. Graph the data, with volume as the x-values and pressure as the y-values.

Solution: Press 2nd **STAT PLOT**. Press ENTER. The parameters for Plot 1 can now be set. Press ENTER to activate Plot 1; the word **On** is highlighted (shaded). Press the down arrow, then press the right-hand arrow to highlight the xyLine type of graph. Press ENTER. Examine the Xlist. **L1** should be highlighted. If it is not, place the cursor on **L1** and press ENTER. Similarly, the Ylist should have **L2** highlighted. Select the desired mark for your points and press ENTER.

Press WINDOW to set the parameters for your graph. Use the down arrow key to move along this menu. Set the Window as: Xmin = 0; Xmax = 3.2; Xscl = 1; Ymin = 0; Ymax = 25; Yscl = 5. Press GRAPH to view your xyLine plot.

b. Trace the plot to determine the volume of the gas when the pressure is 4.13 atm.

Solution: With the graph on the screen, press the up arrow key. Use the arrow keys to place the cursor on the plot as close to y = 4.13 as possible. Press ZOOM and select "2" (**Zoom In**). Press ENTER. Move the arrow keys to get close to $y = 4.13$. You may want to **Zoom In** again. At a pressure of 4.13 atm, the volume is 2.43 L.

c. Calculate the inverse of pressure and plot $1/P$ (y-axis) vs. volume (x-axis).

Solution: Press STAT ENTER to display the lists. Clear List 3, where we'll place the values for $1/P$. Place the cursor at the top of List 3, so that **L3** is highlighted. Press 2nd **L2** x^{-1}, then press ENTER. The $1/P$ values are now in List 3.

Press 2nd **STAT PLOT**, and select "4" (**PlotsOff**). Press ENTER, and all plots have now been deactivated. Press 2nd **STAT PLOT** again, then press the down arrow to highlight Plot 2. Press ENTER. Set up Plot 2 as: **On; Type: xyLine; Xlist:L1; Ylist:L3; Mark:+**.

Press ZOOM, and select "9" (**ZoomStat**). The xyLine plot of $1/P$ vs. volume will be displayed. (*Note:* ZoomStat sets up the window automatically, so we do not need to go through the Window menu manually.)

d. Derive and graph a linear regression equation for the data.

Solution: Press STAT, then press the right-hand arrow to open the CALC menu. Select "5" (**LinReg(ax+b)**), then press 2nd **L1**, 2nd **L3**. Press ENTER and the linear regression will appear. Press Y=, and place the cursor next to the first open line in the Y= screen. Press VARS, and select "5" (**Statistics...**). Press the right-hand arrow key twice, to open the **EQ** menu. Select "7" (**RegEQ**), and the linear regression equation will appear in the Y= screen. Press GRAPH to view the equation.

e. Determine the pressure when the gas volume is 0.418 L.

Solution 1 (tracing): With the graph onscreen, press TRACE, then press the down arrow key to place the cursor on the equation rather than on the xyLine. Use the left- or right-hand arrow keys to move as close to $x = 0.418$ as possible. Press ZOOM, and select "2" (**Zoom In**). Press ENTER. Continue to **Zoom In** until you are satisfied with your answer, which should be very near to $y = 0.0464$. This value is the inverse of the answer. Press **ALPHA Y**, then press x^{-1} ENTER. Your answer should be close to 21.55 atm of pressure.

Solution 2 (calculation): Press 2nd **CALC**. Select "1" (**value**). The graph will appear, and **Eval X** will appear at the bottom of the screen. Type in **0.418** and press ENTER. The direct calculation reveals $1/P$ at a volume of 0.418 L to be 0.0464 . . . , slightly different from your traced answer. Press **ALPHA Y**, then press x^{-1} ENTER. The answer is 21.53 atm of pressure.

In this appendix, we provide graphing calculator solutions for some problems that currently appear in the Chapter Reviews, as well as new problems that can be solved using the graphing calculator. Appendix D provides detailed instruction for using the graphing calculator. The instructions in this section are written specifically for the Texas Instruments TI-82 graphing calculator. The general operations apply to most types of graphing calculators, but the keystroking may be different.

Chapter 2

36. Three students made multiple weighings of a copper cylinder, each using a different balance. The correct mass of the cylinder had been previously determined to be 47.32 g.

	Lissa	**Lamont**	**Leigh Anne**
Weighing 1	47.13	47.45	47.95
Weighing 2	47.94	47.39	47.91
Weighing 3	46.83	47.42	47.89
Weighing 4	47.47	47.41	47.93

a. Complete the following steps on your graphing calculator to prepare a bar chart of Lissa's data. Remember to check for active equations and clear Lists 1 and 2 before beginning. (Refer to Appendix D for detailed instructions.)

- Press STAT ENTER to display the lists. If List 1 contains data, press the up arrow to place the cursor on **L1**. Press CLEAR ENTER to clear the data from List 1. Type in each data point, then press ENTER to place it in the list.
- Press 2nd **STAT PLOT** to display the **STAT PLOTS** menu. Press ENTER to access the commands for Plot 1. Make sure that only Plot 1 is active (or "**On**"). Turn all other plots off. (Refer to Appendix D for detailed instructions.) Use the arrow keys to place the cursor on the appropriate line and set up Plot 1 as: ON ; **Type**: (box plot); **Xlist: L1; Freq: 1**. Press ENTER after high-lighting a setting.
- Press WINDOW to set the screen parameters. Use the arrow keys to place the cursor on the appropriate line to set up the window as: **Xmin: 40; Xmax: 50; Xscl: 1**. (*Note:* the *y*-values are not used for a box plot, but the Ymax must be greater than Ymin for the plot to appear.)
- Press GRAPH to view the box plot of Lissa's weighings. Press TRACE . A blinking cursor will appear; the median value of the weighings will be displayed at the bottom of the screen. Use the left- and right-hand arrow keys to trace across the box plot for maximum and minimum values.
- Follow these steps to enter and graph the weighings for Lamont and Leigh Anne. Use List 2 and Plot 2 for Lamont's data, List 3 and Plot 3 for Leigh Anne's data. Press TRACE . Use the down and up arrow keys to move from one box plot to another. List 1 (Lissa's data) is the top plot.

  What is the median value for each student's set of weighings?

b. Review the box plots and describe the accuracy and precision of each student's measurements.

82. The table below shows how the mass of sulfur increases with an increase in the volume.

Mass of sulfur (g)	**Volume of sulfur (cm^3)**
23.5	11.4
60.8	29.2
115	55.5
168	81.1

a. Complete the following steps on your graphing calculator to prepare a graph of the data. Remember to check for active equations and clear Lists 1 and 2 before beginning. (Refer to Appendix D for detailed instructions.)

- Press STAT ENTER to display the lists. If List 1 contains data, press the up arrow to place the cursor on **L1**. Press CLEAR ENTER to clear the data from List 1. Type in a volume data point, then press ENTER to place it in the list. Enter the mass data in List 2 in a similar manner.

- Press 2nd **STAT PLOT** to display the **STAT PLOTS** menu.
- Press ENTER to access the commands for Plot 1. Make sure that only Plot 1 is active (or "**On**"). Turn all other plots off (see Appendix D for detailed instructions.) Use the arrow keys to place the cursor on the appropriate line and set up Plot 1 as: ON; **Type:** (scatter); **Xlist: L1**; **Ylist: L2**; **Mark:** □. Press ENTER after highlighting a setting.
- Press WINDOW to set the screen parameters. Use the arrow keys to place the cursor on the appropriate line to set up the window as: **Xmin: 0**; **Xmax: 85**; **Xscl: 10**; **Ymin: 0**; **Ymax: 170**; **Yscl: 10**.
- Press GRAPH to view the scatter plot of mass vs. volume.

b. Derive and plot a linear regression equation (best-fit line) for the plotted data.

- Press STAT, then press the right-hand arrow key to display the CALC menu. Select "5" (**LinReg(ax+b)**), then press ENTER. The linear regression equation will appear on the calculator screen.
- Press Y=. Turn off any active equations. An active equation has its = sign highlighted. Place the cursor on the = sign, then press ENTER. The equation is now deactivated, and will not appear on the screen. Place the cursor on the first empty line.
- Press VARS, then select "5" (**Statistics...**). The screen will display various statistical operations. Press the right-hand arrow key twice, to open the **EQ** menu. Select "7" (**RegEQ**). The screen will change to the y= menu, where your linear regression will appear as an active equation. Press GRAPH to view the function and the plotted points.

c. What is the slope of the linear regression equation? What does the slope represent?

d. Press TRACE. The cursor will be flashing. Press the down arrow key to place the cursor on the linear regression (rather than the scatter plot). Use the left- or right-hand arrow keys to trace the line to $x = 1$. What is the y-value at $x = 1$? Compare this estimated density to your answer in part **c.**

Chapter 3

66. Different volumes of the same liquid were added to a flask on a balance. After each addition of liquid, the mass of the flask containing the liquid was measured.

volume (mL)	14	27	41	55	82
mass (g)	103.0	120.4	139.1	157.9	194.1

a. Complete the following steps on your graphing calculator to prepare a graph of the data. Remember to check for active equations and clear Lists 1 and 2 before beginning. (Refer to Appendix D for detailed instructions.)

- Press STAT ENTER to display the lists. If List 1 contains data, press the up arrow to place the cursor on **L1**. Press CLEAR ENTER to clear the data from List 1. Type in the volume data, pressing ENTER after each entry. Enter the mass data in List 2 in a similar manner.
- Press 2nd **STAT PLOT** to display the **STAT PLOTS** menu. Make sure that only Plot 1 is active ("**On**"). Turn all other plots off. (Refer to Appendix D for detailed instructions.) Press ENTER to access the commands for Plot 1. Use the arrow keys to place the cursor on the appropriate line and set up Plot 1 as: **On**; **Type:** (xyLine); **Xlist: L1**; **YList: L2**; **Mark:** □. Press ENTER after highlighting each setting.
- Press WINDOW to set the screen parameters as: **Xmin=0**; **Xmax=100**; **Xscl=10**; **Ymin=100**; **Ymax=200**; **Yscl=10**. Press GRAPH to display the data points. Press the up arrow key, which produces a cursor in the shape of a cross and displays x- and y-values at the bottom of the screen. Use the arrow keys to estimate the mass of a flask of liquid with a volume of 148 mL.

b. Derive a linear regression equation (best-fit line) for the data in Lists 1 and 2. Graph this equation. (Refer to Appendix D for a detailed description of this process.) Use the graph and/or the equation to determine the mass of the flask and the density of the liquid.

c. Press [TRACE], then press the down arrow key to place the cursor on the plot of the linear regression equation. Use the left- and right-hand arrow keys to trace the function to determine the mass of the flask of liquid with a volume of 148 mL. Place the cursor as close to $y = 148$ as possible. Press [ZOOM], then select "2" (**Zoom In**), and press [ENTER]. The graph will be redrawn around a small area near $y = 148$. Press [TRACE] and press the down arrow. Trace the graph to find your answer. The **Zoom In** option may be employed again, if needed. How does this answer compare to your estimate in part **a**?

72. The mass of samples of U.S. pennies minted in various years was measured and tabulated below.

Year minted	Mass (g)	Average mass (g)
1979	3.13, 3.05, 3.10	
1980	3.11, 3.12, 3.08	
1981	3.06, 3.07, 3.14	
1982	3.11, 3.10, 2.51, 2.55	
1983	2.50, 2.45, 2.49	
1984	2.50, 2.53, 2.51	

a. Calculate the average mass of pennies to complete the table.

b. Prepare a graph of average mass (y-axis) vs. year minted (x-axis). Place the year minted data in List 1 and the average mass in List 2. (Refer to Appendix D for detailed instructions.) For the best view of your data, set the screen parameters (**WINDOW**) as: **Xmin=1978.9**; **Xmax=1984.1**; **Xscl=1000**; **Ymin=2.4**; **Ymax=3.2**; **Yscl=.1** Press [GRAPH] to view a plot of mass vs. year.

c. Describe the trend that your graph shows.

d. The volume of a penny is, on average, 0.346 cm^3. Before 1983, all pennies were composed entirely of copper (density = 8.96 g/cm^3). Starting in 1983, pennies were made of zinc (density = 7.13 g /cm3) and copper. Use the table of data to determine whether post-1983 pennies are 50% copper and 50% zinc, 95% copper and 5% zinc, or 5% copper and 95% zinc.

Chapter 4

46. The following table shows some data collected by Rutherford and his colleagues during their gold foil experiment.

Angle of deflection (degrees)	Number of deflections
5	8 289 000
10	502 570
15	120 570
30	7 800
45	1 435
60	477
75	211
105	198

a. Complete the following steps on your graphing calculator to enter the number of deflections in List 1.

- Press [STAT] [ENTER] to display the lists. If List 1 contains data, press the up arrow to place the cursor on **L1**. Press [CLEAR] [ENTER] to clear the data from List 1. Type in each data point, then press [ENTER] to place it in the list.

b. Use the data in List 1 to determine the percent of alpha particle deflections that were 5° or less. (Refer to Appendix D for a sample problem.)

c. What percent were 15° or less?

d. What percent were 60° or greater?

68. The masses of several naturally occurring isotopes of the element mercury are listed below:

Isotope	Atomic mass ($\times 10^{-24}$g)
196	325.303
198	328.625
199	330.287
200	
201	333.611
202	335.271
204	338.596

a. Prepare a graph of atomic mass (y-axis) vs. isotope (x-axis), *omitting mercury-200.* Place the isotopes in List 1 and the atomic masses in List 2. (Refer to Appendix D for detailed instructions.) For the best view of your data, set the screen parameters (**WINDOW**) as: **Xmin=195.9**; **Xmax=204.1**; **Xscl=1**; **Ymin=325**; **Ymax=339**; **Yscl=1**. Press GRAPH to view the plot.

b. Derive a linear regression equation (best-fit line) for your data, and graph the equation.

c. Trace the line to determine the atomic mass of the isotope mercury-200.

d. What is the slope of the linear regression equation? What does the slope represent?

Chapter 5

57. Thousands of different kinds of inorganic chemicals are produced in the United States. The amounts of the top ten inorganic chemicals produced in 1992 are shown in the following data table.

Chemical	Amount produced (billions of kg)
Sulfuric acid	39.4
Nitrogen	25.9
Oxygen	17.7
Ammonia	15.5
Lime	15.3
Phosphoric acid	11.2
Sodium hydroxide	11.0
Chlorine	10.3
Sodium carbonate	9.3
Nitric acid	6.8

a. Complete the following steps on your graphing calculator to enter the amounts produced in List 1.

- Press STAT ENTER to display the lists. If List 1 contains data, press the up arrow to place the cursor on **L1**. Press CLEAR ENTER to clear the data from List 1. Type in each amount, then press ENTER to place it in the list.

b. Use the data in List 1 to determine the percent of the total production that was accounted for by lime (calcium oxide). (Refer to Appendix D for a sample problem.)

c. Three diatomic gases are on the list. What are their names and what was their total production in 1992?

d. Use the data in List 1 to determine the percent of the total production of the top ten inorganic chemicals that was accounted for by the acids.

e. Write the chemical formulas for the top ten inorganic chemicals.

Chapter 6

82. The following table gives the gram formula mass (gfm) and density of seven gases at STP.

Substance	Gram formula mass (gfm)	Density (g/L)g/L)
Oxygen	32.0	1.43
Carbon dioxide	44.0	1.96
Ethane	30.0	1.34
Hydrogen	2.0	0.0893
Sulfur dioxide	64.1	2.86
Ammonia	17.0	0.759
Fluorine	38.0	1.70

a. Complete the following steps on your graphing calculator to prepare a graph of the data. Remember to check for active equations and clear Lists 1 and 2 before beginning. (Refer to Appendix D for detailed instructions.)

- Press STAT ENTER to display the lists. Enter the density data in List 1, pressing ENTER after each entry. Enter the gfm data in List 2 in a similar manner.

- Press 2nd Y= to display the **STAT PLOT** menu.Make sure that only Plot 1 is active ("**On**"). Turn all other plots off (see Appendix D for detailed instructions.) Press ENTER to access the commands for Plot 1. Use the arrow keys to place the cursor on the appropriate line and set up Plot 1 as: On; **Type**: (points); **Xlist: L1**; **YList: L2**;

Mark: □. Press (ENTER) after highlighting each setting.

- Press (WINDOW) to set the screen parameters. Use the arrow keys to place the cursor on the appropriate line to set up the window as: **Xmin=0**; **Xmax=3**; **Xscl=0.1**; **Ymin=0**; **Ymax=65**; **Yscl=10**. Press (GRAPH) to view the graph of the data.

b. Derive a linear regression equation for the data in Lists 1 and 2. Graph this equation. What is the slope of this straight-line plot?

c. Press (TRACE), then press the down arrow key to place the cursor on the plot of the linear regression equation. Use the left- and right-hand arrow keys to trace the function to determine the gfm of a gas at STP that has a density of 1.10 g/L. Place the cursor as close to $x = 1.10$ as possible. Press (ZOOM), then select "2" (**Zoom In**), and press (ENTER). The graph will be redrawn around a small area near $x = 1.10$. Press (TRACE) and press the down arrow. Trace the graph to find your answer. The **Zoom In** option may be employed again, if needed.

d. A mole of a certain gas at STP has a mass of 56.0 g. Trace the linear regression equation to determine the density of this gas.

91. Several pieces of an unknown metal are tested for their densities by water displacement. The test results are given below:

Sample	Mass (g)	Volume (mL)
1	25.19	3.56
2	47.14	6.57
3	19.67	2.83
4	51.94	7.44
5	34.07	4.64
6	6.79	0.98

a. Prepare a graph of the data, placing volume on the x-axis and mass on the y-axis. Derive and graph the linear regression equation (best-fit line) for the data and determine the slope of the line. (Refer to Appendix D for detailed instructions.)

b. The unknown metal is one of the following elements, with its density given in parentheses: manganese (7.44 g/mL), chromium (7.19 g/mL), tin (7.31 g/mL), or zinc (7.13 g/mL). Identify the unknown metal.

c. Trace the best-fit line to determine the volume that 1.00 mole of this metal will occupy.

Chapter 7

69. The white solid calcium chloride, $CaCl_2$, is used as a drying agent. The maximum amount of water absorbed by different quantities of $CaCl_2$ is given in the following table.

$CaCl_2$ (g)	$CaCl_2$ (mol)	H_2O (g)	H_2O (mol)
17.3	—	5.62	—
48.8	—	15.8	—
124	—	40.3	—
337	—	109	—

a. Enter the mass amounts of $CaCl_2$ in List 1 of your graphing calculator by pressing (STAT) (ENTER). Clear List 1 if necessary. Type in the mass data, pressing (ENTER) after each entry.

b. Use the arrow keys to place the cursor at the top of List 2, highlighting **L2**. Press (2nd) **L1/110.98**, then press (ENTER). This step instructs the calculator to divide each value in List 1 by the formula mass of $CaCl_2$ (110.98 g/mol).Thus the values in List 2 become the molar amounts of $CaCl_2$ that correspond to the mass data in List 1.

c. Repeat step **b** above, placing the mass data for water in List 3 and the corresponding molar amounts of water in List 4. Use the data in Lists 2 and 4 to complete the table.

d. Plot the moles of $CaCl_2$ (List 2) on the x-axis and the moles of water absorbed (List 4) on the y-axis. (Refer to Appendix D for detailed instructions.)

e. Derive a linear regression equation for the points that you have plotted, and graph the equation. Based on the graph, how many molecules of water does each formula unit of calcium chloride absorb?

78. Air bags in vehicles employ a reaction involving the substance sodium azide, NaN_3. A series of experiments were conducted at STP and the volume of nitrogen, N_2, was recorded when a given mass of sodium azide reacted. The results were recorded in the table below.

Mass of NaN_3 (g)	**Mol NaN_3**	**Volume of N_2 (L)**	**Mol N_2**
12.5		6.46	
8.26		4.27	
18.9		9.77	
3.45		1.78	
24.7		12.77	

Refer to question 69 to guide you through this problem.

a. Enter the mass amounts of NaN_3 in List 1 of your graphing calculator. Calculate moles of NaN_3 and place these values in List 2.

b. Enter the volume amounts of N_2 in List 3. Calculate the corresponding moles of N_2, and place them in List 4. Complete the table with the values in Lists 2 and 4.

c. Derive a linear regression equation for the mol N_2 (*y*-axis) vs. mol NaN_3 (*x*-axis), and graph the equation. Press WINDOW to set the screen parameters. Use the arrow keys to place the cursor on the appropriate line to set up the window as: **Xmin=0**; **Xmax=0.5**; **Xscl=0.1**; **Ymin=0**; **Ymax=0.6**; **Yscl=0.1**. Press GRAPH to view the graph of the molar relationship. Use the graph or the equation to determine the number of moles of N_2 that are formed per mole of NaN_3 that reacts.

d. Use the graph to determine the volume of N_2 produced when 0.160 mol of NaN_3 react.

e. A certain model of automobile air bag requires the formation of 37.5 L of nitrogen gas to properly inflate in a collision. Use the graph to determine the mass of sodium azide that is needed to produce this volume of gas.

Chapter 9

80. The vapor pressure of a substance changes with temperature, the graph of which can be modeled by a function called a cubic regression. Use the data from Table 9.1 (p. 246) to prepare a graph of the vapor pressure of water and ethanol.

a. Complete the following steps on your graphing calculator to prepare a graph of the data. Remember to check for active equations and clear Lists 1 and 2 before beginning. (Refer to Appendix D for detailed instructions.)

- Press STAT ENTER to display the lists. Type the temperature data for water into List 1, pressing ENTER after each entry. Enter the vapor pressure data in List 2 in a similar manner.
- Press 2nd Y= to display the **STAT PLOTS** menu. Make sure that only Plot 1 is active ("**On**"). Turn all other plots off. (Refer to Appendix D for detailed instructions.) Press ENTER to access the commands for Plot 1. Use the arrow keys to place the cursor on the appropriate line and set up Plot 1 as: **On**; **Type:** (points); **Xlist: L1**; **YList: L2**; **Mark:** □. Press ENTER after highlighting each setting.
- Press WINDOW to set the screen parameters. Use the arrow keys to place the cursor on the appropriate line to set up the window as: **Xmin=0**; **Xmax=110**; **Xscl=10**; **Ymin=0**; **Ymax=110**; **Yscl=10**.
- To derive the cubic regression equation for the vapor pressure of water vs. temperature, press STAT. Press the right-hand arrow key to open the **CALC** menu. Select "7" (**CubicReg**), then press ENTER. The cubic regression will appear on the calculator screen.
- Plot the cubic regression and the data points for water. (Refer to Appendix D for help with plotting points and graphing a regression equation.)

b. Repeat the steps above for the ethanol data in Table 9.1. Use Lists 3 and 4. When you set up **PLOT2** in **STAT PLOTS**, select a different mark for the data points for ethanol. Display the graphs for water and ethanol at the same time. Your graph should be similar to Figure 9.12, p. 248.

c. Press TRACE. Use the up and down arrow keys to place the cursor on the appropriate function, then use the left- and right-hand arrows to move along a graph. What is the vapor pressure of water and ethanol at 62°C? Use the **ZOOM** option to achieve a more accurate answer.

d. Trace the graph to determine the boiling point of each substance with a vapor pressure of 95 kPa. Use the **ZOOM** option for more accurate answers.

e. A liquid mixture is equal parts ethanol and water. Trace the graphs of the temperature of this mixture so that the substances evaporate in equal amounts. (*Hint:* Locate the point where the two functions intersect.)

f. Now try a second method of answering part **e** above. Press 2nd **CALC** to open the **CALCULATE** menu. Select "5" (intersect). The graph will appear, with the cursor displayed as a flashing *x*. Use the arrow keys to place the cursor as close to the intersection of the functions as possible. Press ENTER three times. The intersection of the two functions will be shown at the bottom of the screen. Compare this value to your answer in part **e.**

81. A column of water can be used to make a barometer, in place of mercury (see Biographical Note, p. 240). The difference in column height between a water barometer and a mercury barometer is equal to the ratio of their densities. At 25°C, the ratio of mercury density to water density is 13.59.

a. Use your graphing calculator to plot the relationship between a water barometer and a mercury barometer. Press Y= . Either clear all the equations in the Y= menu (place the cursor next to the = sign of an equation and press CLEAR) *or* turn off all active equations by placing the cursor on an = sign and pressing ENTER . (An active equation has its = sign highlighted.)

b. Enter the following equation on the first open line of the Y= screen:

13.59**X**

c. Press WINDOW to set the screen parameters. Use the arrow keys to place the cursor on the appropriate line to set up the window as: **Xmin=100**; **Xmax=760**; **Xscl=100**; **Ymin=100**; **Ymax=11000**; **Yscl=100**. Press GRAPH to view the graph that relates a water barometer to a mercury barometer.

d. Press TRACE . The displayed *x*-value is the height of a column of mercury and the *y*-value is the corresponding height of a column of water, in mm. Press the left- or right-hand arrow keys to determine the mm of H_2O for an atmospheric pressure of 331.7 mm Hg.

e. A mercury barometer, shown on p. 239, is commonly about 800 mm in length. Press WINDOW and change **Xmax** to 800. Press GRAPH , then presss TRACE . Use the right-hand arrow key to determine the length of a water barometer that would be comparable to an 800 mm mercury barometer.

f. What is the atmospheric pressure, in *kPa,* when a water barometer reads 8342 mm?

Chapter 10

65. The amounts of energy required to change different quantities of carbon tetrachloride, $CCl_4(l)$, into vapor are given in the following table.

Mass of $CCl_4(l)$ (g)	Energy (J)	(cal)
2.90	652	156
7.50	1 689	404
17.0	3 825	915
26.2	5 894	1 410
39.8	8 945	2 140
51.0	11 453	2 740

a. Complete the following steps on your graphing calculator to prepare a graph of the data. Remember to check for active equations and clear Lists 1 and 2 before beginning. (Refer to Appendix D for detailed instructions.)

- Press STAT ENTER to display the lists. Type the mass data for CCl_4 into List 1, pressing ENTER after each entry. Enter the energy data, in joules, in List 2 in a similar manner.

- Press 2nd Y= to display the **STAT PLOTS** menu. Make sure that only Plot 1 is active ("**On**"). Turn all other plots off (see Appendix D for detailed instructions.) Press ENTER to access the commands for Plot 1. Use the arrow keys to place the cursor on the appropriate line and set up Plot 1 as: **On**; **Type:** (points); **Xlist: L1**; **YList: L2**; **Mark:** □. Press ENTER after highlighting each setting.

- Press WINDOW to set the screen parameters. Use the arrow keys to place the cursor on the appropriate line to set up the window as: **Xmin=0; Xmax=60; Xscl=10; Ymin=650; Ymax=12800; Yscl=500**.
- Press GRAPH to view the graph of your data.

b. Derive and graph the linear regression equation for your data. (Refer to Appendix D for help with this process.) What is the slope of the linear regression equation? What does this quantity represent?

c. Calculate the heat of vaporization in cal/g.

d. The accepted value for the heat of vaporization of $CCl_4(l)$ is 53.8 cal/g. How does this value compare to the slope of the line?

90. The specific heat capacity of a type of brass was tested by heating several different samples of the brass by exactly 1°C and measuring the amount of heat energy used. The test results are recorded in the table below.

Mass (g)	Energy (J)
245	094.3
292	112.4
335	129.0
388	149.4
444	170.9

Please refer to question 65, or use Appendix D, to help you with the graphing calculator operations.

a. Prepare a graph of energy (y-axis) vs. mass of brass (x-axis). Derive a linear regression equation for the plotted data, and graph this equation along with the data points. Suggested parameters for the window are: **Xmin=200; Xmax=450; Xscl=50; Ymin=90; Ymax=180; Yscl=10**.

b. What is the slope of the linear regression equation? Include the units with your answer. What does the slope represent?

c. Trace the linear regression equation to determine the amount of energy required to heat a 405-g sample of brass by 1°C. Use the **ZOOM** option if necessary to read the desired information from your graph.

d. How much energy is required to heat a 285-g sample of brass by 28.5°C?

Chapter 11

86. Oxygen can be produced in the laboratory by heating potassium nitrate, KNO_3. The volumes of oxygen that are formed by reacting various masses of potassium nitrate are shown in the table below.

Mass of KNO_3 (g)	Volume of O_2 (cL)
0.84	09.3
1.36	15.1
2.77	30.7
4.82	53.5
6.96	77.3

a. Enter the mass amounts of KNO_3 in List 1 of your graphing calculator by pressing STAT ENTER. Clear List 1 if necessary. Type in the mass data, pressing ENTER after each entry. (Refer to Appendix D for detailed instructions.)

b. Use the arrow keys to place the cursor at the top of List 2, highlighting **L2**. Press 2nd **L1/101.1**, then press ENTER. The values in List 2 are the molar amounts of KNO_3 that correspond to the mass data in List 1.

c. Repeat step **a** above, placing the volume data for oxygen in List 3.

d. Use the arrow keys to place the cursor at the top of List 4, highlighting **L4**. Press 2nd **L2/2240**, then press ENTER. This calculation converts centiliters (cL) of oxygen to moles of O_2 at STP.

e. Plot the moles of KNO_3 (List 2) on the x-axis and the moles of oxygen produced (List 4) on the y-axis. Press WINDOW to set the screen parameters. Use the arrow keys to place the cursor on the appropriate line to set up the window as: **Xmin=0; Xmax=0.08; Xscl=0.01; Ymin=0; Ymax=0.04; Yscl=0.01**. Press GRAPH to view the graph of moles of O_2 vs. moles of KNO_3.

f. Derive a linear regression equation for the points that you have plotted, and graph the equation. Based on the graph, what is the mole ratio by which potassium nitrate and oxygen react?

g. In the decomposition of KNO_3 to form oxygen gas, one other compound is produced. Use this information and the mole ratio to write a balanced equation for this reaction.

93. An experiment was conducted to verify Charles' Law in which the volume of gas trapped above water in a sealed tube was measured at varying temperatures. The results of the experiment are shown in the table below. (The volume readings have been corrected to account for water vapor.)

Temperature (°C)	Volume (mL)
40.0	9.99
35.0	9.86
30.0	9.65
26.0	9.55
20.0	9.34
15.0	9.21
09.0	9.01
05.0	8.88

a. Does the data support Charles' Law?

b. Plot the table of data, placing temperature on the x-axis and volume on the y-axis. Derive the linear regression equation (best-fit line) for the data, and graph this equation along with the plotted points. (Refer to Appendix D for detailed instructions.) Write the equation, rounding to the nearest 0.001.

c. Trace the graph of the linear regression equation to determine the temperature at which the volume equals 0.00 mL.

d. Using 273.15°C as absolute zero, calculate the percent error for this experiment.

Chapter 12

67. The energy of a photon is related to its wavelength and its frequency. Therefore, the simple equations: $\nu = c/\lambda$ (p. 334); and $E = h \times \nu$ (p. 339) are also intimately connected by their common factor, the frequency of a photon.

Energy of photon (J)	Wavelength (m)	Frequency (s^{-1})
3.45×10^{-21}	5.77×10^{-5}	
2.92×10^{-20}	6.82×10^{-6}	
6.29×10^{-20}	3.16×10^{-6}	
1.13×10^{-19}	1.76×10^{-6}	
1.46×10^{-19}	1.36×10^{-6}	
3.11×10^{-19}	6.38×10^{-5}	

This relationship can be viewed and analyzed graphically, as described in the following steps.

a. Enter the photon energy data in List 1 of your graphing calculator by pressing [STAT] [ENTER]. Clear List 1 if necessary. Type in the energy data, pressing [ENTER] after each entry. Enter the corresponding wavelengths in List 2.

b. Use the arrow keys to place the cursor at the top of List 3, highlighting **L3**. Press [2nd] **3E8/L2**, then press [ENTER]. The data in List 3 are the frequency values that correspond to the wavelength data in List 1. Use List 3 to complete the table above.

c. Use **STAT PLOT** to prepare a graph of photon energy (y-axis) versus frequency (x-axis). (See Appendix D for help with this graph.)

d. Derive a linear regression equation for the data that you plotted in part **c**. Graph the line. What is the slope of this linear regression? What does it represent?

69. Bohr's atomic theory can be used to calculate the energy required to remove an electron from an orbit of a hydrogen atom or an ion containing only one electron. This is the ionization energy of that atom or ion. The formula for determining the ionization energy, E, for a mole of electrons is

$$E = (Z^2 \times k) / n^2$$

where Z is the atomic number, k is 1312 kJ per mole, and n is the energy level.

A simple program can be written in your graphing calculator that will evaluate this equation. Follow the steps below to write the program. (Refer to Appendix D for programming assistance.)

- Press PRGM then press the right-hand arrow twice to create a new program. Press ENTER and type in the name **IONIZE**. Press ENTER, and the cursor will move to the first line of the program.
- Enter the program commands as listed below. (Refer to Appendix D for further instructions.)

```
: Lbl A
: Disp "Z?"
: Input Z
: Disp "N?"
: Input N
: ((Z²*1312)/N²)/6.02E23→E
: Disp "E="
: Disp E
: Pause
: Goto A
```

a. Use the program to determine the energy required to eject an electron from a hydrogen atom when the electron is in the ground state ($n = 1$).

b. Press ENTER to restart the program. Determine the energy required if the hydrogen electron is in the second energy level.

c. Press ENTER to restart the program. Determine the energy required to eject a ground state electron from the species Li^{2+}.

d. To exit the program, press ON, then select "2" (**Quit**). (*Note:* This program provides the basic format for solving an equation that contains two variables.)

Chapter 13

56. The melting points of the alkali metals decrease as the atomic numbers increase (see data table below), forming an interesting pattern when graphed.

Element	Atomic number	Melting point (K)
Lithium	3	453.7
Sodium	11	371.0
Potassium	19	336.8
Rubidium	37	312.6
Cesium	**55**	
Francium	87	300.0

a. Prepare a graph of the data, *omitting cesium.* Enter the atomic numbers in List 1 of your graphing calculator and enter the melting point data in List 2. Clear the lists, if necessary, before entering the data.

b. A power regression equation provides a good model for graphing the data. Derive a power regression by pressing STAT, then pressing the right-hand arrow to reveal the **CALC** menu. Select "B" (**PwrReg**), then press ENTER. Write the power regression equation to the nearest 0.001 unit.

c. Press WINDOW to set the screen parameters. Use the arrow keys to place the cursor on the appropriate line to set up the window as: **Xmin=0; Xmax=100; Xscl=10; Ymin=275; Ymax=500; Yscl=100**. Press GRAPH to view the graph of melting point vs. atomic number. Trace the power regression equation to determine the melting point of cesium. Use the **ZOOM** option to achieve a more accurate answer. (Refer to Appendix D for help with the Trace option.)

d. The accepted value of the melting point of cesium is 301.54 K. Calculate the percent error in the melting point determined in part **c**.

59. The chlorine content of a swimming pool or a hot tub can be very accurately determined by spectrometry (see Chapter 12, p. 343). Several samples of water with known concentration of chlorine (mg/L), are tested with a spectrometer. The amount of light at a specific wavelength (565 nm) that the water samples absorb is proportional to the concentration of chlorine in the water. Typical absorbance data are shown in the table below.

Chlorine (mg/L)	Absorbance
0.187	0.00215
0.637	0.05350
1.121	0.10800
1.450	0.14700
1.790	0.18300
2.080	0.22000

a. Prepare a graph of the data, with the chlorine concentration as the x-values and the absorbance data as the y-values. Remember to clear Lists 1 and 2, if necessary. Suggested parameters for the window are: **Xmin=0; Xmax=2.5; Xscl=0.2; Ymin=–0.05; Ymax=0.3; Yscl=0.1**.

b. Derive a linear regression equation for the data. Graph this equation, along with the data points from the table.

c. A certain swimming pool sample is tested via spectroscopy. The absorbance of the pool sample is 0.0852. Trace the graph to determine the chlorine concentration of the sample, in mg/L.

d. A pool owner wished to keep the chlorine concentration of her pool at 1.0 mg/L–1.5 mg/L. Her hand-held portable spectrometer is calibrated according to the data table above. What is the acceptable range of absorbance readings that will assure the desired chlorine concentration?

Chapter 14

67. The reaction of zinc with an acid produces hydrogen gas. The table below gives the amount of hydrogen gas produced at STP when various amounts of zinc react with an excess of hydrochloric acid.

Mass of Zn (g)	Moles of Zn	Volume of H_2 (L)
0.960	—	0.329
2.44	—	0.835
4.18	—	1.43
5.75	—	1.96

a. Enter the mass amounts of zinc in List 1 of your graphing calculator by pressing STAT ENTER. Clear List 1 if necessary. Type in the mass data, pressing ENTER after each entry.

b. Use the arrow keys to place the cursor at the top of List 2, highlighting **L2**. Press 2nd **L1/65.38**, then press ENTER. The values in List 2 are the molar amounts of zinc that correspond to the mass data in List 1. Complete the table with the information in List 2.

c. Enter the volume data for hydrogen gas in List 3. Clear this list first before entering the new data, if necessary. Prepare the Stat Plot for the volume of H_2 (List 3) as the y-values vs. the moles of zinc (List 2) as the x-values. (Refer to Appendix D for help with preparing a Stat Plot graph.)

d. Press WINDOW to set the screen parameters. Use the arrow keys to place the cursor on the appropriate line to set up the window as: **Xmin=0; Xmax=0.1; Xscl=0.01; Ymin=0; Ymax=2.0; Yscl=0.2.** Press GRAPH to view the graph of volume of H_2 vs. moles of Zn.

e. Derive a linear regression equation for the graphed data, and plot the line along with the data points. What is the slope of this line?

f. Based on the value of the slope, what can you surmise about the moles of hydrogen gas produced per mole of zinc that reacted?

75. The values for the first ionization energy and the covalent radius of the Group 5A (IUPAC designation: Group 15) elements are shown in the following table. The covalent radius is one-half the distance between the nuclei of two identical atoms that are covalently bonded. The covalent radius and the atomic radius of a given element are not always the same. (Refer to Chapter 13, Figure 13.5.)

Element	Covalent radius (pm)	First ionization energy (kJ/mol)
N	70	1402
P	110	1012
As	121	947
Sb	141	834
Bi	**152**	

a. Use your graphing calculator to derive the linear regression equation for the table of data omitting bismuth. Plot the data along with the equation. (Refer to Appendix D for help with this process.) Suggested parameters for the window are: **Xmin=200; Xmax=450; Xscl=50; Ymin=90; Ymax=180; Yscl=10**.

b. Trace the graph to determine the first ionization energy of the element bismuth. Use the **ZOOM** option if necessary to achieve a more accurate answer.

c. The actual value for the first ionization energy of bismuth is 703 kJ/mol. Calculate the percent error in the extrapolated value from part **b**.

Chapter 15

70. The graph on p. 430 shows how the percent ionic character of a single bond varies according to the difference in electronegativity between the two elements forming the bond. This graph can be modeled on your graphing calculator by using a cube-root equation.

a. Press Y= . Turn off any active equations by placing the cursor on the = sign of the active equation and pressing ENTER . Place the cursor on the first open equation line, and type in the equation given below *exactly as it appears.*

$$(13.0)(\sqrt[3]{(22X\text{–}35.5)})+44.0$$

(*Note:* The cube-root command can be found by pressing the **MATH** key and selecting "4".)

b. Press WINDOW to set the screen parameters. Use the arrow keys to place the cursor on the appropriate line to set up the window as: **Xmin=0; Xmax=3.2; Xscl=1; Ymin=0; Ymax=100; Yscl=10.** Press GRAPH to view the graph of percent ionic character vs. electronegativity difference.

c. Review the graph and describe the relationship between % ionic character of a single bond and the electronegativity difference between the bonded elements.

d. Trace the graph to determine the electronegativity difference that results in a bond with a 50% ionic character.

e. Trace the graph to determine the % ionic character of the bonds formed between (1) lithium and oxygen, (2) nitrogen and oxygen, (3) magnesium and chlorine, (4) nitrogen and fluorine.

90. The definitions of bond energy (p. 420) and electronegativity (p. 366) suggest that a predictive relationship exists between these two concepts. A graph of this relationship displays an interesting trend. This trend can be observed and analyzed easily by graphing the bond energy for carbon and several elements, and the electronegativity of those elements. The table below is arranged in order of increasing electronegativity.

Element	Electro-negativity	Bond Energy (kJ/mol)
Iodine	2.66	240
Bromine	2.96	276
Nitrogen	3.04	293
Oxygen	3.44	358
Fluorine	3.98	485

a. Enter the electronegativity values in List 1 of your graphing calculator. Enter the corresponding bond energies in List 2. (Refer to Appendix D for detailed instructions.)

b. Graph the data, with electronegativity as the *x*-values and bond energy as the *y*-values. In the **STAT PLOTS** menu, select "xyLine" as the type of graph. After pressing GRAPH to view the plotted points, press ZOOM , then select "9" (**ZoomStat**), which will automatically set the screen parameters to best fit the points. Press the up arrow and use the arrow keys to place the cursor on the graph. Determine the bond energy of carbon with *chlorine* (electronegativity = 3.16) by tracing the graph. (Note: The **Zoom In** option *can* be used with plotted points, if necessary to get a more accurate answer. **Zoom In** is employed by pressing ZOOM and selecting "2".)

c. Derive a linear regression equation for the data and graph the function. Press WINDOW to set the screen parameters. Use the arrow keys to place the cursor on the appropriate line to set up the window as: **Xmin=2.5; Xmax=4; Xscl=1; Ymin=200; Ymax=550; Yscl=100.** Press GRAPH to view the graph of bond energy vs. electronegativity.

d. Trace the linear regression to determine the bond energy of carbon with chlorine, as done in part **b**.

e. The actual value for the C-Cl bond energy is 328 kJ/mol. How do the two bond energy values, from parts **b** and **c**, compare with the actual bond energy? What are the percent errors in the two extrapolated bond energies?

Chapter 16

70. The graph on p. 455 shows the variation in the density of water over the temperature range 0°C to

20°C. This graph can be modeled on your graphing calculator by using a cubic regression equation.

a. Press [Y=]. Turn off any active equations by placing the cursor on the = sign of the active equation and pressing [ENTER]. Place the cursor on the first open equation line, and type in the equation given below *exactly as it appears:*

1.88**E**–7X³–1.51**E**–5X²+1.22**E**–4X+0.9998

(*Note:* The cube command can be found by pressing the **MATH** key and selecting "3". The power of ten can be typed in by pressing [2nd] **EE**.) parameters. Use the arrow keys to place the cursor on the appropriate line to set up the window as: **Xmin= –2**; **Xmax=22**; **Xscl=2**; **Ymin=0.9975**; **Ymax=1.0005**; **Yscl=0.005**. Press [GRAPH] to view the graph of the density of water vs. temperature.

c. Trace the graph to determine the maximum density of water.

d. At what temperature does the maximum density of water occur?

e. Would it be correct to extend the smooth curve of the graph back below 0°C?

105. A hydrate of copper(II) sulfate was examined in the laboratory. The total mass of the hydrate was recorded, then the water of hydration was driven off by heating. The results of several tests were recorded in the following table.

Total hydrate mass (grams)	Mass of water (grams)	Moles of hydrate	Moles of water
29.40	6.154		
42.72	8.941		
67.29	14.08		
8.330	1.743		
94.11	19.70		

a. Enter the values for the mass of hydrate in List 1 of your graphing calculator; enter the water masses in List 2. Clear Lists 3 and 4.

b. Calculate the molar amounts of the hydrate samples and enter them in List 3 by placing the cursor at the top of List 3 (highlighting **L3**), and typing in **L1/172**. Calculate the molar amounts of the water and enter them in List 4 by placing the cursor at the top of List 4 and typing in **L2/18**. Complete the table with the data in Lists 3 and 4.

c. Derive a linear regression equation for the molar amounts of water (y-values) vs. the molar amounts of hydrate (x-axis). Graph the linear regression equation. A suggested window for your graph is: **Xmin=0**; **Xmax=0.6**; **Xscl=0.1**; **Ymin=0**; **Ymax=1.2**; **Yscl=0.1**. Trace the graph to determine the mass of water that would be contained in a copper(II) sulfate sample with a mass of 55.25 grams. Use the **ZOOM** option, if necessary, to achieve a more accurate answer.

d. What is the chemical formula for this substance?

Chapter 17

57. A mixture of glycerol and water is used as antifreeze in automobile engines. The freezing point and specific gravity of the glycerol-water mixture vary with the percent by mass of glycerol in the mixture. On the graph on p. 485, point A represents 20% glycerol by mass; point B, 40%; and point C, 60%. The graph can be modeled by a quadratic equation and displayed on your graphing calculator.

a. Press [Y=]. Turn off any active equations by placing the cursor on the = sign of the active equation and pressing [ENTER]. Place the cursor on the first open equation line, and type in the equation given below *exactly as it appears:*

–1570X²+3211X–1646

b. Press [WINDOW] to set the screen parameters. Use the arrow keys to place the cursor on the appropriate line to set up the window as: **Xmin=1.04**; **Xmax=1.16**; **Xscl=0.02**; **Ymin= –36**; **Ymax= –4**; **Yscl=4**. Press [GRAPH] to view the graph of the freezing point vs. specific gravity.

c. Trace the graph to determine the specific gravity of an antifreeze mixture that freezes at –25°C.

d. What is the freezing point of a mixture that has a specific gravity of 1.06?

e. What is the freezing point of a mixture that is 30% by mass glycerol?

81. One way in which the solubility of a compound can be expressed is by the moles of the compound that will dissolve in 1 kg of water. Solubility depends on temperature; this relationship can be viewed via a graph. The solubility of potassium nitrate, KNO_3, in water is described by the table below.

Temperature (°C)	Solubility KNO_3 (mol/kg)
0	1.61
20	2.80
40	5.78
60	11.20
80	16.76
100	24.50

Use your graphing calculator to work through the following questions. (Refer to Appendix D for help with the graphing calculator operations.)

a. Prepare a graph of solubility (y-axis) vs. temperature (x-axis). Derive and graph a quadratic equation for the plotted points. Trace your graph to determine the following:

b. the solubility of KNO_3 at 76°C and at 33°C

c. the temperature at which the solubility is 17.6 mol/kg of water

d. the temperature at which the solubility is 4.24 mol/kg of water

Chapter 18

101. The following data were collected for decomposition of compound AB into its elements.

[AB] (mol/L)	Time (s)
0.300	0
0.246	50
0.201	100
0.165	150
0.135	200
0.111	250
0.090	300
0.075	350

The reaction is first order in AB. (Refer to Appendix D for help with the graphing calculator steps suggested below.)

a. Prepare a graph of concentration (y-axis) vs. time (x-axis). Derive the exponential regression equation for the data and plot it along with the individual points. Press STAT, then press the right-hand arrow to open the **CALC** menu. Select "A" (**ExpReg**), then press ENTER to calculate an exponential regression. Write the exponential equation that describes this reaction.

b. Without the help of your graphing calculator, use the method shown in Figure 18.24 (p. 524) to determine the rate of this reaction at $t = 100$ seconds and $t = 250$ seconds.

c. Press TRACE. Press the down arrow key (if necessary) to place the cursor on the exponential regression plot. Use the left- or right-hand arrow keys to place the cursor at $x = 100$. Use the Zoom option if necessary to get as close to $x = 100$ as possible. Press 2nd **CALC**, and select "6" (**dy/dx**). This operation takes the numerical derivative (slope) of the function at the point that you've selected with the cursor. Press ENTER. The value displayed at the bottom of the screen is equal to the rate of the reaction at 100 seconds. How does it compare to the rate that you calculated in part **b**?

d. Repeat part **c** to calculate the rate of reaction at 250 seconds. How does this rate compare to your answer in part **b**?

107. The following data were recorded for the reaction:

$$2C_4H_6(g) \rightarrow C_8H_{12}(g)$$

Time (s)	$[C_4H_6]$
0	0.0478
100	0.0395
300	0.0292
500	0.0233
700	0.0193
900	0.0165

a. Prepare graphs of: (1) time vs. $[C_4H_6]$; (2) time vs. ln $[C_4H_6]$; and (3) time vs. $1/[C_4H_6]$. (Refer to

Appendix D for detailed graphing calculator instructions.)

b. Examine the graphs from part **a** and determine the order of the reaction.

c. Use the graph of time vs. $1/[C_4H_6]$ to determine the time at which $[C_4H_6] = 0.0250M$.

Chapter 19

76. The K_w of water varies with temperature according to the table below; thus the pH of water will vary with temperature.

Temperature (°C)	K_w	pH
0	1.137×10^{-15}	
10	2.917×10^{-15}	
20	6.807×10^{-15}	
30	1.469×10^{-14}	
40	2.917×10^{-14}	
50	5.470×10^{-14}	

This relationship can be viewed and analyzed via a graph. (Refer to Appendix D for help with any of the following graphing calculator steps.)

a. Enter the temperature data in List 1 of your graphing calculator. Enter the corresponding K_w values in List 2.

b. You will now use the definitions of K_w (p. 539) and pH to calculate the pH of water at varying temperatures. Clear List 3. Place the cursor at the top of List 3, so that **L3** is highlighted. Enter the following equation, *exactly as shown:*

–log(**L2**/1**E**–7)

Press ENTER. List 3 will be the pH values that correspond to the temperatures in List 1. Complete the table with these values.

c. Prepare a plot of temperature (x-axis) vs. pH (y-axis). Derive a linear regression equation for this data, and graph it along with the plotted points.

d. Trace the graph to determine the pH of water at 5°C.

e. Trace the graph to determine the temperature of a sample of water with pH = 6.85.

82. Many laboratories stock concentrated hydrochloric acid (12*M*) from which all other smaller molar concentrations are prepared by dilution with distilled water. A handy chart can be prepared with a graphing calculator that shows the volume, in mL, of 12*M* HCl needed to prepare 1000 mL of a given concentration of HCl.

a. Press Y=. Turn off, or clear, all of the active equations. Place the cursor next to the first open line, and type in:

83.33X

This simple equation describes the volume of 12*M* HCl needed to prepare 1000 mL of 1.00*M* HCl solution, and all other concentrations possess an equal ratio relationship.

b. Press WINDOW. Suggested parameters for the graph are: **Xmin=0**; **Xmax=10**; **Xscl=1**; **Ymin=0**; **Ymax=900**; **Yscl=100**. Press GRAPH to view the dilution chart for 12*M* HCl.

c. Use the graph to help describe how to prepare a liter of 1.25*M* HCl solution.

d. How would 500 mL of 0.750*M* HCl be prepared from concentrated HCl?

e. Explain how to prepare a second chart (or graph) that can be used for a total solution volume of 250 mL.

64. The data below were collected in a titration of 50.00 mL of ethanoic acid, CH_3COOH, of unknown concentration with 0.100*M* NaOH.

Volume of NaOH (mL)	pH
0	
10.00	4.15
25.00	4.76
40.00	5.36
49.00	6.45
49.99	8.55
50.00	8.73
50.01	8.89
51.00	11.00
60.00	11.96
75.00	12.30
100.00	12.52

a. Plot these data, with pH on the *y*-axis, to obtain a titration curve. As you set the graph parameters in the **PLOT1** menu, select "xyLine" as the **Type**.

b. With the titration curve displayed on your graphing calculator screen, press the up arrow key. The cursor will appear as a cross, with a flashing center. Use the arrow keys to place the cursor on the titration curve. Trace the curve, as closely as possible, to locate the end point of the titration. What is the pH at the end point?

c. Refer to Figures 19.12 and 19.13 (p. 553) to identify one or more indicator solutions that could be used to determine the end point of this titration.

85. A mixture of hydrochloric acid and acetic acid is tested by titrating 10.00 mL of the acid mixture with a 0.20*M* NaOH solution. A summary of the titration data is recorded in the following table.

mL NaOH	pH
2.0	0.96
6.0	1.10
10.0	1.40
14.0	1.85
20.0	2.80
20.2	3.50
20.3	6.00
21.0	6.30
25.0	7.00
30.0	7.80
30.1	8.50
30.4	12.00
32.0	12.02
35.0	12.05

a. Enter the mL NaOH data in List 1 of your graphing calculator. Enter pH in List 2. Prepare a graph of the data, with mL NaOH as the *x*-values and pH as the *y*-values. In the **STAT PLOTS** menu, select "xyLine" as the type of graph. (Refer to Appendix D for detailed instructions.)

b. Press [GRAPH] to view the graph of the titration curve. Press [ZOOM], then select "9" (**ZoomStat**), which will automatically set the screen parameters to best fit the points. Press the up arrow, and use the arrow keys to move the cursor along the titration curve. Trace the curve to determine the molarity of HCl in the mixture. (*Hint:* Locate the region of the titration curve where HCl is neutralized.)

(*Note:* The **Zoom In** option *can* be used with plotted points, if necessary to get a more accurate answer. **Zoom In** is employed by pressing [ZOOM] and selecting "2".)

c. Use the titration curve to determine the molar concentration of acetic acid in the mixture.

Chapter 21

64. The reaction between sodium hypochlorite (the active ingredient in household bleach) and sodium thiosulfate (the "fixer" in photographic film development) produces chloride ions and a sulfur compound. The reaction is summarized as a net ionic equation below:

$$OCl^- + S_2O_3^{2-} \rightarrow Cl^- + \_\_\_\_\_\_$$

This reaction is also exothermic. In one experiment, solutions of the two reactants, each at a 1.0*M* concentration, were mixed in varying proportions so that the total volume of the reaction was constant. The five reactions and their exotherms are shown in the table below.

mL OCl^-	mL $S_2O_3^{2-}$	ΔT(°C)
5	45	5.75
15	35	11.85
25	25	20.85
35	15	29.75
45	5	16.5

a. Prepare a graph of ΔT (y-axis) vs. volume of *either* reactant. As you set the graph parameters in the **PLOT1** menu, select "xyLine" as the **Type**.

b. The reaction has a maximum ΔT when the reactants are in the proper stoichiometric proportion. Use the graph to estimate the mole ratio of the reactants.

c. The sulfur-bearing product could be either SO_2 or $S_2O_6^{2-}$. Based on the mole ratio that you determined in part **a**, which is the more plausible product?

d. Examine the graph and suggest one or two additional reactions that should be run to better confirm the results of the reaction.

65. As you observed in Chapter 13, many properties of the elements exhibit periodic trends. Oxidation numbers are no exception. The *common* oxidation numbers of several elements are listed below.

Element	Atomic number	Common oxidation number
Silicon	14	−4
Phosphorus	15	−3
Chlorine	17	−1
Potassium	19	+1
Calcium	20	+2
Scandium	21	+3
Vanadium	23	+5
Chromium	24	+6

a. Enter the atomic number data in List 1 of your graphing calculator. Enter the corresponding oxidation numbers in List 2. Derive a linear regression equation for the data, with atomic numbers as the x-values and oxidation numbers as the y-values. (Refer to Appendix D for detailed instructions.)

b. Graph the linear regression. Suggested window parameters are **Xmin=10**; **Xmax=25**; **Xscl=5**; **Ymin= −5**; **Ymax=8**; **Yscl=1**.

c. Trace the graph to determine the common oxidation number of sulfur, titanium, and manganese.

d. What oxidation number does the graph predict for argon?

Chapter 22

61. The voltaic cell composed of zinc and copper half-cells (see Example 1, p. 638) has a potential of 1.10 V *as long as the molar concentrations of the zinc and copper ions are the same.* The potential changes as the ion concentrations change. The relationship is linear when potential is graphed with the log of the ratio of ion concentration. The following table provides data for the zinc-copper voltaic cell. (Refer to Appendix D for help with the graphing calculator steps.)

$\log([Zn^{2+}]/[Cu^{2+}])$	E_{cell} (V)
0	1.10
1	1.07
2	1.04
–1	1.13
–2	1.16

a. Prepare a graph of the data, with E_{cell} as the *y*-values. Derive a linear regression equation for the data, and graph the line along with the plotted points.

b. Trace the graph to determine the E_{cell} when the $[Zn^{2+}] = 1.0M$ and the $[Cu^{2+}] = 0.50M$.

c. What is the Zn^{2+} concentration when the E_{cell} = 1.055 and the $[Cu^{2+}] = 0.075M$?

d. According to the graph, if you want a zinc-copper cell to have a potential that is greater than 1.10 V, which ion should have the larger concentration? How does your answer support Le Châtelier's Principle (p. 502)?

62. The progress of certain types of titrations can be monitored and measured by the change in electrical conductivity, as voltage, that occurs. In one such experiment, 0.100*M* sulfuric acid, H_2SO_4, was used to titrate 100.0 mL of a solution of barium hydroxide, $Ba(OH)_2$. A summary of the titration results is given in the following table.

Volume H_2SO_4 (mL)	Potential (volts)
0.0	1.62
3.0	1.33
6.0	1.03
9.0	0.68
10.0	0.50
11.0	0.26
11.1	0.20
11.2	0.16
11.5	0.16
12.0	0.50
14.0	1.83

a. Enter the volume of H_2SO_4 data in List 1 of your graphing calculator. Enter the corresponding potential values in List 2. Graph the data, with acid volume as the *x*-values and the voltage data as the *y*-values. In **STAT PLOTS**, select "xyLine" as the type of graph. A suggested window for your graph is **Xmin= –1.6**; **Xmax=17.6**; **Xscl=1**; **Ymin= –0.1**; **Ymax=2.8**; **Yscl=0.1**. Press GRAPH to view this rather unusual-looking titration curve. (Refer to Appendix D for detailed instructions.)

b. The endpoint of the titration is reached when the conductivity (voltage) is 0.00. Press TRACE. Trace the curve to determine the volume of acid that was added to reach the endpoint of the titration. Use the Zoom option to achieve a more accurate answer.

c. What was the molar concentration of the barium hydroxide solution?

d. The products of this reaction are barium sulfate, a precipitate, and water. What volume of H_2SO_4 was added when 14.67 g of barium sulfate were added?

Chapter 23

53. The data table below shows the quantities of iron ore (Fe_2O_3) and coke (C) that react in a blast furnace to produce pig iron. (Refer to Appendix D for help with the graphing calculator steps.)

Mass of Fe_2O_3 (kg)	Amount of Fe_2O_3 (mol)	Mass of C (kg)	Amount of C (mol)
8.65×10^4		1.95×10^4	
1.26×10^5		2.84×10^4	
2.01×10^5		4.54×10^4	
6.56×10^5		1.48×10^5	
9.61×10^5		2.17×10^5	

a. Enter the data for the mass of iron into List 1 of your graphing calculator. Clear List 2 and place the cursor at the top of the list, with **L2** highlighted. Type in **L1/.1597**, then press ENTER. List 2 now contains the molar quantities of iron ore that correspond to the mass data in List 1. (*Note:* The quantity 0.1579 is the molecular mass of Fe_2O_3 in kg.)

b. Repeat part **a**, placing the mass data for coke in List 3, and calculating the moles of coke to be placed in List 4. Complete the table with the data in Lists 2 and 4.

c. Prepare a plot of the moles of iron ore (y-axis) vs. the moles of coke (x-axis). Derive a linear regression equation for this data, and graph it along with the plotted points. Suggested parameters for the window are: **Xmin=1000000; Xmax=18500000; Xscl=0; Ymin=450000; Ymax=6050000; Yscl=0**. Analyze the graph and/or the linear regression equation to determine the mole ratio by which iron ore reacts with coke in a blast furnace.

d. Trace the graph to determine the mass of coke that is required to react with 100 000 kg of iron ore. Use the **ZOOM** option to achieve a more accurate answer.

63. The data table below lists the melting and boiling points of the halogens.

Halogen	Melting point (°C)	Boiling point (°C)
Fluorine	−219.62	−188.14
Chlorine	−100.98	34.6
Bromine	−7.2	58.78
Iodine	113.5	184.35

a. Enter the atomic numbers for the given elements in List 1. Enter the melting points in List 2 and the boiling points in List 3. (Refer to Appendix D for detailed instructions.) Graph the data so that two plots appear on the screen: melting point (y-axis) vs. atomic number (x-axis), and boiling point vs. atomic number. A suggested window for your graph is: **Xmin=6; Xmax=60; Xscl=10; Ymin= −220; Ymax=190; Yscl=50**. Press GRAPH to view the plots. Describe the trends you observe.

b. Explain these trends. Are they likely to occur with other groups in the periodic table?

c. Delete the information for fluorine from Lists 1, 2, and 3. Derive a linear regression equation for melting point vs. atomic number. Change the window to make **Xmax=90** and **Ymax=400**, and graph the linear regression. Trace the linear regression to determine the melting point of astatine (atomic number = 85).

d. Repeat part **c** to derive a linear regression for boiling point vs. atomic number. Trace this new linear regression to determine the boiling point of astatine.

Chapter 24

40. The seven organic chemicals produced in the largest amounts in the United States in a recent year are listed in the following table.

Chemical	Amount produced (kg × 10^9)
Ethylene	15.9
Propylene	8.4
Urea	6.8
Ethylene dichloride	6.3
Benzene	5.3
Ethyl benzene	4.3
Vinyl chloride	3.7

a. Enter the amounts produced in List 1 on your graphing calculator. (Refer to Appendix D for help with this process.)

b. Use the data in List 1 to determine the percent of the total amount produced that were aromatic compounds. (Refer to Appendix D for a sample problem.)

c. Of the total mass of the seven compounds produced, what percent by mass was made up of compounds with three total carbons in their longest chain?

67. The equilibrium constant, K_{eq}, for a chemical reaction is dependent upon the temperature of the reaction. For example, consider the reaction between nitrogen gas and hydrogen gas:

$$N_2(g) + 3H_2(g) \rightarrow 2NH_3(g)$$

The K_{eq} for the reaction, at a temperature of 573 K, is 1185. (See Practice Problem 21, p. 513.) The K_{eq} at other reaction temperatures is listed below.

Temperature 1/T (K)	K_{eq}	$\ln K_{eq}$
573	1185	
600	580	
650	181.8	
700	62.30	
750	28.05	
800	13.65	

a. Enter the temperature data in List 1 of your graphing calculator. After clearing List 2, place the cursor at the top of List 2 and type in: **L1–1**. Press ENTER. This operation takes the inverse of each value in List 1 and places it in List 2. (Note: The inverse key is the "**x–1**" key on your calculator.)

b. Enter the K_{eq} data in List 3. After clearing List 4, place the cursor at the top of List 4 and type in: **lnL3**. Press ENTER. List 4 is now the natural logarithm values of the data in List 3. Complete the table with the data in Lists 2 and 4.

c. The relationship between $1/T$ and $\ln K_{eq}$ is linear. Derive the linear regression equation for 1/T (List 2) as the x-values and $\ln K_{eq}$ (List 4) as the y-values. (Refer to Appendix D for detailed instructions.) Graph the equation; the suggested window parameters are: **Xmin=0.0012; Xmax=0.0018; Xscl=0; Ymin=2.5; Ymax=7.5; Yscl=1.** Press GRAPH to view the plot of your equation.

d. Trace the graph to determine the value of K_{eq} at a temperature of 350°C.

e. Trace the graph to determine the temperature at which the K_{eq} for this reaction is 75.00.

f. The slope of the linear regression can be used to calculate the enthalpy (ΔH) of the reaction, according to the equation: slope = $-\Delta H/R$; where $R = 8.314$ J/molK. What is the enthalpy of the reaction between nitrogen and hydrogen gas, in kJ/mol?

Chapter 25

93. An experiment was conducted to measure the energy content of various foods. Two food samples were incinerated, and the evolved heat energy was used to warm a given volume of water. The following data were collected for peanuts, an example of a fat, and unbuttered popcorn, an example of a carbohydrate.

Peanuts		Popcorn	
mass (g)	energy (kJ)	mass (g)	energy (kJ)
0.23	2.74	0.052	0.362
0.29	3.50	0.064	0.450
0.34	4.06	0.081	0.565
0.41	4.94	0.104	0.731
0.48	5.77	0.112	0.784

a. Derive a linear regression (best-fit line) equation for the peanut data, and prepare a graph of the equation and the data points.

b. Determine the energy content of the sample of peanuts, in kJ/g.

c. Derive a linear regression equation for the popcorn data, and prepare a graph of the equation and the data points.

d. Determine the energy content of the popcorn sample, in kJ/g.

e. According to the results of the experiment, how many kilocalories of energy are contained, per gram, in the sample of fat (peanuts) and the sample of carbohydrate (popcorn)? Explain how the data supports our understanding of the caloric content of different food types.

94. The heat of combustion of two fuels, paraffin and ethanol, was studied. Paraffin is a huge alkane (straight-chain hydrocarbon), and ethanol is an alcohol with the chemical formula C_2H_5OH. Several samples of each fuel were burned, and the heat energy evolved was recorded in the table below.

Paraffin		Ethanol	
mass (g)	energy (kJ)	mass (g)	energy (kJ)
0.48	10.74	1.19	16.86
1.01	21.93	2.81	41.30
2.13	46.88	4.25	62.44
3.18	69.65	5.78	84.50
4.84	106.41	7.97	117.37

a. Derive a linear regression equation for the paraffin data. Derive a linear regression equation for the ethanol data, and graph both equations on the same screen. A suggested window for your graph is: **Xmin=0; Xmax=10; Xscl=1; Ymin=10; Ymax=120; Yscl=10.** Press GRAPH to view the plot of the equations. (Refer to Appendix D for detailed instructions.)

b. Trace the appropriate equation to determine the heat of combustion for paraffin, in kJ/g.

c. The chemical formula for paraffin is (as an average): $C_{25}H_{52}$. What is the enthalpy of combustion for paraffin, in kJ/mol?

d. Trace the appropriate equation to determine the heat of combustion for ethanol, in kJ/g.

e. What is the enthalpy of combustion for ethanol, in kJ/mol?

Chapter 26

50. The graph on p. 780 shows the radioactive decay curve for thorium-234. Radioactive decay describes an exponential regression relationship between the remaining mass of an isotope and elapsed time. Prepare a model of this curve on your graphing calculator by following the steps below.

a. Press Y= and turn off any active equations. Place the cursor next to the first open line and enter the equation shown below, exactly as written:

95.68*0.976^X

(*Note:* Writing *x* as an exponent is done by pressing the ^ key, then typing in X.)

b. Press WINDOW to set the screen parameters. Use the arrow keys to place the cursor on the appropriate line to set up the window as: **Xmin=0; Xmax=120; Xscl=10; Ymin=0; Ymax=100; Yscl=10.** Press GRAPH to view the decay curve for thorium-234.

c. Trace the graph to determine the percent of the isotope that remains after 60 days.

d. How many grams of a 250-g sample of thorium-234 would remain after 40 days?

e. How many days would pass while 44 g of thorium-234 decayed to 4.4 g?

f. What is the half-life of thorium-234?

71. A sample containing bromine-82 undergoes radioactive decay at a rate described as disintegrations per hour (counts per hour). The following readings were recorded:

Time (hrs)	Decay (cph)
0.0	1 000
10.0	806
40.0	455
70.0	256
100.0	146
125.0	91

a. Prepare a graph of the data and derive the exponential equation that best fits the plotted points. (Refer to Appendix D for graphing calculator assistance.)

b. Use the graph from part **a** to determine the half-life of this isotope of bromine.

c. A sample initially contains 250.0 g of bromine-82. After 50.0 h, what percent of the isotope will remain? What mass of bromine-82 remains after 50.0 h?

Glossary

absolute zero the zero point on the Kelvin temperature scale, equivalent to –273°C; all molecular motion theoretically stops at this temperature. *2.12*

accepted value a quantity used by general agreement of the scientific community. *2.13*

accuracy the closeness of a measurement to the true value of what is being measured. *2.2*

acid a compound containing hydrogen that ionizes to yield hydrogen ions (H^+) in water. *19.2*

acid dissociation constant (K_a) the ratio of the concentration of the dissociated form of an acid to the undissociated form; stronger acids have larger K_a vlaues than weaker acids. *19.10*

acidic solution any solution in which the hydrogen-ion concentration is greater than the hydroxide-ion concentration. *19.3*

activated complex an unstable arrangement of atoms that exists momentarily at the peak of the activation energy barrier; it represents an intermediate or transitional structure formed during the course of a reaction. *18.1*

activation energy the minimum energy colliding particles must have in order to react. *18.1*

activity series of metals a table listing metals in order of decreasing activity. *7.8*

actual yield the amount of product that forms when a reaction is carried out in the laboratory. *8.7*

addition reaction a reaction in which a substance is added at the double bond of an alkene or at the triple bond of an alkyne. 25.6

alcohol an organic compound having an –OH (hydroxyl) group; the general structure is R—OH. *25.4*

aldehyde an organic compound in which the carbon of the carbonyl group is joined to at least one hydrogen; the general formula is RCHO. *25.8*

aliphatic compound a hydrocarbon compound that does not contain a ring structure. *24.8*

alkali metal any metal in Group 1A of the periodic table. *13.3*

alkaline earth metal any metal in Group 2A of the periodic table. *13.3*

alkaline solution a basic solution. *19.3*

alkane a hydrocarbon containing only single covalent bonds; alkanes are saturated hydrocarbons. *24.1*

alkene a hydrocarbon containing one or more carbon–carbon double bonds; alkenes are unsaturated hydrocarbons. *24.5*

alkyl group a hydrocarbon substituent; methyl (CH_3) is an alkyl group. *24.3*

alkyl halide a halocarbon in which one or more halogen atoms are attached to the carbon atoms of an aliphatic chain. *25.2*

alkyne a hydrocarbon containing a carbon–carbon triple bond; alkynes are unsaturated hydrocarbons. *24.5*

allotrope a molecular form of an element that exists in two or more different forms in the same physical state; oxygen, O_2, and ozone, O_3, are allotropes of the element oxygen. *9.7*

alpha particle a positively charged particle emitted from certain radioactive nuclei; it consists of two protons and two neutrons and is identical to the nucleus of a helium atom. *26.2*

alpha radiation alpha particles emitted from a radioactive source. *26.2*

amino acid an organic compound having amino ($-NH_2$) and carboxylic acid (–COOH) groups in the same molecule; proteins are made up of the 20 naturally occurring amino acids. *25.16*

amphoteric a substance that can act both as an acid and a base; water is amphoteric. *19.7*

amplitude the height of a wave from the origin to the crest. *12.6*

amorphous solid a term used to describe a solid that lacks an ordered internal structure; denotes a random arrangement of atoms. *9.7*

analytical chemistry the study of the composition of substances. *1.1*

anion any atom or group of atoms with a negative charge. *5.2*

anode the electrode at which oxidation occurs. *22.2*

antibonding orbital a molecular orbital whose energy is higher than that of the atomic orbitals from which it is formed. *15.7*

aqueous solution (*aq*) a solution in which the solvent is water. *16.6*

arene any member of a special group of unsaturated cyclic hydrocarbons. *24.8*

aromatic compound a name originally given to the arenes because many of them have pleasant odors. *24.8*

aryl halide a halocarbon in which one or more halogens are attached to the carbon atoms of an arene ring. *25.2*

asymmetric carbon a carbon atom that has four different groups attached. *24.7*

atom the smallest particle of an element that retains the properties of that element. *4.1*

atomic emission spectrum the pattern of frequencies obtained by passing light emitted by atoms of an element in the gaseous state through a prism; the emission spectrum of each element is unique to that element. *12.6*

atomic mass the weighted average of the masses of the isotopes of an element. *4.7*

atomic mass unit a unit of mass equal to one-twelfth the mass of a carbon-12 atom. *4.7*

atomic number the number of protons in the nucleus of an atom of an element. *4.4*

atomic orbital a region in space around the nucleus of an atom where there is a high probability of finding an electron. *12.3*

atomic radius one-half the distance between the nuclei in a molecule consisting of identical atoms. *13.4*

atmospheric pressure the pressure exerted by air molecules in the atmosphere surrounding the earth, resulting from collisions of air molecules with objects. *9.2*

Aufbau principle electrons enter orbitals of lowest energy first. *12.4*

Avogadro's hypothesis equal volumes of gases at the same temperature and pressure contain equal numbers of particles. *11.10*

Avogadro's number the number of representative particles contained in one mole of a substance; equal to 6.02×10^{23} particles. *6.2*

balanced equation a chemical equation in which mass is conserved; each side of the equation has the same number of atoms of each element. *7.4*

band of stability the location of stable nuclei on a neutron-vs-proton plot. *26.3*

barometer an instrument used to measure atmospheric pressure. *9.2*

base a compound that ionizes to yield hydroxide ions (OH^-) in water. *19.2*

base dissociation constant (K_b) the ratio of the concentration of the dissociated form of a base to the undissociated form. *19.10*

basic solution any solution in which the hydroxide-ion concentration is greater than the hydrogen-ion concentration. *19.3*

battery a group of voltaic cells that are connected together. *22.4*

Benedict's test a test commonly used to detect the presence of aldehydes. *25.10*

beta particles a fast-moving electron emitted from certain radioactive nuclei; it is formed when a neutron decomposes. *26.2*

beta radiation fast-moving electrons (beta particles) emitted from a radioactive source. *26.2*

binary compound a compound composed of two elements; NaCl and Al_2O_3 are binary compounds. *5.9*

biochemistry the study of the composition and changes in composition of living organisms. *1.1*

boiling point (bp) the temperature at which the vapor pressure of a liquid is just equal to the external pressure on the liquid. *9.6*

boiling point elevation the difference in temperature between the boiling points of a solution and of the pure solvent. *17.7*

bond dissociation energy the amount of energy required to break a bond between atoms; it is usually expressed in kJ per mol of substance. *15.12*

bonding orbital a molecular orbital whose energy is lower than that of the atomic orbitals from which it is formed. *15.7*

Boyle's law for a fixed mass of gas at constant temperature, the volume of the gas varies inversely with pressure. *11.3*

branched-chain alkane an alkane with one or more alkyl groups attached. *24.3*

Brownian motion the chaotic movement of colloidal particles, caused by collision with water molecules of the medium in which they are dispersed. *16.9*

buffer a solution in which the pH remains relatively constant when small amounts of acid or base are added; it consists of a solution of a weak acid and the salt of a weak acid (or a solution of a weak base with the salt of a weak base). *20.6*

buffer capacity a measure of the amount of acid or base that may be added to a buffer solution before a significant change in pH occurs. *20.6*

calorie (cal) the quantity of heat that raises the temperature of 1 g of pure water 1°C. *10.2*

calorimeter an apparatus for measuring heat changes. *10.5*

calorimetry the measurement of heat changes. *10.5*

carbohydrate the name given to a group of monomers and polymers of aldehydes and ketones that have numerous hydroxyl groups attached; sugars and starches are carbohydrates. *25.13*

carbonyl group a functional group having a carbon atom and an oxygen atom joined by a double bond;

$$(\text{—}\overset{\overset{\displaystyle O}{\|}}{C}\text{—})$$

it is found in aldehydes, ketones, esters, and amides. *25.8*

carboxyl group a functional group consisting of a carbonyl group attached to a hydroxyl group;

$$(\text{—}\overset{\overset{\displaystyle O}{\|}}{C}\text{—OH})$$

it is found in carboxylic acids. *25.9*

carboxylic acid an organic acid containing a carboxyl group; the general formula is RCOOH. *25.9*

catalyst a substance that speeds up a reaction without being used up. *7.2, 18.2*

cathode the electrode at which reduction occurs. *22.2*

cathode ray a stream of electrons produced at the negative electrode (cathode) of a tube containing a gas at low pressure. *4.2*

cation any atom or group of atoms with a positive charge. *5.2*

cell potential the difference between the reduction potentials of two half-cells. *22.6*

Celsius temperature scale the temperature scale on which the freezing point of water is 0° and the boiling point is 100°. *2.12*

Charles's law the volume of a fixed mass of gas is directly proportional to its Kelvin temperature if the pressure is kept constant. *11.5*

chemical equation an expression representing a chemical reaction; the formulas of the reactants (on the left) are connected by an arrow with the formulas for the products (on the right). *7.2*

chemical equilibrium a state of balance in which forward and reverse reactions are taking place at the same rate; no net change in the amounts of reactants and products occurs in the chemical system. *18.3*

chemical formula a shorthand method used to show the number and type of atoms present in the smallest representative unit of a substance; the chemical formula of ammonia, with one nitrogen and three hydrogens, is NH_3. *5.4*

chemical potential energy energy stored within the structural units of chemical substances. *10.1*
chemical property the ability of a substance to undergo chemical reactions and to form new substances. *1.9*
chemical reaction the changing of substances to other substances by the breaking of old bonds and the formation of new bonds. *1.9*
chemical symbol a one or two letter representation of an element. *1.8*
chemistry the study of the structure, properties, and composition of substances, and the changes that substances undergo. *1.1*
***cis* configuration** a term applied to geometric isomers; it denotes an arrangement in which the substituted groups are on the same side of the double bond. *24.6*
coefficient a small whole number that appears in front of a formula in a balanced chemical equation. *7.4*
colligative properties a property of a solution that depends on the concentration of the solute particles; boiling point elevation, freezing point depression, and vapor pressure lowering are colligative properties. *17.7*
collision theory atoms, ions, and molecules with sufficient kinetic energy can form chemical bonds when they collide. *18.1*
colloid a liquid mixture containing particles that are intermediate in size between those of a suspension and a true solution; these particles are evenly distributed throughout the liquid and do not settle out with time. *16.9*
combination reaction a chemical change in which two or more substances react to form a single new substance; also called a synthesis reaction. *7.6*
combined gas law a relationship describing the behavior of gases that combines Boyle's law, Charles' law, and Gay-Lussac's law. *11.7*
combustion reaction a chemical change in which oxygen reacts with another substance, often producing energy in the form of heat and light. *7.10*
common ion an ion that is common to both salts in a solution; in a solution of silver nitrate and silver chloride, Ag^+ would be a common ion. *20.8*
common ion effect a decrease in the solubility of a substance caused by the addition of a common ion. *20.8*
complete ionic equation an equation for a reaction in solution showing all strong electrolytes as ions. *7.12*
compound a substance that can be separated into simpler substances (elements or other compounds) only by chemical reactions. *1.7*
concentrated solution a solution containing a large amount of solute. *17.4*
concentration a measurement of the amount of solute that is dissolved in a given quantity of solvent; usually expressed as mol/L. *17.4*
condensed structural formula a structural formula that leaves out some bonds and/or atoms; the presence of these atoms or bonds is understood. *24.2*
conjugate acid the particle formed when a base gains a hydrogen ion; NH_4^+ is the conjugate acid of the base NH_3. *19.7*
conjugate acid-base pair two substances that are related by the loss or gain of a single hydrogen ion. Ammonia (NH_3) and the ammonium ion (NH_4^+) are a conjugate acid-base pair. *19.7*
conjugate base the particle that remains when an acid has donated a hydrogen ion; OH^- is the conjugate base of the acid water. *19.7*
continuous-chain alkane a hydrocarbon that contains any number of carbon atoms in a straight chain. *24.2*
conversion factor a ratio of equivalent units used to express the relationship between quantities expressed in different units. *3.3*
coordinate covalent bond a covalent bond formed when one atom contributes both bonding electrons. *15.4*
coordination number the number of ions of opposite charge that surround each ion in a crystal. *14.5*
cracking the controlled process by which hydrocarbons are broken down or rearranged into smaller, more useful molecules. *24.9*
crystal a substance in which the atoms, ions, or molecules are arranged in an orderly, repeating, three-dimensional pattern called a crystal lattice. *9.7*
cyclic hydrocarbon an organic compound that contains a hydrocarbon ring. *24.8*

Dalton's atomic theory the first theory to relate chemical changes to events at the atomic level. *4.1*
Dalton's law of partial pressures at constant volume and temperature, the total pressure of a mixture of gases is the sum of the partial pressures of all the gases present. *11.9*
de Broglie's equation an equation that describes the wavelength of a moving particle; it predicts that all matter exhibits wavelike motions. *12.10*
decomposition reaction a chemical change in which a single compound is broken down into two or more simpler products. *7.7*
dehydrogenation reaction a reaction in which hydrogen is lost. *25.10*
deliquescent a term describing a substance that removes sufficient water from the air to form a solution; the process occurs when the solution formed has a lower vapor pressure than that of the water in the air. *16.10*
denatured alcohol ethanol to which a poisonous substance has been added to make it unfit to drink. *25.5*
density the ratio of the mass of an object to its volume. *2.10*
dessicant a hygroscopic substance used as a drying agent. *16.10*
diffusion the tendency of molecules and ions to move toward areas of lower concentration until the concentration is uniform throughout the system. *11.11*
dilute solution a solution that contains a small amount of solute. *17.4*
dimensional analysis a technique of problem-solving that uses the units that are part of a measurement to help solve the problem. *3.4*
dipole a molecule that has two electrically charged regions, or poles. *15.11*

dipole interaction a weak intermolecular force resulting from the attraction of oppositely charged regions of polar molecules. *15.13*

diprotic acid any acid that contains two ionizable protons (hydrogen ions); sulfuric acid (H_2SO_4) is a diprotic acid. *19.6*

disaccharide a carbohydrate formed from two monosaccharide units; common table sugar (sucrose) is a disaccharide. *25.13*

dispersion force the weakest kind of intermolecular attraction; thought to be caused by the motion of electrons. *15.13*

distillation a purification process in which a liquid is evaporated and then condensed again to a liquid; used to separate dissolved solids from liquids or liquids from liquids according to boiling point. *1.6*

double covalent bond a covalent bond in which two pairs of electrons are shared by two atoms. *15.2*

double-replacement reaction a chemical change that involves an exchange of positive ions between two compounds. *7.9*

dry cell a commercial voltaic cell in which the electrolyte is a moist paste. *22.3*

effloresce to lose water of hydration; the process occurs when the hydrate has a vapor pressure higher than that of water vapor in the air. *16.10*

effusion a process that occurs when a gas escapes through a tiny hole in its container. *11.11*

electrical potential the ability of a voltaic cell to produce an electric current. *22.6*

electrochemical cell any device that converts chemical energy into electrical energy or electrical energy into chemical energy. *22.1*

electrochemical process the conversion of chemical energy into electrical energy or electrical energy into chemical energy; in an electrochemical cell, all electrochemical processes involve redox reactions. *22.1*

electrode a conductor in a circuit that carries electrons to or from a substance other than a metal. *22.2*

electrolysis a process in which electrical energy is used to bring about a chemical change. *22.9*

electrolyte a compound that conducts an electric current in aqueous solution or in the molten state; all ionic compounds are electrolytes, but most covalent compounds are not. *16.8*

electrolytic cell an electrochemical cell used to cause a chemical change through the application of electrical energy. *22.9*

electromagnetic radiation a series of energy waves that travel in a vacuum at a speed of 3.0×10^{10} cm/s; includes radio waves, microwaves, visible light, infrared and ultraviolet light, x-rays, and gamma rays. *12.6*

electron a negatively charged subatomic particle. *4.2*

electron configuration the arrangement of electrons around the nucleus of an atom in its ground state. *12.4*

electron dot structures a notation that depicts valence electrons as dots around the atomic symbol of the element; the symbol represents the inner electrons and atomic nucleus; also called Lewis dot structures. *14.1*

electronegativity the tendency for an atom to attract electrons to itself when it is chemically combined with another element. *13.7*

element a substance that cannot be changed into a simpler substance under normal laboratory conditions. *1.7*

elementary reaction a reaction in which reactants are converted to products in a single step. *18.13*

empirical formula a formula with the lowest whole-number ratio of elements in a compound; the empirical formula of hydrogen peroxide, H_2O_2, is HO. *6.10*

emulsion the colloidal dispersion of one liquid in another. *16.9*

endothermic process heat absorbing process. *10.4*

end point the point in a titration at which neutralization is just achieved. *20.2*

energy the capacity for doing work; it exists in several forms, including chemical, nuclear, electrical, radiant, mechanical, and thermal energies. *10.1*

energy level a region around the nucleus of an atom where an electron is likely to be moving. *12.1*

enthalpy (H) the amount of heat that a substance has at a given temperature and pressure. *10.5*

entropy (S) a measure of the disorder of a system; systems tend to go from a state of order (low entropy) to a state of maximum disorder (high entropy). *18.7*

enzyme a biological catalyst, almost always a protein. *25.16*

equilibrium constant (K_{eq}) the ratio of product concentrations to reactant concentrations with each raised to a power given by the number of moles of the substance in the balanced chemical equation. *18.9*

equilibrium position the relative concentrations of reactants and products of a reaction that has reached equilibrium; it indicates whether the reactants or products are favored in the reversible reaction. *18.3*

equivalence point the point in a titration at which the number of equivalents of acid and base are equal. *20.4*

equivalent (equiv.) one equivalent is the amount of an acid (or base) that can give one mole of hydrogen (or hydroxide) ions. *20.3*

error the difference between the accepted value and the experimental value. *2.13*

ester a derivative of a carboxylic acid in which the —OH of the carbonyl group has been replaced by the —OR from an alcohol; the general formula is RCOOR. *25.11*

ether an organic compound in which oxygen is bonded to two carbon groups; the general formula is R—O—R. *25.7*

evaporation the vaporization of a liquid in an open container. *9.5*

excess reagent a reagent present in a quantity that is more than sufficient to react with a limiting reagent; any reactant that remains after the limiting reagent is used in a chemical reaction. *8.6*

exergonic a spontaneous reaction that releases free energy. *18.6*

exothermic process a heat dissipating process. *10.4*

experiment a carefully controlled, repeatable procedure for gathering data to test a hypothesis. *1.2*

experimental value the quantitative result of an experimental measurement. *2.13*

fatty acid the name originally given to continuous chain carboxylic acids first isolated from fats. *25.9*

Fehling's test a test used to detect aldehydes. *25.10*

fermentation the production of ethanol from sugars by the action of yeast or bacteria. *25.5*

film badge a small radiation detector worn by persons who work near radiation sources; it is several layers of photographic film covered with black light-proof paper. *26.8*

first order reaction a reaction in which the reaction rate is proportional to the concentration of only one reactant. *18.12*

fission the splitting of a nucleus into smaller fragments, accompanied by the release of neutrons and a large amount of energy. *26.6*

formula unit the lowest whole-number ratio of ions in an ionic compound; in magnesium chloride, the ratio of magnesium ions to chloride ions is 1:2 and the formula unit is $MgCl_2$. *5.4*

free energy the potential energy contained in a reaction system; the energy available to do work. *18.5*

freezing point depression the difference in temperature between the freezing points of a solution and of the pure solvent. *17.7*

frequency (ν) the number of wave cycles that pass a given point per unit of time. *12.6*

fuel cell a voltaic cell in which a fuel substance undergoes oxidation to produce electrical energy. *22.5*

functional group a specific arrangement of atoms in an organic compound that is capable of characteristic chemical reactions; the chemistry of an organic compound is determined by its functional groups. *25.1*

fusion a reaction in which two light nuclei combine to produce a nucleus of heavier mass, accompanied by the release of a large amount of energy. *26.7*

gamma radiation high energy electromagnetic radiation emitted by certain radioactive nuclei; gamma rays have no mass or electrical charge. *26.2*

gas matter that has no definite shape or volume; it adopts the shape and volume of its container. *1.4*

gas pressure a force resulting from the simultaneous collisions of billions of gas particles on an object. *9.2*

Geiger counter a gas-filled metal tube used to detect the presence of beta radiation. *26.8*

geometric isomer an organic compound that differs from another compound only in the geometry of their substituted groups. *24.6*

Gibbs free energy change (ΔG) the maximum amount of energy that can be coupled to another process to do useful work. *18.11*

glass the optically transparent fusion product of inorganic materials that have cooled to a rigid state without crystallizing. *9.7*

Graham's laws of effusion the rate of effusion of a gas is inversely proportional to the square root of its formula mass; this relationship is also true for the diffusion of gases. *11.11*

gram a metric mass unit equal to the mass of 1 cm^3 of water at 4°C. *2.9*

gram atomic mass (gam) the mass, in grams of one mole of atoms in a monatomic element; it is numerically equal to the atomic mass in amu. *6.3*

gram equivalent mass the mass of one equivalent of a substance. *20.3*

gram molecular mass (gmm) the mass of one mole of a moleular substance; it is equal to the formula mass expressed in grams. *6.3*

gram molecular mass (gmm) the mass of one mole of a molecular substance; it is equal to the formula mass expressed in grams. *6.3*

ground state the lowest energy level occupied by an electron when an atom is in its most stable energy state. *12.9*

group a vertical column of elements in the periodic table; the constituent elements of a group have similar chemical and physical properties. *13.2*

half-cell the part of a voltaic cell in which either oxidation or reduction occurs; it consists of a single electrode immersed in a solution of its ions. *22.2*

half-life ($t_{\frac{1}{2}}$) the time required for one-half of the atoms of a radioisotope to emit radiation and decay to products. *26.4*

half-reaction an equation showing either the reduction or the oxidation of a species in an oxidation–reduction reaction. *21.7*

half-reaction method a method of balancing a redox equation by balancing the oxidation and reduction half-reactions. *21.7*

halide ions a negative ion formed when a halogen atom gains an electron. *14.3*

halocarbon any member of a class of organic compounds containing covalently bonded fluorine, chlorine, bromine, or iodine. *25.2*

halogen any member of the nonmetallic elements in Group 7A of the periodic table. *13.3*

heat the energy that is transferred from one body to another because of a temperature difference. *10.1*

heat capacity the quantity of heat required to change an object's temperature by exactly 1°C. *10.2*

heat of combustion the heat absorbed or released during a chemical reaction in which one mole of a substance is completely burned. *10.6*

heat of reaction the heat released or absorbed during a chemical reaction; equivalent to H, the change in enthalpy. *10.6*

Heisenberg uncertainty principle it is impossible to know both the velocity and the position of a particle at the same time. *12.10*

Henry's law at a given temperature the solubility of a gas in a liquid is directly proportional to the pressure of the gas above the liquid. *17.3*

hertz (Hz) the SI unit of frequency, equal to one cycle per second. *12.6*

Hess's law of constant heat summation in going from a particular set of reactants to a particular set of products, the enthalpy change is the same whether the reaction takes place in one step or in a series of steps. *10.8*

heterogeneous mixture a mixture that is not uniform in composition; its components are readily distinguished. *1.6*

heterogeneous reactions a reaction carried out with a heterogeneous mixture of reactants. *18.2*

homogeneous mixture a mixture that is completely uniform in composition; its components are not distinguishable. *1.6*

homologous series a series formed by a group of compounds in which there is a constant increment of change in molecular structure from one compound in the series to the next. *24.2*

Hund's rule when electrons occupy orbitals of equal energy, one electron enters each orbital until all orbitals contain one electron with their spins parallel. *12.4*

hybridization a process in which several atomic orbitals (such as *s* and *p* orbitals) mix to form the same number of equivalent hybrid orbitals. *15.9*

hydration reaction a reaction in which water is added to an alkene. *25.6*

hydrocarbon an organic compound that contains only carbon and hydrogen. *24.0*

hydrogenation reaction a reaction in which hydrogen is added to a carbon–carbon double bond to give an alkane. *25.6*

hydrogen bond a relatively strong intermolecular force in which a hydrogen atom that is covalently bonded to a very electronegative atom is also weakly bonded to an unshared electron pair of an electronegative atom in the same molecule or one nearby. *15.13*

hydrogen-ion acceptor a base, according to the Brønsted-Lowry theory. *19.7*

hydrogen-ion donor an acid, according to the Brønstead-Lowry theory. *19.7*

hydrometer a device used to measure the specific gravity of a liquid. *2.11*

hydronium ion (H_3O^+) the positive ion formed when a water molecule gains a hydrogen ion; all hydrogen ions in aqueous solution are present as hydronium ions. *19.3*

hydroxide ion (OH^-) the negative ion formed when a water molecule loses a hydrogen ion. *19.3*

hydroxyl group the —OH functional group present in alcohols. *25.4*

hygroscopic a term describing salts and other compounds that remove moisture from the air. *16.10*

hypothesis a descriptive model used to explain observations. *1.2*

ideal gas constant (R) a term in the ideal gas law, which has the value 8.31 (L × kPa)/(K × mol). *11.8*

ideal gas law the relationship $P \times V = n \times R \times T$, which describes the behavior of an ideal gas. *11.8*

immiscible liquids that are insoluble in one another; oil and water are immiscible. *17.2*

inhibitor a substance that interferes with catalysis. *18.2*

inorganic chemistry the study of substances that do not contain carbon. *1.1*

intermediate a product of a reaction that immediately becomes a reactant of another reaction. *18.3*

International System of Units (SI) the revised version of the metric system, adopted by international agreement in 1960. *2.6*

ion an atom or group of atoms that has a positive or negative charge; cations are ions with a positive charge, and anions are ions with a negative charge. *5.2*

ionic bond the electrostatic attraction that binds oppositely charged ions together. *14.4*

ionic compound a compound composed of positive and negative ions. *5.3*

ionization energy the energy required to remove an electron from a gaseous atom. *13.5*

ionizing radiation radiation which has enough energy to produce ions by knocking electrons off some of the atoms it strikes. *26.8*

ion product constant for water (K_w) the product of the hydrogen ion and hydroxide ion concentrations of water; it is 1×10^{-14} at 25°C. *19.3*

isotopes atoms of the same element that have the same atomic number but different atomic masses due to a different number of neutrons. *4.6*

IUPAC system an internationally accepted system of naming compounds proposed by the International Union of Pure and Applied Chemistry (IUPAC). *24.2*

joule (j) the SI unit of energy; 4.184 joules equal 1.000 calorie. *2.12*

Kelvin temperature scale the temperature scale in which the freezing point of water is 273 K and the boiling point is 373 K; 0 K is absolute zero. *2.12*

ketone an organic compound in which the carbon of the carbonyl group is joined to two other carbons; the general formula is RCOR. *25.8*

kilogram (kg) the mass of 1 L of water at 4°C; it is the base unit of mass in the metric system. *2.9*

kinetic energy the energy an object has because of its motion. *9.1*

kinetic theory a theory explaining the states of matter, based on the concept that the particles in all forms of matter are in constant motion. *9.1*

law of conservation of energy energy is neither created nor destroyed in an ordinary chemical or physical process. *10.1*

law of conservation of mass mass can be neither created nor destroyed in an ordinary chemical or physical process. *1.12*

law of definite proportions in any chemical compound, the elements are always combined in the same proportion by mass. *5.3*

law of disorder it is a natural tendency of systems to move in the direction of maximum chaos or disorder. *18.7*

law of multiple proportions whenever two elements form more than one compound, the different masses of one element that combine with the same mass of the other element are in the ratio of small whole numbers. *5.5*

Le Châtelier's principle when stress is applied to a system at equilibrium, the system changes to relieve the stress. *18.4*

Lewis acid any substance that can accept a pair of electrons to form a covalent bond. *19.9*

Lewis base any substance that can donate a pair of electrons to form a covalent bond. *19.9*

limiting reagent any reactant that is used up first in a chemical reaction; it determines the amount of product that can be formed in the reaction. *8.6*

lime calcium oxide, CaO; it is sometimes called quicklime. *23.2*

lipid a member of a large class of relatively water-insoluble organic compounds; fats, oils, and waxes are lipids. *25.14*

liquid a form of matter that flows, has a fixed volume, and takes the shape of its container. *1.4*

liter (L) the volume of a cube measuring 10 centimeters on each edge (1000 cm^3); it is the common unprefixed unit of volume in the metric system. *2.8*

mass the amount of matter than an object contains; the SI base unit of mass is the kilogram. *1.3*

mass number the total number of protons and neutrons in the nucleus of an atom. *4.5*

matter anything that takes up space and has mass. *1.3*

melting point (mp) the temperature at which a substance changes from solid to a liquid; the melting point of water is 0°C. *9.7*

metal one of a class of elements that includes a large majority of the known elements; metals are characteristically lustrous, malleable, ductile, and good conductors of heat and electricity. *5.1*

metallic bond the force of attraction that holds metals together; it consists of the attraction of free-floating valence electrons for positively charged metal ions. *14.6*

metalloid one of a class of elements having properties of both metals and nonmetals. *5.1*

metallurgy the various procedures used to separate metals from their ores. *23.10*

meter the base unit of length in the metric and SI measurement systems. *2.7*

miscible liquids that will dissolve in each other. *17.2*

mixture a combination of two or more substances that are not chemically combined. *1.6*

molal boiling point elevation constant (K_b) the change in boiling point for a 1 molal solution of a nonvolatile molecular solute. *17.9*

molal freezing point depression constant (K_f) the change in freezing point for a 1 molal solution of a nonvolatile molecular solute. *17.9*

molality (m) the concentration of solute in a solution expressed as the number of moles of solute dissolved in 1 kilogram (1 000 g) of solvent. *17.8*

molar heat of fusion the energy, in kilojoules, required to melt one mole of a solid. *10.7*

molar heat of vaporization the energy, in kilojoules, required to vaporize one mole of a liquid. *10.7*

molar mass an expression sometimes used in place of gram formula mass to refer to the mass of a mole of any element or compound. *6.4*

molar volume the volume occupied by one mole of a gas at standard temperature and pressure (STP); 22.4 L. *6.6*

molarity (M) the concentration of solute in a solution expressed as the number of moles of solute dissolved in 1 L of solution. *17.4*

mole (mol) the amount of a substance that contains 6.02×10^{23} representative particles of that substance; a gram formula mass of any substance. *6.2*

molecule a neutral chemically bonded group of atoms that act as a unit. *5.3*

molecular compound a compound that is composed of molecules. *5.3*

molecular formula a chemical formula that shows the actual number and kinds of atoms present in a molecule of a compound. *5.4*

molecular orbital an orbital resulting from the overlapping of atomic orbitals when two atoms combine. *15.7*

mole fraction the ratio of the moles of solute in solution to the total number of moles of both solvent and solute. *17.8*

Monel metal a strong, corrosion-resistant alloy of nickel and copper. *23.10*

monomer a simple molecule that combines to form the repeating unit of a polymer. *25.12*

monoprotic acid any acid that contains one ionizable proton (hydrogen ion); nitric acid (HNO_3) is a monoprotic acid. *19.6*

monosaccharide a carbohydrate consisting of one sugar unit; it is also called a simple sugar. *25.13*

net ionic equation an equation for a reaction in solution showing only those particles that are directly involved in the chemical change. *7.12*

network solid a substance in which all of the atoms are covalently bonded to each other. *15.14*

neutralization reaction a reaction in which an acid and a base react in an aqueous solution to produce a salt and water. *20.1*

neutral solution an aqueous solution in which the concentrations of hydrogen and hydroxide ions are 1.0×10^{-7} mol/L; it has a pH of 7.0. *19.3*

neutron a subatomic particle with no charge and a mass of one amu found in the nucleus of the atom. *4.2*

neutron absorption a process used in a nuclear reactor to slow down the chain reaction by decreasing the number of moving neutrons; this is done with control rods made of a material like cadmium that absorbs neutrons. *26.6*

neutron moderation a process used in a nuclear reactor to slow down the neutrons so they can be captured by the reactor fuel to continue the chain reaction; water and carbon are good moderators. *26.6*

noble gas any member of a group of gaseous elements in Group 0 of the periodic table; the *s* and *p* sublevels of their outermost energy level are filled. *13.3*

nonelectrolyte a compound that does not conduct an electric current in aqueous solution or in the molten state. *16.8*

nonmetal one of a class of elements that are not lustrous and are generally poor conductors of heat and electricity; nonmetals are grouped on the right side of the periodic table. *5.1*

nonpolar covalent bond a bond formed when the atoms in a molecule are alike and the bonding electrons are shared equally. *15.10*

nonspontaneous reaction a reaction that does not give products under the specified conditions. *18.6*

normal boiling point the boiling point of a liquid at a pressure of one atmosphere. *9.6*

normality (*N*) the concentration of a solution expressed as the number of equivalents of solute in 1 L of solution. *20.4*

nucleic acid a polymer of ribonucleotides (RNA) or deoxyribonucleotides (DNA) found primarily in cell nuclei; nucleic acids play an important role in the transmission of hereditary characteristics, protein synthesis, and the control of cell activities. *25.16*

nucleotide one of the monomers that make up DNA and RNA; it consists of a nitrogen-containing base (a purine or pyrimidine), a sugar (ribose or deoxyribose), and a phosphate. *25.16*

nucleus the dense central portion of an atom, composed of protons and neutrons. *4.3*

octet rule atoms react by gaining or losing electrons so as to acquire the stable electron structure of a noble gas, usually eight valence electrons. *14.2*

ore a mineral used for commercial production of a metal. *23.10*

organic chemistry the study of compounds that contain the element carbon. *1.1*

oxidation a process that involves complete or partial loss of electrons or a gain of oxygen; it results in an increase in the oxidation number of an atom. *21.1*

oxidation number a positive or negative number assigned to a combined atom according to a set of arbitrary rules; generally it is the charge an atom would have if the electrons in each bond were assigned to the atoms of the more electronegative element. *21.3*

oxidation number change method a method of balancing a redox equation by comparing the increases and decreases in oxidation numbers. *21.5*

oxidation–reduction reaction a reaction that involves the transfer of electrons between reactants during a chemical change. *21.0*

oxidizing agent the substance in a redox reaction that accepts electrons; in the reaction, the oxidizing agent is reduced. *21.2*

paramagnetic a term used to describe a substance that shows a relatively strong attraction to an external magnetic field; these substances have molecules containing one or more unpaired electrons. *15.6*

partial pressure the pressure exerted by each gas in a gaseous mixture. *11.9*

pascal (Pa) the SI unit of pressure. *9.2*

Pauli exclusion principle no more than two electrons can occupy an atomic orbital; these electrons must have opposite spins. *12.4*

peptide an organic compound formed by a combination of amino acids in which the amino group of one acid is united with the carboxylic group of another through an amide bond. *25.15*

peptide bond the bond between the carbonyl group of one amino acid and the nitrogen of the next amino acid in the peptide chain; the structure is

```
  O  H
  ‖  |
—C—N—
```

25.15

percent composition the percent by mass of each element in a compound. *6.9*

$$\textbf{percent error} = \frac{|\text{accepted value} - \text{experimental value}|}{\text{accepted value}} \times 100$$

2.13

percent yield the ratio of the actual yield to the theoretical yield for a chemical reaction expressed as a percentage; a measure of the efficiency of a reaction. *8.7*

period a horizontal row of elements in the periodic table. *13.2*

periodic law when the elements are arranged in order of increasing atomic number, there is a periodic repetition of their physical and chemical properties. *13.2*

periodic table an arrangement of elements into rows and columns according to similarities in their properties. *5.1*

pH a number used to denote the hydrogen-ion concentration, or acidity, of a solution; it is the negative logarithm of the hydrogen ion concentration of a solution. *19.4*

phase any part of a system with uniform composition and properties. *1.6*

phase diagram a diagram showing the conditions at which a substance exists as a solid, liquid, or vapor. *9.9*

photoelectric effect a process in which electrons are ejected by certain metals when light of sufficient frequency shines on them. *12.8*

photon a quantum of light; a discrete bundle of electromagnetic energy that behaves as a particle. *12.8*

physical change an alteration of a substance that does not affect its chemical composition. *1.5*

physical chemistry the study of the theoretical basis of chemical behavior, relying on mathematics and physics. *1.1*

physical property a quality of a substance that can be observed or measured without changing the substance's chemical composition. *1.3*

pi bond (π bond) a bond in which the bonding electrons are most likely to be found in the sausage-shaped regions above and below the nuclei of the bonded atoms. *15.7*

Planck's constant (*h*) a number used to calculate the radiant energy, E, absorbed or emitted by a body from the frequency of radiation. *12.7*

plasma a state of matter consisting of a gaseous mixture of electrons and positive ions. *9.10*

polar bond a bond formed when two different atoms are joined by a covalent bond and the bonding electrons are shared unequally. *15.10*

polar covalent bond see polar bond. *15.10*

polar molecule a molecule in which one or more atoms is slightly negative, and one or more is slightly positive in such a way that the polarities do not cancel; water is a polar molecule. *15.11*

polyatomic ion a tightly bound group of atoms that behaves as a unit and carries a charge. *5.7*

polymer a very large molecule formed by the covalent bonding of repeating small molecules, known as monomers. *25.12*

polypeptide a peptide with more than 10 amino acid residues. *25.15*

polysaccharides a complex carbohydrate polymer formed by the linkage of many monosaccharide monomers; starch, glycogen, and cellulose are polysaccharides. *25.13*

positron a particle which has the same mass as an electron but has a positive charge. *26.3*

precision the reproducibility, under the same conditions, of a measurement. *2.2*

product a substance formed in a chemical reaction. *1.9*

protein any peptide with more than 100 amino acid residues. *25.15*

proton a positively charged subatomic particle found in the nucleus of an atom. *4.2*

qualitative measurement a measurement which gives descriptive, nonnumeric results. *2.1*

quantitative measurement a measurement which gives definite, usually numeric results. *2.1*

quantum a small package, or unit, of electromagnetic energy; the amount of energy required to move an electron from its present energy level to the next higher one. *12.1*

quantum mechanical model the modern description, primarily mathematical, of the behavior of electrons in atoms. *12.2*

radiation the penetrating rays emitted by a radioactive source; also, the giving off of energy in various forms such as heat, light, or radiowaves. *26.1*

radioactive decay the process in which an unstable nucleus loses energy by emitting radiation. *26.1*

radioactivity the property by which an atomic nucleus gives off alpha, beta, or gamma radiation. *26.1*

radioisotopes isotopes that have unstable nuclei and undergo radioactive decay. *26.1*

rate a measure of change within an interval of time. *18.1*

rate law an expression relating the rate of a reaction to the concentration of the reactants. *18.12*

reactant a starting substance in a chemical reaction. *1.9*

reaction mechanism a series of elementary reactions that take place during the course of a complex reaction. *18.13*

redox reaction another name for an oxidation–reduction reaction. *21.0*

reducing agent the substance in a redox reaction that donates electrons; in the reaction, the reducing agent is oxidized. *21.2*

reduction a process that involves a complete or partial gain of electrons or the loss of oxygen; it results in a decrease in the oxidation number of an atom. *21.1*

reduction potential a measure of the tendency of a given half-reaction to occur as a reduction (gain of electrons) in an electrochemical cell. *22.6*

representative element an element that belongs to an A group in the periodic table; they are called representative elements because they illustrate the entire range of chemical properties. *5.1, 13.3*

representative particle the smallest unit into which a substance can be broken down without a change in composition; the term refers to whether a substance commonly exists as atoms, ions, or molecules. *6.2*

resonance a phenomenon that occurs when two or more equally valid electron dot structures can be written for a molecule; the actual bonding is believed to be a hybrid or mixture of the extremes represented by the resonance forms. *15.5*

reversible reaction a reaction in which the conversion of reactants into products and the conversion of products into reactants occur simultaneously. *18.3*

salt bridge a tube containing a conducting solution used to connect half-cells in a voltaic cell; it allows the passage of ions from one compartment to another but prevents the solutions from mixing completely. *22.2*

salt hydrolysis a process in which the cations or anions of a dissociated salt accept hydrogen ions from water or donate hydrogen ions to water; solutions containing hydrolyzed salts may be either acidic or basic. *20.5*

saponification the process used to make soap; it involves the hydrolysis of fats or oils by hot aqueous sodium hydroxide. *25.14*

saturated compound an organic compound in which all carbon atoms are joined by single covalent bonds; it contains the maximum number of hydrogen atoms. *24.5*

saturated solution a solution containing the maximum amount of solute for a given amount of solvent at a constant temperature and pressure; in a saturated solution, the dissolved and undissolved solute are in dynamic equilibrium. *17.2*

scientific law a concise statement that summarizes the results of a broad variety of observations and experiments. *1.2*

scientific notation expression of numbers in the form $N \times 10^n$ where N is equal to or greater than 1 and less than 10 and n is an integer. *2.3*

scintillation counter a device that uses a specially coated surface called a phosphor to detect radiation; ionizing radiation striking this surface produces bright flashes of light (scintillations). *26.8*

self-ionization a term describing the reaction in which two water molecules react to give ions. *19.3*

sigma bond (σ bond) a bond formed when two atomic orbitals combine to form a molecular orbital that is symmetrical along the axis connecting the two atomic nuclei. *15.7*

significant figures all the digits that can be known precisely in a measurement, plus a last estimated digit. *2.4*

single covalent bond a bond formed when a pair of electrons is shared between two atoms. *15.1*

single-replacement reaction a chemical change in which atoms of an element replace atoms of a second element in a compound; also called a displacement reaction. *7.8*

skeleton equation a chemical equation that does not indicate the relative amounts of reactants and products. *7.2*

slaked lime calcium hydroxide, $Ca(OH)_2$. *22.2*

solid matter which has a definite shape and volume. *1.4*

solubility the amount of a substance that dissolves in a given quantity of solvent at specified conditions of temperature and pressure to produce a saturated solution. *17.2*

solubility product constant (K_{sp}) an equilibrium constant that can be applied to the solubility of electrolytes; it is equal to the product of the concentration terms each raised to the power of the coefficient of the substance in the dissociation equation. *20.7*

solute dissolved particles in a solution. *16.6*

solution a homogeneous mixture. *1.6*

solvation a process that occurs when an ionic solute dissolves; in solution, the ions are surrounded by solvent molecules. *16.7*

solvent the dissolving medium in a solution. *16.6*

specific gravity the ratio of the density of a substance to that of a standard substance (usually water). *2.11*

specific rate constant a proportionality constant relating the concentrations of reactants to the rate of the reaction. *18.12*

spectator ion an ion that does not change oxidation number or composition during a reaction. *7.12, 21.7*

spectrum the range of wavelengths and frequencies making up light; the wavelengths are separated when a beam of white light passes through a prism. *12.6*

spontaneous reaction a reaction known to give the products as written in a balanced equation. *18.6*

standard atmosphere (atm) a unit of pressure; it is the pressure required to support 760 mm of mercury in a mercury barometer at 25°C; this is the average atmospheric pressure at sea level. *9.2*

standard cell potential the measured cell potential when the ion concentration in the half-cells are 1.00 *M*, at 1 atm of pressure and 25°C. *22.6*

standard entropy (S^0) the entropy of a substance in its stable state at 25°C and 1 atm. *18.10*

standard heat of formation (H_f^0) the change in enthalpy (*H*) for a reaction in which one mole of a compound is formed from its constituent elements. *10.9*

standard hydrogen electrode an arbitrary reference electrode (half-cell) used with another electrode (half-cell) to measure the standard reduction potential of that cell; the standard reduction potential of the hydrogen electrode is assigned a value of 0.00 V. *22.6*

standard solution a solution of known concentration used in carrying out a titration. *20.2*

standard temperature and pressure (STP) the conditions under which the volume of a gas is usually measured; standard temperature is 0°C and standard pressure is 1 atmosphere (atm). *6.6*

stereoisomers an organic molecule having the same molecular structure as another molecule, but differing in the arrangement of atoms in the space. *24.7*

stoichiometry that portion of chemistry dealing with numerical relationships in chemical reactions; the calculation of quantities of substances involved in chemical equations. *8.0*

strong acid an acid that is completely (or almost completely) ionized in aqueous solution. *19.10*

strong base a base that completely dissociates into metal ions and hydroxide ions in aqueous solution. *19.10*

strong electrolyte a solution in which a large portion of the solute exists as ions. *16.8*

structural formula a chemical formula that shows the arrangement of atoms in a molecule or a polyatomic ion; each dash between two atoms indicates a pair of shared electrons. *15.1*

structural isomer a compound that has the same molecular formula as another compound but has a different molecular structure. *24.4*

sublimation the conversion of a solid to a gas without passing through the liquid state. *9.8*

substance a sample of matter having a uniform and definite composition; it can be either an element or a compound. *1.3*

substituent an atom or group of atoms that can take the place of a hydrogen atom on a parent hydrocarbon molecule. *24.3*

substitution the replacement of an atom or group of atoms by another atom or group of atoms. *25.3*

supersaturated solution a solution that contains more solute than it can theoretically hold at a given temperature. *17.3*

surface tension an inward force that tends to minimize the surface area of a liquid; it causes the surface to behave as if it were covered by a thin skin. *16.2*

surfactant a surface active agent; any substance whose molecules interface with the hydrogen bonding between water molecules, reducing surface tension; soaps and detergents are surfactants. *16.2*

surroundings the remainder of the universe that is outside the system. *10.4*

suspension a mixture from which some of the particles settle out slowly upon standing. *16.9*

system any part of the universe that attention is focused on. *10.4*

temperature the degree of hotness or coldness of an object, which is a measure of the average kinetic energy of the molecules of the object. *2.12*

ternary compound a compound containing atoms of three different elements, with one or more polyatomic ions usually present; Na_2CO_3 and $Mg(OH)_2$ are ternary ionic compounds. *5.11*

tetrahedral angle a bond angle of 109.5° created when a central atom forms four bonds directed toward the corners of a regular tetrahedron. *15.8*

theoretical yield the amount of product that could form during a reaction calculated from a balanced chemical equation; it represents the maximum amount of product that could be formed from a given amount of reactant. *8.7*

theory a thoroughly tested model that explains why experiments give certain results. *1.2*

thermochemical equation a chemical equation that includes the amount of heat produced or absorbed during the reaction. *10.6*

thermochemistry the study of heat changes in chemical reactions. *10.1*
titration a method of reacting a solution of unknown concentration with one of known concentration; this procedure is often used to determine the concentrations of acids and bases. *20.2*
***trans* configuration** a term applied to geometric isomers; it denotes an arrangement in which the substituted groups are on opposite sides of the double bond. *24.6*
transition metal an element found in one of the B groups in the periodic table. *5.1, 13.3*
transition state a term sometimes used to refer to the activated complex. *18.1*
transmutation the conversion of an atom of one element into an atom of another element by the emission of radiation. *26.5*
transuranium element an element in the periodic table whose atomic number is above 92. *26.5*
triglyceride an ester in which all three hydroxyl groups on a glycogen molecule have been replaced by long-chain fatty acids; fats are triglycerides. *25.14*
triple covalent bond a covalent bond in which three pairs of electrons are shared by two atoms. *15.2*
triple point the point on a phase diagram where all three states of a substance are present. *9.9*
triprotic acid any acid that contains three ionizable protons (hydrogen ions); phosphoric acid (H_3PO_4) is a triprotic acid. *19.6*
Tyndall effect the visible path produced by a beam of light passing through a colloidal dispersion or suspension; the phenomenon is caused by the scattering of light by the colloidal and suspended particles. *16.9*

unit cell the smallest group of particles within a crystal that retains the geometric shape of the crystal. *9.7*
universe the totality of all existing things. *10.4*
unsaturated a solution that contains less solute than a saturated solution at a given temperature and pressure. *17.2*
unsaturated compound an organic compound with one or more double or triple carbon–carbon bonds. *24.5*
unshared pair a pair of valence electrons that is not involved in bonding. *15.1*

vacuum a space where no particles of matter exist. *9.2*
valence electron an electron in the highest occupied energy level of an atom. *14.1*
van der Waals force a term used to describe the weakest intermolecular attractions; these include dispersion forces and dipole interactions. *15.13*
vapor a substance in the gaseous state that is ordinarily (at room temperature) a liquid or solid. *1.4*
vapor pressure the pressure produced when vaporized particles above the liquid in a sealed container collide with the container walls; when the container is saturated with vapor, a dynamic equilibrium exists between the gas and the liquid. *9.5*
vaporization the conversion of a liquid to a gas at a temperature below its boiling point. *9.5*
voltaic cell an electrochemical cell used to convert chemical energy into electrical energy; the energy is produced by a spontaneous redox reaction. *22.2*
volume the space occupied by matter. *2.8*
VSEPR theory valence-shell electron-pair repulsion theory; because electron pairs repel, molecules adjust their shapes so that valence-electron pairs are as far apart as possible. *15.8*

water of hydration water molecules that are an integral part of a crystal structure. *16.10*
wavelength (λ) the distance between two adjacent crests of a wave. *12.6*
wax an ester of a long-chain fatty acid and a long-chain alcohol. *25.14*
weak acid an acid that is only slightly ionized in aqueous solution. *19.10*
weak base a base that does not dissociate completely in aqueous solution. *19.10*
weak electrolyte a solution in which only a fraction of the solute exists as ions. *16.8*
weight a measure of the force of attraction between the earth and an object. *2.9*

zwitterion an internal salt of an amino acid. *25.15*

Index

The page on which a term is defined is indicated in **boldface** type.

Photographs

Table of Contents iiiT Robert E. Daemmrich/Tony Stone Images; iiiLC Lowell Georgia/Photo Researchers; iiiRC Seth Joel/Woodfin Camp & Associates; iiiB Barry L. Runk/Grant Heilman Photography; ivT Will Rhyins/Woodfin Camp & Assoc.; ivB Kevin Morris/AllStock; ixT John Terence Turner/AllStock; ixC David Barnes/AllStock; ixB Hobart/Tafa Technologies; viT Peter Menzel/Stock, Boston; viB Lee Snyder/Photo Researchers; viiB Matt Bradley/Bruce Coleman Inc.; viiiT Tony Ward, Tetbury/SPL/Photo Researchers; viiiC National Museum of Athens/Art Resource viiiB William McCoy/Rainbow; xT Henry Groskinsky/Peter Arnold, Inc.; xiT Phil Degginger/Tony Stone Images; xiB Runk-Schoenberger/Grant Heilman Photography; xiiT Pictor/Uniphoto Picture Agency; xiiB Orion Press/Westlight; xiiiT Annie Griffiths Belt/DRK Photo; xiiiB NASA

Chapter 1 4 Robert E. Daemmrich/Tony Stone Images; 7T Scala/Art Resource N.Y., Stradano: The Alchemist, PalazzoVecchio, Florence, Italy; 7B The Bettmann Archives; 20 Nippon Television Network; 21T Seth Joel/Woodfin Camp & Associates; 21B Lowell Georgia/Photo Researchers

Chapter 2 26 Barry L. Runk/Grant Heilman Photography; 33 The Bettmann Archive; 43 NASA/JPL; 53 Uniphoto/Pictor

Chapter 3 71T Peggy/Yoram Kahana/Peter Arnold, Inc.; 71B UPI/Bettmann; 75L Sarah Stone/Tony Stone Images; 78T Will Rhyins/Woodfin Camp & Assoc.

Chapter 4 82 H. R. Bramaz/Peter Arnold, Inc.; 85 Philippe Plailly/SPL/Photo Researchers; 91 Douglas Peebles/Westlight; 95 Runk-Schoenberger/Grant Heilman Photography; 98 Victoria Hurst/Tom Stack and Associates

Chapter 5 112T John Marshall/AllStock; 112B Tom Bean/DRK Photo; 125 John Mead/SPL/Photo Researchers; 128 Jon Feingersh/AllStock; 132 Kevin Morris/AllStock; 135T Jim Richardson/Westlight; 135C Lennart Nilsson/A CHILD IS BORN, Dell Publishing Company; 135B Craig Aurness/Westlight

Chapter 6 140 Jim Zuckerman/Westlight; 144 Leonard Lessin/Peter Arnold, Inc.; 146 Il Servizio di Italiano Posta; 148 Hans Reinhard/Bruce Coleman Inc.; 155 Dewitt Jones/AllStock; 162 Calvin Larsen/Photo Researchers; 165 C. C. Lockwood/DRK Photo; 167 L. L. T. Rhodes/Tony Stone Images

Chapter 7 174 Will & Deni McIntyre/Photo Researchers; 182 Tougaloo College/Coleman Library; 186T Robert Frerck/Tony Stone Images; 186B Akzo Chemicals International B. V.; 196T Larry Lefever/Grant Heilman Photography; 196B Ohn Deeks/Photo Researchers; 201C Courtesy of Bill Denby & DuPont; 201B Stefan Merken/AllStock

Chapter 8 206 Tom Stack/Tom Stack & Associates; 211 D. Cavagnaro/DRK Photo; 212 Grant Heilman/Grant Heilman Photography; 215 Peter Menzel/Stock, Boston; 216 Bob Daemmrich/Stock, Boston; 217 NASA; 220 Ray Pfortner/Peter Arnold, Inc.; 222 Hugo Binz/Bruce Coleman Inc.; 228 Laurance B. Aiuppy/AllStock

Chapter 9 236 Fred Espenak/SPL/Photo Researchers; 240 The Bettmann Archives; 241T Bob Daemmrich/Stock, Boston; 241B Randy Wells/AllStock; 252 Frank Siteman/Stock, Boston; 257 Jack Finch/SPL/Photo Researchers; 258T Wernher Krutein/Photovault; 258B Wernher Krutein/Photovault; 258BR Werner Otto/AllStock

Chapter 10 262 Lee Snyder/Photo Researchers; 264 Stephen Frisch/Stock, Boston; 267 Runk-Schoenberger/Grant Heilman Photography; 269L Hanson Carroll/Peter Arnold, Inc.; 269R Michael P. Gadomski/Bruce Coleman Inc.; 273 Copr. Randy Brandon/AllStock; 275T Lefever-Grushow/Grant Heilman Photography; 275B Chip & Jill Isenhart/Tom Stack and Associates

Chapter 11 304 John Zoiner/Uniphoto Picture Agency; 306 Jim Zipp/Photo Researchers; 308 Copr. E. Masterson/AllStock; 316B Stephen Frink/AllStock; 317T James Stoots/Lawrence Livermore National Laboratory; 317B James Stoots/Lawrence Livermore National Laboratory

Chapter 12 322 Jack Kenner; 329T Matt Bradley/Bruce Coleman Inc.; 329B Rich Treplow/Photo Researchers; 336 Dept. of Physics, Imperial College/SPL/Photo Researchers; 338T Dorothy Miller/Indigo Press; 338B Jerry Jacka/Jerry Jacka Photography; 339 L. West/Bruce Coleman Inc.; 343 GECO UK/SPL/Photo Researchers; 344 Martin Dohrn/SPL/Photo Researchers

Chapter 13 352 Special Collection,Van Pelt Dietrich Library/University of Pennsylvania; 359 Tony Ward, Tetbury/SPL/Photo Researchers; 364 NASA/Goddard Space Flight Center; 368 David Scharf Photography

Chapter 14 372 Pat Lynch/Photo Researchers; 376 U S Postal Service; 379 James Stoots/Lawrence Livermore National Laboratory; 382 Jeremy Burgess/SPL/Photo Researchers; 385RT Dennis Purse/Photo Researchers; 387 Dr. Alton M. Lacy/ UCSF School of Dentistry

Chapter 15 404 William McCoy/Rainbow; 405 Steve Benbow/Stock, Boston; 416 Bob Daemmrich/Stock, Boston; 418 Dr. Arthur Lesk, Laboratory for Molecular Biology/SPL/Photo Researchers; 421 The MIT Museum; 423 Barry L. Runk/Grant Heilman Photography; 426 Pat & Tom Leeson/Photo Researchers; 427L Lawrence Livermore National Laboratory/Hand tinting by Susan Vogel; 427R Lawrence Livermore National Laboratory

Chapter 16 432 David Barnes/AllStock; 435T David M. Dennis/Tom Stack and Associates; 435B John Terence Turner/AllStock; 436B Tom Hollyman/Photo Researchers; 437T Werner H. Muller/Peter Arnold, Inc.; 437B Bob Thomason/Tony Stone Images; 438 Vince Streano/AllStock; 441 Scott Camazine/Photo Researchers; 457 Bob Pool/Tom Stack and Associates

Chapter 17 464 Laurance B. Aiuppy/AllStock; 482 Special Collections, Milbank Memorial Library/Teachers College, Columbia University; 483LT Courtesy of Metco, Inc.; 483RT Hobart/Tafa Technologies; 483C Gregg Mancuso/Stock, Boston; 483BDan McCoy/Rainbow

Chapter 18 488 Henry Groskinsky/Peter Arnold, Inc.; 490 Kashimoto/Pictor/Uniphoto; 493B The Bettmann Archives; 495 Leonard Lessin/Peter Arnold, Inc.; 498 Gerard Fritz/Tony Stone Images; 500 Chris

Cole/Tony Stone Images; 502 Chemical Heritage Foundation; 504 David Ball/AllStock; 506 Ron Sanford/AllStock; 516 James Peter Stuart/AllStock; 518 Andrew Sacks/Tony Stone Images; 525 Ron Watts/Westlight

Chapter 19 544T Adam Hart-Davis/SPL/Photo Researchers; 544BStephen Studd/Tony Stone Images; 548T Ken Sherman/Bruce Coleman Inc.; 549 Special Collections,Van Pelt Dietrich Library/University of Pennsylvania; 555 Leonard Lessin/Peter Arnold, Inc.; 564L James Stoots/Lawrence Livermore National Laboratory; 564C Lawrence Livermore National Laboratory; 564R Astrid & Hanns-Frieder Michler/SPL/Photo Researchers

Chapter 20 David Ryan/Uniphoto; 582 RobertFrerck/Tony Stone Images; 587 Larry Mulvehill/Photo Researchers; 591 Jim Pickerell/Tony Stone Images

Chapter 21 596 Dick Durrance II/The Stock Market; 598T Walter Paul Bebirian/Fundamental Photographs; 598BLeonard Lessin/Peter Arnold, Inc.; 600 Grant Heilman/Grant Heilman Photography; 602 Patricia J. Bruno/Positive Images; 603 Guy Marche/AllStock; 604 Special Collections, Van Pelt Dietrich Library/University of Pennsylvania; 607 E. R. Degginger/Bruce Coleman Inc.; 610 Runk-Schoenberger/Grant Heilman Photography; 612 Ivan Polunin/Bruce Coleman Inc.; 616 Dan McCoy/Rainbow; 617T Railway Technical Research Institute, Japan; 617B Phil Degginger/Tony Stone Images

Chapter 22 622 Paul Silverman/Fundamental Photographs; 628T NASA; 628B Hank Morgan/Photo Researchers; 634 No credit; 641 Occidental Chemical Corp.; 645 Stephen Frisch/Stock, Boston

Chapter 23 650 Jan Halaska/Photo Researchers; 652 Kevin Schafer/AllStock; 653 Richard Megna/Fundamental Photographs; 655L Paul Silverman/Fundamental Photographs; 655R Jim Olive/Uniphoto Picture Agency; 657 Matthew McVay/AllStock; 658L Pictor/Uniphoto Picture Agency; 658RKristen Brochmann/Fundamental Photographs; 659L Jane Grushow/Grant Heilman Photography; 660 Grant Heilman/Grant Heilman Photography; 662L Richard Megna/Fundamental Photographs; 662R Michael Yamashita/Westlight; 664BCalifornia Institute of Technology; 669 Mary Eveans Picture Library/Photo Researchers; 670L Argonne National Laboratory; 670R Dave Woodward/Taurus Photo; 673 © 1992 Roger Ressmeyer/Starlight; 674T Robert Frerck/Tony Stone Images; 674B Paul Silverman/Fundamental Photographs; 675 Sepp Seitz/Woodfin Camp & Associates; 677T Stephen Trimble/DRK Photo; 677C NASA

Chapter 24 682 Vince Streano/Tony Stone Images; 686 Keith Gunnar/Bruce Coleman Inc.; 687 Michael Baytoff/Black Star; 693T Tony Stone Images; 695TChris Noble/AllStock; 695B L. O'Shaughnessy/AllStock; 698 Chemical Heritage Foundation; 701 Clive Freeman, The Royal Institution/SPL/Photo Researchers; 703 Theodore Vogel/Photo Researchers

Chapter 25 710 Orion Press/Westlight; 715 Annie Griffiths Belt/DRK Photo; 720 Chip Henderson/Tony Stone Images; 721 Simon Fraser/SPL/Photo Researchers; 725 Wernher Krutein/Photovault; 728 Karl Weidmann/Photo Researchers; 730 Tom Pantages; 742 Timothy Eagan/Woodfin Camp & Associates; 745 Massachusetts Institute of Technology; 747 Don Kelly/Grant Heilman Photography; 750T Art Wolfe/AllStock; 750B Gerard Lacz/Peter Arnold, Inc.

Chapter 26 764 Patrice Loiez,Cern/SPL/ Photo Researchers; 766 Tom A. Wiewandt/DRK Photo; 771 NASA; 772 Courtesy of JET Joint Undertaking; 774 Richard Falco/Black Star; 776L Bronx Veterans Affairs Medical Center; 776R SUI/Photo Researchers; 777 Larry Mulvehill/Photo Researchers

Anne Dowie*: 32, 51, 61, 75, 157, 248, 271, 476, 507, 775

Stephen Frisch*: 10, 192, 229C, 229L, 229R, 314, 316T, 505, 554, 666

Walter Jebe*: 302, 356, 492, 548B

Wayland Lee*: 245

Geoffrey Nilsen Photography*: v, viiT, x B, 2, 9L, 9C, 9R, 11, 12, 15, 18T, 18B, 19, 28R, 35, 38, 39, 42, 44, 45, 47, 49, 56, 65, 66, 67, 70, 73, 77, 78B, 81, 106, 108, 109, 116L, 116R, 120, 127, 142, 147, 149, 151, 152, 164, 176, 178L, 178R, 184, 188, 193, 201T, 204, 223, 226, 239, 244L, 249, 254, 260L, 260R, 265, 279, 280, 290, 299T, 312L, 312R, 313, 333L, 333R, 341, 348, 350, 374, 380, 381, 383, 385LT, 385LC, 385LB, 392, 401, 436T, 442, 447, 450L, 450R, 451L, 451R, 458, 460L, 460R, 461L, 461R, 465L, 465R, 468, 471L, 471C, 471R, 472, 493LT, 493RT, 512, 534, 536, 540, 552, 553, 566, 568, 572, 574LB, 574CB, 574RB, 574T, 579, 586, 589, 595, 605L, 605R, 608, 620L, 620C, 620R, 624T, 624B, 627, 638, 643, 654L, 654R, 656, 659R, 661, 663, 667, 668j, 672L, 672R, 681, 684, 690, 693B, 694, 697, 708L, 708C, 708R, 723, 734, 736, 737, 738, 740T, 740B, 754LT, 754RT, 754LB, 754RB, 756, 773

Voldi Tanner*: 28L, 48, 72, 118T, 118B

Susan Vogel*: 36, 58, 60, 62, 68,121,158, 208, 446, 494, 584, 664T, 677B, 718,

Basal Feature Logos Walter Jebe*: 7, 51, 71, 77, 98, 118, 132, 144, 165, 220, 241, 275, 338, 356, 364, 379, 405, 426, 437, 446, 467, 498, 518, 544, 561, 572, 602, 628, 676, 688, 695, 717, 735, 762, 773

Chuck O'Rear/Westlight: 20, 39, 102, 186, 196, 215, 253, 280, 306, 316, 329, 387, 474, 591, 616, 634, 665

Special thanks to Acteron Corporation, Redwood City, California; Encore Gymnastics, Walnut Creek, California; California Academy of Sciences, San Francisco, California

*Photographs taken expressly for Addison-Wesley Publishing Company Inc.

Illustrations

Illustrative Art Rolin Graphics

Concept Maps, Charts, and Graphs Tamara Northway

Calligraphy Kei Yamagami: 3,17

Periodic Table of the Elements

1 ← This numbering system is used by the International Union of Pure and Applied Chemistry (IUPAC).

Key: State; Atomic number; Electrons in each energy level; Element symbol; Average atomic mass. Example: (S) 11 **Na** Sodium 22.990 (2-8-1)

State
(S) Solid
(L) Liquid
(G) Gas
(N) Not found in nature

1 1A	2 2A	3 3B	4 4B	5 5B	6 6B	7 7B	8	9 8B	10	11 1B	12 2B	13 3A	14 4A	15 5A	16 6A	17 7A	18 0
(G) 1 **H** Hydrogen 1.0079 (1)																	(G) 2 **He** Helium 4.0026 (2)
(S) 3 **Li** Lithium 6.941 (2-1)	(S) 4 **Be** Beryllium 9.0122 (2-2)											(S) 5 **B** Boron 10.81 (2-3)	(S) 6 **C** Carbon 12.011 (2-4)	(G) 7 **N** Nitrogen 14.007 (2-5)	(G) 8 **O** Oxygen 15.999 (2-6)	(G) 9 **F** Fluorine 18.998 (2-7)	(G) 10 **Ne** Neon 20.179 (2-8)
(S) 11 **Na** Sodium 22.990 (2-8-1)	(S) 12 **Mg** Magnesium 24.305 (2-8-2)											(S) 13 **Al** Aluminum 26.982 (2-8-3)	(S) 14 **Si** Silicon 28.086 (2-8-4)	(S) 15 **P** Phosphorus 30.974 (2-8-5)	(S) 16 **S** Sulfur 32.06 (2-8-6)	(G) 17 **Cl** Chlorine 35.453 (2-8-7)	(G) 18 **Ar** Argon 39.948 (2-8-8)
(S) 19 **K** Potassium 39.098 (2-8-8-1)	(S) 20 **Ca** Calcium 40.08 (2-8-8-2)	(S) 21 **Sc** Scandium 44.956 (2-8-9-2)	(S) 22 **Ti** Titanium 47.90 (2-8-10-2)	(S) 23 **V** Vanadium 50.941 (2-8-11-2)	(S) 24 **Cr** Chromium 51.996 (2-8-13-1)	(S) 25 **Mn** Manganese 54.938 (2-8-13-2)	(S) 26 **Fe** Iron 55.847 (2-8-14-2)	(S) 27 **Co** Cobalt 58.933 (2-8-15-2)	(S) 28 **Ni** Nickel 58.71 (2-8-16-2)	(S) 29 **Cu** Copper 63.546 (2-8-18-1)	(S) 30 **Zn** Zinc 65.38 (2-8-18-2)	(S) 31 **Ga** Gallium 69.72 (2-8-18-3)	(S) 32 **Ge** Germanium 72.59 (2-8-18-4)	(S) 33 **As** Arsenic 74.922 (2-8-18-5)	(S) 34 **Se** Selenium 78.96 (2-8-18-6)	(L) 35 **Br** Bromine 79.904 (2-8-18-7)	(G) 36 **Kr** Krypton 83.80 (2-8-18-8)
(S) 37 **Rb** Rubidium 85.468 (2-8-18-8-1)	(S) 38 **Sr** Strontium 87.62 (2-8-18-8-2)	(S) 39 **Y** Yttrium 88.906 (2-8-18-9-2)	(S) 40 **Zr** Zirconium 91.22 (2-8-18-10-2)	(S) 41 **Nb** Niobium 92.906 (2-8-18-12-1)	(S) 42 **Mo** Molybdenum 95.94 (2-8-18-13-1)	(N) 43 **Tc** Technetium (97) (2-8-18-14-1)	(S) 44 **Ru** Ruthenium 101.07 (2-8-18-15-1)	(S) 45 **Rh** Rhodium 102.91 (2-8-18-16-1)	(S) 46 **Pd** Palladium 106.4 (2-8-18-18)	(S) 47 **Ag** Silver 107.87 (2-8-18-18-1)	(S) 48 **Cd** Cadmium 112.41 (2-8-18-18-2)	(S) 49 **In** Indium 114.82 (2-8-18-18-3)	(S) 50 **Sn** Tin 118.69 (2-8-18-18-4)	(S) 51 **Sb** Antimony 121.75 (2-8-18-18-5)	(S) 52 **Te** Tellurium 127.60 (2-8-18-18-6)	(S) 53 **I** Iodine 126.90 (2-8-18-18-7)	(G) 54 **Xe** Xenon 131.30 (2-8-18-18-8)
(S) 55 **Cs** Cesium 132.91 (2-8-18-18-8-1)	(S) 56 **Ba** Barium 137.33 (2-8-18-18-8-2)	(S) 71 **Lu** Lutetium 174.97 (2-8-18-32-9-2)	(S) 72 **Hf** Hafnium 178.49 (2-8-18-32-10-2)	(S) 73 **Ta** Tantalum 180.95 (2-8-18-32-11-2)	(S) 74 **W** Tungsten 183.85 (2-8-18-32-12-2)	(S) 75 **Re** Rhenium 186.21 (2-8-18-32-13-2)	(S) 76 **Os** Osmium 190.2 (2-8-18-32-14-2)	(S) 77 **Ir** Iridium 192.22 (2-8-18-32-15-2)	(S) 78 **Pt** Platinum 195.09 (2-8-18-32-17-1)	(S) 79 **Au** Gold 196.97 (2-8-18-32-18-1)	(L) 80 **Hg** Mercury 200.59 (2-8-18-32-18-2)	(S) 81 **Tl** Thallium 204.37 (2-8-18-32-18-3)	(S) 82 **Pb** Lead 207.2 (2-8-18-32-18-4)	(S) 83 **Bi** Bismuth 208.98 (2-8-18-32-18-5)	(S) 84 **Po** Polonium (209) (2-8-18-32-18-6)	(S) 85 **At** Astatine (210) (2-8-18-32-18-7)	(G) 86 **Rn** Radon (222) (2-8-18-32-18-8)
(S) 87 **Fr** Francium (223) (2-8-18-32-18-8-1)	(S) 88 **Ra** Radium 226.03 (2-8-18-32-18-8-2)	(S) 103 **Lr** Lawrencium (260) (2-8-18-32-32-9-2)	(N) 104 **Unq** (261) (2-8-18-32-32-10-2)	(N) 105 **Unp** (262) (2-8-18-32-32-11-2)	(N) 106 **Unh** (263) (2-8-18-32-32-12-2)	(N) 107 **Uns** (264) (2-8-18-32-32-13-2)	(N) 108 **Uno** (265) (2-8-18-32-32-14-2)	(N) 109 **Une** (266) (2-8-18-32-32-15-2)									

Series														
Lanthanide Series	(S) 57 **La** Lanthanum 138.91 (2-8-18-18-9-2)	(S) 58 **Ce** Cerium 140.12 (2-8-18-20-8-2)	(S) 59 **Pr** Praseodymium 140.91 (2-8-18-21-8-2)	(S) 60 **Nd** Neodymium 144.24 (2-8-18-22-8-2)	(N) 61 **Pm** Promethium (145) (2-8-18-23-8-2)	(S) 62 **Sm** Samarium 150.4 (2-8-18-24-8-2)	(S) 63 **Eu** Europium 151.96 (2-8-18-25-8-2)	(S) 64 **Gd** Gadolinium 157.25 (2-8-18-25-9-2)	(S) 65 **Tb** Terbium 158.93 (2-8-18-27-8-2)	(S) 66 **Dy** Dysprosium 162.50 (2-8-18-28-8-2)	(S) 67 **Ho** Holmium 164.93 (2-8-18-29-8-2)	(S) 68 **Er** Erbium 167.26 (2-8-18-30-8-2)	(S) 69 **Tm** Thulium 168.93 (2-8-18-31-8-2)	(S) 70 **Yb** Ytterbium 173.04 (2-8-18-32-8-2)
Actinide Series	(S) 89 **Ac** Actinium (227) (2-8-18-32-18-9-2)	(S) 90 **Th** Thorium 232.04 (2-8-18-32-18-10-2)	(S) 91 **Pa** Protactinium 231.04 (2-8-18-32-20-9-2)	(S) 92 **U** Uranium 238.03 (2-8-18-32-21-9-2)	(N) 93 **Np** Neptunium 237.05 (2-8-18-32-22-9-2)	(N) 94 **Pu** Plutonium (244) (2-8-18-32-24-8-2)	(N) 95 **Am** Americium (243) (2-8-18-32-25-8-2)	(N) 96 **Cm** Curium (247) (2-8-18-32-25-9-2)	(N) 97 **Bk** Berkelium (247) (2-8-18-32-27-8-2)	(N) 98 **Cf** Californium (251) (2-8-18-32-28-8-2)	(N) 99 **Es** Einsteinium (254) (2-8-18-32-29-8-2)	(N) 100 **Fm** Fermium (257) (2-8-18-32-30-8-2)	(N) 101 **Md** Mendelevium (258) (2-8-18-32-31-8-2)	(N) 102 **No** Nobelium (259) (2-8-18-32-32-8-2)